The UK Scanning Directory
9th Edition

PW Publishing Limited

The UK Scanning Directory

© Copyright PW Publishing Limited 2005

9th Edition published September 2005

Published by
PW Publishing Limited
Arrowsmith Court, Station Approach, Broadstone, Dorset BH18 8PW
email: UKSD9@pwpublishing.ltd.uk

Printed by Athenaeum Press Ltd, Dukesway, Team Valley, Gateshead, NE11 0PZ

Contents

Introduction 1

Scanning And The Law 2

Using The UK Scanning Directory 4

Long, Medium & Short Wave Allocations 6

Glossary 8

Scanning - A Beginner's Guide 10

Frequencies for the UK and
the Republic of Ireland 23

UK Car Rallying 40

Tuning In Airband Communications 78

Scanning at Formula 1 Grand Prix Meetings 230

Band I & II Channel Allocations 240

More Useful Allocations 246

Tuning in the Military Airband 293

London Metropolitan Police
Divisions and Trunking 366

UK & Irish Airports in Alphabetical Order 515

Late News 538

Acknowledgements

Hundreds of people have contributed to this book and much as I would like to, it's just not possible to thank them all individually.

I must, however, extend special thanks to Paul Wey and the members of PROMA for their willingness to share their extensive knowledge. Whether you're just starting out in the hobby or an experienced frequency collector, I can thoroughly recommend their group at
http://groups.yahoo.com/group/scanpromauk.

Someone else who I have to single out for thanks is Ken Cothliff of Air Supply in Yeadon (www.airsupply.co.uk). Ken is a familiar figure at most air shows where he is often to be heard providing the commentary and his help was invaluable.

Introduction

Welcome to the 9th edition of The UK Scanning Directory, Britain's best selling frequency guide. Over the years, it has become the standard reference book for frequency collectors, scanner enthusiasts, industry and various government departments who'd prefer not to be mentioned. For this edition, we've updated our comprehensive database not only by adding new verified frequencies but also by deleting just as many redundant ones to make sure this book contains the most accurate and up to date information available.

As well as a massive frequency list, we've also included several new articles to help newcomers to the hobby. There's an extensive beginners guide plus articles on scanning the military and aviation bands, motor racing and rallying and tips on how to find elusive frequencies. We've kept our normal layout because readers tell us that dividing the spectrum into separate sections makes it easier to find specific frequencies quickly. It also shows you how the spectrum is organised and might prompt you to explore some new areas.

If you're a regular reader, you'll notice that even though the layout is the same, a lot of the content has changed since our last edition. That's because bandplans have changed, new technologies have been introduced and several large users have bought new equipment and switched frequencies.

A while ago, trunking systems were seen as the way to increase the number of users per frequency but digital techniques are now replacing them. This might be good for radio users but it can make life difficult for frequency collectors. Trunked systems were comparatively easy to monitor but the new digital systems are totally secure and in some bands it's now almost impossible to even find a frequency let alone monitor it.

Even though many of the users who were favourites with scanner users can no longer be heard, the hobby is still rewarding. Enthusiasts are now discovering how interesting some of the less well-known areas of the spectrum can be. For example, anti-shoplifter (Shopwatch) networks operate in most towns and they can be very interesting. Local councils, parking enforcement companies, local buses and taxis, the military and lots of other people all use radios far more than you'd think and most of them are still analogue. Then, of course, there's always the airband. It's still the area that attracts the most listeners and still the easiest to listen to with comparatively inexpensive equipment.

Whatever your interest and whichever area you want to investigate, you should find the relevant frequencies in this book.

The Editor

Scanning and the Law

We are often asked about the legal position of scanning. The law is quite straightforward; if you use a scanner, almost everything you listen to is unlawful! According to the authorities, although it is not illegal to sell, buy or own a scanning or other receiver in the UK, it must only be used to listen to transmissions meant for general reception. The services that you are allowed to listen to include Amateur and Citizens' Band transmissions, licensed broadcast radio and weather and navigation broadcasts. Tuning into the airband, ships or even your local dustcart is definitely not permitted.

We've all heard people say that it's legal to listen so long as you don't tell anyone what you heard - **that is not true!** What is true is that if you listen to something that you shouldn't, you will be breaking the law. If you then tell someone what you heard, you will break another law.

If you'd like to know which laws, Ofcom has the full details on its web site at *www.ofcom.org.uk/radiocomms/ifi/enforcement/ofw156x#content*. If you want more details, you can write to them at: Ofcom Contact Centre, Riverside House, 2a Southwark Bridge Road, London SE1 9HA or you can telephone them on 0845 456 3000, fax them on 0845 456 3333 or e-mail them at: *contact@ofcom.org.uk*.

Before it became a part of Ofcom, the Radiocommunication Agency used to publish the same information as a leaflet called: *'Receive Only - Scanner etc. Information Sheet (RA169)'*, which they would send you free of charge. Ofcom do not seem to offer this service, at least, I can find no mention of it on their main web site. Even their Find a Document search facility doesn't locate RA169. However, the document does still exist and if you would like to download an Adobe Acrobat PDF version of it, you'll find it tucked away in their archives at:
www.ofcom.org.uk/static/archive/ra/publication/ra_info/ra169.htm

The law may be very simple and easy to understand but that doesn't make it a just law. We can all think of situations where listening to transmissions that we are not allowed to might benefit others. I know it's unlikely but we could come across a signal from a baby monitor and maybe overhear someone plotting a crime. What should we do? In a normal society we would simply call the police and they would go and interview the villains. Here you would be admitting to committing a crime yourself and if you did that, who do you think they would decide to prosecute?

We also have the odd situation where it is illegal to listen to aircraft but you can go to any airport or airshow and you will see dozens of people taking photographs and listening to their radios. At some airshows they even announce the frequencies that will be in use, presumably so you know which ones not to listen to!

Some time ago, there was widespread outrage when a group of British plane spotters was arrested in Greece and our national press made great play about the pointlessness of prosecuting harmless hobbyists. No mention was made of the fact that if a spotter in this country doesn't just take photographs but dares to listens to an aircraft, he is liable to prosecution here too, especially if he then tells his friend what he heard. Luckily, most of the police officers on the ground are still equipped with common sense and they tend to ignore spotters.

That is not true everywhere though and over the past few years several people have been successfully prosecuted for listening to police communications even though they were not caught in the act. They had police frequencies programmed into their scanner's memory and that was enough to convict them. The moral there is store sensitive frequencies in your head not in your scanner - not that there are many police frequencies to store anymore now that most forces have moved over to a secure digital system. Even so, there could come a time when just having taxi or motorcycle courier frequencies stored in your scanner could be used as grounds for a prosecution.

Scanning and frequency collecting should be done with common sense and discretion. It is a harmless hobby but not everyone sees it that way. I suppose this is understandable because most people just see the listening aspect of the hobby, not the collecting side. The urge to collect things is normal and widespread but people usually collect objects; stamps, beer mats and so on and many of us cannot understand that. Scanner uses, on the other hand, collect frequencies. They derive great pleasure from winkling out an elusive frequency and once they've found it, they might never listen to it again. It will simply be added to the list and then they will move on to find the next one.

Just as an avid stamp collector might have an album that he hardly ever looks at because it's locked safely away, keen frequency collectors will often have massive frequency lists that they hardly ever refer to because for them the pleasure lies in gathering frequencies, not listening to them. This side of the hobby has become more popular as the introduction of secure digital radio systems has made listening more difficult. Also, frequency collecting is far easier now that the Internet allows enthusiasts around the world to swap information and it usually takes just a few minutes to find a list on a server somewhere that contains the frequency you're looking for.

Of course, we are mere amateurs when it comes to monitoring and information gathering. Governments are the professionals and some seem to be obsessed with eavesdropping on their populations. It's not just the repressive regimes who watch and listen to almost everything. I'm sure we can all think of many free countries where closed circuit television cameras and massive telephone and email intercept stations are employed so that the government can monitor its citizens.

A quick Google search for things like Echelon and Menwith Hill will soon turn up some interesting but dated information. Things have moved on a lot since then and modern monitoring facilities can keep track of almost everything we do. Naturally, that then raises the question – who is watching the watchers?

In America, scanning is a legitimate hobby and their government has accepted the argument that listening to public and emergency services allows the population to see how their tax dollars are being spent. For them, scanning is a way of keeping an eye on the Establishment.

Using the UK Scanning Directory

Each page of *The UK Scanning Directory* is set out in five columns; Base and Mobile frequencies, Mode, Location and User & Notes.

Base Frequency: This column shows the frequency of the base station or the output of a repeater and this is the frequency you're most likely to hear.

As you go through the book, you'll notice frequencies in this column are not always listed in strict numerical order. We've grouped all frequencies in blocks, usually to show who uses that particular section of the spectrum; PMR, Military, Broadcasting and so on. Sometimes you'll find the same section appearing in more than one block. This is because some parts of the spectrum contain two completely different types of user and instead of simply printing a straight frequency list, we've separated the different users to make it easier to find the one you're looking for. A good example of this can be found at 430 MHz. Radio amateurs share this band with military and PMR users and if we'd just printed a simple list, everyone would be mixed in together. If you were looking for, say, an amateur repeater, you would have to plough through a lot of army bases and so on to find it. With this book you don't have to do that because we've grouped together all the amateur radio frequencies and listed them separately. Another good example can be found at the top end of the marine band where PMR frequencies overlap with marine ones.

Mobile Frequency: The second column shows the frequency used by the mobile or handheld radio. If it is different to the one in the first column, it's either the input to a repeater or the other half of a duplex system. If there is no entry in this column, the mobiles use the same frequency as the base.

Mode: This is the mode you should be select on your scanner for best reception. Airband is always AM and almost all the other users listed in this book use NFM but it is worth checking because a few users such as taxis and fire brigades also use AM. Broadcasters often use WFM for their links because they need the higher quality that a wideband connection gives.

Location: This is the general area where the user is located. This will usually be the name of a town or an area. Sometimes the radio system covers that town - a Shopwatch scheme, for instance, or it might be used just in a specific office building, factory or shop, in which case, see column five. If it says 'Nationwide', this means that it is used throughout the country.

User & Notes: This column contains details of who uses a particular frequency, their callsign, channel number and any other relevant notes.

The first part of the last column shows the name of the user. This can be a specific company, a service such as the Fire Brigade or if we haven't been able to narrow it down, something like 'Taxi Company' or 'Docks'.

The first pair of brackets in this column contains the callsign employed by the user, which could be something like (VS) or (Charlie 1). This is handy to know as it helps to verify their identity.

The second set contains the subaudible tone they use. This is a useful piece of information as it helps to identify individual users, especially when there are several companies on the same frequency. If your scanner can show CTCSS or DCS tones, seeing the correct one displayed will confirm you've found the listed user.

Some large companies and services have correspondingly large radio systems with several channels and where they're known, we've listed the channel numbers in this column. If they use a trunked system, we've also shown that along with a note to say whether it's a voice, data or control channel.

Finally, at the end of column five there might be another location. This will usually be because the main location shown in column four is quite large so we've shown a smaller area in this column. For instance, column four might say 'London', which is a big city so whenever possible, we've narrowed it down as much as we can by adding something like 'Ealing' or 'Oxford Street' here.

Space constraints have limited the amount of information we can show for each user but the combination of base frequency and location will usually be enough for you to find a specific user and if you then use either the callsign or subaudible tone you will be able to confirm your find.

Below is an example of a typical page.

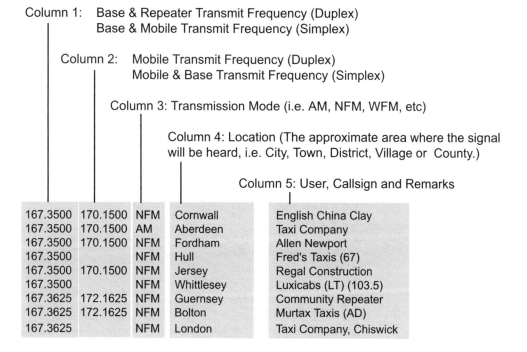

Column 1:   Base & Repeater Transmit Frequency (Duplex)
            Base & Mobile Transmit Frequency (Simplex)

    Column 2:   Mobile Transmit Frequency (Duplex)
                Mobile & Base Transmit Frequency (Simplex)

        Column 3: Transmission Mode (i.e. AM, NFM, WFM, etc)

            Column 4: Location (The approximate area where the signal
            will be heard, i.e. City, Town, District, Village or County.)

                Column 5: User, Callsign and Remarks

167.3500	170.1500	NFM	Cornwall	English China Clay
167.3500	170.1500	AM	Aberdeen	Taxi Company
167.3500	170.1500	NFM	Fordham	Allen Newport
167.3500		NFM	Hull	Fred's Taxis (67)
167.3500	170.1500	NFM	Jersey	Regal Construction
167.3500		NFM	Whittlesey	Luxicabs (LT) (103.5)
167.3625	172.1625	NFM	Guernsey	Community Repeater
167.3625	172.1625	NFM	Bolton	Murtax Taxis (AD)
167.3625		NFM	London	Taxi Company, Chiswick

Long, Medium & Short Wave Allocations

Many scanners now cover frequencies down to 100 kHz and allow access to the exciting world of shortwave radio. They don't work as well as dedicated shortwave receivers but if a decent antenna is used, a surprising amount can be heard. Below is a list of frequency allocations that should give you an idea of where to start looking for various users.

148.5 - 255 kHz	Long Wave Broadcasting AM
255 - 325 kHz	Maritime NDB, Aeronautical Navigation
325 - 405 kHz	Aeronautical Navigation NDB
405 - 435 kHz	Aeronautical Navigation NDB, Maritime Mobiles
435 - 495 kHz	Maritime Mobiles
495 - 505 kHz	Mobile (Distress and Calling)
505 - 526.5 kHz	Maritime Mobiles
526.5 - 1606.5 kHz	Medium Wave Broadcasting
1606.5 -1810 kHz	Maritime
1810 - 2000 kHz	160 metres Amateur Radio
2000 - 2495 kHz	Maritime and Aeronautical
2498 - 2502 kHz	Standard Frequency and Time Signal (2500 kHz)
2502 - 2851 kHz	Maritime and Aeronautical
2851 - 3019 kHz	En-Route Aeronautical Mobiles
3023 - 3155 kHz	Off-Route Aeronautical Mobiles
3155 - 3200 kHz	Fixed and Land & Maritime Mobiles
3200 - 3400 kHz	90 metres Tropical Broadcasting and Fixed & Land Mobiles
3401 - 3497 kHz	En-Route Aeronautical Mobiles
3500 - 3800 kHz	80 metres Amateur Radio
3950 - 4000 kHz	75 metres European Broadcasting
4000 - 4438 kHz	Maritime Fixed & Mobiles
4438 - 4650 kHz	Fixed and Land & Maritime Mobiles
4651 - 4696 kHz	En-Route Aeronautical Mobiles
4700 - 4995 kHz	Off-Route Aeronautical Mobiles
4750 - 5060 kHz	60 metres Tropical Broadcasting
5060 - 5450 kHz	Fixed and Land & Maritime Mobiles
5450 - 5477 kHz	Off-Route Aeronautical Mobiles
5481 - 5676 kHz	En-Route Aeronautical Mobiles
5680 - 5726 kHz	Off-Route Aeronautical Mobiles
5730 - 5960 kHz	Fixed and Land & Maritime Mobiles
5950 - 6200 kHz	49 metres Broadcasting Band
6200 - 6526 kHz	Maritime Mobiles
6526 - 6682 kHz	En-Route Aeronautical Mobiles
6685 - 6765 kHz	Off-Route Aeronautical Mobiles
6765 - 7000 kHz	Fixed and Land Mobiles
7000 - 7100 kHz	40 metres Amateur Radio
7100 - 7300 kHz	41 metres Broadcasting Band
7300 - 8100 kHz	Fixed and Land Mobiles
8100 - 8195 kHz	Fixed and Maritime Mobiles
8195 - 8812 kHz	Maritime Mobiles
8816 - 8960 kHz	En-Route Aeronautical Mobiles
8965 - 9037 kHz	Off-Route Aeronautical Mobiles

9500 - 9900 kHz	31 metres Broadcasting Band
9900 - 9995 kHz	Fixed
10006 - 10096 kHz	En-Route Aeronautical Mobiles
10100 - 10150 kHz	30 metres Amateur Radio
10150 - 11175 kHz	Fixed and Land & Maritime Mobiles
11175 - 11271 kHz	Off-Route Aeronautical Mobiles
11276 - 11396 kHz	En-Route Aeronautical Mobiles
11400 - 12230 kHz	Fixed
11650 - 12050 kHz	25 metres Broadcasting Band
12230 - 13197 kHz	Maritime Mobiles
13200 - 13257 kHz	Off-Route Aeronautical Mobiles
13261 - 13357 kHz	En-Route Aeronautical Mobiles
13360 - 13600 kHz	Fixed and Land & Maritime Mobiles
13600 - 13800 kHz	22 metres Broadcasting Band
13800 - 14000 kHz	Fixed and Land Mobiles
14000 - 14350 kHz	20 metres Amateur Band
14350 - 14990 kHz	Fixed and Land & Maritime Mobiles
15010 - 15097 kHz	Off-Route Aeronautical Mobiles
15100 - 15600 kHz	19 metres Broadcasting Band
15600 - 16360 kHz	Fixed
16360 - 17407 kHz	Maritime Mobiles
17410 - 17550 kHz	Fixed
17550 - 17900 kHz	16 metres Broadcasting Band
17901 - 17967 kHz	En-Route Aeronautical Mobiles
17970 - 18027 kHz	Off-Route Aeronautical Mobiles
18030 - 18068 kHz	Fixed
18068 - 18168 kHz	16 metres Amateur Band
18168 - 18780 kHz	Fixed
18780 - 18900 kHz	Maritime Mobiles
18900 - 19680 kHz	Fixed
19680 - 19797 kHz	Maritime Mobiles
19800 - 21000 kHz	Fixed & Land Mobiles
21000 - 21450 kHz	15 metres Amateur Band
21450 - 21850 kHz	13 metres Broadcasting Band
21850 - 21870 kHz	Fixed
21870 - 21924 kHz	Aeronautical Fixed
21925 - 21998 kHz	En-Route Aeronautical Mobiles
22000 - 22852 kHz	Maritime Mobiles
22855 - 23000 kHz	Fixed
23000 - 23200 kHz	Fixed and Land & Maritime Mobiles
23200 - 23350 kHz	Off-Route Aeronautical Mobiles
23350 - 24890 kHz	Fixed & Land Mobiles
24890 - 24990 kHz	12 metres Amateur Band
24990 - 25070 kHz	Fixed & Land Mobiles
25070 - 25210 kHz	Maritime Mobiles
25210 - 25520 kHz	Fixed and Land & Maritime Mobiles
25550 - 25600 kHz	Radio Astronomy
25600 - 26100 kHz	11 metres Broadcasting Band
26100 - 26172 kHz	Maritime Mobiles
26175 - 26235 kHz	Fixed and Land & Maritime Mobiles

Glossary

AA	Automobile Association
AFIS	Aerodrome Flight Information Service
AFSATCOM	US Air Force Satellite Communications
AM	Amplitude Modulation
ARA	Air Refuelling Area
ATC	Air Traffic Control or Air Training Corps
ATCC	Air Traffic Control Centre
ATIS	Aerodrome Terminal Information Service
AWACS	Airborne Warning & Control System
BAe	British Aerospace
BBC	British Broadcasting Corporation
BGS	British Geological Survey
BNFL	British Nuclear Fuels Ltd
BRS	Business Radio Service (USA)
BT	British Telecom
BTP	British Transport Police
CAC	Centralised Approach Control
CB	Citizens Band
CEGB	Central Electricity Generating Board
CMD	Command
Comms	Communications
CW	Continuous Wave (Morse)
DAB	Digital Audio Broadcasting
DATIS	Digital Aerodrome Terminal Information Service
DME	Distance Measuring Equipment
DoD	Department of Defense (USA)
DTI	Department of Trade and Industry
DSRR	Digital Short Range Radios
FLTSATCOM	US Navy Satellite Communications
FM	Frequency Modulation
FRADU	Fleet Requirements Air Direction Unit
FRS	Family Radio Service (USA)
GCHQ	Government Communications Headquarters
GSM	Global System for Mobile Communications
HF	High Frequency
IBA	Independent Broadcasting Authority
IFR	Instrument Flight Rules
ILR	Independent Local Radio
ILS	Instrument Landing System
ITN	Independent Television News
ITV	Independent Television
JFMG	JFMG Ltd. (issues licences for radio mics etc.)
LBS	Low Band Skip
LSB	Lower Sideband
LWT	London Weekend Television

MoD	Ministry of Defence
Mould	MoD National Home Defence Repeater Network
MRSA	Mandatory Radar Service Area
MURS	Multi Use Radio Service (USA)
MWL	Mid-Wales Railway Line
NATO	North Atlantic Treaty Organisation
NASA	National Aeronautics and Space Administration
NB	Narrow Band
NCB	National Coal Board
NFM	Narrowband Frequency Modulation
O/B	Outside Broadcast
Ofcom	Office of Communications
Ops	Operations
PAR	Precision Approach Radar
PFA	Popular Flying Association
PMR	Private Mobile Radio
PR	Personal Radio
PTT	Press To Talk
R	Runway (Left & Right)
RA	Radiocommunications Agency
RAC	Royal Automobile Club
RAF	Royal Air Force
RAFASU	Royal Air Force Armament Support Unit
RN	Royal Navy
RTTY	Radio Teletype
RX	Receiver
SAR	Search and Rescue
SRBR	Short range Business Radio
SRE	Surveillance Radar Element
SSB	Single Sideband
SSTV	Slow Scan Television
Std	Standard
TACAN	Tactical Air Navigation
TMA	Terminal Manoeuvring Area
TX	Transmitter
UACC	Upper Air Control Centre
UHF	Ultra High Frequency (300 - 3000 MHz)
UKAEA	UK Atomic Energy Authority
UMT	Universal Mobile Telecommunications System (3G)
USAF	US Air Force
USAFE	US Air Force Europe
USB	Upper Sideband
VFR	Visual Flight Rules
VHF	Very High Frequency (30 - 300 MHz)
VOLMET	Aviation Weather Broadcast
VOR	VHF Omni-Directional Radio Range
WFM	Wideband Frequency Modulation

Scanning - A Beginners Guide

Scanning from the ground up!

Beginning a new hobby can often be a daunting prospect. You start out filled with enthusiasm, eager to find out as much as you can and to get the most out of the hobby. Then you begin to have second thoughts because you find the information you need is not that easily available, or you can't find anyone to answer that burning question about some form of transmission. Well, if that's the position you find yourself in, read on because we have the solution to your problems - this beginners' guide to the world of VHF/UHF scanning will give you practical tips and advice, sources of information and most important of all, the names of groups that you can contact to learn more about your hobby and have all those questions answered.

Where can I learn more?

The first stop in your search for information on any hobby should be your local newsagents because there are magazines available that reflect most interests. Luckily, general radio reception and scanning in particular is well catered for by Shortwave Magazine and Radio Active. Both are packed with the latest news, information and useful listening tips from the professionals. They are widely available but if you have trouble finding them they can be obtained direct from the publisher post free. The address is given on page 20.

Listeners groups are also an important source of information. One of the best is available on the Internet. It's called PROMA (The Professional Radio Operators Monitoring Association) and it specialises in monitoring the VHF and UHF bands. It can be found at *http://groups.yahoo.com/group/scanpromauk*.

And while we're on the subject of the Internet, let's not forget that this is now a massive and valuable source of information on scanning. Most web pages focus on scanning in the US but there are many that contain information that is relevant here. I've found UKMidlandscanner at *www.ukmidlandscanner.co.uk* and Big Ears at *http://www.geocities.com/CapeCanaveral/Hangar/4783/curspec.html#b400* to be very good. Also, don't forget the newsgroups. *Alt.radio.scanner* concentrates on US scanning but there are frequent questions and threads that are relevant to UK and European listeners. The best for us is undoubtedly *Alt.radio.scanner.uk* because it concentrates almost entirely on scanning in the UK.

How the VHF/UHF Spectrum works

Many VHF/UHF beginners have graduated from shortwave listening where signals bounce off the ionosphere high above the earth's surface and travel many thousands of miles before reaching your radio. VHF/UHF signals are a little different. You may remember from your school days that energy is directly related to frequency; the higher the frequency, the more energetic the wave. This is true of all waves, including radio waves. At shortwave frequencies, below 30 MHz, wave energies are low enough to be reflected by the ionosphere. At VHF/UHF frequencies the waves are so energetic they pass straight through the ionosphere and continue travelling out into space.

VHF/UHF radio waves might be energetic but they're usually severely attenuated when they travel through brick walls or soil. Often they can't be heard at all from behind a building or a hill so VHF/UHF transmissions are said to operate on the principle of Line of Sight; if you can see it, you can hear it!

That explains why you usually can't hear signals from towns and cities many miles away from your location. On average, you should be able to receive signals within a radius of 25 miles, providing the terrain around you is reasonably flat. As soon as the it begins to change and becomes more uneven, the range of receivable signals is reduced. Aircraft are a bit different. Because they fly so high, they act like radio stations in the sky and it's possible to receive their signals up to 240 miles away. So don't be disappointed if you can't hear a ground signal 30 miles away. It's not your scanner that's at fault, it's just the way the VHF/UHF radio waves work.

There is one exception to all of this. At the bottom end of the VHF bands the lower regions of the ionosphere are capable of reflecting signals if they are suitably excited by solar activity. As we approach more active periods in the 11 year solar cycle, low band skip, as it is known, becomes more common and sometimes we can even pick up US stations on 30 or 40 MHz from here in the UK.

Frequencies and Modes

Transmission modes have always caused confusion amongst beginners. The two basic transmission modes are AM, Amplitude Modulation and FM, Frequency Modulation. If you tune into an AM signal and it seems distorted, it's probably an FM signal and vice versa. Most PMR transmissions are in narrowband FM, NFM. Wideband FM, WFM, is usually only used by broadcasting stations and the audio carriers from TV stations. You just might pick up a few PMR users using AM but they are few and far between.

Another source of confusion is FM on the airbands. Simply put, it never happens. All civil and military aeronautical voice transmissions are carried out in AM. If your scanner is receiving them better in FM, then that is a quirk of your scanner; the original transmission is AM.

Another problem that often confuses a new scanner enthusiast is "How do I tune in a frequency with 5 decimal places if I only have three decimal places on my scanner?"

Let's say you're trying to hear a BBC outside broadcast in Cardiff on a frequency of 141.75625 MHz but your scanner only displays three decimal places. How do you do it? First of all, look at the frequency steps your scanner is capable of tuning. These are usually 25, 12.5, 10, 5, 1 or 0.1 kHz for a table top scanner and 25, 12.5, 10 and 5 kHz for a handheld, although many scanners now allow you to programme which step you want, for example 250 kHz.

Once you've found the smallest tuning step, use the table below to work out which "closest" frequency you should tune. Don't worry about being off frequency. Both AM and FM transmissions are wide enough to allow a small margin of error. So, if your scanner's smallest step is 5 kHz, you should tune 141.755 MHz. You will be 1.25 kHz off frequency but that should not cause any distortion in the audio quality of the signal.

Smallest Step	Frequency to Tune (Decimal Places)			
	2	3	4	5
25 kHz	141.75	141.750	141.7500	141.75000
12.5 kHz	141.75	141.750	141.7500	141.75000
10 kHz	141.75	141.750	141.7500	141.75000
5 kHz		141.755	141.7550	141.75500
1 kHz		141.756	141.7560	141.75600
0.1 kHz			141.7562	141.75620

Simplex or Duplex?

What's the difference? A simplex radio channel is one where both the base and mobile radios transmit on the same frequency, say 81.9375 MHz. With a duplex system, all users transmit on, say, 171.5000 MHz and receive on 166.7000 MHz. This arrangement is often associated with repeaters, which we will look at next.

There is yet another possibility, the dual frequency simplex. In this arrangement, user A transmits on, say, 86.0125 MHz and receives on 72.6250 MHz while user B receives on 86.0125 MHz and transmits on 72.6250 MHz.

Repeaters

The directionality exhibited by VHF/UHF radio waves introduces a unique problem in radio communications. If signals cannot bend around obstacles like mountains, large buildings or even the horizon, how can two radios communicate under these circumstances?

Here's a little thought experiment. Image you are walking down the street of a major city such as Manchester. How much of the city can you see? Well not very much because your view is obstructed by all the buildings. Now imagine that you are standing at the top of one of those buildings looking across the city. How much of the city can you see now? With height on your side, you can see lots more. If you apply that same principle to VHF/UHF radio, a receiver placed on top of a tall building is going to hear much more than one at street level and, similarly, a transmitter is going to be able to transmit further.

Repeaters work on exactly the same principle. By locating a transceiver on top of one of these obstacles and using it to relay radio signals, communications can be carried out over much greater distances. Almost all repeaters use two separate frequencies, one for the input and another for the output. The mobiles and handhelds transmit on the input frequency and this is picked up by the repeater which then rebroadcasts it on a different frequency, usually with more power. This allows relatively low powered radios to communicate with each other far more effectively than if they were to operate simplex.

Trunking

Over the past ten years or so, the demand for frequencies in the VHF/UHF radio spectrum has continued to increase as more and more users take advantage of the benefits of two-way radio communications. This demand, however, has produced an interesting problem in that the number of required frequencies now exceeds the numbers available within the restricted bandwidth of the radio spectrum. In essence, there just isn't enough space to fit in all the users.

One solution is to reduce channel spacing. For example, in a 2 MHz bandwidth there are 80 individual channels, each spaced at 25 kHz. If this spacing is halved to 12.5 kHz, the common channel spacing used in most PMR sub-bands, a total of 160 channels can be fitted into the same bandwidth. This can and has been taken a step further on some sub-bands, particularly those used for public utilities and television outside broadcasts, where channel spacing is now only 6.25 kHz.

Of course, you might think that channel spacing can be reduced indefinitely thus always keeping the problem of spectrum overcrowding at bay. Unfortunately, that is not the case for, at some point, adjacent channels will begin to interfere with each other and all the initially perceived benefits will be lost.

Solving this problem is far more difficult that you might think. To find the solution, we must go back and look at the way frequencies are allocated. One of the major problems of allocating individual channels to each user is that although the channel might be registered for use, it need not actually be in use. So while our 2 MHz sub-band might have all 80 of its 25 kHz channels allocated to 80 different companies, only one or two frequencies might be in use at any one time. With all channels allocated, no new users can join the band even though many of the frequencies are dormant.

The ingenious solution to this seemingly impossible problem is Trunking. Trunking takes all these factors into account and provides a solution that is both user friendly and spectrum-efficient.

So how does a Trunking System work? Each radio in the trunking system monitors a control channel, a data frequency that gives all the radios in the system their instructions. When a call is received or made, the control channel informs the radios who wish to speak to each other which free channel they need to switch to. When speaking on their voice channel, a normal "talk-through" repeater is used to allow the sets to talk to each. Most trunking sites have around a dozen repeaters with the control channel allocating different channels each time a call is made. The real benefit of trunking can be seen when you realised that such a system of repeaters can support several hundred if not a thousand or more customers. Using the old system of one user per channel, that would have required around 12 MHz of bandwidth. With trunking, that can be reduced to less than 2 MHz. Listeners will have noticed that trunking has been adopted by some of their favourite public services in an effort to alleviate spectrum congestion.

If you would like to learn more about trunking systems, how they work and how to follow trunked transmissions, all the information you need is in *Scanner Busters 3* by D.C. Poole

The new digital trunking system, TETRA, (Trans European Trunked Radio) has become more widespread in recent years and as it's a secure digital system, it's of very little interest to scanner users or frequency collectors. The digital nature of the signal combined with a strong encryption system makes monitoring these transmissions impossible.

Paging

Ever wondered exactly what all those data transmissions are around 138 MHz and 153 MHz? The answer is simple: Pagers - those little gadgets that clip onto your belt and tell you all manner of information from "Happy Birthday" to "Come home now, the toilet's blocked." Like mobile telephones, they can be an asset or a hindrance but from the listeners' point of view, they can be a real catch. When digital GSM telephones were introduced a few years ago, many in the scanning community thought that marked the end of the scanning hobby. But the information vacuum did not last long. Enthusiasts throughout Europe and the US focused on Pagers as their next great target. Since the signals when not encrypted, it was only a matter of decoding the data to read the messages.

So, can you read these messages? Well of course you can. All you need is a piece of software that decodes the transmissions and here's the good news, the software is shareware and can be downloaded from the Internet! All you need do is run an audio line from the speaker jack of your scanner to the input port of your PC's soundcard, adjust the volume to the correct level and soon messages will start scrolling up your screen.

So, how do pagers work and what will I hear? The first thing you should know about pagers is that messages are transmitted countrywide. That's because the paging companies don't know exactly where all there pagers are so in order to send a message to any single unit, they must transmit the message all around the country. So don't be too surprised if you read a message for someone in London while you're sitting in your house in Newcastle!

Pagers work like this: The basic signalling pattern used in many pagers is a sequence of coded binary data using the Post Office Code Standardisation Advisory Group (POCSAG) code. The POCSAG code is a synchronous paging format that allows pages to be transmitted in a single-batch structure. The POCSAG code format consists of a preamble and one or more batches of code words. Each batch comprises a 32-bit frame synchronisation code and eight 64-bit address frames of two 32-bit addresses or idle code words each. The frame synchronisation code marks the start of the batch of code words. Data is transmitted as an FSK signal at a bit rate of 512, 1200, or 2400 bits per second. Pager frequencies can be found throughout this book.

If you would like a copy of the pager decoding software, it can be downloaded from *http://www.baycom.de/products/poc32/* or various other sites on the web. A quick Google search will soon find them.

Encryption

Encryption is one of those subjects that keeps on coming up and readers keep on asking if there is any way to beat the system. So, let's take a brief look at how encryption works.

As children, we all played with codes and ciphers, A = 1, B =2, etc. Using such a cipher, any message can be reduced to a series of apparently meaningless numbers. Modern encryption is surprisingly similar, but instead of letters being converted into numbers, whole messages or segments of speech are digitised. Now, prior to transmission, the encryption takes place. This is done by adding a series of pseudo-random numbers to the digitised message, which has the effect of scrambling the message.

Let's assume our original message is APPLE, or 1-16-16-12-5. By adding the series of pseudo-random numbers to our message, it is transformed into 23-13-24-1-5, or WMYAE and this is what is transmitted over the air. To get around the encryption requires that you have some knowledge of the mathematical algorithm that generates the number series. The problem is this: the number series that an encryption algorithm produces depends on the encryption key used by system and encryption keys have literally millions upon millions of possible combinations. In fact, some systems are so secure that to test every possible key at a rate of one key per second would take longer than the age of the universe! Someone once calculated than there are fewer grains of sand on earth than there are possible key combinations for some ciphers. Imagine being asked you find that single grain - truly a daunting prospect. With such a large number of combinations, these codes are said to be computationally infeasible to break. Some experimenters using huge computing power have been rumoured to have had some success but for the average enthusiast, it's just not worth even trying.

So, to answer all these readers out there who would like to tap into the local Regional Crime Squad or Drugs Squad, forget it.

Buying a Scanner

Now let's take a look at buying a scanner. Scanners come is two forms, the base station, which is a table top radio best suited for listening at home, and the handheld scanner, which can easily be slipped into the inside pocket of a jacket so that you can wander around town listening to what is going on.

Before you commit to buying a scanner, first decide what you want to use it for. If you're going to take it out and about, then you need a handheld. If you intend to spend long hours tuning in from the comfort of your own home then a table top radio is for you. Once you've decided that, you now have to choose which is the best scanner for your needs. There are a few essentials that you should look out for: a digital readout is an absolute must, so are both FM and AM reception modes.

Frequency coverage is also very important. Many US scanners only cover selected bands so it's worth reading the small print on the label. If you can, it's usually better to go for a scanner that has continuous coverage. This will often be from around 25 MHz up to about 1 GHz. Always choose a scanner that covers the bands you're interested in.

A quirk of some cheaper scanners is bad image rejection. Simply put, you'll pick up lots of signals but many will be on the wrong frequency. For example, your local skip hire company might transmit on 166.1875 MHz but you could pick it up on 130.4125 MHz. Experienced scanner users who are familiar with bandplans will know that this is right in the middle of the aviation band but if you're new to the hobby and you hear Joe talking about his skips on 130.4125 MHz, you're not going to query the frequency. The real problem occurs when you look up that frequency in *The UK Scanning Directory*. Joe's Skips won't be listed on 130.4125 MHz. Not only will you be listening to the wrong frequency, you will also not be able to get the full benefit of this or any other frequency list. So don't be fooled by that "very reasonable" price tag; buy the best you can afford.

Look through the radio magazines such as *Shortwave Magazine* and *Radio Active* for scanner advertisements and reviews. Find a local scanner dealer who also sells amateur radio equipment and visit them. Talk to the sales people, try out the scanner and find out if it does everything you want. If it does, buy it, if not, keep looking. Of course, there is always the second-hand market and most radio magazines carry advertisements from readers or there's always e-bay.

Antennas
Antenna design is a huge subject that has filled many books. Most handheld scanners come with a short 'rubber duck' antenna already fitted. These are usually fine for strong signals but are a bit lacking with weak ones. Table top radios are usually sold with a trusty telescopic antenna. This is ideal for the novice scanning enthusiast as it has a broad enough bandwidth to capture a wide range of signals and its length can be adjusted for different bands. Once you start to specialise in a particular branch of scanning, maybe military aviation, you might want to either build or buy an antenna for that frequency range. Most radio dealers will happily sell you one, radio magazines publish regular articles on antenna building.or you could investigate scrap yards. They always seem to have VHF/UHF antennas and many companies who operate VHF/UHF radios leave their old antennas behind when they move to new premises! It's worth remembering, the best way to improve the reception of any radio is to get a better antenna.

A Bit of History

Modern scanners have an assortment of features, functions, facilities and frequency ranges and to those who are already involved in the hobby, these new machines hold few mysteries. However, if you're confused by some of the intricacies of microprocessor control, perhaps this explanation of how scanners have evolved over the years will help.

In its simplest form, scanning is nothing more than sequentially listening to a number of pre-programmed channels, stopping whenever a busy one is found. The first scanners were just crystal-controlled receivers with up to 10 channels in the 144MHz (2m) amateur band or the VHF aircraft or marine bands. Pressing the SCAN button on one of these sets would make it check each channel in turn, stopping only when the squelch opened, showing that a carrier was present. It would then stay on that channel until the SCAN button was pressed again, when it would resume scanning until it stopped on the next busy channel.

Some of these sets also had a MANUAL button that allowed the user to move the receiver along one channel at a time with each push of the button. This may seem very primitive by today's standards, but at the time it was a major breakthrough for listeners. Before scanning receivers were invented, it was necessary to manually spin the tuning dial to check for signs of activity and the listener had to keep doing this for as long as he wanted to listen around. The arrival of the first scanner meant that the receiver did the work.

The first, improvement in scanner design came with the advent of auto-resume. This feature removed the need to press the SCAN button again to resume scanning. Whenever the carrier disappeared from the channel being monitored, the squelch would close and the set would then automatically start checking all the channels again until it found another carrier. This was an important new feature because it increased the speed with which a number of channels could be checked for activity. No time was wasted listening to quiet channels as the set would be constantly scanning unless a signal was present.

The next advance was the introduction of the lockout facility. Early scanners had a row of numbered LEDs, one of which lit to show the channel being monitored. Some manufacturers hit on the idea of incorporating a row of miniature toggle switches under these indicators so the listener could switch off one or more of the channels. The scanner would then ignore those frequencies. This facility was useful if, for instance, the scanner had been crystalled up to receive the 144 MHz repeater band. If the local repeater was always transmitting, the set would constantly stop on that channel and have to be restarted manually, only to stop on it again next time round. The lockout switch allowed the listener to skip that channel.

The arrival of frequency synthesisers heralded a new generation of scanners. Instead of having to buy new crystals to change the scanned frequencies, scanners with frequency synthesisers let the user to enter them with a keypad. They were then stored in the set's memories and scanned in the same way as the channels of a crystal-controlled set, but they could be changed at any time.

The Electra Corporation of America is usually credited with making the biggest breakthrough in technology. Their Bearcat range used microprocessors to control all the functions. This allowed them to incorporate several new facilities that had never been seen before and now most modem scanners are controlled this way.

One of the most useful new facilities that came from this breakthrough is searching. This is not the same as scanning, although the two are often confused. To use the search facility, the operator has to define a band by entering upper and lower frequency limits and then, when he presses the search button, the set will check every frequency in that band, usually in 5 kHz steps, stopping whenever a carrier is present. This feature is useful if the listener knows the band that he wants to listen to but does not know the spot frequencies.

For example, if he wants to find out the active frequencies in the 430MHz (70cm) amateur band, all that he has do is enter 440 and 430 as the upper and lower limits and then search the band. When the set finds a busy frequency, it will stop and that frequency can then be entered into one of the memories. In this way, all the memory channels can be filled with active spot frequencies. These can then be scanned and the dead parts of the band are ignored.

A typical Bearcat scanner of that era had numerous features that made great use of the possibilities of microprocessor control. It ran on either 12V dc or 240V AC and covered 66-88, 146-174 and 420-512MHz. It had the usual volume and squelch controls and a keypad for entering frequencies and controlling the functions. There were 50 memories that could be scanned continuously or in separate banks of 10 at either high or low speed and any number of the memories could be locked out. A delay could also be added to any of the channels. This made the scanner stay on that channel for a few seconds after the carrier had dropped, just in case one of the transmitting stations was a little slow replying. Without this feature, the scanner would have rushed off to check the other channels as soon as the carrier disappeared. These were huge advances in their time.

There was also a priority channel. When the priority button was pressed, the set automatically checked the frequency that was stored in Channel 1 every two seconds, regardless of what else it was doing and, if a signal appeared on that frequency, it would override everything else and the set would automatically switch to Channel 1. The good scanners of this time also had both search and scanning facilities that could be set to either 5 or 15 steps per second.

Store was another feature introduced around that time and it's still found on a lot of modern scanners. Instead of having to sit and watch the set while it was searching between pre-programmed limits, the Store button allowed the user to leave the set unattended. When Search and Store were pressed together, the set still checked all the frequencies in the pre-set band, but it did not stop on any of them. Instead, it remembered which ones had signals on them and when the operator returned and pressed the Recall button, it displayed all of the ones that had been active.

One model had an unusual feature that is not found on many scanners today, Count. This facility was used in conjunction with scanning. Whenever the Count button was pressed, the set would display the number of times that it had stopped on a particular channel. This was a great help in sorting out the active channels from the quiet ones.

Another feature that started to appear in those days was the fitting of 3.5mm jack sockets for connecting a tape recorder. Some also had contacts that could be used in conjunction with the Aux button to turn the recorder on and off. When a signal appeared on any of the channels that have had the auxiliary function activated, the recorder would automatically start as the squelch opened. These innovations helped to popularise scanning, but despite having all these features, most scanners from that era became obsolete when another generation of scanners appeared. The first was the AOR AR2001. Its biggest selling point was that it had continuous frequency coverage. Instead of just being able to receive frequencies in pre-set bands, it could receive any frequency between 25 and 550MHz; there were no gaps in its frequency range. At that time, this was seen as massive coverage and it proved to be an extremely popular feature. Most of the good scanners available today have continuous coverage although the range varies between models and the price usually reflects this

As well as having continuous coverage, the AR2001 had some other new features. There was a built-in clock, a liquid crystal display (with a switchable light!) and selectable frequency steps; 5, 12.5 or 25 kHz. It could receive AM or FM transmissions and, as it covered the VHF broadcast band, it also had a wideband FM mode.

Other scanner manufacturers soon realised that this was the way to go and now almost all scanners have continuous coverage up to at least 550MHz and some have extended that to cover up to 800MHz or I.3GHz.

Having stretched the frequency coverage of scanners far further than anyone would have thought possible in the early days; the makers then looked for other features that they could add to their sets. One of the most exciting ideas that they came up with was external computer control.

In 1985, Practical Wireless magazine described how a home microcomputer could be used to control an HF receiver. Scanner manufacturers soon made it possible to use one to control a scanner. One of the first was a box that had only two external controls - volume and squelch. To make it work it was necessary to plug it into a home computer, the two units together forming a very versatile receiver. It had all the usual facilities for searching and scanning but they were controlled from the computer's keyboard. Using an external computer instead of an in-built microprocessor to control the functions meant that memory size was much greater and more features were available. For example, a Memo function allowed the user to write notes about the spot frequencies held in the memories so that whenever the set subsequently stopped on one of those frequencies, the appropriate note would appear on the screen.

If a lot of this sounds familiar, it's because modern scanners have retained most of those early facilities. As microprocessor power has increased, features that used to need an external computer to implement can now be built into a tiny handheld. Similarly, as computer use has spread and more specialist software has been developed, it is now possible to link an ordinary handheld scanner to an average computer and run a monitoring station that would have been the envy of professionals from not that long ago. Logging, spectrum and frequency usage analysis and many other functions are now commonplace and it seems computer control is here to stay. Maybe the next big steps forward in scanning will be made not by manufacturers improving the hardware, but by programmers developing more customised software to allow the user to control the receiver in exactly the way he wants it to be controlled.

I hope this brief history of scanners has shown you what to expect from your scanner and where some of the functions came from.

Useful Addresses

Practical Wireless *Short Wave Magazine* *Radio Active*	PW Publishing Limited Arrowsmith Court Station Approach Broadstone, Dorset BH18 8PW. Tel: 0870 2247830 Fax: 0870 2247850 E-mail: enquiries@pwpublishing.ltd.uk
PROMA	Paul Wey 2 Icknield Way Baldock, Hertfordshire SG7 5AJ. http://groups.yahoo.com/group/scanpromauk
Ofcom	Ofcom Contact Centre Riverside House 2a Southwark Bridge Road London SE1 9HA. Tel: 0845 456 3000 Fax: 0845 456 3333 E-mail: contact@ofcom.org.uk www.ofcom.org.uk
Radio Society of Great Britain	Lambda House Cranborne Road Potters Bar, Hertfordshire EN6 3JE. Tel: 0870 904 7373 Fax: 0870 904 7374 www.rsgb.org

Unfortunately, we are unable to answer questions by telephone.
However, we can be contacted by e-mail at:
UKSD9@pwpublishing.ltd.uk

Frequencies for the UK and the Republic of Ireland

26.1000 - 27.5000 MHz   Fixed, Land & Mobile Except Aeronautical Mobile

26.1000 - 26.1750 MHz   Maritime Mobile USB

26.100 - 27.450 MHz   One-way Paging Systems and Alarms

Base	Mode	Location	User and Notes
26.5880	NFM	Nationwide	Common Paging Channe
26.8350	NFM	Nationwide	Short Term Hire Pagers
26.9200	NFM	Nationwide	Short Term Hire Pagers
26.9950	NFM	Nationwide	Vehicle Radio Keys
27.0450	NFM	Nationwide	Vehicle Radio Keys
27.0950	NFM	Nationwide	Vehicle Radio Keys
27.1200	NFM	Nationwide	Paging Tests & Development
27.1450	NFM	Nationwide	Vehicle Radio Keys
27.1625	NFM	St Helier	Jeanne Jugan Hospital Paging
27.1950	NFM	Nationwide	Vehicle Radio Keys
27.4500	NFM	Nationwide	Short Range Alarms for the Elderly & Infirm

General Telemetry and Telecommand Systems for Industrial, Scientific and Medical Apparatus

Base	Mode	Location	User and Notes
26.995	NFM	Nationwide	Industrial, Scientific and Medical Apparatus
27.045	NFM	Nationwide	Industrial, Scientific and Medical Apparatus
27.095	NFM	Nationwide	Industrial, Scientific and Medical Apparatus
27.145	NFM	Nationwide	Industrial, Scientific and Medical Apparatus
27.195	NFM	Nationwide	Industrial, Scientific and Medical Apparatus

26.9650 - 27.4050 MHz   CEPT (UK & Europe) Citizens Band Radio

Base	Mode	Location	User and Notes
26.965	NFM	Nationwide	Channel 01
26.975	NFM	Nationwide	Channel 02
26.985	NFM	Nationwide	Channel 03
27.005	NFM	Nationwide	Channel 04
27.015	NFM	Nationwide	Channel 05
27.025	NFM	Nationwide	Channel 06
27.035	NFM	Nationwide	Channel 07
27.055	NFM	Nationwide	Channel 08
27.065	NFM	Nationwide	Channel 09
27.075	NFM	Nationwide	Channel 10
27.085	NFM	Nationwide	Channel 11
27.105	NFM	Nationwide	Channel 12
27.115	NFM	Nationwide	Channel 13
27.125	NFM	Nationwide	Channel 14
27.135	NFM	Nationwide	Channel 15
27.155	NFM	Nationwide	Channel 16
27.165	NFM	Nationwide	Channel 17
27.175	NFM	Nationwide	Channel 18
27.185	NFM	Nationwide	Channel 19
27.205	NFM	Nationwide	Channel 20
27.215	NFM	Nationwide	Channel 21
27.225	NFM	Nationwide	Channel 22
27.255	NFM	Nationwide	Channel 23
27.235	NFM	Nationwide	Channel 24
27.245	NFM	Nationwide	Channel 25
27.265	NFM	Nationwide	Channel 26
27.275	NFM	Nationwide	Channel 27
27.285	NFM	Nationwide	Channel 28

Base	Mobile	Mode	Location	User and Notes
27.295		NFM	Nationwide	Channel 29
27.305		NFM	Nationwide	Channel 30
27.315		NFM	Nationwide	Channel 31
27.325		NFM	Nationwide	Channel 32
27.335		NFM	Nationwide	Channel 33
27.345		NFM	Nationwide	Channel 34
27.355		NFM	Nationwide	Channel 35
27.365		NFM	Nationwide	Channel 36
27.375		NFM	Nationwide	Channel 37
27.385		NFM	Nationwide	Channel 38
27.395		NFM	Nationwide	Channel 39
27.405		NFM	Nationwide	Channel 40

26.960 - 27.280 MHz — General Model Control, Surface and Air (Maximum 100 mW)

Base	Mobile	Mode	Location	User and Notes
26.995		NFM	Nationwide	Brown Channel
27.045		NFM	Nationwide	Red Channel
27.095		NFM	Nationwide	Orange Channel
27.145		NFM	Nationwide	Yellow Channel
27.195		NFM	Nationwide	Green Channel
27.245		NFM	Nationwide	Blue Channel

27.60125 - 27.99125 MHz — UK Citizens Band Radio

Base	Mobile	Mode	Location	User and Notes
27.60125	27.60125	NFM	Nationwide	Channel 01
27.61125	27.61125	NFM	Nationwide	Channel 02
27.62125	27.62125	NFM	Nationwide	Channel 03
27.63125	27.63125	NFM	Nationwide	Channel 04
27.64125	27.64125	NFM	Nationwide	Channel 05
27.65125	27.65125	NFM	Nationwide	Channel 06
27.66125	27.66125	NFM	Nationwide	Channel 07
27.67125	27.67125	NFM	Nationwide	Channel 08
27.68125	27.68125	NFM	Nationwide	Channel 09 Emergency
27.69125	27.69125	NFM	Nationwide	Channel 10
27.70125	27.70125	NFM	Nationwide	Channel 11
27.71125	27.71125	NFM	Nationwide	Channel 12
27.72125	27.72125	NFM	Nationwide	Channel 13
27.73125	27.73125	NFM	Nationwide	Channel 14 Calling
27.74125	27.74125	NFM	Nationwide	Channel 15
27.75125	27.75125	NFM	Nationwide	Channel 16
27.76125	27.76125	NFM	Nationwide	Channel 17
27.77125	27.77125	NFM	Nationwide	Channel 18
27.78125	27.78125	NFM	Nationwide	Channel 19 Calling
27.79125	27.79125	NFM	Nationwide	Channel 20
27.80125	27.80125	NFM	Nationwide	Channel 21
27.81125	27.81125	NFM	Nationwide	Channel 22
27.82125	27.82125	NFM	Nationwide	Channel 23
27.83125	27.83125	NFM	Nationwide	Channel 24
27.84125	27.84125	NFM	Nationwide	Channel 25
27.85125	27.85125	NFM	Nationwide	Channel 26
27.86125	27.86125	NFM	Nationwide	Channel 27
27.87125	27.87125	NFM	Nationwide	Channel 28
27.88125	27.88125	NFM	Nationwide	Channel 29
27.89125	27.89125	NFM	Nationwide	Channel 30
27.90125	27.90125	NFM	Nationwide	Channel 31
27.91125	27.91125	NFM	Nationwide	Channel 32

Base	Mobile	Mode	Location	User and Notes
27.92125	27.92125	NFM	Nationwide	Channel 33
27.93125	27.93125	NFM	Nationwide	Channel 34
27.94125	27.94125	NFM	Nationwide	Channel 35
27.95125	27.95125	NFM	Nationwide	Channel 36
27.96125	27.96125	NFM	Nationwide	Channel 37
27.97125	27.97125	NFM	Nationwide	Channel 38
27.98125	27.98125	NFM	Nationwide	Channel 39
27.99125	27.99125	NFM	Nationwide	Channel 40

28.0000 - 29.7000 MHz — 10m Amateur Band

Base	Mobile	Mode	Location	User and Notes
28.1200		NFM	Nationwide	Packet Radio
28.2150		CW	Didcot	Beacon (GB3RAL)
28.6800		NFM	Nationwide	Slow Scan TV and Fax Calling
29.2000		NFM	Nationwide	Packet Radio (FM 2.5 kHz)
29.3000		NFM	Nationwide	Satellite Downlinks
29.6000		NFM	Nationwide	FM Calling Channel
29.6400	29.540	NFM	Northampton	Repeater (GB3CJ) (77)

29.700 - 29.9700 — MOD Tactical Channels 25 kHz Simplex

30.0050 - 31.0250 MHz — NASA Space to Earth Simplex

Base	Mobile	Mode	Location	User and Notes
30.01000		NFM	Space	Downlink

30.0250 - 31.7000 MHz — Military Communications 12.5 kHz Simplex

Base	Mobile	Mode	Location	User and Notes
30.17500		NFM	Salisbury Plain	Army
30.20000		NFM	Salisbury Plain	Army
30.32500		NFM	Salisbury Plain	Army
30.35000		NFM	Nationwide	352 Squadron. Air to Air
30.35000		NFM	Nationwide	Army Forward Air Controllers
30.82500		NFM	Nationwide	1st Battalion Royal Anglia Regiment (98)
31.20000		NFM	Salisbury Plain	Army
31.52500		NFM	Salisbury Plain	Army
31.57500		NFM	Nationwide	RAF Regiment
31.67500		NFM	Salisbury Plain	Army
31.70000		NFM	Salisbury Plain	Army

31.0875 - 31.2125 MHz — Cordless Telephones

Base	Mobile	Mode	Location	User and Notes
31.0375	39.9375	NFM	Nationwide	Channel 1
31.0625	39.9625	NFM	Nationwide	Channel 2
31.0875	39.9875	NFM	Nationwide	Channel 3
31.1125	40.0125	NFM	Nationwide	Channel 4
31.1375	40.0375	NFM	Nationwide	Channel 5
31.1625	40.0625	NFM	Nationwide	Channel 6
31.1875	40.0875	NFM	Nationwide	Channel 7
31.2125	40.1125	NFM	Nationwide	Channel 8

31.7125 - 31.7875 MHz — Hospital Paging Outgoing Speech
(Return Speech in Emergencies Only)

Base	Mobile	Mode	Location	User and Notes
31.725	161.000	NFM	Nationwide	Hospital Paging
31.750	161.025	NFM	Worcester	Ronkwood Hospital Paging
31.750	161.025	NFM	Nationwide	Hospital Paging
31.775	161.050	NFM	Eastbourne	Hospital paging
31.775	161.050	NFM	Nationwide	Hospital Paging

31.8000 - 34.9000 MHz — Military Communications 12.5 kHz Simplex

Base	Mobile	Mode	Location	User and Notes
31.825		NFM	Thetford	Army Training Area
31.900		NFM	Nationwide	Korean Navy Intership
32.250		NFM	Salisbury Plain	Army
32.325		NFM	Salisbury Plain	Army
32.350		NFM	Salisbury Plain	Army
32.425		NFM	Salisbury Plain	Army
32.525		NFM	Salisbury Plain	Army
32.575		NFM	Salisbury Plain	Army
32.700		NFM	Nationwide	RAF Regiment
32.900		NFM	Salisbury Plain	Army
33.125		NFM	Nationwide	Army
33.200		NFM	Salisbury Plain	Army
33.775		NFM	Salisbury Plain	Army
34.125		NFM	Salisbury Plain	Army
34.300		NFM	SW England	Lynx/Gazelle, Exercise Eagles Strike 2005
34.400		NFM	Nationwide	Army Forward Air Controllers

34.9250 - 34.9750 MHz — Low Power Alarms for the Elderly & Infirm

Base	Mobile	Mode	Location	User and Notes
34.925		NFM	Nationwide	Emergency Alarms for the Elderly& Infirm
34.950		NFM	Nationwide	Emergency Alarms for the Elderly& Infirm
34.975		NFM	Nationwide	Emergency Alarms for the Elderly& Infirm

35.0000 - 35.2500 MHz — Radio Controlled Models 10 kHz (100 mW Max)

Base	Mobile	Mode	Location	User and Notes
35.000		NFM	Nationwide	Channel 60
35.010		NFM	Nationwide	Channel 61
35.020		NFM	Nationwide	Channel 62
35.030		NFM	Nationwide	Channel 63
35.040		NFM	Nationwide	Channel 64
35.050		NFM	Nationwide	Channel 65
35.060		NFM	Nationwide	Channel 66
35.070		NFM	Nationwide	Channel 67
35.080		NFM	Nationwide	Channel 68
35.090		NFM	Nationwide	Channel 69
35.100		NFM	Nationwide	Channel 70
35.110		NFM	Nationwide	Channel 71
35.120		NFM	Nationwide	Channel 72
35.130		NFM	Nationwide	Channel 73
35.140		NFM	Nationwide	Channel 74
35.150		NFM	Nationwide	Channel 75
35.160		NFM	Nationwide	Channel 76
35.170		NFM	Nationwide	Channel 77
35.180		NFM	Nationwide	Channel 78
35.190		NFM	Nationwide	Channel 79
35.200		NFM	Nationwide	Channel 80
35.210		NFM	Nationwide	Channel 81
35.220		NFM	Nationwide	Channel 82
35.230		NFM	Nationwide	Channel 83
35.240		NFM	Nationwide	Channel 84
35.250		NFM	Nationwide	Channel 85

35.2500 - 37.7500 MHz — MoD Tactical Communications 12.5 kHz

Base	Mobile	Mode	Location	User and Notes
35.250		NFM	Salisbury Plain	Army
35.275		NFM	Salisbury Plain	Army
35.350		NFM	Brecon Beacons	Army
35.400		NFM	Brecon Beacons	Army

Base	Mobile	Mode	Location	User and Notes
35.575		NFM	Salisbury Plain	Army
35.625		NFM	Salisbury Plain	Army
35.775		NFM	Salisbury Plain	Army
35.975		NFM	Nationwide	Royal Signals
36.025		NFM	Wiltshire	Larkhill Range Tactical
36.200		NFM	Nationwide	847 Naval Air Squadron
36.250		NFM	Nationwide	847 Naval Air Squadron
36.300		NFM	Cinque Ports	Territorial Army
36.350		NFM	Bovington	Army Training Camp
36.350		NFM	Nationwide	27 Squadron Chinook Air-Air
36.450		NFM	Nationwide	JFMG Talkback
36.610		NFM	Nationwide	JFMG Touring Conference Radio Mics
36.750		NFM	Nationwide	Army Forward Air Controllers
36.790		NFM	Nationwide	JFMG Touring Conference Radio Mics
36.800		NFM	Nationwide	Air Training Corps V12
36.850		NFM	Salisbury Plain	Army
37.010		NFM	Nationwide	JFMG Touring Conference Radio Mics
37.025		NFM	Cinque Ports	44 Signal Regiment
37.025		NFM	Nationwide	RAF Regiment
37.025		NFM	Nationwide	Sea Cadet Corps (SV3)
37.190		NFM	Nationwide	JFMG Touring Conference Radio Mics
37.200		NFM	East Anglia	Regiment
37.225		NFM	Thetford	Army, Stanford Battle Area
37.300		NFM	Nationwide	RAF Cadets Channel V11
37.325		NFM	Salisbury Plain	Army

36.6100 - 36.7900 MHz — Cordless Domestic Audio Equipment

37.0100 - 37.1900 MHz — Marine Databuoy Telemetry

37.7500 - 38.2500 MHz — Radio Astronomy Within 80 km of Cambridge

37.9000 - 40.1000 MHz — MoD Tactical Communications 12.5 kHz Simplex

Base	Mobile	Mode	Location	User and Notes
38.000		NFM	Nationwide	Army Air Corps 653 & 663 Squadrons
38.000		NFM	Nationwide	Army Cadet Force
38.000		USB	Nationwide	Racal Comsec
38.025		NFM	Nationwide	Gazelle Close Air Support
38.100		NFM	Nationwide	18 Squadron Chinook Air-Air
38.100		NFM	Nationwide	RAF Cadets Channel V13
38.320		NFM	Nationwide	Fish Tagging (Salmon)
38.325		NFM	Cinque Ports	44 Signal Regiment
38.425		NFM	Cinque Ports	44 Signal Regiment
38.575		NFM	Sennybridge	Army
38.600		NFM	Thetford	RAF Stanford Training Area
38.625		NFM	Okehampton	Army 657 Squadron Ops.
38.825		NFM	Carlisle	Army Ground Station
38.950		NFM	SW England	Exercise Eagles Strike Helo Air-Air 2005
39.000		NFM	Lulworth Cove	Range Patrol Vessel
39.000		NFM	Salisbury Plain	Army
39.250		NFM	Nationwide	36 Signals Regiment
39.500		NFM	Nationwide	Army Tanks Channel

Base	Mobile	Mode	Location	User and Notes
39.600		NFM	Lulworth Cove	Army Patrol Vessel
39.650		NFM	Nationwide	Army Tanks Channel
39.725		NFM	London	Royal Yeomanry, Westminster
39.750		NFM	Nationwide	Royal Signals Public Displays
39.800		NFM	SW England	Puma Air-Air Exercise Eagles Strike 2005
39.800		NFM	Thetford	Army Training Area
39.825		NFM	London	Royal Yeomanry, Westminster
39.850		NFM	Nationwide	Gazelle Close Air Support
39.900		NFM	USAF Fairford	Base Security
40.000		NFM	Salisbury Plain	Army
40.050		NFM	Nationwide	Army Distress Frequency
40.075		NFM	Nationwide	7 Squadron Air-Air
40.200		NFM	Nationwide	RAF Cadets Channel V14
40.225		NFM	Salisbury Plain	Army Tactical Assault Landing

40.6650 - 41.0000 MHz — Radio Controlled Surface Models 10 kHz (e.g. Cars and Boats)

Base	Mobile	Mode	Location	User and Notes
40.665		NFM	Nationwide	Channel 665
40.675		NFM	Nationwide	Channel 675
40.685		NFM	Nationwide	Channel 685
40.695		NFM	Nationwide	Channel 695
40.705		NFM	Nationwide	Channel 705
40.715		NFM	Nationwide	Channel 715
40.725		NFM	Nationwide	Channel 725
40.735		NFM	Nationwide	Channel 735
40.745		NFM	Nationwide	Channel 745
40.755		NFM	Nationwide	Channel 755
40.765		NFM	Nationwide	Channel 765
40.775		NFM	Nationwide	Channel 775
40.785		NFM	Nationwide	Channel 785
40.795		NFM	Nationwide	Channel 795
40.805		NFM	Nationwide	Channel 805
40.815		NFM	Nationwide	Channel 815
40.825		NFM	Nationwide	Channel 825
40.835		NFM	Nationwide	Channel 835
40.845		NFM	Nationwide	Channel 845
40.855		NFM	Nationwide	Channel 855
40.865		NFM	Nationwide	Channel 865
40.875		NFM	Nationwide	Channel 875
40.885		NFM	Nationwide	Channel 885
40.895		NFM	Nationwide	Channel 895
40.905		NFM	Nationwide	Channel 905
40.915		NFM	Nationwide	Channel 915
40.925		NFM	Nationwide	Channel 925
40.935		NFM	Nationwide	Channel 935
40.945		NFM	Nationwide	Channel 945
40.955		NFM	Nationwide	Channel 955

41.0000 - 47.0000 MHz — MoD Tactical Communications 12.5 kHz Simplex

Base	Mobile	Mode	Location	User and Notes
41.1000		NFM	Odiham	Chinook Wing Ops.
41.1250		NFM	Salisbury Plain	Army
41.1750		NFM	Nationwide	Army Ground Station
41.2500		NFM	Cinque Ports	44 Signals Regiment
41.4375		NFM	Thetford	Army Training Area

Base	Mobile	Mode	Location	User and Notes
42.0500		NFM	Jersey	Territorial Army
42.0500		NFM	Salisbury Plain	Army
42.1250		NFM	Nationwide	Army War Training
42.1500		NFM	Cinque Ports	44 Signals Regiment
42.3250		NFM	Salisbury Plain	Royal Artillery
42.3500		NFM	Nationwide	7 Squadron Chinook Air to Air
42.5500		NFM	Salisbury Plain	Army
43.1000		NFM	Salisbury Plain	Army
43.2250		NFM	Salisbury Plain	Army
43.3500		NFM	Nationwide	7 Squadron Chinook Air to Air
43.5500		NFM	Salisbury Plain	Army
43.7250		NFM	North West England	Army Ground Station
43.7750		NFM	Salisbury Plain	Army
44.0000		NFM	Bovington	Army Training Camp
44.0000		NFM	Salisbury Plain	Army
44.4250		NFM	Salisbury Plain	Army
44.4500		NFM	Nationwide	Army War Training
44.9750		NFM	Cinque Ports	44 Signals Regiment
45.3000		NFM	Salisbury Plain	Army
45.3000		NFM	Thetford	Army, Stanford Battle Area
45.4000		NFM	Sennybridge	Army
45.4250		NFM	Thetford	Army, Stanford Battle Area
45.7000		NFM	Wiltshire	Dunge Hill War Games
45.7125		NFM	Nationwide	Army War Training
45.7500		NFM	Nationwide	RAF Regiment
46.0000		NFM	Nationwide	Royal Signals Display
46.1250		NFM	Nationwide	Army War Training
46.3250		NFM	Nationwide	Army War Training

47.0000 - 47.4000 MHz — Future PMR Allocation, Currently MoD

47.309375 - 47.365625 MHz — Vehicle and Long Range Security Alarm Systems 12.5 kHz bandwidth

Base	Mobile	Mode	Location	User and Notes
47.309375		NFM	Nationwide	Long Range Security Alarms Ch 1 (6.25 kHz bandwidth)
47.318750		NFM	Nationwide	Long Range Security Alarms Ch 2
47.331250		NFM	Nationwide	Long Range Security Alarms Ch 3
47.343750		NFM	Nationwide	Long Range Security Alarms Ch 4
47.356250		NFM	Nationwide	Long Range Security Alarms Ch 5
47.365630		NFM	Nationwide	Long Range Security Alarms Ch 6 (6.25 kHz bandwidth)
47.400000		NFM	Nationwide	Car Theft Paging Alarms

47.41875 - 47.43125 MHz — Extended Range Cordless Telephones

Base	Mobile	Mode	Location	User and Notes
47.41875	77.55000	NFM	Nationwide	Extended Range Cordless Telephones
47.43125	77.51250	NFM	Nationwide	Extended Range Cordless Telephones

47.45625 - 47.54375 MHz — Cordless Telephones

Mobile	Base	Mode	Location	User and Notes
47.44375	1.76200	NFM	Nationwide	Channel 7 (Alternate)
47.45625	1.64200	NFM	Nationwide	Channel 1
47.46875	1.66200	NFM	Nationwide	Channel 2
47.48125	1.68200	NFM	Nationwide	Channel 3
47.49375	1.70200	NFM	Nationwide	Channel 4
47.50625	1.72200	NFM	Nationwide	Channel 5
47.51875	1.74200	NFM	Nationwide	Channel 6
47.53125	1.76200	NFM	Nationwide	Channel 7
47.54375	1.78200	NFM	Nationwide	Channel 8

47.5500 - 48.5500 MHz — Broadcasting Links

Base	Mode	Location	User and Notes
47.55000	NFM	Nationwide	JFMG Location Talkback Base
47.57000	NFM	Cardiff	BBC Radio Wales Studio Sound Channel
47.64375	NFM	Nationwide	BBC Radio Microphones
47.64500	NFM	Nationwide	BBC O/B
47.65000	NFM	Suffolk	BBC Radio Suffolk O/B
47.94375	NFM	Nationwide	ITV Engineers Ch.1
47.94375	NFM	Stockport	ITV Engineers
47.95625	NFM	Nationwide	ITV Engineers Ch.2
47.96875	NFM	Nationwide	ITV Engineers Ch.3
48.05625	NFM	Isle of Wight	Isle of Wight Radio Feeder
48.08125	NFM	London	Sky TV Talkback

48.4000 - 48.5000 MHz — Broadcast Sound Links 12.5 kHz

Base	Mode	Location	User and Notes
48.30000	NFM	Nationwide	JFMG Stereo Sound Link
48.42500	NFM	Nationwide	JFMG Mono Sound Link
48.42500	NFM	Wessex	Wessex FM Mono Sound Link
48.45000	WFM	S England	Coastway Hospital Link, South Coast
48.47500	NFM	Nationwide	JFMG Mono Sound Link
48.52500	NFM	Nationwide	JFMG Mono Sound Link
48.80000	NFM	Nationwide	JFMG Location Talkback Base

48.97500 - 48.98750 MHz — Short Term Hire Paging

Base	Mode	Location	User and Notes
48.9750	NFM	Nationwide	On Site & Short Term Hire Paging
48.9875	NFM	Nationwide	On Site & Short Term Hire Paging

48.99375 - 49.49375 MHz — One-Way Non-Speech Paging Systems

Base	Mode	Location	User and Notes
49.0000	NFM	Nationwide	Channel 1
49.0125	NFM	Nationwide	Channel 2
49.0250	NFM	Nationwide	Channel 3
49.0375	NFM	Nationwide	Channel 4
49.0500	NFM	Nationwide	Channel 5
49.0625	NFM	Nationwide	Channel 6
49.0750	NFM	Nationwide	Channel 7
49.0875	NFM	Nationwide	Channel 8
49.1000	NFM	Nationwide	Channel 9
49.1125	NFM	Nationwide	Channel 10
49.1250	NFM	Nationwide	Channel 11
49.1375	NFM	Nationwide	Channel 12
49.1500	NFM	Nationwide	Channel 13
49.1625	NFM	Nationwide	Channel 14
49.1750	NFM	Nationwide	Channel 15
49.1875	NFM	Nationwide	Channel 16
49.2000	NFM	Nationwide	Channel 17
49.2125	NFM	Nationwide	Channel 18
49.2250	NFM	Nationwide	Channel 19
49.2375	NFM	Nationwide	Channel 20
49.2500	NFM	Nationwide	Channel 21
49.2625	NFM	Nationwide	Channel 22
49.2750	NFM	Nationwide	Channel 23
49.2875	NFM	Nationwide	Channel 24
49.3000	NFM	Nationwide	Channel 25
49.3125	NFM	Nationwide	Channel 26

Base	Mobile	Mode	Location	User and Notes
49.3250		NFM	Nationwide	Channel 27
49.3375		NFM	Nationwide	Channel 28
49.3500		NFM	Nationwide	Channel 29
49.3625		NFM	Nationwide	Channel 30
49.3750		NFM	Nationwide	Channel 31
49.3875		NFM	Nationwide	Channel 32
49.4000		NFM	Nationwide	Channel 33
49.4125		NFM	Nationwide	Channel 34

49.4250 - 49.4750 MHz — Hospital Paging

Base	Mobile	Mode	Location	User and Notes
49.4250		NFM	Bournemouth	Hospital Paging
49.4250		NFM	Nationwide	Hospital Channel 35
49.4375		NFM	Nationwide	Hospital Channel 36
49.4500		NFM	Nationwide	Hospital Channel 37
49.4500		NFM	Cardiff	Llandough Hospital Two Way Paging
49.4500		NFM	Oxford	J Radcliff Hospital Emergencies
49.4500		NFM	Jersey	Hospital Cardiac Bleep & Voice
49.4500	454.32500	NFM	Ipswich	Hospital Paging
49.4625		NFM	Nationwide	Hospital Channel 38
49.4750		NFM	Nationwide	Hospital Channel 39

49.8200 - 49.9875 MHz — Low Power Devices, Walkie Talkies, Radio Controlled Toys & Baby Monitors

Base	Mobile	Mode	Location	User and Notes
49.800		WFM	Nationwide	Wireless Headphones
49.820		NFM	Nationwide	JFMG Touring Conference Radio Mics
49.830		NFM	London	Metropolis Motorcycle Training
49.830		NFM	Nationwide	Channel 1
49.830		NFM	Nationwide	Channel A
49.845		NFM	Nationwide	Channel 2
49.845		NFM	Nationwide	Channel B
49.860		NFM	Nationwide	Channel 3
49.860		NFM	Nationwide	Channel C
49.875		NFM	Nationwide	Channel 4
49.875		NFM	Nationwide	Channel D
49.890		NFM	London	CSM Motorcycle Training
49.890		NFM	Nationwide	Channel 5
49.890		NFM	Nationwide	Channel E
49.980		NFM	Nationwide	JFMG Touring Conference Radio Mics

50.0000 - 52.0000 MHz — 6m UK Amateur Radio Band

Base	Mobile	Mode	Location	User and Notes
50.0000		CW	Buxton	Beacon (GB3BUX)
50.0420		CW	St Austell	Beacon (GB3MCB)
50.0500		CW	Potters Bar	Beacon (GB3NHQ)
50.0600		CW	Inverness	Beacon (GB3RMK)
50.0620		CW	Ballymena	Beacon (GB3NGI)
50.0640		CW	Lerwick	Beacon (GB3LER)
50.0655		CW	St Helier	Beacon (GB3IOJ)
50.0900		CW	Nationwide	CW Calling Channel
50.2000		USB	Nationwide	SSB Calling
50.2750		CW	Darlington	Beacon (GB3IFX)
50.3000		CW	Nationwide	CW Calling
50.5100		SSB	Nationwide	Slow Scan TV
50.5500		SSB	Nationwide	Fax

Base	Mobile	Mode	Location	User and Notes
50.6000		SSB	Nationwide	RTTY (afsk)
50.6300		SSB	Nationwide	Packet Radio
50.7200	51.2200	NFM	Tenby	Repeater (GB3AE) (94.8)
50.7200	51.2200	NFM	Kidderminster	Repeater (GB3BY) (67)
50.7200	51.2200	NFM	Martlesham	Repeater (GB3EF) (110.9)
50.7400	51.2400	NFM	Leicester	Repeater (GB3UM) (77)
50.7500	51.2500	NFM	Liverpool	Repeater (GB3LP) (77)
50.7600	51.2600	NFM	Hastings	Repeater (GB3HF) (103.5)
50.7700	51.2700	NFM	Danbury	Repeater (GB3DB) (110.9)
50.7700	51.2700	NFM	Axbridge	Repeater (GB3FH) (77)
50.7800	51.2800	NFM	Barkway	Repeater (GB3PX) (77)
50.7800	51.2800	NFM	Carrickfergus	Repeater (GB3TY) (110.9)
50.7900	51.2900	NFM	Stoke on Trent	Repeater (GB3SX) (103.5)
50.8000	51.3000	NFM	Huddersfield	Repeater (GB3HX) (82.5)
50.8100	51.3100	NFM	Farnham	Repeater (GB3FX) (82.5)
50.8200	51.3200	NFM	Hucknall	Repeater (GB3RR) (71.9)
50.8300	51.3200	NFM	Warminstcr	Repeater (GB3WX) (77)
50.8400	51.3400	NFM	Amersham	Repeater (GB3AM) (77)
50.8500	51.3500	NFM	Portsmouth	Repeater (GB3PN) (71.9)
51.2100		NFM	Nationwide	Raynet
51.4300		NFM	Nationwide	Simplex
51.4500		NFM	Nationwide	Simplex
51.4700		NFM	Nationwide	Simplex
51.4900		NFM	Nationwide	Simplex
51.5100		NFM	Nationwide	Simplex Calling Channel
51.5300		NFM	Nationwide	Simplex (GB2RS News)
51.5300		NFM	Nationwide	Simplex
51.5500		NFM	Nationwide	Simplex
51.5500		NFM	Nationwide	Simplex
51.5700		NFM	Nationwide	Simplex
51.5900		NFM	Nationwide	Simplex
51.9100		NFM	Nationwide	Internet Gateway
51.9300		NFM	Nationwide	Internet Gateway
51.9500		NFM	Nationwide	Raynet
51.9500		NFM	Nationwide	Internet Gateway
51.9700		NFM	Nationwide	Raynet

52.0000 - 52.9500 MHz — Broadcasting Links & Radio Microphones

Base	Mobile	Mode	Location	User and Notes
52.0000		NFM	Nationwide	JFMG Location Talkback Mobile
52.2250		NFM	Nationwide	36 Signals Regiment
52.2250		NFM	Nationwide	BBC TV O/B Link
52.7000		NFM	Nationwide	RAF Regiment
52.7500		NFM	Pontypridd	GTFM Community Radio Link
52.7500		NFM	Nationwide	JFMG Stereo Sound Link
52.8500		WFM	Perth	Hospital Radio
52.8750		NFM	Nationwide	JFMG Mono Sound Link
52.8750		NFM	Sheffield	BBC Radio Sheffield
52.9000		NFM	Cardiff	Rookwood Hospital Radio Link
52.9250		NFM	Nationwide	JFMG Mono Sound Link
52.9250		NFM	Swansea	Swansea University Radio Link
52.9500		NFM	Canvey	OAP Homes Radio Net, Castlepoint
52.9500		NFM	Nationwide	JFMG Location Talkback Mobile
53.5250		NFM	Nationwide	BBC O/B Continuity

53.5750 - 55.7500 MHz — Broadcasting Links & Radio Microphones

Base	Mobile	Mode	Location	User and Notes
53.575		NFM	Taunton	BBC O/B Microphones (Somerset Sound)
53.750		NFM	Nationwide	JFMG Portable Audio Links
53.800		NFM	Nationwide	JFMG Low Power Fixed Site Conference
53.950		NFM	Nationwide	JFMG Portable Audio Links
54.100		NFM	Nationwide	JFMG Low Power Fixed Site Conference
54.150		NFM	Nationwide	JFMG Portable Audio Links
54.300		NFM	Nationwide	JFMG Low Power Fixed Site Conference
54.350		NFM	Nationwide	JFMG Portable Audio Links
54.550		NFM	Nationwide	JFMG Portable Audio Links
54.700		NFM	Nationwide	JFMG Low Power Fixed Site Conference
54.750		NFM	Nationwide	JFMG Portable Audio Links
54.950		NFM	Nationwide	JFMG Portable Audio Links
55.150		NFM	Nationwide	JFMG Portable Audio Links
55.350		NFM	Nationwide	JFMG Portable Audio Links
55.400		NFM	Nationwide	JFMG Low Power Fixed Site Conference
55.500		NFM	Nationwide	JFMG Low Power Fixed Site Conference
55.550		NFM	Nationwide	JFMG Portable Audio Links
55.750		NFM	Nationwide	JFMG Portable Audio Links

54.000 - 60.000 MHz — MoD Tactical Communications 25 kHz

Base	Mobile	Mode	Location	User and Notes
54.775		NFM	Nationwide	36 Signals Regiment
54.800		NFM	Yeovilton	845 Squadron Navy Sea King Air-Air
55.000		NFM	Nationwide	Royal Marines Sec/Movements HMS Albion
56.625		NFM	Nationwide	Royal Signals Public Displays
60.000		NFM	Nationwide	36 Signals Regiment

60.7500 - 62.7500 MHz — Radio Microphones & O/B Links

Base	Mobile	Mode	Location	User and Notes
60.295		NFM	Nationwide	BBC O/B Continuity
60.750		NFM	Nationwide	JFMG Portable Audio Links
60.800		NFM	Nationwide	BBC O/B Microphones
60.900		NFM	Nationwide	BBC O/B Microphones
60.950		NFM	Nationwide	JFMG Portable Audio Links
61.000		NFM	Nationwide	BBC O/B Microphones
61.100		NFM	Nationwide	BBC O/B Microphones
61.150		NFM	Nationwide	JFMG Portable Audio Links
61.300		NFM	Nationwide	BBC O/B Microphones
61.350		NFM	Nationwide	JFMG Portable Audio Links
61.400		NFM	Nationwide	BBC O/B Microphones
61.500		NFM	Nationwide	BBC O/B Microphones
61.550		NFM	Nationwide	JFMG Portable Audio Links
61.700		NFM	Nationwide	BBC O/B Microphones
61.750		NFM	Nationwide	JFMG Portable Audio Links
61.800		WFM	Cardiff	Millennium Stadium Audio Link
61.800		NFM	Essex	BBC Radio Essex Radio Microphones
61.800		NFM	Nationwide	BBC O/B Microphones
61.900		NFM	Nationwide	BBC O/B Microphones
61.950		NFM	Nationwide	JFMG Portable Audio Links
62.150		NFM	Nationwide	JFMG Portable Audio Links
62.200		NFM	Nationwide	BBC O/B Microphones
62.350		NFM	Nationwide	JFMG Portable Audio Links
62.550		NFM	Nationwide	JFMG Portable Audio Links
62.600		NFM	Nationwide	BBC O/B Microphones
62.700		NFM	Nationwide	JFMG Portable Audio Links
62.750		NFM	Nationwide	JFMG Portable Audio Links
62.925		NFM	Nationwide	BBC O/B Microphones (spare)

64.0000 - 68.0000 MHz — MoD Tactical Communications and Broadcast Talkback

Base	Mobile	Mode	Location	User and Notes
67.76875	74.71250	NFM	Nationwide	JFMG Temporary Talkback BBC Main Users
67.79375	75.28125	NFM	Nationwide	JFMG Temporary Talkback BBC Main Users
67.80625		NFM	Nationwide	JFMG Temporary Talkback BBC Main Users
67.83125	75.29375	NFM	Nationwide	JFMG Temporary Talkback BBC Main Users

68.08125 - 69.99375 MHz — PMR Low Band Mobile Simplex

Base	Mobile	Mode	Location	User and Notes
68.22500		NFM	Derbyshire	BBC Engineers Ch. 4
68.47500		NFM	Benbecula	Qinetiq Range
68.52500		NFM	Benbecula	Qinetiq Range
68.67500		NFM	Benbecula	Qinetiq Range
68.87500		NFM	Honington	Army
69.15625	82.65625	NFM	Nationwide	JFMG Location Talkback Duplex
69.16875	82.66875	NFM	Nationwide	JFMG Location Talkback Duplex
69.18125	82.68125	NFM	Nationwide	JFMG Location Talkback Duplex
69.22500		NFM	Berkshire	Cadet Training Net
69.57500		NFM	Benbecula	Qinetiq Range
69.97500		NFM	Berkshire	Cadet Training Net

68.0000 - 69.5000 MHz — MoD Mould & Tactical Communications

Base	Mobile	Mode	Location	User and Notes
68.20000		NFM	Nationwide	Royal Signals
68.22500		NFM	Nationwide	Royal Signals
68.26250		NFM	Nationwide	Royal Signals
68.27500		NFM	Dartmoor	Military Range
68.32500		AM	Nationwide	Military Airfield Ground Services
68.35000		NFM	Dartmoor	Military Range
68.36250		NFM	Nationwide	Army Cadet Force Ch.1
68.38750		NFM	Bristol	MoD Transport
68.42500		NFM	Dartmoor	Military Range
68.42500		NFM	Northern Ireland	British Army
68.50000		NFM	RN Rosyth	Dockyard Ops
68.50000		NFM	Rosyth	RN Dockyards Operations
68.56250		AM	RAE Farnborough	Emergency Services
68.61250		AM	RAE Farnborough	Tractor Control
68.62500		NFM	Larkhill	Army Range
68.63750		NFM	Northern Ireland	British Army
68.67875		NFM	Nationwide	Royal Signals
68.68750		AM	Cheltenham	MoD Transport
68.68750		AM	Hampshire	MoD Transport
68.68750		AM	RAE Farnborough	Ground Services
68.69380		AM	RAE Farnborough	Repair Workshop
68.76250		NFM	Salisbury Plain	Army Transport (Tenor Base)
68.78750		AM	Cheltenham	MoD Transport
68.86880		AM	RAE Farnborough	Fire
68.90630		AM	RAE Farnborough	Medical
68.98750		NFM	Brecon Beacons	Mould
69.07500		NFM	Okehampton	Military Range
69.12125		NFM	Nationwide	Royal Signals
69.12500		NFM	Northern Ireland	British Army
69.15500		NFM	Northern Ireland	British Army
69.17500		NFM	Okehampton	Military Range
69.20000		NFM	Northern Ireland	British Army

Base	Mobile	Mode	Location	User and Notes
69.22500		NFM	Berkshire	Army Cadet Training Net
69.25000		NFM	Northern Ireland	British Army
69.32500		NFM	Brecon Beacons	Army
69.32500		NFM	Northern Ireland	British Army
69.35000		AM	Brecon Beacons	Army Cadets Hike Control
69.37500		NFM	Northern Ireland	British Army
69.40000		NFM	Northern Ireland	British Army
69.47500		NFM	Nationwide	39 Inf Bgd/Sig Ch. A9

69.5000 - 69.9750 MHz — MoD Tactical Communications 25 kHz

Base	Mobile	Mode	Location	User and Notes
69.50000		NFM	Okehampton	Military Range
69.50000		NFM	RN Rosyth	Security
69.55000		NFM	Northern Ireland	British Army
69.75000		NFM	Northern Ireland	British Army
69.95000		NFM	Northern Ireland	British Army
69.97500		NFM	Berkshire	Cadet Training Net

70.0000 - 70.5000 MHz — 4m Amateur Radio Band

Base	Mobile	Mode	Location	User and Notes
70.00000		CW	Buxton	Beacon (GB3BUX)
70.01000		CW	Camberley	Beacon (GB3REB)
70.02000		CW	Dundee	Beacon (GB3ANG)
70.02500		CW	St Austell	Beacon (GB3MCB)
70.05260		CW	Powys	Beacon (GW3MHW)
70.20000		CW	Nationwide	CW Calling Channel
70.20000		SSB	Nationwide	SSB Calling Channel
70.26000		AM	Nationwide	AM Calling Channel
70.30000		NFM	Nationwide	Fax Calling Channel
70.30000		NFM	Nationwide	RTTY Calling Channel
70.31250		NFM	Nationwide	Packet Channel
70.32500		NFM	Nationwide	Packet Channel
70.35000		NFM	Nationwide	Raynet Channel
70.37500		NFM	Nationwide	Raynet Channel
70.38750		NFM	Nationwide	Internet Gateway
70.40000		NFM	Nationwide	Raynet Channel
70.41250		NFM	Nationwide	Internet Gateway
70.42500		NFM	Nationwide	GB2RS News
70.45000		NFM	Nationwide	FM Calling Channel
70.48750		NFM	Nationwide	Packet Channel

70.5000 - 71.5000 MHz — Fire Brigades (England & Wales) 12.5 kHz (Mobiles 80.0000 - 81.5000 MHz)

Base	Mobile	Mode	Location	User and Notes
70.50000	80.00000	AM	Galashiels	Fire Brigade (M2ZF)
70.51250	80.18750	AM	Coventry	Fire Brigade (M2FB)
70.51250	80.42500	NFM	Northumberland	Fire Brigade, Round Meadow (M2LJ)
70.51250	80.43750	AM	West Midlands	Fire Brigade (M2FB)
70.52500	80.10000	AM	London	Fire Brigade (M2FH) Ch.1
70.52500	80.73750	AM	Manchester	Fire Brigade (M2FT) Ch.2
70.53750	80.11250	AM	North Yorkshire	Fire Brigade (M2LY)
70.53750	80.18750	AM	Nottinghamshire	Fire Brigade (M2NZ)
70.55000		AM	Manchester	Fire Brigade HQ (M2FT) Ch.1
70.56250	80.98750	AM	Lincolnshire	Fire Brigade (M2NV)
70.56250	80.60000	AM	Mid Glamorgan	Fire Brigade (M2WF)
70.57500	80.46250	AM	West Midlands	Fire Brigade (M2FBW) Ch.3
70.58750	80.18750	AM	Hampshire	Fire Brigade (M2HX) Ch.2
70.58700	80.76250	AM	Manchester	Fire Brigade (M2FT) Ch.3

Base	Mobile	Mode	Location	User and Notes
70.60000	80.00000	AM	Derbyshire	Fire Brigade (M2ND)
70.60000	81.26250	NFM	Warwickshire	Fire Brigade (M2YS)
70.61250	80.12500	AM	Dyfed	Fire Brigade (M2WV)
70.61250	80.87500	NFM	Surrey	Fire Brigade (M2HF)
70.61250	80.12500	NFM	West Yorkshire	Fire Brigade (M2XF)
70.62500	80.61250	AM	Essex	Fire Brigade (M2VD) Ch.1 Mobilising
70.62500		AM	Merseyside	Fire Brigade (M2FO) Ch.3
70.62500	80.61250	AM	Mid Glamorgan	Fire Brigade (M2WF)
70.63750	80.21250	AM	East Sussex	Fire Brigade (M2KD)
70.63750	80.11250	AM	South Yorkshire	Fire Brigade M2(XV)
70.65000	80.98750	AM	Wiltshire	Fire Brigade (M2QM)
70.66250	80.45000	AM	Leicestershire	Fire Brigade (M2NK)
70.67500	80.55000	NFM	Lancashire	Fire Brigade (M2BE) Ch.1
70.67500	80.55000	AM	Liverpool	Fire Brigade(M2FO)
70.67500	80.52500	AM	South Glamorgan	Fire Brigade (M2WD)
70.68750	80.91250	AM	Hereford & Worcester	Fire Brigade (M2YB)
70.70000	81.12500	NFM	Gwent	Fire Brigade (M2WP) Ch.4
70.70000	80.20000	AM	Merseyside	Fire Brigade (M2FO) Ch.4
70.70000	80.20000	AM	Norfolk	Fire Brigade (M2VF)
70.71250	80.80000	AM	Derbyshire	Fire Brigade (M2ND)
70.71250	80.35000	AM	East Sussex	Fire Brigade (M2KD) Ch.2
70.72500	80.03750	AM	Devon	Fire Brigade (M2QD)
70.72500	80.67500	AM	Essex	Fire Brigade (M2VD) Ch.2
70.74000	70.74000	NFM	West Midlands	Fire Brigade Data Link
70.75000	80.75000	AM	Northamptonshire	Fire Brigade (M2NO)
70.76250	80.15000	AM	East London	Fire Brigade (M2FE) Ch.3
70.76250	80.15000	AM	London	Fire Brigade Ch.3 (M2FE)
70.76250	80.98750	NFM	West Yorkshire	Fire Brigade (M2XF)
70.77500	80.50000	AM	Cheshire	Fire Brigade (M2CF)
70.77500	80.50000	AM	Hampshire	Fire Brigade (M2HX) Ch.1
70.77500	80.42500	NFM	Northumbria	Fire Brigade (M2LJ)
70.78750		NFM	Buckinghamshire	Fire Brigade (M2HK)
70.78750	80.80000	AM	Cornwall	Fire Brigade (M2QA)
70.80000	80.51250	AM	West Sussex	Fire Brigade (M2KW)
70.81250	81.21250	AM	Gwynedd	Fire Brigade (M2WC)
70.81250	81.77500	AM	N. Wales	Fire Brigade Area Command (M2KW)
70.82500	80.03750	AM	Devon	Fire Brigade (M2QD)
70.82500	80.78750	AM	Manchester	Fire Brigade (M2FT) Ch.4
70.83750	80.03750	NFM	Cumbria	Fire Brigade (M2BC)
70.83750	80.03750	AM	Galashiels	Fire Brigade (M2ZF)
70.83750	80.12500	AM	Kent	Fire Brigade (M2KF)
70.83750	80.20000	AM	Norfolk	Fire Brigade (M2VF)
70.85000	80.96250	AM	Powys	Fire Brigade Area Command (M2WB)
70.86250	80.55000	AM	Dorset	Fire Brigade (M2QK)
70.87500	80.66250	NFM	West Yorkshire	Fire Brigade (M2XF) Ch.2
70.88750	80.21250	AM	Durham	Fire Brigade (M2LF)
70.88750		AM	Staffordshire	Fire Brigade (M2YG)
70.90000	80.03750	AM	Hertfordshire	Fire Brigade (M2VI)
70.90000	80.60000	NFM	Lancashire	Fire Brigade (M2BE) Ch.2
70.90000	80.40000	NFM	Suffolk	Fire Brigade (M2VN)
70.91250	80.00000	NFM	Essex	Fire Brigade (M2VD) Ch.3
70.91250		NFM	London	Fire Brigade Data Channel
70.93750		NFM	England & Wales	Fire Brigade Data Channel
70.95000		NFM	West Glamorgan	Fire Brigade (M2WZ)

Base	Mobile	Mode	Location	User and Notes
70.96250	80.11250	AM	London	Fire Brigade (M2FS) Ch.2 NE & SE
70.96250	81.08750	AM	Merseyside	Fire Brigade (M2FO) Ch.2
70.97500	80.65000	AM	Shropshire	Fire Brigade (M2YU)
70.98750	80.42500	NFM	Northumbria	Fire Brigade, Quarry House (M2LJ)
71.01250	80.17500	AM	Avon	Fire Brigade (M2QC)
71.01250	80.17500	AM	Bristol	Fire Brigade (M2QG)
71.03750	81.16250	AM	Merseyside	Fire Brigade (M2FO) Ch.1 Central & South
71.07500	80.15000	AM	Bristol	Fire Brigade (M2QG)
71.07500	80.62500	AM	Gloucester	Fire Brigade (M2QF)
71.07500	80.15000	AM	Humberside	Fire Brigade (M2XT)
71.10000	80.47500	AM	Humberside	Fire Brigade (M2XT) Ch.1
71.10000	80.66250	AM	Oxfordshire	Fire Brigade (M2HI)
71.11250	80.41250	AM	Bedfordshire	Fire Brigade (M2VM)
71.11250	80.00000	AM	Cleveland	Fire Brigade (M2LT) Ch.1 Major Incidents
71.12500	80.11250	AM	Somerset	Fire Brigade (M2QI)
71.13750	80.43750	AM	North Yorkshire	Fire Brigade (M2LY) East Area
71.15000	80.51250	AM	West Midlands	Fire Brigade (M2FBW) Ch.2 Western D+E
71.16250	80.87500	AM	N Wales	Fire Brigade Eastern Area (M2WK)
71.17500	80.21250	AM	London	Fire Brigade West Command (M2FN) Ch.4
71.17500	81.11250	AM	North Yorkshire	Fire Brigade (M2LY) Western Area
71.20000	80.22500	NFM	Berkshire	Fire Brigade (M2HD)
71.20000	80.05000	AM	Humberside	Fire Brigade (M2XT)
71.20000	80.00000	NFM	Lancashire	Fire Brigade (M2BE) Ch.2
71.20000	80.22500	NFM	Scunthorpe	Fire Brigade (M2HQ)
71.25000	80.00000	NFM	Gloucester	Fire Brigade (M2YP)
71.26250		NFM	Windsor Great Park	Royal Park Rangers
71.27500	81.13750	AM	Cleveland	Fire Brigade (M2LT)
71.27500	81.06250	AM	Isle of Wight	Fire Brigade (M2HP)
71.27500	81.08750	NFM	Suffolk	Fire Brigade (M2VN)
71.30000	81.38750	AM	Tyne and Wear	Fire Brigade (M2LP) Ch.1
71.31250		NFM	England & Wales	Fire Brigade Data Channel
71.33750	80.00000	NFM	London	Fire Brigade (M2FHO) Ch.5 1200 Baud
71.33750	80.78750	NFM	South Glamorgan	Fire Brigade (M2WD)
71.33750	81.38750	AM	Tyne and Wear	Fire Brigade (M2LP) Ch.2
71.37500		AM	Gwent	Fire Brigade (M2SD)
71.37500	81.08750	NFM	West Glamorgan	Fire Brigade (M2WF)
71.38750		AM	Gloucestershire	Fire Brigade (M2QC)
71.38750	80.00000	NFM	Lancashire	Fire Brigade (M2BE) Ch.3
71.42500	80.52500	AM	Cambridgeshire	Fire Brigade (M2VC)
71.45000		AM	Nottinghamshire	Fire Brigade (M2NZ)

72.8000 - 73.9250 MHz   MoD Tactical Communications 25 kHz

Base	Mobile	Mode	Location	User and Notes
72.80000		NFM	Brecon Beacons	Army Range Ops.
72.81250		NFM	Portsmouth	Navel Base Transport & Security
72.81250		NFM	Southampton	Royal Navy Loading
72.98750		NFM	Devonport	Naval Provost, HMS Drake
73.00000		NFM	Brecon Beacons	Army Range Ops.
73.00000		NFM	High Wycombe	RAF Police
73.07500		NFM	Cinque Ports	44 Signals Regiment
73.10000		NFM	Aldershot	Military Police
73.21250		NFM	Portsmouth	Royal Navy Transport
73.32500		NFM	Plymouth	Royal Marines
73.33750		NFM	RN Portsdown	Base Ops.
73.33750		NFM	Nationwide	Sea Cadets
73.35000		NFM	Nationwide	MoD Security Police

Base	Mobile	Mode	Location	User and Notes
73.35000		NFM	Lulworth	Range Safety, Land
73.36250		AM	Nationwide	Sea Cadets (Not Within N Ireland)
73.37500		NFM	South Staffs	Army
73.38750		NFM	Nationwide	Sea Cadets
73.40000		NFM	Devonport	MoD Security
73.40000		NFM	Portsmouth	RN Whale Island (151.4)
73.42500		NFM	RN Faslane	Transport
73.42500		NFM	Portsmouth	RN Electricians
73.45000		NFM	Portsmouth	RN Movements
73.46250		NFM	Nationwide	Army Cadet Force
73.47500		NFM	Blandford Forum	Royal Military Police
73.47500		NFM	Nationwide	MoD Police
73.48750		NFM	Nationwide	Sea Cadet Corps Ch.SV5
73.51250		NFM	Fairford	MoD Police Special Events (E Div.)(118.8)
73.51250		NFM	London	MoD Police, Charlton Barracks
73.51250		NFM	Mildenhall	MoD Police Special Events (G Division)
73.51250		NFM	Portsmouth	MoD Police, RN Portsdown
73.53750		NFM	Farnborough	MoD Police at Air Show
73.53750		NFM	Plymouth	MoD Operations
73.53750		NFM	Southampton	RN Marchwoood Military Port
73.55000		NFM	Portland	MoD Police
73.55000		NFM	Harrogate	MoD Police, Menwith Hill
73.56250		NFM	RN Faslane	Security (Alpha Control)
73.56250		NFM	Harrogate	MoD Police, Menwith Hill
73.56750		NFM	RN Poole	Royal Marines
73.57500		NFM	Plymouth	Military Police
73.57500		NFM	Yeovilton	RN Provosts (151.4)
73.57500		NFM	RN Dartmouth	Navy Ops.
73.58750		NFM	London	Royal Military Police Ch 10
73.58750		NFM	Portsmouth	Royal Navy Hospital, Haslar
73.61250		NFM	Plymouth	MoD Police
73.63750		NFM	Plymouth	MoD Police
73.65000		NFM	London	MoD Police
73.65000		NFM	Portsmouth	HMS Dolphin
73.67500		NFM	Devonport	MoD Security
73.67500		NFM	Portsmouth	HMS Dolphin Main Gate
73.70000		NFM	Nationwide	Army Cadet Force
73.70000		NFM	RN Faslane	MoD Police
73.73750		NFM	Bedfordshire	British Intelligence Centre
73.73750		NFM	London	Royal Military Police Ch.11
73.80000		NFM	Brecon Beacons	Army Range Control
73.85000		NFM	Nationwide	Army Cadet Force
73.87500		NFM	Nationwide	Sea Cadet Corps Ch.SV2
73.88750		NFM	London	MoD Police RAF West Ruislip
73.90000		NFM	Devonport	MoD

73.9250 - 74.7875 MHz — MoD Mould & Tactical Channels 12.5 kHz

Base	Mobile	Mode	Location	User and Notes
73.95000		NFM	Portsmouth	RN Electricians
74.01250	79.01250	NFM	London	Mould
74.07500	79.03750	NFM	Catterick	MoD Police (Watchdog)
74.10000		NFM	RAF Honington	RAF Police Ch 3
74.11250		NFM	Colchester	Barracks
74.20000		NFM	Nationwide	Military Transport Security
74.20000	79.30000	NFM	Nationwide	RAF Police Transport
74.21250		NFM	Catterick	MoD Police (Watchdog)

Base	Mobile	Mode	Location	User and Notes
74.22500		NFM	Nationwide	Royal Ordnance Corps
74.30000		NFM	Thetford	Stanford Battle Ground Command Channel
74.42500	79.86250	NFM	London	Mould/Ptarmigan
74.48750	79.60000	NFM	London	Mould/Ptarmigan
74.57500		NFM	Richmond	MoD Police
74.60000	79.91250	NFM	London	Mould/Ptarmigan
74.73750	79.76250	NFM	London	Mould/Ptarmigan

74-8000 - 75.2500 MHz — Civil Aviation Outer, Middle and Inner Runway Markers

Base	Mobile	Mode	Location	User and Notes
75.00000		AM	Nationwide	Runway Marker Beacons

75.2500 - 75.3000 MHz — Broadcasting

Base	Mobile	Mode	Location	User and Notes
75.26250	75.30000	NFM	Nationwide	JFMG Airborne

75.3000 - 76.7000 MHz — MoD 12.5 kHz

Base	Mobile	Mode	Location	User and Notes
75.32500		NFM	Devonport	Royal Navy Devonport
75.46250		NFM	Chichester	163 Provo Company RM Police
75.60000		NFM	Plymouth	MoD
75.66250		NFM	Chichester	163 Provo Company RM Police
75.66250		NFM	Wattisham Barracks	Royal Military Police
75.67500		NFM	Plymouth	MoD Dockyard Ops
75.73750		NFM	Nationwide	Military Close Protection
75.76250		NFM	Salisbury Plain	Close Support Group
75.78750	84.7125	NFM	London	Mould/Ptarmigan
75.81250		NFM	Brecon Beacons	Army
75.82500		NFM	London	Guards, Wellington Barracks/Buckingham Palace
75.82500		NFM	Nationwide	Military Close Protection Ch.12
75.83750		NFM	East Anglia	MoD Police G Division
75.83750		NFM	Portsmouth	MoD Police (151.4)
75.83750		NFM	RN Faslane	Security (Charlie Control)
75.87500	84.71250	NFM	London	Mould/Ptarmigan
75.87500		NFM	Nationwide	Military Close Protection
75.93750		NFM	Salisbury Plain	Army Cadets
75.94000		NFM	Salisbury Plain	Army
75.97500		NFM	Nationwide	Royal Signals
75.98750		NFM	Edinburgh	DVP Military
76.01250		NFM	Plymouth	MoD Dockyard Ops.
76.06250	84.86250	NFM	London	Mould/Ptarmigan
76.06250		NFM	Nationwide	Military Close Protection
76.22500	84.36250	NFM	London	Mould/Ptarmigan
76.25000		NFM	Brecon Beacons	Army
76.26250		NFM	Gwent	Army
76.30000		NFM	RN Culdrose	Ground Services
76.30000		NFM	RN Yeovilton	Navy Provosts
76.32500		NFM	London	MoD Police Ruislip
76.32500		NFM	Nationwide	Military Close Protection
76.43750	84.76250	NFM	London	Mould/Ptarmigan
76.43750		NFM	Nationwide	Military Close Protection
76.43750		NFM	Salisbury Plain	Army
76.44000		NFM	Salisbury Plain	Army
76.50000		NFM	Cardigan Bay	Qinetiq, Aberporth Range
76.50000		NFM	London	MoD Police Ruislip
76.50000		NFM	London	DVP Military, North London
76.50000		NFM	Nationwide	Military Close Protection
76.60000		NFM	Cardigan Bay	Qinetiq, Aberporth Range

UK Car Rallying

If you're thinking about taking your scanner to a motor rally, here's a brief guide to the various communications systems in use along with a selecton of frequencies that are used at these events.

Motor rallies are not races in the accepted sense; instead they are a series of time trials that take place over various stages and they range from small, local events lasting just one day to major international competitions lasting several days.

Don't expect to hear much from the drivers and navigators taking part in a rally. They rarely use radios because they're far too busy trying to complete each stage as quickly as possible. It's the officials who use the radios. Marshals, trackside officials, medical crews and so on can be heard at most rallies.

The communications setup at these events is a little unusual in that individuals do not carry radios. Instead, radio cars are placed around the stages and they are in contact with each other. Anyone on the ground who needs to send or receive a message has to do it through these cars.

There are three basic radio systems in general use at rallies. System C is the minimum communications requirement for all rallies; System B is usually used for larger events and System A is generally only added for the largest events.

System C 81.575 MHz
This system is obligatory at MSA (Motor Sports Association) events. It's the Medical and Safety channel and it's used at all MSA rallies

System B
At larger rallies, this system is used in addition to System C. Events such as the World Rally Championship, now known in the UK as Wales Rally GB but which used to be called the RAC Rally, use this system to pass on the number and time of each car as it passes a checkpoint.

Radio cars are placed at the beginning and end of each stage and usually at regular intervals (normally 5 kilometres) along the way. Different callsigns are used to indicate the stage and the distance so, for example, Rheola 10K would be used by the car at the 10 kilometre marker on the Rheola stage.

These are the System B frequencies; they can be used either simplex or duplex through a repeater:

75.30000 Ch.6	86.83750 Ch.5
76.82500 Ch.4	77.62500 Could Be Repeater Input
78.25000 Ch.7	77.63750 Could Be Repeater Input

System A

At very large events, they often use System A frequencies (either simplex or duplex) as well as those in System C and System B. They will usually be used by the Course Opening cars, the Stage Commanders and other officials when they want to communicate with Rally HQ.

For the Wales Rally GB, senior officials used the callsigns 'Pilot' followed by their own names so they were Pilot Pete, Pilot John and so on.

Here's a selection of System A frequencies that have been used at World Rally Championship events over the years:

82.66250		Crychan (2001)
82.66250		Rally Control, Margam Command & Pilot Philip (2001)
82.66250		Half Way Ch.3 CTCSS 107.2Hz (2004)
82.67500		Rally Control, Brechfa & Trascoed Command (2001)
82.67500		Rally Control & Course Opening cars (2003)
82.67500		Halfway Command, Control & Finish (2003)
82.68750		Rally HQ (2003)
82.68750		Brechfa & Trascoed Command (2003)
82.68750		Rally HQ Ch.1 Brechfa (2004)
82.76250		RAC HQ (1996)
82.78750	77.6125	Hafren/Sweet Lamb to RAC HQ (1997)
82.78750		HQ Chester to Marshals (1994)
82.78750		HQ Chester to Marshals (1995)
82.78750	69.9875	Rhondda Stop & Course Cars (1999)
82.78750	77.6250	(2000)
82.80000		Pantperthog to RAC HQ (1997)
82.80000		HQ Chester to Marshals (1994)
82.80000		HQ Chester to Marshals (1995)
82.80000		HQ Chester to Marshals (1996)
82.80000		RAC HQ (1998)
82.80000		Rally Control Wrexham to Stages (1999)
82.80000		Rally Control (1999)
82.80000	77.6250	Gartheiniog (2000)
82.80000	77.6250	(2000)
82.81250		Dovey (1997)
82.81250	69.9875	HQ Chester to Marshals (1994)
82.81250		HQ Chester to Marshals (1995)
82.81250	73.6375	Rheola Commander & Course Cars (1999)
82.81250	77.6375	Sweet Lamb Ch.3 (2000)
82.81250	77.6250	Myherin Ch.3 (2000)
82.81250	77.6375	Brechfa Ch.3 (2000)
82.81250	77.6250	Trascoed Ch.3 (2000)

76.70625 - 77.99375 MHz — PMR Low Band Mobiles 12.5 kHz Duplex

Base	Mobile	Mode	Location	User and Notes
77.30000		NFM	Scotland	Scottish Office Emergency Voice Network
77.68750		NFM	London	London Underground Contractors (114.8)
77.68750		NFM	Nationwide	St John Ambulance General UK Ch.1
77.70000		NFM	Swansea	Royal Mail Depot

77.8000 - 79.0000 MHz — MoD & Broadcast Links 12.5 kHz

Base	Mobile	Mode	Location	User and Notes
77.87500		NFM	Nationwide	ITN O/B Film Mobiles
78.01250	73.73750	NFM	RNAS Yeovilton	MoD Guard Services (151.4)
78.01250		NFM	Thetford	Army Wardens Land Rover Training Area
78.02500		NFM	Pembroke	Military Range
78.10000		AM	Nationwide	Air Training Corps (V3)
78.11250		NFM	Nationwide	MoD Police South Division E
78.11250	73.17500	NFM	Portsmouth	MoD Guard Service, RN Dockyard (151.4)
78.11250		NFM	RNAS Yeovilton	MoD Police (151.4)
78.11250		NFM	RN Faslane	Security (Papa Control)
78.13750		NFM	Blandford	Royal Signals Security
78.16250		NFM	Aldermaston	Atomic Weapons Establishment
78.16250	73.61250	NFM	Devonport	MoD Police Repeater
78.16250		NFM	Hampshire	MoD Police (Kilo Golf)
78.16250	73.61250	NFM	London	MoD Police Repeater
78.16250	84.66250	NFM	Okehampton	Military Range
78.16250		NFM	RN Faslane	Security (Bravo Control)
78.16250	73.61250	NFM	Salisbury Plain	MoD Police (Scrambled)
78.20000		NFM	Nationwide	BBC O/B Camera Link
78.21250		NFM	Nationwide	BBC O/B Camera Link
78.21250		NFM	London	RAF, West Ruislip
78.22500		NFM	Nationwide	BBC O/B Camera Link
78.23750		NFM	Aldermaston	Atomic Weapons Establishment Ch.1
78.23750		NFM	Aldershot	MoD Police
78.23750		NFM	Devonport	Royal Navy
78.23750		NFM	Larkhill	Regimental Police, Larkhill Range
78.23750		NFM	Nationwide	BBC O/B Camera Link
78.25000		NFM	Nationwide	BBC O/B Camera Link
78.27500		NFM	Nationwide	Army Cadet Force
78.27500		NFM	Nationwide	BBC TV Camera Link
78.28750		NFM	Larkhill	Range Safety Officers
78.30000		NFM	Middle Wallop	Army Air Corps
78.30000		NFM	Nationwide	Combined Cadet Force
78.33750		NFM	Bisley	Army Range Control
78.41250		NFM	Middle Wallop	Army Air Corps
78.45000		NFM	Middle Wallop	Base Security
78.55000		NFM	Middle Wallop	Ops. Ch.1
78.57500		NFM	RNAS Yeovilton	Crash Ops. Ch.7
78.57500		NFM	RN Culdrose	Fire Station Ch.4
78.68750		NFM	Portsmouth	RN Police
78.77500		NFM	Middle Wallop	Ops. Ch.2
78.80000		NFM	Poole	Royal Marines
78.80000		NFM	RNAS Culdrose	Tower Ch.1
78.80000		NFM	RNAS Yeovilton	Ops.
78.82500		NFM	Middle Wallop	Tower to Ground
78.85000		NFM	Middle Wallop	Ops.
78.90000		NFM	RNAS Culdrose	Fire School Ch.2
78.90000		NFM	RNAS Prestwick	Navy Helo Ops. Air-Ground
78.90000		NFM	RNAS Yeovilton	Fuel & Maintenance

Base	Mobile	Mode	Location	User and Notes
78.95000		NFM	RNAS Culdrose	Bowsers Ch.5
78.95000		NFM	RNAS Yeovilton	Ops.
78.95000		NFM	RN Merryfield	Ops.
78.97500		NFM	Larkhill	Firing Control Officers, Larkhill Range

79.0000 - 80.0000 MHz — MoD & RAF Services 12.5 kHz

Base	Mobile	Mode	Location	User and Notes
79.00000		NFM	Longcross	Qinetiq MoD Police
79.00000		NFM	RN Culdrose	Ground Radio Ch.3
79.00000		NFM	RN Yeovilton	Tower-Ground Ch.3
79.20000		NFM	Longcross	Qinetiq MoD Police
79.35000		NFM	Larkhill	Royal Military Police, Larkhill Range
79.37500		NFM	Gosport	RN Security (Tanzy Control)
79.40000		NFM	RAF Honington	Military Police
79.40000		NFM	Tain	Range Control
79.47500		NFM	Lydd	Army Camp Police
79.50000		NFM	Lydd	Army Camp Police
79.50000		NFM	Wattisham	Tower
79.82500	84.82500	NFM	Berkshire	Nuclear Weapons Transport

80.0000 - 82.5000 MHz — Radio Astronomy within 48 km of Cambridge

Base	Mobile	Mode	Location	User and Notes
80.01250		AM/NFM	Nationwide	Fire Brigade Manpacks/Vehicle-Vehicle Ch.21
80.07500		NFM	Hampshire	Fire Brigade Vehicle-Vehicle Ch.07
80.07500		AM/NFM	Nationwide	Fire Brigade Manpacks/Vehicle-Vehicle Ch.22
80.32500	70.5500	NFM	Scotland	Scottish Office Emergency Voice Network Ch.1
80.33750	70.5625	NFM	Scotland	Scottish Office Emergency Voice Network Ch.2
80.35000	70.5750	NFM	Scotland	Scottish Office Emergency Voice Network Ch.3
80.36250	70.5875	NFM	Scotland	Scottish Office Emergency Voice Network Ch.4
80.37500	70.6000	NFM	Scotland	Scottish Office Emergency Voice Network Ch.5
80.55000	70.7750	NFM	Scotland	Scottish Office Emergency Voice Network
80.80000	71.0250	NFM	Scotland	Scottish Office Emergency Voice Network
80.87500	71.1000	NFM	Scotland	Scottish Office Emergency Voice Network

81.5000 - 83.5000 MHz — Low Band PMR (Simplex & Duplex)

Base	Mobile	Mode	Location	User and Notes
81.02500	71.2500	NFM	Scotland	Scottish Office Emergency Voice Network
81.23750	71.4625	NFM	Scotland	Scottish Office Emergency Voice Network
81.57500		NFM	Nationwide	Motor Rally Safety Allocation (From 2003)
81.57500		NFM	N Ireland	Ulster Automobile Club Ch.2
81.80000	68.30000	NFM	Hampshire	Community Repeater, Bullmark
81.80000	68.30000	NFM	Hampshire	Community Repeater, Cleaning Firm
81.80000	68.30000	NFM	Hampshire	Community Repeater, Farm
81.80000	68.30000	NFM	Hampshire	Community Repeater, Sand & Gravel Co.
81.80000	68.30000	NFM	Hampshire	Community Repeater, Security Company
81.80000	68.30000	NFM	Hampshire	Community Repeater, Turfers
81.80000	68.30000	NFM	Herts./Essex	Community Repeater (131.8)
81.80000	68.30000	NFM	Herts./Essex	Community Repeater (173.8)
81.80000	68.30000	NFM	Herts./Essex	Community Repeater (186.2)
81.80000	68.30000	NFM	Isle of Wight	KJ Joyce
81.80000	68.30000	NFM	Mansfield	Community Repeater, Mansfield Skips
81.80000	68.30000	NFM	Poole	Community Repeater
81.80000	68.30000	NFM	Portsmouth	Community Repeater, Council
81.80000	68.30000	NFM	Portsmouth	Red Star Parcels
81.80000	68.30000	NFM	Purbrook	Community Repeater, Battmans
81.80000	68.30000	NFM	Ringwood	Community Repeater, Hall Aggregates
81.80000	68.30000	NFM	Southampton	Community Repeater, Ennimix
81.81250	68.31250	NFM	Kent	Council Highways Department
81.81250	68.31250	NFM	Kent	Doctors Scheme Trunked

Base	Mobile	Mode	Location	User and Notes
81.81250	68.31250	NFM	London	Toni's Radio Cars, Kew Bridge
81.81250	68.31250	NFM	Maidstone	AH Tyler Trunked Repeater
81.85000	68.35000	NFM	Glasgow	Taxi Company
81.85000	68.35000	NFM	London	South London Radio Cars, Wandsworth
81.86250	68.36250	NFM	London	Toni's Radio Cars, Kew Bridge
81.88750	68.38750	NFM	Sussex	PMR Repeater
81.91250	68.31250	NFM	London	Express Taxis
81.91250	68.31250	NFM	London	Swift Couriers, Southgate
81.91250	68.31250	NFM	London	Taxi Company, Ickenham
81.91250	68.41250	NFM	Slough	Express Taxis
81.92500	68.42500	NFM	Birmingham	Taxi Company
81.92500	68.42500	NFM	Hayes	Wings Cabs
81.92500	68.42500	NFM	Redcar	Taxi Company
81.93750	68.43750	NFM	London	Sky Cars, Southall
81.96250	68.46250	AM	Cardiff	City Cars
81.96250	68.46250	AM	Plymouth	Plymouth Taxis
81.98750	68.48750	NFM	Grimsby	Marine Gas and Oil
81.98750	68.48750	NFM	Kent	Courier Service
81.98750	68.48750	NFM	Kent	Doctors' Service Trunked
81.98750	68.48750	NFM	Maidstone	AH Tyler Trunked Repeater
81.98750	68.48750	NFM	Portsmouth	PMR Repeater
82.00000	68.50000	NFM	Sussex	PMR Repeater
82.00000		NFM	London	Royal Military Police, Duke of Yorks HQ
82.01250	68.51250	NFM	Ilford	Atlas Cars
82.01250	68.51250	NFM	London	AJ Cars
82.01250	68.51250	NFM	London	Whetstone Cars
82.01250	68.51250	NFM	Stamford	Premier Taxis (118.8)
82.02500	68.52500	NFM	Erith	Apex Cars
82.02500	68.52500	NFM	Yeadon	SKJ Private Hire (136.5)
82.03750	68.53750	NFM	London	London Car Hire
82.06000	68.56250	NFM	Worcester	Amber Taxis
82.06250	68.56250	NFM	Glasgow	Taxi Company
82.10000	68.60000	NFM	Glasgow	Taxi Company
82.10000	68.60000	NFM	London	Roadrunner Taxis, South Bermondsey
82.10000	68.60000	AM	Swansea	Ryan Mining Ch.1
82.11250	68.61250	NFM	Edinburgh	Taxi Company
82.11250	68.61250	NFM	Glasgow	Taxi Company
82.13750	68.63750	NFM	East Yorkshire	Council Roads Department
82.13750	68.63750	NFM	Humberside	County Council Ch.1
82.13750	68.63750	NFM	Kent	Doctors' Service Trunked
82.13750	68.63750	NFM	London	Building Supplier
83.13750	68.63750	NFM	Maidstone	AH Tyler Trunked Repeater
82.13750	68.63750	NFM	Tonbridge	Doctors' Service
82.17500	85.17500	NFM	Bristol Area	Maintenance Company
82.18750	68.68750	NFM	London	Contract Dustcart
82.21250	68.71250	AM	Swansea	Ryan Mining Ch.2
82.22500	68.72500	NFM	Newcastle	PMR Repeater
82.27500	68.77500	NFM	Kings Lynn	Hughes Electrical
82.30000	68.80000	NFM	Kent	Council Highways Department
82.30000	68.80000	NFM	Kent	Doctors' Service Trunked
82.30000	68.80000	NFM	Leicester	PMR Repeater
82.30000	68.80000	NFM	Maidstone	AH Tyler Trunked Repeater
82.30000	68.80000	NFM	Sussex	PMR Repeater
82.30000	68.80000	NFM	Tonbridge Wells	Doctors' Service
82.36250	68.76250	NFM	Ipswich	TV Repair Company
82.40000	68.90000	NFM	London	Ambassador Car Service, West End

Base	Mobile	Mode	Location	User and Notes
82.40000	68.90000	NFM	London	Embassy/Lady Cars, Archway Area
82.43750	68.93750	NFM	Glasgow	Taxi Company
82.43750	68.93750	NFM	Gravesend	Taxi Company
82.46250	68.96250	NFM	Salford	Mainline Taxis
82.47500	68.97500	NFM	London	Del Cars, Bow
82.47500	68.97500	NFM	London	White Horse Cabs, Stepney
82.48750	68.98750	NFM	London	Senator Cars
82.50000	69.00000	NFM	Arbroath	Geddes Construction
82.50000	69.00000	NFM	London	Great North Cars, Finchley
82.52500	69.02500	NFM	Nationwide	Road Construction Traffic Management
82.55000	69.05000	NFM	Lincoln	PMR Repeater
82.80000	68.50000	NFM	Bournemouth	Securiguard
82.80000	68.50000	NFM	Nationwide	Nynex Telecoms Engineers
83.02500	69.52500	NFM	West Midlands	Seven Trent Water
83.06500	69.56500	NFM	Birmingham	Building Supply Company
83.07500	69.57500	NFM	Birmingham	Seven Trent Water, Aqua Base
83.11250	69.61250	NFM	London	Meter Cabs, Kentish Town
83.35000	69.85000	NFM	Swansea	Council Works Department

83.996 - 84.000 MHz — Industrial, Scientific & Medical Equipment

84.000 - 84.9750 MHz — MoD Communications 25 kHz Simplex

Base	Mobile	Mode	Location	User and Notes
84.05000		NFM	Tweed Valley	Military Police
84.08750		NFM	Nationwide	Military Close Protection
84.12500		NFM	Larkhill	MoD Police, Imber Range Ch.6
84.15000		NFM	Nationwide	Military Close Protection
84.20000		NFM	Larkhill	MoD Police, Imber Range Ch.8
84.22500		NFM	Nationwide	RAF
84.26250		NFM	Nationwide	Military Close Protection
84.30000		NFM	Nationwide	RAF Mountain Rescue Teams
84.31250		NFM	Larkhill	MoD Police, Larkhill Range
84.32500		NFM	Nationwide	RAF Mountain Rescue Ch.2
84.32500		NFM	Wiltshire	MoD Raydex Helicopter Downlink
84.33750		NFM	Blandford	MoD Police
84.36250		NFM	Nationwide	Military Close Protection
84.37500		NFM	Nationwide	Military Police
84.38750		NFM	Nationwide	Military Police
84.40000		NFM	Nationwide	Military Police
84.41250		NFM	Nationwide	Military Police
84.41250		NFM	Lulworth	Range Wardens (218.1)
84.42500		NFM	Nationwide	Military Police
84.43750		NFM	Nationwide	Military Police
84.45000		NFM	Nationwide	Military Police
84.46250		NFM	Nationwide	Military Police
84.47500		NFM	Nationwide	Military Police
84.48750		NFM	England SW	MoD Police
84.48750		NFM	Nationwide	Military Police Escorts
84.50000		NFM	Nationwide	Military Police Royal Escorts
84.51250		NFM	Nationwide	Military Police
84.52500		NFM	Aldershot	Military Police Data
84.53750		NFM	Nationwide	Military Police
84.55000		NFM	London	Military Police
84.56250		NFM	Nationwide	Military Police
84.57500		NFM	Nationwide	Military Police
84.58750		NFM	Nationwide	Military Police
84.60000		NFM	Southampton	Royal Navy

Base	Mobile	Mode	Location	User and Notes
84.61250		NFM	Southampton	Army, Marchwood Camp Shipping Office
84.64000		NFM	Salisbury Plain	Defence Land Services
84.65000	72.85000	NFM	RN Faslane	Medics
84.71250		NFM	Nationwide	Military Close Protection
84.76250		NFM	Nationwide	Military Close Protection
84.77500		NFM	Southampton	Royal Navy
84.82500	79.82500	NFM	Aldermaston	Weapons Transportation
84.82500		NFM	Nationwide	RAF Helicopter Winchmen
84.82500	79.82500	NFM	Nationwide	Royal Ordnance Weapons Transport
84.82500		NFM	RAF Wittering	Military Police Ch. 12
84.83750		NFM	Nationwide	Military Close Protection
84.83750		NFM	Perth	Territorial Army
84.85000		NFM	Nationwide	Military Close Protection
84.87500	78.16250	NFM	Lulworth	Lulworth Range Wardens (218.1)
84.91250		NFM	RNAS Yeovilton	Tower
84.92500		NFM	Southampton	Royal Navy
84.95000		NFM	Lulworth	Range Safety, Sea
84.97500		NFM	Lulworth Cove	Lulworth Camp

84.35000- 84.55000 MHz   Republic of Ireland Fire Brigade and Ambulance Service Duplex

Base	Mobile	Mode	Location	User and Notes
84.35000	74.12500	NFM	Nationwide	Fire Brigade
84.37500	74.15000	NFM	Nationwide	Fire Brigade
84.40000	74.17500	NFM	Nationwide	Fire Brigade
84.42500	74.20000	NFM	Nationwide	Fire Brigade
84.45000	74.22500	NFM	Nationwide	Fire Brigade
84.47500	74.25000	NFM	Nationwide	Fire Brigade
84.50000	74.27500	NFM	Nationwide	Fire Brigade
84.52500	74.30000	NFM	Nationwide	Fire Brigade
84.55000	74.32500	NFM	Nationwide	Fire Brigade
84.57500	74.35000	NFM	Nationwide	Ambulance Service
84.60000	74.37500	NFM	Nationwide	Ambulance Service
84.62500	74.40000	NFM	Nationwide	Ambulance Service
84.65000	74.42500	NFM	Nationwide	Ambulance Service
84.67500	74.45000	NFM	Nationwide	Ambulance Service
84.70000	74.47500	NFM	Nationwide	Ambulance Service
84.72500	74.50000	NFM	Nationwide	Ambulance Service
84.75000	74.52500	NFM	Nationwide	Ambulance Service
84.77500	74.55000	NFM	Nationwide	Ambulance Service
84.80000	74.57500	NFM	Nationwide	Ambulance Service
84.82500	74.60000	NFM	Nationwide	Ambulance Service

85.00625 - 87.5000 MHz   PMR Low Band Base Repeaters 12.5 kHz

Base	Mobile	Mode	Location	User and Notes
85.01250	71.51250	NFM	Birmingham	Vehicle Breakdown Company
85.01250	71.51250	NFM	Brighton	Focsa Street Cleaners
85.01250	71.51250	NFM	Fife	County Council
85.01250	71.51250	NFM	London	Community Repeater, Ealing
85.01250	71.51250	NFM	Sherbourne	Mickey's Taxis (173.8)
85.01250	71.51250	NFM	Suffolk	Anglian Water
85.01250	71.51250	NFM	Sunderland	Sunderland Council Ch.1
85.01250	71.51250	NFM	Telford	Development Corporation
85.01250	71.51250	NFM	Weymouth	MPI Services
85.01250	71.51250	NFM	Widnes	Skip Hire
85.02500	71.52500	NFM	Birmingham	Breakdown Company
85.02500	71.52500	NFM	Exeter	National Rivers Authority

Base	Mobile	Mode	Location	User and Notes
85.02500	71.52500	NFM	Gedling	Gedling Borough Council
85.02500	71.52500	NFM	Nationwide	National Rivers Authority
85.02500	71.52500	NFM	Neath	Council
85.02500	71.52500	NFM	Norfolk	County Highways Department
85.02500	71.52500	NFM	Pickering	Council
85.02500	71.52500	NFM	Port Talbot	Council Services
85.02500	71.55000	NFM	Tranmere	Anchor Taxis
85.03750	71.53750	NFM	Ayr	East Ayrshire Highways Department
85.03750	71.53750	NFM	Cambridge	Regency Cars
85.03750	71.53750	NFM	Dumfries	Council Highways Department
85.03750	71.53750	NFM	Easington	Works Department
85.03750	71.53750	NFM	Exeter	Moorland Garage
85.03750	71.53750	NFM	Hastings	Council
85.03750	71.53750	NFM	Ipswich	Council Repeater
85.03750	71.53750	AM	Killwinning	Council Highways Department
85.03750	71.53750	AM	Leeds	Gritters/Snow Ploughs
85.03750	71.53750	NFM	Strathclyde	Strathclyde Council
85.05000	71.55000	NFM	Aylsham	East Coast Grain
85.05000	71.55000	NFM	Cambridge	Trumpington Farm
85.05000	71.55000	NFM	Ipswich	Cubbit Hire Company
85.05000	71.55000	NFM	Jersey	Abbey
85.05000	71.55000	NFM	London	Baron Cars
85.05000	71.55000	NFM	London	BMC Minicabs, Bermondsey
85.05000	71.55000	NFM	London	Sapphire Cabs
85.05000	71.55000	NFM	Norfolk	Farm Feed Company
85.05000	71.55000	NFM	Peterborough	Royal Taxis
85.05000	71.55000	NFM	Reepham	Salle Farm Company
85.05000	71.55000	NFM	Romford	Atlas Minicabs
85.05000	71.55000	NFM	Sittingbourne	A2 Taxis
85.05000	71.55000	NFM	Southampton	Taxi Company
85.05000	71.55000	NFM	Suffolk	Farm Feed Company
85.05000	71.55000	NFM	Swanage	Associated Taxis
85.05000	71.55000	NFM	Westerfield	Cubbits
85.05500	71.55000	NFM	Maldon	Baron Cars
85.06250	71.56250	NFM	Aberystwyth	Taxi Company
85.06250	71.56250	NFM	Birmingham	Community Ambulance
85.06250	71.56250	NFM	Belfast	Alpha Taxis, Shankill Road
85.06250	71.56250	NFM	Caerphilly	Coddy Cabs
85.06250	71.56250	NFM	Hull	Moss Tyres/Breakdown Recovery
85.06250	71.56250	NFM	Kettering	A-Z Taxis
85.06250	71.56250	NFM	Lincoln	Discount Cabs
85.06250	71.56250	NFM	London	BMC Minicabs, Bermondsey
85.06250	71.56250	NFM	London	Diamond Cars
85.06250	71.56250	NFM	London	Lee Vans
85.06250	71.56250	NFM	Norfolk	James Abbots Ltd.
85.06250	71.56250	NFM	Suffolk	James Abbots Ltd.
85.06250	71.56250	NFM	Swansea	Bryan Twyn Taxis
85.06250	71.56250	NFM	Winterbourne	Simpson Agricultural
85.06250	71.56250	NFM	Witham	Anglia Land Drainage
85.07500	71.57500	NFM	Caerphilly	Taxi Company
85.07500	71.57500	NFM	Downham	WB Chambers
85.07500	71.57500	NFM	Fordingbridge	Newton Farm (110.9)
85.07500	71.57500	NFM	Gt Yarmouth	Wolsey Taxis
85.07500	71.57500	NFM	Hitchin	Castles Taxis
85.07500	71.57500	NFM	Hull	Springhead Taxis
85.07500	71.57500	NFM	Kendal	Castle Taxis

Base	Mobile	Mode	Location	User and Notes
85.07500	71.57500	NFM	Lakenheath	H Palmer Farms
85.07500	71.57500	NFM	Leeds	Gritters/Snow Ploughs
85.07500	71.57500	NFM	Melksham	Dance Taxis
85.07500	71.57500	NFM	Scunthorpe	Taxi Company
85.07500	71.57500	NFM	Woodchurch	Arrow Park Taxis
85.08750	71.58750	NFM	Glasgow	Westbourne Taxis, Barrhead
85.08750	71.58750	NFM	Cambridge	Regency Cars
85.08750	71.58750	NFM	Hillingdon	Sky Radio Cars
85.08750	71.58750	NFM	Newmarket	Six Mile Bottom Estate
85.08750	71.58750	NFM	Poole	Drinkwater Sabey
85.10000	71.60000	NFM	Glasgow	Water Department
85.10000	71.60000	NFM	Ipswich	Anglia Water
85.10000	71.60000	NFM	Leicestershire	Leicester Water Board
85.11250	71.61250	NFM	Colchester	Council Roadworks Depot
85.11250	71.61250	NFM	Ipswich	Council Roadworks Depot
85.11250	71.61250	NFM	Stanway	Council Roadworks Depot
85.11250	71.61250	NFM	West Yorkshire	British Pipelines
85.11250	71.61250	NFM	Yorkshire	National Rivers Authority
85.12500	71.62500	NFM	Ayr	East Ayrshire Highways Department
85.12500	71.62500	NFM	Brighton	Skip Service
85.12500	71.62500	NFM	Nationwide	British Pipelines
85.12500	71.62500	NFM	Strathclyde	Strathclyde Council
85.20000	71.70000	NFM	Liverpool	Taxi Company
85.21000	71.71000	NFM	Ayr	North of Scotland Water Authority
85.22500	71.72500	NFM	Cardiff	South Glamorgan Council
85.22500	71.72500	NFM	Cornwall	County Council
85.22500	71.72500	NFM	Dumbarton	Council
85.22500	71.72500	NFM	Dumfries	West of Scotland Water
85.22500	71.72500	NFM	Kendal	Kendal National Park
85.22500	71.72500	NFM	Kent	Southern Water
85.22500	71.72500	NFM	Thames Valley	Thames Valley Water
85.23750	71.73750	NFM	Thames Valley	Thames Valley Water (Blue Control)
85.25000	71.75000	NFM	Jersey	Jersey Milk
85.25000	71.75000	NFM	Kent	Southern Water
85.26250	71.76250	NFM	Kent	Southern Water
85.26250	71.76250	NFM	Thames Valley	Thames Valley Water
85.27500	71.77500	NFM	Cornwall	South West Water Trunked
85.27500	71.77500	NFM	East Sussex	Southern Water
85.27500	71.77500	NFM	Somerset	Council Housing
85.28750	71.78750	NFM	Kent	National Rivers Authority
85.28750	71.78750	NFM	Kent	Southern Water (Red Base)
85.30000	71.80000	NFM	Aberdeen	Council Dog Catcher
85.30000	71.80000	NFM	Breckland	Council HQ
85.30000	71.80000	NFM	Hampshire	Council Drainage
85.30000	71.80000	NFM	Ipswich	Community Repeater
85.30000	71.80000	NFM	Isle of Wight	Council Roads Department
85.30000	71.80000	NFM	London	Brent Council
85.30000	71.80000	NFM	Trafford	Council Cleansing Department
85.31250	71.81250	NFM	Brighton	Southern Water (Distribution)
85.31250	71.81250	NFM	Dorset	Wessex Water Trunked
85.31250	71.81250	NFM	Humberside	Council
85.32500	71.82500	NFM	Bournemouth	Wessex Water
85.32500	71.82500	NFM	Brighton	Southern Water (Green Base)
85.32500	71.82500	NFM	Folkestone	Community Repeater
85.32500	71.82500	NFM	Kent	Southern Water
85.35000	71.85000	NFM	Barnet	Council

Base	Mobile	Mode	Location	User and Notes
85.35000	71.85000	NFM	Clwyd	Council
85.35000	71.85000	NFM	East Sussex	Bottle Bank Collection
85.35000	71.85000	NFM	Hampshire	Bottle Bank Collection
85.35000	71.85000	NFM	Hawick	Scottish Borders Council Roads Department
85.35000	71.85000	NFM	Kent	Southern Water
85.35000	71.85000	NFM	Portsmouth	City Council
85.35000	71.85000	NFM	Renfrew	Council
85.35000	71.85000	NFM	Saddleworth	Council Highways Department
85.35000	71.85000	NFM	South Wales	Welsh Water
85.35000	71.85000	NFM	Stowmarket	Council Highways Department
85.35000	71.85000	NFM	Sunderland	Sunderland Council Ch.2
85.35000	71.85000	NFM	Swansea	Council
85.36250	71.86250	NFM	Ayr	District Council
85.36250	71.86250	NFM	Chester	Car Transporters
85.36250	71.86250	NFM	Kent	Southern Water
85.37500	71.87500	NFM	Bury St. Edmunds	Council Highways Department
85.37500	71.87500	NFM	Hawick	Tweed Commission Water Bailiffs
85.37500	71.87500	NFM	Leicester	Severn Trent Water
85.38750	71.88750	NFM	Cambridge	Anglia Water
85.38750	71.88750	NFM	Kent	Southern Water
85.38750	71.88750	NFM	Wyre	Council
85.40000	71.90000	NFM	Kent	National Rivers Authority
85.40000	71.90000	NFM	Kent	Southern Water
85.40000	71.90000	NFM	London	Hounslow Council
85.40000	71.90000	NFM	Norfolk	North West Norfolk Highways Department
85.40000	71.90000	NFM	Northampton	Community Repeater, Vet
85.40000	71.90000	NFM	Sheffield	District Council
85.41250	71.91250	NFM	Brighton	Southern Water, Drainage
85.42500	71.92500	NFM	Derby	County Council
85.42500	71.92500	NFM	Kent	Council
85.42500	71.92500	NFM	Kent	Southern Water
85.42500	71.92500	NFM	Northampton	Community Repeater, Social Services
85.42500	71.92500	NFM	Rotherham	Council Cleansing & Dog Wardens
85.43750	71.93750	NFM	Alford	Council Highways Department
85.43750	71.93750	NFM	Lea Valley	Southern Water
85.45000	71.95000	NFM	Ayr	Skip Hire
85.45000	71.95000	NFM	Cumnock	Council
85.45000	71.95000	NFM	Jersey	Blue Coach Tours
85.45000	71.95000	NFM	Kent	National Rivers Authority
85.45000	71.95000	NFM	Kent	Southern Water
85.45000	71.95000	NFM	Pitcaple	Council Highways Department
85.45000	71.95000	NFM	Swansea	Dyfed Council
85.45000	71.95000	AM	Tonbridge	Council
85.46250	71.96250	NFM	Suffolk	Anglia Water
85.47500	71.97500	NFM	Broadstairs	Chauffeur Cars
85.47500	71.97500	NFM	Gatwick	Airport Cars (Kilo Base)
85.47500	71.97500	NFM	Kings Lynn	Dow Chemicals
85.47500	71.97500	NFM	Whitehaven	National Park, Cumbria
85.57500	72.07500	NFM	London	Thames Water
85.60000	72.10000	NFM	Ayrshire	Council Repairs Department
85.60000	72.10000	NFM	Blackpool	Council Parks
85.60000	72.10000	NFM	Exeter	Council Cleansing
85.60000	72.10000	NFM	Forest Heath	Council
85.60000	72.10000	NFM	Scarborough	Council
85.60000	72.10000	NFM	Wigan	Council Plumbers
85.61250	72.11250	NFM	Humberside	Community Repeater

Base	Mobile	Mode	Location	User and Notes
85.61250	72.11250	NFM	Lake District	Lake District National Park
85.61250	72.11250	NFM	London	Concord Ltd.
85.61250	72.11250	NFM	Poole	Adventure Centre
85.61250	72.11250	NFM	Southend on Sea	Council (103.5)
85.62500	72.12500	NFM	Bath	Silversails Taxis
85.62500	72.12500	NFM	Birmingham	Poolview Car Sales
85.62500	72.12500	NFM	Colchester	J Collie Ltd.
85.62500	72.12500	NFM	Denham	Cabline
85.62500	72.12500	NFM	Liverpool	Taxi Company
85.62500	72.12500	NFM	London	Battersea Cars
85.62500	72.12500	NFM	London	Globe Bikes
85.62500	72.12500	NFM	London	Haden Carriers
85.62500	72.12500	NFM	Rendlesham	Regency Cars
85.62500	72.12500	AM	Salisbury	Radio Taxis & Express Deliveries
85.62750	72.12750	NFM	Aberdeen	Taxi Company
85.63750	72.13750	NFM	England	Defence Land Services, S West
85.63750	72.13750	NFM	Guernsey	Fruit Exporters
85.65000	72.15000	NFM	London	Chequers Transport
85.65000	72.15000	NFM	London	Riva Communications Ltd.
85.65000	72.15000	NFM	Mannington	Bascombe Ltd.
85.65000	72.15000	NFM	Portsmouth	Taxi Company
85.65000	72.15000	NFM	Seaforth	Taxi Company
85.65000	72.15000	NFM	St. Ives	Tyrell Contractors
85.65000	72.15000	AM	Stowmarket	Gold Star Taxis
85.66250	72.16250	NFM	Gussage St. Michael	Manor Farm
85.66250	72.16250	NFM	Lochaber	Caledonian Canal
85.66250	72.16250	NFM	London	Anderson Young Ltd.
85.66250	72.16250	NFM	London	Westland Market Tower
85.66250	72.16250	NFM	Maidenhead	Valley Taxis
85.66250	72.16250	NFM	Norfolk/Suffolk	M. Crouch Ltd.
85.67500	72.17500	NFM	Aberdeen	Taxi Company
85.67500	72.17500	NFM	Ayr	Taxi Company
85.67500	72.17500	NFM	Barrow in Furness	Barrow 5 Taxis
85.67500	72.17500	NFM	Brighton	Streamline Taxis
85.67500	72.17500	NFM	Colchester	Eastern Tractors
85.67500	72.17500	NFM	Gillingham	Betta Taxis
85.67500	72.17500	NFM	Gillingham	TA Taxis
85.67500	72.17500	NFM	Jersey	Luxi Cabs
85.67500	72.17500	NFM	London	Petchey & Velite Cars
85.67500	72.17500	NFM	Milton Keynes	Harper Cars
85.67500	72.17500	NFM	Norfolk/Suffolk	Hughes TV Servicing
85.67500	72.17500	NFM	Thetford	Lloyd & Marriot Vets
85.67500	72.17500	NFM	Walsall Wood	Claridge TV & Radio
85.68750	72.18750	NFM	London	Belsize Ltd.
85.68750	72.18750	NFM	Lyndhurst	Hampshire Cattle Breeders
85.68750	72.18750	NFM	Milton Keynes	Skyline Taxis
85.68750	72.18750	NFM	Slough	Castle Radio Cars
85.68750	72.18750	NFM	Suffolk	North Suffolk Parcel Services
85.68750	72.18750	NFM	Wishaw	Myles Taxis
85.70000	72.20000	NFM	Aberdeen	Shanks Transport
85.70000	72.20000	NFM	Bury St. Edmunds	A1 Cars
85.70000	72.20000	NFM	Grimsby	Stoneledge Haulage
85.70000	72.20000	NFM	Hawick	Eildon Taxis
85.70000	72.20000	AM	Hull	Redune Taxis
85.70000	72.20000	NFM	Letchworth	B & D Taxis (123)
85.70000	72.20000	NFM	London	Advance Cars, Walthamstow (127.3)

Base	Mobile	Mode	Location	User and Notes
85.70000	72.20000	NFM	London	Echo Cars
85.70000	72.20000	NFM	London	Gateway Cars, Hounslow
85.70000	72.20000	NFM	Southampton	Fletchwood Vending
85.71250	72.21250	NFM	Goring by Sea	Taxis Company
85.71250	72.21250	NFM	Isle of Wight	Phonographic Hire Ltd.
85.71250	74.21250	NFM	London	Summit Cars
85.72500	72.22500	NFM	Clackmannan	Council
85.72500	72.22500	NFM	London	Ascot & Bracknell
85.72500	72.22500	NFM	Shrewsbury	Taxi Company
85.72500	72.22500	NFM	Weasenham	Farm
85.73750	72.23750	NFM	Cardiff	Council Cleansing Department (114.8)
85.73750	72.23750	NFM	Colchester	Fieldspray Ltd.
85.73750	72.23750	NFM	Eastbourne	Skip Hire
85.73750	72.23750	NFM	Edinburgh	Garage
85.73750	72.23750	NFM	Glasgow	Plant Hire
85.73750	72.23750	NFM	London	Network Cars, Barnet
85.73750	72.23750	NFM	London	Swift & Safe Taxis
85.73750	72.23750	NFM	North Yorkshire	Taxi Company
85.73750	72.23750	NFM	Southampton	Bass Leisure
85.73750	72.23750	AM	St. Austell	Haul-U-Waste
85.75000	72.25000	NFM	Dorchester	Pete's Cabs
85.75000	72.25000	NFM	Guernsey	Warry's Bakery
85.75000	72.25000	NFM	Hitchin	Rural Taxis
85.75000	72.25000	NFM	Lakenheath	Trevor Cobbold
85.75000	72.25000	NFM	London	American Cars
85.75000	72.25000	NFM	London	Headway Cars, East Molesey
85.75000	72.25000	NFM	London	Putney Cars
85.75000	72.25000	NFM	Maidstone	Payless Cabs
85.75000	72.25000	NFM	Manchester	Taxi Company
85.75000	72.25000	NFM	Oldham	Taxi Company
85.76250	72.26250	NFM	Cambridge	Plant Growing Institute
85.76250	72.26250	NFM	Culzean	National Trust for Scotland Rangers
85.76250	72.26250	NFM	Jersey	Regent Radio Cars
85.76250	72.26250	NFM	London	Galaxy Cars
85.76250	72.26250	NFM	Long Stratton	CDS. Fuels
85.76250	72.26250	NFM	St. Leonards	AE Bartholomew Ltd.
85.77500	72.27500	NFM	Alloa	Taxi Company
85.77500	72.27500	NFM	Blackpool	Red Cabs
85.77500	72.27500	NFM	Exeter	Able Taxis (Able)
85.77500	72.27500	NFM	Guernsey	Le Pelley Taxi
85.77500	72.27500	NFM	Leigh on Sea	Taxi Company
85.77500	72.27500	NFM	Levenshulme	Premier Cars
85.77500	72.27500	NFM	Lincoln	County Cars
85.77500	72.27500	NFM	Littlehampton	Arun Taxis
85.77500	72.27500	NFM	London	Allways Ltd.
85.77500	72.27500	NFM	London	Keen Cars, Finchley
85.77500	72.27500	NFM	London	Perwood Cars, Hillingdon
85.77500	72.27500	NFM	Norwich	RC Snelling
85.77500	72.27500	NFM	Oxford	LuxiCabs
85.77500	72.27500	NFM	Perth	Taxi Company
85.77500	72.27500	NFM	Sheffield	Hargreaves Clearwaste Co.
85.77500	72.27500	NFM	Slough	Scorpio Radio Cars
85.77500	72.27500	NFM	Stoke on Trent	Lucky Seven Taxis
85.77500	72.27500	NFM	Weymouth	Portwey Services
85.78250	72.28750	NFM	Birmingham	Wimpey Builders
85.78750	72.28750	NFM	Edinburgh	Taxi Company

Base	Mobile	Mode	Location	User and Notes
85.80000	72.30000	NFM	Aberdeen	City Council
85.80000	72.30000	NFM	Anglia	Parceline Ltd.
85.80000	72.30000	NFM	Brighton	Express Security Vans
85.80000	72.30000	NFM	Cardiff	Cardiff Garage Services
85.80000	72.30000	NFM	Hull	Security Express
85.80000	72.30000	NFM	Nationwide	Express Security Vans
85.80000	72.30000	NFM	Nationwide	Parceline Ltd.
85.80000	72.30000	NFM	Plymouth	City Council Cleansing Department
85.80000	72.30000	NFM	Warrington	Parceline
85.81250	72.31250	NFM	Aberdeen	Taxi Company
85.81250	72.31250	NFM	Cardigan	Vet
85.81250	72.31250	NFM	Dorset	Community Repeater G Crook & Sons
85.81250	72.31250	NFM	Minterne Magna	Community Repeater Century Farm (103.5)
85.81250	72.31250	NFM	Haverfordwest	Community Repeater Vet Service
85.81250	72.31250	NFM	Weymouth	Community Repeater Bennet & Escott
85.81250	72.31250	NFM	Weymouth	Community Repeater Gould Electronics
85.81250	72.31250	NFM	Weymouth	Community Repeater J Bentham
85.81250	72.31250	NFM	Weymouth	Community Repeater Wessex Aerials
85.81250	72.31250	NFM	Weymouth	Community Repeater Western Pipeline
85.82500	72.32500	NFM	Cornwall	Pye Transport
85.82500	72.32500	NFM	Letchworth	Joe & Barry's Taxis
85.82500	72.32500	NFM	London	Kwik Cars
85.82500	72.32500	NFM	Mannings Heath	Drinkwater Sabey
85.82500	72.32500	NFM	Norwich	Beeline Taxis
85.82500	72.32500	NFM	Shoreham by Sea	Taxi Company
85.82500	72.32500	NFM	Southampton	Streamline Taxis
85.83750	72.33750	NFM	Blantyre	Ariel & Art Cabs
85.83750	72.33750	NFM	Cornwall	English China Clay
85.83750	72.33750	NFM	Guernsey	Falles Hire Cars
85.83750	72.33750	NFM	Jersey	Ideal Cars
85.83750	72.33750	NFM	Jersey	Rank Taxis
85.83750	72.33750	NFM	Littleport	JC Rains Ltd
85.83750	72.33750	NFM	London	Belsize Ltd
85.83750	72.33750	NFM	London	Courier 83 Ltd
85.83750	72.33750	NFM	Luton	James Early Ltd
85.83750	72.33750	NFM	St. Andrews	St Andrews Taxis
85.83750	72.33750	AM	St. Austell	Haul-U-Waste
85.83750	72.33750	NFM	Wareham	Hall Waste
85.85000	72.35000	NFM	Cornwall	English China Clay
85.85000	72.35000	NFM	Kirkby	Taxi Company
85.85000	72.35000	NFM	Nationwide	Philips Transport Scheme
85.85000	72.35000	NFM	Newtown	Taxi Company
85.85000	72.35000	NFM	Oldham	Pest Control (Waterhead Control)
85.85000	72.35000	NFM	Skelmersdale	Taxi Company
85.85000	72.35000	NFM	Tyneside	Taxi Company
85.85000	72.35000	NFM	Widnes	Taxi Company
85.85000	72.35000	NFM	Wigan	Taxi Company
85.86250	72.36250	NFM	Guernsey	JH Mahy & Sons Ltd
85.86250	72.36250	NFM	London	Fisher Sylvester Ltd
85.86250	72.36250	NFM	London	G & R Tyres
85.86250	72.36250	NFM	London	Pronto Cars
85.86250	72.36250	NFM	Parkstone	Secure Alarms
85.88750	72.38750	NFM	Aylsham	Aylsham Produce
85.88750	72.38750	NFM	Blackpool	Tower Taxis
85.88750	72.38750	NFM	Burnley	Delta Cabs
85.88750	72.38750	NFM	Coventry	Allens Taxis and Coaches

Base	Mobile	Mode	Location	User and Notes
85.88750	72.38750	NFM	Diss	East Coast Grain
85.88750	72.38750	NFM	London	Teleportation Ltd
85.88750	72.38750	NFM	Perth	Tay Transport
85.88750	72.38750	NFM	Tameside	Tameside Taxis
85.90000	72.40000	NFM	Burnley	Delta Cabs
85.90000	72.40000	NFM	Diss	GW Padley
85.90000	72.40000	NFM	Edinburgh	TV Repair Company
85.90000	72.40000	NFM	Jersey	Rank Taxis
85.90000	72.40000	NFM	Kettering	Headlands Taxis
85.90000	72.40000	NFM	London	Sensechoice
85.90000	72.40000	NFM	Newcastle	Taxi Company
85.90000	72.40000	NFM	Parkstone	Bourne Plasterers
85.90000	72.40000	NFM	Spalding	Glen Heat & Irrigation
85.91250	72.41250	NFM	Aberdeen	Breakdown Services
85.91250	72.41250	NFM	Bradford	Undercliffe Private Hire
85.91250	72.41250	NFM	Brigg	Gallowswood Recovery Service
85.91250	72.41250	NFM	Edinburgh	TV Repair Company
85.91250	72.41250	NFM	Ipswich	Taxi Company
85.91250	72.41250	NFM	Letchworth	Eurocabs (203.5)
85.91250	72.41250	NFM	London	Arrival Couriers
85.91250	72.41250	NFM	London	Central Motors
85.91250	72.41250	NFM	London	K Cars
85.91250	72.41250	NFM	Perth	Tay Breakdown Service
85.91250	72.41250	NFM	Weymouth	West Ham Cars
85.92500	72.42500	NFM	Birmingham	Star Cars
85.92500	72.42500	NFM	Blackpool	Radio Cabs
85.92500	72.42500	NFM	Jersey	LuxiCabs
85.92500	72.42500	NFM	Yeovil	Vets
85.93750	72.42500	NFM	Blandford Forum	Motor Factors
85.93750	72.43750	NFM	Blackpool	Progress Taxis
85.93750	72.43750	NFM	Bury	Moorside Taxis
85.93750	72.43750	NFM	Luton	Home & Away Car & Bus Service
95.93750	72.43750	NFM	Stoke on Trent	ABC Taxis
85.95000	72.45000	NFM	London	Action Cars
85.95000	72.45000	NFM	London	Galaxy Bikes
85.95000	72.43750	NFM	London	Action Cars
85.95000	72.45000	NFM	London	Super Express
85.95000	72.45000	AM	Chichester	Taxi Company
85.95000	72.45000	NFM	Guernsey	Crossways Agricultural
85.95000	72.45000	NFM	Leigh on Sea	Taxi Company
85.95000	72.45000	NFM	Saffron Walden	Lord Braybrooke's Estate
85.96250	72.46250	NFM	Great Massingham	Gilman Ltd
85.96250	72.46250	NFM	London	Globe Cars
85.96250	72.46250	NFM	Norfolk	Don Robin Farms
85.97500	72.47500	NFM	Bristol	Mobile Windscreen Company
85.97500	72.47500	NFM	Cheddington	Colebird & Sons
85.97500	72.47500	NFM	England	Milk Tankers, SW UK
85.97500	72.47500	NFM	Guernsey	Stan Brouard Ltd
85.97500	72.47500	NFM	Hamilton	Bridge Cars
85.97500	72.47500	AM	Leeds	Amber Cars
85.97500	72.47500	NFM	Letheringham	Kerr Farms
85.97500	72.47500	AM	London	Taxi Company, Finsbury Park
85.97500	72.47500	NFM	Martock	M & J Tyres
85.97500	72.47500	NFM	Norfolk	Stanway Taxis
85.97500	72.47500	NFM	Plymouth	Mainline Catering

Base	Mobile	Mode	Location	User and Notes
85.97500	72.47500	NFM	Somerton	Interlink
85.97500	72.47500	NFM	St. Austell	Mobile Windscreens
85.97500	72.47500	NFM	Sutton	Darby Plant
85.97500	72.47500	NFM	Woodbridge	Wm. Kerr Farms
85.97500	72.47500	NFM	Yeovil	Douglas Seatons
85.98750	72.47500	NFM	Ilford	Nations Cars
85.98750	72.48750	NFM	Jersey	Fetch & Carry
85.98750	72.48750	NFM	London	Avery Cars
85.98750	72.48750	NFM	London	City & Suburban
85.98750	72.48750	NFM	London	Commuter Cars
85.98750	72.48750	NFM	London	Parkward Ltd
85.98750	72.48750	NFM	London	Southampton Way Cars
85.98750	72.48750	NFM	St. Neots	Eynsbury Plant Hire
86.00000	72.50000	NFM	Dorchester	Hanford Farms (114.8)
86.00000	72.50000	NFM	Irvine	Taxi Company
86.00000	72.50000	NFM	London	Kilburn Cars
86.00000	72.50000	NFM	London	Windmill Cars
86.00000	72.50000	NFM	Sittingbourne	Pooks Taxis
86.01250	72.51250	NFM	Cheshunt	C & S Taxis
86.01250	72.51250	NFM	Jersey	Blue Coaches
86.01250	72.51250	NFM	Leeds	Premier Cars
86.02500	72.52500	NFM	Brecon	Mountain Rescue
86.03750	72.53750	NFM	Eastbourne	Downland Rangers
86.03750	72.53750	AM	Guernsey	Public Works
86.03750	72.53750	AM	London	Doctors' Service
86.05000	72.55000	NFM	London	Doctors' Service
86.05000	72.55000	NFM	Southampton	Taxi Company
86.06250	72.56250	NFM	Norfolk	Sandringham Royal Estate
86.07500	72.57500	NFM	Annan	District Council
86.08750	72.58750	NFM	Norfolk	Douglas Framlingham
86.10000	72.60000	NFM	Hadleigh	Lemon & Sutherland
86.11250	72.61250	NFM	Humberside	Tyre Company
86.12500	72.62500	NFM	Cardiff	FW Morgan Builders
86.12500	72.62500	NFM	Cheshire	Courier Service
86.12500	72.62500	NFM	Rhonda	Cynon Taff Council Waste Services
86.13750	72.63750	AM	Jersey	De Gruchy Vets
86.15000	72.65000	NFM	Herts/Beds	Skip Hire Company (136.5)
86.16250	72.66250	NFM	Ayrshire	North Ayrshire Highways
86.16250	72.66250	AM	Kent	County Council
86.16250	72.66250	AM	Radnor	County Council
86.17500	72.67500	NFM	Bury St. Edmunds	Hughes TV Servicing
86.17500	72.67500	NFM	Lincolnshire	NCN (Anglia) Couriers
86.17500	72.67500	NFM	Norfolk/Suffolk	Ipswich Transport Ltd
86.20000	72.70000	NFM	Teesside	Teesside Plant Hire
86.21250	72.71250	NFM	East Sussex	County Council
86.21250	72.71250	NFM	London	Enterprise Ltd
86.21250	72.71250	NFM	Needham Market	Quinton Skip Hire
86.21250	72.71250	NFM	Norfolk	William Cory Heating
86.22500	72.72500	NFM	Boothferry	Council
86.22500	72.72500	NFM	Burnley	Breakdown Recovery
86.22500	72.72500	NFM	Ipswich	Biffa Waste Collection (D)
86.22500	72.72500	NFM	Ipswich	Carrow Chip Communications
86.22500	72.72500	NFM	Ipswich	Doctors' Service
86.22500	72.72500	NFM	Ipswich	Mini Skips Company
86.22500	72.72500	NFM	Ipswich	Nighthawk Security (67)
86.22500	72.72500	NFM	Ipswich	Sackers Ltd (Brent)

Base	Mobile	Mode	Location	User and Notes
86.22500	72.72500	NFM	Norfolk	Ipswich Transport Ltd
86.22500	72.72500	NFM	Perth	Amtrac Delivery Service
86.22500	72.72500	NFM	Peterborough	Breakdown Recovery Company
86.22500	72.72500	NFM	Portsmouth	Taxi Company
86.22500	72.72500	NFM	Woodbridge	CALL Alarm Service
86.23750	72.72500	NFM	Great Oakley	Oakley Skip Hire
86.23750	72.72500	NFM	Great Yarmouth	Container Depots
86.23750	72.72500	NFM	Ipswich	Mini Skips Company
86.23750	72.72500	NFM	Ipswich	Nighthawk Security
86.23750	72.72500	NFM	Ipswich	Sachers Ltd
86.23750	72.72500	NFM	Kettering	Farmers
86.23750	72.72500	NFM	Perth	Delivery Company
86.23750	72.73750	NFM	Armagh	Road Construction
86.23750	72.73750	NFM	Felixstowe	CWR Haulage
86.23750	72.73750	NFM	Hull	Jack Pockley Fuels Ltd
86.23750	72.73750	NFM	Ipswich	Hughes TV Servicing (67)
86.23750	72.73750	NFM	Suffolk	Silver Shield Windscreens
86.23750	72.73750	NFM	West Sussex	Doctors' Service
86.25000	72.75000	NFM	Aberdeen	Snow Ploughs
86.25000	72.75000	NFM	East Sussex	County Council
86.26250	72.76250	NFM	Aberdeen	Council
86.26250	72.76250	NFM	Bristol	Zycomm
86.26250	72.76250	NFM	Grampian	Taxi Company
86.26250	72.76250	NFM	Humberside	Council
86.27500	72.77500	NFM	Bournemouth	Cryston Communications
86.27500	72.77500	NFM	Dumfries	Council
86.27500	72.77500	NFM	Hull	Cryston Communications
86.27500	72.77500	NFM	Leeds	Cryston Communications
86.27500	72.77500	NFM	Nationwide	Cryston Communications
86.28750	72.78750	NFM	Ashton under Lyme	Satellite Installation Company
86.28750	72.78750	NFM	Ayrshire	Council Cleansing Department
86.28750	72.78750	NFM	Gt Yarmouth	Container Depot
86.28750	72.78750	NFM	Irvine	North Ayrshire Council
86.30000	72.80000	NFM	East Sussex	County Council
86.30000	72.80000	NFM	Jersey	Jersey Hospital
86.30000	72.80000	NFM	Nationwide	NT Ltd Aerial Riggers
86.30000	72.80000	NFM	Nationwide	Vibroplant Plc

86.3125 - 86.7000 MHz   PMR Low Band 12.5 kHz Simplex

Base	Mobile	Mode	Location	User and Notes
86.31250		NFM	Nationwide	Mountain Rescue Ch.1
86.31250		NFM	Nationwide	UKSAR Ch.105
86.31250		NFM	Yorkshire	North Moors Rangers
86.32500		NFM	Nationwide	Mountain Rescue Ch.2
86.32500		NFM	Nationwide	UKSAR Ch.106
86.33750		NFM	London	London Underground contractors (131.8)
86.33750		NFM	Nationwide	St John Ambulance Ch.2
86.35000		NFM	Cairngorm	Ski Lifts
86.35000		NFM	London	London Underground Contractors (141.3)
86.35000		NFM	Nationwide	Scout Association Ch.2 Reserve
86.35000		NFM	Nationwide	St. John Ambulance Ch.3
86.35000		NFM	N Ireland	Ulster Automobile Club Ch.1
86.36250		NFM	London	London Underground contractors (77)
86.36250		NFM	Nationwide	Scout Association Ch.1 Reserve
86.36250		NFM	Nationwide	St John Ambulance Ch.4
86.37500		NFM	Edinburgh	The Scottish Office
86.37500		NFM	London	London Underground Contractors (107.2)

Base	Mobile	Mode	Location	User and Notes
86.37500		NFM	Nationwide	St John Ambulance Ch.5
86.37500		NFM	N Ireland	Ulster Automobile Club Ch.4
86.38750		NFM	Derby	Council
86.40000		NFM	Nationwide	National Park Rangers
86.40000		NFM	Yorkshire	North Moors Rangers
86.40000		NFM	Yorkshire	Yorkshire Dales Wardens
86.41250		NFM	West Kilbride	Hunterston Power Station
86.42500		NFM	Ettrick & Lauderdale	District Council
86.42500		NFM	London	London Underground Neasden Depot (107.2)
86.42500		NFM	London	London Underground Northumberland Park
86.42500		NFM	London	Bluebird Pleasure Boats, Hyde Park Serpentine
86.42500		AM	Neath	Forestry Commission
86.43750		NFM	Isle of Man	Tudor Manx Rally
86.43750		NFM	Jersey	Jersey Rally Control
86.43750		NFM	Nationwide	RAC Rally Medical/Safety (Pre 2003 - see 81.575)
86.43750		NFM	N Ireland	Ulster Automobile Club Ch.3
86.43750		NFM	Suffolk	Land Rover Rescue Services
86.45000		NFM	Ipswich	Docks
86.45000		AM	Neath	Forestry Commission
86.46250		NFM	Worcester	Council
86.46500		NFM	Glasgow	Skip Hire Company
86.47500		NFM	Cheshire	Gallifords Civil Engineers
86.47500		NFM	Linton	TB Fairy
86.47500		NFM	Nationwide	Network Rail Incidents
86.47500		AM	Neath	Forestry Commission
86.50000		NFM	Suffolk	County Council Emergency Channel
86.50000		NFM	Swindon	Radio Taxis
86.52500		NFM	Dunstable	Taleds Motors Co.
86.52500		NFM	Enfield	Weston Ltd
86.53750		NFM	Derbyshire	Middleton Top Rangers
86.55000		NFM	Guernsey	Cobo Surgery
86.61250	77.90000	NFM	Cornwall	South West Water Trunked
86.62500		AM	Sheffield	Council Repairs
86.63750		NFM	Jersey	Telefitters
86.66250		NFM	Nationwide	Vickers Seismic Surveys
86.67500		NFM	Nationwide	JFMG Talkback (Wales & Western UK Only)
86.68750		NFM	Chester	King Cabs
86.70000		NFM	Dungeness	Power Station

86.7125 - 87.5000 MHz — PMR Low Band Base Duplex

Base	Mobile	Mode	Location	User and Notes
86.73750	76.73750	NFM	Ipswich	Community Repeater
86.75000	76.50000	NFM	Burnley	Plant Hire
86.75000	76.50000	NFM	Cwmbran	Gwent Council
86.75000	76.50000	NFM	Hornsea	East Coast Caravan Security
86.75000	76.50000	NFM	Lowestoft	Hughes TV Rentals
86.76250	76.76250	NFM	Llanelli	Taxi Company
86.76250	76.76250	NFM	Tayside	Community Repeater
86.77500	76.77500	NFM	Merseyside	Plant Hire Company
86.77500	76.77500	NFM	Portsmouth	City Council
86.77500	76.77500	NFM	York	Yorkshire Parcels Group
86.78750	76.78750	NFM	Yorkshire	Andy Plant Hire
86.80000	76.80000	NFM	Brighton	Community Repeater
86.80000	76.80000	NFM	Dyfed	Vets
86.80000	76.80000	NFM	Hampshire	Council
86.80000	76.80000	NFM	Louth	Community Repeater

Base	Mobile	Mode	Location	User and Notes
86.80000	76.80000	NFM	Milford Haven	Taxi Company (131.8)
86.80000	76.80000	NFM	Nationwide	Vibroplant
86.80000	76.80000	NFM	Bradford	Community Transport
86.80000	76.80000	NFM	Oldham	Plant Hire Company
86.80000	76.80000	NFM	West Sussex	Doctors' Service
86.80625	76.80625	NFM	Nationwide	JFMG Wide Area Duplex
86.81000		NFM	Nationwide	JFMG Airborne
86.81250	76.81250	NFM	Nationwide	JFMG Wide Area Duplex
86.81875	76.81875	NFM	Nationwide	JFMG Wide Area Duplex
86.82500		NFM	Bristol	ITV Broadcast Link
86.82500		NFM	Hastings	Meridian TV O/B
86.82500		NFM	Manchester	Granada TV Talkback
86.82500	76.82500	NFM	Nationwide	JFMG Wide Area Duplex
86.82500		NFM	Thames Valley	ITN Talkback
86.83125	76.83125	NFM	Nationwide	JFMG Wide Area Duplex
86.83750		NFM	London	Sky News Talkback
86.83750	76.83750	NFM	Nationwide	JFMG Wide Area Duplex
86.84375	76.84375	NFM	Nationwide	JFMG Wide Area Duplex
86.85000	76.85000	NFM	Clwyd	Delivery Company
86.86250	76.86250	NFM	Louth	Community Repeater
86.86250	76.86250	NFM	Plymouth	Plymouth Vets
86.87500	76.87500	NFM	Lochaber	Council Highways Department
86.87500	76.87500	NFM	Malvern	Abbey Taxis
86.88750	76.88750	NFM	Ballachulish	Highland Council Roads/Snow Ploughs
86.88750	76.88750	NFM	Isle Of Man	Community Repeater, Kennish
86.88750	76.88750	NFM	Lincoln	Murphy Pipeline Contractors
86.88750	76.88750	NFM	Scarborough	T Bermingham Contractor
86.90000	76.90000	NFM	Merseyside	Transport Company
86.90000	76.90000	NFM	Southwold	Suffolk Traffic
86.91250	76.91250	NFM	Lochaber	Highland Regional Council Roads
86.91250	76.91250	NFM	Wirral	A1 Breakdown
86.92500	76.92500	NFM	Cambridgeshire	Community Repeater (203.5)
86.92500	76.92500	NFM	Wiltshire	Council Highways Department
86.96250	76.96250	NFM	Aberystwyth	Forestry Commission
86.96250	76.96250	NFM	Grizedale Forest Park	Forestry Commission
86.96250	76.96250	NFM	Gwynedd	Forestry Commission
86.96250	76.96250	NFM	Keilder	Forestry Commission, Border Forest Park
86.96250	76.96250	NFM	Lochaber	Forestry Commission
86.96250	76.96250	NFM	Nationwide	Forestry Commission
86.96250	76.46250	NFM	Newtown	Wayside Forestry Commission
86.96250	76.96250	NFM	Sherwood Forest	Forestry Commission
86.96250	76.96250	NFM	Thetford Forest	Forestry Commission
86.97500	76.97500	NFM	Cardiff	Biffa Waste Services
86.97500	76.97500	NFM	Louth	Community Repeater
86.98750	76.98750	NFM	Aberystwyth	Ystwyth Vets Llanbadarn
86.98750	76.97500	NFM	Hertfordshire	County Council (Highground)

87.0000 - 87.4875 MHz PMR

Base	Mobile	Mode	Location	User and Notes
87.00000	77.00000	NFM	Berkshire	Council
87.00000	77.00000	NFM	Edinburgh	Data Link
87.00000	77.00000	NFM	Wymondham	Ayton Asphalt
87.05000	77.05000	NFM	Grimsby	Raylor Ltd
87.05000	77.05000	NFM	Leeds	Armor Guard
87.05000	77.05000	NFM	Leeds	Raylor Ltd
87.05000	77.05000	NFM	Perth	Data Link

Base	Mobile	Mode	Location	User and Notes
87.05000	77.05000	NFM	Skelmersdale	Taxi Company
87.05000	77.05000	NFM	Teesside	Raylor Ltd
87.05000	77.05000	NFM	York	Raylor Ltd
87.06250	77.06250	NFM	Bishop Stortford	Rougewell Ltd
87.06250	77.06250	NFM	Didcot	Bob's Taxis
87.06250	77.06250	AM	Gwent	Forestry Commission
87.06250	77.06250	NFM	Haywards Heath	Station Taxis
87.06250	77.06250	NFM	London	Statisted Containers Ltd
87.06250	77.06250	AM	Neath	Forestry Commission
87.06250	77.06250	NFM	Perth	Wilsons Taxis
87.06250	77.06250	NFM	Powys	County Council
87.06250	77.06250	NFM	Wrexham	Derek's Taxis
87.07500	77.07500	NFM	Bristol	Ace Taxis
87.07500	77.07500	NFM	Bury	Red Rose Taxis
87.07500	77.07500	NFM	Droitwich	NY Taxis
87.07500	77.07500	NFM	Glasgow	Taxi Company
87.07500	77.07500	NFM	Ipswich	Council
87.07500	77.07500	AM	Jersey	Taxi Rank
87.07500	77.07500	AM	London	Concorde Minicabs, Wembley
87.07500	77.07500	NFM	Newtownabbey	Glengormley Taxis
87.07500	77.07500	NFM	St. Ives	Bowlers Taxis
87.08750	77.08750	NFM	Halifax	Halifax Council
87.08750	77.08750	NFM	Jersey	Jersey Evening Post
87.08750	77.08750	NFM	Kent	Hotpoint Repair Service
87.08750	77.08750	NFM	Lancashire	Haulage Contractor
87.08750	77.08750	NFM	N Ireland	Castle Cabs
87.10000	77.10000	NFM	Brighton	Taxi Company
87.10000	77.10000	NFM	Guernsey	Gilroy's Taxis
87.10000	77.10000	NFM	Hove	Hove Streamline Taxis
87.10000	77.10000	NFM	Leicester	ABC Taxis
87.10000	77.10000	NFM	London	BJ Transport
87.10000	77.10000	NFM	London	JR Cars
87.10000	77.10000	NFM	Maidenhead	Ace Cars
87.10000	77.10000	NFM	Montrose	Council Housing
87.10000	77.10000	NFM	Preston	Taxi Company
87.12500	77.12500	NFM	Ayr	SRC Building & Works Depart.
87.12500	77.12500	NFM	Hawick	District Council
87.12500	77.12500	AM	Powys	Forestry Commission
87.12500	77.12500	NFM	Strathclyde	Strathclyde Council
87.12500	77.12500	NFM	Suffolk	Babergh Council
87.13750	71.13750	NFM	Cardiff	Highways Department & Gritters (123)
87.13750	77.13750	NFM	Fishguard	Council Highways Department
87.13750	77.13750	NFM	Hampshire	Council
87.13750	77.13750	NFM	Kent	Council Highways Department
87.13750	77.13750	NFM	Leeds	Construction Company
87.13750	77.13750	NFM	Liverpool	Council, Street Lighting
87.13750	77.13750	NFM	Norfolk	South Norfolk District Council
87.13750	77.13750	NFM	Salisbury	Council Highways Department
87.15000	77.15000	NFM	Fishguard	District Council
87.15000	77.15000	NFM	Lancashire	County Highways Department
87.15000	77.15000	NFM	Preston	Council Snow Ploughs & Gritters
87.16250	77.16250	NFM	Aberdeen	Council
87.16250	77.16250	NFM	Buckinghamshire	Council
87.16250	77.16250	NFM	Dunfermline	Fife Regional Council
87.16250	77.16250	NFM	Hawick	District Council

Base	Mobile	Mode	Location	User and Notes
87.16250	77.16250	NFM	Kent	Council Highways Department
87.16250	77.16250	NFM	Lincolnshire	Council Highways Department
87.16250	77.16250	NFM	North Yorkshire	Council Highways Department
87.16250	77.16250	NFM	Shropshire	County Council Emergency Planning
87.17500	77.17500	NFM	Bristol	Council Highways Department
87.17500	77.17500	NFM	Glasgow	Underground Control
87.17500	77.17500	NFM	Lake District	Lake District National Park
87.17500	77.17500	NFM	Lancashire	County Park Rangers
87.17500	77.18750	NFM	London	Chambers Road Haulage
87.17500	77.17500	NFM	Nottinghamshire	Community Repeater
87.18750	77.18750	NFM	Bedfordshire	Council
87.18750	77.18750	NFM	Cambridgeshire	Council
87.18750	77.18750	NFM	Chichester	West Sussex Council
87.18750	77.18750	NFM	Fife	Fife Regional Council Roads
87.18750	77.18750	NFM	Lancashire	Snow Ploughs & Gritters Ch.2
87.18750	77.18750	NFM	Oxford	Council
87.18750	77.18750	NFM	Radnor	Powys Council Highways Department
87.18750	77.18750	NFM	Surrey	Council Ch.2
87.18750	77.18750	NFM	West Yorkshire	Council Highways Department
87.20000	77.20000	NFM	Bury	Bury Council
87.20000	77.20000	NFM	County Durham	County Council
87.20000	77.20000	NFM	Cumbria	Quarry
87.20000	77.20000	NFM	Foreham	Council
87.20000	77.20000	NFM	London	Epping Forrest Rangers (Charlie Control)
87.20000	77.20000	NFM	London	Forest Gate Council
87.20000	77.20000	NFM	Mendip	Council Highways Department
87.20000	77.20000	NFM	Preston	Council
87.20000	77.20000	NFM	Surrey	Council
87.20000	77.20000	NFM	Warwickshire	Council Highways Department
87.21250	77.21250	NFM	Aberfeldy	Council Gritters
87.21250	77.21250	NFM	Buckinghamshire	Council
87.21250	77.21250	NFM	Hertfordshire	Council
87.21250	77.21250	NFM	Humberside	Council
87.21250	77.21250	NFM	London	Merton Council Road Gritters
87.21250	77.21250	NFM	Nationwide	Council Common
87.21250	77.21250	NFM	Rushmoor	Council
87.21250	77.21250	NFM	Sheffield	Council Highways Department
87.21250	77.21250	NFM	Somerset	Council Highways Department
87.21250	77.21250	NFM	Staffordshire	Council
87.22500	77.22500	NFM	Bristol Area	Skip Company
87.22500	77.22500	NFM	Isle of Man	Community Repeater, Kennish
87.22500	77.22500	NFM	Oxford	City Council Ch.3
87.23750	77.23750	NFM	East Sussex	Council Highways Department
87.23750	77.23750	NFM	Eastbourne	Council
87.23750	77.23750	NFM	Fife	Fife Regional Council
87.23750	77.23750	NFM	Gwynedd	Gwynedd Council
87.23750	77.23750	NFM	Lancashire	County Council Ch.3
87.23750	77.23750	NFM	Lincolnshire	Council Highways Department
87.23750	77.23750	NFM	Manchester	Council Sheltered Housing Wardens
87.23750	77.23750	NFM	Oxfordshire	County Council Ch.1
87.23750	77.23750	NFM	Perth	Perth & Kinross Council
87.23750	77.23750	NFM	Plymouth	Council Highways Department
87.23500	77.23750	NFM	St. Annes	Council Highways Department
87.25000	77.25000	NFM	Birmingham	City Council Engineers
87.25000	77.25000	NFM	Brecon	Powys County Highways

| --- | --- | --- | --- | --- |
87.25000	77.25000	NFM	Cardiff	Council Waste Services
87.25000	77.25000	NFM	Congleton	Council
87.25000	77.25000	NFM	Devon	SW Devon Highways
87.25000	77.25000	NFM	East Sussex	Emergency Centre
87.25000	77.25000	NFM	Hampshire	Council
87.25000	77.25000	NFM	Hertfordshire	Council
87.25000	77.25000	NFM	Langholm	Dumfries & Galloway Council Roads Dept.
87.25000	77.25000	NFM	Stevenage	Council
87.25000	77.25000	NFM	West Midlands	Council Snowploughs & Gritters
87.26250	77.26250	NFM	Ayr	Local Council Services
87.26250	77.26250	NFM	Dorset	Council Highways Department
87.26250	77.26250	NFM	England & Wales	Council Common
87.26250	77.26250	NFM	Essex	Council Highways Department
87.26250	77.26250	NFM	Gwent	Islwyn Council
87.26250	77.26250	NFM	Leicester	Council
87.26250	77.26250	NFM	Oxfordshire	County Council
87.26250	77.26250	NFM	Perth	Perth & Kinross Council
87.26250	77.26250	NFM	Slough	Council
87.26250	77.26250	NFM	Stockton	Council Engineers
87.26250	77.26250	NFM	West Sussex	County Council
87.27500	77.27500	NFM	Bury St Edmunds	Taxi Company
87.27500	77.27500	NFM	Devon	Council Highways Department
87.27500	77.27500	NFM	Edinburgh	Council
87.27500	77.27500	NFM	London	London Underground, Upminster (94.8)
87.27500	77.27500	NFM	Lothian & Borders	Lothian Regional Council
87.28750	77.28750	NFM	Fife	Fife Regional Council Drainage
87.28750	77.28750	NFM	Lincolnshire	Council Highways Department
87.30000	77.30000	NFM	Accrington	Town Council Base
87.30000	77.30000	NFM	Breckland	District Council
87.30000	77.30000	NFM	Derbyshire	Derbyshire Council Roads
87.30000	77.30000	NFM	Dumfries	Snowploughs & Gritters
87.30000	77.30000	NFM	Hertfordshire	Council
87.30000	77.30000	NFM	Jersey	Roads & Waterworks
87.30000	77.30000	NFM	Mold	Clwyd County Council
87.31250	77.31250	NFM	London	Royal Parks
87.31250	77.31250	NFM	Perth	Perth & Kinross Council
87.31250	77.31250	NFM	Windsor	Royal Park
87.32500	77.32500	NFM	Bedfordshire	Council Highways Department
87.32500	77.32500	NFM	Dacorum	Refuse/Environmental Services (141.3)
87.32500	77.32500	NFM	Derbyshire	Council
87.32500	77.32500	NFM	Kent	Council Highways Department
87.32500	77.32500	NFM	Perth	Perth & Kinross Council
87.32500	77.32500	NFM	South Yorkshire	Council
87.33750	77.33750	NFM	Collingham	Quarrymix
87.33700	77.33750	NFM	Coventry	Council
87.33750	77.33750	NFM	Edinburgh	Council Highways Department
87.33750	77.33750	NFM	Poole	RBLA Security
87.35000	77.35000	NFM	Castle Douglas	Stewartry Council
87.35000	77.35000	NFM	Guernsey	Gaudion Skip Hire
87.35000	77.35000	NFM	Louth	Community Repeater
87.35000	77.35000	NFM	Stoke	Civil Engineers
87.36250	77.36250	NFM	Buckinghamshire	Highways Agency Roads/Gritters
87.36250	77.36250	NFM	Cambridgeshire	Highways Agency Roads/Gritters
87.36250	77.36250	NFM	Castle Douglas	Forestry Commission
87.36250	77.36250	NFM	Newport Pagnell	Highways Agency Roads/Gritters
87.36250	77.36250	NFM	Northamptonshire	Highways Agency Roads/Gritters

Base	Mobile	Mode	Location	User and Notes
87.36250	77.36250	NFM	Perth	Perth & Kinross Council
87.36250	77.36250	NFM	Rothersthorpe	Highways Agency Roads/Gritters
87.36250	77.36250	NFM	Strathclyde	Forestry Commission
87.36250	77.36250	NFM	Tayside	Forestry Commission
87.36250	77.36250	NFM	Whittlesford	Highways Agency Roads/Gritters
87.37500	77.37500	NFM	Lincolnshire	Community Repeater
87.37500	77.37500	NFM	Oldham	Harris Deliveries
87.38750	77.38750	NFM	Cardiff	TV Repair Company
87.38750	77.38750	NFM	Ipswich	Community Repeater
87.38750	77.38750	NFM	Perth	Community Repeater
87.40000	77.40000	NFM	Aberdeen	Aberdeen Skip Hire
87.41250	77.41250	NFM	Bristol	Community Repeater Ace Skip Hire
87.41250	77.41250	NFM	Bristol	Community Repeater Magnum Scaffolding
87.41250	77.41250	NFM	Bristol	Community Repeater PDG Courier Service
87.41250	77.41250	NFM	Elvington	Community Repeater A1 Haulage
87.41250	77.41250	NFM	Elvington	Community Repeater Elvington Plant Hire
87.41250	77.41250	NFM	Elvington	Community Repeater Silverseal Windscreens
87.41250	77.41250	NFM	Lochaber	Council Highways Department
87.41250	77.41250	NFM	London	Onyx Cleansing Services
87.41250	77.41250	NFM	Perth	Perth & Kinross Council
87.41250	77.41250	NFM	Scotland	Council Highways Common
87.42500	77.42500	NFM	Blackpool	Council Highways Department
87.42500	77.42500	NFM	Guernsey	Remote Gas Detectors
87.42500	77.42500	NFM	Hull	Handy Cars
87.42500	77.42500	NFM	Louth	Community Repeater
87.42500	77.42500	NFM	Stirling	County Council (B)
87.43750	77.43750	NFM	Bedford	County Surveyors
87.43750	77.43750	AM	Mid Wales	Forestry Commission
87.43750	77.43750	NFM	Plymouth	City Engineers
87.43750	77.43750	NFM	Scotland	Council Highways Common
87.43750	77.43750	NFM	York	Council Highways Department
87.45000	77.45000	NFM	Berkshire	Council
87.45000	77.45000	NFM	Cambridge	Council Highways Department
87.45000	77.45000	NFM	Haverfordwest	Preseli Pembroke Council
87.45000	77.45000	NFM	Nottingham	Council Highways Department
87.45000	77.45000	NFM	Pembrokeshire	County Council
87.45000	77.45000	NFM	Trowbridge	Council Highways Department
87.46250	77.46250	NFM	Berkshire	Council Surveyor
87.46250	77.46250	NFM	Ceredigion	County Council
87.46250	77.46250	NFM	Essex	Council Highways Department
87.46250	77.46250	NFM	Fife	NE Fife Council Highways Department
87.46250	77.46250	NFM	Hereford	Council
87.46250	77.46250	NFM	Lincolnshire	Council Highways Department
87.46250	77.46250	NFM	Lothian & Borders	Council Highways Department
87.46250	77.46250	NFM	Scarborough	Snowploughs
87.46250	77.46250	NFM	West Midlands	Snowploughs & Gritters
87.46250	77.46250	NFM	West Sussex	Council
87.46250	77.46250	NFM	Worcester	Council
87.47500	77.47500	NFM	Bedfordshire	Council Highways Department (151.4)
87.47500	77.47500	NFM	Buckinghamshire	County Council
87.48750	77.48750	NFM	Cambridgeshire	Skip Hire Company (141.3)
87.48750	77.48750	NFM	Fife	Council Works Drainage
87.48750	77.48750	NFM	Gainsborough	Council
87.48750	77.48750	NFM	Lincoln	Handsome Cabs
87.48750	77.48750	NFM	Liverpool	Taxi Company
87.48750	77.48750	NFM	Nottingham	DGA Cars Ch 1

87.500 - 108.000 MHz   Nationwide BBC & Independent Local Radio

Base	Mobile	Mode	Location	User and Notes
87.7		WFM	Bangor	Storm 87.7FM, Bangor University
87.7		WFM	Barrow in Furness	Radio Lonsdale, Furness General Hospital
87.7		WFM	Brechin	RNA FM, Brechin Infirmary
87.7		WFM	Carmarthen	Radio Glangwili, W Wales General Hospital
87.7		WFM	Coleg Harlech	Radio Branwen
87.7		WFM	Derriford Hospital	Hospital Radio Plymouth
87.7		WFM	Haverfordwest	Withybush FM, Withybush Hospital
87.7		WFM	Lancaster	Bailrigg FM, Lancaster University
87.7		WFM	Montrose	RNA FM, Montrose Infirmary
87.7		WFM	North Devon	Acorn FM, North Devon College
87.7		WFM	Tayside	Bridge fm, Ashludie Hospital
87.7		WFM	Tayside	Bridge fm, Carseview Centre
87.7		WFM	Tayside	Bridge fm, Ninewells Hospital
87.7		WFM	Tayside	Bridge fm, Royal Victoria Hospital
87.7		WFM	University of Paisley	UCA Radio, University Campus Ayr
87.7		WFM	University of Excter	Xpression FM, Duryard & Birks Halls
87.7		WFM	University of Exeter	Xpression FM, Lafrowda & Exeter Halls
88.1 - 90.3		WFM	Nationwide	BBC Radio 2
87.8		WFM	Aberystwyth	Radio Bronglais, Bronglais Hospital
88.6		WFM	Sheffield	BBC Radio Sheffield
88.8		WFM	Les Platons	Radio Jersey
88.8		WFM	W Hertfordshire	Radio Verulam
89.0		WFM	Isle of Man	Manx Radio, Snaefell
89.8		WFM	Milton Keynes	CRMK
90.0		WFM	Hazler Hill	Radio Shropshire
90.2 - 92.6		WFM	Nationwide	BBC Radio 3
91.2		WFM	Isle of Man	Energy FM, Snaefell
92.4		WFM	Holme Moss	Radio Leeds
92.4 - 96.8		WFM	Wales	BBC Radio Cymru
92.5 - 96.1		WFM	Nationwide	BBC Radio 4
92.5 - 94.7		WFM	Scotland	BBC Radio Scotland
92.7		WFM	Bressay	BBC Radio Scotland
92.7		WFM	Rostrevor Forest	BBC Radio Ulster
92.7 - 95.4		WFM	Ulster	BBC Radio Ulster
92.8		WFM	Peebles	BBC Radio Scotland
93.1		WFM	Cambret Hill	BBC Radio Scotland
93.1		WFM	Camlough	BBC Radio Ulster
93.1		WFM	Londonderry	BBC Radio Foyle
93.1		WFM	Londonderry	BBC Radio Ulster
93.1		WFM	Meldrum	BBC Radio Scotland
93.1		WFM	W Wales	BBC Radio Cymru
93.2		WFM	Les Touillets	BBC Radio Guernsey
93.4		WFM	Isle of Man	Energy FM, Jurby
93.5		WFM	Ashkirk	BBC Radio Scotland
93.5		WFM	Larne	BBC Radio Ulster
93.5		WFM	Mid Wales	BBC Radio Cymru
93.7		WFM	Alderney	Island FM, Fort Albert
93.7		WFM	Keelylang Hill	BBC Radio Scotland
93.7		WFM	SW Wales	BBC Radio Cymru
93.8		WFM	Brougher Mountain	BBC Radio Ulster
93.8		WFM	Durris	BBC Radio Scotland
93.8		WFM	Kilkeel	BBC Radio Ulster
93.9		WFM	Innerleithen	BBC Radio Scotland
93.9		WFM	Kilvey Hill	BBC Radio Wales

Base	Mobile	Mode	Location	User and Notes
94.1		WFM	Eyemouth	BBC Radio Scotland
94.1		WFM	Stranraer	BBC Radio Scotland
94.2		WFM	N Wales	BBC Radio Cymru
94.5		WFM	Divis	BBC Radio Ulster
94.5		WFM	Tullich	BBC Radio Scotland
94.6		WFM	Alsagers Bank	BBC Radio Stoke
94.6		WFM	Henley	BBC Radio Berkshire
94.6		WFM	Porth	BBC Radio Wales
94.7		WFM	Chesterfield	Radio Sheffield
94.7		WFM	Ridge Hill	BBC Hereford & Worcester
94.7		WFM	Sandale	BBC Radio Scotland
94.8		WFM	Huntshaw Cross	BBC Radio Devon
94.8		WFM	Llanddona	BBC Radio Wales
94.8		WFM	Meriden	BBC Coventry and Warks
94.9		WFM	Belmont	BBC Radio Lincolnshire
94.9		WFM	Bristol	BBC Radio Bristol, Ilchester Crescent
94.9		WFM	London	BBC London, Crystal Palace
95.0		WFM	Bilsdale W Moor	BBC Radio Cleveland
95.0		WFM	Ludlow	BBC Radio Shropshire
95.0		WFM	Newhaven	BBC Southern Counties Radio
95.0		WFM	Stroud	BBC Radio Gloucestershire
95.1		WFM	Ballycastle	BBC Radio Ulster
95.1		WFM	Blaenavon	BBC Radio Wales
95.1		WFM	Carmel	BBC Radio Wales
95.1		WFM	Holme Moss	BBC GMR
95.1		WFM	Horsham	BBC Southern Counties Radio
95.1		WFM	Nottingham	BBC Radio Nottingham, Beacon Hill
95.1		WFM	Stoke Holy Cross	BBC Radio Norfolk
95.2		WFM	Caradon Hill	Radio Cornwall
95.2		WFM	Dunfermline	Kingdom FM, Knock Hill
95.2		WFM	Kendal	Radio Cumbria
95.2		WFM	Oxford	BBC Radio Oxford
95.3		WFM	Blaen-Plwyf	BBC Radio Wales
95.3		WFM	Brighton	BBC Southern Counties Radio, Whitehawk Hill
95.3		WFM	Cammoney Hill	BBC Radio Ulster
95.3		WFM	Luddenden	Radio Leeds
95.3		WFM	South Benfleet	BBC Essex
95.3		WFM	Stanton Moor	Radio Derby
95.3		WFM	Wharfedale	Radio Leeds
95.4		WFM	Limavady	BBC Radio Ulster
95.4		WFM	Pontop Pike	Radio Newcastle
95.4		WFM	Windsor	Radio Berkshire
95.4		WFM	Wrexham-Rhos	BBC Radio Wales
95.5		WFM	Hameldon Hill	Radio Lancashire
95.5		WFM	Lowestoft	Radio Suffolk
95.5		WFM	Mansfield	Radio Nottingham, Fishponds Hill
95.5		WFM	Mendip	Radio Bristol
95.5		WFM	Sandy Heath	BBC Three Counties Radio
95.5		WFM	Scarborough	Radio York, Olivers Mount
95.5		WFM	Swansea Valley	BBC Radio Wales
95.6		WFM	Carlisle	Radio Cumbria, Sandale
95.6		WFM	Sutton Coldfield	BBC Radio WM
95.7		WFM	Peterborough	Radio Cambridgeshire
95.8		WFM	Allerton Park	Radio Merseyside
95.8		WFM	Cirencester	Radio Gloucestershire

Base	Mobile	Mode	Location	User and Notes
95.8		WFM	Exeter	Radio Devon, St Thomas
95.8		WFM	London	Capital FM, Croydon
95.8		WFM	Whitby	Radio Cleveland
95.9		WFM	Aldeburgh	Radio Suffolk
95.9		WFM	Christchurch	BBC Radio Wales
95.9		WFM	Haverfordwest	BBC Radio Wales
95.9		WFM	High Hunsley	Radio Humberside
95.9		WFM	Thanet	Invicta FM
96.0		WFM	Bridport	Wessex FM
96.0		WFM	Buxton	Radio Derby
96.0		WFM	Cambridge	Radio Cambridgeshire
96.0		WFM	Chatton	Radio Newcastle
96.0		WFM	Isles of Scilly	Radio Cornwall
96.0		WFM	Okehampton	Radio Devon
96.0		WFM	Shrewsbury	Radio Shropshire, The Wrekin
96.1		WFM	Colchester	SGR Colchester, Wivenhoe Park
96.1		WFM	East Kent	Invicta FM, Wye
96.1		WFM	Glenrothes	Kingdom FM, Purin Hill
96.1		WFM	Morecambe Bay	Radio Cumbria
96.1		WFM	Rowridge	Radio Solent
96.2		WFM	Aylesbury	Mix 96, Quainton Hill
96.2		WFM	Barnstaple	Lantern FM, Huntshaw Cross
96.2		WFM	Coventry City Centre	Kix 96.2FM
96.2		WFM	Fenham	Century FM
96.2		WFM	North Norfolk	North Norfolk Radio, Stody
96.2		WFM	Nottingham	Trent FM, Mapperley Ridge
96.2		WFM	Oldham	96.2 The Revolution, The Civic Centre
96.2		WFM	Scarborough	Yorkshire Coast Radio, Olivers Mount
96.2		WFM	Shetland	SIBC, Bressay
96.2		WFM	Tunbridge Wells	kmfm
96.3		WFM	Benfleet	Essex FM
96.3		WFM	Bristol	GWR FM, Dundry
96.3		WFM	Chelsea	Big Blue (During Home Games Only)
96.3		WFM	Gleniffer Braes	Q96
96.3		WFM	Great Ormes Head	Coast FM
96.3		WFM	Leeds	96.3 Radio Aire, Morley
96.4		WFM	Caldbeck	CFM Radio
96.4		WFM	Congleton	Signal 1, Sutton Common
96.4		WFM	Folkestone	kmfm, Creteway Down
96.4		WFM	Great Barton	SGR FM
96.4		WFM	Grimsby	Compass FM, Bevan House
96.4		WFM	Guildford	96.4 The Eagle
96.4		WFM	Hexham	Century FM, Newton
96.4		WFM	Limavady	Downtown Radio
96.4		WFM	Perth	Tay FM
96.4		WFM	Sutton Coldfield	96.4 FM BRMB
96.4		WFM	Swansea	The Wave, Kilvey Hill
96.4		WFM	Torbay	Gemini FM, Beacon Hill
96.5		WFM	Blackpool Tower	Radio Wave 96.5FM
96.5		WFM	Cairn Pat	South Westsound FM
96.5		WFM	Mansfield	Trent FM, Fishponds Hill
96.5		WFM	Marlborough	GWR FM
96.5		WFM	Taunton	Orchard FM
96.6		WFM	Arbroath Infirmary	RNA
96.6		WFM	Bilsdale	96.6 TFM

Base	Mobile	Mode	Location	User and Notes
96.6		WFM	Blandford	97.4 Vale FM
96.6		WFM	Brougher Mountain	Downtown Radio
96.6		WFM	Cairn Gorm	Moray Firth Radio
96.6		WFM	Chichester	Spirit FM, The Trundle
96.6		WFM	Kirkcaldy	Kingdom FM
96.6		WFM	Mynydd Pencarreg	Radio Ceredigion
96.6		WFM	Northampton	Northants 96
96.6		WFM	St Albans	Mercury FM
96.6		WFM	Tavistock	97FM Plymouth Sound
96.6		WFM	Trislaig	Nevis Radio
96.7		WFM	Belfast	Citybeat 96.7, Black Mountain
96.7		WFM	Bradford	BCB
96.7		WFM	Darvel	West FM
96.7		WFM	Fraserburgh	Moray Firth Radio, Mormond Hill
96.7		WFM	Grantham	Lincs FM
96.7		WFM	Kidderminster	Wyvern FM
96.7		WFM	Kings Lynn	KLFM 96.7, Great Massingham
96.7		WFM	Liverpool	Radio City, Allerton Park
96.7		WFM	Liverpool	Radio City, Mersey Tunnel
96.7		WFM	Winchester	Ocean FM, Crabwood Farm
96.7		WFM	Wrotham	BBC Radio Kent
96.8		WFM	Polbain	Lochbroom FM
96.8		WFM	Selkirk	Radio Borders
96.8		WFM	South Wales	BBC Radio Cymru
96.9		WFM	Aberdeen	Northsound 1
96.9		WFM	Croydon	Choice FM
96.9		WFM	High Hunsley	96.9 Viking FM
96.9		WFM	Manchester	ALL FM 96.9
96.9		WFM	Morecambe Bay	The Bay
96.9		WFM	Newhaven	Southern FM
96.9		WFM	Pye Green	Signal 1
96.9		WFM	Sandy Heath	96.9 Chiltern FM
97.0		WFM	Dover	Invicta FM
97.0		WFM	Dumfries	South Westsound FM, Riddings Hill
97.0		WFM	Exeter	Gemini FM
97.0		WFM	Glencoe	Nevis Radio
97.0		WFM	Millburn Muir	102.5 Clyde 1
97.0		WFM	Plymouth	97FM Plymouth Sound
97.0		WFM	Reading	2-TEN FM, Broad Street Mall
97.0		WFM	Shilton	Mercia FM
97.1		WFM	Burnhope	Metro Radio
97.1		WFM	Carmel	97.1 Radio Carmarthenshire
97.1		WFM	Chedington	Orchard FM
97.1		WFM	Foxhall Heath	SGR FM
97.1		WFM	Haslemere	Delta FM, Holy Cross Hospital
97.1		WFM	Larne	Downtown Radio
97.1		WFM	Morrone	NECR
97.1		WFM	Nottingham	Radio Faza
97.1		WFM	Penistone	Dearne FM
97.1		WFM	Storeton	Wirral's Buzz 97.1
97.1		WFM	Turriff	NECR, Markethill Industrial Estate
97.1		WFM	Tyne Tunnel	Metro Radio
97.1		WFM	Wirral	Buzz 97.1
97.2		WFM	Bincombe	Wessex FM
97.2		WFM	Black Country	Beacon Radio (West Midlands)

Base	Mobile	Mode	Location	User and Notes
97.2		WFM	Blunsdon	GWR FM
97.2		WFM	Bristol	Vibe FM, Pur Down
97.2		WFM	Harrogate	97.2 Stray FM, Harlow Hill
97.2		WFM	Isle of Man	Manx Radio, Carnane
97.2		WFM	Maddybenny More	Q97.2 Causeway Coast Radio
97.2		WFM	Manchester	Wythenshawe FM
97.2		WFM	Wellingborough	Connect FM
97.2		WFM	Wolverhampton	West Midlands' Beacon FM, Turners Hill
97.3		WFM	Craigkelly	Forth One
97.3		WFM	Ilfracombe	Lantern FM
97.3		WFM	London	LBC, Croydon
97.4		WFM	Banbury	Fox FM, Farthinghoe
97.4		WFM	Black Mountain	Cool FM
97.4		WFM	Cardigan Bay	Radio Ceredigion, Penwaun
97.4		WFM	Inverness	97.4 MFR FM, Mounteagle
97.4		WFM	Newmarket	Q103, Icewell Hill
97.4		WFM	Newport	Red Dragon FM, Christchurch
97.4		WFM	Preston & Blackpool	97.4 Rock FM, Winter Hill
97.4		WFM	Shaftesbury	97.4 Vale FM
97.4		WFM	Sheffield	Hallam FM, Tapton Hill
97.4		WFM	Southwold	The Beach, Blythburgh
97.4		WFM	Stamford	Rutland Radio, East Casterton
97.5		WFM	Berwick-upon-Tweed	Radio Borders
97.5		WFM	Bradford	The Pulse of West Yorkshire
97.5		WFM	Carmarthen	97.1 Radio Carmarthenshire
97.5		WFM	Girvan	West FM
97.5		WFM	Horsham	102.7 Mercury FM
97.5		WFM	Llanelli	97.5 Scarlet FM
97.5		WFM	Pitlochry & Aberfeldy	Heartland FM, Faire Mhor
97.5		WFM	Portsmouth	Ocean FM, Fort Widley
97.5		WFM	Southend Town	Essex FM
97.6		WFM	Aberdeen	Northsound 1, Balgownie
97.6		WFM	Edinburgh	97.3 Forth One, Black Hill
97.6		WFM	Folkestone	BBC Radio Kent
97.6		WFM	Hereford	Wyvern FM, Ridge Hill
97.6		WFM	Luton	97.6 Chiltern FM
97.6		WFM	Scunthorpe	Lincs FM 102.2, Trent View Flats
97.7 - 99.8		WFM	Nationwide	Radio 1
98.0		WFM	Beds, Bucks & Herts	BBC Three Counties Radio
98.4		WFM	Isle of Man	Energy FM, Ramsey
98.6		WFM	Isle of Man	Energy FM, Carnane
98.7		WFM	Birmingham	New Style Radio
99.8		WFM	Burnley	2BR, Pendle Forest
99.9		WFM	Cumbria	Classic FM, Sandale
100.0		WFM	Devon	Classic FM, North Hessary Tor
100.0		WFM	London	Kiss 100 FM, Croydon
100.1		WFM	Kendal	Lakeland Radio
100.1		WFM	Sutton Coldfield	Classic FM
100.1		WFM	Tayside	Classic FM, Angus
100.2		WFM	Bath	Classic FM
100.2		WFM	Isle of Man	Classic FM, Douglas
100.2		WFM	Tendring	Dream 100 FM, Telstar Nurseries
100.3		WFM	Bradford	Classic FM
100.3		WFM	Durham	Classic FM, Pontop Pike
100.3		WFM	Glasgow	100-101FM Real Radio, Black Hill

Base	Mobile	Mode	Location	User and Notes
100.3		WFM	Isle of Wight	Classic FM, Rowridge
100.4		WFM	Bedford	Classic FM, Bow Brickhill
100.4		WFM	Hereford	Classic FM, Ridge Hill
100.4		WFM	Medway	kmfm, Hoo St Werburgh
100.4		WFM	NW England	Smooth FM, Winter Hill
100.5		WFM	Belmont	Classic FM
100.5		WFM	Londonderry	Classic FM
100.5		WFM	Meldrum	Classic FM
100.5		WFM	SW Wales	Classic FM, Presely
100.5		WFM	Totnes	South Hams Radio
100.6		WFM	Isle of Man	Ramsey Community Radio, Ramsey
100.6		WFM	London	Classic FM, Crystal Palace
100.7		WFM	NE England	Century FM, Bilsdale
100.7		WFM	NW Wales	Classic FM, Arfon
100.7		WFM	Sutton Coldfield	100.7 Heart fm
100.8		WFM	Dartmouth	South Hams Radio
100.8		WFM	Swindon	Classic FM, Blunsdon
100.8		WFM	W Somerset	Quaywest Radio, Porlock Hill
100.8		WFM	Windermere	Lakeland Radio
100.9		WFM	London	Classic FM
100.9		WFM	Selkirk	Classic FM
101.0		WFM	Mendip	Vibe FM
101.0		WFM	Newcastle	Classic FM, Fenham
101.1		WFM	Cardigan Bay	Classic FM, Blaen Plwyf
101.1		WFM	Havant	Angel Community Radio
101.1		WFM	Craigkelly	100-101FM Real Radio
101.1		WFM	Rosneath	100-101FM Real Radio
101.1		WFM	W Yorkshire	Classic FM, Holme Moss
101.2		WFM	Fermanagh & W Tyrone	Q101 West, Brougher Mountain
101.2		WFM	Peterhead & Fraserburgh	Waves FM, Mormond Hill
101.2		WFM	South Hams	South Hams Radio, Soar
101.3		WFM	Ayrshire	Classic FM, Darvel
101.3		WFM	Oxford	Classic FM
101.3		WFM	W Glamorgan	Classic FM, Kilvey Hill
101.4		WFM	Bristol	Classic FM, Pur Down
101.4		WFM	Derby	SAGA 106.6fm, Drum Hill
101.4		WFM	Moray Firth	Classic FM, Mounteagle
101.5		WFM	Cornwall	Classic FM, Redruth
101.5		WFM	Norfolk	Classic FM, Tacolneston
101.6		WFM	Bilsdale	Classic FM
101.6		WFM	Hindhead	Delta FM
101.6		WFM	Leeds	Classic FM, Beecroft Hill
101.6		WFM	N Wales	Classic FM, Great Ormes Head
101.6		WFM	SE Staffordshire	Centre FM, Lichfield
101.6		WFM	Sevenoaks	kmfm, Wrotham
101.7		WFM	Glasgow	Classic FM, Black Hill
101.7		WFM	Harlow	Ten-17 FM, Rye Hill
101.7		WFM	S Glamorgan	Classic FM, Wenvoe
101.7		WFM	Sheffield	Classic FM
101.8		WFM	Dover	Classic FM
101.8		WFM	Morecambe Bay	Classic FM
101.8		WFM	N E England	Century FM, Burnhope
101.8		WFM	Petersfield	Delta FM, Rams Walk
101.8		WFM	Reading	Classic FM, Hemdean
101.8		WFM	Stoke on Trent	Cross Rhythms City Radio

Base	Mobile	Mode	Location	User and Notes
101.9		WFM	Brighton	Classic FM, Whitehawk Hill
101.9		WFM	Cambridgeshire	Classic FM, Peterborough
101.9		WFM	Ivybridge	South Hams Radio
101.9		WFM	Northern Ireland	Classic FM, Divis
101.9		WFM	Tullich	NECR
102.0		WFM	Alton	Delta FM, Brockham Hill
102.0		WFM	Barnsley	Dearne FM
102.0		WFM	Cowes	Isle of Wight Radio
102.0		WFM	Dundee	Wave 102
102.0		WFM	Hastings	Southern FM
102.0		WFM	Manchester	Galaxy 102, Sunley Building
102.0		WFM	Matlock	Peak FM, Stanton Moor
102.0		WFM	Ryde	Isle of Wight Radio
102.0		WFM	Salisbury	102 Spire FM, Camp Hill
102.0		WFM	Stratford upon Avon	The Bear 102, Lark Stoke
102.0		WFM	Ventnor	Isle of Wight Radio
102.1		WFM	Inverurie	NECR, Meldrum
102.2		WFM	Birmingham	Galaxy 102.2, Metropolitan House
102.2		WFM	East Cornwall	Pirate FM 102, Caradon Hill
102.2		WFM	Lincoln	Lincs FM, Belmont
102.2		WFM	London	102.2 Smooth fm, Croydon
102.2		WFM	Penicuik	97.3 Forth One
102.2		WFM	Shetland	SIBC, Lerwick
102.2		WFM	Ullapool	Lochbroom FM
102.2		WFM	West Cumbria	CFM, Broughton Moor
102.2		WFM	West Wiltshire	GWR FM, Naish Hill
102.3		WFM	Ballymena	Downtown Radio, Portglenone
102.3		WFM	Bournemouth	102.3 2CR FM, Nine Barrow Down
102.3		WFM	Glasgow	102.5 Clyde 1, Rothesay
102.3		WFM	Littlehamptont	Spirit FM, Hammerpo
102.3		WFM	Skye/Mallaig	Nevis Radio, Cnoc Malagan
102.3		WFM	Thirsk	Minster FM, Calvert's Carpets
102.3		WFM	Windermere	The Bay
102.4		WFM	Bridlington	Yorkshire Coast Radio, Buckton Barn
102.4		WFM	Eastbourne	Southern FM, Heathfield
102.4		WFM	Gloucester & Cheltenham	Severn Sound, Churchdown Hill
102.4		WFM	Great Yarmouth & Norwich	Radio Broadland, Stoke Holy Cross
102.4		WFM	Isle of Man	Energy FM, Beary
102.4		WFM	Loch Leven	Nevis Radio, Glenachulish
102.4		WFM	Londonderry	Downtown Radio
102.4		WFM	SE Staffordshire	Centre FM, Burton
102.4		WFM	West Somerset	Quaywest Radio, Minehead North
102.4		WFM	Wigan	102.4 Wish FM, Billinge Hill
102.5		WFM	Caithness	Caithness FM, Ben Dorrery
102.5		WFM	Glasgow	102.5 Clyde 1, Black Hill
102.5		WFM	Halifax & Huddersfield	The Pulse of West Yorkshire, Vicars Lot
102.5		WFM	Pembrokeshire	Radio Pembrokeshire, Haverfordwest
102.5		WFM	Penrith	CFM Radio
102.6		WFM	Alnwick	Metro Radio, Shilbottle
102.6		WFM	Chelmsford	Essex FM, Bakers Wood
102.6		WFM	Kildrummy	NECR, Scar Hill
102.6		WFM	Oxford	FOX FM
102.6		WFM	Somerset	Orchard FM, Mendip
102.6		WFM	Stoke-on-Trent	Signal 1, Alsagers Bank
102.7		WFM	Aston Villa	The Villan (During Home Games Only)

Base	Mobile	Mode	Location	User and Notes
102.7		WFM	Keighley	BBC Radio Leeds
102.7		WFM	Peterborough	Hereward FM, Gunthorpe
102.7		WFM	Reigate & Crawley	Mercury FM
102.8		WFM	Derby	Ram FM, Drum Hill
102.8		WFM	Dundee	Tay FM, Angus
102.8		WFM	East Kent	Invicta FM, Dunkirk
102.8		WFM	Keith	Moray Firth Radio, Tor Sliasg
102.8		WFM	West Cornwall	Pirate FM, Redruth
102.8		WFM	Worcester	Wyvern FM, Malvern
102.9		WFM	Barnsley	Hallam FM, Ardsley
102.9		WFM	Basingstoke & Andover	2-TEN FM, Hannington
102.9		WFM	Leamington Spa	Mercia FM
102.9		WFM	Londonderry	Q102 FM
103.0		WFM	Bath	GWR FM (West)
103.0		WFM	Caernarfon	Champion 103, Arfon
103.0		WFM	Cambridge	Q103 FM, Madingley
103.0		WFM	Dumbarton	YOURradio FM
103.0		WFM	East Devon	Gemini FM, Stockland Hill
103.0		WFM	Isle of Lewis	Isles fm, Eitshal
103.0		WFM	Kirkcudbright	South Westsound FM, Cambret Hill
103.0		WFM	Manchester	Key 103, Saddleworth
103.0		WFM	Peterhead	Northsound 1, Stirling Hill
103.0		WFM	Stroud	Severn Sound
103.0		WFM	Tyne & Wear	Metro Radio, Fenham
103.1		WFM	Borders	Radio Borders, Peebles
103.1		WFM	Maidstone	Invicta FM, Bluebell Hill
103.1		WFM	Shrewsbury	Beacon Radio, The Wrekin
103.1		WFM	South Newry	Downtown Radio, Camlough
103.1		WFM	Stirling	Central FM, Earls Hill
103.1		WFM	Whitby	Yorkshire Coast Radio
103.2		WFM	Bradford	Sunrise Radio
103.2		WFM	Cardiff	Red Dragon FM, Wenallt
103.2		WFM	Colpy	NECR, Hill of Foudland
103.2		WFM	Darlington	Alpha 103.2
103.2		WFM	Hexham	Metro Radio, Newton
103.2		WFM	Kendal	The Bay
103.2		WFM	Leicester	Takeover Radio
103.2		WFM	Mansfield	Mansfield 103.2, Fishponds Hill
103.2		WFM	N Norfolk	North Norfolk Radio, Aylmerton
103.2		WFM	N Norfolk	North Norfolk Radio, Bunkers Hill
103.2		WFM	Southampton	Power FM, Chillerton Down
103.3		WFM	Buxworth	High Peak Radio
103.3		WFM	Cardigan Bay	Radio Ceredigion, Blaen Plwyf
103.3		WFM	Haringey	London Greek Radio, Alexandra Palace
103.3		WFM	Hope Valley	High Peak Radio
103.3		WFM	Milton Keynes	FM 103 Horizon, Bow Brickhill
103.3		WFM	Oban	Oban FM, Pulpit Hill
103.3		WFM	Rosneath	102.5 Clyde 1
103.4		WFM	Borders	Radio Borders, Eyemouth
103.4		WFM	Doncaster	Hallam FM, Clifton
103.4		WFM	Gt Yarmouth & Lowestoft	The Beach
103.4		WFM	Henley	2-TEN FM
103.4		WFM	Newcastle	Downtown Radio
103.4		WFM	Plymouth Tor	BBC Radio Devon, North Hessary
103.4		WFM	Sunderland	Sun FM, Haining

Base	Mobile	Mode	Location	User and Notes
103.4		WFM	West Cumbria	CFM Radio, Whitehaven
103.4		WFM	West Lothian	River FM, Bathgate
103.4		WFM	Wrexham	MFM
103.5		WFM	Brighton	Southern FM, Whitehawk Hill
103.5		WFM	Great Braxted	BBC Essex
103.5 - 104.9		WFM	Nationwide	BBC Radio 4
103.5		WFM	Newton Barrow	BBC Radio Wiltshire
103.5 - 104.9		WFM	Scotland	BBC Radio nan Gaidheal
103.5 - 104.9		WFM	Wales	BBC Radio Cymru
103.6		WFM	Blunsdon	Radio Swindon
103.6		WFM	Corby	Radio Northampton, Geddington
103.7		WFM	Acklam Wold	BBC Radio York
103.7		WFM	Isle of Man	Manx Radio, Jurby
103.7		WFM	Jersey	Channel 103 FM, Fremont Point
103.7		WFM	Lark Stoke	BBC WM
103.7		WFM	Merthyr Tydfil	BBC Radio Wales
103.7		WFM	Newton	BBC Radio Newcastle
103.8		WFM	Beds, Bucks & Herts	BBC Three Counties Radio, Zouches Farm
103.8		WFM	Bincombe Hill	BBC Radio Solent
103.8		WFM	Mapperley Ridge	BBC Radio Nottingham
103.9		WFM	Beecroft Hill	BBC Radio Leeds
103.9		WFM	Cardiff	BBC Radio Wales, Wenallt
103.9		WFM	Manningtree	BBC Radio Suffolk
103.9		WFM	Redruth	BBC Radio Cornwall
103.9		WFM	Sussex	SkyWave Radio
103.9		WFM	Winter Hill	BBC Radio Lancashire
104.0		WFM	Great Malvern	BBC Hereford & Worcester
104.0		WFM	Nuneaton	BBC WM
104.0		WFM	Reigate	BBC Southern Counties Radio
104.1		WFM	Clun	BBC Radio Shropshire
104.1		WFM	Hannington	BBC Radio Berkshire
104.1		WFM	Holme Moss	BBC Radio Sheffield
104.1		WFM	Keswick Forest	BBC Radio Cumbria
104.1		WFM	Stafford	BBC Radio Stoke
104.1		WFM	Whitehaven	BBC Radio Cumbria
104.2		WFM	Isle of Man	3FM, Port St Mary
104.2		WFM	Isle of Man	3FM, Ramsey
104.2		WFM	Northampton	BBC Radio Northampton
104.2		WFM	SE Wales	BBC Radio Cymru
104.2		WFM	Swingate	BBC Radio Kent
104.2		WFM	Windermere	BBC Radio Cumbria
104.3		WFM	Beacon Hill (North)	BBC Radio Devon
104.3		WFM	Naish Hill	BBC Radio Wiltshire
104.3		WFM	NE Wales	BBC Radio Cymru
104.3		WFM	Woolmoor	BBC Radio York
104.4		WFM	Fenham	BBC Radio Newcastle
104.4		WFM	Gt Massingham	BBC Radio Norfolk
104.4		WFM	London	Resonance104.4fm, Southbank
104.4		WFM	Reading	BBC Radio Berkshire
104.5		WFM	Bow Brickhill	BBC Three Counties Radio
104.5		WFM	Drum Hill	BBC Radio Derby
104.5		WFM	Heathfield	BBC Southern Counties Radio
104.5		WFM	Lancaster	BBC Radio Lancashire
104.6		WFM	Bath	BBC Radio Bristol
104.6		WFM	Great Barton	BBC Radio Suffolk
104.6		WFM	Guildford	BBC Southern Counties Radio

Base	Mobile	Mode	Location	User and Notes
104.6		WFM	Kidderminster	BBC Hereford & Worcester
104.6		WFM	Mid Wales	BBC Radio Cymru
104.6		WFM	Saddleworth	BBC GMR
104.7		WFM	Churchdown Hill	BBC Radio Gloucestershire
104.7		WFM	Grantham	BBC Radio Lincolnshire
104.7		WFM	Guernsey	Island FM, Les Touillets
104.7		WFM	York	Minster FM, Acklam Wold
104.8		WFM	Burton Down	BBC Southern Counties R
104.9		WFM	Copt Oak	BBC Radio Leicester
104.9		WFM	London	Xfm, Crystal Palace
104.9		WFM	Marlborough	BBC Radio Wiltshire
104.9		WFM	Stockport	Imagine FM, Romiley
105.0		WFM	S & E Isle of Man	3FM
105.1		WFM	Yorkshire	Galaxy 105-106, Emley Moor
105.2		WFM	Carmarthenshire	105-106FM Real Radio, Carmel
105.2		WFM	Glasgow	SAGA 105.2fm, Black Hill
105.2		WFM	Isle of Man	Energy FM, Maughold
105.2		WFM	Solent	Wave 105, Chillerton Down
105.2		WFM	Sutton Coldfield	Kerrang!
105.3		WFM	N E England	Galaxy 105-106, Burnhope
105.4		WFM	Cardiff	105-106FM Real Radio, St Hilary
105.4		WFM	Leicester	Leicester Sound, Billesdon
105.4		WFM	London	Magic 105.4, Croydon
105.4		WFM	N W England	105.4 Century FM, Winter Hill
105.4		WFM	St Andrews	Kingdom FM, Allanhill Farm
105.6		WFM	Bradford	Galaxy 105-106
105.6		WFM	Cambridge	Vibe FM, Madingley
105.6		WFM	Isle of Man	3FM
105.6		WFM	Maidstone	CTR FM, Coxheath
105.6		WFM	N E England	Galaxy 105-106, Fenham
105.6		WFM	Newbury	Kick FM, Wash Common Water Tower
105.6		WFM	Sheffield	Galaxy 105-106, Tapton Hill
105.6		WFM	Yeovil	Ivel FM, Coker Hill
105.7		WFM	Central Scotland	Beat 106, Craigkelly
105.7		WFM	Pembrokeshire	105-106FM Real Radio, Preseli
105.7		WFM	W Midlands	SAGA 105.7fm, Sutton Coldfield
105.8		WFM	Hexham	Galaxy 105-106, Newton
105.8		WFM	London	Virgin Radio, Crystal Palace
105.8		WFM	N Humberside	Galaxy 105-106, High Hunsley
105.8		WFM	Poole	Wave 105
105.9		WFM	Newport	105-106FM Real Radio, Christchurch
106.0		WFM	Canterbury	kmfm
106.0		WFM	Carmarthen	105-106FM Real Radio
106.0		WFM	Cookstown	Mid FM, Tulnagee Quarry
106.0		WFM	E Midlands	106 Century FM, Copt Oak
106.0		WFM	Ross-shire	Two Lochs Radio, Cnoc na Sgaid
106.0		WFM	Swansea	105-106FM Real Radio, Kilvey Hill
106.1		WFM	Central Scotland	Beat 106, Black Hill
106.1		WFM	Norwich	Vibe FM, Stoke Holy Cross
106.2		WFM	Carmarthenshire	105-106FM Real Radio, Fishguard
106.2		WFM	Isle of Man	3FM, Peel
106.2		WFM	Isle of Skye	Cuillin FM, Portree
106.2		WFM	London	Heart 106.2, Croydon
106.2		WFM	Yorkshire	105-106FM Real Radio, Emley Moor
106.3		WFM	Bridgend	106.3 Bridge FM
106.3		WFM	Chester	Dee 106.3, The Steam Mill

Base	Mobile	Mode	Location	User and Notes
106.3		WFM	Fife	Kingdom FM, The East, NE UK
106.4		WFM	Buxton	High Peak Radio
106.4		WFM	Glossop	High Peak Radio
106.4		WFM	Haywards Heath	Bright 106.4
106.4		WFM	Hill of Allargue	NECR
106.4		WFM	Mendlesham	Vibe FM
106.4		WFM	N E England	Galaxy 105-106, Bilsdale
106.5		WFM	Campbeltown	Argyll FM
106.6		WFM	Chapel en le Frith	High Peak Radio
106.6		WFM	Chard	Ivel FM, Windwhistle
106.6		WFM	Cliff Hill	Two Lochs Radio
106.6		WFM	Midhurst	Spirit FM
106.6		WFM	Slough	Star 106.6
106.6		WFM	Waltham	SAGA 106.6fm
106.7		WFM	Isle of Wight	Angel Community Radio
106.7		WFM	Knowsley	106.7 The Rocket
106.7		WFM	Old Knebworth	Hertbeat fm
106.8		WFM	Dover	kmfm, Guston
106.8		WFM	Peterborough	106.8 Lite FM, Gunthorpe
106.8		WFM	Thamesmead	Time 106.8, Shooters Hill
106.8		WFM	Wakefield	Ridings FM, Birkwood Farm
106.9		WFM	Helensburgh	YOURradio, Rosneath
106.9		WFM	Hertford	Hertbeat fm, Cole Green
106.9		WFM	Macclesfield	106.9 Silk FM, Sutton Common
106.9		WFM	Pontypridd	GTFM
107.0		WFM	Isle of Wight	Isle of Wight Radio, Chillerton Down
107.0		WFM	Loughborough	Oak 107, Loughborough University
107.0		WFM	Reading	Reading 107 FM, Tilehurst Water Tower
107.1		WFM	Ballygroggan	Argyll FM
107.1		WFM	Doncaster	Trax FM, Clifton
107.1		WFM	Ely Cathedral	Star 107
107.1		WFM	N London	Choice FM, Alexandra Palace
107.1		WFM	Rugby	107.1 Rugby FM, Royal Court Rounds Garden
107.2		WFM	Brighton	Juice 107.2, Sussex Heights
107.2		WFM	Bristol	Star 107.9, Pur Down
107.2		WFM	Broadstairs	kmfm
107.2		WFM	Dungannon	Mid FM
107.2		WFM	Dursley	Star 107.2
107.2		WFM	Glasgow	Awaz FM
107.2		WFM	Manton	Rutland Radio
107.2		WFM	Warrington	107.2 Wire FM, High Warren Reservoir
107.2		WFM	Winchester	The New 107.2 Win FM, Crabwood Farm
107.3		WFM	Bredgar	Time FM
107.4		WFM	Bolton	107.4 Tower FM, Tottington
107.4		WFM	Bridgwater	BCR fm
107.4		WFM	Chesterfield	Peak FM
107.4		WFM	Geddington	Connect FM
107.4		WFM	High Wycombe	Mix 107
107.4		WFM	Hungerford	Kick FM
107.4		WFM	Portsmouth	The Quay, Fort Southwick
107.4		WFM	Telford	107.4 Telford FM, Heath Hill
107.5		WFM	Cheltenham	Star 107.5
107.5		WFM	Cumbernauld	107 The Edge
107.5		WFM	Eastbourne	107.5 Sovereign Radio, Butt's Brow
107.5		WFM	Fenland	Fen Radio 107.5, Friday Bridge
107.5		WFM	Havering	Time FM, Lambourne House

Base	Mobile	Mode	Location	User and Notes
107.5		WFM	Pembrokeshire	Radio Pembrokeshire, Fishguard
107.5		WFM	Pembrokeshire	Radio Pembrokeshire, Tenby
107.5		WFM	Warminster	3TR FM
107.6		WFM	Ashford	Kmfm
107.6		WFM	Basingstoke	107.6 Kestrel FM, Fanum House
107.6		WFM	Bournemouth	Fire 107.6, West Howe
107.6		WFM	Bradford	106-108FM Real Radio
107.6		WFM	Liverpool	107.6 Juice FM, Liverpool Cathedral
107.6		WFM	Liverpool	107.6 Juice FM, Mersey Tunnels
107.7		WFM	Amersham	Mix 107
107.7		WFM	Chelmsford	Dream 107.7, Church Green
107.7		WFM	Peterborough	Vibe FM, Gunthorpe
107.7		WFM	S Yorkshire	106-108FM Real Radio, Tapton Hill
107.7		WFM	Somerset	Star 107.7, Worlebury Hill
107.7		WFM	South Knapdale	Argyll FM
107.7		WFM	West Lothian	River FM, Linlithgow
107.7		WFM	Wolverhampton	107.7 The Wolf, Mander House
107.7		WFM	Worthing	107.7 Splash FM, Guildbourne Centre
107.8		WFM	Hastings	107.8 Arrow FM
107.8		WFM	Kingston upon Thames	107.8 Radio Jackie, Tolworth Tower
107.8		WFM	Southampton	The Saint, Midanbury
107.9		WFM	Bath	Bath FM
107.9		WFM	Cambridge	Star 107, Gog Magog Hill
107.9		WFM	Hinckley	Fosseway Radio, Barwell
107.9		WFM	Huddersfield	Home 107.9, Ainley Top
107.9		WFM	Lanarkshire	107 The Edge, Hamilton
107.9		WFM	Medway	kmfm, Gillingham
107.9		WFM	Oxford	Passion 107.9, Boars Hill
107.9		WFM	Southport	107.9 Dune FM, Gaw Hill
107.9		WFM	Stroud	Star 107
107.9		WFM	Worksop	Trax FM

108.0000 - 112.0000 MHz   TACAN, DME Idents & ILS Localisers

Base	Mobile	Mode	Location	User and Notes
108.100		AM	Belfast	DME (I-BFH)
108.100		AM	Dundee Airport	DME Ident (DDE)
108.100		AM	Guernsey	ILS Localiser Runway 09 (I-UY)
108.100		AM	Guernsey	ILS Localiser Runway 27 (I-GH)
108.100		AM	RAF Chivenor	ILS Localiser Runway 28 (CV)
108.100		AM	RAF Cottesmore	TACAN Ident (CTM)
108.100		AM	USAF Mildenhall	ILS Localiser Runway 11 (I-MIL)
108.100		AM	USAF Mildenhall	ILS Localiser Runway 29 (I-MLD)
108.150		AM	Blackpool	DME Ident
108.150		AM	Blackpool	ILS Localiser Runway 28 (I-BPL)
108.150		AM	Lydd Airport	DME Ident
108.150		AM	Lydd Airport	ILS Localiser Runway 22 (I-LYX)
108.200		AM	Boscombe Down (MoD)	TACAN Ident (BDN)
108.300		AM	Londonderry	ILS/DME Rwy 26 (EGT)
108.300		AM	USAF Lakenheath	ILS Localiser Runway 24 (I-LKH)
108.400		AM	RAF Valley	TACAN Ident (VYL)
108.500		AM	RAF Benson	ILS Localiser Runway 19 (BO)
108.500		AM	Inverness Airport	ILS Localiser Runway 05 (I-LN)
108.500		AM	Inverness Airport	ILS Localiser Runway 23 (I-DX)
108.500		AM	RAF Northolt	ILS /DME
108.500		AM	Sumburgh Airport	DME Ident
108.500		AM	Sumburgh Airport	ILS Localiser Runway 09 (SUB)
108.500		AM	Sumburgh Airport	ILS Localiser Runway 27 (I-SG)

Base	Mobile	Mode	Location	User and Notes
108.500		AM	Teesside Airport	DME Ident
108.500		AM	Teesside Airport	ILS Localiser Runway 05 (I-TSE)
108.500		AM	Teesside Airport	ILS Localiser Runway 23 (I-TD)
108.600		AM	Kirkwall Airport	VOR/DME Ident (KWL)
108.700		AM	Newton Point	TACAN Ident (NTP)
108.700		AM	RAF Leuchars	ILS Localiser Runway 27 (LU)
108.700		AM	RAF Shawbury	ILS Localiser Runway 19 (SY)
108.700		AM	RAF St Mawgan	ILS Localiser Runway 31 (SM)
108.750		AM	Humberside Airport	DME Ident
108.750		AM	Humberside Airport	ILS Localiser Runway 21 (I-HS)
108.800		AM	Weathersfield	TACAN Ident (WET)
108.900		AM	Cranfield	ILS Localiser Runway 22 (I-CR)
108.900		AM	Dublin	ILS/DME Rwy 10
108.900		AM	Dublin	ILS/DME Rwy 28
108.900		AM	Edinburgh Airport	DME Ident
108.900		AM	Edinburgh Airport	ILS Localiser Runway 07 (I-VG)
108.900		AM	Edinburgh Airport	ILS Localiser Runway 25 (I-TH)
108.900		AM	Kerry	DME/ILS R25 KER
108.900		AM	Ventnor	TACAN Ident (VNR)
108.950		AM	Woodford	DME Ident (I-WU)
108.950		AM	Woodford	ILS Localiser Runway 25 (I-WU)
109.050		AM	Yeovil Aerodrome	DME Ident (YVL)
109.100		AM	Southampton Airport	ILS Localiser Runway 20 (I-SN)
109.150		AM	Luton Airport	DME Ident
109.150		AM	Luton Airport	ILS Localiser Runway 26 (I-LJ)
109.150		AM	Luton Airport	ILS Localiser Rwy 08 (I-LTN)
109.150		AM	Woodford Airport	ILS/DME
109.200		AM	Inverness Airport	VOR/DME Ident (INS)
109.200		AM	Swansea Aerodrome	DME Ident (SWZ)
109.300		AM	Glasgow	ILS Localiser Runway 23 (I-OO)
109.350		AM	Biggin Hill	ILS Localiser Runway 21 (I-BGH)
109.350		AM	Notts/East Midlands	ILS Localiser Runway 09 (I-EMW)
109.350		AM	Notts/East Midlands	ILS Localiser Runway 27 (I-EME)
109.400		AM	Barrow Airport	DME Ident (WL)
109.400		AM	Guernsey	ATIS
109.400		AM	Guernsey	VOR/ATIS (GUR)
109.500		AM	London, Heathrow	DME Ident
109.500		AM	London, Heathrow	ILS Localiser Runway 09R (I-BB)
109.500		AM	London, Heathrow	ILS Localiser Runway 27L (I-LL)
109.500		AM	Manchester Airport	DME Ident
109.500		AM	Manchester Airport	ILS Localiser Runway 06 (I-MM)
109.500		AM	Manchester Airport	ILS Localiser Runway 24 (I-NN)
109.500		AM	Plymouth Airport	DME Ident
109.500		AM	Plymouth Airport	ILS Localiser Runway 31 (I-PLY)
109.500		AM	Shannon Airport	ILS Runway 24 (SA)
109.600		AM	RAF Linton on Ouse	TACAN Ident (LOZ)
109.600		AM	RAF Odiham	TACAN Ident (ODH)
109.700		AM	Belfast (Aldergrove)	ILS Localiser Runway 25 (I-AG)
109.700		AM	RAF Cranwell	ILS Localiser Runway 26 (CW)
109.700		AM	RAF Kinloss	ILS Localiser Runway 26 (KS)
109.700		AM	RAF Lyneham	ILS Localiser Runway (LA)
109.700		AM	RAF Valley	ILS Localiser Runway 14 (VY)
109.750		AM	Coventry Airport	ILS Localiser Runway 23 (I-CT)
109.800		AM	RAF Kinloss	TACAN Ident (KSS)
109.800		AM	RAF Lyneham	TACAN (LYE)
109.850		AM	Fair Oaks Aerodrome	DME Ident (FRK)

Base	Mobile	Mode	Location	User and Notes
109.900		AM	Aberdeen (Dyce Airport)	ILS Localiser Runway 16 (I-AX)
109.900		AM	Aberdeen (Dyce Airport)	ILS Localiser Runway 34 (I-ABD)
109.900		AM	Belfast Airport	ILS Localiser Runway 25 (I-AG)
109.900		AM	Cork Airport	ILS Runway 17 (ICA)
109.900		AM	Cork Airport	ILS Runway 35 (ICN)
109.900		AM	East Midlands Airport	ILS Localiser Runway 09 (I-EMW)
109.900		AM	East Midlands Airport	ILS Localiser Runway 27 (I-EME)
109.900		AM	Exeter Airport	ILS Localiser Runway 26 (I-XR)
109.900		AM	Stornoway Airport	ILS Localiser Runway 18 (I-SV)
109.900		AM	Warton (MoD)	DME Ident
109.900		AM	Warton (MoD)	ILS Localiser Runway 26 (WQ)
110.000		AM	Galway	DME (CRN)
110.100		AM	RAF Benson	TACAN (BSO)
110.100		AM	Birmingham International	DME Ident
110.100		AM	Birmingham International	ILS Localiser Runway 15 (I-BIR)
110.100		AM	Birmingham International	ILS Localiser Runway 33 (I-BM)
110.100		AM	Glasgow	ILS Localiser Runway 05 (I-UU)
110.100		AM	RAF Marham	ILS Localiser Runway 24 (MR)
110.150		AM	Bristol Airport	ILS Localiser Runway 09 (I-BON)
110.150		AM	Bristol Airport	ILS Localiser Runway 27 (I-BTS)
110.150		AM	USAF Mildenhall	ILS Localiser Runway 11 (I-MIL)
110.150		AM	USAF Mildenhall	ILS Localiser Runway 29 (I-MLD)
110.200		AM	USAF Lakenheath	TACAN Ident (LKH)
110.300		AM	RAF Cottesmore	ILS Localiser Runway 23 (CTM)
110.300		AM	Jersey Airport	ILS Localiser Runway 27 (I-DD)
110.300		AM	London, Heathrow	DME Ident
110.300		AM	London, Heathrow	ILS Localiser Runway 09L (I-AA)
110.300		AM	London, Heathrow	ILS Localiser Runway 27R (I-RR)
110.300		AM	Prestwick Airport	ILS Localiser Runway 13 (I-PP)
110.300		AM	Prestwick Airport	ILS Localiser Runway 31 (I-KK)
110.300		AM	RAF Cottesmore	ILS Localiser Runway 23 (CM)
110.300		AM	RAF Leeming	ILS Localiser Runway 16 (LI)
110.350		AM	Harwarden Airport	DME/ILS Localiser Runway 05 (HDN) &
110.350		AM	Harwarden Airport	DME/ILS Localiser Runway 23 (HDN)
110.400		AM	Perth Aerodrome	VOR (PTH)
110.500		AM	Bournemouth (Hurn)	DME Ident
110.500		AM	Bournemouth (Hurn)	ILS Localiser Runway 08 (I-BMH)
110.500		AM	Bournemouth (Hurn)	ILS Localiser Runway 26 (I-BH)
110.500		AM	RAF Leuchars	TACAN Ident (LUK)
110.500		AM	Stansted	DME Ident
110.500		AM	Stansted	ILS Localiser Runway 05 (I-SED)
110.500		AM	Stansted	ILS Localiser Runway 23 (I-SX)
110.550		AM	Filton (BAe), Bristol	ILS Localiser Runway 10 (I-BRF)
110.550		AM	Filton (BAe), Bristol	ILS Localiser Runway 28 (I-FB)
110.700		AM	Cardiff Airport	DME Ident
110.700		AM	Cardiff Airport	ILS Localiser Runway 12 (I-CD)
110.700		AM	Cardiff Airport	ILS Localiser Runway 30 (I-CWA)
110.700		AM	Carlisle Airport	DME Ident (CO)
110.700		AM	Connaught (Knock)	ILS Localiser Rwy 27 (I-CK)
110.700		AM	London, Heathrow	DME Ident (HHT)
110.700		AM	London, Heathrow	ILS Localiser Runway 23 (I-CC)
110.700		AM	RAF Coningsby	ILS Localiser Runway 26 (CY)
110.700		AM	RAF Linton on Ouse	ILS Localiser Runway 22 (LO) &
110.700		AM	RAF Linton on Ouse	ILS Localiser Runway 04 (LO)
110.900		AM	Belfast (Aldergrove)	ILS Runway 17 (I-FT)
110.900		AM	Jersey Airport	DME Ident (I-JJ)

Base	Mobile	Mode	Location	User and Notes
110.900		AM	Jersey Airport	ILS Localiser Runway 09 (I-JJ)
110.900		AM	Leeds/Bradford Airport	ILS Localiser Runway 09 (I-LBF)
110.900		AM	Leeds/Bradford Airport	ILS Localiser Runway 32 (I-LF)
110.900		AM	London, Gatwick	DME Ident
110.900		AM	London, Gatwick	ILS Localiser Runway 08R (I-GG)
110.900		AM	London, Gatwick	ILS Localiser Runway 26L (I-WW)
110.900		AM	Norwich Airport	ILS Localiser Runway 14 (I-NH)
111.000		AM	RNAS Yeovilton	TACAN Ident (VLN)
111.100		AM	RAF Coningsby	TACAN Ident (CGY)
111.100		AM	RAF Lossiemouth	ILS Localiser Runway 23 (LM)
111.100		AM	RAF Waddington	ILS Localiser Runway 21 (WA)
111.100		AM	USAF Fairford	ILS Localiser Runway 09 (I-FFA)
111.100		AM	USAF Fairford	ILS Localiser Runway 27 (I-FFD)
111.150		AM	Ronaldsway, Isle of Man	ILS Localiser Runway 08 (I-RH)
111.150		AM	Ronaldsway, Isle of Man	ILS Localiser Runway 26 (I-RY)
111.500		AM	London, City Airport	ILS Localiser Runway 10 (LST)
111.500		AM	London, City Airport	ILS Localiser Runway 28 (LST)
111.500		AM	Newcastle Airport	DME Ident
111.500		AM	Newcastle Airport	ILS Localiser Runway 07 (I-NC)
111.500		AM	Newcastle Airport	ILS Localiser Runway 25 (I-NWC)
111.500		AM	RAF Coltishall	ILS Localiser Runway 22 (CS)
111.500		AM	USAF Fairford	TACAN Ident (FFA)
111.550		AM	Farnborough	ILS/DME Localiser Runway 06(FRG)
111.550		AM	Farnborough	ILS/DME Localiser Runway 24(FNB)
111.550		AM	Manchester Airport	ILS/DME Localiser Runway 06R (I-MC)
111.600		AM	RAF Chivenor	TACAN Ident (CVR)
111.700		AM	Boscombe Down (MoD)	ILS Localiser Runway 24 (BD)
111.750		AM	Liverpool Airport	DME Ident
111.750		AM	Liverpool Airport	ILS Localiser Runway 09 (LVR)
111.750		AM	Liverpool Airport	ILS Localiser Runway 27 (I-LQ)
111.750		AM	Woodford (BAe)	ILS/DME Localiser Runway 10/28
111.900		AM	RAF Brize Norton	ILS Localiser Runway 08 (BZA)
111.900		AM	RAF Brize Norton	ILS Localiser Runway 26 (BZB)
111.900		AM	RAF Brize Norton	TACAN Ident (BZN)
111.900		AM	RAF Honington	ILS Localiser Runway 27 (HT)

112.0000 - 117.9750 MHz — TACAN & DME Idents, ATIS & VOR Aero

Base	Mobile	Mode	Location	User and Notes
112.100		AM	Berry Head	VOR/DME Ident (BHD)
112.100		AM	Pole Hill	VOR/DME Ident (POL)
112.200		AM	Jersey Airport	VOR/ATIS (JSY)
112.200		AM	Ronaldsway, Isle of Man	VOR/DME Ident (IOM)
112.500		AM	St Abbs	VOR/DME Ident (SAB)
112.600		AM	RAF Leeming	TACAN Ident (LEE)
112.600		AM	RAF St Mawgan	TACAN Ident (SMG)
112.700		AM	Donegal Aerodrome	DME Ident (CFN)
112.800		AM	Gamston Aerodrome	VOR/DME Ident (GAM)
112.800		AM	Rennes Airport	VOR (RNE) France
113.100		AM	Strumble	VOR/DME Ident (STU)
113.200		AM	Warton (MoD)	TACAN Ident (WTN)
113.300		AM	Shannon Airport	DVOR/DME (SHA)
113.350		AM	Southampton Airport	VOR/ATIS (SAM)
113.400		AM	RAF Fairford (USAFE)	TACAN Ident (FFA)
113.550		AM	Manchester Airport	VOR/DME Ident (MCT)
113.600		AM	London, Heathrow	VOR/DME Ident (LON)
113.600		AM	Wick Aerodrome	TACAN Ident (WIZ)

Base	Mobile	Mode	Location	User and Notes
113.600		AM	Wick Aerodrome	VOR (WIK)
113.650		AM	Honiley	VOR/DME Ident (HON)
113.750		AM	Bovingdon	VOR/DME Ident (BNN)
113.900		AM	Ottringham	VOR/DME Ident (OTR)
113.950		AM	Benbecula	VOR/DME Ident (BEN)
114.000		AM	Midhurst	VOR/DME Ident (MID)
114.050		AM	Lydd Airport	VOR (LYD)
114.100		AM	Wallasey	VOR/DME Ident (WAL)
114.200		AM	Land's End Airport	VOR/DME Ident (LND)
114.250		AM	Newcastle Airport	VOR/ATIS (NEW)
114.300		AM	Aberdeen (Dyce Airport)	ATIS
114.300		AM	Aberdeen (Dyce Airport)	VOR/DME Ident (ADN)
114.350		AM	Compton	VOR/DME Ident (CPT)
114.550		AM	Clacton Aerodrome	VOR/DME Ident (CLN)
114.600		AM	Cork Airport	DVOR/DME Ident (CRK)
114.750		AM	Chichester/Goodwood	VOR (GWC)
114.800		AM	RAF St Athan	TACAN Ident (SAT)
114.900		AM	Dublin	VOR/DME Ident (DUB)
114.900		AM	Vallafield	TACAN Ident (VFD)
114.950		AM	Dover	VOR/DME Ident (DVR)
115.100		AM	Biggin Hill	VOR/DME Ident (BIG)
115.100		AM	Stornoway Airport	TACAN Ident (STZ)
115.100		AM	Stornoway Airport	VOR (STN)
115.200		AM	Dean Cross	VOR/DME Ident (DCS)
115.300		AM	Ockham	VOR/DME Ident (OCK)
115.400		AM	Glasgow	VOR/ATIS/DME Ident (GOW)
115.550		AM	Gloucestershire Airport	DME Ident (GOS)
115.600		AM	Lambourne	VOR/DME Ident (LAM)
115.700		AM	Stoke on Trent	VOR/DME Ident (TNT)
115.800		AM	Baldonnel, Eire	VOR Ident (BAL)
115.900		AM	USAF Mildenhall	TACAN Ident (MLD)
115.950		AM	Lashenden	VOR/DME Ident (HLS)
116.000		AM	RAF Machrihanish	DVOR (MAC)
116.200		AM	Blackbushe	DME Ident (BLC)
116.250		AM	Barkway	VOR/DME Ident (BKY)
116.400		AM	Daventry	VOR/DME Ident (DTY)
116.500		AM	Cranfield	VOR Ident (CFD)
116.500		AM	RAF Coltishall	TACAN Ident (CSL)
116.750		AM	Cambridge Airport	DME Ident (CAB)
116.750		AM	Enniskillen	DME Ident (ENN)
116.750		AM	Haverfordwest	DME Ident (HDW)
117.000		AM	Seaford	VOR/DME Ident (SFD)
117.100		AM	Burnham	VOR (BUR)
117.200		AM	Belfast	VOR/DME Ident (BEL)
117.300		AM	Detling	VOR/DME Ident (DET)
117.350		AM	Sumburgh Airport	VOR/DME Ident (SUM)
117.400		AM	Connaught (Knock)	VOR/DME Ident (CON)
117.400		AM	RAF Cranwell	TACAN Ident (CWZ)
117.450		AM	Brecon	VOR/DME Ident (BCN)
117.500		AM	Brookmans Park	VOR/DME Ident (BPK)
117.500		AM	Turnberry	VOR/DME Ident (TRN)
117.550		AM	Cumbernauld Airport	DME Ident (CBN)
117.600		AM	RAF Wittering	TACAN Ident (WIT)
117.700		AM	Oxford/Kidlington Airport	DME Ident (OX)
117.700		AM	Tiree	VOR/DME Ident (TIR)
117.900		AM	Mayfield	VOR/DME Ident (MAY)

Tuning in Air Band Communications
by Peter G. Clark

One of the most exciting and entertaining aspects of scanning is listening to the civil aviation band. Whether it's in the comfort of your own home or at your local airport, civil air band listening will always have a surprise in store for you. It's also probably the most visible form of the scanning hobby. Just look around any airport or air display and you'll see scanner users by the dozen. It is unlawful but it's the part of the hobby that's least likely to land you in trouble!

Airband listening (118.000 to 136.975 MHz) is an easily accessible form of scanning with a plethora of dedicated handheld receivers on the market but from the begginner's point of view, it can often be a daunting prospect. Not knowing where to look for frequencies and then trying to understand the various confusing terms and phrases used by pilots and air traffic controllers are the first hurdles to be overcome so here's a brief guide to get you started. Of course, many of you will not live near an airport, but that shouldn't spoil your airband listening - you will still be able to hear aircraft checking in with controllers as they track through the airways. And if that isn't enough, someone once calculated that almost the entire UK population lives no more than 25 miles away from an airport or aerodrome!

Getting Started in Airband Radio

If you're just starting out in the hobby, you'll probably just want to hear your first aircraft. The table below should help as it shows how the civil airband is broken down into sections and lists a few frequencies where you'll almost certainly be able to hear something.

Control Tower Frequencies	118 - 123 MHz
	118.300 MHz Birmingham Tower
	118.625 MHz Manchester Tower
	118.700 MHz London Heathrow Tower
	118.800 MHz Glasgow Tower
General Airways Frequencies	123 - 130 MHz
	126.075 MHz Swanwick ACC Sector 6
	127.650MHz Shanwick Oceanic
	128.600 MHz London VOLMET
	129.225 MHz Scottish ACC
Company Frequencies	130 - 132 MHz
	131.050 MHz Swanwick ACC Sector 4
	131.500 MHz Heathrow Airline Operations
	131.550 MHz ACARS Data Worldwide
General Airways Frequencies	132 - 136 MHz
	132.300 MHz Swanwick ACC Sector 21
	133.600 MHz Swanwick ACC Sector 5
	133.675 MHz Scottish ACC
	135.375 MHz London VOLMET

How far can I hear?

As you will have probably discovered by now, VHF signals don't seem to travel very far. That's a function of their frequency; as a rule of thumb, the lower the frequency, the further it will travel around the world. If you've ever listened to frequencies in the shortwave bands, those below 30 MHz, you will probably have heard a variety of weird and wonderful stations from all over the world. You can hear them because shortwave signals bounce off the different layers that make up our sky and travel around the globe by bouncing up and down. They can travel great distances this way. On the other hand, VHF signals are pretty energetic and they don't bounce off the sky. Instead, they pass straight through the atmosphere and out into space. That's why VHF transmitters should be line of sight if you want to be sure of hearing them. If they are over the horizon, typically only about 20 miles away, then you probably won't be able to hear them. Airband signals are no different to any other VHF ones but you can hear them from a lot further away because aircraft fly at altitude and that means even when they are dozens of miles away, they can still be above the horizon. In fact, an aircraft flying at 37,000 feet can be heard up to 240 miles away! So, as you can see, airband radio opens up new possibilities in VHF listening and can increase your reception range tenfold.

What can I hear?

You should be able to hear most of the airports in your area so the first thing to do is to find a good atlas or even local road map and search for the location of all your local airports and aerodromes, those within a distance of about 60 miles. Now turn to the Alphabetical List of Airports section in this book and find the frequencies for each of those airports; then load those frequencies into your scanner and just wait. You might like to programme the frequencies into your scanner's memories so that you can rapidly scan a number of channels for activity and sooner or later the scanner will stop and airband communications will pour from your speaker! You could also programme in the air traffic control frequencies like Swanwick and Scottish. You might not be able to hear the ground stations but you will almost certainly hear the aircraft talking to them. Working out which frequencies are best to listen to can be easily solved with an excellent book by Mike Simkins called *North Atlantic Flight Communications*. This is an indispensable guide to airband radio on both VHF and the shortwave bands and will help you pinpoint the best airways frequencies to tune to at your location.

It's worth remembering that the civil airband normally uses 25 kHz channel spacing but 8.33 kHz spacing is gradually being introduced so you might come across some odd looking frequencies in the future. Also, don't forget all airband communications are carried out in the AM mode.

Now let's take a quick look at one of the more complex aspects of airband radio, understanding what pilots and air traffic controllers are talking about. Luckily for us, the universal language for airband communications is English so you won't have to learn a new language as well as new words and phrases.

Departures

Let's begin at the beginning, the departure. Once we passengers (self-loading cargo as we're called by some of the more cynical aviators) are safely aboard and the doors are closed, that's when the pilots' job really begins. Before anything else can happen, engine start, taxi and departure clearances must all be obtained. This will generally take place on the Ground Frequency with a call like "Speedbird 175 on stand 43 request push and start." One thing you will quickly discover with airband listening is that pilots and controllers operate in a world of precision and this is very evident in the way they speak. That short and apparently simple radio call has identified the flight as Speedbird 175, which is a scheduled British Airways flight from London Heathrow to New York JFK, parked on Stand 43 and it is requesting clearance to start his engines and for the tug crew to push him back onto the taxi way.

Once clearance for engine start and taxi has been received, the all important airways clearance quickly follows:

ATC: "Speedbird 175. Clearance when you're ready."
BA175: "Go ahead."
ATC: "Speedbird 175 is cleared to New York Kennedy via UA1 UR3 55
            North. Airways frequency 133.45 and the squawk will be 4026."

That short exchange has just cleared the flight from London Heathrow to its Oceanic entry point at 55° North 10° West, about 110 nautical miles west of Belfast via two Upper Air Routes, UA1 and UR3.

As the aircraft begins to move, it will be asked to change frequency to the Tower where it will be guided along the taxiways and onto the runway in use. Once the "cleared for take-off" message is received, the aircraft will begin its acceleration run, then lift off from the runway and begin its journey.

Once airborne, the aircraft will switch to the Radar Frequency and begin to follow the Standard Instrument Departure or SID in force for that day. Like approach procedures, which we will look at later, these are a set of precise instructions that get aircraft from the runway and onto a heading and position so that they can join the airway.

So, let's quickly recap on frequency usage at major airports. The use of three frequencies is not uncommon; Ground is used for ground movements, Tower is responsible for getting aircraft to and from the runways and Approach or Radar takes over as soon as the flight is airborne.

More detailed information on Upper Air Routes, flight procedures and radio communications across the North Atlantic can be found in *North Atlantic Flight Communications*. This comprehensive book is accompanied by software that allows you to plot the progress of flights as they cross the 'pond'.

The Flight

Once the flight has left the confines of the airport and has entered controlled airspace, responsibility for separation is handed over to air traffic controllers who watch the progress of individual flights across various sectors of the country. During the flights of yesteryear, a pilot's workload remained high for the duration of the flight. Today, however, that is not always the case. Certainly, flight instruments still have to be monitored and forward estimates calculated but, essentially, the work of flying the aircraft has been handed over to onboard computers in the form of the autopilot.

With the flight plan entered into the flight management system, pilots rarely communicate with air traffic control centres except when checking in on a new frequency, requesting a slight course deviation to avoid CB's or Cumulonimbus clouds, which are responsible for much of the unpleasant flying weather, or requesting flight level changes.

Over land, most navigation involves flying between two radio navigation beacons, such as VORs, which operate in the 108-118 MHz band and NDBs (Non-Directional Beacons) which operate in the 283.5-435.0 kHz band. Coupled with some VORs are DMEs or Distance Measuring Equipment, which provide a readout on board the aircraft of the distance left to run to a beacon. Over water, where beacons are not practical, aircraft rely on their internal navigation systems. Of course, where VHF radio navigation does not work, neither does VHF voice communication. The solution is to use an HF or shortwave frequency between 3 - 30 MHz, a band that many scanners now cover and which is well worth exploring. This is the main communications mode in use for flights crossing the Atlantic. It's an interesting aspect of airband listening and if you want to explore it, *North Atlantic Flight Communications* is without doubt the book to have, along with another invaluable book, *World Airline Fleet and Selcal Directory*.

Arrivals

Arriving at the destination might be the time when passengers can relax but behind the scenes the workload is frantic. All flights arriving at an airport must be positioned to ensure safety and flight separation. Airport approach frequencies positively buzz with instructions and clearances as pilots fly Instrument Approaches or what are known as plates; diagrams of the procedures to be flown to land safely. In fact, many flights end with the pilots only gaining visual contact with the runway a few hundred feet from their touchdown point. Plates form an essential part of Instrument Flying and allow pilots to fly between two airports even if there is cloud all the way.

A final word on airband listening. One of the more popular airband pastimes these days is tuning in to air display teams like the Red Arrows. If you've never done it, then there is a real treat in store for you. Just imagine being able to listen to the same instructions that the display pilots are receiving! Check out the team frequencies later in this book - you might be surprised by what you can hear!

Base	Mobile	Mode	Location	User and Notes

117.9750 - 136.0000 MHz   International Aviation Band 50 kHz

Base	Mobile	Mode	Location	User and Notes
118.000		AM	Nationwide	Air-Air Common
118.000		AM	Nationwide	Honda Display Team Air-Air
118.000		AM	Nationwide	Shape Sky Divers Discrete
118.000		AM	Nationwide	Utterly Butterly Wing Walking Team
118.000		AM	USAF Mildenhall	Interplane
118.000		AM	Yeovil	Westland Helicopter Tests
118.000		AM	Wattisham (Army Airfield)	Air-Air
118.025		AM	Leeds/Bradford Airport	ATIS
118.050		AM	Birmingham International	Radar/Approach
118.050		AM	North Sea	Frigg Oil Field Deck
118.050		AM	Oban	Air-Ground
118.075		AM	Barra, Scotland	AFIS
118.075		AM	London, City Airport	Tower
118.075		AM	Newcastle Helipad	Air-Ground
118.100		AM	Aberdeen (Dyce Airport)	Tower
118.100		AM	Penzance Heliport	Tower
118.125		AM	RAF St Athan	Tower
118.150		AM	Clacton on Sea	Air-Ground
118.150		AM	Plymouth City Airport	Tower
118.150		AM	Prestwick Airport	Tower
118.200		AM	Lossiemouth (RAF)	Ground
118.200		AM	Lossiemouth (RAF)	Tower
118.200		AM	Ronaldsway, Isle of Man	Radar
118.200		AM	Southampton Airport	Tower
118.250		AM	Brittas Bay	Air-Ground
118.250		AM	Sumburgh Airport	Tower
118.275		AM	Fishburn	Air-Ground
118.275		AM	Middle Wallop (Army)	Approach
118.275		AM	Middle Wallop (Army)	Tower
118.300		AM	Belfast (Aldergrove)	Tower
118.300		AM	Birmingham International	Tower
118.300		AM	Kirkwall Airport	Tower/Approach/Weather
118.325		AM	Ipswich Airport	AFIS
118.350		AM	Derby (Burnaston)	Air-Ground
118.350		AM	Kinloss (RAF)	Talkdown
118.375		AM	Newcastle Airport	ATIS
118.400		AM	Blackpool	Tower
118.400		AM	London City Airport	Tower
118.425		AM	Lyneham (RAF)	Approach
118.425		AM	Lyneham (RAF)	Director
118.450		AM	Liverpool John Lennon	Radar
118.475		AM	Swanwick Civil ATC	London Control
118.500		AM	Dublin Airport	Director
118.500		AM	London Heathrow	Tower
118.500		AM	Newcastle Airport	Radar
118.550		AM	Jersey Airport	Radar
118.575		AM	Manchester Airport	Approach
118.575		AM	Manchester Airport	Radar Standby
118.600		AM	Dublin Airport	Tower
118.625		AM	Manchester Airport	Tower
118.650		AM	Bournemouth (Hurn)	Radar
118.675		AM	Nationwide	Paragliding Below 5000 Feet
118.700		AM	Edinburgh Airport	Tower
118.700		AM	London Heathrow	Tower
118.700		AM	Shannon Airport	Tower

Base	Mobile	Mode	Location	User and Notes
118.725		AM	Nationwide	CAA Temporary Event Allocation
118.775		AM	Manchester Control Centre	Control
118.800		AM	Cork Airport	Radar
118.800		AM	Glasgow	Tower
118.825		AM	London TCC (Terminal Control)	Brookmans Park
118.825		AM	Swanwick Civil ATC	London Control ACC
118.850		AM	Tees Valley/Durham Airport	Approach
118.850		AM	Tees Valley/Durham Airport	Radar
118.900		AM	Guernsey	Radar
118.900		AM	Kemble	AFIS
118.900		AM	Kinloss (RAF)	Departures
118.900		AM	Lossiemouth (RAF)	Departures
118.900		AM	Ronaldsway, Isle of Man	Tower
118.950		AM	London Gatwick	Approach
118.950		AM	London Gatwick	Radar
118.950		AM	London TCC (Terminal Control)	Gatwick
118.950		AM	Mona (RAF)	AFIS
119.000		AM	Brize Norton	Radar
119.000		AM	Fairford (USAF)	Radar
119.000		AM	Shetlands	East Shetland Information
119.050		AM	Aberdeen (Dyce Airport)	Approach
119.050		AM	Aberdeen (Dyce Airport)	Radar
119.050		AM	Exeter Airport	Radar
119.100		AM	Glasgow	Approach
119.100		AM	Glasgow	Radar
119.125		AM	Humberside Airport	Approach
119.125		AM	Humberside Airport	Radar
119.150		AM	Fairford (USAF)	Tower
119.175		AM	Mona (RAF)	Flying Club
119.200		AM	Benbecula	Approach/Tower & AFIS
119.225		AM	Lyneham (RAF)	Tower
119.250		AM	Coventry Airport	Approach
119.250		AM	Coventry Airport	Tower
119.275		AM	Sandown, Isle of Wight	Air-Ground
119.300		AM	Cork Airport	Tower
119.300		AM	Glasgow	Radar
119.325		AM	Exeter Airport	ATIS
119.350		AM	Coltishall (RAF)	MATZ
119.350		AM	Inverness Airport	Radar
119.350		AM	Kinloss (RAF)	Approach
119.350		AM	Lossiemouth (RAF)	Radar
119.350		AM	Norwich Airport	Approach
119.350		AM	Norwich Airport	Radar
119.375		AM	Barkston Heath (RAF)	Departure
119.375		AM	Cranwell (RAF)	Approach
119.375		AM	Cranwell (RAF)	MATZ
119.400		AM	Haydock Park Racecourse	Air-Ground
119.400		AM	Manchester Control Centre	Control
119.425		AM	Farway Common	Air-Ground
119.425		AM	Stubton Park	Air-Ground
119.450		AM	Hinton in the Hedges	Air-Ground
119.450		AM	Jersey Airport	Tower
119.450		AM	Prestwick Airport	Radar
119.475		AM	Bournemouth (Hurn)	Approach
119.475		AM	Bournemouth (Hurn)	Europe Air Charter
119.525		AM	Manchester Airport	Approach

Base	Mobile	Mode	Location	User and Notes
119.550		AM	Dublin Airport	Approach
119.550		AM	Shipdam	Air-Ground & AFIS
119.600		AM	Redhill Aerodrome	Tower/AFIS
119.650		AM	Aberporth (MoD)	AFIS
119.700		AM	Newcastle Airport	Tower
119.700		AM	Swansea Airport	Air-Ground
119.700		AM	Wick	Air-Ground
119.725		AM	London Heathrow	Approach (Director)
119.725		AM	London TCC (Terminal Control)	Heathrow
119.750		AM	Perranporth	Air-Ground
119.750		AM	Valley (RAF)	MATZ
119.750		AM	Woodvale (RAF)	Tower
119.775		AM	London TCC (Terminal Control)	Bovingdon
119.775		AM	Swanwick Civil ATC	London Control
119.800		AM	Exeter Airport	Tower
119.800		AM	London Gatwick	Police Helicopter Ops
119.800		AM	Perth (Scone)	Air-Ground & AFIS
119.800		AM	Tees Valley/Durham Airport	Tower
119.850		AM	Liverpool John Lennon	Approach
119.850		AM	Liverpool John Lennon	Radar
119.875		AM	Scottish Air Traffic Control - Prestwick	Scottish ACC (Information)
119.900		AM	Cork Airport	Approach
119.900		AM	Dunstable Downs	Gliders Air-Ground
119.925		AM	Dublin Airport	Approach
119.925		AM	Manston	Approach
119.925		AM	Manston	Tower
119.950		AM	Blackpool	Approach/Radar
119.950		AM	Guernsey	Tower
119.975		AM	Coningsby (RAF)	Tower
119.975		AM	Wyton (RAF)	Tower
120.025		AM	London TCC (Terminal Control)	Logan
120.025		AM	Swanwick Civil ATC	London Control
120.075		AM	Colerne (RAF)	Approach
120.075		AM	Colerne (RAF)	Tower
120.075		AM	North Sea	Trent Oil Field Deck
120.075		AM	North Sea	Tyne Oil Field Deck
120.075		AM	North Sea	Viking Oil Field Log
120.125		AM	East Midlands Airport/ Nottingham	Radar
120.150		AM	North Coates	Air-Ground
120.175		AM	London TCC (Terminal Control)	TIMBA
120.175		AM	Swanwick Civil ATC	London Control Inbound
120.200		AM	Shannon Airport	Approach
120.225		AM	Southampton Airport	Zone
120.250		AM	Panshanger	Air-Ground
120.250		AM	Solent	Initial Contact Frequency
120.300		AM	Jersey Airport	Approach
120.300		AM	Jersey Airport	Radar
120.300		AM	Leeds/Bradford Airport	Tower
120.325		AM	Northolt (RAF)	Departures
120.350		AM	Glasgow	Oceanic Clearance
120.350		AM	Shanwick Oceanic Area Control Centre	ATC Shanwick Oceanic
120.375		AM	Beccles Heliport	Air-Ground
120.400		AM	London Heathrow	Approach
120.400		AM	London TCC (Terminal Control)	Heathrow
120.425		AM	Barkston Heath (RAF)	Tower
120.450		AM	Jersey Airport	ATZ Zone/Radar

Base	Mobile	Mode	Location	User and Notes
120.450		AM	Jersey Airport	Radar
120.450		AM	North Sea	Oil Rig Heliports Common
120.475		AM	London TCC (Terminal Control)	London
120.475		AM	Swanwick Civil ATC	London Control SIDs
120.500		AM	Leeming (RAF)	Tower
120.525		AM	London TCC (Terminal Control)	Biggin
120.525		AM	Swanwick Civil ATC	London Control ACC
120.550		AM	Prestwick Airport	Approach
120.550		AM	Prestwick Airport	Radar
120.575		AM	Luton Airport	ATIS
120.600		AM	Cumbernauld Airport	Air-Ground
120.625		AM	Audley End	Air-Ground
120.625		AM	London TCC (Terminal Control)	Stansted
120.625		AM	Stansted	Approach
120.650		AM	Cardiff Airport	Tremorfa Heliport
120.675		AM	Northolt (RAF)	Tower
120.700		AM	Lydd Airport	AFIS
120.700		AM	Woodford (BAe)	Tower
120.725		AM	Valley (RAF)	ATIS
120.775		AM	Shawbury (RAF)	MATZ
120.800		AM	Coningsby (RAF)	Approach
120.800		AM	Nationwide	Battle of Britain Flights
120.850		AM	Ronaldsway, Isle of Man	Approach
120.850		AM	Ronaldsway, Isle of Man	Radar
120.900		AM	Ballykelly (Army)	Approach (Aldergrove)
120.900		AM	Belfast (Aldergrove)	Radar
120.900		AM	Belfast (City)	Radar (Belfast)
120.900		AM	Benson (RAF)	Approach
120.900		AM	Benson (RAF)	MATZ
120.925		AM	Cork Airport	ATIS
120.975		AM	Gloucestershire Staverton	Radar
121.000		AM	Woodvale (RAF)	Approach
121.025		AM	London TCC (Terminal Control)	Cowley
121.050		AM	Leeds/Bradford Airport	Radar
121.075		AM	Silverstone	Air-Ground
121.100		AM	Dublin Airport	Approach
121.100		AM	Henlow (RAF)	Air-Ground
121.125		AM	Prestwick Airport	ATIS
121.175		AM	Duxford	Air-Ground
121.175		AM	Nationwide	CAA Events/Airshows
121.175		AM	North Sea	Nam Noordwinning
121.200		AM	Edinburgh Airport	Approach
121.225		AM	London TCC (Terminal Control)	REDFA
121.225		AM	Swanwick Civil ATC	London Control
121.250		AM	Plymouth Military Radar (RN)	Radar
121.275		AM	London TCC (Terminal Control)	Bovingdon
121.275		AM	Swanwick Civil ATC	London Control
121.300		AM	Glasgow	Radar
121.300		AM	Lochaber	Air Ambulance
121.325		AM	Scottish Air Traffic Control - Prestwick	Scottish Air Traffic Control
121.325		AM	Swanwick Civil ATC	London Control TMA
121.350		AM	Manchester Airport	Approach (Director)
121.350		AM	Manchester Airport	Director
121.375		AM	Manchester Airport	Ground
121.400		AM	Shannon Airport	Approach
121.400		AM	Shannon Airport	Radar

Base	Mobile	Mode	Location	User and Notes
121.500		AM	Nationwide	Civil Aviation Distress Channel
121.600		AM	Aberdeen (Dyce Airport)	Fire Service
121.600		AM	Birmingham International	Fire Service
121.600		AM	Bournemouth (Hurn)	Fire Service
121.600		AM	Brize Norton	Crew Commander
121.600		AM	Cambridge Airport	Fire Service
121.600		AM	Coventry Airport	Fire Service
121.600		AM	Derry	Fire Service
121.600		AM	East Midlands Airport/ Nottingham	Fire Service
121.600		AM	Edinburgh Airport	Fire Service
121.600		AM	Farnborough	Fire Service
121.600		AM	Glasgow	Fire Service
121.600		AM	Gloucestershire Staverton	Fire Service
121.600		AM	Jersey Airport	Fire Service
121.600		AM	Kerry	Ground
121.600		AM	London Gatwick	Fire Service
121.600		AM	Lyneham (RAF)	Crew Commander
121.600		AM	Manchester Airport	Fire Service
121.600		AM	Manston	Fire Service
121.600		AM	Nationwide	Airfield Fire & Rescue
121.600		AM	Ronaldsway, Isle of Man	Fire Service
121.600		AM	Sumburgh Airport	Fire Service
121.600		AM	Waterford	Fire Service
121.700		AM	Aberdeen (Dyce Airport)	Ground
121.700		AM	Bournemouth (Hurn)	Ground
121.700		AM	Cork Airport	Tower
121.700		AM	Coventry Airport	Ground
121.700		AM	Glasgow	Ground
121.700		AM	London Heathrow	Ground
121.700		AM	Manchester Airport	Clearance
121.700		AM	Manchester Airport	Delivery
121.700		AM	Nationwide	CAA Events (Rarely Used)
121.700		AM	Shannon Airport	Clearance
121.700		AM	Shannon Area Control Centre	Centre
121.725		AM	Brize Norton	Ground
121.725		AM	Stansted	Ground
121.725		AM	Waddington (RAF)	Approach
121.725		AM	Warton (BAe)	ATIS
121.725		AM	Waterford	ATIS
121.750		AM	Belfast (Aldergrove)	Ground
121.750		AM	Blackpool	ATIS
121.750		AM	Edinburgh Airport	Ground
121.750		AM	Luton Airport	Ground
121.775		AM	London City Airport	Ground
121.775		AM	Southampton Airport	Ground
121.775		AM	Wycombe Air Park (Booker)	Ground
121.800		AM	Birmingham International	Ground
121.800		AM	Cork Airport	Ground
121.800		AM	Dublin Airport	Ground
121.800		AM	Guernsey	Ground
121.800		AM	London Gatwick	Ground
121.800		AM	Prestwick Airport	Tower
121.800		AM	Shannon Airport	Ground
121.800		AM	Southend Airport	ATIS
121.850		AM	Aberdeen (Dyce Airport)	ATIS
121.850		AM	London Heathrow	ATIS (Departures)

Base	Mobile	Mode	Location	User and Notes
121.850		AM	Manchester Airport	Ground
121.850		AM	Manchester Airport	Tower
121.875		AM	Biggin Hill	ATIS
121.875		AM	Cranfield	ATIS
121.875		AM	Dublin Airport	Clearance/Delay
121.900		AM	Connaught (Knock) Airport	Ground
121.900		AM	East Midlands Airport/ Nottingham	Ground
121.900		AM	Jersey Airport	Ground
121.900		AM	London Heathrow	Ground
121.950		AM	Bournemouth (Hurn)	ATIS
121.950		AM	Church Fenton	Ground
121.950		AM	Liverpool John Lennon	Ground
121.950		AM	London Gatwick	Clearance
121.950		AM	London Gatwick	Delivery
121.950		AM	Oxford (Kidlington Airport)	Ground
121.975		AM	London Heathrow	Clearance/Delivery
121.975		AM	Manchester Airport	ATIS (Departures)
122.000		AM	Baldonnel	Approach
122.000		AM	Baldonnel	Dublin Military Radar
122.000		AM	Coventry Airport	Radar
122.000		AM	Lashenden (Headcorn)	Air-Ground
122.000		AM	North Sea	BP Buchan Field
122.000		AM	North Sea	BP Cyprus Field
122.000		AM	North Sea	BP Forties Field
122.000		AM	North Sea	BP Gyda Field
122.000		AM	North Sea	Unity Oil Field Deck
122.025		AM	North Sea	BP Cleeton Field Deck
122.025		AM	North Sea	Caister Oil Field Deck
122.025		AM	North Sea	Murdoch Oil Field Deck
122.050		AM	Birmingham International	Goldstar Ops.
122.050		AM	Blackpool Airport	Keenair Ops
122.050		AM	Bristol Airport	City Express Ops
122.050		AM	Guernsey	FlyBe Ops
122.050		AM	London Gatwick	Groundstar Ops.
122.050		AM	Luton Airport	Aviance Ops.
122.050		AM	Manchester Airport	Swissport Handling Ops
122.050		AM	North Sea	Brent Oil Field Deck
122.050		AM	North Sea	Chevron Ninian Field Log
122.050		AM	North Sea	Conoco Murchison Field Deck
122.050		AM	North Sea	Ninian Field Log
122.050		AM	North Sea	Shell/Esso Auk Field
122.050		AM	North Sea	Shell/Esso Kittiwake Field
122.050		AM	North Sea	Thistle Field Deck
122.050		AM	Nottingham/Tollerton	Hutchins Crop Sprayers
122.050		AM	Prestwick Airport	Greer Aviation Ops
122.050		AM	Ronaldsway, Isle of Man	FlyBe Ops
122.050		AM	Southend Airport	Heavilift Ops
122.050		AM	Stansted Airport	Swissport Handling Ops
122.050		AM	Stapleford Tawney	Aeromega Ops (Helicopter Ops)
122.075		AM	Duxford	AFIS
122.075		AM	Whitchurch (Tilstock)	Air-Ground
122.100		AM	Benson (RAF)	Radar
122.100		AM	Church Fenton	Tower
122.100		AM	Coltishall (RAF)	Approach
122.100		AM	Coltishall (RAF)	Tower
122.100		AM	Coningsby (RAF)	Approach

Base	Mobile	Mode	Location	User and Notes
122.100		AM	Coningsby (RAF)	Ground
122.100		AM	Coningsby (RAF)	Tower
122.100		AM	Cottesmore (RAF)	Ground
122.100		AM	Cottesmore (RAF)	Tower
122.100		AM	Culdrose (RN)	Talkdown
122.100		AM	Culdrose (RN)	Tower
122.100		AM	Dishforth (Army)	Approach
122.100		AM	Dishforth (Army)	Ground
122.100		AM	Dishforth (Army)	Tower
122.100		AM	Honington (RAF)	Tower
122.100		AM	Kinloss (RAF)	Tower
122.100		AM	Kirkcudbridght Ranges	Kirkcoobree Range
122.100		AM	Lakenheath (USAF)	Tower
122.100		AM	Leeming (RAF)	Tower
122.100		AM	Leuchars (RAF)	Ground
122.100		AM	Leuchars (RAF)	Tower
122.100		AM	Linton on Ouse (RAF)	Ground
122.100		AM	Linton on Ouse (RAF)	Tower
122.100		AM	Lyneham (RAF)	Tower
122.100		AM	Marham (RAF)	Tower
122.100		AM	Merryfield (RN)	Tower
122.100		AM	Nationwide	Fisheries Protection
122.100		AM	Nationwide	Military Tower Common
122.100		AM	Odiham (RAF)	Flight Information
122.100		AM	Odiham (RAF)	Tower
122.100		AM	Portland (RN)	Approach
122.100		AM	Portland (RN)	Tower
122.100		AM	Predannack (RN)	Tower(Culdrose)
122.100		AM	Shawbury (RAF)	Tower
122.100		AM	Sligo	Tower/AFIS
122.100		AM	Spadeadam (RAF)	Radar
122.100		AM	St. Mawgan (RAF)	Approach
122.100		AM	St. Mawgan (RAF)	Tower
122.100		AM	Ternhill (RAF)	Tower
122.100		AM	Topcliffe (RAF)	Approach
122.100		AM	Topcliffe (RAF)	Tower
122.100		AM	Valley (RAF)	Ground
122.100		AM	Valley (RAF)	Tower
122.100		AM	Waddington (RAF)	Tower
122.100		AM	Wattisham (Army Airfield)	Tower
122.100		AM	Wethersfield (RAF)	MATZ
122.100		AM	Wyton (RAF)	Ground
122.100		AM	Yeovilton (RN)	Tower
122.125		AM	Flotta Airfield	Tower
122.125		AM	Leicester Aerodrome	Air-Ground
122.125		AM	North Sea	Hamilton Argyll Field
122.175		AM	North Sea	Mobil Beryl Field
122.175		AM	Turweston Aerodrome	Air-Ground
122.200		AM	Cambridge Airport	Tower
122.200		AM	Gormanston, Eire (Military)	Approach/Tower
122.200		AM	Haverfordwest	Air-Ground
122.250		AM	Caernarfon Aerodrome	Air-Ground
122.250		AM	North Sea	Shell/Esso Brent Field
122.250		AM	Rochester Aerodrome	AFIS
122.250		AM	Valley (RAF)	Approach
122.275		AM	Nationwide	CAA Calibrator Aircraft

Base	Mobile	Mode	Location	User and Notes
122.275		AM	Stansted	Hijack Negotiations
122.300		AM	Alderney	Aurigny Airlines
122.300		AM	Baldonnel	Dublin Military Radar
122.300		AM	Blackbushe	AFIS & Air-Ground
122.300		AM	Peterborough (Sibson)	Approach/Radar
122.325		AM	North Sea	Amoco Montrose Field
122.325		AM	North Sea	Gannet Oil Field deck
122.325		AM	North Sea	Hamilton Esmond Field
122.325		AM	North Sea	Hamilton Forbes Field
122.325		AM	North Sea	Hamilton Gordon Field
122.325		AM	North Sea	Lomond Oil Field deck
122.350		AM	Brooklands	Air-Ground
122.350		AM	Cardiff Airport	Execair Ops
122.350		AM	Dublin Airport	Air Contractor Ops
122.350		AM	East Midlands Airport/ Nottingham	Air Bridge Carriers Ops
122.350		AM	Edinburgh Airport	Execair Operations
122.350		AM	Glasgow	Execair Ops
122.350		AM	Grimsby (Cuxwold)	Air-Ground
122.350		AM	Guernsey	Aurigny Air Services
122.350		AM	Hethel	Air-Ground
122.350		AM	Hitchin (Rush Green)	Air-Ground
122.350		AM	Liverpool John Lennon	Reed Aviation Ops
122.350		AM	Lochaber	PLM Helicopters
122.350		AM	London Gatwick	Aviance Handling
122.350		AM	London Gatwick	Thos. Cook Airlines
122.350		AM	London Heathrow	Gulf Air Terminal 3
122.350		AM	Luton Airport	Aviance
122.350		AM	Luton Airport	Reed Aviation
122.350		AM	Manchester Airport	Air Kilroe Ops
122.350		AM	Manchester Airport	Thos Cook Airlines
122.350		AM	North Sea	Total Alwyn Field
122.350		AM	Tees Valley/Durham Airport	Air Cam
122.375		AM	Blackpool	Scotia Helibus Ops
122.375		AM	Humberside Airport	Scotia Helibus Ops
122.375		AM	North Sea	BP Magnus Field Deck
122.375		AM	North Sea	Lennox Oil Field Deck
122.375		AM	Peterhead/Longside	Air-Ground Bond Helicopters
122.375		AM	Strubby Heliport	Air-Ground
122.375		AM	North Sea	Magnus BP
122.400		AM	Bantry, Eire	Air-Ground
122.400		AM	Dounreay Aerodrome	Tower
122.400		AM	Elstree Aerodrome	Air-Ground & AFIS
122.400		AM	Scatsa	Radar
122.400		AM	Weston (Dublin), Eire	Air-Ground
122.425		AM	Earls Colne	Air-Ground
122.450		AM	Chichester (Goodwood)	AFIS
122.450		AM	North Sea	Claymore & Tartan
122.450		AM	North Sea	Occidental Claymore Field
122.450		AM	North Sea	Piper Oil Field deck
122.450		AM	North Sea	Saltire Oil Field deck
122.450		AM	North Sea	Texaco Tartan Field
122.450		AM	Sleap Aerodrome	Air-Ground
122.450		AM	Wickenby Aerodrome	Air-Ground
122.475		AM	Nationwide	Hot Air Ballooning Air-Ground
122.500		AM	Bitteswell Aerodrome	Air-Ground
122.500		AM	Farnborough	Tower

Base	Mobile	Mode	Location	User and Notes
122.500		AM	Galway, Eire	Tower & AFIS
122.500		AM	Llanbedr	Air-Ground
122.500		AM	Weston-super-Mare	Tower
122.525		AM	Ashcroft farm	Air-Ground
122.525		AM	North Sea	Clyde Oil Field deck
122.525		AM	North Sea	Hamilton Pipe Field
122.525		AM	North Sea	Judy Oil Field deck
122.550		AM	Mildenhall (USAF)	Tower
122.600		AM	Abbeyshrule, Eire	Air-Ground
122.600		AM	Castlebar, Eire	Air-Ground
122.600		AM	Inverness Airport	Approach/Tower
122.600		AM	Lerwick (Tingwall)	Air-Ground & Air Ambulance
122.600		AM	Seething Aerodrome	Air-Ground
122.600		AM	Sherburn in Elmet Aerodrome	Air-Ground
122.600		AM	Stansted	Fire
122.600		AM	White Waltham Aerodrome	Air-Ground
122.625		AM	North Sea	Conoco Viking Field
122.650		AM	North Sea	Nelson Oil Field Deck
122.675		AM	Duxford	AFIS
122.700		AM	Barton Aerodrome, Manchester	Air-Ground
122.700		AM	Bodmin	Tower
122.700		AM	Compton Abbas Aerodrome	Air-Ground
122.700		AM	Nationwide	Battle of Britain Flight
122.700		AM	Tiree	AFIS
122.725		AM	Filton (BAe) Bristol	Approach
122.750		AM	Cardiff Airport	Execair
122.750		AM	Cowden Range	Range Control
122.750		AM	Donna Nook Range	Control
122.750		AM	Eskmeals Range (MOD)	Range
122.750		AM	Highland Ranges/Tain(RAF)	Range
122.750		AM	North Coates	Air-Ground Donna Nook Range
122.750		AM	North Sea	Shell/Esso Fulmar Field
122.750		AM	Pembrey Range (RAF)	Range
122.750		AM	Salisbury Plain (Army)	Air-Ground
122.750		AM	Tain Range (RAF)	Range
122.750		AM	Wainfleet Range (RAF)	Range
122.775		AM	Crowfield Aerodrome	Air-Ground
122.775		AM	North Sea	Scott Oil Field deck
122.775		AM	Oaksey Park	Air-Ground
122.800		AM	Baldonnel	Area Control
122.800		AM	North Sea	Beatrice Field deck
122.800		AM	North Sea	Unionoil Heather Field
122.800		AM	Stapleford Tawney	Air-Ground
122.825		AM	Bruntingthorpe	Air-Ground
122.850		AM	Cranfield	Approach
122.850		AM	Eshott	Air-Ground
122.875		AM	North Sea	Excalibur Oil Field Deck
122.875		AM	North Sea	Galahad Oil Field Deck
122.875		AM	North Sea	Guinevere Oil Field Deck
122.875		AM	North Sea	Lancelot Oil Field Deck
122.875		AM	North Sea	Phillips Hewett Field
122.875		AM	North Sea	Pickerill Oil Field Deck
122.900		AM	Dundalk	Air-Ground
122.900		AM	Gloucestershire Staverton	Tower
122.900		AM	Kilkenny	Air-Ground
122.900		AM	London, Westland Heliport	Tower (Battersea)

Base	Mobile	Mode	Location	User and Notes
122.925		AM	Fenland	Air-Ground & AFIS
122.925		AM	North Sea	Phillip Ekofisk Field
122.950		AM	Birr Aerodrome, Eire	Air-Ground
122.950		AM	Glasgow Heliport	Air-Ground
122.950		AM	Great Yarmouth (North Denes)	Air-Ground
122.950		AM	London	Air Ambulance G-HEMS
122.950		AM	Nationwide	Air Ambulance Common Use
122.950		AM	North Sea	Eko/Tees Pip Oil Field Deck
122.950		AM	North Sea	Kotter Oil Field Deck
122.950		AM	North Sea	Logger Oil Field Deck
122.950		AM	North Sea	Nam Nam Field
122.950		AM	North Sea	Penzoil Noordwinning
122.950		AM	North Sea	Petroland Petroland Field
122.950		AM	North Sea	Placid Placid Field
122.950		AM	North Sea	Zanddijk
123.000		AM	Connemara, Eire	Air-Ground
123.000		AM	Eaglescott	Air-Ground
123.000		AM	Halfpenny Green (see Wolverhampton)	AFIS
123.000		AM	Inisheer, Eire	Air-Ground
123.000		AM	Inishman, Eire	Air-Ground
123.000		AM	Inishmore, Eire	Air-Ground
123.000		AM	North Sea	Ivanhoe Oil Field Deck
123.000		AM	Wolverhampton (Halfpenny Green)	Air-Ground
123.025		AM	North Sea	Gryphon Oil Field Deck
123.025		AM	North Sea	Hamilton Ravenspurnn North
123.050		AM	Beverley (Linley Hill)	Tower
123.050		AM	Leconfield (RAF)	Air-Ground
123.050		AM	North Sea	Brent Oil Field Log
123.050		AM	North Sea	North Cormorant Log
123.050		AM	North Sea	Shell/Esso Eider Field Log
123.050		AM	North Sea	Shell/Esso Tern Field Log
123.050		AM	North Sea	South Cormorant Log
123.050		AM	Nuthampstead, Royston	Air-Ground
123.050		AM	Wigtown	Tower
123.100		AM	Baldonnel	Ground
123.100		AM	Boulmer (RAF)	Air-Ground SAR
123.100		AM	London	Special Flypasts Air-Ground
123.100		AM	Nationwide	Search & Rescue (Primary)
123.150		AM	Fair Isle	Air-Ground
123.150		AM	Islay Airport	AFIS
123.150		AM	Shoreham by Sea	Approach/Tower
123.150		AM	Sumburgh Airport	Approach
123.150		AM	Sumburgh Airport	North Sea Offshore
123.175		AM	Badminton	Air-Ground
123.200		AM	Barrow (Walney Island)	Air-Ground
123.200		AM	Enniskillen (St. Angelo)	Air-Ground
123.200		AM	Old Sarum	Air-Ground
123.200		AM	St. Angelo	Tower
123.225		AM	Fadmoor Aerodrome	Air-Ground
123.225		AM	North Sea	Arco Thames Field
123.225		AM	North Sea	Bruce Oil Field Deck
123.225		AM	North Sea	Welland Oil Field Log
123.250		AM	Bagby (Thirsk)	Air-Ground
123.250		AM	Bembridge, Isle of Wight	AFIS & Air-Ground
123.275		AM	Netherthorpe	Air-Ground
123.300		AM	Barkston Heath (RAF)	Talkdown

Base	Mobile	Mode	Location	User and Notes
123.300		AM	Church Fenton	Talkdown
123.300		AM	Coltishall (RAF)	Director
123.300		AM	Coltishall (RAF)	Talkdown
123.300		AM	Coningsby (RAF)	Talkdown
123.300		AM	Cottesmore (RAF)	Director
123.300		AM	Cottesmore (RAF)	Talkdown
123.300		AM	Cranwell (RAF)	Talkdown
123.300		AM	Culdrose (RN)	Talkdown
123.300		AM	Culdrose (RN)	Tower
123.300		AM	Dublin Airport	Dublin Military ATC
123.300		AM	Kinloss (RAF)	Director
123.300		AM	Leeming (RAF)	Talkdown
123.300		AM	Leuchars (RAF)	Director
123.300		AM	Linton on Ouse (RAF)	Radar
123.300		AM	Linton on Ouse (RAF)	Talkdown
123.300		AM	Lossiemouth (RAF)	Approach
123.300		AM	Lossiemouth (RAF)	Director
123.300		AM	Lossiemouth (RAF)	Talkdown
123.300		AM	Lyneham (RAF)	Talkdown
123.300		AM	Marham (RAF)	Talkdown
123.300		AM	Middle Wallop (Army)	Tower
123.300		AM	Nationwide	Military Airfield Radar
123.300		AM	Odiham (RAF)	Talkdown
123.300		AM	Portland (RN)	Tower
123.300		AM	Shawbury (RAF)	Talkdown
123.300		AM	Spanish Point, Eire	Air-Ground
123.300		AM	St. Athan (RAF)	Talkdown
123.300		AM	St. Mawgan (RAF)	Radar
123.300		AM	St. Mawgan (RAF)	Talkdown
123.300		AM	Topcliffe (RAF)	Talkdown
123.300		AM	Trim, Eire	Air-Ground
123.300		AM	Valley (RAF)	Radar
123.300		AM	Valley (RAF)	Talkdown
123.300		AM	Waddington (RAF)	Radar
123.300		AM	Wattisham (Army Airfield)	Approach
123.300		AM	Wattisham (Army Airfield)	Director
123.300		AM	Wattisham (Army Airfield)	Talkdown
123.300		AM	Wethersfield (RAF)	Radar
123.300		AM	Wittering (RAF)	Talkdown
123.300		AM	Yeovilton (RN)	Director
123.300		AM	Yeovilton (RN)	Talkdown
123.325		AM	Kerry	Tower
123.350		AM	Hawarden/Chester	Approach
123.375		AM	Morecambe Bay	British Gas Helicopters
123.400		AM	Lyneham (RAF)	Approach
123.400		AM	Lyneham (RAF)	Radar
123.400		AM	North Sea	Dab Duc Skjold Field
123.400		AM	St. Mawgan (RAF)	Tower
123.425		AM	Fairoaks	Tower & AFIS
123.450		AM	Aberdeen (Dyce Airport)	Bristow Helicopters
123.450		AM	Errol Aerodrome	Drop Zone Control
123.450		AM	Mull	Mull Traffic
123.450		AM	Nationwide	Air-Air Common
123.450		AM	North Sea	Dab Duc Dan Field
123.450		AM	North Sea	Dab Duc Gorm Field
123.450		AM	North Sea	Marathon East Kinsale

Base	Mobile	Mode	Location	User and Notes
123.450		AM	North Sea	Marathon West Kinsale
123.450		AM	North Sea	Noordwinning/Zanddijk Field
123.450		AM	North Sea	Rolf Oil Field Deck
123.450		AM	North Sea	Tyra Oil Field Deck
123.450		AM	Unst (Saxa Vord)	Ops
123.475		AM	Dunkeswell Aerodrome	Air-Ground
123.500		AM	Baldonnel	Tower
123.500		AM	Berwick on Tweed (Winfield)	Winfield Radio
123.500		AM	Felthorpe Aerodrome	Tower
123.500		AM	Scottish Air Traffic Control - Prestwick	Scottish Control (Stornoway)
123.500		AM	Shobdon Aerodrome	Air-Ground
123.500		AM	Stornoway Airport	Approach/Tower & AFIS
123.500		AM	Swanton Morley Aerodrome	Air-Ground
123.525		AM	North Weald	Air-Ground
123.550		AM	North Sea	Andrew Oil Field Deck
123.550		AM	North Sea	Captian Oil Field Deck
123.550		AM	North Sea	Sun Balmoral Field
123.575		AM	North Sea	Tiffany Oil Field Deck
123.600		AM	Belmullet, Eire	AFIS & Air-Ground
123.600		AM	Cambridge Airport	Approach
123.600		AM	Carlisle Airport	Approach/Tower/Ground
123.600		AM	Rathkenny	Air-Ground
123.600		AM	Scatsa	Approach/Tower
123.625		AM	Ballykelly (Army)	Approach (Eglington)
123.625		AM	Derry	Approach
123.625		AM	Londonderry	Approach
123.625		AM	North Sea	Amoco Indefatigable Field
123.625		AM	North Sea	Amoco Leman Field
123.625		AM	North Sea	Bessemer Oil Field Deck
123.625		AM	North Sea	Camelot Oil Field Deck
123.625		AM	North Sea	Davey Oil Field Deck
123.625		AM	North Sea	Shell/Esso Indefatigable
123.625		AM	North Sea	Shell/Esso Leman Field
123.625		AM	North Sea	Shell/Esso Sean Field
123.625		AM	North Sea	Thames Oil Field Deck
123.625		AM	North Sea	Welland Oil Field Deck
123.625		AM	Walton Wood	Air-Ground
123.650		AM	Bournemouth (Hurn)	FR Aviation (Broadway Ops)
123.650		AM	Hayes Heliport	A/G (Macline Hayes)
123.650		AM	London Heathrow	Excelair
123.650		AM	Nationwide	Fisheries Protection
123.650		AM	North Sea	Brae Oil Field deck
123.650		AM	North Sea	East Brae Oil Field Deck
123.725		AM	Brize Norton	Tower
123.750		AM	Leeds/Bradford Airport	Approach
123.775		AM	Scottish Air Traffic Control - Prestwick	Scottish Control
123.800		AM	Stansted	Tower
123.825		AM	Scilly Isles (St. Marys)	Approach/Tower
123.875		AM	North Sea	Maureen Oil Field Deck
123.875		AM	Ronaldsway, Isle of Man	ATIS
123.900		AM	London TCC (Terminal Control)	Lambourne
123.925		AM	Little Staughton	Air-Ground
123.950		AM	Shanwick Oceanic Area Control	ATC Shanwick Oceanic
124.000		AM	East Midlands Airport/ Nottingham	Radar
124.000		AM	East Midlands Airport/ Nottingham	Tower
124.025		AM	Wellesbourne Mountford	Air-Ground

Base	Mobile	Mode	Location	User and Notes
124.050		AM	Scottish Air Traffic Control - Prestwick	Scottish Control
124.075		AM	Tatenhill Aerodrome	Air-Ground
124.125		AM	Humberside Airport	ATIS
124.150		AM	Little Snoring Aerodrome	Air-Ground
124.150		AM	Marham (RAF)	MATZ
124.150		AM	Marham (RAF)	Radar
124.150		AM	Plymouth Military Radar (RN)	Radar
124.150		AM	Portland (RN)	Approach
124.150		AM	Portland (RN)	MATZ
124.150		AM	Portland (RN)	Radar
124.150		AM	Shawbury (RAF)	Radar
124.200		AM	Pembrey Range (RAF)	Air-Ground
124.225		AM	London Gatwick	Tower
124.250		AM	Norwich Airport	Tower
124.275		AM	Brize Norton	MATZ
124.275		AM	Fairford (USAF)	CAC (Brize)
124.275		AM	Fairford (USAF)	MATZ
124.275		AM	Swanwick Civil ATC	London Control
124.325		AM	Liverpool John Lennon	ATIS
124.350		AM	Bourn Aerodrome	Air-Ground
124.375		AM	Newcastle Airport	Approach
124.375		AM	Newcastle Airport	Radar
124.375		AM	Spadeadam (RAF)	LARS
124.450		AM	Nationwide	YAK Display Team
124.475		AM	London Heathrow	Stand-by Tower
124.500		AM	Guernsey	Radar
124.500		AM	Scottish Air Traffic Control - Prestwick	Scottish Control
124.525		AM	Dublin Airport	ATIS
124.600		AM	Holbeach Range	Control
124.600		AM	Swanwick Civil ATC	London Control FIR Information
124.650		AM	Dublin Area Control Centre	Control South
124.700		AM	Galway, Eire	CAC
124.700		AM	Shannon Area Control Centre	Control
124.700		AM	Waterford	CAC
124.750		AM	Staxton Wold (RAF)	Danger Area Info.
124.750		AM	Swanwick Civil ATC	London Control Information
124.750		AM	Trevose Head (RAF)	Danger Area Info.
124.800		AM	Coventry Airport	Tower
124.825		AM	Scottish Air Traffic Control - Prestwick	Scottish Control (0630-2130)
124.875		AM	Wolverhampton (Halfpenny Green)	ATIS
124.900		AM	Humberside Airport	Tower
124.925		AM	London TCC (Terminal Control)	Dogga
124.950		AM	Filton (BAe) Bristol	Radar
124.950		AM	Hawarden/Chester	Tower
124.975		AM	Cambridge Airport	Radar
124.975		AM	Northolt (RAF)	Ground
125.000		AM	Cardiff Airport	Tower
125.000		AM	Dishforth (Army)	Approach
125.000		AM	Topcliffe (RAF)	Approach
125.050		AM	Braintree Airfield	Air-Ground
125.050		AM	Cranwell (RAF)	Tower
125.100		AM	Manchester Control Centre	Control
125.125		AM	Northolt (RAF)	ATIS
125.175		AM	North Sea	Markham Oil Field Deck
125.175		AM	North Sea	Petroland Oil Field Deck
125.175		AM	North Sea	Placid Oil Field Deck

Base	Mobile	Mode	Location	User and Notes
125.200		AM	Jersey Airport	ATZ Zone/Radar
125.200		AM	Jersey Airport	Radar
125.225		AM	Valley (RAF)	Director
125.250		AM	Farnborough	Radar
125.250		AM	Lasham Aerodrome	Approach (Farnborough)
125.250		AM	Odiham (RAF)	MATZ
125.300		AM	Ronaldsway, Isle of Man	Radar
125.300		AM	Shoreham by Sea	ATIS
125.325		AM	Oxford (Kidlington Airport)	Approach
125.350		AM	Alderney	Tower
125.350		AM	Waddington (RAF)	Radar
125.400		AM	Castleforbes, Eire	Tower
125.400		AM	Yeovil (Westland)	Air-Ground
125.400		AM	Yeovil (Westland)	Tower
125.425		AM	Syerston (RAF)	Air-Ground
125.475		AM	Eskmeals Range (MOD)	London Information
125.475		AM	Swanwick Civil ATC	London Control Information
125.525		AM	Wittering (RAF)	Tower
125.550		AM	St. Mawgan (RAF)	Radar
125.550		AM	Stansted	Tower
125.600		AM	Bournemouth (Hurn)	Tower
125.625		AM	London Heathrow	Radar
125.625		AM	London Heathrow	Tower (Special Flights)
125.625		AM	London TCC (Terminal Control)	Thames
125.675		AM	Scottish Air Traffic Control - Prestwick	Scottish Control
125.725		AM	Scottish Air Traffic Control - Prestwick	Scottish VOLMET
125.800		AM	Swanwick Civil ATC	London Control Radar Dep.
125.800		AM	Wattisham (Army Airfield)	Approach
125.800		AM	Wattisham (Army Airfield)	MATZ
125.850		AM	Cardiff Airport	Approach
125.850		AM	Cardiff Airport	Radar
125.850		AM	St. Athan (RAF)	Approach
125.850		AM	Sumburgh Airport	ATIS
125.875		AM	Northolt (RAF)	Talkdown
125.900		AM	Campbeltown	AFIS
125.900		AM	Coltishall (RAF)	MATZ
125.900		AM	Coltishall (RAF)	Radar
125.950		AM	Manchester Control Centre	Control
126.025		AM	Bristol Airport	ATIS
126.050		AM	Coventry Airport	ATIS
126.075		AM	Swanwick Civil ATC	London Control
126.100		AM	Prestwick Airport	Highland Radar
126.225		AM	Doncaster (Robin Hood)	Approach
126.250		AM	Scottish Air Traffic Control - Prestwick	Scottish Control (Information)
126.275		AM	Birmingham International	ATIS
126.300		AM	Scottish Air Traffic Control - Prestwick	Scottish Control (2131-0629)
126.300		AM	Swanwick Civil ATC	London Control Inbound
126.350		AM	Canterbury	Traffic Information (Manston)
126.350		AM	Liverpool John Lennon	Tower
126.350		AM	Manston	Approach
126.350		AM	Manston	Radar
126.450		AM	Northolt (RAF)	Approach
126.500		AM	Brize Norton	Talkdown
126.500		AM	Church Fenton	Approach
126.500		AM	Leuchars (RAF)	Approach
126.500		AM	Leuchars (RAF)	MATZ

Base	Mobile	Mode	Location	User and Notes
126.500		AM	St. Mawgan (RAF)	MATZ
126.500		AM	Trevose Head (RAF)	Danger Area Information
126.550		AM	Wycombe Air Park (Booker)	Tower/AFIS
126.625		AM	Cardiff Airport	Radar
126.650		AM	Bristol Airport	Approach
126.700		AM	Boscombe Down (MoD)	MATZ
126.725		AM	Luton Airport	Radar
126.825		AM	London Gatwick	Approach
126.825		AM	London TCC (Terminal Control)	Gatwick
126.850		AM	Scottish Air Traffic Control - Prestwick	Scottish Control
126.875		AM	Swanwick Civil ATC	London Control Inbound
126.900		AM	Aberdeen (Dyce Airport)	Lion Ops
126.925		AM	Scottish Air Traffic Control - Prestwick	Scottish Control
126.950		AM	London TCC (Terminal Control)	Stansted
126.950		AM	Stansted	Radar
127.000		AM	Dublin Airport	Dublin VOLMET
127.050		AM	Nationwide	CAA Test Flights
127.100		AM	Swanwick Civil ATC	London Control
127.150		AM	Benson (RAF)	Tower
127.175		AM	Stansted	ATIS
127.250		AM	Brize Norton	Approach
127.250		AM	Fairford (USAF)	Approach
127.275		AM	Scottish Air Traffic Control - Prestwick	Scottish ACC (Information)
127.350		AM	Waddington (RAF)	MATZ
127.350		AM	Yeovilton (RN)	MATZ
127.350		AM	Yeovilton (RN)	Radar
127.425		AM	Swanwick Civil ATC	London Control Upper East
127.450		AM	Swanwick Military/London Joint Area Org.	Lower Airspace (Northwest)
127.450		AM	Swanwick Military/London Joint Area Org.	Middle Airspace (Northwest)
127.475		AM	Gloucestershire Staverton	ATIS
127.500		AM	Shannon Area Control Centre	Control
127.525		AM	London Heathrow	Approach
127.525		AM	London TCC (Terminal Control)	Heathrow
127.650		AM	Shanwick Oceanic Area Control	ATC Shanwick Oceanic
127.650		AM	Swanwick Civil ATC	Oceanic Clearance (E of 30W)
127.700		AM	Swanwick Civil ATC	London Control
127.725		AM	Southend Airport	Tower
127.750		AM	Leeming (RAF)	Approach
127.750		AM	Leeming (RAF)	MATZ
127.875		AM	Swanwick Civil ATC	London Control
127.900		AM	Shanwick Oceanic Area Control	Air-Ground Shanwick Radio
127.900		AM	West Midlands	Air Ambulance
127.950		AM	London TCC (Terminal Control)	Vaton
127.975		AM	Warton (BAe)	Ops
128.000		AM	Welshpool	Air-Ground
128.025		AM	London City Airport	Radar(City Radar)
128.050		AM	Manchester Control Centre	Control
128.075		AM	London Heathrow	ATIS (Arrivals)
128.100		AM	St. Kilda (RAF)	Tower
128.125		AM	Swanwick Civil ATC	London Control North Sea
128.175		AM	Manchester Airport	ATIS (Arrivals)
128.200		AM	Belfast (Aldergrove)	ATIS
128.225		AM	East Midlands Airport/ Nottingham	ATIS
128.300		AM	Aberdeen (Dyce Airport)	Radar
128.300		AM	Netheravon (Army)	AFIS
128.300		AM	Netheravon (Army)	Air-Ground (Salisbury Plain)

Base	Mobile	Mode	Location	User and Notes
128.300		AM	Netheravon (Army)	Drop Zone Radio
128.300		AM	Netheravon (Army)	Information
128.300		AM	Newtownards	Air-Ground
128.325		AM	Norwich Airport	Radar
128.375		AM	Huddersfield (Crosland Moor)	Air-Ground
128.400		AM	Farnborough	ATIS
128.425		AM	Swanwick Civil ATC	London Control
128.475		AM	London TCC (Terminal Control)	Welin
128.500		AM	Belfast (Aldergrove)	Approach
128.500		AM	Belfast (City)	Approach (Belfast)
128.525		AM	Sheffield City	Air-Ground
128.550		AM	Clonbullogue, Eire	Air-Ground
128.550		AM	Gloucestershire Staverton	Approach
128.600		AM	Swanwick Civil ATC	London VOLMET (South)
128.625		AM	Norwich Airport	ATIS
128.650		AM	Alderney	Approach (Guernsey)
128.650		AM	Cosford (RAF)	Tower
128.650		AM	Guernsey	Approach
128.675		AM	Manchester Control Centre	Pennine Radar
128.725		AM	St. Mawgan (RAF)	Approach
128.750		AM	London TCC (Terminal Control)	Luton
128.750		AM	Luton Airport	Approach
128.750		AM	Luton Airport	Director
128.775		AM	Doncaster (Robin Hood)	Tower
128.850		AM	Cosford (RAF)	Ground
128.850		AM	Southampton Airport	Approach
128.850		AM	Southampton Airport	Radar
128.850		AM	Tees Valley/Durham Airport	Radar
128.900		AM	Honington (RAF)	Radar
128.900		AM	Lakenheath (USAF)	Civil Transit
128.900		AM	Stanford (Army)	Danger Area Information
128.950		AM	Southend Airport	Radar
128.975		AM	Exeter Airport	Approach
128.975		AM	Exeter Airport	Radar
129.025		AM	London Gatwick	Approach
129.025		AM	London Gatwick	Radar Standby
129.025		AM	London TCC (Terminal Control)	Gatwick
129.050		AM	Doncaster (Robin Hood)	Radar
129.075		AM	London TCC (Terminal Control)	Low
129.075		AM	Swanwick Civil ATC	London Control
129.100		AM	Swanwick Civil ATC	London Control
129.150		AM	Linton on Ouse (RAF)	Approach
129.150		AM	Linton on Ouse (RAF)	Radar
129.150		AM	Linton on Ouse (RAF)	Talkdown
129.175		AM	Dublin Area Control Centre	Control North
129.200		AM	Swanwick Civil ATC	London Control
129.250		AM	Humberside Airport	Radar
129.275		AM	London TCC (Terminal Control)	Lorel
129.375		AM	Swanwick Civil ATC	London Control
129.400		AM	Biggin Hill	Approach
129.425		AM	Swanwick Civil ATC	London Control
129.450		AM	Manston	Approach
129.450		AM	Manston	Director
129.475		AM	Lyneham (RAF)	Ground
129.525		AM	Warton (BAe)	Approach
129.525		AM	Warton (BAe)	Radar

Base	Mobile	Mode	Location	User and Notes
129.550		AM	London TCC (Terminal Control)	Luton
129.550		AM	Luton Airport	Approach
129.575		AM	Glasgow	ATIS
129.600		AM	London TCC (Terminal Control)	Sabre
129.600		AM	Swanwick Civil ATC	London Control
129.650		AM	North Sea	Statfjord Oil Field Deck
129.700		AM	Alderney	Trinity Lightship Heliport
129.700		AM	Baldonnel	Talkdown
129.700		AM	Blackbushe	ATS
129.700		AM	Cambridge Airport	Marshalls Ops
129.700		AM	English Channel	Trinity House Lightships
129.700		AM	Jersey Airport	Aviation Beauport Ops
129.700		AM	Nationwide	Trinity House Helicopters
129.700		AM	North Sea	Amoco Arbroath Field
129.700		AM	North Sea	Everest Oil Field Deck
129.700		AM	Prestwick Airport	PIK Handling
129.700		AM	Southend Airport	Express Flight Handling
129.725		AM	Jersey Airport	ATIS
129.725		AM	Lewes (Deanland)	Air-Ground
129.725		AM	Peterborough (Conington)	Air-Ground
129.750		AM	Belfast (City)	Handling
129.750		AM	Bournemouth (Hurn)	Servisair/GlobeGround
129.750		AM	Cardiff Airport	Aviance
129.750		AM	Filton (BAe) Bristol	Rolls Royce Ops
129.750		AM	Leeds/Bradford Airport	Coney Park Heliport
129.750		AM	North Sea	Elf Aquataine Norge Frigg
129.750		AM	North Sea	Kewanee Nordsee Field
129.750		AM	North Sea	Total/Elf Frigg Field
129.750		AM	Ronaldsway, Isle of Man	Manx Handling
129.750		AM	Ronaldsway, Isle of Man	Citiexpress Ops
129.750		AM	Stansted	Servisair/GlobeGround
129.775		AM	North Sea	Noordwinning Oil Field Deck
129.775		AM	North Sea	North Hamilton Oil Field Deck
129.800		AM	Breighton	Air-Ground
129.800		AM	Donegal, Eire	Tower
129.800		AM	Popham Aerodrome	Air Ground
129.800		AM	Truro Aerodrome	Air-Ground
129.825		AM	Cromer (Northrepps)	Air-Ground (Microlight)
129.825		AM	Insch Airfield	Air-Ground
129.825		AM	Nationwide	Microlight Common
129.825		AM	Swindon (Draycott)	Air-Ground
129.850		AM	Waterford	Tower and AFIS
129.875		AM	Enstone Aerodrome	Air-Ground
129.875		AM	Hethersett Aerodrome	Air-Ground
129.875		AM	North Sea	Amethyst Field Deck
129.875		AM	North Sea	BP Ravenspurn North Field Deck
129.875		AM	North Sea	BP West Sole Field Deck
129.875		AM	North Sea	British Gas Rough Field Deck
129.875		AM	North Sea	Ravenspun Deck
129.875		AM	North Sea	West Sole Oil Field Deck
129.900		AM	Cark	Cark Radio
129.900		AM	Coonagh, Eire	Air-Ground
129.900		AM	Langar Airfield	Drop Zone
129.900		AM	Limerick (Coonagh)	Air-Ground
129.900		AM	Liskeard	Civil Heliport
129.900		AM	Nationwide	Hang Gliding

Base	Mobile	Mode	Location	User and Notes
129.900		AM	Nationwide	Hot Air Ballooning
129.900		AM	Nationwide	Parachute DZ
129.900		AM	North Sea	Eider Oil Field Deck
129.900		AM	North Sea	Phillips Eko/EMB Pipe Deck
129.900		AM	Strathallan Aerodrome	Air-Ground
129.925		AM	Donegal, Eire	ATIS
129.950		AM	Ballykelly (Army)	Dropping Zone
129.950		AM	North Sea	Conoco Oil Rig
129.950		AM	North Sea	North Cormorant Deck
129.950		AM	North Sea	Shell/Esso Dunlin Field Deck
129.950		AM	North Sea	Shell/Esso Tern Field Deck
129.950		AM	North Sea	South Cormorant Oil Field Deck
129.950		AM	Shetlands	Viking Approach
129.950		AM	Sumburgh Airport	Helicopter Information
129.975		AM	Filton (BAe) Bristol	Radar
129.975		AM	Nationwide	Gliding
129.975		AM	North Sea	Helicopter Common
129.975		AM	North Weald	Gliders
129.975		AM	Pocklington	Gliders
129.975		AM	Rufforth, York	Air-Ground
129.975		AM	Swansea Airport	ATC Glider Training
129.975		AM	Tibenham	Air-Ground
130.000		AM	Boscombe Down (MoD)	Approach
130.025		AM	Biggin Hill	Srikair
130.025		AM	London	Capital Radio Flying Eye Ops
130.050		AM	Farnborough	Precision Approach Radar
130.050		AM	Kirkcudbridght Ranges	West Freugh Range
130.050		AM	West Freugh (MoD)	Approach
130.075		AM	Brize Norton	Ops
130.075		AM	Coventry Airport	Handling
130.075		AM	Liverpool John Lennon	Gemstone Ops Emerald Airways
130.075		AM	London Gatwick	Excelair Ops.
130.100		AM	Ballykelly (Army)	Ops (Bellarena Ops)
130.100		AM	Bellarena	Air-Ground Gliders
130.100		AM	Dishforth (Army)	Air-Ground
130.100		AM	Nationwide	Gliders
130.100		AM	Perranporth	Air-Ground Gliders
130.100		AM	Pocklington	Air-Ground Gliders
130.100		AM	Strubby Aerodrome	Air-Ground Gliders
130.100		AM	Tibenham	Air-Ground Gliders
130.125		AM	Long Marston Aerodrome	Tower
130.125		AM	Nationwide	Glider Training
130.125		AM	Scarborough	Air-Ground
130.175		AM	Blackbushe	Premiair Ops.
130.175		AM	Blackbushe	Air Lynton Ops.
130.175		AM	Cambridge Airport	Magnet Air
130.175		AM	Cambridge Airport	Scot Airways Ops
130.175		AM	Cambridge Airport	Suckling Ops.
130.175		AM	Exeter Airport	Handling
130.175		AM	Exeter Airport	Markair Ops
130.175		AM	Liverpool John Lennon	Gemstone Ops Emerald Airways
130.175		AM	Liverpool John Lennon	Raven Air Ops
130.175		AM	Liverpool John Lennon	Royal Mail Ops
130.175		AM	London Gatwick	Interflight Ops
130.175		AM	London Heathrow	Corporate Jet Ops
130.175		AM	Luton Airport	Magec Ops

Base	Mobile	Mode	Location	User and Notes
130.175		AM	Luton Airport	Signature Executive Ops
130.175		AM	Manchester Airport	Ryanair Ops
130.175		AM	North Weald	Aceair Company Channel
130.175		AM	Ronaldsway, Isle of Man	Manxair Ops
130.175		AM	Ronaldsway, Isle of Man	Woodgate Aviation
130.175		AM	Stansted Airport	Ryanair Ops
130.200		AM	Chivenor (RAF)	Air-Ground
130.200		AM	Cottesmore (RAF)	Approach
130.200		AM	Cottesmore (RAF)	MATZ
130.200		AM	Langar Airfield	Approach
130.200		AM	North Sea	Alwyn North Oil Field Log
130.200		AM	North Sea	Dunbar Oil Field Deck
130.200		AM	North Sea	Ninian Field Deck
130.200		AM	Wittering (RAF)	Approach
130.200		AM	Wittering (RAF)	MATZ
130.250		AM	Benson (RAF)	Radar
130.250		AM	East Midlands Airport/ Nottingham	Donington Aviation
130.250		AM	Hawarden/Chester	Radar
130.250		AM	Henstridge	Air-Ground
130.250		AM	Tresco	Civil Heliport Air-Ground
130.300		AM	Sturgate Aerodrome	Air-Ground
130.350		AM	Northolt (RAF)	Director
130.350		AM	Unst (Saxa Vord)	Air-Ground
130.350		AM	Unst (Saxa Vord)	Flight Information
130.375		AM	Farnborough	TAG Executive Ops
130.375		AM	Manchester Airport	FLS Engineering Ops
130.375		AM	Southampton Airport	Signature Executive Ops
130.375		AM	Wick	Fuellers (FarNor)
130.400		AM	Nationwide	Gliders
130.400		AM	Punchestown	Air-Ground (Parachute/Glider Ops)
130.400		AM	Spalding (Crowland)	Tower (Gliders)
130.400		AM	Thirsk (Sutton Bank)	Air-Ground Gliders
130.425		AM	Halton (RAF)	Air-Ground
130.425		AM	Nationwide	SAR Incident
130.425		AM	Sandtoft	Tower
130.450		AM	Fife	Air-Ground
130.450		AM	Glenrothes	Air-Ground
130.450		AM	Skegness Aerodrome	Air-Ground
130.450		AM	Thruxton Aerodrome	Air-Ground
130.475		AM	London, Lippits Hill	Met Police Helicopter Air-Ground
130.475		AM	Retford	Air-Ground
130.500		AM	Alderney	Ground
130.500		AM	Castleforbes, Eire	Air-Ground
130.500		AM	Nationwide	Aquilla Spanish Display Team
130.500		AM	Nationwide	CAA Events/Airshows
130.525		AM	Nationwide	Parachute DZ
130.550		AM	Andrewsfield	Air-Ground
130.550		AM	Brough Aerodrome	Tower & Air-Ground
130.550		AM	North Sea	Amoco Valhall Field
130.550		AM	North Sea	Phillips Albuskjell Field
130.550		AM	North Sea	Phillips Cod Field
130.550		AM	North Sea	Phillips Edda Field
130.550		AM	North Sea	Phillips Ekofisk Field
130.550		AM	North Sea	Phillips Eldfisk Field
130.550		AM	North Sea	Phillips Tor Field
130.550		AM	North Sea	Valhall Oil Field Deck

Base	Mobile	Mode	Location	User and Notes
130.575		AM	Aberdeen (Dyce Airport)	Scotia Ops
130.575		AM	Stansted	Universal Air Handling
130.600		AM	Aberdeen (Dyce Airport)	Servisair/GlobeGround
130.600		AM	Blackpool	Servisair/GlobeGround
130.600		AM	Bournemouth (Hurn)	Channel Express
130.600		AM	Bristol Airport	Servisair/GlobeGround
130.600		AM	Cardiff Airport	Servisair/GlobeGround
130.600		AM	Edinburgh Airport	Servisair/GlobeGround
130.600		AM	Glasgow Airport	Servisair/GlobeGround
130.600		AM	Guernsey	Servisair/GlobeGround
130.600		AM	Jersey Airport	Servisair/GlobeGround
130.600		AM	Leeds/Bradford Airport	Servisair/GlobeGround
130.600		AM	Liverpool John Lennon	Servisair/GlobeGround
130.600		AM	Luton Airport	Servisair/GlobeGround
130.600		AM	Manchester Airport	Servisair/GlobeGround
130.600		AM	Stansted Airport	Servisair/GlobeGround
130.600		AM	Newcastle Airport	Servisair/GlobeGround
130.625		AM	Aberdeen (Dyce Airport)	Caledonian Ops
130.625		AM	Bristol Airport	Clifton Ops
130.625		AM	Coventry Airport	Air Atlantique Ops
130.625		AM	East Midlands Airport/ Nottingham	Donington Aviation Ops
130.625		AM	Edinburgh Airport	Fishery Protection
130.625		AM	London City Airport	KGS Handling Ops
130.625		AM	Ronaldsway, Isle of Man	Islavia Ops
130.625		AM	Stansted Airport	Zap Ops Titan Airways
130.625		AM	Stapleford Tawney	Stapleford Ops
130.650		AM	Birmingham International	Birmingham Executive
130.650		AM	Cardiff Airport	Red Dragon Ops
130.650		AM	Foulsham Aerodrome	Tower
130.650		AM	Glasgow	Loganair Ops
130.650		AM	Kyle of Lochalsh	RN Heliport
130.650		AM	Leeds/Bradford Airport	Multiflight Ops
130.650		AM	London Gatwick	Aviance
130.650		AM	London Gatwick	Korean Airlines
130.650		AM	Luton Airport	Thames Valley Police Ops
130.650		AM	Manchester Airport	Northern Executive Handling Ops
130.650		AM	Newcastle Airport	Apron (Samson Ops.)
130.650		AM	Plockton Airfield	Air-Ground
130.650		AM	Skye	Air-Ground
130.650		AM	Southampton Airport	Ops
130.675		AM	London Heathrow	Singapore Airlines Ops.
130.675		AM	Nationwide	CAA Events/Airshows
130.700		AM	Connaught (Knock) Airport	Tower
130.700		AM	Land's End (St Just)	Air-Ground
130.700		AM	Old Warden (Biggleswade)	Tower (Display Days Only)
130.725		AM	Denham	Air-Ground & AFIS
130.725		AM	North Sea	FRG/STFS Pipe
130.750		AM	Boscombe Down (MoD)	Ground
130.750		AM	Boscombe Down (MoD)	Talkdown
130.750		AM	Boscombe Down (MoD)	Tower
130.750		AM	Woodford (BAe)	Approach
130.775		AM	Southend Airport	Approach
130.775		AM	Southend Airport	Radar
130.800		AM	English Channel	Fisheries Protection
130.800		AM	Hucknall Aerodrome	Air-Ground
130.800		AM	North Sea	Amoco NW Hutton Deck

Base	Mobile	Mode	Location	User and Notes
130.800		AM	North Sea	Conoco Hutton Deck
130.800		AM	Warton (BAe)	Approach
130.800		AM	Warton (BAe)	Tower
130.800		AM	Yeovil (Westland)	Approach
130.800		AM	Yeovil (Westland)	Radar
130.850		AM	Belfast (City)	Tower
130.850		AM	Little Gransden Aerodrome	Air-Ground
130.875		AM	North Sea	Kittiwake Oil Field Deck
130.900		AM	Elmsett	Air-Ground
130.900		AM	Nationwide	Dutch F-16 Display Team
130.925		AM	London TCC (Terminal Control)	Welin
130.925		AM	Swanwick Civil ATC	London Control TMA
130.950		AM	Shannon Airport	ATIS
131.025		AM	Lasham Aerodrome	Glider Ops
131.050		AM	Swanwick Civil ATC	London Control North East UIR
131.125		AM	Swanwick Civil ATC	London Control
131.150		AM	Shannon Area Control Centre	Control (Cork Sector)
131.175		AM	Liverpool John Lennon	Liverpool Aviation (Keenair) Ops
131.300		AM	Odiham (RAF)	Approach/Radar
131.300		AM	Sumburgh Airport	Radar (N Sea Offshore)
131.325		AM	Birmingham International	Radar
131.350		AM	Edinburgh Airport	ATIS
131.375		AM	Glasgow	Air Canada
131.400		AM	London Heathrow	CSA
131.400		AM	Luton Airport	easyJet Ops.
131.425		AM	Birmingham International	Ogden Aviation
131.425		AM	Birmingham International	Servisair
131.425		AM	Dublin Airport	British Midland/Aviance
131.425		AM	London Gatwick	Air New Zealand Ops
131.425		AM	London Gatwick	Flystar Ops
131.425		AM	London Gatwick	Ogden Aviation Ops
131.425		AM	London Gatwick	Virgin Ops
131.425		AM	London Heathrow	Aviance
131.425		AM	London Heathrow	Royal Jordanian Ops
131.425		AM	London Heathrow	Saudia Ops
131.425		AM	London Heathrow	Virgin Ops
131.450		AM	Dublin Airport	Servisair
131.450		AM	London Heathrow	Air Canada Ops
131.450		AM	London Heathrow	Alitalia Ops
131.450		AM	London Heathrow	Pakistan International Ops
131.450		AM	London Heathrow	Thai Airways Ops
131.450		AM	Prestwick Airport	Air Canada Ops
131.450		AM	Shannon Airport	Servisair/GlobeGround
131.475		AM	Dublin Airport	Translift Ops
131.475		AM	London City Airport	City Handling Ops
131.475		AM	London Gatwick	British Airways Maintenance
131.475		AM	London Heathrow	All Nippon Airlines Ops
131.475		AM	Stansted Airport	FedEx Ops
131.500		AM	Cork Airport	Aer Lingus Ops
131.500		AM	Dublin Airport	Aer Lingus Shamrock Ops
131.500		AM	London Heathrow	Air France Ops
131.500		AM	London Heathrow	Air Singapore Ops
131.500		AM	London Heathrow	Kuwait Airways Ops
131.525		AM	Luton Airport	Monarch Airlines
131.525		AM	Luton Airport	Ryanair Ops
131.525		AM	Nationwide	ACARS Frequency

Base	Mobile	Mode	Location	User and Notes
131.550		AM	Dublin Airport	Ryanair Ops
131.550		AM	London Heathrow	British Airways Terminal 1
131.575		AM	Belfast (Aldergrove)	British Midland
131.575		AM	Birmingham International	Loganair
131.575		AM	Birmingham International	TEA Operations
131.575		AM	East Midlands Airport/ Nottingham	British Midland
131.575		AM	East Midlands Airport/ Nottingham	Excalibur Ops
131.575		AM	Edinburgh Airport	British Midland
131.575		AM	Guernsey	British Midland Ops
131.575		AM	Jersey Airport	British Midland Jersey Ops
131.575		AM	Leeds/Bradford Airport	Aviance
131.575		AM	London Heathrow	British Midland Ops
131.575		AM	London Heathrow	El Al
131.575		AM	Manchester Airport	Aviance
131.575		AM	Stansted Airport	Aviance
131.600		AM	East Midlands Airport/ Nottingham	UPS Ops
131.600		AM	London Gatwick	City Flyer Ops
131.600		AM	Stansted Airport	Ryanair Ops
131.625		AM	London Gatwick	British Airways/GB Air
131.625		AM	Portishead	Aero Radio Telephones
131.650		AM	London Heathrow	Air Malta Ops
131.650		AM	London Heathrow	KLM Ops
131.650		AM	Luton Airport	Gemstone Ops Emerald Airways
131.675		AM	Belfast (Aldergrove)	Aviance
131.675		AM	Luton Airport	Britannia Airways
131.700		AM	Glasgow	Jetset Ops Air 2000
131.700		AM	London Gatwick	First Choice
131.700		AM	London Gatwick	Jetset Ops Air 2000
131.700		AM	London Heathrow	British Midlands Ops
131.700		AM	London Heathrow	Delta Ops
131.700		AM	London Heathrow	SAS Ops
131.700		AM	Manchester Airport	Swissair Ops
131.725		AM	Nationwide	ACARS Frequency
131.750		AM	London Gatwick	Continental Airlines Ops
131.750		AM	London Heathrow	Aer Lingus Ops
131.750		AM	London Heathrow	Swissair Ops
131.750		AM	London Heathrow	TAP Air Portugal
131.750		AM	Manchester Airport	Aer Lingus Ops
131.775		AM	London Heathrow	Aeroflot
131.775		AM	London Heathrow	British Airways Ops
131.775		AM	London Heathrow	British Mediterranean
131.775		AM	London Heathrow	Korean Air Ops
131.775		AM	London Heathrow	LOT
131.775		AM	Luton Airport	BA Maintenance
131.775		AM	Stansted	Air Foyle
131.800		AM	Edinburgh Airport	British Airways Ops
131.800		AM	Glasgow Airport	British Airways Ops
131.800		AM	London Heathrow	British Airways Ops
131.800		AM	Nationwide	Fisheries Protection
131.825		AM	Dublin Airport	Park Aviation
131.825		AM	London Heathrow	Federal Express Ops
131.825		AM	London Heathrow	Globe Air Ops
131.825		AM	Nationwide	ACARS Frequency
131.850		AM	Belfast (Aldergrove)	British Airways Ops
131.850		AM	Birmingham International	British Airways Ops
131.850		AM	Cork Airport	Aer Lingus

Base	Mobile	Mode	Location	User and Notes
131.850		AM	Glasgow	British Airways Ops
131.850		AM	Inverness Airport	British Airways Ops
131.850		AM	Jersey Airport	British Airways Jersey Ops
131.850		AM	London Heathrow	United Airlines Ops
131.850		AM	Newcastle Airport	British Airways Ops
131.850		AM	Manchester Airport	British Airways Ops
131.875		AM	Liverpool John Lennon	Aviance
131.875		AM	London Gatwick	British Airways Ops
131.875		AM	London Heathrow	Quantas Ops.
131.875		AM	London Heathrow	Singapore Airlines Ops
131.875		AM	Manchester Airport	Euro Manx Ops
131.875		AM	Ronaldsway, Isle of Man	Gemstone Ops Emerald Airways
131.900		AM	London Heathrow	British Airways Terminal 4
131.900		AM	London Heathrow	South African Airlines
131.925		AM	London Heathrow	Air India Ops
131.925		AM	London Heathrow	American Airlines Maintenance
131.925		AM	London Heathrow	American Ops
131.925		AM	London Heathrow	Cathay Pacific Ops
131.925		AM	London Heathrow	Lufthansa Ops
131.925		AM	Manchester Airport	Lufthansa
131.950		AM	London Heathrow	British Airways Ops
131.950		AM	London Heathrow	Iberia Airlines Ops.
131.950		AM	London Heathrow	Olympic Airways Ops.
131.950		AM	Manchester Airport	Federal Express
131.975		AM	London Heathrow	United Airlines Ops
131.975		AM	Stansted	Ryanair Engineering Ops
132.150		AM	Shannon Area Control Centre	Control
132.325		AM	Full Sutton	Air-Ground
132.350		AM	Filton (BAe) Bristol	Tower
132.450		AM	Swanwick Civil ATC	London Control
132.475		AM	Cardiff Airport	ATIS
132.475		AM	Carlisle Airport	ATIS
132.550		AM	Luton Airport	Tower
132.600		AM	Swanwick Civil ATC	London Control SW Approach
132.650		AM	Kent	Air Ambulance
132.650		AM	London Heathrow	Medivac
132.650		AM	Nationwide	Air Ambulance Common
132.650		AM	Nationwide	Coastguard Standby
132.650		AM	Nationwide	Royal Flights Helicopters Air-Ground
132.650		AM	Nationwide	Royal Navy Lynx Duo
132.650		AM	Oxford	Churchill Hospital Helicopter
132.650		AM	Swansea Airport	Air Sea Rescue
132.700		AM	London City Airport	Approach/Thames Radar
132.700		AM	London City Airport	Radar (Thames Radar)
132.700		AM	London Heathrow	Thames Radar
132.700		AM	London TCC (Terminal Control)	Thames
132.800		AM	Swanwick Civil ATC	London Control (Bristol)
132.8416		AM	Swanwick Civil ATC	London Control
132.900		AM	Nationwide	CAA Events/Airshows
132.950		AM	Swanwick Civil ATC	London Control
133.050		AM	Manchester Control Centre	Control
133.075		AM	London TCC (Terminal Control)	Cowly
133.175		AM	London TCC (Terminal Control)	Willo
133.175		AM	Swanwick Civil ATC	London Control
133.400		AM	Manchester Control Centre	Control
133.425		AM	Manchester Control Centre	Control

Base	Mobile	Mode	Location	User and Notes
133.425		AM	Oxford (Kidlington Airport)	Tower
133.450		AM	Swanwick Civil ATC	London Control
133.525		AM	North Sea	Barque Oil Field Deck
133.525		AM	Swanwick Civil ATC	London Control North Sea
133.550		AM	Plymouth City Airport	Approach
133.575		AM	North Sea	Clipper Oil Field Deck
133.575		AM	North Sea	Galleon Oil Field Deck
133.600		AM	Swanwick Civil ATC	London Control
133.650		AM	Weston on the Green	Weston Radio
133.675		AM	Scottish Air Traffic Control - Prestwick	Scottish ACC (Entire Route)
133.675		AM	Scottish Air Traffic Control - Prestwick	Scottish Control
133.700		AM	Cambridge Airport	ATIS
133.700		AM	Swanwick Civil ATC	London Control
133.750		AM	Brize Norton	Director
133.800		AM	Manchester Control Centre	Control
133.850		AM	Bristol Airport	Tower
133.875		AM	Manston	ATIS
133.875		AM	Scottish Air Traffic Control - Prestwick	Scottish Control
133.975		AM	London TCC (Terminal Control)	London
134.050		AM	Culdrose (RN)	Approach
134.050		AM	Culdrose (RN)	MATZ
134.050		AM	Predannack (RN)	Approach(Culdrose)
134.050		AM	Wyton (RAF)	Air-Ground
134.050		AM	Wyton (RAF)	Approach
134.100		AM	Prestwick Airport	Highland Radar
134.125		AM	London TCC (Terminal Control)	Ockham
134.125		AM	Swanwick Civil ATC	London Control
134.150		AM	Ballykelly (Army)	Approach (Eglington Tower)
134.150		AM	Derry	Tower
134.150		AM	Londonderry	Tower
134.150		AM	Shetlands	Radar
134.175		AM	Derby (Burnaston)	Approach (East Midlands)
134.175		AM	East Midlands Airport/ Nottingham	Approach
134.175		AM	East Midlands Airport/ Nottingham	Radar
134.225		AM	London Gatwick	Tower
134.250		AM	Swanwick Civil ATC	London Control North Sea
134.275		AM	Shannon Area Control Centre	Control
134.300		AM	Scottish Air Traffic Control - Prestwick	Scottish Military
134.300		AM	Swanwick Military/London Joint Area Org.	Middle Airspace (Scottish)
134.300		AM	Weston-super-Mare	Danger Area Information
134.350		AM	Farnborough	Approach
134.350		AM	Valley (RAF)	Approach
134.350		AM	Valley (RAF)	Radar
134.425		AM	Swanwick Civil ATC	London Control Irish Sea
134.450		AM	London Heathrow	London Zone
134.450		AM	Swanwick Civil ATC	London Control (Hurn)
134.500		AM	Filton (BAe) Bristol	Filton Ops
134.550		AM	Nationwide	CAA Events/Airshows
134.650		AM	Nationwide	Flight Checker Navaid Calibrator
134.750		AM	Swanwick Civil ATC	London Control Upper West
134.800		AM	Biggin Hill	Tower
134.875		AM	Northampton (Sywell)	AFIS
134.875		AM	Nottingham/Tollerton	Air-Ground
134.900		AM	Swanwick Civil ATC	London Control
134.925		AM	Cranfield	Tower
134.950		AM	Doncaster (Robin Hood)	ATIS

Base	Mobile	Mode	Location	User and Notes
134.975		AM	London Heathrow	Approach
134.975		AM	London TCC (Terminal Control)	Heathrow
134.975		AM	Nationwide	CAA Test Flights
135.000		AM	Nationwide	CAA Test Flights
135.050		AM	Swanwick Civil ATC	London Control
135.125		AM	Brimpton	Air-Ground
135.150		AM	Swanwick Military/London Joint Area Org.	Middle Airspace (West)
135.175		AM	Nationwide	Los Halcones Chilean Display Team
135.225		AM	Shannon Area Control Centre	Control Southern Sector
135.250		AM	Swanwick Civil ATC	London Control (Cardiff)
135.275		AM	Swanwick Military/London Joint Area Org.	Middle Airspace (East)
135.325		AM	Swanwick Civil ATC	London Control (Cardiff)
135.375		AM	London Gatwick	London VOLMET (Main)
135.375		AM	London Heathrow	London VOLMET (Main)
135.375		AM	Swanwick Civil ATC	London VOLMET (Main)
135.425		AM	Swanwick Civil ATC	London Control
135.475		AM	Nationwide	SAFETYCOMM
135.525		AM	Scottish Air Traffic Control - Prestwick	Shanwick Oceanic (Clearances)
135.575		AM	London Gatwick	Approach
135.575		AM	London TCC (Terminal Control)	Gatwick
135.600		AM	Shannon Area Control Centre	Control
135.675		AM	Cranwell (RAF)	DATIS
135.700		AM	Fowlemere	Air-Ground
135.700		AM	Lee on Solent (Fleetlands)	Tower
135.750		AM	Nationwide	CAA Test Flights/Events
135.800		AM	London TCC (Terminal Control)	Compton
135.850		AM	Scottish Air Traffic Control - Prestwick	Scottish Air Traffic Control
135.875		AM	Cosford (RAF)	Approach
135.875		AM	Scottish Air Traffic Control - Prestwick	Scottish Control UIR
135.925		AM	Nationwide	Moroccan Green March Display Team
135.950		AM	Blackpool	Radar
135.950		AM	Nationwide	AAC Blue Eagles Display Team
135.975		AM	Liverpool John Lennon	Mail Flights (Air-Air)
135.975		AM	Nationwide	AAC Blue Eagles Display Team
135.975		AM	Nationwide	Army Air-Air

136.0000 - 138.0000 MHz — National & International Air Traffic Control Centres, Airline Ops, Meteorology & Space Operations & Research

Base	Mobile	Mode	Location	User and Notes
136.050		AM	Dublin Area Control Centre	Control North
136.050		AM	Dublin Area Control Centre	Control South
136.075		AM	Bristol Airport	Radar
136.080		NFM	Nongeostationary	Canada Isis 2
136.100		NFM	Nongeostationary	NASA Explorer 15
136.110		NFM	Nongeostationary	NASA Explorer 35
136.111		NFM	Nongeostationary	NASA Explorer 18
136.112		NFM	Nongeostationary	France/US Ayame 2
136.112		NFM	Nongeostationary	Japan MOS-1
136.125		NFM	Nongeostationary	NASA Explorer 28
136.141		NFM	Nongeostationary	NASA Explorer 34
136.142		NFM	Nongeostationary	NASA Explorer 21
136.145		NFM	Nongeostationary	NASA Explorer Series
136.150		AM	Dublin Area Control Centre	Control North
136.150		AM	Dublin Area Control Centre	Control South
136.159		NFM	Nongeostationary	Japan Ohsumi 1

Base	Mobile	Mode	Location	User and Notes
136.160		NFM	Nongeostationary	ESRO Aurorae
136.170		NFM	Nongeostationary	NASA Explorer 42
136.170		NFM	Nongeostationary	US Echo 2
136.171		NFM	Nongeostationary	NASA Explorer 22
136.200		NFM	Nongeostationary	US Cameo 1
136.200		NFM	Nongeostationary	US ERS 20
136.200		NFM	Nongeostationary	US Injun SR3
136.200		NFM	Nongeostationary	US Nimbus 2
136.200		NFM	Nongeostationary	US SERT 2
136.200		AM	Tees Valley/Durham Airport	ATIS
136.220		NFM	Nongeostationary	US OAO 1
136.225		AM	Oxford (Kidlington Airport)	ATIS
136.230		NFM	Nongeostationary	US ESSA 1
136.231		NFM	Nongeostationary	US Tiros 9
136.233		NFM	Nongeostationary	US Tiros 8
136.234		NFM	Nongeostationary	US Tiros 7
136.250		NFM	Nongeostationary	France Castor
136.260		NFM	Nongeostationary	NASA OV5-3
136.273		NFM	Nongeostationary	NASA Explorer Series
136.275		NFM	Nongeostationary	NASA Explorer 26
136.290		NFM	Nongeostationary	NASA Explorer 40
136.290		NFM	Nongeostationary	NASA Hawkeye
136.293		NFM	Nongeostationary	NASA Explorer 25
136.300		NFM	Nongeostationary	NASA SMS 1
136.319		NFM	Nongeostationary	USAF GGSE 1
136.320		NFM	Nongeostationary	NASA GEOS 3
136.320		NFM	Nongeostationary	USAF Ferret
136.348		NFM	Nongeostationary	Australia WRESAT 1
136.350		AM	London City Airport	ATIS
136.350		NFM	Nongeostationary	France EOLE 1
136.350		NFM	Nongeostationary	France FR 1
136.350		NFM	Nongeostationary	USAF SR 11B
136.380		NFM	Nongeostationary	US ERS 27
136.410		NFM	Nongeostationary	Canada Isis 1
136.410		NFM	Nongeostationary	ITSO Intelsat
136.415		NFM	Nongeostationary	USAF ERS 6
136.430		NFM	Nongeostationary	India Bhaskara
136.440		NFM	Nongeostationary	USAF ERS 15
136.450		AM	Benson (RAF)	Director
136.468		NFM	Nongeostationary	NASA SYNCOM 2
136.500		AM	Lakenheath (USAF)	Approach
136.500		AM	Lakenheath (USAF)	RAPCon
136.500		NFM	Nongeostationary	NASA ATS Series
136.500		NFM	Nongeostationary	NASA Injun
136.500		NFM	Nongeostationary	NASA SR 3
136.500		NFM	Nongeostationary	US NOAA 10
136.510		NFM	Nongeostationary	NASA OVS 9
136.521		NFM	Nongeostationary	US SOLRAD 11B
136.525		AM	London Gatwick	ATIS
136.530		NFM	Nongeostationary	US OV 5-9
136.530		NFM	Nongeostationary	US SOLRAD 11B
136.530		NFM	Nongeostationary	US Vela Hotel 8
136.560		NFM	Nongeostationary	Germany GRS-A
136.563		NFM	Nongeostationary	US RADSAT 43
136.590		NFM	Nongeostationary	Canada Alouette 1
136.590		NFM	Nongeostationary	Canada Isis 1 & 2

Base	Mobile	Mode	Location	User and Notes
136.600		AM	Swanwick Civil ATC	London Control (Standby)
136.610		NFM	Nongeostationary	ESA Arian LO3
136.610		NFM	Nongeostationary	ESA CAT 1
136.620		NFM	Nongeostationary	Italy Sirio 1
136.620		NFM	Nongeostationary	USAF OV 5
136.625		AM	Belfast (City)	ATIS
136.630		NFM	Nongeostationary	France Signe 3
136.650		AM	Manchester Airport	Ringway Handling
136.650		NFM	Nongeostationary	US TRAAC
136.650		NFM	Nongeostationary	US Transit 5B5
136.650		NFM	Nongeostationary	USAF OV 5-5
136.651		NFM	Nongeostationary	USAF SN-43
136.678		NFM	Nongeostationary	US SMS
136.694		NFM	Nongeostationary	Japan Shinsei
136.695		NFM	Nongeostationary	Japan Jiki'ken
136.710		NFM	Nongeostationary	US OSO-4
136.712		NFM	Nongeostationary	US OGO-2
136.713		NFM	Nongeostationary	Japan Tansei
136.713		NFM	Nongeostationary	NASA OSO-2
136.725		NFM	Nongeostationary	Japan CORSA B
136.740		NFM	Nongeostationary	France ERS-A
136.750		AM	Nationwide	ACARS Frequency
136.768		NFM	Nongeostationary	ESA ERS-17 ORS3
136.770		NFM	Nongeostationary	US NOAA 6
136.770		NFM	Nongeostationary	US NOAA 8
136.770		NFM	Nongeostationary	US NOAA 9
136.771		NFM	Nongeostationary	USAF ERS-13 TRS6
136.775		AM	Nationwide	CAA Events Air-Ground
136.800		AM	Manchester Airport	Kestrel Ops My Travel
136.801		NFM	Nongeostationary	USAF SOLRAD 7B
136.804		NFM	Nongeostationary	US EGRS SECOR
136.809		NFM	Nongeostationary	Japan UME 1 & 2
136.810		NFM	Nongeostationary	Japan ETS-1 KIKU
136.825		AM	Dublin	City Jet Ops
136.825		AM	London City Airport	City Jet Ops
136.825		AM	Manchester Airport	American Airlines Ops
136.830		NFM	Nongeostationary	USAF EGRS 8
136.830		NFM	Nongeostationary	USAF ERS 28
136.840		NFM	Nongeostationary	USAF EGRS 9
136.840		NFM	Nongeostationary	USAF TOPO 1
136.860		NFM	Nongeostationary	NASA IUE TETR 2
136.860		NFM	Nongeostationary	NASA RMS
136.860		NFM	Nongeostationary	US ERS 21
136.860		NFM	Nongeostationary	USA Landsat 2
136.860		NFM	Nongeostationary	USAF Cannonball 2
136.860		NFM	Nongeostationary	USAF OV5-4
136.870		NFM	Nongeostationary	US Injun 3
136.875		AM	London Gatwick	Monarch Airlines Ops
136.875		AM	Luton Airport	Monarch Airlines Ops
136.875		AM	Manchester Airport	Monarch Airlines Ops
136.887		NFM	Nongeostationary	USAF SOLRAD 7A
136.890		NFM	Nongeostationary	NASA Explorer 47
136.890		NFM	Nongeostationary	USAF ERS 9 TRS4
136.890		NFM	Nongeostationary	USAF SOLRAD 6
136.891		NFM	Nongeostationary	USAF ERS 9
136.892		NFM	Nongeostationary	USAF ERS 5

Base	Mobile	Mode	Location	User and Notes
136.900		AM	Nationwide	ACARS Frequency
136.919		NFM	Nongeostationary	US Tiros 9
136.920		NFM	Nongeostationary	USAF OSO 8
136.920		NFM	Nongeostationary	USAF SERT 28
136.925		AM	Nationwide	ACARS Frequency
136.950		NFM	Nongeostationary	ESA COS B1
136.975		AM	Nationwide	AAC Blue Eagles Display Team
136.975		AM	Royston	Bassingbourn Barracks Air-Ground
137.025		NFM	Rosyth	Superfast Ferries Bridge/Loaders/On Board
137.040		NFM	Nongeostationary	USAF Ferret
137.080		NFM	Nongeostationary	ESA Meteorsat 1/2
137.110		NFM	Nongeostationary	US ATS 6
137.140		NFM	Nongeostationary	ERS ECS 2
137.170		NFM	Nongeostationary	ERS MARECS A
137.170		NFM	Nongeostationary	France MAROTS
137.190		NFM	Nongeostationary	US GEOS 3
137.200		AM	USAF Lakenheath	Departures
137.200		AM	USAF Mildenhall	Departures
137.230		NFM	Nongeostationary	India/USSR Bhaskara 2
137.230		NFM	Nongeostationary	NOAA 61
137.260		NFM	Nongeostationary	NOAO-A2
137.300		NFM	Nongeostationary	Meteor 3-2
137.300		NFM	Nongeostationary	US Timation 2
137.380		NFM	Nongeostationary	USAF OVS 3
137.400		NFM	Nongeostationary	USAF SMS-2
137.410		NFM	Nongeostationary	USAF Explorer 30
137.420		NFM	Nongeostationary	India Rohini
137.440		NFM	Nongeostationary	India Aryabhata
137.440		NFM	Nongeostationary	India Bhaskari 3
137.450		AM	Nationwide	100 Sqdn. Air/Air Ch. V05
137.500		AM	Nationwide	56R Sqdn. Air/Air
137.500		NFM	Nongeostationary	NOAA 10
137.500		NFM	Nongeostationary	NOAA 12
137.560		NFM	Nongeostationary	UK 6
137.570		NFM	Nongeostationary	NASA Explorer Series
137.620		NFM	Nongeostationary	NOAA 9
137.620		NFM	Nongeostationary	NOAA 11
137.620		NFM	Nongeostationary	NOAA 13
137.675		NFM	Nongeostationary	US P76-5
137.800		NFM	Nongeostationary	USAF SOLRAD 11
137.850		NFM	Nongeostationary	Intercosmos 18
137.850		NFM	Nongeostationary	Meteor 2-16
137.850		NFM	Nongeostationary	Meteor 2-17
137.850		NFM	Nongeostationary	Meteor 2-18
137.850		NFM	Nongeostationary	Meteor 2-19
137.850		NFM	Nongeostationary	Meteor 2-20
137.850		NFM	Nongeostationary	Meteor 3-3
137.850		NFM	Nongeostationary	Meteor 3-4
137.850		NFM	Nongeostationary	Meteor 3-5
137.860		NFM	Nongeostationary	US Landsat 2
137.890		NFM	Nongeostationary	NASA RMS
137.890		NFM	Nongeostationary	US ANS-1
137.950		NFM	Nongeostationary	Canada Isis
137.950		NFM	Nongeostationary	NASA Explorer 45
137.975		NFM	Nationwide	Wide Area Paging (Pocsag 1200)
137.980		NFM	Nongeostationary	NASA Explorer 50
138.000		NFM	Nongeostationary	USAF Hilat 1

Base	Mobile	Mode	Location	User and Notes

138.0000 - 138.2125 MHz — Nationwide Paging 12.5 kHz

Base	Mobile	Mode	Location	User and Notes
138.07500		NFM	Nationwide	Wide Area Paging (POCSAG 1200)
138.15000		NFM	Nationwide	Wide Area Paging (POCSAG 1200)
138.17500		NFM	Nationwide	Wide Area Paging (POCSAG 512/1200)

138.01675 - 138.30625 MHz — Police Air to Ground

Base	Mobile	Mode	Location	User and Notes
138.09375		NFM	England & Wales	Police Helicopter Air-Ground Ch.1
138.09375		NFM	Humberside	Police Helicopter Air-Ground Ch.1
138.09375		NFM	London	Police Helicopter Ch.1
138.09375		NFM	Merseyside	Police Air Support Group (M1)
138.09375		NFM	Thames Valley	Police Helicopter Ch.1 (XA97/99)
138.10625		NFM	England & Wales	Police Helicopter Air-Ground Ch.2
138.10625		NFM	London	Police Helicopter Ch.2
138.10625		NFM	Manchester	Police Helicopter
138.10625		NFM	Thames Valley	Police Helicopter Ch.2 (XA97/99)
138.10625		NFM	West Midlands	Police Helicopter Ch.2
138.29375		NFM	England & Wales	Police Helicopter Ch.3
138.29375		NFM	London	Police Helicopter Ch.3
138.29375		NFM	Thames Valley	Police Helicopter Ch.3 (XA97/99)
138.30625		NFM	England & Wales	Police Helicopter Ch.4
138.30625		NFM	Lancashire	Police Helicopter
138.30625		NFM	London	Police Helicopter Ch.4
138.30625		NFM	Thames Valley	Police Helicopter Ch.4 (XA97/99)

138.00625 - 140.96875 MHz — VHF High Band Public Utilities

Base	Mobile	Mode	Location	User and Notes
138.30000		AM	Nationwide	USAF Air-Air
138.50000		AM	Mildenhall	Airlift Ops.
138.55000		AM	Nationwide	US Marines (KC130 Raider)
138.67500		AM	Nationwide	USAF 52 FW
138.70000		AM	Wattisham	Used When 123.100 Is Not Available
139.12500		AM	Nationwide	USAF Air-Air
139.47500		NFM	Nationwide	USS Winston Churchill On Board Trunked

M/N/Y/N/W = MANWEB/NORWEB/Yorkshire Electricity/Northern Electric/Western Power
SP/SH = Scottish Power/ Scottish Hydro

Base	Mobile	Mode	Location	User and Notes
139.51875	148.01875	NFM	M/N/Y/N/W	MPT 1327Trunked (8 Channels per Area)
139.51875	148.01875	NFM	SP/SH	MPT 1327Trunked (8 Channels per Area)
139.51875	148.01875	NFM	Nationwide	Electricity Boards Trunked J22
139.53125	148.03125	NFM	M/N/Y/N/W	MPT 1327Trunked (8 Channels per Area)
139.53125	148.03125	NFM	SP/SH	MPT 1327Trunked (8 Channels per Area)
139.53125	148.03125	NFM	Nationwide	Electricity Boards Trunked J23
139.54375	148.04375	NFM	M/N/Y/N/W	MPT 1327Trunked (8 Channels per Area)
139.54375	148.04375	NFM	SP/SH	MPT 1327Trunked (8 Channels per Area)
139.54375	148.04375	NFM	Nationwide	Electricity Boards Trunked J24
139.55625	148.05625	NFM	M/N/Y/N/W	MPT 1327Trunked (8 Channels per Area)
139.55625	148.05625	NFM	SP/SH	MPT 1327Trunked (8 Channels per Area)
139.55625	148.05625	NFM	Nationwide	Electricity Boards Trunked J25
139.56875	148.06875	NFM	M/N/Y/N/W	MPT 1327Trunked (8 Channels per Area)
139.56875	148.06875	NFM	SP/SH	MPT 1327Trunked (8 Channels per Area)
139.56875	148.06875	NFM	Nationwide	Electricity Boards Trunked J26
139.57500		AM	Nationwide	Dutch Air Force THG Falcon Stoter A/G
139.58125	148.08125	NFM	M/N/Y/N/W	MPT 1327Trunked (8 Channels per Area)
139.58125	148.08125	NFM	SP/SH	MPT 1327Trunked (8 Channels per Area)
139.58125	148.08125	NFM	Nationwide	Electricity Boards Trunked J27
139.59375	148.09375	NFM	M/N/Y/N/W	MPT 1327Trunked (8 Channels per Area)

Base	Mobile	Mode	Location	User and Notes
139.59375	148.09375	NFM	SP/SH	MPT 1327Trunked (8 Channels per Area)
139.59375	148.09375	NFM	Nationwide	Electricity Boards Trunked J28
139.60000		NFM	Nationwide	Illegal Bugging Devices
139.60625	148.10625	NFM	M/N/Y/N/W	MPT 1327Trunked (8 Channels per Area)
139.60625	148.10625	NFM	SP/SH	MPT 1327Trunked (8 Channels per Area)
139.60625	148.10625	NFM	Nationwide	Electricity Boards Trunked J29
139.61875	148.11875	NFM	M/N/Y/N/W	MPT 1327Trunked (8 Channels per Area)
139.61875	148.11875	NFM	SP/SH	MPT 1327Trunked (8 Channels per Area)
139.61875	148.11875	NFM	Nationwide	Electricity Boards Trunked J30
139.63125	148.13125	NFM	M/N/Y/N/W	MPT 1327Trunked (8 Channels per Area)
139.63125	148.13125	NFM	SP/SH	MPT 1327Trunked (8 Channels per Area)
139.63125	148.13125	NFM	Nationwide	Electricity Boards Trunked J31
139.64375	148.14375	NFM	M/N/Y/N/W	MPT 1327Trunked (8 Channels per Area)
139.64375	148.14375	NFM	SP/SH	MPT 1327Trunked (8 Channels per Area)
139.64375	148.14375	NFM	Nationwide	Electricity Boards Trunked J32
139.65625	148.15625	NFM	M/N/Y/N/W	MPT 1327Trunked (8 Channels per Area)
139.65625	148.15625	NFM	SP/SH	MPT 1327Trunked (8 Channels per Area)
139.65625	148.15625	NFM	Nationwide	Electricity Boards Trunked J33
139.66875	148.16875	NFM	M/N/Y/N/W	MPT 1327Trunked (8 Channels per Area)
139.66875	148.16875	NFM	SP/SH	MPT 1327Trunked (8 Channels per Area)
139.66875	148.16875	NFM	Nationwide	Electricity Boards Trunked J34
139.68125	148.18125	NFM	M/N/Y/N/W	MPT 1327Trunked (8 Channels per Area)
139.68125	148.18125	NFM	SP/SH	MPT 1327Trunked (8 Channels per Area)
139.68125	148.18125	NFM	Nationwide	Electricity Boards Trunked J35
139.69375	148.19375	NFM	M/N/Y/N/W	MPT 1327Trunked (8 Channels per Area)
139.69375	148.19375	NFM	SP/SH	MPT 1327Trunked (8 Channels per Area)
139.69375	148.19375	NFM	Nationwide	Electricity Boards Trunked J36
139.70625	148.20625	NFM	M/N/Y/N/W	MPT 1327Trunked (8 Channels per Area)
139.70625	148.20625	NFM	SP/SH	MPT 1327Trunked (8 Channels per Area)
139.70625	148.20625	NFM	Nationwide	Electricity Boards Trunked J37
139.71875	148.21875	NFM	M/N/Y/N/W	MPT 1327Trunked (8 Channels per Area)
139.71875	148.20625	NFM	SP/SH	MPT 1327Trunked (8 Channels per Area)
139.71875	148.20625	NFM	Nationwide	Electricity Boards Trunked J38
139.73125	148.23125	NFM	M/N/Y/N/W	MPT 1327Trunked (8 Channels per Area)
139.73125	148.23125	NFM	SP/SH	MPT 1327Trunked (8 Channels per Area)
139.73125	148.23125	NFM	Nationwide	Electricity Boards Trunked J39
139.74375	148.24375	NFM	M/N/Y/N/W	MPT 1327Trunked (8 Channels per Area)
139.74375	148.24375	NFM	SP/SH	MPT 1327Trunked (8 Channels per Area)
139.74375	148.24375	NFM	Nationwide	Electricity Boards Trunked J40
139.75625	148.25625	NFM	M/N/Y/N/W	MPT 1327Trunked (8 Channels per Area)
139.75625	148.25625	NFM	SP/SH	MPT 1327Trunked (8 Channels per Area)
139.75625	148.25625	NFM	Nationwide	Electricity Boards Trunked J41
139.76875	148.26875	NFM	M/N/Y/N/W	MPT 1327Trunked (8 Channels per Area)
139.76875	148.26875	NFM	SP/SH	MPT 1327Trunked (8 Channels per Area)
139.76875	148.26875	NFM	Nationwide	Electricity Boards Trunked J42
139.78125	148.28125	NFM	M/N/Y/N/W	MPT 1327Trunked (8 Channels per Area)
139.78125	148.28125	NFM	SP/SH	MPT 1327Trunked (8 Channels per Area)
139.78125	148.28125	NFM	Nationwide	Electricity Boards Trunked J43
139.79375	148.29375	NFM	M/N/Y/N/W	MPT 1327Trunked (8 Channels per Area)
139.79375	148.29375	NFM	SP/SH	MPT 1327Trunked (8 Channels per Area)
139.79375	148.29375	NFM	Nationwide	Electricity Boards Trunked J44
139.80000		NFM	Nationwide	Illegal Bugging Devices
139.80625	148.30625	NFM	M/N/Y/N/W	MPT 1327Trunked (8 Channels per Area)
139.80625	148.30625	NFM	SP/SH	MPT 1327Trunked (8 Channels per Area)
139.80625	148.30625	NFM	Nationwide	Electricity Boards Trunked J45
139.81875	148.31875	NFM	M/N/Y/N/W	MPT 1327Trunked (8 Channels per Area)

Base	Mobile	Mode	Location	User and Notes
139.81875	148.31875	NFM	SP/SH	MPT 1327Trunked (8 Channels per Area)
139.81875	148.31875	NFM	Nationwide	Electricity Boards Trunked J46
139.83125	148.33125	NFM	M/N/Y/N/W	MPT 1327Trunked (8 Channels per Area)
139.83125	148.33125	NFM	SP/SH	MPT 1327Trunked (8 Channels per Area)
139.83125	148.33125	NFM	Nationwide	Electricity Boards Trunked J47
139.84375	148.34375	NFM	M/N/Y/N/W	MPT 1327Trunked (8 Channels per Area)
139.84375	148.34375	NFM	SP/SH	MPT 1327Trunked (8 Channels per Area)
139.84375	148.34375	NFM	Nationwide	Electricity Boards Trunked J48
139.85625	148.35625	NFM	M/N/Y/N/W	MPT 1327Trunked (8 Channels per Area)
139.85625	148.35625	NFM	SP/SH	MPT 1327Trunked (8 Channels per Area)
139.85625	148.35625	NFM	Nationwide	Electricity Boards Trunked J49
139.86875	148.36875	NFM	M/N/Y/N/W	MPT 1327Trunked (8 Channels per Area)
139.86875	148.36875	NFM	SP/SH	MPT 1327Trunked (8 Channels per Area)
139.86875	148.36875	NFM	Nationwide	Electricity Boards Trunked J50
139.87250		AM	Nationwide	USAF Air-Air
139.87500		AM	Mildenhall	USAF Interplane
139.87500		AM	Nationwide	USAF Refuelling
139.88125	148.38125	NFM	M/N/Y/N/W	MPT 1327Trunked (8 Channels per Area)
139.88125	148.38125	NFM	SP/SH	MPT 1327Trunked (8 Channels per Area)
139.88125	148.38125	NFM	Nationwide	Electricity Boards Trunked J51
139.89375	148.39375	NFM	M/N/Y/N/W	MPT 1327Trunked (8 Channels per Area)
139.89375	148.39375	NFM	SP/SH	MPT 1327Trunked (8 Channels per Area)
139.89375	148.39375	NFM	Nationwide	Electricity Boards Trunked J52
139.90000		AM	Fairford	Chase Car (U2) April 2005
139.90625	148.40625	NFM	M/N/Y/N/W	MPT 1327Trunked (8 Channels per Area)
139.90625	148.40625	NFM	SP/SH	MPT 1327Trunked (8 Channels per Area)
139.90625	148.40625	NFM	Nationwide	Electricity Boards Trunked J53
139.91875	148.41875	NFM	M/N/Y/N/W	MPT 1327Trunked (8 Channels per Area)
139.91875	148.41875	NFM	SP/SH	MPT 1327Trunked (8 Channels per Area)
139.91875	148.41875	NFM	Nationwide	Electricity Boards Trunked J54
139.93125	148.43125	NFM	M/N/Y/N/W	MPT 1327Trunked (8 Channels per Area)
139.93125	148.43125	NFM	SP/SH	MPT 1327Trunked (8 Channels per Area)
139.93125	148.43125	NFM	Nationwide	Electricity Boards Trunked J55
139.94375	148.44375	NFM	M/N/Y/N/W	MPT 1327Trunked (8 Channels per Area)
139.94375	148.44375	NFM	SP/SH	MPT 1327Trunked (8 Channels per Area)
139.94375	148.44375	NFM	Nationwide	Electricity Boards Trunked J56
139.95625	148.45625	NFM	M/N/Y/N/W	MPT 1327Trunked (8 Channels per Area)
139.95625	148.45625	NFM	SP/SH	MPT 1327Trunked (8 Channels per Area)
139.95625	148.45625	NFM	Nationwide	Electricity Boards Trunked J57
139.96875	148.46875	NFM	M/N/Y/N/W	MPT 1327Trunked (8 Channels per Area)
139.96875	148.46875	NFM	SP/SH	MPT 1327Trunked (8 Channels per Area)
139.96875	148.46875	NFM	Nationwide	Electricity Boards Trunked J58
139.98125	148.48125	NFM	M/N/Y/N/W	MPT 1327Trunked (8 Channels per Area)
139.98125	148.48125	NFM	SP/SH	MPT 1327Trunked (8 Channels per Area)
139.98125	148.48125	NFM	Nationwide	Electricity Boards Trunked J59
139.99375	148.49375	NFM	M/N/Y/N/W	MPT 1327Trunked (8 Channels per Area)
139.99375	148.49375	NFM	SP/SH	MPT 1327Trunked (8 Channels per Area)
139.99375	148.49375	NFM	Nationwide	Electricity Boards Trunked J60
140.00000		NFM	Nationwide	Illegal Bugging Devices
140.00625	148.50625	NFM	M/N/Y/N/W	MPT 1327Trunked (8 Channels per Area)
140.00625	148.50625	NFM	SP/SH	MPT 1327Trunked (8 Channels per Area)
140.00625	148.50625	NFM	Nationwide	Electricity Boards Trunked J61
140.01875	148.51875	NFM	M/N/Y/N/W	MPT 1327Trunked (8 Channels per Area)
140.01875	148.51875	NFM	SP/SH	MPT 1327Trunked (8 Channels per Area)
140.01875	148.51875	NFM	Nationwide	Electricity Boards Trunked J62
140.02500		AM	Nationwide	USAF 31st FW Ch.V10

Base	Mobile	Mode	Location	User and Notes
140.02500		NFM	Rosyth	Superfast Ferries Bridge/Loaders
140.03125	148.53125	NFM	M/N/Y/N/W	MPT 1327Trunked (8 Channels per Area)
140.03125	148.53125	NFM	SP/SH	MPT 1327Trunked (8 Channels per Area)
140.03125	148.53125	NFM	Nationwide	Electricity Boards Trunked J63
140.04375	148.54375	NFM	M/N/Y/N/W	MPT 1327Trunked (8 Channels per Area)
140.04375	148.54375	NFM	SP/SH	MPT 1327Trunked (8 Channels per Area)
140.04375	148.54375	NFM	Nationwide	Electricity Boards Trunked J64
140.05000		NFM	Nationwide	Mine Rescue Channel
140.05625	148.55625	NFM	M/N/Y/N/W	MPT 1327Trunked (8 Channels per Area)
140.05625	148.55625	NFM	SP/SH	MPT 1327Trunked (8 Channels per Area)
140.05625	148.55625	NFM	Nationwide	Electricity Boards Trunked J65
140.06875	148.56875	NFM	M/N/Y/N/W	MPT 1327Trunked (8 Channels per Area)
140.06875	148.56875	NFM	SP/SH	MPT 1327Trunked (8 Channels per Area)
140.06875	148.56875	NFM	Nationwide	Electricity Boards Trunked J66
140.08125	148.58125	NFM	M/N/Y/N/W	MPT 1327Trunked (8 Channels per Area)
140.08125	148.58125	NFM	SP/SH	MPT 1327Trunked (8 Channels per Area)
140.09370	148.59370	NFM	Nationwide	Electricity Boards Trunked J67
140.09375	148.59375	NFM	M/N/Y/N/W	MPT 1327Trunked (8 Channels per Area)
140.09375	148.59375	NFM	SP/SH	MPT 1327Trunked (8 Channels per Area)
140.09375	148.59375	NFM	Nationwide	Electricity Boards Trunked J68
140.10625	148.60625	NFM	M/N/Y/N/W	MPT 1327Trunked (8 Channels per Area)
140.10625	148.60625	NFM	SP/SH	MPT 1327Trunked (8 Channels per Area)
140.10625	148.60625	NFM	Nationwide	Electricity Boards Trunked J69
140.11875	148.61875	NFM	M/N/Y/N/W	MPT 1327Trunked (8 Channels per Area)
140.11875	148.61875	NFM	SP/SH	MPT 1327Trunked (8 Channels per Area)
140.11875	148.61875	NFM	Nationwide	Electricity Boards Trunked J70
140.13125	148.63125	NFM	M/N/Y/N/W	MPT 1327Trunked (8 Channels per Area)
140.13125	148.63125	NFM	SP/SH	MPT 1327Trunked (8 Channels per Area)
140.13125	148.63125	NFM	Nationwide	Electricity Boards Trunked J71
140.14375	148.64375	NFM	M/N/Y/N/W	MPT 1327Trunked (8 Channels per Area)
140.14375	148.64375	NFM	SP/SH	MPT 1327Trunked (8 Channels per Area)
140.14375	148.64375	NFM	Nationwide	Electricity Boards Trunked J72
140.15625	148.65625	NFM	M/N/Y/N/W	MPT 1327Trunked (8 Channels per Area)
140.15625	148.65625	NFM	SP/SH	MPT 1327Trunked (8 Channels per Area)
140.15625	148.65625	NFM	Nationwide	Electricity Boards Trunked J73
140.16875	148.66875	NFM	M/N/Y/N/W	MPT 1327Trunked (8 Channels per Area)
140.16875	148.66875	NFM	SP/SH	MPT 1327Trunked (8 Channels per Area)
140.16875	148.66875	NFM	Nationwide	Electricity Boards Trunked J74
140.18125	148.68125	NFM	M/N/Y/N/W	MPT 1327Trunked (8 Channels per Area)
140.18125	148.68125	NFM	SP/SH	MPT 1327Trunked (8 Channels per Area)
140.18125	148.68125	NFM	Nationwide	Electricity Boards Trunked J75
140.19375	148.69375	NFM	M/N/Y/N/W	MPT 1327Trunked (8 Channels per Area)
140.19375	148.69375	NFM	SP/SH	MPT 1327Trunked (8 Channels per Area)
140.19375	148.69375	NFM	Nationwide	Electricity Boards Trunked J76
140.20625	148.70625	NFM	M/N/Y/N/W	MPT 1327Trunked (8 Channels per Area)
140.20625	148.70625	NFM	SP/SH	MPT 1327Trunked (8 Channels per Area)
140.20625	148.70625	NFM	Nationwide	Electricity Boards Trunked J77
140.21875	148.71875	NFM	M/N/Y/N/W	MPT 1327Trunked (8 Channels per Area)
140.21875	148.71875	NFM	SP/SH	MPT 1327Trunked (8 Channels per Area)
140.21875	148.71875	NFM	Nationwide	Electricity Boards Trunked J78
140.23125	148.73125	NFM	M/N/Y/N/W	MPT 1327Trunked (8 Channels per Area)
140.23125	148.73125	NFM	SP/SH	MPT 1327Trunked (8 Channels per Area)
140.23125	148.73125	NFM	Nationwide	Electricity Boards Trunked J79
140.24375	148.74375	NFM	M/N/Y/N/W	MPT 1327Trunked (8 Channels per Area)
140.24375	148.74375	NFM	SP/SH	MPT 1327Trunked (8 Channels per Area)
140.24375	148.74375	NFM	Nationwide	Electricity Boards Trunked J80

Base	Mobile	Mode	Location	User and Notes
140.25625	148.75625	NFM	M/N/Y/N/W	MPT 1327Trunked (8 Channels per Area)
140.25625	148.75625	NFM	SP/SH	MPT 1327Trunked (8 Channels per Area)
140.25625	148.75625	NFM	Nationwide	Electricity Boards Trunked J81
140.26875	148.76875	NFM	M/N/Y/N/W	MPT 1327Trunked (8 Channels per Area)
140.26875	148.76875	NFM	SP/SH	MPT 1327Trunked (8 Channels per Area)
140.26875	148.76875	NFM	Nationwide	Electricity Boards Trunked J82
140.28125	148.78125	NFM	M/N/Y/N/W	MPT 1327Trunked (8 Channels per Area)
140.28125	148.78125	NFM	SP/SH	MPT 1327Trunked (8 Channels per Area)
140.28125	148.78125	NFM	Nationwide	Electricity Boards Trunked J83
140.29375	148.79375	NFM	M/N/Y/N/W	MPT 1327Trunked (8 Channels per Area)
140.29375	148.79375	NFM	SP/SH	MPT 1327Trunked (8 Channels per Area)
140.29375	148.79375	NFM	Nationwide	Electricity Boards Trunked J84
140.30000		AM	Nationwide	USAF 31st FW Ch.V11
140.30625	148.80625	NFM	M/N/Y/N/W	MPT 1327Trunked (8 Channels per Area)
140.30625	148.80625	NFM	SP/SH	MPT 1327Trunked (8 Channels per Area)
140.30625	148.80625	NFM	Nationwide	Electricity Boards Trunked J85
140.31875	148.81875	NFM	M/N/Y/N/W	MPT 1327Trunked (8 Channels per Area)
140.31875	148.81875	NFM	SP/SH	MPT 1327Trunked (8 Channels per Area)
140.31875	148.81875	NFM	Nationwide	Electricity Boards Trunked J86
140.33125	148.83125	NFM	M/N/Y/N/W	MPT 1327Trunked (8 Channels per Area)
140.33125	148.83125	NFM	SP/SH	MPT 1327Trunked (8 Channels per Area)
140.33125	148.83125	NFM	Nationwide	Electricity Boards Trunked J87
140.34375	148.84375	NFM	M/N/Y/N/W	MPT 1327Trunked (8 Channels per Area)
140.34375	148.84375	NFM	SP/SH	MPT 1327Trunked (8 Channels per Area)
140.34375	148.84375	NFM	Nationwide	Electricity Boards Trunked J88
140.35000		AM	Nationwide	USAF 31st FW Ch.V16
140.35625	148.85625	NFM	M/N/Y/N/W	MPT 1327Trunked (8 Channels per Area)
140.35625	148.85625	NFM	SP/SH	MPT 1327Trunked (8 Channels per Area)
140.35625	148.85625	NFM	Nationwide	Electricity Boards Trunked J89
140.36875	148.86875	NFM	M/N/Y/N/W	MPT 1327Trunked (8 Channels per Area)
140.36875	148.86875	NFM	SP/SH	MPT 1327Trunked (8 Channels per Area)
140.36875	148.86875	NFM	Nationwide	Electricity Boards Trunked J90
140.38125	148.88125	NFM	M/N/Y/N/W	MPT 1327Trunked (8 Channels per Area)
140.38125	148.88125	NFM	SP/SH	MPT 1327Trunked (8 Channels per Area)
140.38125	148.88125	NFM	Nationwide	Electricity Boards Trunked J91
140.39375	148.89375	NFM	M/N/Y/N/W	MPT 1327Trunked (8 Channels per Area)
140.39375	148.89375	NFM	SP/SH	MPT 1327Trunked (8 Channels per Area)
140.39375	148.89375	NFM	Nationwide	Electricity Boards Trunked J92
140.40625	148.90625	NFM	M/N/Y/N/W	MPT 1327Trunked (8 Channels per Area)
140.40625	148.90625	NFM	SP/SH	MPT 1327Trunked (8 Channels per Area)
140.40625	148.90625	NFM	Nationwide	Electricity Boards Trunked J93
140.41875	148.91875	NFM	M/N/Y/N/W	MPT 1327Trunked (8 Channels per Area)
140.41875	148.91875	NFM	SP/SH	MPT 1327Trunked (8 Channels per Area)
140.41875	148.91875	NFM	Nationwide	Electricity Boards Trunked J94
140.43125	148.93125	NFM	M/N/Y/N/W	MPT 1327Trunked (8 Channels per Area)
140.43125	148.93125	NFM	SP/SH	MPT 1327Trunked (8 Channels per Area)
140.43125	148.93125	NFM	Nationwide	Electricity Boards Trunked J95
140.44375	148.94375	NFM	M/N/Y/N/W	MPT 1327Trunked (8 Channels per Area)
140.44375	148.94375	NFM	SP/SH	MPT 1327Trunked (8 Channels per Area)
140.44375	148.94375	NFM	Nationwide	Electricity Boards Trunked J96
140.45625	148.95625	NFM	M/N/Y/N/W	MPT 1327Trunked (8 Channels per Area)
140.45625	148.95625	NFM	SP/SH	MPT 1327Trunked (8 Channels per Area)
140.45625	148.95625	NFM	Nationwide	Electricity Boards Trunked J97
140.46875	148.96875	NFM	M/N/Y/N/W	MPT 1327Trunked (8 Channels per Area)
140.46875	148.96875	NFM	SP/SH	MPT 1327Trunked (8 Channels per Area)
140.46875	148.96875	NFM	Nationwide	Electricity Boards Trunked J98

Base	Mobile	Mode	Location	User and Notes
140.48125	148.98125	NFM	M/N/Y/N/W	MPT 1327Trunked (8 Channels per Area)
140.48125	148.98125	NFM	SP/SH	MPT 1327Trunked (8 Channels per Area)
140.48125	148.98125	NFM	Nationwide	Electricity Boards Trunked J99
140.49375	148.99375	NFM	M/N/Y/N/W	MPT 1327Trunked (8 Channels per Area)
140.49375	148.99375	NFM	SP/SH	MPT 1327Trunked (8 Channels per Area)
140.49375	148.99375	NFM	Nationwide	Electricity Boards Trunked J100
140.60000		AM	Nationwide	Frecce Tricolori Display Team

140.9400 - 141.4750 MHz — ILR, BBC and Local Radio Talkback

Base	Mobile	Mode	Location	User and Notes
140.94375		NFM	Nationwide	LWT Engineering Talkback
140.95000		AM	Nationwide	USAF 52 FW
140.99375		NFM	London	ITV & GMTV Talkback
140.99375		NFM	London	ITN 6 O'Clock News
140.99375		NFM	London	South Bank Studios
140.99375		NFM	London	Screen TV O/B
141.00000		NFM	Nationwide	Latvia Navy On Board Handhelds, LNS Versaitis
141.01250		NFM	Nationwide	ILR Talkback Ch.1
141.01250		NFM	Nationwide	ITN Ch.1
141.01875		NFM	Inverness	Moray Firth Radio O/B
141.02500		NFM	Humberside	Viking Radio Links
141.02500		NFM	Nationwide	ILR Talkback Ch.2
141.03125		NFM	Leeds	Flying Eye - Magic 828/Hallam FM/Viking AM
141.03125		NFM	London	Heart FM O/B
141.03125		NFM	London	Kiss FM O/B
141.03125		NFM	London	Sky Patrol Air to Ground
141.03125		NFM	Nationwide	ITN O/B
141.03125		NFM	Stoke on Trent	Signal Radio
141.03750		NFM	Nationwide	Channel 4 TV Engineering/News
141.03750		NFM	Nationwide	ILR Engineering Ch.4
141.03750		NFM	Nationwide	ITN Ch.3
141.04375		NFM	Wolverhampton	Beacon Radio O/B
141.04375		NFM	Berkshire	Radio 210
141.05000		NFM	Nationwide	Independent Local Radio Ch.4
141.05000		NFM	Andover	Independent Local Radio
141.05000		NFM	Bristol	Independent Local Radio
141.05000		NFM	Chelmsford	Independent Local Radio
141.05000		NFM	Cornwall	Independent Local Radio
141.05000		NFM	Hereward	Independent Local Radio
141.05000		NFM	Inverness	Independent Local Radio
141.05000		NFM	Liverpool	Independent Local Radio
141.05000		NFM	Newcastle	Independent Local Radio
141.05000		NFM	Oxford	Independent Local Radio
141.05000		NFM	Peterborough	Independent Local Radio
141.05000		NFM	Reigate	Independent Local Radio
141.05000		NFM	Sheffield	Independent Local Radio
141.05000		NFM	Wolverhampton	Independent Local Radio
141.05625		NFM	Preston	Red Rose Radio
141.06250		NFM	Nationwide	Independent Local Radio Ch.5
141.06250		NFM	Exeter	Independent Local Radio
141.06250		NFM	Gloucester	Independent Local Radio
141.06250		NFM	Great Yarmouth	Independent Local Radio
141.06250		NFM	Gwynedd	Independent Local Radio
141.06250		NFM	Hereford	Independent Local Radio
141.06250		NFM	Huddersfield	Independent Local Radio
141.06250		NFM	Leicester	Independent Local Radio
141.06250		NFM	Maidstone	Independent Local Radio

Base	Mobile	Mode	Location	User and Notes
141.06250		NFM	SE England	2CR Eye in the Sky
141.06250		NFM	Reading	Independent Local Radio
141.06250		NFM	Shrewsbury	Independent Local Radio
141.06875		NFM	Essex	Breeze AM O/B
141.06875		NFM	Essex	Essex Radio Eye-In-The-Sky O/B
141.06875		NFM	Liverpool	Radio City
141.07500		NFM	Nationwide	Independent Local Radio Ch.6
141.07500		NFM	Aberdeen	Independent Local Radio
141.07500		NFM	Barnsley	Independent Local Radio
141.07500		NFM	Berwick upon Tweed	Independent Local Radio
141.07500		NFM	Cardiff	Independent Local Radio
141.07500		NFM	Coventry	Independent Local Radio
141.07500		NFM	Glasgow	Independent Local Radio
141.07500		NFM	London	Independent Local Radio
141.07500		NFM	Manchester	Independent Local Radio
141.07500		NFM	Portsmouth	Independent Local Radio
141.07500		NFM	Stoke on Trent	Independent Local Radio
141.07500		NFM	Swindon	Independent Local Radio
141.08125		NFM	London	Heart FM Studio Link
141.08125		NFM	London	Kiss FM O/B
141.08125		NFM	Manchester	Piccadilly Radio
141.08750		NFM	Nationwide	Independent Local Radio Ch.7
141.08750		NFM	Bedford	Independent Local Radio
141.08750		NFM	Bournemouth	Independent Local Radio
141.08750		NFM	Eastbourne	Independent Local Radio
141.08750		NFM	Edinburgh	Independent Local Radio
141.08750		NFM	Essex	Breeze AM O/B
141.08750		NFM	Guildford	Independent Local Radio
141.08750		NFM	Hereford	Independent Local Radio
141.08750		NFM	Humberside	Independent Local Radio
141.08750	187.40000	NFM	Ipswich	SGR FM O/B
141.08750		NFM	Manchester	Independent Local Radio
141.08750		NFM	Nottingham	Independent Local Radio
141.08750		NFM	Plymouth	Independent Local Radio
141.08750		NFM	Swansea	Swansea Sound O/B
141.08750		NFM	Trent	Independent Local Radio
141.08750		NFM	Whitehaven	Independent Local Radio
141.10000		NFM	Nationwide	Independent Local Radio Ch.8
141.10000		NFM	Aylesbury	Independent Local Radio
141.10000		NFM	Belfast	Independent Local Radio
141.10000		NFM	Birmingham	Independent Local Radio
141.10000		NFM	Blackpool	Independent Local Radio
141.10000		NFM	Bognor Regis	Independent Local Radio
141.10000		NFM	Bradford	Independent Local Radio
141.10000		NFM	Bury St Edmunds	Independent Local Radio
141.10000		NFM	Cambridge	Independent Local Radio
141.10000		NFM	Canterbury	Independent Local Radio
141.10000		NFM	Derby	Independent Local Radio
141.10000		NFM	Dorchester	Independent Local Radio
141.10000		NFM	Dover	Independent Local Radio
141.10000		NFM	Dumfries	Independent Local Radio
141.10000		NFM	Dundee	Independent Local Radio
141.10000		NFM	Gwent	Independent Local Radio
141.10000		NFM	Ipswich	SGR FM O/B
141.10000		NFM	Leeds	Independent Local Radio

Base	Mobile	Mode	Location	User and Notes
141.10000		NFM	London	Capitol Radio Link
141.10000		NFM	London	Independent Local Radio
141.10000		NFM	Londonderry	Independent Local Radio
141.10000		NFM	Middlesbrough	Independent Local Radio
141.10000		NFM	Milton Keynes	Independent Local Radio
141.10000		NFM	Newmarket	Independent Local Radio
141.10000		NFM	Newport	Independent Local Radio
141.10000		NFM	Northampton	Independent Local Radio
141.10000		NFM	Perth	Independent Local Radio
141.10000		NFM	Preston	Independent Local Radio
141.10000		NFM	Southampton	Independent Local Radio
141.10000		NFM	Stranraer	Independent Local Radio
141.10000		NFM	Weymouth	Independent Local Radio
141.10000		NFM	Wrexham	Independent Local Radio
141.10000		NFM	Yeovil	Independent Local Radio
141.11250		NFM	Nationwide	Independent Local Radio Ch.9
141.11250	141.06250	NFM	Norfolk	Radio Broadland O/B
141.11875		NFM	Derby	GEM AM 945/999
141.11875		NFM	Derby	Trent FM 96.2
141.11875		NFM	London	Capital FM O/B
141.12500		NFM	Nationwide	Independent Local Radio Ch.10
141.12500		NFM	Birmingham	96.4 FM BRMB Radio Talkback
141.13750		NFM	Nationwide	Independent Local Radio Ch.11
141.13750		NFM	Nationwide	Local Radio Engineers
141.13750		NFM	West of England	HTV Clean Feed
141.14375		NFM	Kent	Invicta FM O/B
141.14375	447.23125	NFM	Newmarket	Q103 Radio O/B
141.15000		NFM	Humberside	Viking Radio O/B
141.15000		NFM	Ipswich	SGR FM O/B
141.15000		NFM	Nationwide	Local Radio Engineers
141.15000		NFM	Nationwide	Independent Local Radio Ch.12
141.15000		NFM	Swansea	Swansea Sound O/B
141.15000		NFM	Trent	Independent Local Radio Talkback
141.15625		NFM	London	LBC Radio O/B
141.15625		NFM	Nationwide	ITN O/B
141.16250		NFM	Dorset	2CR Studio Talkback
141.16250		NFM	Nationwide	ITN Ch.13
141.16875		NFM	Coventry	Mercia Sound O/B
141.17500		NFM	Nationwide	Independent Local Radio Ch.14
141.18125		NFM	Leicester	Sunrise Radio O/B
141.18125		NFM	London	Independent Radio O/B
141.18125		NFM	Midlands	Gem AM O/B
141.18125		NFM	Midlands	Ram FM O/B
141.18125		NFM	Midlands	Trent AM O/B
141.18750		NFM	Nationwide	Independent Local Radio Ch.15
141.18750		NFM	Cowley	Fox FM Flying Eye
141.18750		NFM	Humberside	Viking Radio O/B
141.18750	141.00000	NFM	Norfolk	SGR FM O/B
141.19375		NFM	Birmingham	Xtra AM
141.19375		NFM	London	LBC O/B
141.20000		NFM	Nationwide	Independent Local Radio Ch.16
141.20000		NFM	Hampshire	BBC Radio Solent
141.20000		NFM	Northamptonshire	BBC Radio Northampton O/B
141.20000		NFM	Yorkshire	BBC Radio Yorkshire O/B Link
141.21875		NFM	Hereford & Worcester	BBC Radio Worcester

Base	Mobile	Mode	Location	User and Notes
141.21875		NFM	London	BBC Radio Car O/B
141.21875		NFM	Lincoln	BBC Radio Lincs Talkback
141.21875	455.30625	NFM	Suffolk	BBC Radio Suffolk O/B
141.21875	455.31875	NFM	Suffolk	BBC Radio Suffolk O/B
141.22500		NFM	Leicester	BBC O/B Cricket Commentary
141.23125	446.83750	NFM	Kent	BBC Radio Kent
141.23125		NFM	Sheffield	BBC Radio Sheffield O/B
141.23125		NFM	Surrey	BBC Radio Surrey
141.23750		NFM	Taunton	BBC Radio Talkback
141.24375		NFM	Berkshire	BBC Radio Surrey & Berkshire
141.24375		NFM	Bristol	BBC Radio O/B
141.24375		NFM	Channel Islands	ITN
141.24375		NFM	Cornwall	ITN
141.24375		NFM	Coventry	CWR Radio O/B
141.24375		NFM	Essex	BBC Radio Essex O/B
141.24375		NFM	London	BBC Radio Car O/B
141.24375		NFM	Norfolk	ITN
141.24385		NFM	Leeds	BBC Radio Talkback
141.24385		NFM	Nottingham	BBC Radio Talkback
141.24385		NFM	Newcastle	BBC Radio Talkback
141.25625		NFM	Cambridge	ITN talkback
141.25625		NFM	London	BBC Radio Car O/B
141.25625		NFM	Peterborough	BBC Radio Peterborough Studio Link
141.25625		NFM	Stoke on Trent	BBC Radio Stoke
141.25625		NFM	West Sussex	BBC Radio Sussex
141.28750		NFM	London	BBC Radio 5 Live O/B
141.29375		NFM	London	BBC Radio 4 Car O/B
141.29375		NFM	Newcastle	BBC Radio Talkback
141.29375		NFM	Shrewsbury	BBC Radio Shrewsbury
141.29385		NFM	Southampton	BBC Radio Solent Talkback
141.29500		NFM	London	BBC Radio News Studio
141.29750		NFM	York	Radio York O/B
141.30000		AM	Nationwide	USAF 31st FW Ch.17
141.30625		NFM	Leicester	BBC Radio Leicester
141.30625		NFM	Manchester	BBC Radio Talkback
141.31250		NFM	Gloucester	BBC Radio Gloucester
141.31250		NFM	Nationwide	BBC Radio 5 Live O/B
141.31825		NFM	London	BBC Radio 4 Car O/B
141.31875		NFM	Nationwide	BBC Radio 4 O/B
141.35000		NFM	Belfast	Data Link
141.35000		NFM	London	BBC1 Clean Feed
141.35000		NFM	London	ITN Music Links
141.35000		NFM	Nationwide	BBC Radio 2 Engineering
141.37500		NFM	Nationwide	BBC O/B Talkback
141.37500	224.23350	NFM	Nationwide	BBC Radio 1 O/B
141.38000		WFM	West Midlands	Pebblemill Studio
141.38750		NFM	Manchester	Key 103 O/B
141.42500		AM	Nationwide	USAF 31st FW Ch.13
141.46250		NFM	Leicester	BBC1 West Midlands Link
141.46250		NFM	Lincolnshire	BBC TV/Radio O/B link
141.46250		NFM	London	BBC TV O/B link
141.46250		NFM	Manchester	BBC TV
141.46250		NFM	Nationwide	BBC Radio 5 Live Talkback
141.46250		NFM	Nationwide	Sky TV O/B Open Link
141.46250		NFM	Nottingham	BBC1 Nottingham Clean Feed
141.47500		WFM	Southampton	BBC TV South Feed to O/B

141.5000 - 141.98750 MHz — Government Agencies & Military

Base	Mobile	Mode	Location	User and Notes
141.50000		AM	Nationwide	USAF Air-Air
141.57500		NFM	Norfolk	Police Link 452.450/452.400/154.375
141.62500		AM	Nationwide	NATO AWACS Test Frequency
141.72500		AM	Nationwide	Swiss PC7 Team
141.82500		AM	Nationwide	Patrouille De France Display Team
141.91250		NFM	RAF Chicksands	British Intelligence Centre (DVP and Mould)
141.91250		NFM	Salisbury Plain	Army Training Net Trunked (MPT1327)
141.91250		NFM	Sandfields Base	Territorial Army
141.91250		NFM	Swansea	Government Surveillance Teams (D)
141.92500		AM	Nationwide	USAF Air-Air
141.93750		NFM	England	Mould (Speech), North West
141.93750	149.47500	NFM	London	DVP/Cougarnet/Voice
141.93750		NFM	London	MI5/Anti-Terrorist Branch (Operation Resolve)
141.93750		NFM	Newhaven	Government Agency
141.96250		NFM	Berkshire	Mould Link
141.96250		NFM	Nationwide	Army
141.98750		NFM	Berkshire	Mould Link
141.98750		NFM	England	Government Agency, North West
141.98750		NFM	Newhaven	Government Agency
141.98750		NFM	Sandfields Base	Territorial Army

142.0000 - 142.9750 MHz — MoD, USAF & Soviet Space Communications

Base	Mobile	Mode	Location	User and Notes
142.01250		NFM	Thetford	Stanford Battle Training Ground (Mainly Scrambled)
142.02500		AM	Nationwide	MoD Aircraft
142.02500		AM	Nationwide	USAF Air to Air
142.02500		NFM	Thetford	Stanford Battle Training Ground (Mainly Scrambled)
142.05000		AM	Leeming	Interplane
142.05000		AM	Nationwide	100 Squadron Air-Air CH.V04
142.05000		AM	Nationwide	USAF Air-Air
142.05000		NFM	Thetford	Stanford Army Exercise Area
142.07500		AM	Home Counties	Army Network
142.07500		AM	Nationwide	USAF Air-Air
142.08750		NFM	North Yorkshire	Army
142.10000		NFM	England	Government Agency Cougarnet/DVP, North West
142.10000		AM	Nationwide	USAF 52 FW Air to Air
142.11250		NFM	London	Mould Linked to 74.425 MHz
142.15000		AM	Nationwide	USAF Air-Air
142.15000		NFM	RAF Chicksands	British Intelligence Centre (DVP)
142.16250		NFM	Home Counties	Army Network
142.16250		NFM	Salisbury Plain	Army Training Net Trunked (MPT1327)
142.20000		NFM	Nationwide	Korean Navy On Board Handhelds, Chun Jee
142.20000		AM	Nationwide	USAF 31st FW Ch.18
142.21250		NFM	Home Counties	Army Network
142.22500		NFM	Home Counties	Army Network
142.22500		NFM	Salisbury Plain	Army Training Net Trunked (MPT1327)
142.26250		NFM	Belfast	Army Cougarnet
142.26250		NFM	London	Cougarnet, N1
142.27500		AM	USAF Mildenhall	Ground
142.28750		NFM	Porton Down	Army Range
142.30000		AM	Nationwide	USAF Air-Air
142.30000		NFM	RAF Chicksands	British Intelligence Centre (DVP/Voice)
142.32500		AM	Leeming	Interplane
142.32500		AM	Nationwide	100 Squadron Air to Air Ch.V03
142.37500		NFM	Home Counties	Army Network
142.37500		AM	USAF Mildenhall	Blackhat Ops.

Base	Mobile	Mode	Location	User and Notes
142.37500		AM	Nationwide	100 Squadron Air-Air Ch.V02
142.37500		AM	RAF Conningsby	RAF 56 (R) 5QN
142.37500		NFM	Salisbury Plain	Army Training Net Trunked (MPT1327)
142.40000		NFM	RAF Chicksands	Defence Intelligence Centre (DVP/Voice)
142.41250		NFM	RAF Welford	Armaments Store
142.42500		NFM	Dover	Government Agency Surveillance
142.42500		NFM	Gosport	Fort Monkton Camp
142.42500		NFM	RAF Chicksands	Defence Intelligence Centre (DVP/Voice)
142.42500		NFM	Sussex	Royal Signals Exercise
142.42500		NFM	Thetford	Stanford Army Exercise Area (Mainly Scrambled)
142.47500		AM	Nationwide	Dutch Air Force Display Team Air-Air/Ground Crew
142.47500	149.17500	NFM	RAF Chicksands	British Intelligence Centre (DVP/Voice)
142.50000		NFM	Coulport	MoD Police
142.51250		NFM	Nationwide	RSPCA Surveillance
142.55000		AM	Nationwide	USAF 52 FW Air-Air
142.58750		NFM	RAF Chicksands	British Intelligence Centre (Voice/DVP)
142.60000		NFM	Salisbury Plain	Army Training Net Trunked (MPT1327)
142.60000		NFM	Thetford	Stanford Army Exercise Area (Mainly Scrambled)
142.65000		AM	USAF Mildenhall	Blackhat Ops.
142.70000		AM	Nationwide	USAF Air-Air
142.72500		AM	Nationwide	USAF Air-Air
142.72500		AM	RAF Brize Norton	101 Squadron Air-Air
142.75000		NFM	Salisbury Plain	Army Training Net Trunked (MPT1327)
142.77500		AM	Nationwide	Dutch Army Parachute DZ
142.77500		AM	RAF Valley	Interplane
142.78750		FM	England	Military, South West
142.80000		NFM	Belfast	Army Cougarnet
142.80000		NFM	Thetford	Stanford Army Exercise Area (Mainly Scrambled)
142.82500		AM	Nationwide	USAF Air-Air
142.82500		NFM	Thetford	Stanford Army Exercise Area (Mainly Scrambled)
142.82500		AM	USAF Lakenheath	Approach
142.82500		AM	USAF Mildenhall	Approach
142.87500		AM	Leeming	Interplane
142.87500		AM	Nationwide	100 Squadron Air-Air Ch.V01
142.87500	149.57500	NFM	RAF Chicksands	British Intelligence Centre (DVP & Voice)
142.87500		AM	RAF Conningsby	RAF 56 (R) 5QN
142.90000		NFM	England	Government Agency (DVP), North West
142.90000		NFM	Home Counties	Army Network
142.90000		AM	RAF Coltishall	Ops
142.90000		NFM	Salisbury Plain	Army Training Net Trunked (MPT1327)
142.95000		AM	USAF Mildenhall	Dust Off Ops.
142.95000		AM	Nationwide	USAF Air-Air
142.95000		NFM	Salisbury Plain	Army Training Net Trunked (MPT1327)
142.96250		NFM	Ramsgate	Government agency (DVP)
142.97500		NFM	Belfast	Army Cougar
142.97500		NFM	Salisbury Plain	Army Training Net Trunked (MPT1327)

143.0000 - 144.0000 MHz   Metropolitan and SW Scottish Police

Base	Mobile	Mode	Location	User and Notes
143.00000		AM	Nationwide	USAF Air-Air
143.01250		NFM	Strathclyde	Police
143.07500		NFM	Strathclyde	Police Special Use Back-Back
143.08750		NFM	W Yorkshire	Police Air Support
143.10000		AM	Nationwide	Patrouille de France Display Team
143.11250		NFM	Strathclyde	Police Special Use Back-Back
143.15000		NFM	Strathclyde	Police
143.21250		NFM	Strathclyde	Police Special Use Back-Back

Base	Mobile	Mode	Location	User and Notes
143.27500		AM	Nationwide	Dutch F-16 Air-Air
143.30000		NFM	Strathclyde	Police Special Use Back-Back
143.35000		NFM	Strathclyde	Police Special Use Back-Back
143.40000		NFM	Strathclyde	Police Motorcycles/VIP Escort
143.42500		NFM	Strathclyde	Police Special Use Back-Back
143.45000		AM	Nationwide	A2A Retro 61 - was USAF F16s
143.45000		NFM	Staffordshire	Police Trunked Network Link
143.50000		NFM	Staffordshire	Police Helicopter Air Support Unit
143.55000		NFM	Strathclyde	Police Special Use Back-Back
143.56250		NFM	Strathclyde	Police Main Used Back-Back
143.57500		NFM	Sussex	Police Helicopter VHF Gateway
143.58750		NFM	Strathclyde	Police Special Use Back-Back
143.60000		AM	Nationwide	USAF Air-Air
143.61250		NFM	Staffordshire	Police Trunked Network Link
143.61250		NFM	Strathclyde	Police Special Use Back-Back
143.62500		NFM	Nationwide	ISS Space Walk Space-Earth, 2005
143.63750		NFM	Strathclyde	Police (Little Used)
143.68750		NFM	Strathclyde	Police Ex-Special Branch Back-Back
143.70000		NFM	Nationwide	Korean Navy On Board Handhelds
143.75000		NFM	Nationwide	Used Illegally By Hang Gliders/Microlights
143.77500		NFM	Nationwide	Used Illegally By Hang Gliders/Microlights
143.80000		NFM	Nationwide	Used Illegally By Hang Gliders/Microlights
143.80000		AM	Nationwide	USAF Air-Air
143.82500		NFM	Nationwide	Used Illegally By Hang Gliders/Microlights
143.82500		NFM	Space	Soviet Military Satellite Coded Channel
143.82500		NFM	Staffordshire	Police Trunked Net Link
143.85000		NFM	Nationwide	Used Illegally By Hang Gliders/Microlights
143.86250		NFM	Strathclyde	Police Special Use Back-Back
143.87500		NFM	Nationwide	Used Illegally By Hang Gliders/Microlights
143.88750		NFM	Belfast	Data link
143.90000		NFM	London	Police Bomb Jamming Van Used With 154.600
143.90000		NFM	Nationwide	Used Illegally By Hang Gliders/Microlights
143.90000		AM	Nationwide	USAF Air-Air
143.92500		NFM	Nationwide	Used Illegally By Hang Gliders/Microlights
143.93750		NFM	London	National Football Intelligence Unit (DVP/Cougarnet)
143.93750		NFM	Manchester	National Football Intelligence Unit (DVP/Cougarnet)
143.95000		NFM	Nationwide	Used Illegally By Hang Gliders/Microlights

144.0000 - 146.0000 MHz   2m Amateur Radio

Base	Mobile	Mode	Location	User and Notes
144.00000		CW	Nationwide	EME
144.05000		CW	Nationwide	CW Calling Frequency
144.10000		CW	Nationwide	Random MS Telegraphy
144.13800		CW	Nationwide	PSK31 Centre of Activity
144.15000		CW	Nationwide	FAI & EME Activity
144.16000		CW	Nationwide	FAI & EME Activity
144.17500		NFM	Nationwide	Microwave Talkback
144.19500		CW/SSB	Nationwide	Random MS
144.26000		SSB	Nationwide	Raynet
144.30000		SSB	Nationwide	SSB Calling Frequency
144.37000		CW/SSB	Nationwide	FSK 441 Random Calling Frequency
144.40700		CW	Nationwide	UK Transatlantic Beacon
144.43000		CW	Wrotham, Kent	Beacon (GB3VHF)
144.44500		CW	Shetland	Beacon (GB3LER)
144.45300		CW	Angus	Beacon (GB3ANG)
144.46900		CW	St Austell	Beacon (GB3MCB)
144.48200		CW	Ballymena	Beacon (GB3NGI)
144.50000		NFM	Nationwide	SSTV Calling

Base	Mobile	Mode	Location	User and Notes
144.50000		CW	Space	OSCAR 5 Telemetry Beacon
144.52500		SSB	Nationwide	ATV Talkback
144.60000		NFM	Nationwide	RTTY Calling
144.62500		NFM	Nationwide	Raynet
144.65000		NFM	Nationwide	Raynet
144.67500		NFM	Nationwide	Packet
144.70000		NFM	Nationwide	FAX Calling
144.75000		NFM	Nationwide	ATV Calling and Talkback
144.77500		NFM	Nationwide	Raynet
144.80000		NFM	Nationwide	Unconnected Nets - APRS, UIVIEW etc.
144.85000		NFM	Nationwide	AX25 BBS User Access
144.87500		NFM	Nationwide	TCP/IP User Access
144.88750		NFM	Nationwide	DX Cluster User Access
144.90000		NFM	Nationwide	DX Cluster User Access
144.95000		CW	Nationwide	AX25 BBS User Access
144.98300		CW	Space	OSCAR 1 & 2 Beacon
145.00000		AM	Nationwide	USAF/RAF Air-Air Exercise April 2005
145.20000		NFM	Nationwide	Raynet 08
145.21250		NFM	Nationwide	Internet Voice Gateway
145.22500		NFM	Nationwide	Raynet 09
145.23750		NFM	Nationwide	Internet Voice Gateway
145.25000		NFM	Nationwide	Channel 10
145.27500		NFM	Nationwide	Channel 11
145.30000		NFM	Nationwide	Channel 12 RTTY Calling
145.32500		NFM	Nationwide	Channel 13
145.33750		NFM	Nationwide	Internet Voice Gateway
145.35000		NFM	Nationwide	Channel 14
145.37500		NFM	Nationwide	Channel 15
145.40000		NFM	Nationwide	Channel 16
145.42500		NFM	Nationwide	Channel 17
145.45000		NFM	Nationwide	Channel 18
145.47500		NFM	Nationwide	Channel 19
145.50000		NFM	Nationwide	Channel 20 Mobile Calling Channel
145.52500		NFM	Nationwide	Channel 21 GB2RS RSGB News
145.55000		NFM	Nationwide	Channel 22 Rally/Exhibition Talk-In
145.57500		NFM	Nationwide	Channel 23
145.60000	145.00000	NFM	Brighton	Repeater (GB3SR) (88.5)
145.60000	145.00000	NFM	Bury	Repeater (GB3MB) (82.5)
145.60000	145.00000	NFM	Wigton, Cumbria	Repeater (GB3AS) (77.0)
145.60000	145.00000	NFM	East London	Repeater (GB3EL) (82.5)
145.60000	145.00000	NFM	Elgin	Repeater (GB3SS) (67.1)
145.60000	145.00000	NFM	Burntisland	Repeater (GB3FF) (94.8)
145.60000	145.00000	NFM	Leicester	Repeater (GB3CF) (77.0)
145.60000	145.00000	NFM	Limavady	Repeater (GB3LY) (110.9)
145.60000	145.00000	NFM	Scarborough	Repeater (GB3YC) (88.5)
145.60000	145.00000	NFM	Wells	Repeater (GB3WR) (94.8)
145.61250	145.01250	NFM	Northampton	Repeater (GB3TO) (77.0)
145.61250	145.01250	NFM	Wooferton	Repeater (GB3VM) (103.5)
145.62500	145.02500	NFM	Bournemouth	Repeater (GB3SC) (71.9)
145.62500	145.02500	NFM	Douglas	Repeater (GB3GD) (110.9)
145.62500	145.02500	NFM	Dover	Repeater (GB3KS) (103.5)
145.62500	145.02500	NFM	Fraserburgh	Repeater (GB3NG) (67.1)
145.62500	145.02500	NFM	London, West	Repeater (GB3WL) (82.5)
145.62500	145.02500	NFM	Renfrewshire	Repeater (GB3PA) (103.5)
145.62500	145.02500	NFM	Ripon	Repeater (GB3HG) (88.5)
145.62500	145.02500	NFM	St. Ives	Repeater (GB3SI) (77.0)
145.62500	145.02500	NFM	Worcester	Repeater (GB3NW) (67.0)
145.62500	145.02500	NFM	Wymondham	Repeater (GB3NB) (94.8)

Base	Mobile	Mode	Location	User and Notes
145.63750	145.03750	NFM	Mansfield	Repeater (GB3IN) (71.9)
145.63750	145.03750	NFM	Torrington	Repeater (GB3DN) (77.0)
145.65000	145.05000	NFM	Birmingham	Repeater (GB3EC) (67.0)
145.65000	145.05000	NFM	Dalry	Repeater (GB3AY) (103.5)
145.65000	145.05000	NFM	Hull	Repeater (GB3HS) (88.5)
145.65000	145.05000	NFM	Ipswich	Repeater (GB3PO) (110.9)
145.65000	145.05000	NFM	Jersey	Repeater (GB3GJ) (77.0)
145.65000	145.05000	NFM	Orkney	Repeater (GB3OC) (77.0)
145.65000	145.05000	NFM	Orpington	Repeater (GB3OK) (103.5)
145.65000	145.05000	NFM	Selkirk	Repeater (GB3SB) (118.8)
145.65000	145.05000	NFM	Stockport	Repeater (GB3MN) (82.5)
145.65000	145.05000	NFM	Swindon	Repeater (GB3WH) (118.8)
145.65000	145.05000	NFM	Torquay	Repeater (GB3TR) (94.8)
145.66250	145.06250	NFM	Ballycastle	Repeater (GB3PK) (110.9)
145.66250	145.06250	NFM	Criccieth, Gwynedd	Repeater (GB3DW) (118.8)
145.66250	145.06250	NFM	Herne Bay	Repeater (GB3KI) (103.5)
145.66250	145.06250	NFM	Rotherham	Repeater (GB3YR) (71.9)
145.66250	145.06250	NFM	Southampton	Repeater (GB3SH) (71.9)
145.67500	145.07500	NFM	Amersham	Repeater (GB3AJ) (77.0)
145.67500	145.07500	NFM	Asgarby	Repeater (GB3JF) (71.9)
145.67500	145.07500	NFM	Barnsley	Repeater ((GB3NA) (71.9)
145.67500	145.07500	NFM	Hastings	Repeater (GB3ES) (103.5)
145.67500	145.07500	NFM	Lancaster	Repeater (GB3LD) 110.9)
145.67500	145.07500	NFM	Lerwick	Repeater (GB3LU) (77.0)
145.67500	145.07500	NFM	Lochgilphead	Repeater (GB3LG) (103.5)
145.67500	145.07500	NFM	Peterborough	Repeater (GB3PE) (94.8)
145.67500	145.07500	NFM	Perth	Repeater (GB3PR) (94.8)
145.67500	145.07500	NFM	Reading	Repeater (GB3RD) (118.8)
145.67500	145.07500	NFM	Swansea	Repeater (GB3SA) (94.8)
145.67500	145.07500	NFM	Weston Super Mare	Repeater (GB3WE) (77.0)
145.67500	145.07500	NFM	Wolverhampton	Repeater (GB3BX) (67.0)
145.70000	145.10000	NFM	Aylesbury	Repeater (GB3VA) (118.8)
145.70000	145.10000	NFM	Berwick	Repeater (GB3BT) (118.8)
145.70000	145.10000	NFM	Buxton	Repeater (GB3HH) (71.9)
145.70000	145.10000	NFM	Caernarfon	Repeater (GB3AR) (110.9)
145.70000	145.10000	NFM	Eden Vale	Repeater (GB3EV) (77.0)
145.70000	145.10000	NFM	Maidstone	Repeater (GB3KN) (103.5)
145.70000	145.10000	NFM	Isle of Mull	Repeater (GB3HI) (88.5)
145.70000	145.10000	NFM	Plymouth	Repeater (GB3WD) (77.0)
145.71250	145.11250	NFM	Birmingham	Repeater (GB3DX) (67.0)
145.71250	145.11250	NFM	Kings Lynn	Repeater (GB3KY) (94.8)
145.71250	145.11250	NFM	Manchester	Repeater (GB3MI) (82.5)
145.72500	145.12500	NFM	Cheltenham	Repeater (GB3CG) (118.8)
145.72500	145.12500	NFM	Four marks	Repeater (GB3SN) (71.9)
145.72500	145.12500	NFM	Belfast	Repeater (GB3NI) (110.9)
145.72500	145.12500	NFM	Chelmsford	Repeater (GB3DA) (110.9)
145.72500	145.12500	NFM	Durham	Repeater (GB3TW) (118.8)
145.72500	145.12500	NFM	Forfar	Repeater (GB3AG) (94.8)
145.72500	145.12500	NFM	Inverness	Repeater (GB3BI) (67.0)
145.72500	145.12500	NFM	Keighley	Repeater (GB3TP) (82.5)
145.72500	145.12500	NFM	Lincoln	Repeater (GB3LM) (71.9)
145.72500	145.12500	NFM	St. Austell	Repeater (GB3NC) (77.0)
145.72500	145.12500	NFM	Stoke-on-Trent	Repeater (GB3VT) (103.5)
145.73750	145.13750	NFM	Amersham	Repeater (GB3AL) (77.0)
145.73750	145.13750	NFM	Dorchester	Repeater (GB3DR) (71.9)
145.73750	145.13750	NFM	Hereford	Repeater (GB3ZA) (118.8)
145.73750	145.13750	NFM	Tamworth	Repeater (GB3TA) (67)
145.75000	145.15000	NFM	Crawley	Repeater (GB3WS) (88.5)

Base	Mobile	Mode	Location	User and Notes
145.75000	145.15000	NFM	Folkestone	Repeater (GB3FK) (103.5)
145.75000	145.15000	NFM	Kilsyth	Repeater (GB3CS) (103.5)
145.75000	145.15000	NFM	Mansfield	Repeater (GB3MX) (71.9)
145.75000	145.15000	NFM	Moel-y-Parc	Repeater (GB3MP) (110.9)
145.75000	145.15000	NFM	Newport, Gwent	Repeater (GB3BC) (94.8)
145.75000	145.15000	NFM	Royston	Repeater (GB3PI) (77.0)
145.76250	145.16250	NFM	Bradley	Repeater (GB3IP) (103.5)
145.76250	145.16250	NFM	Gunnislake	Repeater (GB3PL) (77.0)
145.76250	145.16250	NFM	Newbury	Repeater (GB3NE) (118.8)
145.76250	145.16250	NFM	Richmond Yorks.	Repeater (GB3IR) (88.5)
145.77500	145.17500	NFM	Aberdeenshire	Repeater (GB3GN) (67.0)
145.77500	145.17500	NFM	Accrington	Repeater (GB3RF) (82.5)
145.77500	145.17500	NFM	Carmarthenshire	Repeater (GB3WW) (94.8)
145.77500	145.17500	NFM	Clacton-on-Sea	Repeater (GB3TE) (103.5)
145.77500	145.17500	NFM	Dumfriesshire	Repeater (GB3DG) (103.5)
145.77500	145.17500	NFM	Enfield	Repeater (GB3NL) (82.5)
145.77500	145.17500	NFM	Leamington Spa	Repeater (GB3WK) (67.0)
145.77500	145.17500	NFM	Newtown, Powys	Repeater (GB3PW) (103.5)
145.77500	145.17500	NFM	Omagh	Repeater (GB3WT) (110.9)
145.77500	145.17500	NFM	Portsmouth	Repeater (GB3PC) (71.9)
145.77500	145.17500	NFM	Spilsby	Repeater (GB3FR) (71.9)
145.77500	145.17500	NFM	Stornoway	Repeater (GB3IG) (88.5)
145.78750	145.18750	NFM	Bedford	Repeater (GB3BF) (77.0)
145.78750	145.18750	NFM	Kidderminster	Repeater (GB3KD) (118.8)
145.78750	145.18750	NFM	Llandudno	Repeater (GB3GO) (110.9)
145.78750	145.18750	NFM	Wakefield (Proposed)	Repeater (GB3YW) (82.5)
145.78750	145.18750	NFM	Bedford	Repeater (GB3BF) (77.0)
145.80000		NFM	Space	ISS Space-Earth Amateur Radio
145.80900		CW	Space	OSCAR 10 Beacon (Unmodulated)
145.81200		CW	Space	OSCAR 13 Beacon
145.82000		CW	Space	RS-10 Robot A Uplink
145.82200		CW	Space	Oscar 21 (RS-14) Beacon
145.82438		NFM	Space	Oscar 17 Beacon
145.82516		NFM	Space	Oscar 17 Beacon
145.82600		NFM	Space	OSCAR 11 Beacon
145.85000		CW	Space	OSCAR 10 Mode B Downlink
145.85700		CW	Space	RS-10 Beacon
145.86000		CW/SSB	Space	RS10 Mode B Uplink
145.86200		CW	Space	RS13 Beacon/Robot
145.90300		CW	Space	RS-10 Beacon
145.90700		CW	Space	RS-10 Beacon/Robot
145.90800		CW	Space	RS-13 Beacon/Robot
145.91200		CW	Space	RS-12 Beacon/Robot
145.92500		NFM	Space	PO-28 POSAT-1 Uplink
145.95200		SSB	Space	Oscar-21 (RS-14) Beacon
145.95300		CW	Space	RS-10 Beacon/Robot
145.95900		CW	Space	RS-12 Beacon/Robot
145.97500		NFM	Space	PO-28 POSAT-1 Uplink
145.98300		SSB	Space	Oscar-21 (RS-14) Beacon
145.98500		CW	Space	OSCAR 13 Engineering Beacon
145.98750		NFM	Space	OSCAR 21 Calling Channel

ARISS - Amateur Radio on the International Space Station

Voice/Packet Downlink	145.800 MHz	Crossband FM Repeater Downlink	145.800 MHz
Voice Uplink	145.200 MHz	Crossband FM Repeater Uplink	437.800 MHz
Packet Uplink	145.990 MHz	Space Walk Space-Earth 2005	143.625 MHz

www.rac.ca/ariss/oindex.htm#Frequencies%20in%20use

146.0000 - 148.0000 MHz — Police & Fire Brigades

Base	Mobile	Mode	Location	User and Notes
146.02500		NFM	Surrey	Fire Brigade Input Link
146.05000		NFM	Derbyshire	Fire Brigade Input Link (M2ND)
146.05000		NFM	Nationwide	National Crime Squad (DVP/Cougarnet/Voice)
146.07500		NFM	West Sussex	Police (M2KB) Ch.3
146.08750		NFM	Nationwide	Illegal Chinese Cordless Phones
146.10000	152.85000	NFM	Suffolk	Police (M2VL) Ch.1
146.10000	155.81250	NFM	Suffolk	Police (M2VL) Ch.1
146.10000	154.70000	NFM	Suffolk	Police (M2VL) Ch.1
146.15000		NFM	Hertfordshire	Police Link (M2VH) Ch.1
146.17500		NFM	Cambridgeshire	Fire Brigade Link (M2VC)
146.32500		NFM	Humberside	Fire Brigade (M2XT) Ch.2
146.32500		NFM	Nationwide	Special Branch Royalty Protection
146.42500		NFM	Kent	Fire Brigade (M2KF)
146.42500		NFM	Nationwide	Illegal Chinese Cordless Phones
146.47500		NFM	West Sussex	Police (M2KB) Ch.2
146.47500		NFM	Nationwide	UKSAR Ch. 92 (94)
146.55000	152.97500	NFM	Cambridgeshire	(M2VB) Ch.2
146.57500	154.27500	AM	Suffolk	Hill Top Link (M2VL) Ch.2
146.57500	154.75000	AM	Suffolk	Hill Top Link (M2VL) Ch.2
146.57500	154.85000	AM	Suffolk	Hill Top Link (M2VL) Ch.2
146.68750		NFM	Kent	Police (M2KA) Ch.3 Base Link
146.70000		NFM	City of London	Police Vehicle-Vehicle Ch.76
146.71250		NFM	Gwynedd	Fire Brigade (M2WC)
146.71250		NFM	Kent	Police (M2KA) Base Link Ch.4
146.72500		NFM	City of London	Police Vehicle-Vehicle Ch.77
146.72500	154.36250	NFM	Gloucester	Fire Brigade (M2GL)
146.72500		NFM	Norfolk	Fire Brigade (M2VF)
146.75000		NFM	Kent	Police (M2KA) Ch.1 Link
146.77500		NFM	Humberside	Fire Brigade Ch.1 Output Link
146.77500		NFM	Kent	Police (M2KA) Ch.2 Base Link
146.78750	154.80000	NFM	Norfolk	Police (M2VK) Ch.2
146.80000	154.35000	NFM	Cambridgeshire	Police (M2VB) Ch.1
146.80000	154.37500	NFM	Norfolk	Police (M2VK) Ch.1
146.86250		NFM	West Glamorgan	Fire Brigade (M2WZ)
146.95000		NFM	Lewes	Police (M2KB) Ch.1
146.97500		NFM	Cheltenham	Gloucestershire Fire Brigade Link
147.01250	154.40000	NFM	Bedfordshire	Police (M2VA) Ch.1
147.05000		AM	Nationwide	National Crime Squad DVP/Cougarnet/Voice
147.06250		AM	West Sussex	Police (M2KB) Ch.5
147.07500		NFM	Suffolk	Fire Brigade (M2VN)
147.08750		NFM	Staffordshire	Police & Fire Trunk Input
147.35000		NFM	Nationwide	UKSAR Ch.96 Rebroadcast Feeder Link
147.37500		NFM	West Sussex	Fire Brigade Hilltop Link
147.47500		NFM	Nationwide	UKSAR Ch.92
147.52500		NFM	Lincoln	Fire Brigade (M2NV)
147.65000		NFM	West Sussex	Police (M2KB) Ch.4
147.70000		NFM	Nationwide	National Crime Squads (DVP/Cougarnet)
147.72500		NFM	Nationwide	National Crime Squads (DVP/Cougarnet)
147.75000		NFM	Nationwide	National Crime Squads (DVP/Cougarnet)
147.77500		NFM	London	Robbery Squad/CID/Special Use Ch.18
147.77500		NFM	Nationwide	National Crime Squads (DVP/Cougarnet)
147.80000		NFM	Nationwide	Fire Brigade Alert Paging
147.80000		AM	USAF Mildenhall	Navy Ops.
147.83750		NFM	Nationwide	National Crime Squads (DVP/Cougarnet)

Base	Mobile	Mode	Location	User and Notes
147.86250		NFM	London	Police Anti-Terrorist Stops/Checks (Legion) Ch.98
147.86250		NFM	London	CID Surveillance/Handhelds
147.86250		NFM	London	Police TSG Van-Van Ch.92 (127.3)
147.87500		NFM	London	Police CID/TSG /POLSA Handhelds
147.87500		NFM	London	Police Special Escort Group Ch.16
147.87500		AM	Nationwide	CID & Special Escorts Ch.21
147.88750		NFM	Kent	Police (M2KA)
147.88750		NFM	Kent Motorways	Police (M2TD) Ch.3
147.90000		NFM	Gwent	Fire Brigade (M2WP)
147.90000		NFM	London	Police CID/TSG Van-Van
147.91250		NFM	London	CID Ops on Illegal Street Traders Oxford/Regent St.
147.91250		AM	London	Police Ch.17 CID/TSG/POLSA Handhelds
147.91250		NFM	Nationwide	Police Ch.22 CID & Special Escorts
147.92500		NFM	London	Police TSG Van-Van Ch.91 (127.3)
147.93750		NFM	London	Police TSG Van-Van Ch.19
147.95000		NFM	London	Police TSG Van-Van Ch.97 (146.2)
147.95000		NFM	Nationwide	Close Protection Squads (DVP/Cougarnet)
147.97500		NFM	London	Police TSG Van-Van Ch.93

149.0000 - 149.9000 MHz   Government & MoD

Base	Mobile	Mode	Location	User and Notes
149.01000		NFM	Space	Russian Low Orbit Navigation Satellite (RTTY)
149.01250		NFM	Sennybridge	Army Firing Range
149.01250		NFM	Teesside	MoD Police
149.03750		NFM	Aberfield	MoD Police
149.03750	153.83750	NFM	Aldershot	Army Range Wardens (Beaver Control)
149.04000		NFM	Space	Russian Low Orbit Navigation Satellite (RTTY)
149.05000		NFM	Cardigan Bay	Qinetiq Aberporth Range Tower/Fire
149.06250		NFM	England	Army Voice Communications, North West
149.06250		NFM	Suffolk	Military Data Link
149.07000		NFM	Space	Russian Low Orbit Navigation Satellite (RTTY)
149.07500		AM	Nationwide	Air Training Corps Ch.V5
149.10000		AM	Nationwide	USAF Rescue Helicopter
149.11250		NFM	Cardigan Bay	Qinetiq Aberporth Range General Use
149.11250		NFM	Salisbury	Mould
149.12500		NFM	RAF Caerwent	Security
149.13750		NFM	Hampshire	Unidentified Military Security
149.16250		NFM	Torpoint	HMS Raleigh
149.16250		NFM	Cardigan Bay	Llanbedr Range Tower
149.18750		NFM	Cardigan Bay	Qinetiq Aberporth Range General Use
149.20000		NFM	Hampshire	Voice, Solent Area - possibly SBS
149.21250		NFM	Cardigan Bay	Qinetiq Aberporth Range Emergency/Medical
149.22500		NFM	Nationwide	Danish Navy On Board Handhelds, HDMS Ebden Snare
149.22500		NFM	Thetford	Stanford Army Training Ground
149.23750		NFM	Cardigan Bay	Qinetiq Aberporth Range Jindevix Control
149.27500	153.80000	AM	Nationwide	Air Training Corps Repeater Ch.V6/V10
149.27500		NFM	Nationwide	Air Training Corps Ch.V6
149.27500		NFM	Northumbria	Otterburn Range
149.27500		NFM	RAF Spadeadam	Forward Air Controller
149.31250		NFM	Thetford	Stanford Army Training Ground
149.32500		NFM	Cardigan Bay	Qinetiq Aberporth Missile Range
149.32500		NFM	Thetford	Stanford Army Training Ground
149.32500		NFM	MoD Aberporth	Ops
149.33750		AM	Nationwide	Air Training Corps Ch.V7
149.37500		NFM	Aldershot	Range Controllers
149.37500		NFM	Nationwide	Army Cadet Force

Base	Mobile	Mode	Location	User and Notes
149.38750		NFM	Aberporth	MoD Link
149.38750	142.06250	NFM	Shoeburyness	Army
149.40000		AM	Nationwide	Air Training Corps Ch.V2
149.40000		NFM	Porton Down	MoD Police
149.41250		NFM	Boscombe Down	MoD Police
149.41250		NFM	Gosport	Fort Monkton MI6 Training (103.5)
149.41250		AM	Nationwide	Air Training Corps Ch.V9
149.41250		NFM	Porton Down	MoD Police
149.42500		NFM	Thetford	Stanford Army Training Ground
149.43750		NFM	Gosport	Fort Monckton MI6 Training
149.46250		NFM	Gosport	Fort Monckton MI6 Training
149.46250		NFM	London	Mould
149.53750		NFM	London	Mould
149.55000		AM	USAF Mildenhall	352 SOG Air/Air (Talon)
149.63750		NFM	Larkhill	Range Security
149.63750	142.28750	NFM	Porton Down	Range
149.65000		NFM	USAF Lakenheath	Radar
149.65000		NFM	USAF Mildenhall	US Navy
149.65000		NFM	Nationwide	USAF Air-Air
149.68750		NFM	Porton Down	Direct Link to Middle Wallop
149.70000		NFM	Hampshire	DVP/Cougarnet Solent Area - possibly SBS
149.73750		NFM	Caerwent	MoD Ops
149.73750		NFM	London	Mould
149.73750		NFM	Wattisham	MoD Army Air Corp.
149.76250		NFM	Salisbury Plain	Army Bio-Warfare Firing
149.77500		NFM	London	MI5 and Police Anti-Terrorist Branch
149.77500		NFM	Nationwide	USAF Air-Air
149.78750		NFM	Aldermaston	Atomic Weapons Establishment Fire/Rescue
149.81250		NFM	Salisbury Plain	Army
149.82500		NFM	Portsmouth	MoD Police, Whale Island (PD)
149.82500		NFM	London	MoD Police
149.85000		NFM	Colchester	MoD Police
149.85000		NFM	Hadleigh	MoD Police
149.85000		NFM	Nationwide	MoD Police Ch.3
149.85000		NFM	Portsmouth	Whale Island MoD Police (PD)
149.85000		NFM	Aldershot	MoD Police, Barracks

149.9000 - 150.0500 MHz Radionavigation & Soviet Satellite Beacons

Base	Mobile	Mode	Location	User and Notes
149.970		NFM	Space	Polar Bear 8688A
149.980		NFM	Space	Soviet Cosmos Satellites
150.000		NFM	Space	Russian Low Orbit Navigation Satellite

150.0500 - 152.0000 MHz Radio Astronomy, Paging & MoD

Base	Mobile	Mode	Location	User and Notes
150.03000		NFM	Space	Russian Low Orbit Navigation Satellite (RTTY)
150.11000		NFM	Nationwide	Oil Slick Markers
150.18500		NFM	Nationwide	Oil Slick Markers
150.30000		NFM	Space	Russian Cosmos Geodetic
151.62500		NFM	USA	BRS Handhelds Often Used Illegally in UK (Red Dot)
151.67500		NFM	Newmarket	Paging
151.77500		NFM	Galway	University Hospital Paging
151.82000		NFM	USA	MURS 2W Handhelds Often Used Illegally in UK CH.1
151.88000		NFM	USA	MURS 2W Handhelds Often Used Illegally in UK Ch.2
151.94000		NFM	USA	MURS 2W Handhelds Often Used Illegally in UK Ch.3
151.95500		NFM	USA	BRS Handhelds Often Used Illegally in UK (Purple Dot)

Base	Mobile	Mode	Location	User and Notes
152.0000 - 152.9875 MHz				**Police & Fire PMR 12.5 kHz**
152.01250	143.05000	NFM	Glasgow	Traffic Police
152.01250	143.56250	AM	West Yorkshire	Police (M2XW) Ch.3
152.02500	143.02500	NFM	Glasgow	Traffic Police
152.02500		NFM	Humberside	Fire Brigade (M2XT) Ch.1
152.02500		NFM	Leek	Fire Brigade Trunked (Cell 12)
152.02500	143.06250	NFM	London	Police Ch.3 South Linked To Ch.4
152.03750	143.05000	NFM	Glasgow	Traffic Police
152.03750	143.07500	AM	Leicester	Police (M2NL) Ch.1
152.05000	143.05000	NFM	Glasgow	Traffic Police
152.05000	143.11250	NFM	London	Police Ch.5 City Wide Secondary Channel
152.05000	143.58750	AM	West Yorkshire	Police (M2XW) Ch.5
152.06250	143.31250	AM	North Yorkshire	Police (M2XN) Ch.2
152.06250	143.31250	AM	Scarborough	Police 'D' Division
152.07500	143.47500	NFM	London	Police Helicopter Trunking Gateway Cell 14 (107.2)
152.07500	143.45000	NFM	Strathclyde	Traffic Police
152.08750	143.07500	AM	Northumberland	Police (M2LB) Ch.1
152.08750	143.08750	NFM	Strathclyde	Special Events/Football/Traffic
152.08750	143.08750	NFM	Edinburgh	Police at Fringe Festival
152.10000	143.26250	NFM	London	Police (M2MP) GT/Special Events Ch.11
152.10000	143.45000	NFM	Ayrshire	Traffic Police
152.12500		NFM	Strathclyde	Police Special Events/VIP Escorts/Long Pursuits
152.13750	143.31250	NFM	London	Police (M2MP) GT/Special Events Ch.13
152.13750		NFM	Staffordshire	Fire Brigade Trunked (M2YF/YG)
152.15000	143.20000	NFM	Strathclyde	Police Special Events/VIP Escorts/Long Pursuits
152.15000	143.36250	AM	N Yorkshire	Police (M2XN) Ch.4
152.15000		NFM	Staffordshire	Fire Brigade Trunked (M2YF/YG)
152.16250	143.21250	NFM	London	Police Traffic/Tunnels/Special Events Ch.9
152.16250	143.37500	NFM	Strathclyde	Police Ch.3
152.16250	143.42500	AM	South Yorkshire	Police (M2XS) Ch.5
152.17500	143.10000	AM	Leicester	Police (M2NL) Ch.2
152.17500	143.20000	NFM	Strathclyde	Police Ch.12
152.18750	143.10000	AM	Northumbria	Police (M2LB) Ch.2
152.20000	143.20000	NFM	Strathclyde	Police Special Events/VIP Escorts/Long Pursuits
152.20000	143.36250	NFM	London	Police Ch.15
152.21250	143.05000	NFM	Glasgow	Traffic Police
152.21250	143.41250	NFM	Strathclyde	Police Ch.36
152.22500	143.13750	NFM	London	Police GT/Mainset Backup Ch.6 (M2MP)
152.22500	143.27500	NFM	Strathclyde	Police Ch.18 (PNC/CRO Checks Only)
152.25000	143.27500	NFM	Strathclyde	Police Ch.5
152.26250	143.18750	NFM	London	Police (Diplomatic & Royalty Protection) (Ranger)
152.26250	143.38750	AM	North Yorkshire	Police (M2XN) Channel 5
152.26250		NFM	Staffordshire	Fire Brigade Trunked (M2YF/YG)(Cell 6)
152.27500	143.45000	NFM	Strathclyde	Traffic Police
152.30000	143.23750	NFM	London	Police Area Traffic Control Ch.10
152.30000	143.27500	NFM	Strathclyde	Police (PNC/CRO Checks Only)
152.30000	143.20000	NFM	Strathclyde	Police Special Events/VIP Escorts/Long Pursuits
152.31250	143.16250	AM	Humberside	Police (M2XH) Ch.1
152.31250		NFM	Staffordshire	Fire Brigade Trunked (M2YF/YG) (Cell 6 South)
152.32500	143.16250	NFM	London	Police SO19 Firearm & Robbery Squad Ch.7 (Trojan)
152.33750	143.03750	AM	West Yorkshire	Police (M2XW) Ch.1
152.33750	143.46250	NFM	Strathclyde	Police Ch. 26
152.35000	143.12500	AM	Leicester	Police (M2NL) Ch.3
152.35000	143.20000	NFM	Strathclyde	Police Special Events/VIP Escorts/Long Pursuits
152.36250	143.03750	NFM	London	Police Ch 2 (M2MP) North Linked To Ch.1
152.37500	143.45000	NFM	Ayr	Traffic Police (M2CH)

Base	Mobile	Mode	Location	User and Notes
152.38750	143.01250	NFM	London	Police Ch.1 (M2MP) North Linked To Ch.2
152.38750	143.23750	AM	Cleveland	Police (M2LZ) Ch.1
152.40000	143.20000	AM	Nottinghamshire	Police (M2NH) Ch.1
152.40000	143.27500	NFM	Strathclyde	Police (PNC/CRO Checks Only)
152.41250	143.12500	NFM	London	Police, City of London Ch.42
152.41250	143.12500	AM	Northumberland	Police (M2LB) Ch.3
152.41250	143.12500	NFM	Staffordshire	Fire Brigade Trunked (Cell 6 South C)
152.42500	143.22500	AM	Nottinghamshire	Police (M2NH) Ch.2
152.42500	143.53750	NFM	Strathclyde	Lanarkshire Traffic Division
152.43750	143.51250	NFM	London	Police City of London Ch.43
152.43750		NFM	Staffordshire	Fire Brigade Trunked (M2YF/YG) (Cell 18)
152.43750	143.45000	NFM	Strathclyde	Ayrshire Traffic Police
152.45000	143.18750	AM	Humberside	Police (M2XH) Ch.2
152.45000	143.45000	NFM	Strathclyde	Ayrshire Traffic Police
152.46250	143.08750	NFM	London	Police Ch 4 (M2MP) South Linked To Ch.3
152.48750	143.26250	AM	Cleveland	Police Ch.2
152.48750	143.53750	NFM	Strathclyde	Lanarkshire Traffic Police
152.48750		NFM	Surrey	Fire Brigade Repeater Input
152.50000	143.25000	AM	Nottinghamshire	Police Air Support (M2NH) Ch.3
152.50000	143.53750	NFM	Strathclyde	Lanarkshire Traffic Police
152.51250	143.33750	NFM	London	Police Ch.14
152.51250	143.08750	AM	West Yorkshire	Police (M2XW) Ch.4
152.52500		NFM	Humberside	Fire Brigade Input Link Ch.2
152.53750		NFM	Staffordshire	Fire Brigade Trunked (M2YF/YG) (Cell 6 South)
152.55000	143.28750	NFM	London	Police City Wide Main Traffic Channel Ch.12
152.55000	143.15000	AM	Northumberland	Police (M2LB) Ch.4
152.55000		NFM	Staffordshire	Fire Brigade Trunked (M2YF/YG)
152.56250	143.65000	NFM	Strathclyde	Lanarkshire Traffic Police
152.57500	143.02500	NFM	Glasgow	Traffic Police
152.57500	143.02500	AM	Northamptonshire	Police (M2NG) Ch.1
152.58750	143.43750	NFM	London	Police Royal Palaces/Royalty Protection
152.58750	143.11250	AM	West Yorkshire	Police (M2XW) Ch.6
152.60000		NFM	Kent	Government Agency (DVP/Cougarnet)
152.60000	143.17500	AM	Northumberland	Police (M2LB) Ch.5
152.61250	143.90000	AM	Humberside	Police
152.62500	143.70000	NFM	Strathclyde	W Dunbartonshire Traffic Police
152.63750		NFM	Northern Ireland	Fire Brigade Handhelds Ch.10
152.65000	143.90000	NFM	Strathclyde	Police Argyll Sub-Division Dunoon
152.68750	143.21250	AM	Humberside	Police (M2XH) Ch.3
152.68750		AM	London	Police Helicopter Trunking Gateway Cell 14 Control
152.70000	143.05000	AM	Northamptonshire	Police (M2NG) Ch.2
152.70000	143.70000	NFM	Strathclyde	W Dunbartonshire Traffic Police
152.71250		NFM	Strathclyde	Police Argyll Sub-Division Oban
152.71250	143.06250	AM	West Yorkshire	Police (M2XW) Ch.2
152.72500	143.37500	AM	Lincolnshire	Police (M2NC) Ch.1
152.73750		NFM	Humberside	Fire Brigade Input Link Ch.2
152.75000	143.53750	NFM	Strathclyde	Lanarkshire Traffic Police
152.76250		NFM	Strathclyde	Police Argyll Sub-Division Lochgilphead
152.77500	143.46250	AM	Lincolnshire	Police (M2NC) Ch.2
152.78750	143.27500	AM	South Yorkshire	Police (M2XS) Ch.1
152.80000	143.02500	AM	County Durham	Police (M2LA) Ch.1
152.81250	143.45000	NFM	Strathclyde	Traffic Police, Ayrshire
152.81250	143.13750	AM	West Yorkshire	Police (M2XW) Ch.7
152.82500		NFM	Humberside	Fire Brigade Input Link Ch.1
152.82500	143.72500	NFM	London	Police Helicopter Trunking Gateway Cell 14 (107.2)

Base	Mobile	Mode	Location	User and Notes
152.82500		NFM	Staffordshire	Fire Brigade Trunked (YF/YG) (Cell 6 South)
152.82500	143.70000	NFM	Strathclyde	Police W Dunbartonshire Sub-Division
152.83750	143.05000	AM	Durham	Police (M2LA) Ch.2
152.83750		NFM	Staffordshire	Fire Brigade Trunked (YF/YG) (Cell 7 North)
152.85000		NFM	Nationwide	UKSAR Ch.93 (Line Searches/Stretcher Lowering)
152.85000	143.32500	AM	South Yorkshire	Police (M2XS) Ch.3
152.86250		NFM	Humberside	Fire Brigade (M2XT) Input Link Ch.1
152.88750	143.08750	NFM	Strathclyde	Police Special Events/Football/Traffic
152.90000	143.30000	AM	South Yorkshire	Police (M2XS) Ch.2
152.91250	143.35000	NFM	Nationwide	Communications Commission
152.92500	143.35000	AM	South Yorkshire	Police (M2XS) Ch.4
152.92500	143.27500	NFM	Strathclyde	Police (PNC/CRO Checks Only)
152.95000	143.28750	AM	North Yorkshire	Police (M2XN) Ch.1
152.97500	143.33750	AM	North Yorkshire	Police (M2XN) Ch.3
152.97500		NFM	Staffordshire	Police & Fire Trunked (YF/YG) (Cell 18)
152.98000	152.53750	NFM	Strathclyde	Traffic Police Lanarkshire

153.0125 - 153.3750 MHz   National Paging

Base	Mobile	Mode	Location	User and Notes
153.02500		NFM	Nationwide	Wide Area Paging FLEX 3200
153.12500		NFM	Nationwide	Wide Area Paging POCSAG 1200
153.15000		NFM	Nationwide	Wide Area Paging POCSAG 1200
153.17500		NFM	Nationwide	Wide Area Paging POCSAG 512/1200/FLEX 3200
153.20000		NFM	Nationwide	UK Paging Test & Development
153.22500		NFM	Nationwide	Wide Area Paging POCSAG 1200
153.25000		NFM	Nationwide	Wide Area Paging POCSAG 1200
153.32500		NFM	Nationwide	Wide Area Paging FLEX 1600
153.35000		NFM	Nationwide	Wide Area Paging POCSAG 1200/2400
153.37500		NFM	Nationwide	Wide Area Paging POCSAG

153.5000 - 154.0000 MHz   MoD Tactical Communications & Red Cross

Base	Mobile	Mode	Location	User and Notes
153.58750		NFM	Boscombe Down	Qinetiq Range
153.58750		NFM	Cardigan Bay	Qinetiq Aberporth Range Security
153.60000		NFM	Belfast	Army
153.60000		NFM	Nationwide	RAF Mountain Rescue Teams
153.63750		NFM	Boscombe Down	Qinetiq Range
153.66250	149.0500	NFM	Boscombe Down	Qinetiq Range
153.67500		NFM	Portsmouth	RN Portsmouth
153.68750		NFM	Boscombe Down	Qinetiq Range
153.68750		NFM/AM	Nationwide	Air Training Corps Ch.V8
153.71250		NFM	Boscombe Down	Qinetiq Range
153.71250		NFM	Nationwide	Red Cross (Allocation Shared with Military)
153.71250		NFM	Nationwide	St John Ambulance
153.71250		NFM	Suffolk	Army
153.72500		NFM	Portsmouth	RN Portsmouth
153.76250		NFM	Belfast	Army
153.78750		NFM	Cardigan Bay	Qinetiq Aberporth Range General Use
153.80000		NFM/AM	Nationwide	Air Training Corps Ch.V1
153.80000	149.27500	NFM/AM	Nationwide	Air Training Corps Ch.V10
153.82500		NFM	Galway	Garda Paging
153.82500		NFM/AM	Nationwide	Air Training Corps Ch.V4
153.83750	149.03750	NFM	Aldershot	Range Wardens (Beaver Control)
153.83750		NFM	Portsmouth	RN Portsmouth
153.85000		NFM	Belfast	Army
153.86250		NFM	Portsmouth	RN Serco Tugs
153.93750	149.18750	NFM	Boscombe Down	Qinetiq Range
153.97500		NFM	Nationwide	National Crime Squad DVP/Cougarnet/Voice

Base	Mobile	Mode	Location	User and Notes

154.0000 - 155.9875 MHz   Police & Fire Brigades 12.5 kHz

Base	Mobile	Mode	Location	User and Notes
154.01250	146.65000	NFM	Badenoch	Highland & Island Fire Brigade
154.01250	146.06250	NFM	Fife	Fire Brigade
154.01250	146.12500	NFM	London	Police M25 North (M2SM) Ch.1
154.02500	146.05000	NFM	Fife	Police Traffic Division (ZM2T)
154.02500	146.13750	NFM	Dingwall	Northern Constabulary
154.02500	146.51250	AM	West Mercia	Police (M2YK) Ch.1
154.03750	146.06250	NFM	Fife	Fire Brigade
154.03750	146.21250	NFM	Inverness	Highland & Island Fire Brigade
154.05000	146.95000	NFM	Brighton	Police (M2KB) Ch.1 Microwave Link Return
154.05000	146.05000	NFM	Fife	Police Traffic Division (ZT)
154.05000	146.53750	AM	West Mercia	Police (M2YK) Ch.2
154.06250	146.21250	NFM	Inverness	Highland & Island Fire Brigade (UF)
154.06250		NFM	W Sussex	Fire Brigade Microwave Link Return
154.07500	146.13750	NFM	Dingwall	Northern Constabulary
154.07500	146.17500	NFM	Fife	Police Leven Area (L)
154.07500	146.17500	NFM	Lancashire	Police (M2BD) Ch.4
154.07500	146.47500	AM	Sussex	Police (M2KB) Ch.3 Microwave Link Return
154.08750	146.06250	NFM	Fife	Fire Brigade
154.08750	146.21250	NFM	Inverness	Highland & Island Fire Brigade
154.08750	146.16250	NFM	London	Police M25 South Ch.2
154.08750		NFM	Staffordshire	Fire Brigade Trunked (YF/YG) (Cell 7 North)
154.10000	146.10000	NFM	Fife	Police Dalgety Bay
154.11250	146.06250	NFM	Fife	Fire Brigade
154.11250	146.21250	NFM	Inverness	Highland & Island Fire Brigade
154.11250	146.31250	NFM	Norfolk	Police Ch.7
154.11250	146.82500	NFM	Sussex	Police (M2KB) Microwave Link Return
154.11250	146.56250	AM	West Midlands	Police (M2MA) Central Motorway Patrols
154.12500	146.13750	NFM	Dingwall	Northern Constabulary
154.12500	146.05000	NFM	Fife	Police Traffic Division (ZT)
154.12500		NFM	Humberside	Fire Brigade Input Link Ch.2
154.13750	146.36250	AM	Cambridge	Police (VB) Ch.3
154.13750	146.13750	NFM	Dingwall	Northern Constabulary
154.13750	146.22500	NFM	Dyfed	Police Ch.5
154.13750	146.05000	NFM	Fife	Police (ZT)
154.15000		NFM	Glasgow	Police Drug Squad
154.15000	146.67500	AM	Gloucester	Police (QL) Ch.1
154.15000		AM	Kent	Police (M2KA) Ch.3 Mobile Link
154.15000	146.48750	NFM	Lothian & Borders	Police
154.15000		NFM	Stirling	Fire Brigade
154.16250	146.16250	NFM	Fife	Police
154.16250	146.07500	NFM	Dingwall	Northern Constabulary
154.17500	146.17500	NFM	Dunfermline	Police (D)
154.17500		NFM	Stirling	Fire Brigade (F)
154.17500	147.06250	NFM	Sussex	Police (M2KB) Ch.2 Microwave Link Return
154.18750	146.05000	NFM	Fife	Police (ZT)
154.18750	154.18750	NFM	Inverness	Fire Brigade
154.18750	146.42500	NFM	Lochaber	Northern Constabulary (UR)
154.18750	146.47500	NFM	Sussex	Police (M2KB) Ch.4 Microwave Link Return
154.20000	146.20000	NFM	Fife	Police, Cowdenbeath
154.20000	146.58750	AM	Staffordshire	Police (YF) Ch.1
154.20000	146.95000	NFM	Sussex	Police (M2KB) Ch.5 Microwave Backup
154.21250	146.65000	NFM	Badenoch	Highland & Island Fire Brigade
154.21250	146.06250	NFM	Fife	Fire Brigade
154.22500	146.22500	NFM	Fife	Police, Glenrothes
154.22500	146.70000	AM	Gloucester	Police (QL) Ch.2

154.22500	146.98750	NFM	Norfolk	Police Ch.4
154.22500	147.65000	NFM	Sussex	Police (M2KB) Ch.4 Microwave Backup
154.23750		NFM	Surrey	Fire Brigade Repeater Link
154.23750	146.23750	NFM	West Lothian	Police
154.25000	146.28750	NFM	Inverness	Northern Constabulary
154.25000	146.25000	NFM	Lothian & Borders	Police (ZHE) East/Mid Lothian
154.25000	146.87500	NFM	Sussex	Police (M2KB) Ch.3 Microwave Link Return
154.26250	146.25000	AM	Lothian	Lothian & Borders Police Special Use
154.26250	146.47500	AM	W Midlands	Police (M2MA) Central Motorway Patrols
154.27500		NFM	Surrey	Police Hilltop Link for 155.83750
154.28750	146.30000	NFM	Edinburgh	Lothian & Borders Police
154.28750	146.28750	NFM	Inverness	Northern Constabulary Aviemore
154.30000	146.30000	NFM	Edinburgh	Police, Fettes (ZH) Ch.1
154.30000	146.28750	NFM	Inverness	Northern Constabulary Drumochter
154.30000		NFM	Kent	Police Ch.4 Mobile Link
154.31250	146.45000	AM	Birmingham	Police (YM) Ch.5
154.31250	146.30000	NFM	Lothian & Borders	Police, Ayton (G & ZH)
154.31250	146.65000	NFM	Sussex	Police (M2KB) Ch.2 Microwave Link Return
154.32500	147.30000	NFM	Kelso	Police
154.33750	146.73750	NFM	Dyfed	Police (WH) Ch.3
154.33750	147.17500	NFM	Manchester	Police Ch.7
154.33750	147.17500	NFM	Manchester	Metrolink Trams Police
154.33750	146.30000	NFM	Lothian & Borders	Police Common Incident
154.35000	146.35000	NFM	Edinburgh	Police, Fettes (ZH) Ch.2
154.35000	146.42500	NFM	Lochaber	Northern Constabulary (UR)
154.35000	146.30000	NFM	Lothian	Police Special Use
154.36250	146.72500	AM	Gloucester	Police (QL) Ch.3
154.37500	146.30000	NFM	Lothian & Borders	Police Special Use
154.37500	146.33750	NFM	Norfolk	Police (M2VK) Ch.8
154.38750	146.48750	NFM	Lothian & Borders	Police (ZHE)
154.38750	146.48750	NFM	Scotland, Central	Police, South of Region
154.38750		NFM	Surrey	Fire Brigade Repeater
154.40000	146.48750	NFM	Galashiels	Police
154.40000	147.87500	NFM	Orkney	Highland & Island Fire Brigade, Helmsdale
154.41250	146.08750	AM	Warwickshire	Police (YJ) Ch.1
154.41250	146.48750	NFM	Lothian & Borders	Police, Duns
154.41250	147.65000	NFM	Sussex	Police (M2KB) Ch.2 Microwave Link Return
154.42500		NFM	Galashiels	Police (D)
154.42500	146.48750	NFM	Peebles	Police
154.43750	146.48750	NFM	Lothian & Borders	Police Special Use
154.43750		NFM	Edinburgh	Police (T) Traffic Division
154.45000	146.35000	AM	West Midlands	Police (M2MA) Central Motorway Patrols
154.45000	147.18750	NFM	Tayside	Police, North of Region
154.46250	146.42500	NFM	Lochaber	Northern Constabulary (UR)
154.46250	146.25000	NFM	Lothian & Borders	Police (ZHE) East/Mid Lothian
154.46250		NFM	N Ireland	Fire Brigade
154.46250	146.06250	NFM	Sussex	Police (M2KB) Microwave Link Return
154.47500	146.60000	AM	Dyfed	Police (WH) Ch.1
154.47500	146.62500	NFM	Edinburgh	Fire Brigade (F)
154.48750	147.48750	NFM	Central Scotland	Police, South of Region
154.48750	147.65000	NFM	Sussex	Police (M2KB) Ch.4 Beddingham Microwave Backup
154.50000	147.65000	NFM	Sussex	Police (M2KB) Ch 4 Lewes Microwave Link Return
154.50000	146.50000	AM	Jersey	Police (M2GS) Ch.1
154.51250	146.25000	NFM	Lothian & Borders	Police (ZHE) East/Mid Lothian
154.51250	146.42500	NFM	Lochabar	Northern Constabulary
154.51250	146.47500	NFM	Sussex	Police (M2KB) Beddingham Microwave Link Backup

Base	Mobile	Mode	Location	User and Notes
154.52500	146.52500	NFM	Caithness	Northern Constabulary
154.52500	146.48750	NFM	Central Scotland	Police, South of Region
154.52500		NFM	Humberside	Fire Brigade Input Link Ch.2
154.52500	146.70000	NFM	Orkney	Northern Constabulary Sanday
154.52500	146.85000	NFM	Sutherland	Northern Constabulary
154.52500	146.58750	NFM	Western Isles	Northern Constabulary Urgha
154.53750	146.53750	NFM	Edinburgh	Fire Brigade (F)
154.53750	143.87500	AM	Orkney	Highland & Island Fire Brigade Melvich
154.53750	146.93750	NFM	Ross-shire	Highland & Island Fire Brigade Braemore
154.55000	146.55000	AM	Jersey	Fire Brigade Ch.4
154.55000		NFM	Kent	Fire Brigade (M2KF)
154.55000	146.71250	NFM	Kyle of Lochalsh	Northern Constabulary (UR)
154.55000	146.25000	NFM	Selkirk	Police
154.55000		NFM	Staffordshire	Fire Brigade Trunked (YF) (Cell 18)
154.56250	146.52500	NFM	Caithness	Northern Constabulary
154.56250	146.48750	NFM	Central Scotland	Police, South of Region
154.56250	146.86250	NFM	Easter Ross	Northern Constabulary
154.57000		NFM	USA	BRS Handhelds Often Used Illegally in UK (Blue Dot)
154.57000		NFM	USA	MURS Handhelds Often Used Illegally in UK Ch.4
154.57500	146.65000	NFM	Kyle of Lochalsh	Highland & Island Fire Brigade
154.57500		NFM	Staffordshire	Police & Fire Trunked (YF) (Cell 12)
154.58750	146.52500	NFM	Caithness	Northern Constabulary
154.58750	146.52500	NFM	Hawick	Police (ZH) Ch.4
154.58750	146.63750	NFM	Shetland	Northern Constabulary Bressay
154.58750		NFM	Surrey	Police Hilltop Link for 155.8625
154.58750	146.58750	NFM	Western Isles	Northern Constabulary South Harris
154.60000		NFM	London	Police bomb Jamming Van Used With 143.900
154.60000		NFM	USA	BRS Handhelds Often Used Illegally in UK (Green Dot)
154.60000		NFM	USA	MURS Handhelds Often Used Illegally in UK Ch.5
154.60000	147.23750	NFM	Tayside	Police, West of Division (W)
154.61250	146.52500	NFM	Caithness	Northern Constabulary Beabstermire
154.61250	147.03750	NFM	Lochaber	Highland & Island Fire Brigade
154.61250	147.23750	NFM	Lothian & Borders	Police (S)
154.61250	154.41250	FM	Norfolk	Police (VK) Ch 6
154.61250	146.63750	NFM	Shetland	Northern Constabulary Gonfirth
154.61250	146.58750	NFM	Western Isles	Northern Constabulary Eitshal, Grein Head
154.61250	147.07500	AM	Wiltshire	Police (M2QJ) Ch.4
154.62500	146.32500	AM	Birmingham	Police (M2YM) Ch.1
154.62500	146.62500	NFM	Edinburgh	Fire Brigade (F)
154.62500	146.62500	AM	Jersey	Police (M2GS) Ch.2
154.62500	146.87500	NFM	Orkney	Highland & Island Fire Brigade Ben-A-Chielt
154.62500	146.77500	NFM	Shetland	Highland & Island Fire Brigade Bressay
154.62500	146.06250	NFM	Sussex	Police (M2KB) Ch.2 Microwave Link Return
154.62500	146.87500	NFM	Western Isles	Highland & Island Fire Brigade Rodel
154.63750	146.52500	NFM	Caithness	Northern Constabulary Olrig
154.63750	147.23750	NFM	Lothian & Borders	Police Mosspaul Grantshouse
154.63750	146.63750	NFM	Shetland	Northern Constabulary Collinforth
154.63750	146.86250	NFM	Strathbran	Northern Constabulary
154.65000	146.65000	NFM	Kyle of Lochalsh	Highland & Island Fire Brigade Applecross
154.65000	146.87500	NFM	Orkney	Highland & Island Fire Brigade Forsinard
154.65000	146.82500	NFM	Sussex	Police (M2KB) Ch.1 Microwave Link Return
154.65000	146.11250	AM	West Midlands	Police (M2MA) Central Motorway Patrols
154.66250	146.66250	NFM	Perth	Fire Brigade (Fire Control)
154.66250	146.77500	NFM	Shetland	Highland & Islands Fire Brigade Gonfirth
154.66250	146.93750	NFM	Strathbran	Highland & Islands Fire Brigade

Base	Mobile	Mode	Location	User and Notes
154.66250	146.47500	NFM	Sussex	Police (M2KB) Ch.3 Microwave Link Return
154.68750	146.65000	NFM	Kyle of Lochalsh	Highland & Islands Fire Brigade Skriag
154.68750	154.68750	NFM	Northern Ireland	Fire Brigade Handhelds Ch.3
154.68750	146.87500	NFM	Orkney	Highland & Islands Fire Brigade Thurso
154.68750	146.77500	NFM	Shetland	Highland & Islands Fire Brigade Collafirth
154.70000	146.37500	AM	Birmingham	Police Ch.3
154.70000	147.82500	NFM	Jedburgh	Police
154.70000	146.70000	NFM	Orkney	Northern Constabulary Maroquoy
154.70000	146.82500	NFM	Sussex	Police (M2KB) Ch.1 Microwave Link Return
154.70000	146.80000	NFM	Sutherland	Northern Constabulary (UR)
154.71250	146.52500	NFM	Caithness	Northern Constabulary Helmsdale, Ben Tongue
154.71250	146.71250	NFM	Kyle of Lochalsh	Northern Constabulary Stormy Hill (UR)
154.71250	146.96250	NFM	Tayside	Police Angus (W)
154.72500	146.76250	NFM	Fife	Police Special Events (RAF Leuchars Airshow)
154.72500		NFM	Kent	Police Ch.2 Mobile Link
154.72500	146.71250	NFM	Kyle of Lochalsh	Northern Constabulary Applecross (UR)
154.72500		NFM	Staffordshire	Fire Brigade (YF/YG) Trunked (Cell 7 North)
154.73750	146.52500	NFM	Caithness	Northern Constabulary Wick County Yard
154.73750	146.15000	NFM	Scotland, Central	Police, West of Division
154.73750	146.63750	NFM	Shetland	Northern Constabulary Scousbrough
154.73750	146.58750	NFM	Western Isles	Northern Constabulary Benadrove
154.75000	146.28750	NFM	Inverness	Northern Constabulary Mount Eagle (UR)
154.75000	147.95000	NFM	Nationwide	Police National Crime Squad DVP/Cougarnet/Voice
154.75000		NFM	Staffordshire	Fire Brigade Trunked (Cell 12)
154.75000	151.15000	NFM	Suffolk	Police (VL) H/T Link
154.75000		NFM	Sussex	Police (M2KB) Microwave Link Return
154.75000	146.58750	NFM	Western Isles	Northern Constabulary Maeruig
154.76250	146.80000	NFM	Sutherland	Northern Constabulary Merkland (UR)
154.76250	147.23750	NFM	Tayside	Police, West of Division (W)
154.77500	146.77500	NFM	Shetland	Highland & Islands Fire Brigade
154.77500	146.93750	NFM	Ross-shire	Highland & Islands Fire Brigade
154.77500	146.80000	NFM	Tayside	Fire Brigade
154.78750	146.02500	AM	Cambridge	Police (VB) Ch.1
154.78750	146.05000	AM	Grampian	Police
154.78750	146.80000	AM	Gwent	Police (WE) Ch.2
154.78750	146.86250	NFM	Easter Ross	Northern Constabulary
154.78750	146.70000	NFM	Orkney	Northern Constabulary Wideford
154.80000		NFM	Kent	Police (M2KA) Ch.2 Mobile Link
154.80000	146.18750	AM	Dorset	Police (QC) Ch.3
154.80000	146.72500	AM	Lancashire	Police (BD) Ch.5
154.80000	146.80000	NFM	Sutherland	Northern Constabulary (UR)
154.81250	146.48750	NFM	Scotland, Central	Police, South of Region
154.81250	146.80000	NFM	Sutherland	Northern Constabulary Helmsdale (UR)
154.82500	146.68750	AM	Cambridge	Police (VB) Ch.2
154.82500		NFM	Humberside	Fire Brigade Ch.1 Input Link
154.83750	146.85000	NFM	Sutherland	Northern Constabulary Struie Hill
154.83750	146.96250	NFM	Tayside	Police Angus (W)
154.83750	146.58750	NFM	Western Isles	Northern Constabulary Rodell
154.85000		NFM	Sussex	Police (M2KB) Microwave Link Return
154.85000	146.85000	NFM	Sutherland	Northern Constabulary Hilton Farm (UR)
154.85000	146.58750	NFM	Western Isles	Northern Constabulary Dalbeg, Brevaig
154.86250	146.12500	AM	Bridgend	Police (WL) Ch.1
154.86250	146.86250	NFM	Easter Ross	Northern Constabulary
154.86250	146.82500	AM	Merseyside	Police (CH) Ch.1
154.86250	146.90000	AM	Suffolk	Police (VL) Ch.1

Base	Mobile	Mode	Location	User and Notes
154.87500	146.65000	AM	Badenoch	Highland & Islands Fire Brigade
154.87500	146.87500	AM	Orkney	Highland & Islands Fire Brigade
154.87500	146.66250	NFM	Perth	Fire Brigade (Fire Control)
154.87500	146.87500	AM	Western Isles	Highland & Islands Fire Brigade
154.88750	146.71250	NFM	Kyle of Lochalsh	Northern Constabulary Skriag (UR)
154.88750	146.15000	AM	South Wales	Police (M2WL) Ch.2
154.88750		NFM	Staffordshire	Fire Brigade (YF/YG) Trunked (Cell 7 North)
154.88750	146.92500	AM	Suffolk	Police (M2VL) Ch.2
154.88750	146.95000	NFM	Sussex	Police (M2KB) CH.2 Microwave Link Return
154.88750	147.23750	NFM	Tayside	Police, West of Division (W)
154.90000	146.83750	AM	Bedfordshire	Police (M2VA) Ch.1
154.90000	146.85000	AM	Merseyside	Police (M2CH) Ch.2
154.91250		NFM	Lochaber	Fire Brigade
154.91250	146.48750	AM	Norfolk	Police (VK) Ch.1
154.91250	147.05000	NFM	Tayside	Police
154.92500	147.05000	NFM	Grampian	Police
154.92500	146.90000	AM	Merseyside	Police (CH) Ch.3
154.93750	146.61250	AM	Kent	Police (KA) Ch.2
154.93750		NFM	Nationwide	Illegal Chinese Cordless Phones
154.93750	146.87500	NFM	Orkney	Highland & Islands Fire Brigade
154.93750	146.17500	AM	South Wales	Police (WL) Ch.4
154.93750	146.93750	NFM	Tayside	Fire Brigade (Fire Control)
154.95000	146.93750	NFM	Aberdeen	Fire Brigade (Fire Control)
154.95000	146.01250	AM	Thames Valley	Police (HB) Ch.7
154.95000	146.87500	NFM	Western Isles	Highland & Islands Fire Brigade
154.96250	146.63750	AM	Kent	Police Ch.3
154.96250	146.96250	NFM	Tayside	Police Angus
154.96250	146.07500	AM	South Wales	Police (WL) Ch.3
154.97500	147.05000	NFM	Aberdeen	Fire Brigade (Fire Control)
154.97500	146.42500	AM	Birmingham	Police (YM) Ch.4
154.97500	146.68750	NFM	Hampshire	Police (HC) Ch.5
154.97500	146.68750	NFM	Hampshire	Police Ch.5
154.97500	147.05000	NFM	Tayside	Police
154.97500	146.87500	NFM	Western Isles	Highland & Islands Fire Brigade
154.98750	147.06000	NFM	Aberdeen	Fire Brigade
154.98750	147.05000	NFM	Grampian	Police
154.98750	146.67500	NFM	Norfolk	Police (VK) Ch.5
155.00000	147.00000	NFM	Fife	Police (Special Events/Royalty Protection)
155.00000	146.31250	AM	West Sussex	Police (M2KB) Ch.1
155.01250	147.56250	NFM	Grampian	Police (UBE)
155.01250	146.21250	AM	Manchester	Police (CK) Ch.1
155.01250	147.32500	AM	Scotland, Central	Police, North of Region
155.02500	147.02500	NFM	Dundee	Police (ZS)
155.02500	147.13750	AM	Essex	Police Ch.1
155.02500	147.13750	AM	Manchester	Police (Traffic)
155.03750	147.13750	NFM	Sutherland	Highland & Islands Fire Brigade (Fire Control)
155.03750	147.06250	NFM	Tayside	Fire Brigade
155.05000	146.66250	AM	Powys	Police (WA) Ch.1
155.05000	147.05000	NFM	Tayside	Police
155.05000	146.36250	AM	West Sussex	Police (M2KB) Ch.3
155.06250	147.23750	AM	Manchester	Police (CK) Ch.4
155.06250	147.06250	NFM	Perth	Fire Brigade (Fire Control)
155.06250	147.13750	NFM	Sutherland	Highland & Islands Fire Brigade
155.07500	147.06250	NFM	Aberdeen	Fire Brigade (Fire Control)
155.07500	147.18750	AM	Essex	Police (VG) Ch.3
155.07500		NFM	N Ireland	Fire Brigade Ch.8

Base	Mobile	Mode	Location	User and Notes
155.07500		NFM	Staffordshire	Fire Brigade (YF/YG) Trunked (Cell 7 North)
155.07500	146.87500	NFM	Western Isles	Highland & Islands Fire Brigade Urgha
155.08750	146.40000	AM	Hampshire	Police (HC) Ch.1
155.08750	147.10000	AM	Manchester	Police (CK) Ch.5
155.08750	146.87500	NFM	Western Isles	Highland & Islands Fire Brigade Dalbeg
155.10000	146.43750	AM	North Wales	Police Ch.2
155.10000	146.58750	AM	Kent	Police (KA) Ch.1
155.10000	147.18750	NFM	Tayside	Police North of Region (W)
155.11250	147.06250	NFM	County Down	Fire Brigade
155.11250	146.43750	AM	Hampshire	Police (HC) Ch.2
155.12500	147.48750	NFM	Edinburgh	Fire Brigade (ZF)
155.12500	147.87500	NFM	Western Isles	Highland & Islands Fire Brigade Maaruig
155.13750	147.08750	NFM	County Armagh	Fire Brigade
155.13750	146.66250	AM	Kent	Police (KA) Ch.4
155.13750	147.13750	NFM	Sutherland	Highland & Islands Fire Brigade
155.13750	147.13750	NFM	Tayside	Fire Brigade (Fire Control)
155.15000	146.07500	AM	Manchester	Police (CK) Ch.6
155.15000	147.22500	NFM	Perth	Police (W)
155.16250	147.11250	NFM	County Tyrone	Fire Brigade
155.16250	146.46250	AM	Hampshire	Police (HC) Ch.4
155.16250	147.61250	AM	Warwickshire	Police (YJ) Ch.3
155.17500	146.16250	AM	Essex	Police (VG) Ch.2
155.17500	146.92500	AM	Merseyside	Police (CH) Ch.4
155.17500	147.48750	NFM	Lothian & Borders	Fire Brigade (ZF)
155.18750	146.38750	AM	Essex	Police (VG)
155.18750	147.48750	NFM	Lothian & Borders	Fire Brigade (ZF)
155.18750	146.38750	AM	Manchester	Police (Traffic)
155.18750	147.18750	NFM	Tayside	Police North of Region (W)
155.18750	146.38750	AM	West Sussex	Police (M2KB) Ch.4
155.20000	146.65000	AM	Dyfed	Police (WH) Ch.2
155.20000	146.60000	AM	Hertfordshire	Police (VH) Ch.1
155.20000	146.65000	NFM	Kyle of Lochalsh	Highland & Islands Fire Brigade
155.20000	146.60000	AM	Manchester	Police
155.20000	147.06250	NFM	Tayside	Fire Brigade (Fire Control)
155.21250	147.08750	AM	Avon	Police (M2QP) Ch.1
155.21250	147.22500	NFM	Perth	Police (W)
155.21250		NFM	Staffordshire	Fire Brigade (YF/YG) Trunked (Cell 6 South)
155.22500	146.95000	AM	Merseyside	Police (CH) Ch.5
155.22500	147.22500	NFM	Perth	Police (W)
155.22500	146.33750	AM	West Sussex	Police (M2KB2) Control & Traffic Ch.2
155.23750	147.03750	NFM	N Ireland	Fire Brigade B, C & E Districts
155.23750	147.23750	NFM	Perth	Police (W)
155.25000	147.06250	NFM	Kent	Police (KA) Ch.3 Mobile Link
155.25000	146.52500	AM	Avon	Police (M2QP) Ch.2
155.25000	147.48750	NFM	Lothian & Borders	Fire Brigade (ZF)
155.26250	146.31250	AM	Cheshire	Police (BA) Ch.2
155.26250	146.48750	NFM	Hampshire	Police (HC) Ch.3
155.26250		AM	Manchester	Traffic Police
155.26250	146.4875	NFM	Tayside	Police Helicopter Base
155.27500	146.05000	NFM	Grampian	Police
155.27500	146.62500	AM	Dyfed	Police (WH) Ch.4
155.27500	146.90000	AM	Devon/Cornwall	Police Ch.2
155.28750	147.22500	NFM	Grampian	Police (UBG)
155.28750	147.22500	NFM	Perth	Police (W)
155.28750	146.41250	AM	Sussex	Police (M2KB) Ch.5
155.30000	146.97500	AM	Devon/Cornwall	Police Ch.7

Base	Mobile	Mode	Location	User and Notes
155.30000	147.22500	NFM	Grampian	Fire Brigade
155.30000	147.13750	NFM	Londonderry	Fire Brigade
155.30000		NFM	Staffordshire	Fire Brigade (YF/YG) Trunked (Cell 7 North)
155.31250	147.23750	NFM	Perth	Police (W)
155.32500	146.23750	AM	Devon/Cornwall	Police Ch.4
155.32500	146.97500	NFM	Merseyside	Police (CH, D) Ch.6
155.32500	147.32500	NFM	Scotland, Central	Police North of Region
155.33750	147.18750	NFM	Perth	Police, North of Region
155.33750		NFM	West Midlands	Fire Brigade (M2FB) Hilltop Repeater
155.35000	147.56250	NFM	Grampian	Police
155.35000		NFM	Nationwide	UKSAR Ch.91 (94) (Regional Restrictions)
155.36250	146.26250	AM	Devon/Cornwall	Police (QB) Ch.5
155.36250	147.13750	NFM	Sutherland	Highland & Islands Fire Brigade
155.36250	147.13750	NFM	Tayside	Police, North of Region
155.37500	147.18750	NFM	Grampian	Police
155.37500		NFM	Londonderry	Fire Brigade
155.38750	146.95000	AM	Devon/Cornwall	Police (QB) Ch.6
155.40000	146.87500	NFM	Orkney	Highland & Islands Fire Brigade
155.40000	147.18750	NFM	Perth	Fire Brigade (Fire Control)
155.41250	146.62500	AM	Dyfed	Police (WH) Ch.2
155.41250	147.03750	NFM	Lochaber	Highlands and Islands Fire Brigade (UF)
155.41250	147.48750	NFM	Lothian	Fire Brigade Data Channel
155.41250		NFM	Staffordshire	Fire Brigade (YF/YG) Trunked (Cell 7 North)
155.42500	146.38750	AM	Manchester	Police (CK) Ch.2
155.42500	147.23750	NFM	Perth	Police (W)
155.43750	147.48750	AM	Galashiels	Fire Brigade
155.43750	147.23750	NFM	Perth	Fire Brigade (Fire Control)
155.43750		NFM	Staffordshire	Fire Brigade (YF/YG) Trunked (Cell 7 North)
155.45000	147.56250	NFM	Grampian	Police
155.46250	146.21250	AM	Devon/Cornwall	Police Ch.1
155.47500	146.60000	AM	Dyfed	Police (WH) Ch.1
155.47500	147.56250	NFM	Grampian	Police (UBE)
155.48750	147.48750	NFM	Lothian	Fire Brigade (ZF)
155.50000	146.65000	AM	Dyfed	Police (WH)
155.50000	147.56250	NFM	Grampian	Police
155.51250	146.92500	AM	Devon/Cornwall	Police Ch.3
155.51250	147.48750	NFM	Dunbar	Fire Brigade
155.51250	147.48750	NFM	Peebles	Fire Brigade
155.52500		NFM	Staffordshire	Fire Brigade (YF/YG) Trunked (Cell 6 South)
155.53750	146.46250	AM	Powys	Police (WA) Ch.3
155.53750	147.56250	NFM	Grampian	Police
155.55000		NFM	Staffordshire	Fire Brigade (YF/YG) Trunked (Cell 6 South)
155.56250		NFM	Perth	Police (W)
155.56250		NFM	Staffordshire	Fire Brigade (YF/YG) Trunked (Cell 7 North)
155.56250	147.01250	NFM	Northern Ireland	Fire Brigade A & F districts
155.56250	147.48750	NFM	Lothian	Fire Brigade (ZF)
155.57500	146.28750	AM	Devon/Cornwall	Police (QB) Ch.8
155.57500	147.56250	NFM	Grampian	Police (UBG)
155.57500	147.48750	NFM	Perth	Police (W)
155.58750	147.05000	NFM	Grampian	Police
155.58750	146.25000	AM	Cumbria	Police (BB) Ch.3 M6 Motorway
155.61250	146.41250	AM	Devon/Cornwall	Police Ch.9
155.61250	146.41250	AM	Manchester	Police (CK) Ch.3
155.61250		NFM	Lochaber	Fire Brigade (UF)
155.61250	147.48750	NFM	Lothian	Fire Brigade (ZF)
155.61250		NFM	Staffordshire	Fire Brigade (YF/YG) Trunked (Cell 6 South)

Base	Mobile	Mode	Location	User and Notes
155.62500		NFM	Derbyshire	Fire Brigade Repeater
155.62500		NFM	Grampian	Police (UB)
155.62500	146.48750	AM	North Wales	Police Ch.4
155.63750	146.11250	AM	Cumbria	Police (BB) Ch.2
155.65000	146.26250	AM	Derbyshire	Police (NA) Ch.1
155.67500	146.65000	NFM	Badenoch	Highlands and Islands Fire Brigade
155.67500		NFM	Nationwide	Police Regional Crime Squads (DVP/Voice)
155.70000		NFM	Nationwide	Police Regional Crime Squads (DVP/Voice)
155.72500		NFM	Nationwide	Police Regional Crime Squads (DVP/Voice)
155.73750	147.03750	NFM	Lochaber	Highlands & Islands Fire Brigade
155.75000		NFM	Nationwide	Police Regional Crime Squads
155.77500		NFM	Nationwide	Police Regional Crime Squads
155.78750		NFM	Grampian	Fire Brigade (Fire Control)
155.78750		NFM	N Ireland	Security Forces
155.80000	147.03750	NFM	Grampian	Police
155.80000	147.76250	AM	Guernsey	Police (QY) Ch.1
155.80000		AM	Kent	Police Ch.45
155.80000	146.20000	AM	Surrey	Police (HJ) Ch.1
155.81250		AM	Gloucester	Police (QL)
155.81250		NFM	Grampian	Police
155.81250		NFM	Staffordshire	Fire Brigade (YF/YG) Trunked (Cell 7 North)
155.81250		NFM	Suffolk	Police H/T Link (VL) Ch.3
155.81250	146.91250	AM	Wiltshire	Police (QJ) Ch.1
155.83750	146.22500	AM	Surrey	Police (HJ) Ch.2
155.83750	146.28750	AM	Derbyshire	Police (NA) Ch.2
155.85000	146.93750	AM	Wiltshire	Police (QJ) Ch.
155.86250		NFM	Humberside	Police Helicopter Link (XT/XF)
155.86250	147.75000	NFM	Jersey	Police (M2GS) Ch.3
155.86250	146.25000	AM	Surrey	Police (HJ) Ch.3
155.87500	146.10000	AM	Dorset	Police (QC) Ch.1
155.87500		NFM	Dunfermline	Fire Brigade (F)
155.87500		NFM	Staffordshire	Fire Brigade (YF/YG) Trunked (Cell 6 South)
155.88750	146.20000	AM	Cumbria	Police (BB) Ch.1 South Lakes
155.90000	147.85000	AM	Guernsey	Police (QY) Ch.2
155.90000	146.96250	NFM	Norfolk	Police Ch.3
155.90000	146.96250	AM	Wiltshire	Police (QJ) Ch.3
155.91250		NFM	Hertfordshire	Police (VH) Ch.1 Hilltop Link
155.92500	147.01250	AM	Dorset	Police (QC) Ch.2
155.92500	146.38750	NFM	Norfolk	Police Ch.5
155.95000		AM	Merseyside	Police (Radio Engineers)
155.96250	146.23750	AM	Essex	Police (VG) Ch.4
155.96250		NFM	Jersey	Police and Fire Services
155.97500	147.67500	AM	Devon	Police (QB) Ch.7
155.97500		NFM	West Midlands	Fire Brigade (FB) Link

156.0000 - 161.6750 MHz   Maritime Band 25 kHz

Base	Mobile	Mode	Location	User and Notes
156.000		NFM	Nationwide	Marine Emergency/Helicopters
156.00000		NFM	Nationwide	Channel 00 (HM Coastguard)
156.00000		NFM	Nationwide	Channel 00 (UKSAR under HMCG Control)
156.02500	160.62500	NFM	Nationwide	Channel 60
156.02500	160.62500	NFM	Port of Heysham	British Gas
156.05000	160.65000	NFM	Nationwide	Channel 01
156.05000	160.65000	NFM	Portsmouth	Wightlink Ferries
156.07500	160.67500	NFM	Nationwide	Channel 61
156.07500	160.67500	NFM	Troon	P & O Operations
156.10000	160.70000	NFM	Nationwide	Channel 02
156.10000	160.70000	NFM	Portsmouth	Harbour Boat Tours

Base	Mobile	Mode	Location	User and Notes
156.10000	160.70000	NFM	Thames	Working Channel
156.12500	160.72500	NFM	Nationwide	Channel 62
156.12500	160.72500	NFM	Forth	Working Channel
156.12500		NFM	Nationwide	UKSAR Ch.62a (Emergency Calling Channel)
156.15000	160.75000	NFM	Nationwide	Channel 03
156.15000	160.75000	NFM	Bacton	Working Channel
156.15000	160.75000	NFM	Cardigan Bay	Working Channel
156.17500	160.77500	NFM	Nationwide	Channel 63
156.17500		NFM	Nationwide	UKSAR Ch.63a (Team Working Channel)
156.20000	160.80000	NFM	Nationwide	Channel 04
156.20000	160.80000	NFM	Grimsby	Working Channel
156.20000	160.80000	NFM	Morecombe	Working Channel
156.20000	160.80000	NFM	Niton	Working Channel
156.22500	160.82500	NFM	Nationwide	Channel 64
156.22500		NFM	Nationwide	UKSAR Ch.64a (Team Default Channel)
156.22500	160.82500	NFM	Lands End	Working Channel
156.25000	160.85000	NFM	Nationwide	Channel 05
156.25000	160.85000	NFM	Liverpool	Alfred Dock Ops.
156.25000	160.85000	NFM	Liverpool	Gladstone Dock Ops.
156.25000	160.85000	NFM	Weymouth	Working Channel
156.27500	160.87500	NFM	Nationwide	Channel 65
156.27500	160.87500	NFM	North Foreland	Working Channel
156.30000		NFM	Nationwide	Channel 06
156.30000		NFM	Nationwide	Marine Emergency/Helicopters
156.30000		NFM	Cowes	Sally Water Taxis
156.30000		NFM	Larne NI	Port Ops.
156.30000		NFM	London	Woolwich Ferry
156.32500	160.92500	NFM	Nationwide	Channel 66
156.32500	160.92500	NFM	North Foreland	Working Channel
156.35000	160.95000	NFM	Nationwide	Channel 07
156.35000	160.95000	NFM	Eastham	Manchester Ship Canal
156.35000	160.95000	NFM	Hastings	Working Channel
156.35000	160.95000	NFM	Ilfracombe	Working Channel
156.37500		NFM	Nationwide	Channel 67
156.37500		NFM	Cork	Working Channel
156.37500		NFM	Jersey	Working Channel
156.37500		NFM	Minehead	Working Channel
156.37500		NFM	Rosslare	Working Channel
156.40000		NFM	Nationwide	Channel 08
156.42500		NFM	Nationwide	Channel 68
156.45000		NFM	Nationwide	Channel 09
156.45000		NFM	Thames Estuary	Pilots
156.47500		NFM	Nationwide	Channel 69
156.47500		NFM	Holyhead	Irish Ferries
156.47500		NFM	S Wales	Barry Docks
156.50000		NFM	Nationwide	Channel 10
156.52500		NFM	Nationwide	Channel 70
156.55000		NFM	Nationwide	Channel 11
156.55000		NFM	Portsmouth	Queens Harbour Master
156.57500		NFM	Nationwide	Channel 71 Port Operations
156.57500		NFM	Belfast	River Warden
156.57500		NFM	Manchester	Weather Navigation, Manchester Ship Canal
156.57500		NFM	Portsmouth	Dockyard Tours
156.57500		NFM	Rosyth	Docks
156.57500		NFM	Swansea	Port Tugs
156.60000		NFM	Nationwide	Channel 12
156.60000		NFM	Avonmouth	Avonmouth Docks (Avonmouth Radio)

Base	Mobile	Mode	Location	User and Notes
156.60000		NFM	Humber	Vessel Traffic Service
156.60000		NFM	Isle of Man	Douglas Harbour Control
156.60000		NFM	Langstone Harbour	Port
156.60000		NFM	Leith	Harbour
156.60000		NFM	Liverpool	Mersey Radio
156.60000		NFM	Milford Haven	Milford Haven Docks, Patrol & Pilot Launch
156.60000		NFM	Padstow	Working Channel
156.60000		NFM	Plymouth	Royal Navy Marine Traffic
156.60000		NFM	Plymouth	Sutton Lock
156.60000		NFM	Portsmouth	Royal Navy Marine Traffic
156.60000		NFM	Southampton	Vessel Traffic Service
156.60000		NFM	St Malo	Port
156.60000		NFM	St Peter Port	Working Channel
156.61250		NFM	Plymouth	Warships Calling Ferry
156.62500		NFM	Nationwide	Channel 72
156.62500		NFM	Poole	Harbour Police
156.65000		NFM	Nationwide	Channel 13
156.65000		NFM	Gravesend	Shipping Channel
156.65000		NFM	Nationwide	UKSAR Ch.53a Ground-Air (Ceiling 6,500 feet)
156.65000		NFM	Plymouth	Tug to Tug
156.65000		NFM	Portsmouth	Queens Harbour Master
156.67500		NFM	Nationwide	Channel 73
156.67500		NFM	Firth of Forth	Weather Reports
156.67500		NFM	Nationwide	UKSAR Ch.73 Ground-Air Overflow Channel
156.67500		NFM	Nationwide	Intership
156.67500		NFM	Plymouth	Tugs
156.70000		NFM	Nationwide	Channel 14
156.70000		NFM	Ayr	Harbour Control
156.70000		NFM	Bristol Channel	Pilots (Cardiff)
156.70000		NFM	Bristol Channel	Pilots (Newport)
156.70000		NFM	Chichester	Harbour Radio
156.70000		NFM	Eastham	Manchester Ship Canal
156.70000		NFM	Glensanda	Super Quarry
156.70000		NFM	Grangemouth	Grangemouth Locks
156.70000		NFM	Harwich	Port
156.70000		NFM	Heysham	Port Ops
156.70000		NFM	Humber	Pilot
156.70000		NFM	Itchenor	Ferry
156.70000		NFM	Larne NI	Port Ops
156.70000		NFM	Liverpool	Out-Bound Ships
156.70000		NFM	Manchester	Eastham Control, Manchester Ship Canal
156.70000		NFM	Milford Haven	Elf & Gulf Oil Terminals
156.70000		NFM	Milford Haven	Milford Haven Docks
156.70000		NFM	Milford Haven	Patrol & Pilot Launch
156.70000		NFM	Milford Haven	Texaco Oil Terminal
156.70000		NFM	Plymouth	Plymouth Pilots
156.70000		NFM	Portsmouth	Harbour Radio
156.70000		NM	Poole	Harbour Control
156.70000		NFM	Ramsgate	Ramsgate Port Control (Romeo)
156.70000		NFM	Shoreham by Sea	Port
156.70000		NFM	Southampton	Vessel Traffic Service
156.70000		NFM	St Helier	Port & Marina
156.70000		NFM	Teesside	Tees Harbour Radio
156.70000		NFM	Woolwich	Thames Pilot
156.72500		NFM	Nationwide	Channel 74
156.72500		NFM	Alderney	Working Channel

Base	Mobile	Mode	Location	User and Notes
156.72500		NFM	Cullercoats	Harbour
156.72500		NFM	Gloucester	Docks
156.72500		NFM	Heysham	Isle of Man Steam Packet
156.72500		NFM	Kent	Medway Radio
156.72500		NFM	Land's End	Transatlantic Shipping
156.72500		NFM	Lochaber	Caledonian Canal
156.72500		NFM	Nationwide	Ports, Lock
156.72500		NFM	Plymouth	Liberty Boats
156.75000		NFM	Gt Yarmouth	Water Taxi
156.75000		NFM	Nationwide	Channel 15
156.75000		NFM	Liverpool Bay	Offshore Gas Rig Supply Vessels
156.75000		NFM	Nationwide	On-board Handhelds
156.77500		NFM	Nationwide	Channel 75 (Guard Channel - Not in Use)
156.80000		NFM	Nationwide	Channel 16 Calling, Distress & Safety
156.82500		NFM	Nationwide	Channel 76 (Guard Channel - Not in Use)
156.85000		NFM	Nationwide	Channel 17
156.85000		NFM	English Channel	Ferries
156.85000		NFM	Holyhead	Stena Line
156.85000		NFM	Ramsgate	Trans Europa Ferries
156.87500		NFM	Nationwide	Channel 77
156.87500		NFM	Swansea Docks	Swansea-Cork Ferry
156.90000	161.50000	NFM	Nationwide	Channel 18
156.90000	161.50000	NFM	Manchester Canal	Barton & Irlam Docks
156.90000	161.50000	NFM	Milford Haven	Elf & Gulf Oil Terminals
156.90000	161.50000	NFM	Port En Bessin	Marina Channel
156.90000	161.50000	NFM	Southampton	Vessel Traffic Service
156.92500	161.52500	NFM	Nationwide	Channel 78
156.92500	161.52500	NFM	St Peter Port	Working Channel
156.95000	161.55000	NFM	Nationwide	Channel 19
156.95000	161.55000	NFM	Southampton	Esso Dock
156.95000	161.55000	NFM	Southend on Sea	Patrol Boats
156.95000	161.55000	NFM	Tranmere	Shell Oil Terminal
156.97500	161.57500	NFM	Nationwide	Channel 79
157.00000	161.60000	NFM	Nationwide	Channel 20
157.00000	161.60000	NFM	Liverpool	Garston Docks
157.00000	161.60000	NFM	Manchester Canal	Stanlow Docks
157.00000	161.60000	NFM	Stanlow	Shell Refinery
157.00000	161.60000	NFM	Southampton	Vessel Traffic Service
157.02500	161.62500	NFM	Nationwide	Channel 80
157.02500	161.62500	NFM	Bangor	Marina
157.02500	161.62500	NFM	Dover	Coastguard
157.02500	161.62500	NFM	Hull	Marina
157.02500	161.62500	NFM	London	St Katherine's Yacht Haven
157.02500	161.62500	NFM	Nationwide	Marina Common
157.02500	161.62500	NFM	Milford Haven	Marine & Yacht Station
157.02500	161.62500	NFM	Brighton	Marina Ops.
157.05000	161.65000	NFM	Nationwide	Channel 21
157.05000	161.65000	NFM	Liverpool	Manchester Canal, Langton Docks
157.05000	161.65000	NFM	Milford Haven	Texaco Oil Terminal
157.07500	161.67500	NFM	Nationwide	Channel 81
157.07500	161.67500	NFM	Anglesey	Working Channel
157.10000	161.70000	NFM	Nationwide	Channel 22
157.10000	161.70000	NFM	Kent	Medway Radio
157.10000	161.70000	NFM	Southampton	Vessel Traffic Service
157.12500	161.72500	NFM	Nationwide	Channel 82
157.12500	161.72500	NFM	Jersey	Working Channel

Base	Mobile	Mode	Location	User and Notes
157.12500	161.72500	NFM	Morecombe Bay	Working Channel
157.15000	161.75000	NFM	Nationwide	Channel 23
157.15000	161.75000	NFM	Bantry	Working Channel
157.15000	161.75000	NFM	Malin Head	Working Channel
157.15000	161.75000	NFM	Rosslare	Working Channel
157.17500	161.77500	NFM	Nationwide	Channel 83
157.17500		NFM	Nationwide	UKSAR Ch.83a Team Working Channel
157.17500	161.77500	NFM	Dublin	Working Channel
157.17500	161.77500	NFM	Minehead	Working Channel
157.17500	161.77500	NFM	Thames	Working Channel
157.20000	161.80000	NFM	Nationwide	Channel 24
157.20000		NFM	Nationwide	UKSAR Ch.24a (Eventual Ground-Air)
157.20000	161.80000	NFM	Forth	Working Channel
157.20000	161.80000	NFM	Glen Head	Working Channel
157.20000	161.80000	NFM	Humber	Working Channel
157.20000	161.80000	NFM	Isle of Skye	Working Channel
157.20000	161.80000	NFM	Shannon	Working Channel
157.20000	161.80000	NFM	Valentia	Working Channel
157.22500	161.82500	NFM	Nationwide	Channel 84
157.22500	161.82500	NFM	Cromarty	Working Channel
157.25000	161.85000	NFM	Nationwide	Channel 25
157.25000	161.85000	NFM	Bristol Channel	Working Channel
157.25000	161.85000	NFM	Jersey	Working Channel
157.25000	161.85000	NFM	Whitby	Working Channel
157.27500	161.87500	NFM	Nationwide	Channel 85
157.27500		NFM	Nationwide	UKSAR Ch.85a Team Default Channel
157.27500	161.87500	NFM	Bantry	Working Channel
157.27500	161.87500	NFM	Humber	Working Channel
157.27500	161.87500	NFM	Lands End	Working Channel
157.27500	161.87500	NFM	Niton	Working Channel
157.30000	161.90000	NFM	Nationwide	Channel 26
157.30000	161.90000	NFM	Anglesey	Working Channel
157.30000	161.90000	NFM	Cork	Working Channel
157.30000	161.90000	NFM	Humber	Working Channel
157.30000	161.90000	NFM	Orkney	Working Channel
157.30000	161.90000	NFM	Star Point	Working Channel
157.32500	161.92500	NFM	Nationwide	Channel 86
157.35000	161.95000	NFM	Nationwide	Channel 27
157.35000	161.95000	NFM	Grimsby	Working Channel
157.35000	161.95000	NFM	Lands End	Working Channel
157.35000	161.95000	NFM	Shetland	Working Channel
157.37500	161.97500	NFM	Nationwide	Channel 87
157.37500	161.97500	NFM	Bristol Channel	Working Channel
157.37500	161.97500	NFM	Niton	Working Channel
157.40000	162.00000	NFM	Nationwide	Channel 28
157.40000	162.00000	NFM	Anglesea	Working Channel
157.40000	162.00000	NFM	Cromarty	Working Channel
157.40000	162.00000	NFM	Niton	Working Channel
157.40000	162.00000	NFM	Shannon	Working Channel
157.40000	162.00000	NFM	Valentia	Working Channel
157.42500	162.02500	NFM	Nationwide	Channel 88
157.45000	162.05000	NFM	Nationwide	Channel 29
157.45000	162.05000	NFM	Channel Islands	Ferries
157.45000	162.05000	NFM	Holyhead	Irish Ferries
157.45000	162.05000	NFM	Jersey	Local Fishing Boats
157.45000	162.05000	NFM	Plymouth	Torpoint Ferries

Base	Mobile	Mode	Location	User and Notes
157.45000	162.05000	NFM	Portsmouth	Continental Ferries
157.45000	162.05000	NFM	Southampton	Vessel Traffic Service
157.47500	162.07500	NFM	Nationwide	Channel 89
157.47500	162.07500	NFM	Southampton	Red Funnel Ferries
157.50000	162.10000	NFM	Nationwide	Channel 30
157.50000	162.10000	NFM	English Channel	Herm Seaway
157.50000	162.10000	NFM	Swansea Docks	Trinity Lighthouse Crews
157.52500	162.12500	NFM	Nationwide	Channel 90
157.55000	162.15000	NFM	Nationwide	Channel 31
157.55000		NFM	Nationwide	RNLI Channel (Training/Non-Search & Rescue)
157.55000		NFM	Cowes	Coastguard
157.55000		NFM	Gosport	Ferry
157.55000	162.15000	NFM	Holyhead	Lifeboat
157.55000	162.15000	NFM	Orkney	Pentland Ferries (Gills Bay-St Margarets Hope)
157.55000	162.15000	NFM	Sark	Working Channel
157.55000	162.15000	NFM	Scotland	Caledonian MacBrayne Ops.
157.57500	162.17500	NFM	Nationwide	Channel 91
157.60000	162.20000	NFM	Nationwide	Channel 32
157.60000	162.20000	NFM	Hampshire	Naval Tugs
157.62500	162.22500	NFM	Nationwide	Channel 92
157.65000	162.25000	NFM	Nationwide	Channel 33
157.65000	162.25000	NFM	Dover	Hovercraft
157.65000	162.25000	NFM	English Channel	Fishermen's Co-operative
157.65000	162.25000	NFM	Gosport	Gosport-Portsmouth Private Ferry
157.65000		NFM	Norfolk	Broadlands River Inspectors Ch.33A
157.67500	162.27500	NFM	Nationwide	Channel 93
157.67500	162.27500	NFM	Greencastle	Fishermen's Cooperative
157.70000	162.30000	NFM	Nationwide	Channel 34
157.70000	162.30000	NFM	Nationwide	RNLI Channel
157.70000	162.30000	NFM	English Channel	Herm
157.70000	162.30000	NFM	Portsmouth	Naval Tugs
157.70000	162.30000	NFM	Southend on Sea	Patrol Boats
157.72500	162.32500	NFM	Nationwide	Channel 94
157.72500		NFM	Jersey	Local Fishing Boats
157.75000	162.35000	NFM	Nationwide	Channel 35
157.75000		NFM	Dover	Hoverspeed Ops.
157.75000		NFM	Humberside	North Sea Ferries
157.75000		NFM	Jersey	Local Fishing Boats
157.77500	162.37500	NFM	Nationwide	Channel 95
157.77500	162.37500	NFM	Thames	Pilot to Tug
157.80000	162.40000	NFM	Nationwide	Channel 36
157.80000		NFM	Brighton	Marina Security
157.80000		NFM	Heysham	Norse Merchant Ferries
157.80000		NFM	Holyhead	Stena Ops.
157.80000		NFM	Ryde	Hovertravel Base
157.80000		NFM	Scilly Isles	St Mary's Boatmens' Association
157.82500	162.42500	NFM	Nationwide	Channel 96
157.85000	162.45000	NFM	Nationwide	Channel 37
157.85000		NFM	Nationwide	Marina Channel M1
157.85000		NFM	Brighton	Marina
157.85000		NFM	Hartlepool	Yacht Marina
157.85000		NFM	Jersey	St Catherine's Yacht Club
157.85000		NFM	Nationwide	Marina Common
157.85000		NFM	Milford Haven	Marine & Yacht Station
157.85000		NFM	Penarth	Penarth Marina (Camper Base)
157.85000		NFM	Plymouth	Queen Anne's Battery

Base	Mobile	Mode	Location	User and Notes
157.87500	162.47500	NFM	Nationwide	Channel 97
157.90000	162.50000	NFM	Nationwide	Channel 38
157.90000	162.50000	NFM	English Channel	British Ferries
157.90000	162.50000	NFM	Guernsey	Sealink
157.90000	162.50000	NFM	Heysham	Isle of Man Steam Packet Ferries
157.90000	162.50000	NFM	Southampton	Pilots' Private Channel
157.92500	162.52500	NFM	Nationwide	Channel 98
157.95000	162.55000	NFM	Nationwide	Channel 39
157.95000	162.55000	NFM	London	Port of London Authority
157.95000	162.55000	NFM	Runcorn	Shipping Company
157.97500	162.57500	NFM	Nationwide	Channel 99 (USA)
157.97500		NFM	London	Port of London Authority
157.97500	162.57500	NFM	Montrose Docks	Cam Shipping
157.97500	162.57500	NFM	Scarborough	Rescue
158.00000	162.60000	NFM	Nationwide	Channel 40
158.00000		NFM	Cowes	Harbour Radio
158.00000		NFM	Portsmouth	Blue Funnel Ferries
158.00000		NFM	Scotland	Western Ferries
158.02500	162.62500	NFM	Nationwide	Channel 100
158.02500	162.62500	NFM	Dover	P & O Ferries
158.05000	162.65000	NFM	Nationwide	Channel 41
158.05000	162.65000	NFM	English Channel	Battricks
158.05000	162.65000	NFM	Harwich	Scandinavian Seaways
158.05000	162.65000	NFM	Jersey	Local Fishing Boats
158.07500	162.67500	NFM	Nationwide	Channel 101
158.07500	162.67500	NFM	Holyhead	Irish Ferries
158.07500		NFM	Portsmouth	Harbour Boat Tours
158.10000	162.70000	NFM	Nationwide	Channel 42
158.10000	162.70000	NFM	Jersey	Local Fishing Boats
158.10000	162.70000	NFM	Medway	Marine Services
158.12500	162.72500	NFM	Nationwide	Channel 102
158.12500	162.72500	NFM	Dover	P & O Phone Link
158.12500		NFM	Gt Yarmouth	Beach Patrol/Medical
158.12500		NFM	Hartlepool	Tees Tugs
158.15000	162.75000	NFM	Nationwide	Channel 43
158.15000		NFM	Portsmouth	Wightline Cruises
158.15000	162.75000	NFM	Swansea	Shipping Pilots for Docks Pilot HQ
158.17500	162.77500	NFM	Nationwide	Channel 103
158.17500	162.77500	NFM	Dover	P & O Ferries
158.17500		NFM	Reading	Pipers Island Pleasure Boats
158.20000	162.80000	NFM	Nationwide	Channel 44
158.20000	162.80000	NFM	Moray Firth	Beatrice Alpha/Bravo Platform
158.20000	162.80000	NFM	Solent	Kilmart Base Ops.
158.22500	168.82500	NFM	Nationwide	Channel 104
158.25000	162.85000	NFM	Nationwide	Channel 45
158.25000	162.85000	NFM	Holyhead	Stena Line Freight
158.25000	162.85000	NFM	Ipswich	Docks Transport
158.25000	162.85000	NFM	Jersey	Local Fishing Boats
158.25000	162.85000	NFM	Moray Firth	Beatrice Alpha/Bravo Platform
158.27500	162.87500	NFM	Nationwide	Channel 105
158.30000	162.90000	NFM	Nationwide	Channel 46
158.30000	162.90000	NFM	Jersey	Local Fishing Boats
158.30000	162.90000	NFM	Moray Firth	Beatrice Alpha/Bravo Platform
158.30000	162.90000	NFM	Solent	Grant & Denholme Cargo Ops.
158.32500	162.92500	NFM	Nationwide	Channel 106
158.35000	162.95000	NFM	Nationwide	Channel 47

Base	Mobile	Mode	Location	User and Notes
158.35000	162.95000	NFM	Moray Firth	Beatrice Alpha/Bravo Platform
158.37500	162.97500	NFM	Nationwide	Channel 107
158.40000	163.00000	NFM	Nationwide	Channel 48
158.40000	163.00000	NFM	Aberdeen	Dockside
158.40000	163.00000	NFM	Dover	Stena Line
158.40000	163.00000	NFM	Holyhead	Stena Line Freight
158.42500	163.02500	NFM	Nationwide	Channel 108
158.42500	163.02500	NFM	English Channel	Condor Hydrofoils
158.42500		NFM	Hartlepool	Tees Tugs
158.42500		NFM	Holyhead	Irish Ferries
158.42500		NFM	Portsmouth	Wightlink Ferries
158.42500		NFM	Southport	Rescue
158.45000	163.05000	NFM	Nationwide	Channel 49
158.45000		NFM	Bo'ness	Lake Windermere Steamers
158.45000		NFM	Isle of Rhum	Scottish National Heritage
158.45000		NFM	Jersey	Channel Islands Yacht Services
158.45000		NFM	Lowestoft	Lifeguards
158.45000		NFM	Moray Firth	Beatrice Alpha/Bravo Platform
158.45000		NFM	Nigg Bay	Oil Tanker
158.45000		NFM	Orkney	Orkney Ferries
158.45000		NFM	Poole	Brittany Ferries
158.45000		NFM	Portsmouth	Butchers Tugs
158.47500		NFM	Nationwide	Channel 109
158.47500		NFM	Aberdeen	Shipping Info
158.47500		NFM	Harwich	Irish Ferries
158.47500		NFM	Heysham	Isle of Man Steam Packet
158.47500		NFM	Holyhead	Tugs
158.47500		NFM	Jersey	Agriculture & Fisheries
158.50000		NFM	Nationwide	Channel 50
158.50000		NFM	Dorset	Police Marine Division
158.50000		NFM	English Channel	Emeraude Line
158.50000		NFM	Great Yarmouth	Pleasure Boats
158.50000		NFM	Gosport & Fareham	Inshore Rescue
158.50000		NFM	Isle of Wight	Inshore Rescue
158.50000		NFM	Nationwide	Private Shipping
158.50000		NFM	Nigg Bay	Oil Tanker
158.50000		NFM	Ryde	Inshore Rescue
158.52500		NFM	Nationwide	Channel 110
158.52500		NFM	Medway	Marine Services
158.55000	163.15000	NFM	Nationwide	Channel 51 (Used for PMR in UK)
158.60000	163.20000	NFM	Nationwide	Channel 52 (Used for PMR in UK)
158.65000	163.25000	NFM	Nationwide	Channel 53 (Used for PMR in UK)
158.65000		NFM	Nationwide	UKSAR Ch.53a Air-Ground (Ceiling 6,500 feet)
158.70000	163.30000	NFM	Nationwide	Channel 54 (Used for PMR in UK)
158.75000	163.15000	NFM	Nationwide	Channel 55 (Used for PMR in UK)
158.80000	163.35000	NFM	Nationwide	Channel 56 (Used for PMR in UK)
158.85000	163.40000	NFM	Nationwide	Channel 57 (Used for PMR in UK)
158.90000	163.45000	NFM	Nationwide	Channel 58 (Used for PMR in UK)
158.95000	163.50000	NFM	Nationwide	Channel 59 (Used for PMR in UK)
159.00000		NFM	North Sea	Amoco Oil Ch.1
159.03750		NFM	Gloucester	Docks
159.10000	163.60000	NFM	Nationwide	RNLI Ch.3 Private (Simple Inversion Scrambling)
159.20000		NFM	North Sea	Amoco Oil Ch.2
160.60000		NFM	Nationwide	Channel 99 (UK)
160.60000		NFM	Nationwide	HM Coastguard
160.60000		NFM	Aberdeen	Aberdeen Coastguard

Base	Mobile	Mode	Location	User and Notes
160.60000		NFM	Brixham	Brixham Coastguard
160.60000		NFM	Crail	Crail Coastguard
160.60000		NFM	Falmouth	Falmouth Coastguard
160.60000		NFM	Redcar	Redcar Coastguard
160.72500		NFM	Nationwide	UKSAR Ch.62b Team Default Channel
160.77500		NFM	Nationwide	UKSAR Ch.63b Team Default Channel
160.82500		NFM	Nationwide	UKSAR Ch.64b Team Default Channel
161.12500		NFM	Nationwide	Channel 111
161.15000		NFM	Nationwide	Channel 112
161.15000		NFM	London	Westminster Dredging
161.17500		NFM	Nationwide	Channel 113
161.20000		NFM	Nationwide	Channel 114
161.20000		NFM	Yarmouth	Yarmouth Harbour
161.22500		NFM	Nationwide	Channel 115 (Old Yacht Channel M3)
161.25000		NFM	Nationwide	Channel 116
161.25000		NFM	Portsmouth	Gosport Rescue
161.27500		NFM	Nationwide	Channel 117
161.30000		NFM	Nationwide	Channel 118
161.32500		NFM	Nationwide	Channel 119
161.35000		NFM	Nationwide	Private On-Board Communications
161.35000		NFM	Nationwide	P & O Ch.P1
161.37500		NFM	Medina Valley	Sailing Centre
161.40000		NFM	Nationwide	Radio Navigation
161.42500		NFM	Nationwide	Old Yacht Channel M2
161.45000		NFM	Nationwide	Private On-Board Communications
161.67500		NFM	Nationwide	Marina Channel M2

158.5250 - 160.54375 MHz   PMR, Marine and Data 12.5 kHz

Base	Mobile	Mode	Location	User and Notes
158.55000		NFM	Nationwide	Private Shipping Channel 51
158.60000		NFM	Nationwide	Private Shipping Channel 52
158.62500		NFM	London	Community Security Trust (Linked to Israeli Security Forces) (77)
158.65000		NFM	Nationwide	Private Shipping Channel 53
158.65000		NFM	Nationwide	UKSAR Ch.53a Air-Ground (Ceiling 6,500 feet)
158.70000		NFM	Nationwide	Private Shipping Channel 54
158.75000		NFM	Nationwide	Private Shipping Channel 55
158.78750		NFM	Southsea	White Swan Pub/Club
158.80000		NFM	Nationwide	Private Shipping Channel 56
158.85000		NFM	Nationwide	Private Shipping Channel 57
158.90000		NFM	Nationwide	Private Shipping Channel 58
158.95000		NFM	Nationwide	Private Shipping Channel 59
159.00000		NFM	Nationwide	Shipping Rescue
159.01250		NFM	Tamworth	Alfred McAlpine Construction
159.05000		NFM	Nationwide	National Crime Squad (DVP/Cougarnet/Voice)
159.05000		NFM	Scotland	Scottish Crime Squad
159.07500		NFM	Nationwide	National Crime Squad (DVP/Cougarnet/Voice)
159.07500		NFM	Scotland	Scottish Crime Squad
159.18750		NFM	Cumbria	Dalton Wild Animal Park
159.18750		NFM	Jersey	Surveyors
159.35000		NFM	Renfrewshire	Erskine Bridge Control
159.40000		NFM	Bar Hill	AR Benstead
159.40000		NFM	Belfast	A1 Taxis
159.40000		NFM	Bury St Edmunds	A1 & A3 Cars
159.40000		NFM	Douglas, IoM	A1 Radio Cabs
159.40000		NFM	Ely	AK Taxis
159.40000		NFM	Fulbourn	AM Alarms Maintenance
159.40000		NFM	Haverhill	AM Cars
159.40000		NFM	Kings Lynn	AA Taxis

Base	Mobile	Mode	Location	User and Notes
159.40000		NFM	Kings Lynn	AB Cars
159.40000		NFM	Reading	APC Comms
159.40000		NFM	Sandy	AJ Hart & Son Ltd
159.40000		NFM	Thetford	A1 Cars
159.42500		NFM	Newmarket	Racecourse Staff
159.42500		NFM	Sheffield	Gllson Builders
159.43750		NFM	Preston	Tarmac
159.45000		NFM	Stevenage	Academy Bar, Kings Leisure Site
159.45000		NFM	Swansea	Jinks Taxis
159.48750		NFM	Brighton	Dome/Star Academy
159.48750		NFM	Chepstow	Pink Nash Bird Gardens
159.48750		NFM	Exeter	Imperial Club Doormen
159.48750		NFM	London	Arsenal Football Club Ticket Office
159.48750		NFM	London	Disney Store Staff, Piccadilly (69)
159.48750		NFM	London	Plaza Shopping Centre, Oxford Street
159.48750		NFM	London	Royal Opera House Security
159.48750		NFM	London	Stratford Shopping Centre (69.3)
159.48750		NFM	London	Westminster Council Emergency Planning (173.8)
159.48750		NFM	Nationwide	Channel 4 Productions Ch.1
159.48750		NFM	Nationwide	Ordnance Survey Teams (69.3)
159.48750		NFM	Nationwide	SEP Events Traffic Management (107.3)
159.50000		NFM	Cardiff	Cardiff Arms Park Rugby Stewards (82.5)
159.50000		NFM	Carlisle	B & Q Store
159.50000		NFM	Llanelli	Tostre Tinplate Works
159.50000		NFM	London	Brent Cross Shopping Centre
159.50000		NFM	London	Cafe de Paris Security, Coventry Street
159.50000		NFM	London	Diana Memorial Security Staff (69.3)
159.50000		NFM	London	Plaza Shopping Centre Security
159.50000		NFM	London	Shaw Park Plaza Hotel
159.50000		NFM	Nationwide	Channel 4 Productions Ch.2
159.51250		NFM	Fleetwood	P & O Ferries
159.51250		NFM	Felixstowe	Dock Transport
159.51250		NFM	Larne	P & O Ferries (110.9)
159.51250		NFM	London	Integrated Security Group
159.51250		NFM	Nationwide	P & O Ferries Common
159.51250		NFM	West Drayton	O'Rourke Construction
159.52500		NFM	Channel Tunnel	Euroscan X-Ray Machine Ch.2 (F)
159.52500		NFM	Chessington	World of Adventures
159.52500		NFM	Bristol	Balloon Festival
159.52500		NFM	Edinburgh	Hillend Ski Slope
159.52500		NFM	Gosport & Fareham	Inshore Rescue
159.52500		NFM	Heathrow	Pink Elephant Parking (250.3)
159.52500		NFM	London	Chelsea Football Club Stewards
159.52500		NFM	London	Posthouse Hotel, Kensington Close (103.5)
159.52500		NFM	Portsmouth	Venture Scouts
159.52500		NFM	Southampton	Pink Elephant Airport Parking Courtesy Coaches
159.52500		NFM	Stoke on Trent	Foxfield Railway, Blythe Bridge
159.53750		NFM	Corby	Rockingham Speedway Commentary Link Ch.5
159.55000		NFM	Diss	Golf Club Stewards
159.55000		NFM	Edinburgh	Sheriffs Court
159.55000		NFM	Gatwick	Porters
159.56250		NFM	Nationwide	National Crime Squad (DVP/Cougarnet/Voice)
159.56250		NFM	Scotland	Scottish Crime Squad
159.58750		NFM	Bath	Ashley Communications Ltd
159.58750		NFM	Bexleyheath	Abercorn Car Hire
159.58750		NFM	Bury St Edmunds	Bonnet Ltd

Base	Mobile	Mode	Location	User and Notes
159.58750		NFM	Cambridge	Ace Taxis
159.58750		NFM	Cambridge	Bourn Hall Clinic
159.58750		NFM	Cambridge	Botany School, Cambridge University
159.58750		NFM	Cambridge	G Asbridge
159.58750		NFM	Ely	Allen Skip Hire
159.58750		NFM	Folkestone	Rotunda Amusement Park
159.58750		NFM	Fulbourn	Abington Farms Ltd.
159.58750		NFM	Glasgow	Argyll Communications Ltd
159.58750		NFM	Holyhead	Anglesey Comms
159.58750		NFM	Hounslow	Midas Security Primark Clothes
159.58750		NFM	Hunstanton	Ace Cabs
159.58750		NFM	London	Next Security, Oxford Circus
159.58750		NFM	London	Stratford Shopping Centre Security
159.58750		NFM	Llandudno	Wern Bach Farm
159.58750		NFM	Milton Keynes	Ace Cars
159.58750		NFM	Newmarket	Anglia Windscreens
159.58750		NFM	Newmarket	CW Bradfield & Son
159.58750		NFM	Nationwide	Channel 4 Productions Ch.3 Set Construction
159.58750		NFM	Redditch	Arca Ltd
159.58750		NFM	Rugby	Rugby Cement
159.58750		NFM	Stansted	Anglia Cars
159.58750		NFM	Swanton	Academy Cars
159.58750		NFM	Thetford	Ace Taxis
159.58750		NFM	Thetford	Andy's Taxis
159.58750		NFM	Totness	RM Arnold Ltd
159.62500		NFM	Corby	ASCAR (2004) Ben Collins Team Turn Four Car 42
159.62500		NFM	Coventry	MR Investigations
159.62500		NFM	Llanelli	Tostre Tinplate Works
159.62500		NFM	London	Oval Cricket Ground
159.62500		NFM	London	Queens Club Stella Artois Championships
159.62500		NFM	Luton	Vauxhall Car Plant
159.62500		NFM	Nationwide	Channel 4 Productions Ch.4 Set Construction
159.62500		NFM	Rugby	Rugby Cement
159.62500		NFM	West Drayton	O'Rouke Construction
159.68750		NFM	Coventry	MR Investigations
159.68750		NFM	London	Town & Country Outside Events Security
159.68750		NFM	Nationwide	NSR Events Communications, Short Term Hire
159.68750		NFM	Rugby	Rugby Cement
159.68750		NFM	Silverstone	Driving School
159.93750		NFM	Hastings	Priory Meadow Shopping Centre Security
159.95000		NFM	Worcester	AW Taxis
159.98750		NFM	Bedford	Oak Park Security
160.05000		NFM	Hull	Dynorod
160.06000		NFM	Southampton	Doctors' Service
160.06250		NFM	Bolton	Doctors' Service
160.07500		NFM	Kent	Roger's Refuse Collections
160.07500		NFM	Maidstone	Scan Electronics
160.11500		NFM	Yorkshire	Recovery Service
160.15000		NFM	Blackpool	Doctors' Service
160.15000		NFM	Bristol	Doctors' Service
160.15000		NFM	Sheffield	Forge Alert Security
160.17500		NFM	Seven Bridge	Toll collection
160.18750		NFM	Co. Durham	Doctors' Service
160.18750		NFM	London	Seymour Car Services
160.20000		NFM	Nationwide	Teleacoustic Ltd
160.23750		NFM	Hayes	Crosse & Blackwell

Base	Mobile	Mode	Location	User and Notes
160.25000		NFM	Oxford	John Hadcliffe Hospital
160.30000		NFM	Eastbourne	Doctors' Service
160.32500		NFM	London	St. Mary's Hospital
160.32500		NFM	Swansea	BJ Security
160.37500		NFM	N Ireland	Milk Tankers
160.46250		NFM	Birmingham	AS Security
160.50000		NFM	London	North West Cars, New Malden
160.51250		NFM	Bath	University
160.51250		NFM	London	British Oxygen, Hammersmith
160.52500		NFM	Bath	University
160.52500		NFM	Dover	Dover Castle

160.54375 - 160.58125 MHz — Local Authority Emergency Alarms

Base	Mobile	Mode	Location	User and Notes
160.55000		NFM	Nationwide	OAP Alarm Systems
160.56250		NFM	Nationwide	OAP Alarm Systems
160.57500		NFM	Nationwide	OAP Alarm Systems

160.6000 - 160.9750 MHz — International Maritime Band (Including 156 MHz to show Bandplan)

Base	Mobile	Mode	Location	User and Notes
160.60000		NFM	Nationwide	Channel 99 Coastguard Auxiliary
160.62500	156.02500	NFM	Nationwide	Channel 60
160.65000	156.05000	NFM	Nationwide	Channel 01 Port Ops
160.67500	156.07500	NFM	Nationwide	Channel 61
160.70000	156.10000	NFM	Nationwide	Channel 02
160.72500	156.12500	NFM	Nationwide	Channel 62
160.75000	156.15000	NFM	Nationwide	Channel 03
160.77500	156.17500	NFM	Nationwide	Channel 63
160.80000	156.20000	NFM	Nationwide	Channel 04
160.82500	156.22500	NFM	Nationwide	Channel 64
160.85000	156.25000	NFM	Nationwide	Channel 05
160.87500	156.27500	NFM	Nationwide	Channel 65
156.30000	156.30000	NFM	Nationwide	Channel 06 Ship-Ship & SAR with Aircraft
160.92500	156.32500	NFM	Nationwide	Channel 66
160.95000	156.35000	NFM	Nationwide	Channel 07
156.37500	156.37500	NFM	Nationwide	Channel 67 Coastguard Small Craft Safety
156.40000	156.40000	NFM	Nationwide	Channel 08 Intership
156.42500	156.42500	NFM	Nationwide	Channel 68 Port Ops & Ship Movements
156.45000	156.45000	NFM	Nationwide	Channel 09 Port Ops, Intership & Ship Movements
156.47500	156.47500	NFM	Nationwide	Channel 69 Port Ops & Ship Movements
156.50000	156.50000	NFM	Nationwide	Channel 10 Pollution
156.52500	156.52500	NFM	Nationwide	Channel 70 Digital Selcall - Distress/Safety/Calling
156.55000	156.55000	NFM	Nationwide	Channel 11 Port Ops & Ship Movements
156.57500	156.57500	NFM	Nationwide	Channel 71 Port Ops & Ship Movements
156.60000	156.60000	NFM	Nationwide	Channel 12 Port Ops & Ship Movements
156.62500	156.62500	NFM	Nationwide	Channel 72 Intership Comms
156.65000	156.65000	NFM	Nationwide	Channel 13 Primarily Intership Navigation Safety
156.67500	156.67500	NFM	Nationwide	Channel 73 Coastguard
156.70000	156.70000	NFM	Nationwide	Channel 14 Port Ops & Ship Movements
156.72500	156.72500	NFM	Nationwide	Channel 74 Port Ops & Ship Movements
156.75000	156.75000	NFM	Nationwide	Channel 15 Port Ops, Intership & Ship Movements
156.76250	156.76250	NFM	Nationwide	Channel 75 Guard Band
156.80000	156.80000	NFM	Nationwide	Channel 16 Distress & Calling
156.81250	156.81250	NFM	Nationwide	Channel 76 Guard Band
156.85000	156.85000	NFM	Nationwide	Channel 17 Port Ops, Intership & Ship Movements
156.87500	156.87500	NFM	Nationwide	Channel 77 Intership
161.50000	156.90000	NFM	Nationwide	Channel 18 Port Ops & Ship Movements
161.52500	156.92500	NFM	Nationwide	Channel 78

Base	Mobile	Mode	Location	User and Notes
161.55000	156.95000	NFM	Nationwide	Channel 19 Port Ops & Ship Movements
161.57500	156.97500	NFM	Nationwide	Channel 79 Port Ops & Ship Movements
161.60000	157.00000	NFM	Nationwide	Channel 20 Port Ops & Ship Movements
161.62500	157.02500	NFM	Nationwide	Channel 80 Port Ops, Ship Movements & Marinas
161.65000	157.05000	NFM	Nationwide	Channel 21 Port Ops & Ship Movements
161.67500	157.07500	NFM	Nationwide	Channel 81
161.70000	157.10000	NFM	Nationwide	Channel 22 Port Ops & Ship Movements
161.72500	157.12500	NFM	Nationwide	Channel 82
161.75000	157.15000	NFM	Nationwide	Channel 23
161.77500	157.17500	NFM	Nationwide	Channel 83
161.80000	157.20000	NFM	Nationwide	Channel 24
161.82500	157.22500	NFM	Nationwide	Channel 84
161.85000	157.25000	NFM	Nationwide	Channel 25
161.87500	157.27500	NFM	Nationwide	Channel 85
161.90000	157.30000	NFM	Nationwide	Channel 26
161.92500	157.32500	NFM	Nationwide	Channel 86 Calling/Automatic Telephone Systems
161.95000	157.35000	NFM	Nationwide	Channel 27
161.97500	157.37500	NFM	Nationwide	Channel 87
162.00000	157.40000	NFM	Nationwide	Channel 28
162.02500	157.42500	NFM	Nationwide	Channel 88

160.9750 - 161.4750 MHz — International Marine, Business Marine & Local Community Services 25 kHz Simplex

Base	Mode	Location	User and Notes
160.97500	NFM	Eastbourne	Beach Wardens
161.15000	NFM	Edinburgh	Forth Engineering Vessel
161.15000	NFM	Harwich	Dredging Ops.
161.15000	NFM	Nationwide	P & O Crew On Board Ferries
161.15000	NFM	Nationwide	Sealink Crew On Board Ferries
161.20000	NFM	Bacton	Philips Petroleum
161.20000	NFM	Dover	Hoverspeed
161.20000	NFM	Holyhead	Stena Security
161.22500	NFM	Brighton	Sea Front Office Beach Wardens (100)
161.22500	NFM	Newquay	Beach Wardens
161.22500	NFM	Weymouth	Beach Wardens& Lifeguards
161.25000	NFM	Gosport & Fareham	Inshore Rescue
161.25000	NFM	Holyhead	Docks
161.25000	NFM	London	River Thames Ops.
161.27500	NFM	Nationwide	Radio Alarms
161.30000	NFM	Cowes	UK Sailing Association
161.30000	NFM	Felixstowe	Alexandra Tugs
161.30000	NFM	Holyhead	Docks
161.30000	NFM	Liverpool	Alexandra & Cowey Towage Company
161.30000	NFM	Southampton	Trinity House Pilots
161.30000	NFM	Swansea Docks	Associated British Ports/Tugs
161.32500	NFM	Newmarket	Turners of Soham Ltd
161.35000	NFM	Dover-Calais	P & O Ferries Bridge/Loaders
161.35000	NFM	Felixstowe	P & O Ferries Ch.1
161.35000	NFM	Fleetwood	P & O Ferries Bridge/Loaders
161.35000	NFM	Jersey	P & O Ferries
161.35000	NFM	Larne NI	P & O Ferries Ops.
161.35000	NFM	North Sea	Amoco Oil Ch.3
161.35000	NFM	Portsmouth	P & O Ferries Bridge/Loaders
161.35000	NFM	Portsmouth	Serco Tugs
161.42500	NFM	Jersey	Local Fishing Boats
161.42500	NFM	Jersey	Marina
161.42500	NFM	Nationwide	Marina Common
161.45000	NFM	Felixstowe	Docks

161.4750 - 162.0500 MHz   International Maritime & PMR

Base	Mobile	Mode	Location	User and Notes
161.47500		NFM	Heysham	Seacat Ops.
161.47500		NFM	Troon	Seacat Ops.
161.57500		NFM	Manchester	Canal Tugs - Outgoing
161.60000	157.00000	NFM	Brixham	Fishing Trawlers
161.62500		NFM	Penarth	Penarth Marina (Camper Base)
161.65000	157.05000	NFM	Liverpool	Langton Dock Ops
161.67500		NFM	Nationwide	Marinas and Yacht Clubs Ch.M2
161.72500		NFM	Liverpool	Dredgers
161.77500		NFM	Dover	Sally Line Ferries
161.80000		NFM	Nationwide	UKSAR Ch.24b Team Default Channel
161.82500		NFM	Poole	Cross Channel Ferries
161.87500		NFM	London	Thames Barge Traffic
161.87500		NFM	Nationwide	UKSAR Ch.85b Team Default Channel
161.90000		NFM	Portsmouth	Dockyard Cranes
161.92500		NFM	Poole	Fishing Trawlers
161.95000		NFM	Poole	Police, Harbour
161.97500		NFM	Lyme Regis	Dredgers
162.00000		NFM	Plymouth	Tugs

162.0500 - 163.03125 MHz   Private Marine Allocation & PMR 25 kHz

Base	Mobile	Mode	Location	User and Notes
162.05000		NFM	Tamworth	Keywatch Security
162.07500	157.47500	NFM	Hartlepool	Harbour Pilot
162.10000		NFM	Jersey	Herm Seaway
162.14375	157.54375	NFM	Nationwide	RNLI Lifeboats Ch.1 (Simple Inversion Scrambling)
162.15000		NFM	Isle of Sark	Shipping
162.15625	157.55625	NFM	Nationwide	RNLI Lifeboats Ch.2 (Simple Inversion Scrambling)
162.17500		NFM	Driffield	JR Hood
162.17500	157.67500	NFM	London	Parking Enforcement Kilburn/W Hampstead (203.5)
162.20000		NFM	London	Target Couriers
162.20000		NFM	Merry Hill	Drinks Machines Company
162.21250	157.61250	NFM	Birmingham	Motorola Trunked System Voice
162.22500		NFM	Bristol	Security Company
162.22500		NFM	Cheshire	Delivery Company
162.22500		NFM	Lincoln	Taxi Service
162.25000		NFM	Jersey	Fishermen's Co-operative
162.25000		NFM	Norfolk	Broadlands River Inspectors Ch.33B
162.27500		NFM	Hull	Container Terminal
162.27500		NFM	Manchester	Delivery Company
162.30000		NFM	Felixstowe	Shipping Company
162.30000		NFM	Jersey	Shipping Company
162.32500		NFM	Boston	Fossitt & Thorne Tyres Ltd
162.32500		NFM	Felixstowe	Shipping Company
162.32500		NFM	London	Contract Buses
162.32500		NFM	London	Courier
162.32500		NFM	London	Doctors' Service
162.35000		NFM	Bournemouth	Off-Shore Drilling
162.35000		NFM	Hull	North Sea Ferries
162.36250		NFM	Solihull	Courier
162.37500	157.77500	NFM	London	Doctors' Service
162.37500		NFM	Northampton	Camelot Lottery Warehouse Security
162.37500		NFM	Swindon	Skip Company
162.40000		NFM	Hull	Humber Tugs
162.42500		NFM	Blackpool	Hospital Cleaners
162.42500		NFM	Liverpool	Engineers
162.42500		NFM	London	Taxi Company
162.45000		NFM	Nationwide	Differential GPS

Base	Mobile	Mode	Location	User and Notes
162.47500		NFM	Manchester	Delivery Company
162.47500		NFM	Preston	Meals on Wheels
162.47500		NFM	Warrington	Newton Recovery
162.50000	157.90000	NFM	Dieppe	Ferry Company
162.50000	157.90000	NFM	Guernsey	Sealink
162.50000	157.90000	NFM	Harwich	Pilots
162.50000	157.90000	NFM	Heysham	Isle of Man Steam Packet Ferries
162.50000	157.90000	NFM	Newhaven	Sealink
162.50000		NFM	Norfolk	Broadlands River Inspectors Ch.38B
162.52500		NFM	Leatherhead	Taxi Company
162.52500		NFM	Norfolk	Broadlands River Inspectors Ch.39B
162.52500		NFM	Staffordshire	Haulage Company
162.55000	157.95000	NFM	Nationwide	P & O
162.65000		NFM	Liverpool	Shipping Agents
162.65000	158.02500	NFM	Wallasey	Mersey Ferries
162.67500		NFM	North Sea	Amoco Oil Ch.101
162.70000	158.10000	NFM	Bristol	Dock Tugs
162.70000		NFM	Lowestoft	Beach Wardens
162.75000		NFM	Holyhead	Stena Line Primary
162.85000		NFM	Holyhead	Stena Line On-Board Communications
162.85000		NFM	Liverpool	Ship Ops.
162.87500		NFM	Manchester	Delivery Company
162.92500		NFM	Boston	Fossitt & Thorne Tyres Ltd
162.92500		NFM	London	Bus Hoppas, Wembley
162.92500	158.42500	NFM	London	Community Repeater (218.1)
162.92500		NFM	Manchester	Delivery Company
162.97500		NFM	Boston	Fossitt & Thorne Tyres Ltd
162.97500		NFM	Oldham	Service Engineers
163.00000		NFM	London	BB Securities Ltd.
163.00000		NFM	Southampton	Doctors' Service
163.02500		NFM	Nationwide	Differential GPS

163.03125 - 165.0000 MHz   PMR Band

Base	Mobile	Mode	Location	User and Notes
163.05000	158.55000	NFM	Cumnock	Gibson Whyte, Heating Engineers
163.05000	158.55000	NFM	Hatfeild	Shopwatch (254.1)
163.05000	158.55000	NFM	Hertford	Shopwatch (250.3)
163.05000	158.55000	NFM	Jersey	Amal-Grow
163.05000	158.55000	NFM	Jersey	Besco
163.05000	158.55000	NFM	Jersey	Dynarod
163.05000	158.55000	NFM	Jersey	Gorey Cabs
163.05000	158.55000	NFM	Newcastle	Newcastle City Trunked
163.05000	158.55000	NFM	St Austell	Games Machine Company
163.07500	158.57500	NFM	Brighton	Construction Company
163.07500	158.57500	NFM	Glasgow	Puma Coaches & Buses
163.07500	158.57500	NFM	Colchester	Community Repeater Oak Park Security (119.9)
163.07500	158.57500	NFM	Colchester	Community Repeater Parcel Company
163.07500	158.57500	NFM	Colchester	Community Repeater R & J Electronics
163.07500	158.57500	NFM	Colchester	Community Repeater Repair Company
163.07500	158.57500	NFM	Colchester	Pub & Nightclub Link to Police
163.07500		NFM	Manchester	Bus Inspectors (114.8)
163.07500	158.57500	NFM	Manchester	Parking Enforcement, Trafford
163.08750	158.48750	NFM	Nationwide	Road Construction
163.11250	158.61250	NFM	Canterbury	Community Patrols
163.12500	158.62500	NFM	London	Parking Enforcement, Camden (192.8)
163.13750		NFM	Duxford	Imperial War Museum Car Park (146.2)
163.13750		NFM	London	Alexandra Palace Leisure Centre Car Park (146.2)
163.13750		NFM	London	Wembley Complex Car Park (146.2)

Base	Mobile	Mode	Location	User and Notes
163.15000		NFM	Bletchley	Museum Security
163.15000		NFM	Chessington	World of Adventures
163.15000		NFM	Corby	Rockingham Speedway ASCAR Ops.
163.15000		NFM	London	Police Royal Parks (Probably all now on Airwave)
163.15000		NFM	Newmarket	Oaks Security (Oscar)
163.15000	158.55000	NFM	Swansea	Townhill Estate Security
163.20000	158.70000	NFM	Bangor	DSS
163.20000	158.70000	NFM	Birmingham	City Hospital Medical Engineers
163.20000		NFM	Jersey	Amal-Grow
163.20000		NFM	Jersey	Besco
163.20000		NFM	Jersey	Dynarod
163.20000		NFM	Jersey	Gorey Cabs
163.20000		NFM	Preston	Lowe's Plant Hire
163.21250		NFM	Lincoln	Acorn Haulage
163.21250	158.71250	NFM	London	Doctors' Service
163.21250	158.71250	NFM	Sunderland	Protector Security
163.21250	158.71250	NFM	Tayside	Heating Engineers
163.22500	158.72500	NFM	Handcross	Community Repeater
163.22500	158.72500	NFM	Ipswich	Community Repeater Farm
163.22500	158.72500	NFM	Manchester	Steve's Bakery, Gorton
163.22500	158.72500	NFM	Oldham	Emergency Doctor
163.22500	158.72500	NFM	Peterborough	Community Repeater
163.22500	158.72500	NFM	Preston	Vet on Emergency Calls
163.22500	158.72500	NFM	Salisbury	Community Repeater Farm (123)
163.22500	158.62500	NFM	Shaftesbury	Starbridge Laundry
163.22500	158.62500	NFM	Suffolk	Kesgrave Aggregates
163.22500	158.72500	NFM	Wiltshire	Compton Chamberlayne Estate (250.3)
163.28750	158.78750	NFM	Coventry	Shopwatch, Ball Hill (114.8)
163.28750	158.78750	NFM	Edinburgh	Murrayfield Stadium Admin/Catering/Stewards (107.2)
163.28750	158.78750	NFM	London	Network Rail Maintenance Crews, Kings Cross (71.9)
163.28750	158.78750	NFM	London	Town And Country Outside Events
163.28750		NFM	London	Zoo Bar Security, Bear Street
163.28750	158.78750	NFM	Nationwide	EP Events Car Parking (233.6)
163.28750	158.78750	NFM	Nationwide	NSR Events Communications (DCS 051)
163.28750		NFM	Suffolk	Somerleyton Hall Grounds
163.30000	158.80000	NFM	Nationwide	Road Construction
163.32500	158.82500	NFM	Hatfield	Skyline Taxis
163.32500	158.82500	NFM	London	Islington Refuse Collection
163.35000		NFM	Co. Durham	Waste Disposal
163.35000		NFM	Devon	Associated Leisure
163.35000		NFM	Jersey	Amal-Grow
163.35000		NFM	Jersey	Besco
163.35000		NFM	Jersey	Dynarod
163.35000		NFM	Jersey	Gorey Cabs
163.35000	158.85000	NFM	Newcastle	City Trunked
163.35000		NFM	Okehampton	Target Express
163.36250	158.76250	NFM	Cambridge	Vehicle Towaway
163.36250	158.76250	NFM	Manchester	Battery Deliveries, Lees
163.36250	158.76250	NFM	Newcastle	Security Company
163.37500	158.87500	NFM	Nationwide	Road Construction
163.45000	158.95000	NFM	Wolverhampton	Albro Taxis (Data Link)
163.47500		NFM	Nationwide	National Crime Squad
163.51250	159.01250	NFM	Nationwide	Road Construction
163.52500	159.02500	NFM	Birkenhead	Argyle Taxis
163.52500	159.02500	NFM	Wolverhampton	Wednesfield Radio Cars (Data Link)
163.60000		NFM	Tyneside	UK Security
163.61250	159.11250	NFM	Nationwide	Road Construction
163.68750	159.18750	NFM	London	Community Repeater
163.71250	159.21250	NFM	Southport	Community Wardens

Base	Mobile	Mode	Location	User and Notes
163.71250	159.21250	NFM	Wolverhampton	Central Taxis (Data Link)
163.73750	159.23750	NFM	Cardiff	Medical/Ambulances
163.85000	159.35000	NFM	Northamptonshire	Althorp Estate Staff/Security
163.86250	159.36250	NFM	Cheltenham	Starline Taxis (MDT Data)
163.86250	159.36250	NFM	Wolverhampton	ABC Countdown Taxis (Data Link)
163.90000		NFM	Bridlington	Leisure World Catering Staff
163.90000	159.40000	NFM	Cardiff	St Davids Bay Hotel & Spa (167.9)
163.90000		NFM	Chepstow	Racecourse Betting (103.5)
163.90000	158.40000	NFM	Edinburgh	Murrayfield Stadium Admin/Catering/Stewards (107.2)
163.90000	159.40000	NFM	Grimsby	Murphy Construction
163.90000	159.40000	NFM	Haverhill	AM Cars
163.90000	159.40000	NFM	Huntingdon	A & D Private Hire
163.90000	159.40000	NFM	Isle of Man	Taxi Company, Douglas
163.90000		NFM	Leicestershire	Scouts Ch. White 3
163.90000	159.40000	NFM	Lichfield	Tarmac
163.90000	159.40000	NFM	London	Town And Country Outside Events Catering
163.90000		NFM	Nationwide	Channel 4 Productions Ch.5 Repairs
163.90000	159.40000	NFM	Newport	Royal Gwent Hospital Security/Porters
163.90000	159.40000	NFM	Sheffield	Murphy Hire Ltd
163.90000	159.40000	NFM	S Ayrshire	South Ayrshire Highways Department
163.91250	159.41250	NFM	Jersey	Island Cabs
163.91250		NFM	Cambridge	Data Link
163.92500	159.42500	NFM	Edinburgh	Murrayfield Stadium Admin/Catering/Stewards (107.2)
163.92500		NFM	Leicestershire	Scouts Ch. White 4
163.92500		NFM	Letchworth	Superkarts Go Kart Track (67)
163.92500		NFM	London	Oval Cricket Ground Stewards
163.92500		NFM	London	Saddlers Wells Theatre Front of House Staff (77)
163.92500		NFM	London	Satellite Electronic News Gathering (118.8)
163.92500	159.42500	NFM	Rhyl	Taxi Company (123)
163.92500	159.42500	NFM	Sheffield	Gleason Builders
163.92500	159.42500	NFM	Sheffield	Murphy Hire Ltd
163.92500		NFM	Ufford	Golf Course (186.2)
163.93750	159.43750	NFM	Harrogate	Mainline Taxis
163.93750	159.43750	NFM	Rickmansworth	Fleet Cars Voice/Data
163.95000	159.45000	NFM	Chesterfield	Royal Hospital Porters
163.95000		NFM	Felixstowe	Docks (123)
163.95000		NFM	Langford	D Jays Taxis
163.95000	159.45000	NFM	Liverpool	Royal Liverpool Hospital Security
163.95000		NFM	Wigan	Bridgewater Business Park Security
163.96250	159.46250	NFM	Birmingham	School Maintenance
163.96250	159.46250	NFM	Cardiff	Kevin Kahill Transport Trunked
163.96250	159.46250	NFM	Fleetwood	Pharmacy Agency
163.97500	159.47500	NFM	Lichfield	Taxi Company
163.97500	159.47500	NFM	M25	Recovery Company
163.98750		NFM	Chessington	World of Adventures
163.98750		NFM	Coventry	MR Investigations
163.98750		NFM	Ipswich	Docks Security
163.98750		NFM	Reading	Madejski Stadium Ch.4 Medical/Red Cross
163.98750		NFM	Rugby	Rugby Cement
164.00000		NFM	Bletchley	Bletchley Park Security
164.00000		NFM	Jersey	Motor Traffic Department
164.00000		NFM	Kings Lynn	AB Cars
164.00000		NFM	Nationwide	Channel 4 Productions Ch.6 Security
164.00000		NFM	Rugby	Rugby Cement
164.00000		NFM	Severn Valley	Railway Preservation Society
164.01250		NFM	Chessington	World of Adventures
164.01250		NFM	Corby	Rockingham Speedway Ch.6 Yellow Flag
164.01250	164.01250	NFM	Guernsey	Aurigny Airlines

Base	Mobile	Mode	Location	User and Notes
164.01250	159.51250	NFM	Kent	Eurotunnel Traffic/Loading
164.01250		NFM	London	St Pauls Cathedral Staff
164.01500		NFM	England (Southern)	O'Rourke Construction
164.02500		NFM	Cardiff	BJ Skip Hire Company
164.02500		NFM	Chessington	World of Adventures Parking/Admin
164.02500		NFM	Gosport	Brune Park Community School
164.02500	159.52500	NFM	Kent	Eurotunnel Euroscan Machine
164.02500		NFM	London	London Zoo Graze Cafe Catering Staff (82.5)
164.02500		NFM	Lowestoft	Port Security (114.8)
164.03750	159.53750	NFM	Dover	Eurotunnel (T)
164.03750		NFM	Hendon	RAF Museum (Blue Control)
164.03750		NFM	Jersey	Aurigny Airlines Handhelds
164.05000		NFM	Cardiff	Docks Security
164.05000		NFM	Duxford	Imperial War Museum Car Park (151.4)
164.05000		NFM	Edinburgh	Sheriff Court Security
164.05000		NFM	Essex	Boy Scouts Ch.1
164.05000	159.55000	NFM	Gloucester	Docks Security
164.05000		NFM	Leicestershire	Boy Scouts Ch. White 1
164.05000		NFM	London	Alexandra Palace Car Park (151.4)
164.05000		NFM	London	Warner Bros Cinema Staff/Security at O2 Centre
164.05000		NFM	Nationwide	City & Suburban Car Parking Ltd (151.4)
164.05000		NFM	Nationwide	MG Car Club Events
164.05000		NFM	Nationwide	Used for Surveillance by Government Agencies
164.05000		NFM	Nationwide	St. John Ambulance Ch.5 UK General
164.05000		NFM	Nationwide	Scouts Association Ch.1
164.05000		NFM	Newmarket	Security Company
164.05000		NFM	Northampton	Golf Club
164.05000		NFM	Sussex	Sussex Land Search & Rescue (250.3)
164.06250		NFM	Essex	Boy Scouts Ch.2
164.06250		NFM	Leicestershire	Scouts Ch. White 2
164.06250		NFM	London	English Heritage, Wellington Arch
164.06250		NFM	Morecambe	Sea Scouts
164.06250		NFM	Nationwide	MG Car Club Events
164.06250		NFM	Nationwide	Used for Surveillance by Government Agencies
164.06250		NFM	Nationwide	Scouts Association Ch.2
164.06250		NFM	Nationwide	St. John Ambulance Ch.3 UK General
164.06250		NFM	Woodbridge	Site Security, Old Woodbridge Airbase (156.7)
164.07500		NFM	Cardiff	Docks Ops.
164.07500		NFM	Kent	Eurotunnel Security
164.07500		NFM	Larne NI	P & O Superstar Express Ops. (110.9)
164.07500		NFM	Merthyr Tydfil	Keith's Cabs
164.07500		NFM	Portsmouth	University Students Union
164.08750		NFM	Glasgow	Taxi Company
164.08750		NFM	Heathrow	Train Terminal Building
164.08750		NFM	Nationwide	NSR Events Communications (94.8)
164.08750		NFM	Nationwide	Whitby Davison Productions (Films)
164.08750		NFM	Rugby	Rugby Cement
164.12500		NFM	Leicestershire	Scouts Ch. White 5
164.12500		NFM	London	Cafe de Paris Security/Staff, Piccadilly
164.12500		NFM	London	Village Gay Pub Doorman, Soho
164.12500		NFM	Nationwide	NSR Events Communications (77)
164.12500		NFM	Nationwide	Channel 4 Productions Ch.7 Lighting
164.12500		NFM	Nationwide	O'Rourke Construction
164.12500		NFM	Rugby	Rugby Cement
164.12500		NFM	Southampton	Taxi Company
164.13750		NFM	Corby	Rockingham Speedway Race Control Ch.7
164.13750		NFM	Portsmouth	University Students Union
164.18750		NFM	Cambridge	EF Language School

Base	Mobile	Mode	Location	User and Notes
164.18750		NFM	Ipswich	Anglian Water Sewage Works Staff
164.18750		NFM	Leicestershire	Scouts Ch. White 6
164.18750		NFM	London	Alexandra Palace security
164.18750		NFM	Nationwide	Channel 4 Productions Ch.8 Camera Crews
164.18750		NFM	Reading	Madejski Stadium Ch.3 (DCS 023)
164.18750		NFM	Reading	Oracle Shopping Centre Cleaners (127.3)
164.18750		NFM	Rhyl	A & J Taxis (110.9)
164.18750		NFM	Rugby	Rugby Cement
164.22500	159.77500	NFM	Galway	Community Repeater
164.27500		NFM	Ashton under Lyme	Tyre Company Deliveries
164.30000		NFM	Blackburn	DMC Private Hire
164.37500		NFM	Blackburn	Chippy's Private Hire
164.37500		NFM	Newmarket	Security Company
164.38750		NFM	Manchester	Lewis Food Company, Hyde
164.40000		NFM	Blackburn	C & M Private Hire
164.40000		NFM	Manchester	Service Engineers
164.43750	159.93750	NFM	Birmingham	Security Company
164.43750	159.93750	NFM	Essex	Airlink Communications
164.43750	159.93750	NFM	London	Community Repeater Patient Transport (192.8)
164.43750	159.93750	NFM	Norfolk	Community Repeater Darndan Security
164.43750	159.93750	NFM	Norwich	Community Repeater Breakdown Recovery
164.43750	159.93750	NFM	Norwich	Autotec Communications Trunked
164.43750	159.93750	NFM	Wakefield	Calderdale Council (162.2)
164.45000	159.94500	NFM	Dyfed	Riverlea Tractors
164.45000	159.95000	NFM	Cleveland	Security Company
164.45000	159.95000	NFM	Haverfordwest	Coin Machines Company
164.45000		NFM	Isle of Man	Taxi Company
164.45000	159.95000	NFM	London	Vehicle Recovery/Car Repair Company (71.9)
164.45000	159.95000	NFM	Manchester	Airport Car Park Ferry Buses
164.45000	159.95000	NFM	Newmarket	Taxi Company
164.45000	159.95000	NFM	Oxford	Community Repeater Parcel Company (141.3)
164.45000	159.95000	NFM	Worcester	A W Taxis
164.46250	159.96250	NFM	Devon, North	Vet
164.46250	159.96250	NFM	Glasgow	Community Repeater
164.46250	159.96250	NFM	Gloucester	Security Firm
164.46250		NFM	Holyhead	Taxi Company
164.46250	159.96250	NFM	Penrith	County Taxis
164.46250		NFM	Pembroke	Taxi Company (173.8)
164.46250	159.96250	NFM	St. Ives, Cambs	Vehicle Recovery Company
164.47500	159.97500	NFM	Coventry	City Council Engineers
164.47500	159.97500	NFM	London	Doctors' Service
164.47500	159.97500	NFM	Sussex	Doctors' Service
164.47500	159.97500	NFM	Warwick	Council Boarding-Up Service
164.48750	159.98750	NFM	Cambridge	Oak Park Security Ch.2
164.48750		NFM	Bishop Stortford	Taxi Company
164.48750	159.98750	NFM	Crewe	Recovery Vehicles
164.48750	159.98750	NFM	Poole	Community Repeater
164.48750		NFM	Southampton	Taxi Company
164.50000	160.00000	NFM	Bolton	Transport Company
164.50000	160.00000	NFM	Bournemouth	Doctors' Service
164.50000	160.00000	NFM	Cardiff	Doctors' Service
164.50000	160.00000	NFM	Glasgow	Doctors' Service
164.50000	160.00000	NFM	Hertfordshire	Business Post
164.50000	160.00000	NFM	London	School Bus Service
164.50000	160.00000	NFM	Manchester	Security Firm, Hyde
164.50000	160.00000	NFM	Nationwide	Doctors' Service
164.50000	160.00000	NFM	Poole	Doctors' Service
164.50000	160.00000	NFM	Sheffield	Doctors' Service

Base	Mobile	Mode	Location	User and Notes
164.50000	160.00000	NFM	Southampton	Skip Hire Company
164.50000	160.00000	NFM	Wakefield	Doctors' Service
164.50000	160.00000	NFM	Warrington	Garden Centre
164.51250	160.01250	NFM	Bristol	Doctors' Service
164.51250	160.01250	NFM	Cardiff	Doctors' Service (151.4)
164.51250	160.01250	NFM	Cleveland	Doctors' Service
164.51250	160.01250	NFM	Kent	Skip Hire Company (88.5)
164.51250	160.01250	NFM	Oldham	Parking Enforcement
164.51250	160.01250	NFM	Wales	Taxi Company, Church Village (141.3)
164.52500	160.02500	NFM	Ashford	Ashbridge Domestic Appliances
164.52500	160.02500	NFM	Derbyshire	Bus Company
164.52500	160.02500	NFM	Dunstable	Doctors' Service
164.52500	160.02500	NFM	Kent	Community Repeater Flowers Vets (94.8)
164.52500	160.02500	NFM	Kent	Community Repeater Drainage Engineers (MD)
164.52500	160.02500	NFM	London	Doctors' Service
164.52500	160.02500	NFM	Maidstone	Gold Taxis
164.52500	160.02500	NFM	Nationwide	Doctors' Service
164.52500	160.02500	NFM	Worthing	Taxi Company
164.53750	160.03750	NFM	East Durham	Doctors' Service
164.53750	160.03750	NFM	Avon	Severnside Area Rescue Association Ch.77
164.53750	160.03750	NFM	Galway	Community Repeater
164.53750	160.03750	NFM	Nottingham	Doctors' Service
164.55000	160.05000	NFM	Blackburn	CRM Private Hire
164.55000	160.05000	NFM	Cardiff	Doctors' Service
164.55000	160.05000	NFM	Co. Durham	Alarm Engineers
164.55000	160.05000	NFM	Hull	East Yorkshire Buses
164.55000	160.05000	NFM	Manchester	Builders Yard, Hyde
164.55000	160.05000	NFM	Swansea	BJ Security
164.56250	160.06250	NFM	Bournemouth	Doctors' Service
164.56250	160.06250	NFM	Bristol	Doctors' Service
164.56250	160.06250	NFM	Coventry	Doctors' Service
164.56250	164.56250	NFM	Manchester	Doctors' Service
164.56250	160.06250	NFM	Newcastle	Doctors' Service
164.56250	160.06250	NFM	Sheffield	Doctors' Service
164.56250	160.06250	NFM	Southampton	Doctors' Service
164.56250	160.06250	NFM	South Yorkshire	Doctors' Service
164.56250	160.06250	NFM	Tyne & Wear	Doctors' Service
164.57500	160.07500	NFM	Kent	Roger's Refuse Collection
164.57500	160.07500	NFM	London	Doctors' Service
164.57500	160.07500	NFM	Maidstone	Scan Electronics TV & Audio
164.57500	160.07500	NFM	Reading	Borough Council
164.58750	160.08750	NFM	Bury	Doctors' Service
164.58750	160.08750	NFM	Croydon	Minicab Company
164.58750	160.08750	NFM	Hull	Doctors' Service
164.58750	160.08750	NFM	Manchester	Doctors' Service
164.60000	160.10000	NFM	Nationwide	Doctors' Service
164.60000	160.10000	NFM	Newcastle	UK Waste Skip Hire
164.60000	160.10000	NFM	Poole	Community Repeater
164.60000	160.10000	NFM	Sheffield	Community Repeater SABA Communications
164.60000	160.10000	NFM	Sheffield	Community Repeater Forge Alert Security Ch.2
164.61250	160.11250	NFM	Bournemouth	Council Road Gangs
164.61250	160.11250	NFM	Norwich	Autotec Communications, Trunked
164.61250	160.11250	NFM	Poole	Community Repeater
164.62500	160.12500	NFM	Bristol	Hospital Transport
164.62500	160.12500	NFM	Glasgow	Springburn College
164.62500	160.12500	NFM	Hampshire	St John Ambulance Ch.9
164.62500	160.12500	NFM	Kent	Tunbridge Freight
164.62500	160.12500	NFM	London	Doctors' Service

Base	Mobile	Mode	Location	User and Notes
164.62500	160.12500	NFM	Nationwide	Doctors' Service
164.62500	160.12500	NFM	Parkstone	Aristoview
164.62500	160.12500	NFM	Plymouth	Doctors' Service
164.62500	160.12500	NFM	Poole	Community Repeater
164.62500	160.12500	NFM	Staffordshire	Doctors' Service
164.63750	160.13750	NFM	Birmingham	Doctors' Service
164.63750	160.13750	NFM	Glasgow	Doctors' Service
164.63750	160.13750	NFM	Leicester	Doctors' Service
164.63750	160.13750	NFM	Newport, Gwent	Doctors' Service
164.63750	160.13750	NFM	Portsmouth	Doctors' Service (114.8)
164.63750	160.13750	NFM	Southampton	Taxi Company
164.63750	160.13750	NFM	Swansea	Doctors' Service
164.63750	160.13750	NFM	Tyne & Wear	Taxi Company
164.63750	160.13750	NFM	Wolverhampton	Doctors' Service
164.65000	160.15000	NFM	Birmingham	Doctors' Service
164.65000	160.15000	NFM	Bournemouth	Doctors' Service
164.65000	160.15000	NFM	Bristol	Doctors' Service
164.65000	160.15000	NFM	Cannock	Doctors' Service
164.65000	160.15000	NFM	Cardiff	Doctors' Service (206.3)
164.65000	160.15000	NFM	Newcastle	Doctors' Service
164.65000	160.15000	NFM	Newport, Gwent	Doctors' Service
164.65000	160.15000	NFM	South Glamorgan	Doctors' Service
164.66250	160.16250	NFM	Leeds	Vanguard Security
164.66250	160.16250	NFM	Poole	Community Repeater
164.67500	160.17500	NFM	Essex	Community Repeater St John Ambulance (110.9)
164.67500	160.17500	NFM	Maidstone	Scan Electronics TV & Audio
164.67500	160.17500	NFM	Preston	Business Post
164.67500	160.17500	NFM	Severn Bridge	Toll Booths
164.68/50	160.18750	NFM	Co. Durham	Doctors' Service
164.68750	160.18750	NFM	Cheltenham	Community Repeater Doctors' Service (250.3)
164.68750	160.18750	NFM	Gloucestershire	Dial-A-Ride, Newent (141.3)
164.68750	160.18750	NFM	Lincoln	Rainbow Cabs
164.68750	160.18750	NFM	London	CB Motors Vehicle Recovery, Golders Green (71.9)
164.68750	160.18750	NFM	London	Seymour Car Services Ltd
164.68750	160.18750	NFM	Norfolk	Community Repeater Darndan Security
164.68750	160.18750	NFM	Norfolk	Community Repeater INC Security
164.70000	160.20000	NFM	Berkhampstead	Norcom Communications
164.70000	160.20000	NFM	Newcastle	Council, Trunked
164.70000	160.20000	NFM	Tyneside	Plumbing Repairs
164.70000	160.20000	NFM	West Midlands	Burglar Alarm Company
164.71250	160.21250	NFM	Buckinghamshire	Community Repeater Flower Delivery Company (74.4)
164.71250	160.21250	NFM	Gloucester	Community Repeater
164.71250	160.21250	NFM	Kent	Doctors' Service
164.71250	160.21250	NFM	London	Doctors' Service
164.71250	160.21250	NFM	Sheffield	Community Repeater SABA Communications
164.72500	160.22500	NFM	Bexley	Bexley Park Ranger Service (67)
164.72500	160.22500	NFM	Crewe	Taxi Company
164.72500	160.22500	NFM	Essex	Community Repeater Centaur Security
164.72500	160.22500	NFM	Kent	Doctors' Service
164.72500	160.22500	NFM	London	Security Company
164.72500	160.22500	NFM	Newry	Doctors' Service (136.5)
164.72500	160.22500	NFM	Poole	Community Repeater
164.73750	160.23750	NFM	Cleveland	Doctors' Service
164.75000	160.25000	NFM	Ely	Taxi Company
164.75000	160.25000	NFM	London	Council Contractors
164.75000	160.25000	NFM	Oxford	Hospital Services
164.75000	160.25000	NFM	S England	Saxon Security
164.75000	160.25000	NFM	Wrexham	Haulage Contractor

Base	Mobile	Mode	Location	User and Notes
164.76250		NFM	Cambridge	Community Repeater Comms Engineers (167.9)
164.76250	160.26250	NFM	Leeds	Taxi Company
164.76250	160.26250	NFM	London	Doctors' Service
164.76250	160.26250	NFM	Newmarket	Transport Company
164.76250	160.26250	NFM	Perthshire	Delivery Company
164.76250	160.26250	NFM	Portsmouth	Taxi Company
164.76250	160.26250	NFM	Shelford	Clothing Distributor (183)
164.77500	160.27500	NFM	London	Doctors' Service
164.77500	160.27500	NFM	Sheffield	Community Repeater SABA Communications
164.78750	160.28750	NFM	Blackpool	Haulage Contractors
164.78750	160.28750	NFM	Nottinghamshire	Community Repeater Skip Company
164.80000	160.30000	NFM	Biggleswade	Community Repeater Sandy Skips
164.80000	160.30000	NFM	Biggleswade	Community Repeater Travis Perkins
164.80000	160.30000	NFM	Bodmin	Vet Services
164.80000	160.30000	NFM	Staffordshire	Community Repeater Skip Company
164.80000	160.30000	NFM	Walsall	Refuse Collectors
164.81250	160.01250	NFM	Bristol	Taxi Company
164.81250	160.01250	NFM	Leicester	Vending Machine Company
164.81250	160.31250	NFM	Norwich	Community Repeater Airport Taxis
164.81250	160.01250	NFM	Poole	Community Repeater
164.82500	160.32500	NFM	London	Vehicle Recovery Company
164.82500	160.32500	NFM	Byfleet	National Rescue
164.82500	160.32500	NFM	London	St Mary's Hospital
164.82500	160.32500	NFM	Poole	Community Repeater
164.82500	160.32500	NFM	Swansea	BJ Security
164.82500	160.32500	NFM	Tamworth	Bluebell Taxis
164.82500	160.32500	NFM	West Sussex	Vehicle Recovery Company
164.83750	160.33750	NFM	Birmingham	Glaziers
164.83750	160.33750	NFM	Bournemouth	Express Carriers
164.83750	160.33750	NFM	Crumlin NI	M & M Group Taxis
164.83750	160.33750	NFM	Ipswich	Community Repeater Ipswich Communications
164.83750	160.33750	NFM	Poole	Community Repeater
164.83750	160.33750	NFM	Suffolk	Doctors' Service
164.85000	160.35000	NFM	N Hertfordshire	Security Company
164.85000	160.35000	NFM	Wadesbridge	Builders' Merchant
164.86250	160.36250	NFM	Manchester	Bouncy Castle Hire
164.86250	160.36250	NFM	SW Wales	Community Repeater DSS Fraud Teams
164.86250	160.86250	NFM	Swansea	Taxi Company (179.9)
164.87500	160.37500	NFM	Norfolk	Alpha Drains
164.87500	160.37500	NFM	Poole	Community Repeater
164.87500	160.37500	NFM	Sussex Coast	Coastway Hospital Radio
164.87500	160.37500	NFM	Swansea	Community Repeater Crimewatch Security
164.87500	160.37500	NFM	Swansea	Community Repeater Building Company
164.88750	160.38750	NFM	Bedfordshire	Vehicle Recovery Company
164.88750	160.38750	NFM	Burton	Skip Company
164.88750	160.38750	NFM	Kent/Essex	Procom Communications Engineers
164.90000	160.40000	NFM	Bedfordshire	Community Repeater
164.90000	160.40000	NFM	Cheshire	Tyre Services
164.90000	160.40000	NFM	Lincoln	Gas Suppliers
164.90000	160.40000	NFM	Manchester	Delivery Company
164.90000	160.40000	NFM	Wiltshire	Fonthill Estate
164.91250	160.41250	NFM	Bournemouth	Taxi Company
164.91250	160.41250	NFM	Ipswich	Community Repeater Brent Walker
164.91250	160.41250	NFM	Ipswich	Community Repeater County Communications
164.91250	160.41250	NFM	Ipswich	Community Repeater Garage
164.91250	160.41250	NFM	Ipswich	Community Repeater HELP Security (127.3)
164.91250	160.41250	NFM	Ipswich	Community Repeater Unicorn Communications (67)
164.91250	160.41250	NFM	Newport	Central Heating Company

Base	Mobile	Mode	Location	User and Notes
164.92500	160.42500	NFM	Brighton	Community Repeater
164.92500		NFM	Cardiff	Bessemer Market
164.92500	160.42500	NFM	Hastings	Refuse Collectors
164.92500	160.42500	NFM	Norfolk	ANC Parcels
164.92500	160.42500	NFM	Norfolk	Community Repeater Darndan Security
164.92500	160.42500	NFM	Norwich	Autotec Communications Trunked
164.92500	160.42500	NFM	Suffolk	Morlings TV Rentals
164.93750	160.43750	NFM	Bristol	Security Company
164.93750	160.43750	NFM	Poole	Community Repeater
164.93750	160.43750	NFM	Truro	Cowlings Security
164.95000	160.45000	NFM	Glasgow	Taxi Company
164.95000	160.45000	NFM	Nottingham	Taxi Company
164.95000	160.45000	NFM	Redcar	Parking Enforcement
164.96250	160.46250	NFM	Birmingham	AS Security
164.96250	160.46250	NFM	London	Winters Skip Hire
164.97500	160.47500	NFM	Merseyside	Surveyors
164.97500	160.47500	NFM	Mildenhall	Community Repeater HHH Cars
164.98750	160.48750	NFM	Hertfordshire	Community Repeater Vehicle Recovery (192.8)
164.98750	160.48750	NFM	Hertfordshire	Community Repeater Vehicle Recovery (210.7)
164.98750	160.48750	NFM	Hertfordshire	Community Repeater Vehicle Recovery (179.9)
164.98750		NFM	Shropshire	Severn Valley Railway

Garda VHF Frequencies Nationwide

Base	Mobile	Mode	Ch	Base	Mobile	Mode	Ch
164.0250	159.5250	NFM	1	164.2250		NFM	32
164.0375		NFM	2	164.2250	159.7250	NFM	33
164.0375	159.5375	NFM	3	164.2375		NFM	34
164.0500		NFM	4	164.2375	159.7375	NFM	35
164.0500	159.550	NFM	5	164.2500		NFM	36
164.0625		NFM	6	164.2500	159.7500	NFM	37
164.0625	159.5625	NFM	7	164.2625		NFM	38
164.0750		NFM	8	164.2625	159.7625	NFM	39
164.0750	159.5750	NFM	9	164.2750		NFM	40
164.0875		NFM	10	164.2750	159.7750	NFM	41
164.0875	159.5875	NFM	11	164.2875		NFM	42
164.1000		NFM	12	164.2875	159.7875	NFM	43
164.1000	159.6000	NFM	13	164.3000		NFM	44
164.1125		NFM	14	164.3000	159.8000	NFM	45
164.1125	159.6125	NFM	15	164.3125		NFM	46
164.1250		NFM	16	164.3125	159.8125	NFM	47
164.1250	159.6250	NFM	17	164.3250		NFM	48
164.1375		NFM	18	164.3250	159.8250	NFM	49
164.1375	159.6375	NFM	19	164.3375		NFM	50
164.1500		NFM	20	164.3375	159.8375	NFM	51
164.1500	159.6500	NFM	21	164.3500		NFM	52
164.1625		NFM	22	164.3500	159.8500	NFM	53
164.1625	159.6625	NFM	23	164.3625		NFM	54
164.1750		NFM	24	164.3625	159.8625	NFM	55
164.1750	159.6750	NFM	25	164.3750		NFM	56
164.1875		NFM	26	164.3750	159.8750	NFM	57
164.1875	159.6875	NFM	27	164.3875		NFM	58
164.2000		NFM	28	164.3875	159.8875	NFM	59
164.2000	159.7000	NFM	29	164.4000		NFM	60
164.2125		NFM	30	164.4000	159.9000	NFM	61
164.2125	159.7125	NFM	31				

Base	Mobile	Mode	Location	User and Notes
165.0125- 168.2250 MHz			**VHF High Band PMR Base/Repeaters**	
			Ambulance Services (England & Wales)	
165.00000	160.50000	NFM	Aberdeen	Northern Garaget
165.00000	160.50000	NFM	Bath	Bath University Research Department
165.00000	160.50000	NFM	Cornwall	Community Repeater
165.00000	160.50000	NFM	Dorking	Community Repeater Ch. 3
165.00000	160.50000	NFM	Ipswich	Community Repeater Ipswich Communications
165.00000	160.50000	NFM	Kent	Doctors' Service
165.00000	160.50000	NFM	London	Doctors' Service
165.00000	160.50000	NFM	Manchester	Plant Hire Company
165.00000	160.50000	NFM	Manchester	Security Company
165.00000	160.50000	NFM	Morecambe	Security Vans
165.00000	160.50000	NFM	New Malden	North West Cars
165.00000	160.50000	NFM	Newmarket	Doctors' Service
165.00000	160.50000	NFM	Poole	Taxi Company
165.00000	160.50000	NFM	West Suffolk	Doctors' Service
165.01250	160.51250	NFM	London/Kent	British Oxygen
165.01250	160.51250	NFM	South London	Doctors' Service
165.01250	160.51250	NFM	Tamworth	Quarry
165.01250	160.51250	NFM	West Midlands	Vehicle Recovery Company (186.2)
165.02500	169.52500	NFM	Avon	Severnside Area Rescue Association Ch.44
165.02500	169.52500	NFM	Bath	Bath University Research Department
165.02500	169.52500	NFM	Blackpool	First Aid Council
165.02500	169.52500	NFM	Burnley	Delivery Service
165.02500	169.52500	NFM	Cardiff	Commercial Rigging
165.02500	169.52500	NFM	Dover Castle	Security/Works Department
165.02500	169.52500	NFM	Gosforth	Papa Taxis
165.02500	169.52500	NFM	Hull	Capital Security
165.02500	169.52500	NFM	North Yorkshire	Doctors' Service
165.02500	169.52500	NFM	Staffordshire	ForestryRangers
165.03750	169.53750	NFM	Avon	Severnside Area Rescue Association Ch.66
165.03750	169.53750	NFM	Bristol	Bristol Dogs Home
165.03750	169.53750	NFM	Cardiff	Community Repeater Wentloog Security
165.03750	169.53750	NFM	Jersey	Eurocar Hire
165.03750	169.53750	NFM	Newport	Community Repeater
165.03750	169.53750	NFM	Nottingham	Taxi Company
165.03750	169.53750	NFM	Poole	Community Repeater
165.03750	169.53750	NFM	Preston	Farm Suppliers
165.05000	169.85000	NFM	Ballymena	TC Taxis
165.05000	169.85000	NFM	Bathgate	Taxi Company
165.05000	169.85000	NFM	Blackburn	B & B Private Hire
165.05000	169.85000	NFM	Bournemouth	Critax Taxis
165.05000	169.85000	NFM	Bradford	Barkerend Taxis
165.05000	169.85000	NFM	Cheetham	Ekko Private Hire
165.05000	169.85000	NFM	Dumfries	Taxi Company
165.05000	170.85000	NFM	Gt Yarmouth	Premier TV Repairs (67)
165.05000	169.85000	NFM	Guernsey	Circuit Skips
165.05000	169.85000	NFM	Hull	Taxi Company
165.05000	169.85000	NFM	Jersey	SGB Scaffolding Erectors
165.05000	169.85000	NFM	Lincoln	A2B Taxis
165.05000	169.85000	NFM	Manchester	Taxi Company
165.05000	169.85000	NFM	Newbury	Broadway Cars
165.05000	169.85000	NFM	Newtown	Newtown Taxis
165.05000	169.85000	NFM	Peterborough	Osbourne Plumbing
165.05000	169.85000	NFM	Plymouth	AA Taxis
165.05000	169.85000	NFM	Southend on Sea	Parking Enforcement (114.8)

Base	Mobile	Mode	Location	User and Notes
165.05000	169.85000	NFM	Swindon	Inta-Car Taxis
165.06250	169.86250	NFM	Bristol	AutoGlass
165.06250	169.86250	NFM	Carlisle	Biffa Skips
165.06250	169.86250	NFM	Cromer	Tylers Waste Management
165.06250	169.86250	NFM	Essex	Doctors' Service (West)
165.06250	169.86250	NFM	Essex	Warrior Skips
165.06250	169.86250	NFM	Guernsey	Community Repeater
165.06500	165.06500	NFM	Haverfordwest	Taxi Company
165.06250	169.86250	NFM	London	London Underground Line Ch.5
165.06250	169.86250	NFM	London	London Underground Victoria Line
165.06250	169.86250	NFM	Londonderry	Special Care Buses (110.9)
165.06250	169.86250	NFM	Perth	King Contractors (King Base)
165.06250	169.86250	NFM	Pocklington	Town Travel Taxis
165.06250	169.86250	NFM	Poole	Community Repeater
165.06250	169.86250	NFM	Rillington	H Atkinson Slaughter House
165.06250	169.86250	NFM	Suffolk	Garage Supplies
165.07500	169.87500	NFM	Coventry	Security Company
165.07500	169.87500	NFM	Dover Castle	Security/Works Department
165.07500	169.87500	NFM	London	Amey Roadstone Road Maintenance Teams
165.07500	169.87500	NFM	M1	Associated Asphalt
165.07500	169.87500	NFM	Nationwide	Road Construction Engineers
165.07500	169.87500	NFM	Norfolk/Suffolk	May Gurney & Co.
165.07500	169.87500	NFM	Perth	Community Repeater
165.08750	169.88750	NFM	Ambleside	Kevin's Taxis
165.08750	169.88750	NFM	Biggleswade	Jordans Cereals Ch.1
165.08750	169.88750	NFM	Blackpool	C Cabs
165.08750	169.88750	NFM	Chestwood	Chestwood Mushrooms
165.08750	169.88750	NFM	Darlington	Bus Company
165.08750	169.88750	NFM	Ipswich	Motorway Vehicle Recovery M5
165.08750	169.88750	NFM	Jersey	Normans Ltd Ch.1
165.08750	169.88750	NFM	Leicester	Garage
165.08750	169.88750	NFM	London	Penge Minicabs
165.08750	169.88750	NFM	London NW	Parking Enforcement, Wembley (77)
165.08750	169.88750	NFM	Peterborough	A Touch of Class Cabs (107.2)
165.08750	169.88750	NFM	Plymouth	University Security
165.10000	169.90000	NFM	Abingdon	Vargas Taxis
165.10000	169.90000	NFM	Blackpool	C Cabs
165.10000	169.90000	NFM	Bournemouth	Wade's Taxis
165.10000	169.90000	NFM	Bristol	Durston Plant
165.10000	169.90000	NFM	Carlisle	Abbey Skip Hire
165.10000	169.90000	NFM	Clacton	Clacton Taxis
165.10000	169.90000	NFM	Coventry	Taxi Company
165.10000	169.90000	NFM	Edinburgh	Taxi Company
165.10000	169.90000	NFM	Fordham	D Jenkins TV
165.10000	169.90000	NFM	Glasgow	Drumchapel Taxis
165.10000	169.00000	NFM	Gt Cornard	Wood's Radio Taxis
165.10000	169.90000	NFM	Gorleston on Sea	Ace Day & Night Taxis
165.10000	169.90000	NFM	Guernsey	Transfer Taxis
165.10000	169.90000	NFM	Havant	Taxi Company
165.10000	169.90000	NFM	Hazelgrove	Lynx Private Hire
165.10000	169.90000	NFM	Kings Lynn	Geoff's Taxis
165.10000	169.90000	NFM	Kirkcaldy	Taxi Company
165.10000	169.90000	NFM	Leeds	Speedline
165.10000	169.90000	NFM	Leigh	Swift Next Day Deliveries
165.10000	169.90000	NFM	Letchworth	Jaspals Taxis
165.10000	169.90000	NFM	Lincoln	City Taxis

Base	Mobile	Mode	Location	User and Notes
165.10000	169.90000	NFM	Lincolnshire	Earl of Yarborough Farm
165.10000	169.90000	NFM	Little Downham	Mott Farmers
165.10000	169.90000	NFM	London	SEB Scaffolding Company
165.10000	169.90000	NFM	London	White City Taxis
165.10000	169.90000	NFM	London	Minicab Firm, Acton
165.10000	169.90000	NFM	London	Minicab Firm, Croydon
165.10000	169.90000	NFM	Lurgan	HB Taxis
165.10000	169.90000	NFM	Manchester	Bishop's Security Company
165.10000	169.90000	NFM	Manchester	Taxi Company, Gorton
165.10000	169.90000	NFM	Montrose	Taxi Company
165.10000	169.90000	NFM	Morecambe	Morecambe Market Security & Caretaker (167.9)
165.10000	169.90000	NFM	Newcastle	Taxi Company
165.10000	169.90000	NFM	Peterborough	Diamond Cars
165.10000	169.90000	NFM	Saxmundham	Fishwick Vets
165.10000	169.90000	NFM	Seaforth	Dale's Taxis
165.10000	169.90000	NFM	Stockport	Taxi Company
165.10000	169.90000	NFM	Stoke on Trent	Taxi Company
165.10000	169.90000	NFM	Tarrant Rawston	Farm (67)
165.10000	169.90000	NFM	Walton	Copsey Taxis
165.10000	169.90000	NFM	Wickford	Allied Taxis
165.10000	169.90000	NFM	Woodbridge	TV Repair Company
165.11000	169.91000	NFM	Kilmarnock	Taxi Company
165.11000	169.91000	NFM	Wakefield	Taxi Company
165.11250	169.91250	NFM	Barrow	Taxi Company
165.11250	169.91250	NFM	Bournemouth	Brown Motors
165.11250	169.91250	NFM	Bradford	Bank Top Private Hire
165.11250	169.91250	NFM	Cambridge	Inter-City Taxis (159.8)
165.11250	169.91250	NFM	Carlisle	Borders Cabs
165.11250	169.91250	NFM	Durweston	Folly Farm (67)
165.11250	169.91250	NFM	Dyfed	J Lawrence Tractors
165.11250	169.91250	NFM	Glasgow	Taxi Company
165.11250	169.91250	NFM	Guernsey	Fuel Supplies
165.11250	169.91250	NFM	Hull	Midgeleys Scrap
165.11250	169.91250	NFM	Hull	University
165.11250	169.91250	NFM	Isle of Man	Taxi Company (107.5)
165.11250	169.91250	NFM	Jersey	Beeline Taxis Ch.1
165.11250	169.91250	NFM	Kent	Romney, Hythe & Dymchurch Light Railway
165.11250	169.91250	NFM	London	Minicab Firm, N London
165.11250	169.91250	NFM	Oxford	Parking Enforcement (141.3)
165.11250	169.91250	NFM	Pembrokeshire	J Lawrence Tractors
165.11250	169.91250	NFM	Peterborough	Cab Line (71.9)
165.11250	169.91250	NFM	Sheffield	Network Cars
165.11250	169.91250	NFM	Swansea	Abba Taxis
165.11250	169.91250	NFM	Walton on Thames	Vending Machine Company
165.12500	169.92500	NFM	Aberdeen	Amtrak
165.12500	169.92500	NFM	Alderton	Mortiers, Cedar Farms
165.12500	169.92500	NFM	Aylesbury	Fosters Taxis
165.12500	169.92500	NFM	Burnley	Taxi Company
165.12500	169.92500	NFM	Cardiff	Starline Taxis
165.12500	169.92500	NFM	Cosham	Taxi Company
165.12500	169.92500	NFM	Edinburgh	Taxi Company
165.12500	169.92500	NFM	Failsworth	Embassy Cars
165.12500	169.92500	NFM	Glasgow	Taxi Company
165.12500	169.92500	NFM	Guernsey	C Richard Vehicle Recovery
165.12500	169.92500	NFM	Hadleigh	Wilsons Corn & Milling
165.12500	169.92500	NFM	Hawick	Stuarts Taxis

Base	Mobile	Mode	Location	User and Notes
165.12500	169.92500	NFM	Hinkley	Station Taxis
165.12500	169.92500	NFM	Huntingdon	Mercury Bluebird Taxis
165.12500	169.92500	NFM	Immingham	Taxi Company
165.12500	169.92500	NFM	Jersey	Farm
165.12500	169.92500	NFM	Llandudno	Taxi Company
165.12500	169.92500	NFM	London	M & J Cars, Surrey Quays
165.12500	169.92500	NFM	London	Temple Cars (Data)
165.12500	169.92500	NFM	Manchester	Security Company, Gorton
165.12500	169.92500	NFM	Oldham	Embassy Cars
165.12500	169.92500	NFM	Perth	Taxi Company
165.12500	169.92500	NFM	Portsmouth	Taxi Company
165.12500	169.92500	NFM	Sheffield	Security Company
165.12500	169.92500	NFM	Slough	Topcars
165.12500	169.92500	NFM	Sudbury	Wilsons Corn & Milling
165.12500	169.92500	NFM	Sudbury	Woods Taxis
165.12500	169.92500	NFM	Weymouth	Taxi Company
165.13750	169.93750	NFM	Baldock	Wheat Farm (167.9)
165.13750	169.93750	NFM	Cardington	Building Research Establishment Fire Safety Centre
165.13750	169.93750	NFM	Gt Yarmouth	Shopwatch/Pubwatch/Street Patrols/TVEye (67)
165.13750	169.93750	NFM	Guernsey	Stan Brouard Ltd
165.13750	169.93750	NFM	Hull	Reckitts Security
165.13750	169.93750	NFM	Isle of Man	Manx Energy Generation Ch.1
165.13750	169.93750	NFM	Lancaster	Parking Enforcement (88.5)
165.13750	169.93750	NFM	London	Royal ParksPolice (Now Mainly on Airwave)
165.13750	169.93750	NFM	Poole	Community Repeater
165.13750	169.93750	NFM	Swaffham	Reed & Milkik Ltd.
165.15000	169.95000	NFM	Anglesey	Council Refuse Collection
165.15000	169.95000	NFM	Bury St Edmunds	United Taxis
165.15000	169.95000	NFM	Coventry	Walsgrave Hospital Porters (151.4)
165.15000	169.95000	NFM	Edinburgh	Private Traffic Wardens (APCOA)
165.15000	169.95000	NFM	Glasgow	Taxi Company
165.15000	169.95000	NFM	Grimsby	Doctors' Service
165.15000	169.95000	NFM	Guernsey	Norman Piette
165.15000	169.95000	NFM	Jersey	RG Romeril Plant Hire
165.15000	169.95000	NFM	London	Construction Company (218.1)
165.15000	169.95000	NFM	Loudham Melton	Warburg Hall Farm (94.8)
165.15000	169.95000	NFM	Merry Hill	Centre Maintenance
165.15000	169.95000	NFM	Nationwide	Group 4 Security Ch.1
165.15000	169.95000	NFM	Oxford	Timbmet Ltd
165.15000	169.95000	NFM	Salford	Parking Enforcement (71.9)
165.15000	169.95000	NFM	Swansea	Group 4 Security
165.16250	169.96250	NFM	Alton Towers	Ch.3 Monorail (118.8)
165.16250	169.96250	NFM	Birmingham	Queen Elizabeth Hospital Porters (146.2)
165.16250	169.96250	NFM	Bedfordshire	Community Repeater
165.16250	169.96250	NFM	Bonnybridge	United Distillers Security
165.16250	169.96250	NFM	Bournemouth	Beach Security/ Lifeguard Patrols (94.8)
165.16250	169.96250	NFM	Bridgewater	Shopwatch (156.7)
165.16250	169.96250	NFM	Cambridge	University
165.16250	169.96250	NFM	Carlisle	Pubwatch
165.16250	169.96250	NFM	Chessington	World of Adventures Ch. 1(82.5)
165.16250	169.96250	NFM	Doncaster	Transline Bus Stations Security Network
165.16250	169.96250	NFM	Elgin	Shopwatch
165.16250	169.96250	NFM	Elverdon	Centre Parcs, First Aid & Security (103.5)
165.16250	169.96250	NFM	Exeter	Shopping Centre Security (88.5)
165.16250	169.96250	NFM	Gt Yarmouth	Holiday Park (77)
165.16250	169.96250	NFM	Guernsey	Vehicle Recovery Service

Base	Mobile	Mode	Location	User and Notes
165.16250	169.96250	NFM	Hastings	Swallow Security
165.16250	169.96250	NFM	Hatfield	University of Hatfield Resident Assistants
165.16250	169.96250	NFM	Haydock	Haydock Park Racecourse
165.16250	169.96250	NFM	Heathrow	Parking Enforcement NCP Car Parks (114.8)
165.16250	169.96250	NFM	Hull	Reckitts Security
165.16250	169.96250	NFM	Ipswich	Spotcheck Security
165.16250	169.96250	NFM	Kettering	Shopwatch (203.5)
165.16250	169.96250	NFM	London	Ealing Hospital Security/Car Park Clampers (225)
165.16250	169.96250	NFM	London	Harvey Nicholls Security, Knightsbridge (67)
165.16250	169.96250	NFM	London	Heathrow Airport Parking Enforcement
165.16250	169.96250	NFM	London	Nortel (Northern Telecom) Staff (162.2)
165.16250	169.96250	NFM	London	Tottenham Hotspur Football Club (218.1)
165.16250	169.96250	NFM	Londonderry	Seagate Factory (131.8)
165.16250	169.96250	NFM	Lowestoft	Neptune Accommodation (88.5)
165.16250	169.96250	NFM	Newport	Gwent House Security
165.16250	169.96250	NFM	Newton Abbot	Shopwatch (67)
165.16250	169.96250	NFM	Nottingham	Nottingham University Security
165.16250	169.96250	NFM	Penrith	Oasis Holiday Park (82.5)
165.16250	169.96250	NFM	Perth	Perth Royal Infirmary Security/Porters
165.16250	169.96250	NFM	Redcar	Corus Coal Loading .
165.16250	169.96250	NFM	Ripon	Lightwater Valley Theme Park
165.16250	169.96250	NFM	Skegness	Pleasure Beach Amusements (PBA)
165.16250	169.96250	NFM	Sutton Hoo	Historic Burial Site (192.8)
165.16250	169.96250	NFM	S Wales	Royal Gwent Hospital Security (131.8)
165.16250	169.96250	NFM	Wakefield	The Ridings Centre Security Ch.1
165.16250	169.96250	NFM	Winsford	Shopping Centre Security
165.16250	169.96250	NFM	Worthing	Southlands Hospital Porters (156.7)
165.17500	169.97500	NFM	Luton Airport	On Site Security
165.18750	169.98750	Fm	Alton Towers	Ch.6 Hotel/Admin (225)
165.18750	169.98750	NFM	Ashington	Shopwatch
165.18750	169.98750	NFM	Bedford	Parking Enforcement
165.18750	169.98750	NFM	Belfast	International Airport Ground Ops/Security (88.5)
165.18750	169.98750	NFM	Birmingham	Selly Oak Hospital Porters (146.2)
165.18750	169.98750	NFM	Bognor Regis	Butlins Ch.1
165.18750	169.98750	NFM	Bournemouth	Securitas Security
165.18750	169.98750	NFM	Bristol	Shopwatch
165.18750	169.98750	NFM	Burnley	CCTV System
165.18750	169.98750	NFM	Cambridge	Abbey Security
165.18750	169.98750	NFM	Cardiff	Cardiff Museum (67)
165.18750	169.98750	NFM	Castleford	Shopwatch
165.18750	169.98750	NFM	Chelmsford	Anglia Polytechnic University
165.18750	169.98750	NFM	Chessington	World of Adventures Ch.3 (114.8)
165.18750	169.98750	NFM	Darwen	Shopwatch
165.18750	169.98750	NFM	Elverdon	Centre Parcs Leisure Centre Lifeguards (107.2)
165.18750	169.98750	NFM	Exeter	Shopwatch (67)
165.18750	169.98750	NFM	Gloucester	Shopwatch (156.7)
165.18750	169.98750	NFM	Hinckley	Shopwatch (118.8)
165.18750	169.98750	NFM	Hull	SPS Security
165.18750	169.98750	NFM	Leeds	Street Patrols
165.18750	169.98750	NFM	London	Coca Cola/Schweppes Depot Shunters, Edmonton
165.18750	169.98750	NFM	London	Dept of Environment Transport (Ergum)
165.18750	169.98750	NFM	London	John Lewis Undercover Security, Oxford Street (250)
165.18750	169.98750	NFM	London	Nortel Security, Southgate (131.8)
165.18750	169.98750	NFM	Manchester	Manchester United Football Club Security
165.18750	169.98750	NFM	Manchester	Manchester University Security
165.18750	169.98750	NFM	Minehead	Butlins Holiday Camp (103.5)

Base	Mobile	Mode	Location	User and Notes
165.18750	169.98750	NFM	Newport	Shopwatch (167.9)
165.18750	169.98750	NFM	Newquay	Pubwatch/Clubwatch
165.18750	169.98750	NFM	Newtownards	Kool Kabs
165.18750	169.98750	NFM	Norfolk	Pritchard Security
165.18750	169.98740	NFM	Penrith	Oasis Holiday Park (71.9)
165.18750	169.98750	NFM	Perth	Taxi Company
165.18750	169.98750	NFM	Portsmouth	Historic Dockyard (103.5)
165.18750	169.98750	NFM	Preston	Preston Hospital
165.18750	169.98650	NFM	Reading	Madejski Stadium Ch.2 (241.8)
165.18750	169.98750	NFM	Scunthorpe	Corus Steel Security
165.18750	169.98750	NFM	Sheffield	Benefits Agency/Job Centres Security
165.18750	169.98750	NFM	Southend on Sea	Southend College
165.18750	169.98750	NFM	Stevenage	Shopwatch (203.5)
165.18750	169.98750	NFM	Stoke	Keele University
165.18750	169.98750	NFM	Sunderland	Parking Enforcement
165.18750	169.98750	NFM	Wigan	Royal Albert Edward Infirmary Hospital Security (77)
165.20000	170.00000	NFM	Aberdeen	Aberdeen Vets
165.20000	170.00000	NFM	Derc Regis	Ferndown Skips
165.20000	170.00000	NFM	Butley Capel	St Andrew Farms
165.20000	170.00000	NFM	Croydon	Borough Council (71.9)
165.20000	170.00000	NFM	Cheshire	Alternative Taxis
165.20000	170.00000	NFM	Dudley	Russells Hall Hospital Porters (156.7)
165.20000	170.00000	NFM	Edinburgh	Taxi Company
165.20000	170.00000	NFM	Glencoe	Mountain Rescue
165.20000	170.00000	NFM	Isle of Man	Manx Energy Ch.2
165.20000	170.00000	NFM	Newport	University Of Wales College Security (141.3)
165.20000	170.00000	NFM	Norwich	Esso Heating
165.20000	170.00000	NFM	Peterborough	Cabco
165.20000	170.00000	NFM	Poole	Repeater
165.20000	170.00000	NFM	Powys	Welshpool & Llanfair Railway
165.20000	170.00000	NFM	Stevenage	Apollo Taxis
165.21250	170.01250	NFM	Alton Towers	Ch.2 Rides & Shows (82.5)
165.21250	170.01250	NFM	Ayr	Haven Craig Tara Holiday Camp
165.21250	170.01250	NFM	Barnsley	Barnsley Market
165.21250	170.01250	NFM	Birkenhead	Market Security (186.2)
165.21250	170.01250	NFM	Birmingham	Aston Villa Football Club Stewards
165.21250	170.01250	NFM	Blantyre	Forge Centre Security
165.21250	170.01250	NFM	Bolton	University Of Bolton
165.21250	170.01250	NFM	Bournemouth	Beach Patrols
165.21250	170.01250	NFM	Bressingham	Steam Museum Staff
165.21250	170.01250	NFM	Cambridge	Grafton Centre (71.9)
165.21250	170.01250	NFM	Cardiff	Cardiff University Security (123)
165.21250	170.01250	NFM	Coventry	GPT Telecoms Security
165.21250	170.01250	NFM	Elverdon	Centre Parcs, Grounds & Technical Services (107.2)
165.21250	170.01250	NFM	Exeter	University Security & Porters (71.9)
165.21250	170.01250	NFM	Fleetwood	Fleetwood Freeport Security
165.21250	170.01250	NFM	Glasgow	The Forge Shopping Centre Security
165.21250	170.01250	NFM	Hatfield	University Of Hertfordshire Security (94.8)
165.21250	170.01250	NFM	Hull	Scamps Security
165.21250	170.01250	NFM	Huntingdon	Huntingdon Life Sciences Security
165.21250	170.01250	NFM	Inverness	Nexfor Ltd Wood & Timber, Morayhill
165.21250	170.01250	NFM	Ipswich	Axa Insurance (94.8)
165.21250	170.01250	NFM	London	Alexandra Palace Leisure Centre Ch.2 (146.2)
165.21250	170.01250	NFM	London	John Lewis Security, Oxford Street Ch.2
165.21250	170.01250	NFM	London	Natwest Tower Security
165.21250	170.01250	NFM	London	Stratford Shopping Centre Security/Parking (218.1)

Base	Mobile	Mode	Location	User and Notes
165.21250	170.01250	NFM	London	The Horniman Museum Staff/Security (173.8)
165.21250	170.01250	NFM	Lowestoft	Shopwatch
165.21250	170.01250	NFM	Milford on Sea	Shorefield Country Park Admin/Maintenance (136.5)
165.21250	170.01250	NFM	Milton Keynes	Milton Keynes Taxis
165.21250	170.01250	NFM	Portsmouth	Historic Dockyard (173)
165.21250	170.01250	NFM	Romsey	Paultons Park Staff
165.21250	170.01250	NFM	Rotherham	College Of Art & Technology
165.21250	170.01250	NFM	Shap	Shap Quarry
165.21250	170.01250	NFM	Shepperton	Shepperton Studios Maintenance (DCS 143)
165.21250	170.01250	NFM	Southend on Sea	Adventure Island Ch.1 Staff/Security (DCS 043)
165.21250	170.01250	NFM	Stevenage	Dixons/Currys Warehouse (123)
165.21250	170.01250	NFM	Stretford	Shopwatch, Arndale Centre (123)
165.21250	170.01250	NFM	Suffolk	Bressingham Steam Museum Staff
165.21250	170.01250	NFM	Swansea	Quadrant Shopping Centre Security
165.21250	170.01250	NFM	Swindon	Shopwatch (110.9)
165.21250	170.01250	NFM	Windsor	Legoland (77)
165.21250	170.01250	NFM	Worthing	Shopwatch (114.8)
165.21250	170.01250	NFM	Yeovil	Shopwatch
165.22500	170.02500	NFM	Ballymena	Sharp Taxis
165.22500	170.02500	NFM	Bangor	Taxi Company
165.22500	170.02500	NFM	Blackburn	Arcade Private Hire
165.22500	170.02500	NFM	Frome	Blue Taxis
165.22500	170.02500	NFM	Halifax	4 Ways Taxis
165.22500	170.02500	NFM	Hawick	WE Taxis
165.22500	170.02500	NFM	Hitchin	Castle Taxis
165.22500	170.02500	NFM	Jersey	Flying Dragon Cabs
165.22500	170.02500	NFM	Langley	Station Minicabs
165.22500	170.02500	NFM	Leicester	LCL Cable Comms
165.22500	170.02500	NFM	Letchworth	Duggans Taxis (186.2)
165.22500	170.02500	NFM	London	Minicab Company, Woodford
165.22500	170.02500	NFM	Nottingham	Taxi Company
165.22500	170.02500	NFM	Portishead	Docks, Esso Fuels
165.22500	170.02500	NFM	Scarborough	Atlas Taxis
165.22500	170.02500	NFM	Slough	Minicab Company
165.22500	170.02500	NFM	Southampton	Taxis
165.22500	170.02500	NFM	Tamworth	A2B Taxis
165.22500	170.02500	NFM	Weymouth	Dorset Alarms
165.23750	170.03750	NFM	Anglesey	Benji's Taxis
165.23750	170.03750	NFM	Barrow	Acacia Taxis (77)
165.23750	170.03750	NFM	Birmingham	Castle Taxi
165.23750	170.03750	NFM	Bristol	Black & White Taxis
165.23750	170.03750	NFM	Cardiff	Amber Taxis Ch 2
165.23750	170.03750	NFM	Cardiff	Premier Taxis Ch 2 (250.3)
165.23750	170.03750	NFM	Carlisle	Taxi Company
165.23750	170.03750	NFM	Coventry	Dixon Group Warehouse
165.23750	170.03750	NFM	Crewe	Taxi Company
165.23750	170.03750	NFM	Glasgow	Taxi Company
165.23750	170.03750	NFM	Glossop	Thameside Council
165.23750	170.03750	NFM	Guernsey	Access Skips
165.23750	170.03750	NFM	Hastings	Phoenix Taxis
165.23750	170.03750	NFM	Isle of Man	Ramsey Hospital
165.23750	170.03750	NFM	Leighton Buzzard	Choake Billington
165.23750	170.03750	NFM	London	Minicab Firm, Ealing
165.23750	170.03750	NFM	Orford	Orfordness National Trust
165.23750	170.03750	NFM	Plymouth	Taxi Company
165.23750	170.03750	NFM	Poole	Repeater

Base	Mobile	Mode	Location	User and Notes
165.23750	170.03750	NFM	Reading	Parking Enforcement
165.23750	170.03750	NFM	Rhos on Sea	Gwynn's Taxis
165.23750	170.03750	NFM	Torpoint	Taxi Company
165.23750	170.03750	NFM	Wales	Black & White Taxis
165.25000	170.05000	NFM	Airdrie	Monkland Independent Taxis
165.25000	170.05000	NFM	Aylesbury	Waddesdon Manor Estate Staff/Beaters (71.9)
165.25000	170.05000	NFM	Belfast	Cregagh Cabs (67)
165.25000	170.05000	NFM	Birmingham	Taxi Company, Northfield
165.25000	170.05000	NFM	Bradford	Taxi Company
165.25000	170.05000	NFM	Cardiff	City Council Safety Events Ch.1
165.25000	170.05000	NFM	Chingford	Bell Cabs
165.25000	170.05000	NFM	Coventry	Taxi Company
165.25000	170.05000	NFM	Elvington	Warter Estate Farms
165.25000	170.05000	NFM	Glasgow	Taxi Company
165.25000	170.05000	NFM	Guernsey	Island Taxis
165.25000	170.05000	NFM	Gwynedd	Taxi Company
165.25000	170.05000	NFM	Hawick	D & G Taxis
165.25000	170.05000	NFM	Kent	Tankerton Gaming Machines
165.25000	170.05000	NFM	Lancing	Taxi Company
165.25000	170.05000	NFM	London	London Bridge Cars
165.25000	170.05000	NFM	London	Ruby Radio Cars, Walthamstow
165.25000	170.05000	NFM	Manchester	Taxi Company
165.25000	170.05000	NFM	Milton Keynes	Ace Cars
165.25000	170.05000	NFM	Montrose	Radio & TV Company
165.25000	170.05000	NFM	Newcastle	Taxi Company
165.25000	170.05000	NFM	Norwich	Millennium Bettacars
165.25000	170.05000	NFM	Sheffield	Confederate Cars
165.25000	170.05000	NFM	Slough	Compass Cars
165.25000	170.05000	NFM	Southend	Taxi Company
165.25000	170.05000	NFM	St Andrews	Williamson Taxis
165.25000	170.05000	NFM	Stantstead Abbots	RSPB Rye Meads Nature Reserve (71.9)
165.25000	170.05000	NFM	Swansea	Kingsway Cabs
165.25000	170.05000	NFM	Swansea	Swallow Taxis
165.25000	170.05000	NFM	Tenby	Taxi Company
165.25000	170.05000	NFM	Wirral	Taxi Company
165.26250	170.06250	NFM	Ashington	Heating Repairs
165.26250	170.06250	NFM	Belfast	Rank Taxis
165.26250	170.06250	NFM	Cheltenham	Bus Engineers
165.26250	170.06250	NFM	Dudley	TV Repair Company
165.26250	170.06250	NFM	Hampshire	Community Repeater Breakdown Recovery (136.5)
165.26250	170.06250	NFM	Herne Bay	Community Repeater Icom UK
165.26250	170.06250	NFM	Ipswich	Security
165.26250	170.06250	NFM	Isle of Man	Repeater, Snaefell
165.26250	170.06250	NFM	Jersey	CSL Repeater
165.26250	170.06250	NFM	Kent	St. John Ambulance Brigade Ch.6 (173.8)
165.26250	170.06250	NFM	Kent	Tankerton Gaming Machines (67)
165.26250	170.06250	NFM	Poole	Repeater
165.26250	170.06250	NFM	Preston	Council Dog Warden
165.26250	170.06250	NFM	Reading	Centurion Security
165.26250	170.06250	NFM	Sheffield	Crystal Peaks Security
165.26250	170.06250	NFM	Southampton	B & K Security
165.26250	170.06250	NFM	Southampton	Ravenscroft Motors
165.26250	170.06250	NFM	Swansea	Taxi Company
165.26250	170.06250	NFM	Walsall	GB Engineering
165.26250	170.06250	NFM	Worcester	Quarry Mill
165.27500	170.07500	NFM	Andover	Middleton & Portway Farms (203.5)

Base	Mobile	Mode	Location	User and Notes
165.27500	170.07500	NFM	Ashington	Ashington Taxis
165.27500	170.07500	NFM	Bath	Orange Grove Taxis
165.27500	170.07500	NFM	Benfleet	Wheel's Taxis
165.27500	170.07500	NFM	Brierley Hill	Lady Cabs
165.27500	170.07500	NFM	Dover	A2B Cars
165.27500	170.07500	NFM	Exeter	City Minibus Company
165.27500	170.07500	NFM	Felling	Taxi Company
165.27500	170.07500	NFM	Glasgow	Taxi Company
165.27500	170.07500	NFM	Guernsey	HF Gaudion
165.27500	170.07500	NFM	Halstead	Gosling Bros
165.27500	170.07500	NFM	Isle of Man	Electra Systems
165.27500	170.07500	NFM	London	Minicab Company, Holloway
165.27500	170.07500	NFM	London	Minicab Company, Kingston
165.27500	170.07500	NFM	Manchester	Taxi Company
165.27500	170.07500	NFM	Mansfield	Ace Taxis
165.27500	170.07500	NFM	Montrose	Taxi Company
165.27500	170.07500	NFM	Newport	Show Taxis (123)
165.27500	170.07500	NFM	Newtownabbey	Newtownabbey Taxis
165.27500	170.07500	NFM	Poole	Repeater
165.27500	170.07500	NFM	Portsmouth	Taxi Company
165.27500	170.07500	NFM	Romsey	Paultons Park Staff
165.27500	170.07500	NFM	Shire Oaks	Shire Oaks Colliery Security
165.27500	170.07500	NFM	Swindon	Swindon Taxis
165.27500	170.07500	NFM	Swinton	Lynch Taxis
165.28750	170.08750	NFM	Bangor	Taxi Company
165.28750	170.08750	NFM	Belfast	Stormont Cabs (110.9)
165.28750	170.08750	NFM	Blaxhall	Greenfields, Lime Tree Farm
165.28750	170.08750	NFM	Carmarthen	Taxi Company (71.9)
165.28750	170.08750	NFM	Chesterford	Park Research
165.28750	170.08750	NFM	Cleveland	Boro Taxis
165.28750	170.08750	NFM	Colchester	Taxi Company
165.28750	170.08750	NFM	Downham Market	Lindsay Smith
165.28750	170.08750	NFM	Falkirk	Taxi Company
165.28750	170.08750	NFM	Ferndown	Taxi Company
165.28750	170.08750	NFM	Jersey	Polar Car Hire
165.28750	170.08750	NFM	Lincoln	Imp Taxis
165.28750	170.08750	NFM	London	Minicab Company, Beckenham
165.28750	170.08750	NFM	London	Minicab Company, Bromley
165.28750	170.08750	NFM	Macclesfield	Silvertown Taxis
165.28750	170.08750	NFM	Montrose	Taxi Company
165.28750	170.08750	NFM	New Quay	New Quay Taxis
165.28750	170.08750	NFM	Peterborough	King Cabs (146.2)
165.28750	170.08750	NFM	Rochdale	Streamline Taxis
165.28750	170.08750	NFM	Rochester	Marconi Avionics Fire/Security
165.28750	170.08750	NFM	Spalding	Baytree Nurseries
165.28750	170.08750	NFM	Stotford	Bewes Electrical
165.28750	170.08750	NFM	Suffolk	Farm (118.8)
165.28750	170.08750	NFM	Warwickshire	Farm
165.28750	170.08750	NFM	Woolwich	Taxi Company
165.30000	170.10000	NFM	Colwyn Bay	Taxi Company
165.30000	170.10000	NFM	East Dereham	Dereham Taxis
165.30000	170.10000	NFM	Edinburgh	Taxi Company
165.30000	170.10000	NFM	Fleet	Crystal Taxis
165.30000	170.10000	NFM	Fleet	Jockey Taxis
165.30000	170.10000	NFM	Guernsey	Links Community Repeater 2
165.30000	170.10000	NFM	Hook	Crystal Taxis

Base	Mobile	Mode	Location	User and Notes
165.30000	170.10000	NFM	Lichfield	Taxi Company
165.30000	170.10000	NFM	London	Doctors' Service
165.30000	170.10000	NFM	London	St John Ambulance Special Events (186.2)
165.30000	170.10000	NFM	Midlands	Delta Delivery
165.30000	170.10000	NFM	Midlands	Target Delivery
165.30000	170.10000	NFM	Newbury	Cabco
165.30000	170.10000	NFM	Oxfordshire	Security Firm
165.30000	170.10000	NFM	Taplow	Farm (131.8)
165.30000	170.10000	NFM	Worcester	Security Company
165.31250	170.10000	NFM	Bristol	Abba Cabs
165.31250	170.11250	NFM	Caerphilly	Taxi Company (123)
165.31250	170.11250	NFM	Christchurch	Taxi Company
165.31250	170.11250	AM	Cleethorpes	Taxi Company
165.31250	170.11250	NFM	Coventry	MJ DeCourcey Coaches
165.31250	170.11250	NFM	Croydon	The Croydon Carriage Company
165.31250	170.11250	NFM	Glasgow	Taxi Company
165.31250	170.11250	NFM	Glossop	Padtax Taxis
165.31250	170.11250	NFM	Launceston	Roscar Electronics
165.31250	170.11250	NFM	Leigh	Avacab
165.31250	170.11250	NFM	London	Minicab Company, Putney
165.31250	170.11250	NFM	Luton	Skyline Cars
165.31250	170.11250	NFM	Manchester	Taxi Company
165.31250	170.11250	NFM	Merseyside	Taxi Company
165.31250	170.11250	NFM	Morecambe	Taxi Company
165.31250	170.11250	NFM	Northampton	Taxi Company
165.31250	170.11250	NFM	Newbury	Cabco
165.31250	170.11250	NFM	N Herts	Taxi Company (218.1)
165.31250	170.11250	NFM	Nottingham	Taxi Company
165.31250	170.11250	NFM	Oxfordshire	Government Use (94.8)
165.31250	170.11250	NFM	Pembroke	Taxi Company (82.5)
165.31250	170.11250	NFM	Peterborough	Euro A2B Cabs (88.5)
165.31250	170.11250	NFM	Plymouth	Council Security
165.31250	170.11250	NFM	Southampton	Taxi Company
165.31250	170.11250	NFM	Stansted	Aircars
165.31250	170.11250	NFM	Swindon	Ace Taxis
165.31250	170.11250	NFM	Tamworth	Refuse Collectors (203.5)
165.31250	170.11250	NFM	Taunton	Alpha/Apex Taxis
165.32500	170.12500	NFM	Bristol	Paramedics
165.32500	170.12500	NFM	Coventry	Linkline Parcels
165.32500	170.12500	NFM	Edinburgh	Taxi Company
165.32500	170.12500	NFM	Humberside	Haulage Company
165.32500	170.12500	NFM	London	London Underground Line Ch.6
165.32500	170.12500	NFM	Plymouth	City Security (Papa Control)
165.32500	170.12500	NFM	Poole	Repeater
165.32500	170.12500	NFM	Sheffield	Kay & Hodgkinson Plant Hire
165.32500	170.12500	NFM	Southampton	Taxi Company
165.32500	170.12500	NFM	Swansea	A & M Parcel Delivery Service
165.32500	170.12500	NFM	Warwickshire	Farm
165.33750	170.13750	NFM	Calne	Taxi Company
165.33750	170.13750	NFM	Cambridge	Lion Yard Shopping Centre Security
165.33750	170.13750	NFM	Cardiff	Cardiff cars (107.2)
165.33750	170.13750	NFM	Carlisle	Auto Recoveries
165.33750	170.13750	NFM	Cheltenham	A to B Taxis
165.33750	170.13750	NFM	Clacton on Sea	Ace Taxis
165.33750	170.13750	NFM	Clacton on Sea	Bernie's Taxis
165.33750	170.13750	NFM	Cleethorpes	AA Taxis

Base	Mobile	Mode	Location	User and Notes
165.33750	170.13750	NFM	Coventry	Linkline Parcels
165.33750	170.13750	NFM	Debach	Green Label Poultry
165.33750	170.13750	NFM	Eccles	Minicabs Company
165.33750	170.13750	NFM	Glasgow	Clydeside Taxi
165.33750	170.13750	NFM	Gt Yarmouth	Farm (123)
165.33750	170.13750	NFM	Inverness	Eastgate Shopping Centre Security
165.33750	170.13750	NFM	Kings Lynn	Simons
165.33750	170.13750	NFM	Letchwood	John's Taxis
165.33750	170.13750	NFM	Lisburn	Central Taxis (77)
165.33750	170.13750	NFM	London	Minicab Company, Camden
165.33750	170.13750	NFM	Lytham	Lytham Taxis
165.33750	170.13750	NFM	Manchester	Taxi Company
165.33750	170.13750	NFM	Peterborough	Goldstar Cabs
165.33750	170.13750	NFM	Southampton	Taxi Company
165.33750	170.13750	NFM	Stoke on Trent	Z Cars Taxis
165.33750	170.13750	NFM	Swindon	Taxi Company
165.33750	170.13750	NFM	Winchester	Taxi Company
165.33750	170.13750	NFM	Wool	Monkey World Staff Ch.1 (118.8)
165.33750	170.13750	NFM	Wrexham	Atax Taxis
165.35000	170.15000	NFM	Bath	Twerton Taxis
165.35000	170.15000	NFM	Belfast	Taxi Company, Oldpark Road
165.35000	170.15000	NFM	Bournemouth	Ace Taxis
165.35000	170.15000	NFM	Bury	Star Taxis
165.35000	170.15000	NFM	Cambridge	Cambridge Cabs
165.35000	170.15000	NFM	Clacton	Ace Taxis
165.35000	170.15000	NFM	Dumfries	Diamond Taxis
165.35000	170.15000	NFM	Felling	Taxi Company
165.35000	170.15000	NFM	Glasgow	Taxi Company
165.35000	170.15000	NFM	Great Melton	Downham Farm Services
165.35000	170.15000	NFM	Lichfield	Taxi Company
165.35000	170.15000	NFM	Lincoln	Security
165.35000	170.15000	NFM	London	Minicab Company, Lewisham
165.35000	170.15000	NFM	Luton	Victor Taxis
165.35000	170.15000	NFM	Manchester	Taxi Company
165.35000	170.15000	NFM	Newcastle	Northumbria University
165.35000	170.15000	NFM	Nottingham	Doctors Service
165.35000	170.15000	NFM	Peterborough	ABC Taxis
165.35000	170.15000	NFM	West Parley	Parley Court Farm (77)
165.36250	170.15000	NFM	Bedfordshire	Eastern Counties Farmers
165.36250	165.36250	NFM	Birkenhead	Car Breakdown Recovery
165.36250	170.16250	NFM	Bournemouth	Lynx Carriers
165.36250	170.16250	NFM	Derby	Community Repeater
165.36250	170.16250	NFM	Dundee	Car Hire Service
165.36250	170.16250	NFM	Edinburgh	Community Repeater
165.36250	170.16250	NFM	Gosport	Taxi Company
165.36250	170.16250	NFM	Greenham	Council
165.36250	170.16250	NFM	Isle of Wight	Steve Porter Transport, Cowes
165.36250	170.16250	NFM	Leicester	Taxi Company
165.36250	170.16250	NFM	Liverpool	Taxi Company
165.36250	170.16250	NFM	London	Net Cars
165.36250	170.16250	NFM	London	Streetline Buses
165.36250	170.16250	NFM	London	Tosca Skips
165.36250	170.16250	NFM	London	West London Skips
165.36250	170.16250	NFM	Matlock	Haulage Company
165.36250	170.16250	NFM	Mendlesham	Trident Recovery (94.8)
165.36250	170.16250	NFM	Milford Haven	Skip Lorries

Base	Mobile	Mode	Location	User and Notes
165.36250	170.16250	NFM	Oxfordshire	Security Company
165.36250	170.16250	NFM	Pembroke	Taxi Company
165.36250	170.16250	NFM	Perth	Community Repeater
165.36250	170.16250	NFM	Plymouth	Devro Security
165.36250	170.16250	NFM	Poole	Repeater
165.36250	170.16250	NFM	Portsmouth	Docks, Steve Porter Transport
165.36250	170.16250	NFM	Portsmouth	St John Ambulance at Events (71.9)
165.36250	170.16250	NFM	Southampton	Security Company
165.36250	170.16250	NFM	Thanet	Thanet Buses
165.36250	170.16250	NFM	St. Monans	Bass Rock Oil Company
165.37500	170.17500	NFM	Bath	Rainbow Taxis
165.37500	170.17500	NFM	Birkenhead	All The 3s Taxis
165.37500	170.17500	NFM	Blaxhall	Blaxhall Farm
165.37500	170.17500	NFM	Cambridge	Able Cars
165.37500	170.17500	NFM	Chelmsford	Taxi Company
165.37500	170.17500	NFM	Cheltenham	727 Taxis (136.5)
165.37500	170.17500	NFM	Dumfries	Bee Hive Taxis
165.37500	170.17500	NFM	Glasgow	Taxi Company
165.37500	170.17500	NFM	Harlow	Regency Cars
165.37500	170.17500	NFM	Holyhead	Taxi Company (71.9)
165.37500	170.17500	NFM	Isle of Man	Taxi Company
165.37500	170.17500	NFM	London	Minicab Company, Nine Elms
165.37500	170.17500	NFM	Newtownards	A&G/Scrabo Taxis (82.5)
165.37500	170.17500	NFM	Plymouth	Olympic Taxis
165.37500	170.17500	NFM	Ramsbottom	Snobs Private Hire
165.37500	170.17500	NFM	Reading	Checkers Cars
165.37500	170.17500	NFM	Redcar	Allied Central Taxis
165.38750	170.18750	NFM	Biggleswade	Maurices Cars (77)
165.38750	170.18750	NFM	Bradford	FTB Private Hire
165.38750	170.18750	NFM	Carlisle	Taxi Company
165.38750	170.18750	NFM	Clacton-on-Sea	Apollo Taxis
165.38750	170.18750	NFM	Clydach	Cwmtawe Travel (Buses & Taxis)
165.38750	170.18750	NFM	Cumbria	Community Repeater S. Lakes
165.38750	170.18750	NFM	Fakenham	Selective Fertilisers
165.38750	170.18750	NFM	Glasgow	Taxi Company
165.38750	170.18750	NFM	Hoylake	Hoylake Station Radio Taxis
165.38750	170.18750	NFM	Jersey	F. Brown Recovery
165.38750	170.18750	NFM	Louth	Community Repeater
165.38750	170.18750	NFM	Luton Airport	LEP Internetional Freight Handling
165.38750	170.18750	NFM	Medway	Kingsferry Coaches
165.38750	170.18750	NFM	Middlesbrough	Taxi Company
165.38750	170.18750	NFM	Morecambe	Joe's Taxis
165.38750	170.18750	NFM	Motherwell	United Taxis
165.38750	170.18750	NFM	Newport	Greenline Taxis (179.9)
165.38750	170.18750	NFM	Newport	Red Dragon Taxis Ch.1
165.38750	170.18750	NFM	Peterlee	Yellow Cabs
165.38750	170.18750	NFM	Portsmouth	Taxi Company
165.38750	170.18750	NFM	Retford	Malcolm's Taxis
165.38750	170.18750	NFM	Sheffield	City Cars
165.38750	170.18750	NFM	Sherborne	Beaver Cabs (88.5)
165.38750	170.18750	NFM	Soham	Tompsett Burgess Growers
165.38750	170.18750	NFM	Tayside	Farm Workers
165.38750	170.18750	NFM	Wilshaw	Taxi Company
165.38750	170.18750	NFM	Wool	Monkey World Ch.2 Keepers (107.2)
165.40000	170.20000	NFM	Abingdon	Top Cabs (77)
165.40000	170.20000	NFM	Bedford	Community Repeater

Base	Mobile	Mode	Location	User and Notes
165.40000	170.20000	NFM	Cambourne	Vending Company
165.40000	170.20000	NFM	Cornwall	Houpers Haulage
165.40000	170.20000	NFM	Cumbria	Community Repeater, South Lakes
165.40000	170.20000	NFM	Ipswich	Repeater
165.40000	170.20000	NFM	Lancashire	Andersons Pumps
165.40000	170.20000	NFM	London	London Underground Stations Ch.2
165.40000	170.20000	NFM	Morecambe	Delivery Service
165.40000	170.20000	NFM	Morpeth	Garden Centre
165.40000	170.20000	NFM	Nottingham	Taxi Company
165.40000	170.20000	NFM	Worthing	Transport Company
165.41250	170.21250	NFM	Ballymoney	Route Taxis (250.3)
165.41250	170.21250	NFM	Brighton	Devils Dyke Golf Club
165.41250	170.21250	NFM	Leeds	Motor Factors
165.41250	170.21250	NFM	London	London Underground Bakerloo Line
165.41250	170.21250	NFM	London	London Underground District Line
165.41250	170.21250	NFM	London	London Underground Line Ch.1
165.41250	170.21250	NFM	London	London Underground Piccadilly Line
165.41250	170.21250	NFM	Lowestoft	Waveney Couriers
165.41250	170.21250	NFM	Newcastle	Plumbers
165.41250	170.21250	NFM	Norfolk	General Refrigeration
165.41250	170.21250	NFM	Perth	King Contractors
165.41250	170.21250	NFM	Wilby	TG Askew Haulage
165.42500	170.22500	NFM	Birmingham	Taxi Company, Sparkhill
165.42500	170.22500	NFM	Calne	Taxi Company
165.42500	170.22500	NFM	Cleethorpes	Beavers Cars
165.42500	170.22500	NFM	Cornwall	Associated Leisure
165.42500	170.22500	NFM	Falkirk	Bruce Taxis
165.42500	170.22500	NFM	Farnborough	Farnborough College
165.42500	170.22500	NFM	Hull	Taxi Company
165.42500	170.22500	NFM	Letchworth	Taxi Company (114.8)
165.42500	170.22500	NFM	Lichfield	Taxi Company
165.42500	170.22500	NFM	Llanelli	Taxi Company
165.42500	170.22500	NFM	Milford Haven	Taxi Company
165.42500	170.22500	NFM	Newcastle	Taxi Company
165.42500	170.22500	NFM	Ormskirk	Green Line Taxis
165.42500	170.22500	NFM	Plymouth	Night Watch Security
165.42500	170.22500	NFM	Pontypridd	Regal Taxis
165.42500	170.22500	NFM	Swinton	Swinton 1010 Taxis
165.42500	170.22500	NFM	Wakefield	Taxi Company
165.43750	170.23750	NFM	Abingdon	Superior Suppers (107.2)
165.43750	170.23750	NFM	Barrow in Furness	CAW Skip Hire & Haulage
165.43750	170.23750	NFM	Birmingham	Castle Security
165.43750	170.23750	NFM	Brecon	Mountain Rescue (S) (114.8)
165.43750	170.23750	NFM	Bristol	Taxi Company
165.43750	170.23750	NFM	Carlisle	H & E Trotter
165.43750	170.23750	NFM	Colchester	General Refrigeration
165.43750	170.23750	NFM	Colchester	Trident Recovery
165.43750	170.23750	NFM	Derbyshire	Riber Security
165.43750	170.23750	NFM	Haverfordwest	Taxi Company
165.43750	170.23750	NFM	Humberside	Cash Register Company
165.43750	170.23750	NFM	London	London Underground City Line
165.43750	170.23750	NFM	London	London Underground Metropolitan Line
165.43750	170.23750	NFM	London	London Underground Piccadilly Line Main
165.43750	170.23750	NFM	Manchester	Taxi Company
165.43750	170.23750	NFM	Mansfield	Doctors' Service
165.43750	170.23750	NFM	Merthyr Tydfil	Mountain Rescue (118.8)

Base	Mobile	Mode	Location	User and Notes
165.43750	170.23750	NFM	Oxford	Freight Company (141.3)
165.43750	170.23750	NFM	Pembroke	Taxi Company
165.43750	170.23750	NFM	Peterborough	City Aerials Ltd
165.43750	170.23750	NFM	Staffordshire	Security Company
165.43750	170.23750	NFM	Truro	Pellows Waste
165.43750	170.23750	NFM	West Midlands	Castle Security
165.43750	170.23750	NFM	Woodsford	Woodsford Farm (123)
165.45000	170.25000	NFM	Ashmore	Glebe Farm (118.8)
165.45000	170.25000	NFM	Brighton	Blood/Medical Courier Service (82.5)
165.45000	170.25000	NFM	Cambridgeshire	Farm (114.8)
165.45000	170.25000	NFM	Edinburgh	Council Cleansing Department
165.45000	170.25000	NFM	Frome	Taxi Company
165.45000	170.25000	NFM	Hastings	Conquest Hospital Porters/Security (67)
165.45000	170.25000	NFM	Isle of Man	Taxi Company
165.45000	170.25000	NFM	London	Club Cars, Southal
165.45000	170.25000	NFM	London	Minicab Company, Greenford
165.45000	170.25000	NFM	Newport	Alfa Taxis
165.45000	170.25000	NFM	Poole	Repeater
165.45000	170.25000	NFM	Southminster	Badnocks Farm
165.45000	170.25000	NFM	Truro	Treliske Hospital
165.46250	170.26250	NFM	Belfast	Water Board
165.46250	170.26250	NFM	Bristol	Community Repeater
165.46250	170.26250	NFM	Eye, Suffolk	TG Asher Haulage
165.46250	170.26250	NFM	Glasgow	Salone Services
165.46250	170.26250	NFM	Gloucester	Repeater
165.46250	170.26250	NFM	Ipswich	Kesgrave Aggregates (K-Base)
165.46250	170.26250	NFM	Ipswich	Nightfreight (East) Ltd (B)
165.46250	170.26250	NFM	Ipswich	Polar Base Freezers
165.46250	170.26250	NFM	London	London Underground Central Line
165.46250	170.26250	NFM	London	London Underground Jubilee Line
165.46250	170.26250	NFM	London	London Underground Line Ch.8
165.46250	170.26250	NFM	Needham Market	TG Concrete
165.46250	170.26250	NFM	Poole	Repeater
165.46250	170.26250	NFM	Southport	Southport Hospital
165.46250	170.26250	NFM	Suffolk	Biffa Bins
165.46250	170.26250	NFM	Suffolk	General Refrigeration
165.46250	170.26250	NFM	Tayside	Vets
165.46250	170.26250	NFM	Worthing	Nynex Cable Comms
165.46250	170.26250	NFM	Wilby	TG Askew Haulage
165.47500	170.27500	NFM	Haddenham	Anglia Cars
165.47500	170.27500	NFM	Kent	Doctors' Service
165.47500	170.27500	NFM	Newport	Community Repeater
165.47500	170.27500	NFM	Plymouth	Red Lightning Dispatch
165.47500	170.27500	NFM	Poole	Repeater
165.47500	170.27500	NFM	Scunthorpe	Courier Service
165.47500	170.27500	NFM	Southampton	Doctors' Service Ch.3
165.48750	170.28750	NFM	Ashton under Lyme	Stamford Private Hire
165.48750	170.28750	NFM	Barry	Flat Holm Island Maintenance (173)
165.48750	170.28750	NFM	Belfast	Amber Taxis, Creagh Road
165.48750	170.28750	NFM	Birmingham	Taxi Company
165.48750	170.28750	NFM	Bristol	Severn Bridge Maintenance (Jasmine)
165.48750	170.28750	NFM	Carlisle	Taxi Company
165.48750	170.28750	NFM	Exeter	Club Taxis
165.48750	170.28750	NFM	Exeter	Maxi Cabs
165.48750	170.28750	NFM	Leicestershire	Farm
165.48750	170.28750	NFM	Little Hulton	Radio Cars Ltd Taxis

Base	Mobile	Mode	Location	User and Notes
165.48750	170.28750	NFM	Manchester	Taxi Company
165.48570	170.28750	NFM	Millom	Pete's Taxis (88.5)
165.48750	170.28750	NFM	Milton Keynes	Quicker Cars
165.48750	170.28750	NFM	Montrose	Taxi Company
165.48750	170.28750	NFM	Oldham	Delta Cars
165.48750	170.28750	NFM	Runcorn	Taxi Company
165.48750	170.28750	NFM	West Midlands	Arrow Taxis
165.50000	170.30000	NFM	Bournemouth	Token Amusements Ltd
165.50000	170.30000	NFM	Bristol	Taxi Company
165.50000	170.30000	NFM	Cambridge	Institute of Animal Physiology, Babraham
165.50000	170.30000	NFM	Cleethorpes	Fon-a-Car
165.50000	170.30000	NFM	Dover	P & O Ferries
165.50000	170.30000	NFM	Glasgow	Taxi Company
165.50000	170.30000	NFM	Gorton	Belle Vue Cars
165.50000	170.30000	NFM	Hemel Hempstead	Rainbow Cars (118.8)
165.50000	170.30000	NFM	Holyhead	Star Taxis
165.50000	170.30000	NFM	Letchwood	G Folly Builders
165.50000	170.30000	NFM	London	Fitzpatrick Builders
165.50000	170.30000	NFM	London	Ron's Cars, Stoke Newington
165.50000	170.30000	NFM	Martlesham	Independent Taxis Ltd Ch.1
165.50000	170.30000	NFM	Paisley	Taxi Company
165.50000	170.30000	NFM	Plymouth	Tower Cabs
165.50000	170.30000	NFM	Swansea	Phoenix Security
165.50000	170.30000	NFM	Swansea	Ystrad Cabs, Ystradgynlais
165.51250	170.31250	NFM	Aberdeen	Taxi Company
165.51250	170.31250	NFM	Aberystwyth	Aber Cars
165.51250	170.31250	NFM	Ashton under Lyme	Courier Service
165.51250	170.31250	NFM	Birkenhead	Delta Cars
165.51250	170.31250	NFM	Bishop Stortford	Taxi Company
165.51250	170.31250	NFM	Bolton	Halliwell Taxis
165.51250	170.31250	NFM	Bristol	Taxi Company
165.51250	170.31250	NFM	Cadishead	Cadishead Cars (141.3)
165.51250	170.31250	NFM	Cambridge	Browns Taxis
165.51250	170.31250	NFM	Gloucester	TV Repair Company
165.51250	170.31250	NFM	Holyhead	Taxi Company (67)
165.51250	170.31250	NFM	Liverpool	Taxi Company
165.51250	170.31250	NFM	Manchester	Taxi Company
165.51250	170.31250	NFM	Nottingham	Apex Taxis, Hucknall
165.51250	170.31250	NFM	Oxenholme	Blue Star Taxis (67)
165.51250	170.31250	NFM	Poole	Repeater
165.51250	170.31250	NFM	Sheerness	Val's Cars
165.51250	170.31250	NFM	Sheffield	Bradwell Skips Services
165.51250	170.31250	NFM	Stockport	Taxi Company
165.51250	170.31250	NFM	Swansea	Lakes Taxis
165.51250	170.31250	NFM	Worthing	Taxi Company
165.51250	170.31250	NFM	Wrexham	Club Taxis
165.52500	170.32500	NFM	Basildon	Taxi Company
165.52500	170.32500	NFM	Bedfordshire	Manor Farm
165.52500	170.32500	NFM	Belfast	Serviceforce Washing Machine Repairs
165.52500	170.32500	NFM	Bristol	Community Repeater
165.52500	170.32500	NFM	Cambridgeshire	Farm (162.2)
165.52500	170.32500	NFM	Exmouth	Shopwatch (71.9)
165.52500	170.32500	NFM	Gt Yarmouth	Haulage Company Ch.1 (107.2)
165.52500	170.32500	NFM	Halifax	ABC Taxis
165.52500	170.32500	NFM	Kent	Farm (123)
165.52500	170.32500	NFM	Kent	Stanfast Alarms

Base	Mobile	Mode	Location	User and Notes
165.52500	170.32500	NFM	Knowlton	New Barn Farm (94.8)
165.52500	170.32500	NFM	London	Embassy Cars
165.52500	170.32500	NFM	Luton	Parking Enforcement (110.9)
165.52500	170.32500	NFM	Manchester	Taxi Company
165.52500	170.32500	NFM	Reading	1st Yellow Cars
165.52500	170.32500	NFM	Swansea	Taxi Company
165.52500	170.32500	NFM	Urmston	Phoenix Taxis
165.52500	170.32500	NFM	Wickham Market	A Hayward & Sons, Low Farm (94.8)
165.52500	170.32500	NFM	Wiltshire	TV Repair Company
165.53750	170.33750	NFM	Abingdon	Eagle Security Company
165.53750	170.33750	NFM	Askam in Furness	Furness Vehicle Recovery Service
165.53750	170.33750	NFM	Birmingham	Travel West Midland Buses
165.53750	170.33750	NFM	Bradford	Cosy Cars
165.53750	170.33750	NFM	Cardiff	Celtic Cars
165.53750	170.33750	NFM	Carrickfergus	Carrick Cabs
165.53750	170.33750	NFM	Gateshead	Shopwatch
165.53750	170.33750	NFM	Norfolk	General Refrigeration
165.53750	170.33750	NFM	Norfolk	Waveney Couriers
165.53750	170.33750	NFM	N Yorkshire	Doctors' Service
165.53750	170.33750	NFM	Oxfordshire	Car Windscreen Repair Company
165.53750	170.33750	NFM	Oxfordshire	Central Heating Company
165.53750	170.33750	NFM	Oxfordshire	Courier Company
165.53750	170.33750	NFM	Scarborough	Shopwatch, Brunswick Shopping Centre
165.53750	170.33750	NFM	Scunthorpe	Corus Steel Emergency Services
165.53750	170.33750	NFM	Stamford	Stamford Cars (127.3)
165.53750	170.33750	NFM	Wells	Taxi Company
165.53750	170.33750	NFM	Wolverhampton	Skip Hire Company
165.55000	170.35000	NFM	Blackburn	Intack Private Hire
165.55000	170.35000	NFM	Bradford	Thornbury Private Hire
165.55000	170.35000	NFM	Edinburgh	Tarmac Roadstone
165.55000	170.35000	NFM	Eskdale	Ravenglass & Eskdale Railway
165.55000	170.35000	NFM	London	Breakdown Recovery Company (192.8)
165.55000	170.35000	NFM	London	Red Cross Ch.5 (67)
165.55000	170.35000	NFM	Rhyl	Station Taxis
165.55000	170.35000	NFM	Southampton	Taxi Company
165.55000	170.35000	NFM	S Warwickshire	Farm
165.56250	170.36250	NFM	Brighton	Royal Sussex County Hospital
165.56250	170.36250	NFM	Bristol	Community Repeater
165.56250	170.36250	NFM	Cambridge	Community Repeater Oak Park Security Ch.1
165.56250	170.36250	NFM	Cheltenham	Community Repeater Bus Inspectors
165.56250	170.36250	NFM	Cheltenham	Community Repeater Gaming Machine Repairs
165.56250	170.36250	NFM	Cheltenham	Community Repeater Monarch Security
165.56250	170.36250	NFM	Cheltenham	Community Repeater Refuse Collectors
165.56250	170.36250	NFM	Cleveland	Stagecoach Buses
165.56250	170.36250	NFM	Derbyshire	Derbyshire Council Rangers
165.56250	170.36250	NFM	Edinburgh	Community Repeater Carpet Fitting Company
165.56250	170.36250	NFM	Edinburgh	Community Repeater Castle Security
165.56250	170.36250	NFM	Edinburgh	Community Repeater Trinity Roofing
165.56250	170.36250	NFM	Glasgow	Taxi Company
165.56250	170.36250	NFM	Hartlepool	Bus Company
165.56250	170.36250	NFM	London	Thames Water Engineers
165.56250	170.36250	NFM	Norwich	Blueline Taxis
165.56250	170.36250	NFM	Poole	Fernside Recovery
165.56250	170.36250	NFM	Portsmouth	Bus Company
165.56250	170.36250	NFM	Preston	Parking Enforcement NCP/Parkwise (67)
165.56250	170.36250	NFM	Starford	Tree Surgeons

Base	Mobile	Mode	Location	User and Notes
165.56250	170.36250	NFM	Stoke on Trent	PMT Buses (103.5)
165.56250	170.36250	NFM	Suffolk	East Counties Farmers Ch.2
165.56250	170.36250	NFM	Swindon	Games Machine Company
165.56250	170.36250	NFM	Truro	Shopwatch
165.56250	170.36250	NFM	Tyne & Wear	Doctors' Service
165.56250	170.36250	NFM	Wirral	Brombourgh Cabs
165.56750	170.37500	NFM	Worksop	Trumpet Taxis
165.57500	170.37500	NFM	Accrington	D-Line Cars
165.57500	170.37500	NFM	Bedfordshire	Manor Farm
165.57500	170.37500	NFM	Coleraine	SB Taxis (118.8)
165.57500	170.37500	NFM	Cymmer	Taxi Company (131.8)
165.57500	170.37500	NFM	Edinburgh	Eden Aerial Riggers
165.57500	170.37500	NFM	Felixstowe	Taxi Company
165.57500	170.37500	NFM	Grimsby	Taxi Company
165.57500	170.37500	NFM	Grundisburgh	Tuckwell Engineering
165.57500	170.37500	NFM	Haverhill	Jennings Transport
165.57500	170.37500	NFM	Manchester	New United Taxis
165.57500	170.37500	NFM	Montrose	Farm Workers
165.57500	170.37500	NFM	Newport	Star Taxis (110.9)
165.57500	170.37500	NFM	Sheffield	Star Cars
165.57500	17.037500	NFM	Southend on Sea	Borough Council Maintenance (71.9)
165.57500	17.037500	NFM	Spilsby	Yates & Greenough Television
165.57500	170.37500	NFM	Weston Super Mare	Woodspring Taxis
165.57500	170.37500	NFM	Wiltshire	Ambulance Major Incident Channel (67)
165.57500	170.37500	NFM	Woodbridge	K Tuckwell Engineers
165.58750	170.38750	NFM	Blackburn	A&B Private Hire
165.58750	170.38750	NFM	Coventry	Neil Bartlett Haulage
165.58750	170.38750	NFM	Letchworth	Arrotaxis
165.58750	170.38750	NFM	London	Riverside Cabs, Richmond
165.58750	170.38750	NFM	Macclesfield	Taxi Company
165.58750	170.38750	NFM	Manchester	Taxi Company
165.58750	170.38750	NFM	Newhaven	Taxi Company
165.58750	170.38750	NFM	Sheffield	F W Collins Skips
165.58750	170.38750	NFM	Stockport	Taxi Company
165.58750	170.38750	NFM	Swinton	Radio Cars Ltd
165.60000	170.40000	NFM	Aldridge	Alpha Taxis
165.60000	170.40000	NFM	Bridlington	Coastline Cabs
165.60000	170.40000	NFM	Bristol	NCP Car Parks
165.60000	170.40000	NFM	Bury	Taxi Company
165.60000	170.40000	NFM	Cornwall	English China Clay
165.60000	170.40000	NFM	Glasgow	Taxi Company
165.60000	170.40000	NFM	Glossop	Shadow Taxis
165.60000	170.40000	NFM	Ipswich	Elite Taxis & Fleet Cabs
165.60000	170.40000	NFM	London	Z Car Hire, Paddington
165.60000	170.40000	NFM	Manchester	Taxi Company
165.60000	170.40000	NFM	Paisley	Taxi Company
165.60000	170.40000	NFM	Port Talbot	Corus Steelworks (71.9)
165.60000	170.40000	NFM	Stockport	Taxi Company
165.60000	170.40000	NFM	Suffolk	Council Beach Wardens
165.60000	170.40000	NFM	West Lexham	Lodge Farm
165.61250	170.41250	NFM	Castleton	Castleton Cars
165.61250	170.41250	NFM	Dunstable	Hunter Taxis
165.61250	170.41250	NFM	Kirkham	Taxi Company
165.61250	170.41250	NFM	Lakenheath	Base Taxis
165.61250	170.41250	NFM	Linlithgow	Taxi Company
165.61250	170.41250	NFM	Mildenhall	M & L Taxis

Base	Mobile	Mode	Location	User and Notes
165.61250	170.41250	NFM	Neath	Dragon Cabs
165.61250	170.41250	NFM	Newcastle	Buses
165.61250	170.41250	NFM	Perth	Council Plumbers
165.61250	170.41250	NFM	Scunthorpe	Steel Works Maintenance
165.61250	170.41250	NFM	Sheffield	Indoor Market Security
165.61250	170.41250	NFM	St Austell	ECC Pits
165.61250	170.41250	NFM	Stansted	Taxi Company
165.62500	170.42500	NFM	Bangor	University of Wales Security
165.62500	170.42500	NFM	Bolton	Tonge Moor Private Hire
165.62500	170.42500	NFM	Bridlington	Star Cars
165.62500	170.42500	AM	Bristol	Bond Delivery
165.62500	170.42500	NFM	Co. Durham	Haulage, Coal Wagons
165.62500	170.42500	NFM	East Dereham	Acab Taxis
165.62500	170.42500	NFM	Glasgow	Taxi Company
165.62500	170.42500	NFM	Leicester	City Buses
165.62500	170.42500	NFM	Newcastle	Taxi Company
165.62500	170.42500	NFM	Newmarket	Newtax Taxis
165.62500	170.42500	NFM	Oxford	Royal Taxis (94.8)
165.62500	170.42500	NFM	Plymouth	Central Taxis
165.62500	170.42500	NFM	Sheffield	Sheffield United Football Club Stewards
165.62500	170.42500	NFM	Sittingbourne	Swale Taxis
165.62500	170.42500	NFM	Southampton	First Bus Limited
165.62500	170.42500	NFM	Swansea	Swallow Cars
165.62500	170.42500	NFM	Walton	Dancabs Taxis
165.62500	170.42500	NFM	Worcester	Take-Away Delivery Service
165.63750	170.43750	NFM	London	British Transport Police Ch.1 (All Now Mainly Airwave)
165.63750		NFM	Nationwide	British Transport Police Ch.3 (All Now Mainly Airwave)
165.63750	170.43750	NFM	Nationwide	Royal Parks Police Ch.1 (All Now Mainly Airwave)
165.63750	170.43750	NFM	Tadworth	British Transport Police Training Centre Ch.3 (118.8)
165.65000	170.45000	NFM	Cambridge	Cambridge Council
165.65000	170.45000	NFM	Chichester	District Council Car Parks/Patrols
165.65000	170.45000	NFM	Halifax	Calderdale Council Transport (118.8)
165.65000		NFM	London	British Transport Police Ch.4 (All Now Mainly Airwave)
165.65000	170.45000	NFM	London	British Transport Police London Underground Ch.2 (118.8)
165.65000	170.45000	NFM	Somerset	South Somerset Council
165.65000	170.45000	NFM	Warrington	Warrington Council Environmental Services
165.66250	170.46250	NFM	Belfast	Sure Cabs, Antrim Road
165.66250	170.46250	NFM	Bristol	City Line Buses
165.66250	170.46250	NFM	Consett	Taxi Company
165.66250	170.46250	NFM	Hatfield	Hilltop Taxis (103.5)
165.66250	170.46250	NFM	Llandudno	Taxi Service
165.66250	170.46250	NFM	London	Auto Car Repair
165.66250	170.46250	NFM	Lowestoft	Bluebird Taxis
165.66250	170.46250	NFM	Macclesfield	Macc Radio Cars
165.66250	170.46250	NFM	Manchester	Taxi Company
165.66250	170.46250	NFM	Medway	Hydro Descaling
165.66250	170.46250	NFM	Rochdale	Strand Private Hire
165.66250	170.46250	AM	Scarborough	Laker Taxis
165.66250	170.46250	NFM	Sheffield	Direct & Class Cars
165.66250	170.46250	NFM	Aberkenfig	Village Cars
165.66250	170.46250	NFM	Banbridge	Bann Taxis
165.67500	170.47500	NFM	Bolton	Taxi Company
165.67500	170.47500	NFM	Cambridge	Camdoc Doctors' Service (88.5)
165.67500	170.47500	NFM	Carrickfergus	BP Taxis
165.67500	170.47500	NFM	Dunstable	E J Allan
165.67500	170.47500	AM	Ipswich	Crown Taxis

Base	Mobile	Mode	Location	User and Notes
165.67500	170.47500	NFM	Leeds	Aireborough Private Hire
165.67500	170.47500	NFM	London	Amber Radio Cars, Southall
165.67500	170.47500	NFM	Manchester	Manchester Airport Taxis
165.67500	170.47500	NFM	Port Talbot	Corus Steel (71.9)
165.67500	170.47500	NFM	Reading	ABC Cars
165.67500	170.47500	AM	Scarborough	Laker Taxis
165.67500	170.47500	NFM	Scunthorpe	Corus Steel Trains
165.67500	170.47500	NFM	Sheffield	AK Cars
165.67500	170.47500	NFM	St Annes	West Star Taxis
165.67500	170.47500	NFM	Wolds	Tennants Farms
165.68750	170.48750	NFM	Cambridgeshire	Potato Farm (141.3)
165.68750	170.48750	NFM	Cardiff	City Council Safety Events Ch.2
165.68750	170.48750	NFM	Derbyshire	Derbyshire Council Rangers
165.68750	170.48750	NFM	East Midlands	Highways Agency Gritters/Road Gangs Ch.2 (141.3)
165.68750	170.48750	NFM	Gloucester	Gloucester Airport, Crash
165.68750	170.48750	NFM	Lincolnshire	Highways Agency Gritters/Road Gangs Ch.2 (141.3)
165.68750	170.48750	NFM	Nationwide	Bell Fruit Machines
165.68750	170.48750	NFM	Sheffield	Paymaster Ltd.
165.68750	170.48750	NFM	Trimley	Goslings Farm/Plant Centre
165.68750	170.48750	NFM	Yorkshire	Highways Agency Gritters/Road Gangs Ch.2 (141.3)
165.70000	170.50000	NFM	Brighton	Taxi Company
165.70000	170.50000	NFM	Cardiff	Delta Cars
165.70000	170.50000	NFM	Chatteris	Catwood Potatoes
165.70000	170.50000	AM	Christchurch	Critax Taxis
165.70000	170.50000	NFM	Glasgow	Taxi Company
165.70000	170.50000	NFM	Guernsey	T & D Services
165.70000	170.50000	NFM	Hamilton	Cadzow Cars
165.70000	170.50000	NFM	Holyhead	RSPCA, South Stack
165.70000	170.50000	NFM	Humberside	Transport Company
165.70000	170.50000	NFM	Ipswich	Clarke Demolition
165.70000	170.50000	NFM	Ipswich	Thompson & Morgan
165.70000	170.50000	NFM	Jersey	T & D Services
165.70000	170.50000	NFM	Kings Lynn	Ambassador Taxis
165.70000	170.50000	NFM	Luton	District Cars
165.70000	170.50000	NFM	Pontefract	Slatters Taxis
165.70000	170.50000	NFM	Portsmouth	Aqua Taxis
165.70000	170.50000	NFM	Saffron Walden	Crusader Cars
165.70000	170.50000	NFM	Scarborough	Station Taxis
165.70000	170.50000	NFM	Southampton	Taxi Company
165.70000	170.50000	NFM	Wolverhampton	Wednesfield Radio Cars
165.71250	170.51250	NFM	Aldershot	Taxi Company
165.71250	170.51250	NFM	Basildon	Taxi Company
165.71250	170.51250	NFM	Bedford	Key Cars
165.71250	170.51250	NFM	Birmingham	Northfield Radio Cars (118.8)
165.71250	170.51250	NFM	Bognor Regis	Taxi Company
165.71250	170.51250	NFM	Bradford	Listers/Carlisle Private Hire
165.71250	170.51250	NFM	Bristol	Blue Iris Coaches
165.71250	170.51250	NFM	Cambridge	Four Four Taxis
165.71250	170.51250	NFM	Carnforth	PR Taxis
165.71250	170.51250	NFM	Crewe	Taxi Company
165.71250	170.51250	NFM	Edinburgh	Taxi Company
165.71250	170.51250	NFM	Folkestone	Folkestone City Buses
165.71250	170.51250	NFM	Headham	Gower Ltd
165.71250	170.51250	NFM	Hollesley	WJ Mills
165.71250	170.51250	NFM	Ipswich	EH Roberts
165.71250	170.51250	NFM	Newcastle	Castle Cars

Base	Mobile	Mode	Location	User and Notes
165.71250	170.51250	NFM	Tamworth	Acorn Taxis
165.71250	170.51250	NFM	Valley, Wales	Ted's Taxis
165.72500	165.52500	NFM	Ayr	Network Rail Workmen
165.72500	170.52500	NFM	Blackburn	Manhattan Private Hire
165.72500	170.52500	NFM	Bolton	MacArthur Private Hire
165.72500	170.52500	NFM	Bournemouth	Southern Dispatch Couriers
165.72500	170.52500	NFM	Cardiff	Taxi Company
165.72500	170.52500	NFM	Carlisle	Q Doc Doctors' Service
165.72500	170.52500	NFM	Grimsby	Ibwest Security
165.72500	170.52500	NFM	Hatfield	Tarmac Construction
165.72500	170.52500	NFM	Hockwold Cum Wilton	Bob's Taxis
165.72500	170.52500	NFM	Medway	Council Housing Department (82.5)
165.72500	170.52500	NFM	Oxfordshire	Isis Accord Motorway Repairs (167.9)
165.72500	170.52500	NFM	Rickmansworth	Taxi Company (186.2)
165.72500	170.52500	NFM	Scunthorpe	Corus Steel Transport
165.72500	170.52500	NFM	Stoke on Trent	Hawks Private Hire (203.5)
165.72500	170.52500	NFM	Truro	Treliske Hospital
165.72500	170.52500	NFM	Woodbridge	Notcutts Nurseries
165.73750	170.53750	NFM	Bradford	Eccleshill Private Hire
165.73750	170.53750	NFM	Brighton	City College Security
165.73750	170.53750	NFM	Bury	Royal Taxis
165.73750	170.53750	NFM	Coventry	Lion Taxis
165.73750	170.53750	NFM	Leeds	Crossgates Private Hire
165.73750	170.53750	NFM	Newport	Globe Taxis (141.3)
165.73750	170.53750	NFM	Runcorn	Taxi Company
165.73750	170.53750	NFM	Stockton on Tees	Taxi Service
165.73750	170.53750	NFM	Sudbury	Amey Roadstones
165.73750	170.53750	NFM	Swindon	Tramps Radio Cars
165.73750	170.53750	NFM	Widnes	Taxi Company
165.75000	170.55000	NFM	Bournemouth	Council
165.75000	170.55000	NFM	Carlisle	Council Highways
165.75000	170.55000	NFM	Dundee	Taxi Company
165.75000	170.55000	NFM	Enfield	Council
165.75000	170.55000	NFM	Exeter	Council (82.5)
165.75000	170.55000	NFM	Fylde	Town Council
165.75000	170.55000	NFM	Halifax	Refuse Collection FOCSA
165.75000	170.55000	NFM	Hastings	Parking Enforcement
165.75000	170.55000	NFM	Hove	Council
165.75000	170.55000	NFM	Lancaster	City Council
165.75000	170.55000	NFM	Leamington Spa	Council
165.75000	170.55000	NFM	Luton	Luton Borough Council
165.75000	170.55000	NFM	Machynlleth	Hendre Quarry
165.75000	170.55000	NFM	Newark	Taxis
165.75000	170.55000	NFM	Norwich	Eastern Counties Buses (67)
165.75000	170.55000	NFM	Perth	Taxi Company
165.75000	170.55000	NFM	Reading	Council
165.75000	170.55000	NFM	Southend on Sea	Southend Borough Council
165.75000	170.55000	NFM	Stoke on Trent	Council
165.75000	170.55000	NFM	Swindon	Town Council
165.75000	170.55000	NFM	Torbay	NCP Parking Enforcement
165.75000	170.55000	NFM	Wiltshire	Thamesdown Council
165.75000	170.55000	NFM	Wirral	A-Z Private Hire, Woodchurch
165.75000	170.55000	NFM	Woking	Woking Community Transport (162.2)
165.76250	170.56250	NFM	Aberdeen	Waste Masters
165.76250	170.56250	NFM	Barnsley	Council
165.76250	170.56250	NFM	Bedfordshire	District Council

Base	Mobile	Mode	Location	User and Notes
165.76250	170.56250	NFM	Bolton	District Council
165.76250	170.56250	NFM	Bridlington	Borough Council Repairs
165.76250	170.56250	NFM	Brierley Hill	Council
165.76250	170.56250	NFM	Cardiff	City Council Parks
165.76250	170.56250	NFM	Dartmoor	Dartmoor National Park Rangers
165.76250	170.56250	NFM	Dundee	City Council Dog Catcher
165.76250	170.56250	NFM	Doncaster	Doncaster Council
165.76250	170.56250	NFM	Dundee	Council Refuse Contractors
165.76250	170.56250	NFM	Edinburgh	Lothian Regional Council
165.76250	170.56250	NFM	Ipswich	Council Housing Department
165.76250	170.56250	NFM	Llanelli	Town Council Depot
165.76250	170.56250	AM	London	Southall Council
165.76250	170.56250	NFM	Luton	Contractor
165.76250	170.56250	NFM	Norfolk	Norfolk County Council
165.76250	170.56250	NFM	Poole	Repeater
165.76250	170.56250	NFM	Preston	District Council
165.76250	170.56250	NFM	Southampton	City Council Refuse Collectors
165.76250	170.56250	NFM	Suffolk	County Council
165.77500	170.57500	NFM	Barrow	Council Dog Wardens
165.77500	170.57500	NFM	Congleton	Taxi Company
165.77500	170.57500	NFM	Cwmbran	Cwmbran Plumbing Company
165.77500	170.57500	NFM	Dudley	Council
165.77500	170.57500	NFM	Glasgow	Strathkelvin District Council
165.77500	170.57500	NFM	Gloucester	Dial A Ride
165.77500	170.57500	NFM	Havant	Council
165.77500	170.57500	NFM	Hayling Island	Council
165.77500	170.57500	NFM	High Wycombe	Council Parks Department
165.77500	170.57500	NFM	Huntingdon	Council
165.77500	170.57500	NFM	Ipswich	Brough Transport
165.77500	170.57500	NFM	N Yorkshire	Doctors' Service
165.77500	170.57500	NFM	Norwich	Norwich City Council
165.77500	170.57500	NFM	Portsmouth	City Council
165.77500	170.57500	NFM	Skegness	Council
165.77500	170.57500	NFM	Somerset	County Council
165.77500	170.57500	NFM	Southend on Sea	District Council
165.77500	170.57500	NFM	Southport	Coast Rangers (127.3)
165.77500	170.57500	NFM	Stoke-on-Trent	Council Parks Department
165.77500	170.57500	NFM	Swindon	Council (71.9)
165.77500	170.57500	NFM	Tendring	Lifeguards/Beach Staff
165.77500	170.57500	NFM	Torbay	Parking Enforcement
165.77500	170.57500	NFM	West Cambs	District Council
165.77500	170.57500	NFM	Wiltshire	County Council (71.9)
165.78750	170.58750	NFM	Bangor	Balloo Hire Company (94.8)
165.78750	170.58750	NFM	Birmingham	St John Ambulance Ch.12 Events (114.8)
165.78750	170.58750	NFM	Boston	Organic Growers Association
165.78750	170.58750	NFM	Bournemouth	Council
165.78750	170.58750	NFM	Bromley	Borough Council
165.78750	170.58750	NFM	Carlisle	County Contractors
165.78750	170.58750	NFM	Coventry	Mercia Gas
165.78750	170.58750	NFM	Darlington	Stagecoach Buses
165.78750	170.58750	NFM	Fawley	Power Station
165.78750	170.58750	NFM	Gt Yarmouth	Breakdown Recovery (103.5)
165.78750	170.58750	NFM	Hyndburn	Accrington Bus Control
165.78750	170.58750	NFM	Manchester	Tameside Patrollers
165.78750	170.58750	NFM	Newquay	Shopwatch
165.78750	170.58750	NFM	Peterborough	Betta Cars Amalgamated

Base	Mobile	Mode	Location	User and Notes
165.78750	170.58750	NFM	Poole	Repeater
165.78750	170.58750	NFM	Runnymede	Borough Council (71.9)
165.78750	170.58750	NFM	Stoke on Trent	Skip Hire
165.78750	170.58750	NFM	Shoreham by Sea	Adur District Council Street Refuse Teams
165.78750	170.58750	NFM	Suffolk	Mid Suffolk District Council
165.78750	170.58750	NFM	Swindon	Thamesdown Council
165.78750	170.58750	NFM	West Midlands	Council Refuse
165.80000	170.60000	NFM	Brighton	Streamline Taxis
165.80000	170.60000	NFM	Bridgend	Allways Cars (103.5)
165.80000	170.60000	NFM	Cwmbran	Checker Taxis
165.80000	170.60000	NFM	Derby	Taxi Company, Langley Mill
165.80000	170.60000	NFM	Dudley	Five Star Taxis
165.80000	170.60000	NFM	Dundee	Taxi Company
165.80000	170.60000	NFM	Exeter	Castle Cars
165.80000	170.60000	NFM	Felixstowe	Peewit Caravans
165.80000	170.60000	NFM	Jersey	Normans Ch.22
165.80000	170.60000	NFM	Kilmarnock	Taxi Company
165.80000	170.60000	NFM	London	Taxi Company
165.80000	170.60000	NFM	Luton	CJ Private Hire
165.80000	170.60000	NFM	Newtownabbey	Jock's Cabs
165.80000	170.60000	NFM	Norwich	Beeline & Dolphin Taxis
165.80000	170.60000	NFM	Sheffield	Taxi Company
165.80000	170.60000	NFM	Snowdonia	Snowdon Mountain Railway
165.80000	170.60000	NFM	Summercourt	Tonkins Garage
165.80000	170.60000	NFM	Swansea	Hooper Taxis
165.80000	170.60000	NFM	Wickham Market	Haywards Farms
165.81250	170.61250	NFM	Bath	Abbey Taxis Ch.2
165.81250	170.61250	NFM	Belfast	Park Taxis, Falls Road
165.81250	170.61250	NFM	Cambridge	Panther Cars
165.81250	170.61250	NFM	Cleethorpes	Bob's Cars
165.81250	170.61250	NFM	Coventry	Godiva Taxis
165.81250	170.61250	NFM	Coventry	Lewis Taxis
165.81250	170.61250	NFM	Preston	Cabtax Taxis
165.81250	170.61250	NFM	St Austell	Taxi Company
165.81250	170.61250	NFM	Swansea	AA Taxis, Mumbles
165.82500	170.62500	NFM	Bath	Abbey Taxis Ch 1
165.82500	170.62500	NFM	Bolton	ABA Private Hire
165.82500	170.62500	NFM	Bradford	Heaton Private Hire
165.82500	170.62500	NFM	Dudley	Midland Taxis
165.82500	170.62500	NFM	Glasgow	Taxi Company
165.82500	170.62500	NFM	Hull	Ennerdale Cars
165.82500	170.62500	NFM	Ipswich	Wilding & Smith
165.82500	170.62500	NFM	March	Worrall Potatoes
165.82500	170.62500	NFM	Oxford	ABC Taxis
165.82500	170.62500	NFM	Peterborough	Anglia ABC Cars (103.5)
165.82500	170.62500	NFM	West Country	Taxi Company (82.5)
165.83750	170.62750	NFM	Blackpool	Bus Company
165.83750	170.63750	NFM	Caistor	Hurdiss Quarries
165.83750	170.62750	NFM	Cardiff	Transport Company
165.83750	170.62750	NFM	Ely	AE Lee Farms
165.83750	170.62750	NFM	Glasgow	Taxi Company
165.83750	170.62750	NFM	Gloucester	Andy Cars
165.83750	170.63730	NFM	Halifax	Vinneys Taxis
165.83750	170.63750	NFM	Leeds	New Bramley Private Hire
165.83750	170.63750	NFM	Liverpool	Allerton Taxis, Garston
165.83750	170.62750	NFM	Macclesfield	Taxi Company

Base	Mobile	Mode	Location	User and Notes
165.83750	170.62750	NFM	Newtownabbey	Fernagh Taxis, Whiteabbey (127.3)
165.83750	170.62750	NFM	Oldham	Limeline Private Hire
165.83750	170.62750	NFM	Peterborough	Hereward Ace Taxis
165.83750	170.62750	NFM	Plymouth	Taxi Company
165.83750	170.62750	NFM	Sheffield	Airport Express (Tex)
165.83750	170.62750	NFM	St. Osyth	Tudor Taxis
165.85000	170.65000	NFM	Birmingham	Lucas Aerospace Securit
165.85000	170.65000	NFM	Falkirk	Blue Star Taxis (Star)
165.85000	170.65000	NFM	Haddenham	A.F. Buck
165.85000	170.65000	NFM	Leigh	Avacabs
165.85000	170.65000	NFM	Liverpool	City Cars
165.85000	170.65000	NFM	London	Dial A Cab Data Boxes
165.85000	170.65000	NFM	Manchester	Avacabs
165.85000	170.65000	NFM	Newport, Gwent	Royal Cars
165.85000	170.65000	NFM	Three Holes	Hallsworth Framing Company
165.86000	170.66000	NFM	Ayr	Taxi Company
165.86250	170.66250	NFM	Cambridge	Securicor
165.86250	170.66250	NFM	Hythe	Hythe Ferry & Pier Trunked
165.86250	170.66250	NFM	Isle of Man	Securicor
165.86250	170.66250	NFM	Jersey	Pony Express Delivery
165.86250	170.66250	NFM	Leeds	Courier Service
165.86250	170.66250	NFM	London	Securicor Prisoner Transport
165.86250	170.66250	NFM	Nationwide	Securicor Trunked Network Ch.6
165.87500	170.67500	NFM	Birmingham	Black Cabs
165.87500	170.67500	NFM	Birmingham	Driving School
165.87500	170.67500	NFM	Edinburgh	Pony Express Couriers
165.87500	170.67500	NFM	Fleetwood	Nightwatchmen
165.87500	170.67500	NFM	Guernsey	Securicor
165.87500	170.67500	NFM	Nationwide	Securicor Trunked Network Ch.2
165.87500	170.67500	NFM	Wokington	Council
165.88750	170.67500	NFM	Cramlington	Target Taxis
165.88750	170.68750	NFM	Bournemouth	Council Tarmac Gang
165.88750	170.68750	NFM	Horwich	Duval Security
165.88750	170.68750	NFM	Hythe	Hythe Ferry and Pier Trunked
165.88750	170.68750	NFM	Nationwide	Securicor Trunked Network Ch.3
165.90000	170.70000	NFM	Airdrie	Twin Cabs
165.90000	170.70000	NFM	Belfast	Circle Taxis, Crumlin Road
165.90000	170.70000	NFM	Biggleswade	AT Taxis
165.90000	170.70000	AM	Bury St Edmunds	Fairways Taxis
165.90000	170.70000	NFM	Cambridgeshire	Huntingdon & District Buses
165.90000	170.70000	NFM	Colchester	Town Cars
165.90000	170.70000	AM	Dartford	Abba Dart Taxis
165.90000	170.70000	NFM	Dundee	Taxi Company
165.90000	170.70000	NFM	Exeter	City Central Cabs
165.90000	170.70000	NFM	Exeter	J I Cabs
165.90000	170.70000	NFM	Hitchin	Duggan's Taxis
165.90000	170.70000	NFM	Ipswich	Taxi Company
165.90000	170.70000	NFM	London	Automania Breakdown Recovery
165.90000	170.70000	NFM	Manchester	Atherton Cab Company
165.90000	170.70000	NFM	Rochdale	Norden Cars
165.90000	170.70000	NFM	Sevenoaks	Beeline Radio Taxis
165.90000	170.70000	NFM	Sheffield	Amusement Machine Servicing
165.90000	170.70000	NFM	Sheffield	Paymaster Ltd.
165.90000	170.70000	NFM	Swansea	Lloyds Taxis
165.90000	170.70000	AM	Swindon	Viking Taxis
165.90000	170.70000	NFM	Tilbury	Tilbury Taxis (151.4)

Base	Mobile	Mode	Location	User and Notes
165.90000	170.70000	NFM	Wantage	Robert's Taxis
165.90000	170.70000	NFM	West Drayton	LHR Express Cars
165.91250	170.71250	NFM	Devizes	Community Repeater
165.91250	170.71250	NFM	Hythe	Hythe Ferry & Pier Trunked
165.91250	170.71250	NFM	Jersey	A1 Double Glazing
165.91250	170.71250	NFM	Nationwide	Securicor Trunked Network Ch.7
165.91250	170.71250	NFM	Walsall	MFI Deliveries
165.92500	170.72500	NFM	Aberystwyth	Taxi Company
165.92500	170.72500	NFM	Aberdeen	Oil Industry
165.92500	170.72500	NFM	Brighton	Car Mechanics Ch.1
165.92500	170.72500	NFM	Cambridge	Alpha Express Parcel
165.92500	170.72500	NFM	Chester Le Street	Shopwatch
165.92500	170.72500	NFM	Cirencester	Gerry's Cars
165.92500	170.72500	NFM	Cleveland	6767 Taxis
165.92500	170.72500	NFM	Jersey	Hire Cars
165.92500	170.72500	NFM	Larne	McBurney Taxis
165.92500	170.72500	NFM	Manchester	Taxi Company
165.92500	170.72500	NFM	Middleton	Middleton Radio Cars
165.92500	170.72500	NFM	Nationwide	Securicor Prisoner Transport
165.92500	170.72500	NFM	Newcastle	Taxi Company
165.92500	170.72500	NFM	Nottingham	Bells Taxis, Hucknall
165.92500	170.72500	NFM	Poole	Data Repeater
165.92500	170.72500	NFM	Portsmouth	Aqua Cabs
165.92500	170.72500	NFM	Scarborough	Castle Taxis
165.92500	170.72500	NFM	Sheffield	Arc Taxis (Aztec)
165.92500	170.72500	NFM	Sheffield	Valley Taxis
165.92500	170.72500	NFM	Stockton-on-Tees	Taxi Company
165.92500	170.72500	NFM	Tenby	Taxi Company
165.92500	170.72500	NFM	Wolverhampton	ABC Countdown Cabs
165.93750	170.73750	NFM	Liverpool	Gas Fitters
165.93750	170.73750	NFM	Nationwide	Securicor Trunked Network Ch.8
165.93750	170.73750	NFM	Newcastle	Central Heating Company
165.95000	170.75000	NFM	Baldock	Farm (131.8)
165.95000	170.75000	NFM	Brighton	Car Mechanics Ch.2
165.95000	170.75000	NFM	Colwyn Bay	Station Taxis
165.95000	170.75000	NFM	Cumbria	South Lakes Refuse Collection
165.95000	170.75000	NFM	Dundee	Taxi Company
165.95000	170.75000	NFM	Ellesmere Port	Cosy Cars
165.95000	170.75000	AM	Grimsby	Fletchers Taxis
165.95000	170.75000	NFM	Gt Yarmouth	Anglia Taxis
165.95000	170.75000	NFM	Hemel Hempstead	Millennium Cars
165.95000	170.75000	NFM	Jersey	Collas & Le Sueur Electrical Contractor
165.95000	170.75000	NFM	Kendal	District Council
165.95000	170.75000	NFM	London	Minicab Company, Southall
165.95000	170.75000	NFM	Norfolk	Norfolk Farm Produce
165.95000	170.75000	NFM	Northampton	Taxi Company
165.95000	170.75000	NFM	Norwich	Taxi Company
165.95000	170.75000	NFM	Portrush	Andy Brown Taxis (77 Input Only)
165.95000	170.75000	NFM	Stamford	Phoenix/Starline Cabs (136.5)
165.96250	170.76250	NFM	Birmingham	Car Repair Company
165.96250	170.76250	NFM	Birmingham	Driving School
165.96250	170.76250	NFM	Birmingham	Gas Contractors
165.96250	170.76250	NFM	Bournemouth	Council Parks
165.96250	170.76250	NFM	Hythe	Hythe Ferry & Pier Trunked
165.96250	170.76250	NFM	Isle of Wight	Landscaping Service
165.96250	170.76250	NFM	Liverpool	Taxi Company

Base	Mobile	Mode	Location	User and Notes
165.96250	170.76250	NFM	Nationwide	Securicor Trunked Network Ch.4
165.97500	170.77500	NFM	Brighton	Securicor
165.97500	170.77500	NFM	Bristol	AC Taxis
165.97500	170.77500	NFM	Haverfordwest	Securicor
165.97500	170.77500	NFM	Isle of Man	Securicor
165.97500	170.77500	NFM	London	Omega Parcels
165.97500	170.77500	NFM	Nationwide	Securicor Trunked Network Ch.1
165.97500	170.77500	NFM	St Annes	Night Security
165.98750	170.78750	NFM	Hythe	Hythe Ferry and Pier Trunked
165.98750	170.78750	NFM	Jersey	Securicor
165.98750	170.78750	NFM	London	Securicor Prisoner Transport
165.98750	170.78750	NFM	Nationwide	Securicor Trunked Network Ch.5
166.00000	170.80000	NFM	Barnstaple	North Devon College
166.00000	170.80000	NFM	Barrow in Furness	Z-Cars Taxis
166.00000	170.80000	NFM	Cannock	Taxi Company
166.00000	170.80000	NFM	Chelmsford	Farmers Supplies
166.00000	170.80000	NFM	Croydon	Roadrunners Mini Cabs
166.00000	170.80000	NFM	Cwmbran	Tiger Taxis (110.9)
166.00000	170.80000	NFM	Glasgow	Taxi Company
166.00000	170.80000	NFM	Guernsey	Vaudins Taxi
166.00000	170.80000	NFM	Hull	Taxi Company
166.00000	170.80000	NFM	Kenilworth	Taxi Company
166.00000	170.80000	NFM	Linlithgow	Taxi Company
166.00000	170.80000	NFM	Mansfield	Ace ABC Taxis
166.00000	170.80000	NFM	Perth	Taxi Company
166.00000	170.80000	NFM	Prestatyn	Robert's Taxis
166.00000	170.80000	AM	Sheffield	Ace of Cars Taxis
166.00000	170.80000	NFM	South Shields	Taxi Company
166.00000	170.80000	NFM	Stevenage	Parker Cars
166.00000	170.80000	NFM	Swansea	Taxi Company
166.00000	170.80000	NFM	Tollerton	Gadd's Farm
166.00000	170.80000	NFM	Torpoint	Taxi Company
166.00000	170.80000	NFM	West Drayton	Station Cars
166.00000	170.80000	NFM	Winton	M & G Electronics
166.00000	170.80000	NFM	Woolerstone	AW Mayhew Farms
166.01250	170.81250	NFM	Aberdeen	Taxi Company
166.01250	170.81250	NFM	Aberystwyth	Taxi Company
166.01250	170.81250	NFM	Bedford	BC Cars
166.01250	170.81250	NFM	Birmingham	Taxi Company
166.01250	170.81250	NFM	Bradford	Preston Street Private Hire
166.01250	170.81250	NFM	Cardiff	Roath Taxis
166.01250	170.81250	NFM	Cwmbran	Tiger Taxis
166.01250	170.81250	NFM	Glasgow	Taxi Company
166.01250	170.81250	NFM	Hamilton	Taxi Owners Association
166.01250	170.81250	NFM	Kings Lynn	Baconpac Company
166.01250	170.81250	NFM	Newport	Taxis Company (123)
166.01250	170.81250	NFM	Peterborough	On Site Tyres
166.01250	170.81250	NFM	Sheffield	Swallownest Taxis
166.01250	170.81250	NFM	St Neots	Steve's Taxis (110.9)
166.02500	170.82500	AM	Aberdeen	Oil Industry
166.02500	170.82500	NFM	Bedfordshire	Verdant Ltd, Recycling Refuse for Council (118.8)
166.02500	170.82500	NFM	Bedworth	Autoway Taxis
166.02500	170.82500	NFM	Birmingham	Taxi Company, Sheldon
166.02500	170.82500	NFM	Bolton	Taxi Company
166.02500	170.82500	NFM	Cornwall	English China Clay
166.02500	170.82500	NFM	Doncaster	Mucks Taxis

Base	Mobile	Mode	Location	User and Notes
166.02500	170.82500	NFM	Hillingdon	Civic Centre Security
166.02500	170.82500	NFM	Hitchin	Allpoints Taxis
166.02500	170.82500	NFM	Kennyhill	JA Butcher
166.02500	170.82500	NFM	Manchester	Taxi Company
166.02500	170.82500	NFM	Newcastle	Taxi Company
166.02500	170.82500	NFM	Norwich	A Tolver Taxis
166.02500	170.82500	NFM	Oldham	Taxi Company
166.02500	170.82500	AM	Peterborough	Nene Park Rangers
166.02500	170.82500	NFM	Scarborough	Dial A Car Taxis
166.02500	170.82500	NFM	Swindon	Science Museum, Wroughton Ch.2
166.02500	170.82500	NFM	Woodbridge	Council Vans
166.03750	170.83750	NFM	Aberdeen	Taxi Company
166.03750	170.83750	NFM	Cambridge	Cabco Taxis
166.03750	170.83750	NFM	Cardiff	Black Cab Taxis
166.03750	170.83750	NFM	Cromer	Biffa Ltd
166.03750	170.83750	NFM	Croydon	Kendall Cars
166.03750	170.83750	AM	Grimsby	Taxi Company
166.03750	170.83750	NFM	Jersey	Pentagon Ltd
166.03750	170.83750	NFM	London	Alpine Radio Cars (A), NW2
166.03750	170.83750	NFM	London	Biffa Waste Disposal
166.03750	170.83750	NFM	London	Taxi Company, E London
166.03750	170.83750	NFM	Macclesfield	Atax
166.03750	170.83750	NFM	Motherwell	Forgewood Security
166.03750	170.83750	NFM	Newport	A1 Skip Hire
166.03750	170.83750	NFM	Newport	Diamond Taxis
166.03750	170.83750	NFM	Peterborough	A2B Taxis
166.03750	170.83750	NFM	Peterborough	City Cabs (107.2)
166.05000	170.85000	NFM	Cardiff	Council
166.05000	170.85000	NFM	Chelmsford	Borough Council
166.05000	170.85000	NFM	Deal	Council
166.05000	170.85000	NFM	Doncaster	Council Manual Workers
166.05000	170.85000	NFM	Dover	District Council
166.05000	170.85000	NFM	Glasgow	City Council
166.05000	170.85000	NFM	Gloucester	District Council
166.05000	170.85000	NFM	Hawick	Roxburg
166.05000	170.85000	NFM	Lake Windermere	Rangers & Wardens
166.05000	170.85000	NFM	Lancashire	Road Repairs
166.05000	170.85000	NFM	Leicester	Council
166.05000	170.85000	NFM	Liverpool	Bruno Security
166.05000	170.85000	NFM	London	Hillingdon Council (127.3)
166.05000	170.85000	NFM	Manchester	Security Company
166.05000	170.85000	NFM	Milton Keynes	Council
166.05000	170.85000	NFM	Motherwell	District Council
166.05000	170.85000	NFM	Oxford	Oxford City Council
166.05000	170.85000	NFM	Powys	Ambulance
166.05000	170.85000	NFM	Preston	Council (131.8)
166.05000	170.85000	NFM	Southampton	Council Engineering
166.05000	170.85000	NFM	Southport	Sefton Council (123)
166.05000	170.85000	NFM	Walsall	Environmental Health
166.05000	170.85000	NFM	Wokinghan	Council
166.05000	170.85000	NFM	Woodbridge	Suffolk Coastal District Council
166.06250	170.86250	NFM	Ballymoney	Borough Council
166.06250	170.86250	NFM	Barrow in Furness	SITA Cleansing Department
166.06250	170.86250	NFM	Blackburn	Silverline Private Hire
166.06250	170.86250	NFM	Bournemouth	Council Engineers
166.06250	170.86250	NFM	Cleethorpes	Borough Council

Base	Mobile	Mode	Location	User and Notes
166.06250	170.86250	NFM	Colchester	Borough Council
166.06250	170.86250	NFM	Deeside	Deeside Council
166.06250	170.86250	NFM	Derbyshire	Amber Valley County Council
166.06250	170.86250	NFM	Dudley	Meals on Wheels (77)
166.06250	170.86250	NFM	Dundee	City Council Workshop
166.06250	170.86250	NFM	Eakring	BP Depot
166.06250	170.86250	NFM	Forest of Dean	Gritters
166.06250	170.86250	NFM	Gt Yarmouth	Shopwatch/Pubwatch/Patrols/TVEye Ch.1 (186.2)
166.06250	170.86250	NFM	Hertfordshire	County Council
166.06250	170.86250	NFM	Kent	WPS Parcels
166.06250	170.86250	NFM	London	Brent Council
166.06250	170.86250	NFM	Lowestoft	Street Warden Patrols (186.2)
166.06250	170.86250	NFM	Luton	Repeater
166.06250	170.86250	NFM	Manchester	City Council
166.06250	170.86250	NFM	Newbury	Council
166.06250	170.86250	NFM	Newcastle	City Council
166.06250	170.86250	NFM	Peterborough	Council
166.06250	170.86250	NFM	Sheffield	Council Housing Department Area 5
166.06250	170.86250	NFM	Slough	Borough Council
166.06250	170.86250	NFM	Taunton	Taunton Borough Council
166.06250	170.86250	NFM	Tonbridge	Tonbridge & Malling Council
166.07500	170.87500	NFM	Berkhamstead	Parking Enforcement (67)
166.07500	170.87500	NFM	Cannock	Council
166.07500	170.87500	NFM	Cardiff	City Council Security (94.8)
166.07500	170.87500	NFM	Carlisle	Council Contractors
166.07500	170.87500	NFM	Chelmsford	Council Refuse Collection
166.07500	170.87500	NFM	Cleveland	Council Gritters
166.07500	170.87500	NFM	Edinburgh	City of Edinburgh Parks Department
166.07500	170.87500	NFM	Ipswich	Borough Council Parks Department
166.07500	170.87500	NFM	Jersey	Elizabeth Castle
166.07500	170.87500	NFM	London	Council Flood Control, Haringey
166.07500	170.87500	NFM	London	Parking Enforcement, Harrow (67)
166.07500	170.87500	NFM	London	Sutton Borough Council (151.4)
166.07500	170.87500	NFM	Luton	Community Repeater
166.07500	170.87500	NFM	Manchester	Trafford Council
166.07500	170.87500	NFM	Rochester	Council
166.07500	170.87500	NFM	Sevenoaks	Council
166.07500	170.87500	NFM	Strabane	Council
166.07500	170.87500	NFM	Stroud	Council Gritters
166.07500	170.87500	NFM	Wirral	Community Patrols Ch.2
166.07500	170.87500	NFM	Surrey	Surrey Heath Borough Council
166.07500	170.87500	NFM	Wirral	Council Parks and Gardens
166.08750	170.88750	NFM	Berkshire	Council Ch.1
166.08750	170.88750	NFM	Birmingham	Council
166.08750	170.88750	NFM	Bolton	District Council
166.08750	170.88750	NFM	Burton	Council
166.08750	170.88750	NFM	Cardiff	Margam Park Staff/Rangers
166.08750	170.88750	NFM	Cleethorpes	GC Transport
166.08750	170.88750	NFM	Edinburgh	Lothian Regional Council
166.08750	170.88750	NFM	Essex	Havering Council
166.08750	170.88750	NFM	Exmouth	Haven Holidays Devon Cliffs Caravan Park (94.8)
166.08750	170.88750	NFM	Fleetwood	Wyre Council
166.08750	170.88750	NFM	Grimsby	Stagecoach Buses
166.08750	170.88750	NFM	Halifax	Council
166.08750	170.88750	NFM	Havering	Council
166.08750	170.88750	NFM	London	Westminster Council

Base	Mobile	Mode	Location	User and Notes
166.08750	170.88750	NFM	Oldham	Council Refuse Collection
166.08750	170.88750	NFM	Perth	Council Leisure & Recreation
166.08750	170.88750	NFM	Poulton	Council
166.08750	170.88750	NFM	Romford	Parking Enforcement
166.08750	170.88750	NFM	Southampton	City Buses
166.08750	170.88750	NFM	Surrey	Surrey Council (Zulu)
166.08750	170.88750	NFM	Windsor	Windsor & Maidenhead Council
166.08750	170.88750	NFM	Wirral	Community Patrols Ch.1
166.10000	170.90000	NFM	Birmingham	City Hospital (114.8)
166.10000	170.90000	NFM	Birmingham	Good Hope Hospital (88.5)
166.10000	170.90000	NFM	Birmingham	Sandwell Hospital (67)
166.10000	170.90000	NFM	East Midlands	East Midlands Ambulance Service
166.10000	170.90000	NFM	Merseyside	Merseyside Ambulance Service
166.10000	170.90000	NFM	Norfolk	East Anglian Ambulance Patient Transport
166.10000	170.90000	NFM	North Yorkshire	North Yorkshire Ambulance Service
166.10000	170.90000	NFM	Oxford	Oxfordshire Ambulance Service Ch.8 (94.8 Input)
166.10000	170.90000	NFM	Scotland	Scottish Ambulance Service
166.10000	170.90000	NFM	West Midlands	West Midlands Ambulance Patient Transport
166.10000	170.90000	NFM	West Yorkshire	West Yorkshire Ambulance Patient Transport
166.11250	170.91250	NFM	Ashington	Wansbeck District Council
166.11250	170.91250	NFM	Cambridgeshire	Council (151.4)
166.11250	170.91250	NFM	Cardiff	Crown Cars
166.11250	170.91250	NFM	Doncaster	Council Metro Cleansing
166.11250	170.91250	NFM	Grimsby	Town Council
166.11250	170.91250	NFM	Isle of Man	Local Government
166.11250	170.91250	NFM	Lincolnshire	Council
166.11250	170.91250	NFM	London	Camden Council
166.11250	170.91250	NFM	London	Tower Hamlets Council
166.11250	170.91250	NFM	Lowestoft	Council (186.2)
166.11250	170.91250	NFM	Newcastle	Council
166.11250	170.91250	NFM	Newmarket	British Legion Security
166.11250	170.91250	NFM	Poole	Repeater
166.11250	170.91250	NFM	Stoke on Trent	Council Refuse Collection (151.4)
166.11250	170.91250	NFM	South Glamorgan	Council
166.11250	170.91250	NFM	Wakefield	District Council
166.11250	170.91250	NFM	Wrexham	Council Dog Wardens
166.12500	170.92500	NFM	Atherstone	Council
166.12500	170.92500	NFM	Aylesbury	District Council (136.5)
166.12500	170.92500	NFM	Bexley	Council & At-Night Ward Security
166.12500	170.92500	NFM	Bristol	City Council
166.12500	170.92500	NFM	Buckinghamshire	Council
166.12500	170.92500	NFM	Canterbury	City Council
166.12500	170.92500	NFM	Canterbury	Parking Enforcement (203.5)
166.12500	170.92500	NFM	Cardiff	Cardiff International Arena Security
166.12500	170.92500	NFM	Carlisle	Council Contractors
166.12500	170.92500	NFM	Coleraine	Borough Council (71.9)
166.12500	170.92500	NFM	Doncaster	Council Emergency Callout
166.12500	170.92500	NFM	Llanelli	Council Works Department
166.12500	170.92500	NFM	London	Bexleyheath Council
166.12500	170.92500	NFM	Newcastle	Council Housing Repairs
166.12500	170.92500	NFM	Newport	Council Estate Rangers, Community Wardens
166.12500	170.92500	NFM	Norwich	Biffa Bins
166.12500	170.92500	NFM	Peterborough	Holland Farms
166.12500	170.92500	NFM	Poole	Repeater
166.12500	170.92500	NFM	Plymouth	Parking Enforcement
166.12500	170.92500	NFM	Reading	Reading Council (82.5)

Base	Mobile	Mode	Location	User and Notes
166.12500	170.92500	NFM	Salford	Quaywatch Security Company (82.5)
166.12500	170.92500	NFM	Scarborough	Council
166.12500	170.92500	NFM	Stevenage	Council Housing Repairs (103.5)
166.12500	170.92500	NFM	Suffolk	Council Highways Department
166.12500	170.92500	NFM	Swansea	Council Highways Department
166.12500	170.92500	NFM	Watford	Council
166.12500	170.92500	NFM	Windsor	Council Refuse Collection (82.5)
166.13750	170.93750	NFM	Ayr	Haven Craig Tara Holiday Camp
166.13750	170.93750	NFM	Barnard Castle	GlaxoSmithKline
166.13750	170.93750	NFM	Basildon	District Council
166.13750	170.93750	NFM	Chippenham	Council
166.13750	170.93750	NFM	Doncaster	Council Highways Department
166.13750	170.93750	NFM	East Midlands	Highways Agency Gritters/Road Gangs Ch.1
166.13750	170.93750	NFM	Glasgow	Taxi Company
166.13750	170.93750	NFM	Gt Yarmouth	Shopwatch/Pubwatch/Patrols/TVEye (67)
166.13750	170.93750	NFM	Hertfordshire	District Council
166.13750	170.93750	NFM	Kent	Medina Council
166.13750	170.93750	NFM	Lincolnshire	Highways Agency Gritters/Road Gangs Ch.1
166.13750	170.93750	NFM	London	Brent Council
166.13750	170.93750	NFM	London	Harrow Council Maintenance
166.13750	170.93750	NFM	Milton Keynes	MK Security (167.9)
166.13750	170.93750	NFM	Newport	Refuse Skip Company
166.13750	170.93750	NFM	N Ireland	Northern Ireland Railways Ch.2 (156.7)
166.13750	170.93750	NFM	Oxford	City Link Coaches (107.2)
166.13750	170.93750	NFM	Preston	District Nurses (88.5)
166.13750	170.93750	NFM	Saffron Walden	Council
166.13750	170.93750	NFM	Sheffield	Brown Construction
166.13750	170.93750	NFM	S Glamorgan	Council
166.13750	170.93750	NFM	Surrey	Council
166.13750	170.93750	NFM	Yorkshire	Highways Agency Gritters/Road Gangs Ch.1
166.15000	170.95000	NFM	Aberdeen	Dee Van Hire
166.15000	170.95000	NFM	Berkshire	Council Ch.2
166.15000	170.95000	NFM	Brighton	Sussex Ambulance Emergency Reserve Channel
166.15000	170.95000	NFM	Bristol	City Council
166.15000	170.95000	NFM	Cheltenham	Council
166.15000	170.95000	NFM	Colchester	Council
166.15000	170.95000	NFM	Doncaster	City Council
166.15000	170.95000	NFM	Kettering	Council Refuse Collection
166.15000	170.95000	NFM	Leicester	Council
166.15000	170.95000	NFM	Lichfield	Council
166.15000	170.95000	NFM	Liverpool	City Council
166.15000	170.95000	NFM	Llandudno	Flood Planning
166.15000	170.95000	NFM	London	Bromley Council
166.15000	170.95000	NFM	London	Enfield Council
166.15000	170.95000	NFM	London	Epping Forest Council
166.15000	170.95000	NFM	London	Southwark Council
166.15000	170.95000	NFM	Macclesfield	Cheshire County Council Cleansing Department
166.15000	170.95000	NFM	Milton Keynes	Council
166.15000	170.95000	NFM	Newport	Council Ch.1
166.15000	170.95000	NFM	Poole	Repeater
166.15000	170.95000	NFM	Southampton	Council City Car Parks
166.15000	170.95000	NFM	Southend on Sea	Council Elderly Care Wardens (110.9)
166.15000	170.95000	NFM	S Glamorgan	Council Contractors
166.15000	170.95000	NFM	Suffolk	Council Highways Department
166.15000	170.95000	NFM	Telford	Council
166.15000	170.95000	NFM	Torbay	Torwatch, Torbay Council Patrols

Base	Mobile	Mode	Location	User and Notes
166.15000	170.95000	NFM	Windsor	Windsor & Maidenhead Council
166.15000	170.95000	NFM	Wirral	Community Patrols Ch.3
166.16250	170.96250	NFM	Ayrshire	ADOC Doctors' Service
166.16250	170.96250	NFM	Berkshire	South East Berks Emergency Volunteers (114.8)
166.16250	170.96250	NFM	Bracknell	District Council
166.16250	170.96250	NFM	Corby	Rockingham Speedway ASCAR Pit Ops. Ch.1
166.16250	172.96250	NFM	Eastbourne	Community Transport
166.16250	170.96250	NFM	Forest Heath	Council
166.16250	170.96250	NFM	London	Hammersmith & Fulham Council
166.16250	170.96250	NFM	Rotherham	Council
166.16250	170.96250	NFM	Salford	District Council
166.16250	170.96250	NFM	Solihull	Council
166.16250	170.96250	NFM	Wimborne	Council
166.17500	170.97500	NFM	Abingdon	Council
166.17500	170.97500	NFM	Bridlington	Council Car Parks
166.17500	170.97500	NFM	Brighton	Council Environmental/Refuse (127.3)
166.17500	170.97500	NFM	Burnley	Council Inspectors
166.17500	170.97500	NFM	Burton	Council
166.17500	170.97500	NFM	Cambridge	City Council (67)
166.17500	170.97500	NFM	Cardiff	Council
166.17500	170.97500	NFM	Christchurch	Council
166.17500	170.97500	NFM	Cumbria	Lake District National Park
166.17500	170.97500	NFM	Gateshead	Council
166.17500	170.97500	NFM	Grays	District Council
166.17500	170.97500	NFM	Grimsby	Council
166.17500	170.97500	NFM	Heysham	Power Station
166.17500	170.97500	NFM	Kings Lynn	District Council
166.17500	170.97500	NFM	Lanark	Council Repairs
166.17500	170.97500	NFM	Lancaster	Council
166.17500	170.97500	NFM	Lincolnshire	Council
166.17500	170.97500	NFM	London	Harrow Council
166.17500	170.97500	NFM	London	Lewisham Council
166.17500	170.97500	NFM	London	Noise Abatement Patrols
166.17500	170.97500	NFM	London	Thames Ditton Council
166.17500	170.97500	NFM	Macclesfield	Taxis
166.17500	170.97500	NFM	Manchester	City Council
166.17500	170.97500	NFM	Morecambe	Parking Enforcement, Parkwise (88.5)
166.17500	170.97500	NFM	Newcastle	Council Housing Repairs
166.17500	170.97500	NFM	Newport	Council Dustbins
166.17500	170.97500	NFM	N Ireland	Northern Ireland Railways Ch.1 (156.7)
166.17500	170.97500	NFM	St Albans	Council Maintenance
166.17500	170.97500	NFM	Southend on Sea	Borough Council (141.3)
166.17500	170.97500	NFM	Staffordshire	Council
166.17500	170.97500	NFM	Stirling	Stirling Council
166.17500	170.97500	NFM	Suffolk	Council Highways Department
166.17500	170.97500	NFM	Thanet	District Council (94.8)
166.17500	170.97500	NFM	Vale of White Horse	District Council
166.17500	170.97500	NFM	Welwyn	Welwyn & Hatfield Council
166.17500	170.97500	NFM	West Norfolk	District Council
166.18750	170.98750	NFM	Aberdeen	Council Highways Department
166.18750	170.98750	NFM	Bedfordshire	Council
166.18750	170.98750	NFM	Carlisle	City Council
166.18750	170.98750	NFM	Christchurch	Council
166.18750	170.98750	NFM	Crawley	Council
166.18750	170.98750	NFM	Dudley	Ambulance Service
166.18750	170.98750	NFM	Folkestone	District Council

Base	Mobile	Mode	Location	User and Notes
166.18750	170.98750	NFM	Hull	City Council
166.18750	170.98750	NFM	Isle of Man	Douglas Corporation
166.18750	170.98750	NFM	Kilwinning	Eglington Park Rangers
166.18750	170.98750	NFM	Kings Lynn	Council
166.18750	170.98750	NFM	Leeds	Council Redhall Security & Services
166.18750	170.98750	NFM	London	Ealing Borough Council Maintenance
166.18750	170.98750	NFM	Maidstone	Borough Council (192.8)
166.18750	170.98750	NFM	Merseyside	MTL Asset Protection Teams
166.18750	170.98750	NFM	Newcastle	Council
166.18750	170.98750	NFM	Nottingham	County Council
166.18750	170.98750	NFM	Poole	Repeater
166.18750	170.98750	NFM	Ramsgate	Council
166.18750	170.98750	NFM	Southend on Sea	Borough Council (192.8)
166.18750	170.98750	NFM	Spelthorne	Council (71.9)
166.18750	170.98750	NFM	Stockton on Tees	Borough Council Security
166.18750	170.98750	NFM	Tandridge	Council
166.18750	170.98750	NFM	Telford	Council
166.18750	170.98750	NFM	Trafford	Council Highways Department
166.18750	170.98750	NFM	Vale of Glamorgan	Council Repairs (107.2)
166.18750	170.98750	NFM	Waveney	District Council
166.18750	170.98750	NFM	West Midlands	Council Environmental Health
166.20000	171.00000	NFM	Chichester	St Richards Hospital
166.20000	171.00000	NFM	Edinburgh	Scottish Ambulance Service Trunked Control
166.20000	171.00000	NFM	Hampshire	Ambulance Service
166.20000	171.00000	NFM	London	Ambulance Service
166.20000	171.00000	NFM	Merseyside	Ambulance Service Rapid Response Medics
166.20000	171.00000	NFM	Port Talbot	Wales Ambulance Trust A&E
166.20000	171.00000	NFM	N Yorkshire	North Yorkshire Ambulance Trust
166.20000	171.00000	NFM	W Midlands	Ambulance Service Patient Transport
166.20000	171.00000	NFM	W Yorkshire	Ambulance Service Emergencies
166.21250	171.01250	NFM	Amersham	Chiltern Council
166.21250	170.01250	NFM	Cardiff	Bunnon
166.21250	170.01250	NFM	Castle Point	Borough Council
166.21250	171.01250	NFM	Essex	Council Ch.1
166.21500	171.01500	NFM	Gateshead	Council
166.21250	171.01250	NFM	Gloucester	District Council
166.21250	171.01250	NFM	Hampshire	Council
166.21250	171.01250	NFM	Hinchley	Council
166.21250	171.01250	NFM	Hinckley	Council
166.21250	171.01250	NFM	London	Greenwich Council
166.21250	171.01250	NFM	Manchester	District Council
166.21250	171.01250	NFM	Newport	Gwent Council Decorators
166.21250	171.01250	NFM	Northern Ireland	Northern Ireland Railways Ch.3 (156.7)
166.21250	171.01250	NFM	Poole	RBLA security
166.21250	171.01250	NFM	Suffolk	Hasketon Farms
166.21250	171.01250	NFM	Swindon	Cooper's Metals
166.21250	171.01250	NFM	Uttlesford	Council
166.21250	171.01250	NFM	Woking	Council
166.21500	171.01500	NFM	Worcester	City Council Depot
166.22500	171.02500	NFM	Aberdeen	Fish Market
166.22500	171.02500	NFM	Ashford	District Council Ch.4
166.22500	171.02500	FM	Ayr	Sewer Maintenance
166.22500	171.02500	NFM	Birmingham	Park Patrols Central Control
166.22500	171.02500	NFM	Blaenau	Gwent Council
166.22500	171.02500	NFM	Bridgnorth	Bridgnorth District Council
166.22500	171.02500	NFM	Cambridge	Council

Base	Mobile	Mode	Location	User and Notes
166.22500	171.02500	NFM	Chester	Council Vandal Line Team (186.2)
166.22500	171.02500	NFM	Coventry	Council Environmental Dept. Noise Abatement
166.22500	171.02500	NFM	Eastbourne	Borough Council
166.22500	171.02500	NFM	Eastleigh	Council
166.22500	171.02500	NFM	Gloucester	Council
166.22500	171.02500	NFM	Guildford	Council
166.22500	171.02500	NFM	Kilmarnock	Council Parks Department
166.22500	171.02500	NFM	Lincoln	Local Authority
166.22500	171.02500	NFM	Livingston	West Lothian District Council
166.22500	171.02500	NFM	London	Kensington & Chelsea Council
166.22500	171.02500	NFM	London	Lewisham Council
166.22500	171.02500	NFM	London	Newham Council
166.22500	171.02500	NFM	Nationwide	Local Authorities
166.22500	171.02500	NFM	Newcastle	Council
166.22500	171.02500	NFM	Preston	Council Maintenance
166.22500	171.02500	NFM	Reigate & Banstead	Council (131.8)
166.22500	171.02500	NFM	Southend on Sea	Borough Council (123)
166.22500	171.02500	NFM	Stevenage	Borough Council
166.22500	171.02500	NFM	Sunderland	Council
166.22500	171.02500	NFM	Woking	District Council
166.22500	171.02500	NFM	Worcester	Council
166.23750	171.03750	NFM	Aberdeen	TV Repair Company
166.23750	171.03750	NFM	Bathgate	Streamline Taxis (Streamline)
166.23750	171.03750	NFM	Chichester	Council
166.23750	171.03750	NFM	Coventry	National Agricultural Centre, Stoneleigh
166.23750	171.03750	NFM	Cwmbran	Council
166.23750	171.03750	NFM	Gt Yarmouth	Skip Hire Company (94.8)
166.23750	171.03750	NFM	London	Kingston Council (82.5)
166.23750	171.03750	NFM	Manchester	Thameside Council
166.23750	171.03750	NFM	Mansfield	District Council
166.23750	171.03750	NFM	Norfolk	Haller's Skip Hire
166.23750	171.03750	NFM	Oldham	Halroyd Skips
166.23750	171.03750	NFM	Pembroke	Taxi Company (123)
166.23750	171.03750	NFM	Weymouth	Council
166.25000	171.05000	NFM	Basingstoke	Council
166.25000	171.05000	NFM	Beverly	Council Parks Department
166.25000	171.05000	NFM	Birmingham	Traffic Lights Maintenance
166.25000	171.05000	NFM	Brighton	Brighton Council
166.25000	171.05000	NFM	Bury St Edmunds	District Council
166.25000	171.05000	NFM	Chandlers Ford	Taxi Company
166.25000	171.05000	NFM	Elmbridge	Council
166.25000	171.05000	NFM	Harlow	Council
166.25000	171.05000	NFM	Hertfordshire	District Council
166.25000	171.05000	NFM	Hull	Council Parks Department
166.25000	171.05000	NFM	Ipswich	GIS/Goldlink Guards Security
166.25000	171.05000	NFM	Jersey	Tantivy Holiday Coaches
166.25000	171.05000	NFM	London	Lambeth Council
166.25000	171.05000	NFM	Manchester	House Calls
166.25000	171.05000	NFM	Mid Glamorgan	Council
166.25000	171.05000	NFM	Newcastle	Tyne Tunnel Control
166.25000	171.05000	NFM	Northern Ireland	Northern Ireland Railways
166.25000	171.05000	NFM	Poole	Repeater
166.25000	171.05000	NFM	Tayside	Council Building Works
166.25000	171.05000	NFM	Trowbridge	Housing Association
166.25000	171.05000	NFM	Tyneside	Tyne Tunnel Control
166.26250	171.06250	NFM	Bolton	Council Dog Warden

Base	Mobile	Mode	Location	User and Notes
166.26250	171.06250	NFM	Braintree	Borough Council
166.26250	171.06250	NFM	Edinburgh	Citadel Couriers (City)
166.26250	171.06250	NFM	Essex	Council Highways Department Ch.2
166.26250	171.06250	NFM	Leicester	Council Refuse Collection
166.26250	171.06250	NFM	London	Merton Council Refuse Collection
166.26250	171.06250	NFM	London	Newham Borough Council
166.26250	171.06250	NFM	Nuneaton & Bedworth	Council
166.26250	171.06250	NFM	Rochford	Council
166.26250	171.06250	NFM	Salford	Council Cleansing Department
166.26250	171.06250	NFM	Sheffield	Hallam University
166.26250	171.06250	NFM	Thetford	Broadland Council
166.26500	171.06250	NFM	Newcastle	Taxi Company
166.27500	171.07500	NFM	Edinburgh	Scottish Ambulance Service Trunked
166.27500	171.07500	NFM	Lincolnshire	Ambulance Service Southern Area A&E
166.27500	171.07500	NFM	London	Ambulance Ch.11 East/Central
166.27500	171.07500	NFM	Northern Ireland	Ambulance Ch.09 (Spare Channel)
166.27500	171.07500	NFM	Scotland	Scottish Ambulance Service Trunked
166.27500	171.07500	NFM	West Country	Ambulance Service
166.27500	171.07500	NFM	West Midlands	Ambulance Service Data Vehicle Location System
166.28750	171.08750	NFM	Ashford	Doctors' Service
166.28750	171.08750	NFM	East Midlands	Ambulance Service
166.28750	171.08750	NFM	Kent	Ambulance Service Ch.5
166.28750	171.08750	NFM	Manchester	Greater Manchester Ambulance Service Ch.5
166.28750	171.08750	NFM	NE England	North East Ambulance Trust Emergency
166.28750	171.08750	NFM	N Ireland	Ambulance Service Ch.5 (67 Input)
166.28750	171.08750	NFM	Scotland	Scottish Ambulance Service Trunked
166.28750	171.08750	NFM	Wales	Wales Ambulance Trust
166.28750	171.08750	NFM	West Country	Ambulance Service
166.30000	171.10000	NFM	Cumbria	Ambulance Service Patient Transport
166.30000	171.10000	NFM	East Midlands	Ambulance Service
166.30000	171.10000	NFM	London	Ambulance Service Ch.9 South East
166.30000	171.10000	NFM	Manchester	Greater Manchester Ambulance Service Ch.3
166.30000	171.10000	NFM	N Yorkshire	North Yorkshire Ambulance Trust
166.30000	171.10000	NFM	Scotland	Scottish Ambulance Service Trunked
166.30000	171.10000	NFM	Wales	Wales Ambulance Trust
166.31250	171.11250	NFM	Cambridgeshire	Ambulance Service
166.31250	171.11250	NFM	East Midlands	Ambulance Service
166.31250	171.11250	NFM	London	Ambulance Ch.1 West
166.31250	171.11250	NFM	N Ireland	Ambulance Service East Patient Transport Ch.6
166.31250	171.11250	NFM	Plymouth	West Country Ambulance Trust
166.31250	171.11250	NFM	Scotland	Scottish Ambulance Service Trunked
166.31250	171.11250	NFM	S Wales	Wales Ambulance Trust
166.32500	171.12500	NFM	London	Ambulance S. East
166.32500	171.12500	NFM	Merseyside	Ambulance Service
166.32500	171.12500	NFM	N Ireland	Ambulance Service North A&E Ch.1 (67 Input)
166.32500	171.12500	NFM	Scotland	Scottish Ambulance Service Trunked
166.32500	171.12500	NFM	Sussex	Chubb Alarms
166.32500	171.12500	NFM	Wales	Wales Ambulance Trust
166.32500	171.12500	NFM	Warwickshire	Ambulance Service
166.33750	171.13750	NFM	Herts/Beds	Hertfordshire & Bedfordshire Ambulance Service
166.33750	171.13750	NFM	Isle of Wight	Ambulance Service
166.33750	171.13750	NFM	Kent	Ambulance Service
166.33750	171.13750	NFM	Lincolnshire	Ambulance Service A&E Patient Transport
166.33750	171.13750	NFM	Merseyside	Ambulance Service
166.33750	171.13750	NFM	Northern Ireland	Ambulance Service West A&E Ch.4 (67 Input)
166.33750	171.13750	NFM	Scotland	Scottish Ambulance Service Trunked

Base	Mobile	Mode	Location	User and Notes
166.33750	171.13750	NFM	West Country	Ambulance Trust
166.35000	171.15000	NFM	Cumbria	Ambulance Service
166.35000	171.15000	NFM	Dorset	Dorset Ambulance Trust Patient Transport
166.35000	171.15000	NFM	London	Ambulance Service Ch.3 North East
166.35000	171.15000	NFM	N Ireland	Ambulance Service South A&E Ch.3 (67 Input)
166.35000	171.15000	NFM	NE England	North East Ambulance Trust Patient Transport
166.35000	171.15000	NFM	Scotland	Scottish Ambulance Service Trunked
166.35000	171.15000	NFM	Wales	Wales Ambulance Trust
166.36250	171.16250	NFM	Essex	Ambulance Service
166.36250	171.16250	NFM	Gloucestershire	Ambulance Service
166.36250	171.16250	NFM	Hampshire	Ambulance Service East Ch.2
166.36250	171.16250	NFM	Merseyside	Ambulance Service
166.36250	171.16250	NFM	Scotland	Scottish Ambulance Service Trunked
166.36250	171.16250	NFM	Wales	Wales Ambulance Trust
166.36250	171.16250	NFM	W Yorkshire	Ambulance Service Patient Transport
166.37500	171.17500	NFM	Cumbria	Ambulance Service
166.37500	171.17500	NFM	E Midlands	Ambulance Service
166.37500	171.17500	NFM	Hereford & Worcester	Ambulance Service
166.37500	171.17500	NFM	London	Ambulance Service South East
166.37500	171.17500	NFM	Scotland	Scottish Ambulance Service Trunked
166.38750	171.18750	NFM	Berkshire	Ambulance Service
166.38750	171.18750	NFM	Kent	Ambulance Service Ch.3
166.38750	171.18750	NFM	Lancashire	Ambulance Trust Patient Transport
166.38750	171.18750	NFM	Scotland	Scottish Ambulance Service Trunked
166.38750	171.18750	NFM	Staffordshire	Ambulance Service A&E Ch.3
166.38750	171.18750	NFM	S Wales	Wales Ambulance Trust
166.38750	171.18750	NFM	West Midlands	St John Ambulance
166.38750	171.18750	NFM	West Yorkshire	Ambulance Service Patient Transport
166.40000	171.20000	NFM	East Midlands	Ambulance Service
166.40000	171.20000	NFM	Lancashire	Ambulance Service
166.40000	171.20000	NFM	N Ireland	Ambulance Service East A&E Ch.2 (67 Input)
166.40000	171.20000	NFM	Scotland	Scottish Ambulance Service Trunked
166.40000	171.20000	NFM	Sussex	Sussex Ambulance Trust (210.7)
166.40000	171.20000	NFM	Wales	Wales Ambulance Trust Ambulance Data
166.41250	171.21250	NFM	East Midlands	Ambulance Service
166.41250	171.21250	NFM	London	Ambulance Service South East Ch.3
166.41250	171.21250	NFM	Shropshire	Ambulance Service
166.41250	171.21250	NFM	Scotland	Scottish Ambulance Service Trunked
166.41250	171.21250	NFM	Wales	Wales Ambulance Trust
166.41250	171.21250	NFM	Wiltshire	Ambulance Service
166.42500	171.22500	NFM	Birmingham	Doctors' Service
166.42500	171.22500	NFM	Cardiff	Robert Bosch Security
166.42500	171.22500	NFM	Gt Yarmouth	M & M Services Working On Farms (67)
166.42500	171.22500	NFM	London	Ambulance/Paramedics & G-Hems Ch.7
166.42500	171.22500	NFM	Norwich	Doctors' Service
166.42500	171.22500	NFM	Rotherham	Rotherham Football Club Stewards
166.42500	171.22500	NFM	West Country	Ambulance Service
166.43750	171.23750	NFM	Hampshire	Common Air Ambulance Channel
166.43750	171.23750	NFM	Hampshire	Emergency Reserve/Police ASU Boxer 10
166.43750	171.23750	NFM	Kent	Common Air Ambulance Channel
166.43750	171.23750	NFM	Kent	St. John Ambulance Brigade Ch.10
166.43750	171.23750	NFM	London	Ambulance Service G-Hems Pilot-Doctor Comms
166.43750	171.23750	NFM	London	St. John Ambulance Ch.10
166.43750	171.23750	NFM	Manchester	Greater Manchester Ambulance Service
166.43750	171.23750	NFM	Nationwide	Helimed/Cross Country/Incident Control Ch.1
166.43750	171.23750	NFM	Nationwide	St. John Ambulance

Base	Mobile	Mode	Location	User and Notes
166.43750	171.23750	NFM	N Ireland	Ambulance Service Reserve Channel Ch.10
166.43750	171.23750	NFM	Oxford	Ambulance Service Ch.9 Patient Transport (94.8 Input)
166.43750	171.23750	NFM	Scotland	Scottish Ambulance Service Trunked
166.43750	171.23750	NFM	Surrey	Ambulance Emergency Relay
166.43750	171.23750	NFM	West Midlands	Ambulance Service Midwives & Helimed (110.9)
166.45000	171.25000	NFM	Birmingham	Community Midwives (82.5)
166.45000	171.25000	NFM	Bradford	Doctors' Deputy Service
166.45000	171.25000	NFM	Derby	District Nurses
166.45000	171.25000	NFM	Gravesend	Medway District Hospital Security/Porters
166.45000	171.25000	NFM	London	Ambulance Service Ch.6 Reserve
166.45000	171.25000	NFM	Newport, Gwent	Breakdown Recovery Company
166.45000	171.25000	NFM	W Yorkshire	Lexicon Deputising Service
166.45000	171.25000	NFM	Wantage	Doctors' Deputy Service
166.45000	171.25000	NFM	Wisbech	Clarkson Health Centre
166.46250	171.26250	NFM	Herts/Beds	Hertfordshire & Bedfordshire Ambulance Service
166.46250	171.26250	NFM	Scotland	Scottish Ambulance Service Trunked
166.46250	171.26250	NFM	Sussex	Ambulance Trust Portable Repeater (210.7)
166.46250	171.26250	NFM	Wales	Wales Ambulance Trust
166.46250	171.26250	NFM	West Midlands	Ambulance Service (110.9)
166.46250	171.26250	NFM	West Yorkshire	Ambulance Service Patient Transport
166.47500	171.27500	NFM	Hereford & Worcester	Ambulance Service
166.47500	171.27500	NFM	London	Ambulance North West
166.47500	171.27500	NFM	Merseyside	Ambulance Service
166.47500	171.27500	NFM	Scotland	Scottish Ambulance Service Trunked
166.47500	171.27500	NFM	Southend on Sea	Essex Ambulance Service
166.47500	171.27500	NFM	Wales	Wales Ambulance Trust
166.48750	171.28750	NFM	Dorset	Ambulance Trust Emergency (123 Input)
166.48750	171.28750	NFM	Essex	Ambulance Service
166.48750	171.28750	NFM	Liverpool	Ambulance Service
166.48750	171.28750	NFM	Manchester	Greater Manchester Ambulance Service Ch.7
166.48750	171.28750	NFM	North Yorkshire	Ambulance Service
166.48750	171.28750	NFM	Oxfordshire	Ambulance Service
166.48750	171.28750	NFM	Scotland	Scottish Ambulance Service Trunked
166.48750	171.28750	NFM	South Yorkshire	Ambulance Service
166.48750	171.28750	NFM	Tyne and Wear	Ambulance Service
166.50000	171.30000	NFM	Avon	Ambulance Service (Blue Base)
166.50000	171.30000	NFM	Birmingham	NHS Drug & Medical Supplies (67)
166.50000	171.30000	NFM	London	Ambulance Service
166.50000	171.30000	NFM	Manchester	Greater Manchester Ambulance Service Ch.6
166.50000	171.30000	NFM	N Ireland	Ambulance Ch.3 South A&E (67 Input)
166.50000	171.30000	NFM	Scilly Isles	Ambulance Service
166.50000	171.30000	NFM	Scotland	Scottish Ambulance Service Trunked
166.50000	171.30000	NFM	Staffordshire	Ambulance Service
166.50000	171.30000	NFM	West Midlands	Ambulance Service Selly Oak Hospital PTS
166.50000	171.30000	NFM	West Yorkshire	Ambulance Service Patient Transport Service
166.51250	171.31250	NFM	Cambridge	East Anglian Ambulance Service
166.51250	171.31250	NFM	Dorset	Ambulance Service Mobile Data
166.51250	171.31250	NFM	Manchester	Greater Manchester Ambulance Service Ch.2
166.51250	171.31250	NFM	Scotland	Ambulance Service
166.52500	171.32500	NFM	Erith	Council Refuse Collection (136.5)
166.52500	171.32500	NFM	Hampshire	Ambulance Service
166.52500	171.32500	NFM	Lancashire	Lancashire Ambulance Trust Emergency
166.52500	171.32500	NFM	London	Ambulance Service Ch.4 South West
166.52500	171.32500	NFM	Manchester	Greater Manchester Ambulance Service Ch.8
166.52500	171.32500	NFM	North Yorkshire	Ambulance Service
166.52500	171.32500	NFM	Scotland	Scottish Ambulance Service Trunked

Base	Mobile	Mode	Location	User and Notes
166.52500	171.32500	NFM	Suffolk	East Anglian Ambulance Service
166.52500	171.32500	NFM	Wales	Wales Ambulance Trust
166.52500	171.32500	NFM	Warwickshire	Ambulance Service Patient Transport Service
166.52500	171.32500	NFM	West Yorkshire	Ambulance Service Emergency
166.53750	171.33750	NFM	East Midlands	Ambulance Service
166.53750	171.33750	NFM	Scotland	Scottish Ambulance Service Trunked
166.53750	171.33750	NFM	Surrey	Ambulance Service
166.53750	171.33750	NFM	West Yorkshire	Ambulance Service
166.55000	171.35000	NFM	Essex	Ambulance Service
166.55000	171.35000	NFM	Hampshire	Ambulance Service
166.55000	171.35000	NFM	Lancashire	Ambulance Service Emergency
166.55000	171.35000	NFM	Northants/Bucks	Two Shires Ambulance Service
166.55000	171.35000	NFM	South Yorkshire	Ambulance Service
166.55000	171.35000	NFM	Scotland	Scottish Ambulance Service Trunked
166.55000		NFM	West Midlands	West Mercia Air Ambulance Doctor & Team
166.56250	171.36250	NFM	Hereford & Worcester	Ambulance Service
166.56250	171.36250	NFM	Norfolk	East Anglian Ambulance Service
166.56250	171.36250	NFM	N Ireland	Ambulance Ch.8 West Patient Transport (67 Input)
166.56250	171.36250	NFM	Scotland	Scottish Ambulance Service Trunked
166.56250	171.36250	NFM	South Yorkshire	Ambulance Service
166.56250	171.36250	NFM	Sussex	Ambulance Trust Red Base East (210.7)
166.56250	171.36250	NFM	Wales	Wales Ambulance Trust
166.56250	171.36250	NFM	West Country	Ambulance Service
166.57500	171.37500	NFM	London	Ambulance Service Ch.10 Central South
166.57500	171.37500	NFM	Merseyside	Ambulance Service (127.3)
166.57500	171.37500	NFM	Norfolk	East Anglian Ambulance Service A&E Link
166.57500	171.37500	NFM	Northants/Bucks	Two Shires Ambulance Service
166.57500	171.37500	NFM	Scotland	Scottish Ambulance Service Trunked
166.57500	171.37500	NFM	Suffolk	East Anglian Ambulance Service
166.57500	171.37500	NFM	Wales	Wales Ambulance Trust
166.58750	171.38750	NFM	Durham	Ambulance Service
166.58750	171.38750	NFM	Hampshire	Ambulance Service
166.58750	171.38750	NFM	Herts/Beds	Hertfordshire & Bedfordshire Ambulance
166.58750	171.38750	NFM	Lincolnshire	Ambulance Service A&E Northern Area
166.58750	171.38750	NFM	Merseyside	Ambulance Service
166.58750	171.38750	NFM	N Ireland	Ambulance Ch.7 South Patient Transport (67 Input)
166.58750	171.38750	NFM	Scotland	Scottish Ambulance Service Trunked
166.58750	171.38750	NFM	Staffordshire	Ambulance Service Ch.4 (major accidents)
166.60000	171.40000	NFM	Chertsey	St Peters Hospital (71.9)
166.60000	171.40000	NFM	Essex	North East Essex Doctors' Service
166.60000	171.40000	NFM	Manchester	Greater Manchester Ambulance Service Ch.4 (131.8)
166.60000	171.40000	NFM	Scotland	Scottish Ambulance Service Trunked
166.60000	171.40000	NFM	West Midlands	Ambulance Service A Div Ch.3 A&E (110.9)
166.61250	171.41250	NFM	Barking	Council
166.61250	171.41250	NFM	Belfast	Belfast Cab Company
166.61250	171.41250	NFM	Berkshire	Ambulance Service
166.61250	171.41250	NFM	Havant	Dixie's Taxis
166.61250	171.41250	NFM	Herts/Beds	Ambulance Service
166.61250	171.41250	NFM	Humberside	Ambulance Service
166.61250	171.41250	NFM	North Yorkshire	Ambulance Service
166.61250	171.41250	NFM	Oxfordshire	Ambulance Service
166.61250	171.41250	NFM	Scotland	Scottish Ambulance Service Trunked
166.61250	171.41250	NFM	Staffordshire	Ambulance Service Ch.2 A&E
166.61250	171.41250	NFM	Wiltshire	Ambulance Service
166.62500	171.42500	NFM	Antrim	Regency Cabs (67)
166.62500	171.42500	NFM	Bath	Francis Plant Hire

Base	Mobile	Mode	Location	User and Notes
166.62500	171.42500	NFM	Bolton	Cobra Taxis
166.62500	171.42500	NFM	Bournemouth	Breakdown Recovery Company
166.62500	171.42500	NFM	Bristol	Red Taxis
166.62500	171.42500	NFM	Cardiff	Blue Cabs
166.62500	171.42500	NFM	Dundee	Taxi Company
166.62500	171.42500	NFM	Gorseinon	Direct Taxis
166.62500	171.42500	NFM	Hampshire	Streamline Cabs
166.62500	171.42500	NFM	Hatfield	University Bus (118.8)
166.62500	171.42500	NFM	Ipswich	DSS Inspectors Ch.1
166.62500	171.42500	NFM	London	Congestion Charge Enforcement Officers
166.62500	171.42500	NFM	Lytham	Whitesides Taxis
166.62500	171.42500	NFM	Milford Haven	Taxi Company (103.5)
166.62500	171.42500	NFM	Manchester	Taxi Company
166.62500	171.42500	NFM	Poole	Repeater
166.62500	171.42500	NFM	St Austell	ECC Pits
166.62500	171.42500	NFM	Stirling	Thistle Centre
166.62500	171.42500	NFM	Worcester	Delta Taxis
166.63750	171.43750	NFM	Ashington	Toward Taxis
166.63750	171.43750	NFM	Bolton	Taxi Company
166.63750	171.43750	NFM	Caerphilly	Taxi Company (127.3)
166.63750	171.43750	NFM	Collyhurst	Taxi Company
166.63750	171.43750	NFM	Coventry	Lewis Taxis
166.63750	171.43750	NFM	Drayton	Draytax Taxis
166.63750	171.43750	NFM	Glasgow	DSS, Pitt Street
166.63750	171.43750	NFM	Isle of Wight	Grange Taxis
166.63750	171.43750	NFM	Lancing	Access Cars
166.63750	171.43750	NFM	Limavady	Bells Taxis (162.2)
166.63750	171.43750	NFM	Lowestoft	Union Taxis
166.63750	171.43750	NFM	Manchester	Cresta Car Hire
166.63750	171.43750	NFM	Middlesbrough	Docks
166.63750	171.43750	NFM	Oldham	Taxi Company
166.63750	171.43750	NFM	Peacehaven	Dave's Taxis
166.63750	171.43750	NFM	Ramsgate	Taxi Company
166.63750	171.43750	NFM	Whittlesey	S & S Tractors
166.63750	171.43750	NFM	Woodbridge	Greenwell Farms
166.65000	171.45000	NFM	Bedfordshire	Bedfordshire Growers
166.65000	171.45000	NFM	Belfast	Ferguson Flowers (94.8)
166.65000	171.45000	NFM	Bury	Byford Taxis
166.65000	171.45000	NFM	Flixton	Beaumont's Private Hire
166.65000	171.45000	NFM	Glasgow	Taxi Company
166.65000	171.45000	NFM	Halifax	Crossleys Taxis
166.65000	171.45000	NFM	Hampshire	Wessex Plant Hire
166.65000	171.45000	NFM	Ipswich	Taxi Association
166.65000	171.45000	NFM	Maidstone	Streamline Taxis
166.65000	171.45000	NFM	Shefford	K Cars
166.66250	171.46250	NFM	Barkway	British Sugar
166.66250	171.46250	NFM	Belfast	Need-A-Cab (114.8)
166.66250	171.46250	NFM	Bradford	Quickline
166.66250	171.46250	NFM	Cantley	British Sugar
166.66250	171.46250	NFM	Cheltenham	Celtax Couriers
166.66250	171.46250	NFM	Chester	Countess of Chester Hospital
166.66250	171.46250	NFM	Exeter	Al Cars
166.66250	171.46250	NFM	Felixstowe	Wizard Taxis Ch.2
166.66250	171.46250	NFM	Grimsby	Peter Sheffield Buses
166.66250	171.46250	NFM	London	Scorpio Cars
166.66250	171.46250	NFM	Manchester	Taxi Company

Base	Mobile	Mode	Location	User and Notes
166.66250	171.46250	NFM	Perth	Taylor's Taxis
166.66250	171.46250	NFM	Sudbury	A Line Taxis
166.66250	171.46250	NFM	Swinton	Skytax
166.67500	171.47500	NFM	Alconbury	Steve's Taxis
166.67500	171.47500	NFM	Alderney	Alderney Taxi
166.67500	171.47500	NFM	Bolton	Best Way Taxis
166.67500	171.47500	NFM	Burnley	Parking Enforcement (192.8)
166.67500	171.47500	NFM	Coleraine	Crown Cabs (173.8)
166.67500	171.47500	NFM	Elvington	Rolawn Turf Suppliers
166.67500	171.47500	NFM	Glasgow	Taxi Company
166.67500	171.47500	NFM	Hampshire	Ace Taxis
166.67500	171.47500	NFM	Hartlepool	Station Taxis
166.67500	171.47500	NFM	Hounslow	Minicab Company
166.67500	171.47500	NFM	Hinckley	Station Taxis
166.67500	171.47500	NFM	Hull	Sentry Security
166.67500	171.47500	NFM	Huntingdon	Steve's Taxis
166.67500	171.47500	NFM	Ipswich	Hawk Express
166.67500	171.47500	NFM	Ipswich	Premier Cabs
166.67500	171.47500	NFM	Leeds	B Line Cabs
166.67500	171.47500	NFM	London	Minicab Company, Ealing
166.67500	171.47500	NFM	London	Minicab Company, Wimbledon
166.67500	171.47500	NFM	Mostyn	Dave's Taxis
166.67500	171.47500	NFM	Newtownabbey	Bellevue Taxis
166.67500	171.47500	NFM	Norwich	Norwich Courtesy Cars
166.67500	171.47500	NFM	Radcliffe	Harvey's Taxis
166.67500	171.47500	NFM	Scarborough	Nippy Taxis
166.67500	171.47500	NFM	Skegness	Sid Dennis Skips
166.67500	171.47500	NFM	Southampton	A2B Taxis
166.68750	171.48750	NFM	Anglesey	Anglesey Doctors
166.68750	171.48750	NFM	Berinsfield	Star Cars
166.68750	171.48750	NFM	Blackpool	Doctors (103.5)
166.68750	171.48750	NFM	Buxton	Crane & Son
166.68750	171.48750	NFM	Chatteris	Whitworth Produce
166.68750	171.48750	NFM	East Kilbride	Kelvin Kabs
166.68750	171.48750	NFM	Glasgow	Taxi Company
166.68750	171.48750	NFM	Guernsey	AC Heating
166.68750	171.48750	NFM	Guernsey	Cobo Building
166.68750	171.48750	NFM	Harold Wood	Amber Car Services (88.5)
166.68750	171.48750	NFM	Ipswich	Ransomes Ltd
166.68750	171.48750	NFM	Kings Lynn	British Sugar
166.68750	171.48750	NFM	London	20th Century Taxis, Harrow
166.68750	171.48750	NFM	Newport	ABC Taxis
166.68750	171.48750	NFM	Peterborough	Co-Op TV Services
166.68750	171.48750	NFM	Sittingbourne	Swift Taxis
166.68750	171.48750	NFM	Swindon	Starlight Taxis
166.70000	171.50000	NFM	Belfast	AA Taxis (94.8)
166.70000	171.50000	NFM	Birmingham	Taxi Company, Shard End
166.70000	171.50000	NFM	Boyton	Valley Farm (94.8)
166.70000	171.50000	NFM	Cardiff	Supertax Taxis (162.2)
166.70000	171.50000	NFM	Cirencester	Radio Cars
166.70000	171.50000	NFM	Colchester	Incabs
166.70000	171.50000	NFM	Gosport	Kingfisher Caravan Park Security/Maint. (118.8)
166.70000	171.50000	NFM	Hampshire	Haverson Electronics
166.70000	171.50000	NFM	Hull	Council Parks Department
166.70000	171.50000	NFM	Methwold	Darby Bros Farms
166.70000	171.50000	NFM	Montrose	Taxi Company

Base	Mobile	Mode	Location	User and Notes
166.70000	171.50000	NFM	Murriston	Samlet Cabs
166.70000	171.50000	NFM	Norwich	Bestway Taxis
166.70000	171.50000	NFM	Nottingham	Phoenix Cars, Hucknall
166.70000	171.50000	NFM	Portstewart NI	Ultra Taxis
166.70000	171.50000	NFM	Sheffield	Abbeytax Taxis
166.70000	171.50000	NFM	Sheffield	Sheftax Taxis
166.70000	171.50000	NFM	Southampton	RMS Motors
166.70000	171.50000	NFM	Stoke on Trent	Taxi Company (203.5)
166.70000	171.50000	NFM	Swansea	Samlet Cabs
166.71250	171.51250	NFM	Abingdon	JMB Plant Hire
166.71250	171.51250	NFM	Canvey Island	Taxi Company
166.71250	171.51250	NFM	Chelmsford	Ali's Cabs
166.71250	171.51250	NFM	Coleraine	Haz Kabs
166.71250	171.51250	NFM	Coventry	Taxi Company
166.71250	171.51250	NFM	Edinburgh	Festival Cars
166.71250	171.51250	NFM	Frome	C&C Taxis
166.71250	171.51250	NFM	Grimsby	Taxi Company
166.71250	171.51250	NFM	Havant	Jacks Taxis
166.71250	171.51250	NFM	Keighley	Crown Taxis
166.71250	171.51250	NFM	Londonderry	Rosemount Taxis (94.8)
166.71250	171.51250	NFM	London	Mogul Radio Cars, Surbiton
166.71250	171.51250	NFM	London	West End Mini Cabs, Soho
166.71250	171.51250	NFM	Morecambe	Taxi Company
166.71250	171.51250	NFM	Sheffield	RD Cars
166.71250	171.51250	NFM	Southampton	Taxi Company
166.71250	171.51250	NFM	Trumpington	Ciba Agricultural Farm Workers (136.5)
166.71250	171.51250	NFM	Trumpington	Ciba Agricultural Security (186.2)
166.72500	171.52500	NFM	Limavady	Alpha Taxis (186.2)
166.72500	171.52500	NFM	Manchester	Parking Enforcement
166.72500	171.52500	NFM	Northamptonshire	Council Gritters/Highways
166.73750	171.53750	NFM	Bolton	Cross Private Hire
166.73750	171.53750	AM	Colchester	Rainbow Taxis
166.73750	171.53750	NFM	Exeter	Line 49 Cars
166.73750	171.53750	NFM	Gt Yarmouth	Shopwatch /Pubwatch/ Patrols/TVEye (77)
166.73750	171.53750	NFM	Hintlesham	Northlands Farm
166.73750	171.53750	NFM	London	National Radio Cars
166.73750	171.53750	NFM	London	Alpha Cars, Hounslow
166.73750	171.53750	NFM	Maidstone	Leeds Castle Ch.1 Maintenance (103.5)
166.73750	171.53750	NFM	Pitsea	Taxi Company
166.73750	171.53750	NFM	Poulton	Poulton Cabs
166.73750	171.53750	NFM	Rochdale	Globe Taxis
166.73750	171.53750	NFM	Widnes	Kay Cabs
166.75000	171.55000	NFM	Banchory	Taxi Company
166.75000	171.55000	NFM	East Anglia	Ambulance Service Emergency Support
166.75000	171.55000	NFM	Hull	DSS Datalink
166.75000	171.55000	NFM	Surrey	Ambulance Service Mobile Data
166.75000	171.55000	NFM	Tyne & Wear	North East Ambulance Trust
166.75000	171.55000	NFM	West Midlands	Ambulance Service Data
166.76250	171.56250	NFM	Alton Towers	Ch.1 Security/Car Parks (94.8)
166.76250	171.56250	NFM	Belfast	Ulster University, Jordanstown Campus (131.8)
166.76250	171.56250	NFM	Bognor Regis	Butlins Ch.2
166.76250	171.56250	NFM	Burnley	Shopwatch (203.5)
166.76250	171.56250	NFM	Burton on Trent	Hospital Porters
166.76250	171.56250	NFM	Cambridge	Girton College (Tower)
166.76250	171.56250	NFM	Canterbury	Shopwatch (103.5)
166.76250	171.56250	NFM	Castle Donington	Race Control (141.3)

Base	Mobile	Mode	Location	User and Notes
166.76250	171.56250	NFM	Chessington	World of Adventures Security (131.8)
166.76250	171.56250	NFM	Coleraine	Ulster University, Coleraine Campus (131.8)
166.76250	171.56250	NFM	Coventry	Coventry University Maintenance
166.76250	171.56250	NFM	Crosby	Shopwatch
166.76250	171.56250	NFM	Derby	Derby City Hospital Porters
166.76250	171.56250	NFM	Dudley	Delivery Company
166.76250	171.56250	NFM	Dumfries	District Council
166.76250	171.56250	NFM	Harlow	Harvey Centre Security
166.76250	171.56250	NFM	Harrogate	Shopwatch
166.76250	171.56250	NFM	Hatfield	Hertfordshire University Resident Assistants (173.8)
166.76250	171.56250	NFM	Holbrook	Royal Hospital School
166.76250	171.56250	NFM	Hornchurch	St Georges Hospital
166.76250	171.56250	NFM	Hull	DSS Inspectors
166.76250	171.56250	NFM	Ipswich	Taxi Company
166.76250	171.56250	NFM	Irvine	Rivergate Shopping Centre Security
166.76250	171.56250	NFM	Isle of Man	Manx Domestic Airline, Ronaldsway Airport
166.76250	171.56250	NFM	Kirkcaldy	Mercat Shopping Centre Security
166.76250	171.56250	NFM	London	John Lewis Security Ch.1, Brent Cross
166.76250	171.56250	NFM	London	John Lewis Undercover Security Ch.1, Oxford Street
166.76250	171.56250	NFM	Londonderry	Ulster University, Magee Campus (131.8)
166.76250	171.56250	NFM	Maggor	Tesco Distribution Warehouse SW UK (136.5)
166.76250	171.56250	NFM	Norwich	Pubwatch/SOS Bus (123)
166.76250	171.56250	NFM	Plymouth	Shopwatch
166.76250	171.56250	NFM	Poole	Guardforce Security
166.76250	171.56250	NFM	Port Talbot	Corus Steelworks (107.2)
166.76250	171.56250	NFM	Portsmouth	Cascade Shopping Centre (127.3)
166.76250	171.56250	NFM	Preston	University Of Central Lancashire Maint. (186.2)
166.76250	171.56250	NFM	Preston	University Of Central Lancashire Security (127.3)
166.76250	171.56250	NFM	Rugby	Shopwatch
166.76250	171.56250	NFM	Sheffield	Rother Valley Sports Centre
166.76250	171.56250	NFM	Shepperton	Shepperton Studios Security (DCS 031)
166.76250	171.56250	NFM	Southport	Pleasureland Theme Park (151.4)
166.76250	171.56250	NFM	St Andrews	Shopwatch
166.76250	171.56250	NFM	Stoke on Trent	Parking Enforcement (71.9)
166.76250	171.56250	NFM	Suffolk	Royal Hospital School, Holbrook
166.76250	171.56250	NFM	Swindon	Oasis Leisure Centre
166.76250	171.56250	NFM	Swillington	St Aidan's Open Cast Coal Mine Ch.1
166.76250	171.56250	NFM	Wakefield	The Ridings Centre Security Ch.2
166.76250	171.56250	NFM	Warrington	Golden Square Shopping Centre Security
166.76250	171.56250	NFM	Wentworth	Wentworth Golf Club Staff (151.4)
166.77500	171.57500	NFM	Burnley	Doctors' Service
166.77500	171.57500	NFM	Cardiff	Taxi Company
166.77500	171.57500	NFM	Dover	Council
166.77500	171.57500	NFM	East Anglia	Ambulance Ch.8 Link to St. John Ambulance
166.77500	171.57500	NFM	Herts/Beds	Ambulance Service
166.77500	171.57500	NFM	Scotland	Scottish Ambulance Service Trunked
166.77500	171.57500	NFM	Suffolk	District Nurses
166.78750	171.58750	NFM	Bournemouth	Castle Recovery
166.78750	171.58750	NFM	Bristol	Taxi Company (210.7)
166.78750	171.58750	NFM	Cornwall	Vetco Base
166.78750	171.58750	NFM	Dorking	Kings Recover
166.78750	171.58750	NFM	Dumfries	District Council
166.78750	171.58750	NFM	Edinburgh	Diamond Security
166.78750	171.58750	NFM	Grimsby	Lincs Vending
166.78750	171.58750	NFM	Grimsby	Mariner Gas
166.78750	171.58750	NFM	Hampshire	Council

Base	Mobile	Mode	Location	User and Notes
166.78750	171.58750	NFM	Ipswich	Taxi Company
166.78750	171.58750	NFM	Kent	St. John Ambulance Brigade Ch.11 Training
166.78750	171.58750	NFM	Lancaster	District Nurse
166.78750	171.58750	NFM	Lincolnshire	Community Repeater
166.78750	171.58750	NFM	London	Bus/Coach Company (131.8)
166.78750	171.58750	NFM	London	Breakdown Recovery (97.4)
166.78750	171.58750	NFM	Newcastle	Auto Breakdowns
166.80000	171.60000	NFM	Cheshire	Doctors' Service
166.80000	171.60000	NFM	Darlington	Darlington Hospital
166.80000	171.60000	NFM	Doncaster	Royal Infirmary
166.80000	171.60000	NFM	Glossop	District Nurses
166.80000	171.60000	NFM	Gloucester	Ambulance Service Ch.2
166.80000	171.60000	NFM	London	Haringey Council
166.80000	171.60000	NFM	London	Lambeth Council
166.80000	171.60000	NFM	Manchester	Hospital Porters
166.80000	171.60000	NFM	Mansfield	Kings Mill Hospital
166.80000	171.60000	NFM	Preston	Preston Hospital (179.9)
166.80000	171.60000	NFM	Poole	General Hospital
166.80000	171.60000	NFM	Scotland	Scottish Ambulance Service Trunked
166.80000	171.60000	NFM	Sussex	Sussex Ambulance Trust Blue Base
166.80000	171.60000	NFM	Wigan	Royal Albert Edward Infirmary Porters/Security (67)
166.80000	171.60000	NFM	Wiltshire	Ambulance Service
166.80000	171.60000	NFM	Winsford	Doctors' Service
166.81250	171.61250	NFM	Chapmanslade	Barters Farm
166.81250	171.61250	NFM	Doncaster	Health Centre
166.81250	171.61250	NFM	Essex	Havering Council
166.81250	171.61250	NFM	Haverfordwest	E Williams Transport
166.81250	171.61250	NFM	Herts/Beds	Herts & Beds Ambulance Service Paramedics
166.81250	171.61250	NFM	Kings Lynn	District Nurses
166.81250	171.61250	NFM	Llanelli	Doctors' Service
166.81250	171.61250	NFM	Merseyside	Doctors' Service
166.81250	171.61250	NFM	Nationwide	Doctors' Service Ch.1
166.81250	171.61250	NFM	Norfolk	Doctors' Service
166.81250	171.61250	NFM	North Lancashire	Doctors' Service
166.81250	171.61250	NFM	Northampton	Doctors' Service
166.81250	171.61250	NFM	Oxfordshire	Doctors' Service
166.81250	171.61250	NFM	Runcorn	Doctors' Service
166.81250	171.61250	NFM	Stoke-on-Trent	Doctors' Service
166.81250	171.61250	NFM	Sussex	Brighton Council
166.81250	171.61250	NFM	Scotland	Scottish Ambulance Service Trunked
166.81250	171.61250	NFM	Upwell	Health Centre
166.81250	171.61250	NFM	Yorkshire	Doctors' Service
166.82500	171.62500	NFM	Burnley	Council Security Patrols
166.82500	171.62500	NFM	Coventry	Chemtek Cleansing Liquids
166.82500	171.62500	NFM	Hartlepool	Hartlepool Hospital
166.82500	171.62500	NFM	Hastings	Council
166.82500	171.62500	NFM	Ipswich	Wilding & Smith
166.82500	171.62500	NFM	Jersey	Yellow Cabs
166.82500	171.62500	NFM	Kent	Ambulance Service Ch.4
166.82500	171.62500	NFM	London	Islington Flood Control
166.82500	171.62500	NFM	Manchester	Doctors' Service
166.82500	171.62500	NFM	Nationwide	DSS Fraud Teams
166.82500	171.62500	NFM	Scotland	Scottish Ambulance Service Trunked
166.82500	171.62500	NFM	Stirling	Stirling Hospital
166.82500	171.62500	AM	Thanet	Ambulance Service
166.82500	171.62500	NFM	Wales	Wales Ambulance Trust

Base	Mobile	Mode	Location	User and Notes
166.82500	171.62500	NFM	Wirral	District Nurses
166.82500	171.62500	NFM	Worcestershire	Ambulance Service
166.83750	171.63750	NFM	Castle Donington	Race Track Medical Control
166.83750	171.63750	NFM	Downham Market	Doctors' Service
166.83750	171.63750	NFM	Emsworth	John's Cabs
166.83750	171.63750	NFM	Gateshead	Doctors' Service
166.83750	171.63750	NFM	Hampshire	District Nurse
166.83750	171.63750	NFM	Hockley	Doctors' Service
166.83750	171.63750	NFM	Kent	Health Service
166.83750	171.63750	NFM	London	Haringey Council
166.83750	171.63750	NFM	Mid Glamorgan	Doctors' Service
166.83750	171.63750	NFM	Peterborough	Doctors' Service
166.83750	171.63750	NFM	S Essex	Doctors' Service
166.83750	171.63750	NFM	Sunderland	Doctors' Service
166.83750	171.63750	NFM	Wirral	Doctors' Service
166.85000	171.65000	NFM	Bristol	Domestic Appliance Engineers (159)
166.85000	171.65000	NFM	Cambridgeshire	Community Nurses
166.85000	171.65000	NFM	Dundee	Christian Salvesen
166.85000	171.65000	NFM	East Sussex	Doctors' Service
166.85000	171.65000	NFM	Edinburgh	Taxi Company
166.85000	171.65000	NFM	Gt. Yarmouth	Doberman Security
166.85000	171.65000	NFM	Haverfordwest	Gillmans Quarry
166.85000	171.65000	NFM	Kent	Winters 24hr Vehicle Recovery
166.85000	171.65000	NFM	Medway	Doctors' Service
166.85000	171.65000	NFM	Poole	Taxi Company
166.85000	171.65000	NFM	Sittingbourne	Britton & Hobbs TV & Video (127.3)
166.85000	171.65000	NFM	S Glamorgan	Doctors' Service
166.85000	171.65000	NFM	Swansea	Brisco Skip Hire Waste Disposal Service
166.86250	171.66250	NFM	Belfast	Dynorod (94.8)
166.86250	171.66250	NFM	Birmingham	Car Breakdown Recovery (103.5)
166.86250	171.66250	NFM	Coventry	Mayfair Security Ch.1
166.86250	171.66250	NFM	Crewe	City Council
166.86250	171.66250	NFM	Edinburgh	Housing Department
166.86250	171.66250	NFM	London	Emergency Radio System, Hillingdon Council
166.86250	171.66250	NFM	London	Lambeth Council (71.9)
166.86250	171.66250	NFM	Jersey	Pioneer Coaches
166.86250	171.66250	NFM	Newcastle	Taxi Company
166.86250	171.66250	NFM	Sheffield	Night Security Services
166.86250	171.66250	NFM	Wigan	Council Highways Department
166.87350	171.63750	NFM	Portsmouth	Doctors' Service
166.87350	171.63750	NFM	St Helens	Doctors' Service
166.87500	171.67500	NFM	Dundee	Doctors' Service
166.87500	171.67500	NFM	Freethorpe	Aitchison Bros
166.87500	171.67500	NFM	Gt Yarmouth	Doberman Security
166.87500	171.67500	NFM	Letchworth	Mick's Taxis (94.8)
166.87500	171.67500	NFM	London	Scaffolding Company
166.87500	171.67500	NFM	London	Shopwatch, Hampstead (71.9)
166.87500	171.67500	NFM	Manchester	Porter's Dairies
166.87500	171.67500	NFM	Morpeth	Council
166.87500	171.67500	NFM	Norfolk	Auto Windscreens
166.87500	171.67500	NFM	Northumberland	Farm Workers
166.87500	171.67500	NFM	Poole	Taxi Company
166.87500	171.67500	NFM	Preston	Dynorod
166.87500	171.67500	NFM	Somerset	Council
166.87500	171.67500	NFM	Warwick	Vet
166.87500	171.67500	NFM	Worcester	Gaming Machine Repairs

Base	Mobile	Mode	Location	User and Notes
166.87500	171.67500	NFM	Worcester	Silver Cars
166.88750	171.68750	NFM	Baildon	Baildon Private Hire
166.88750	171.68750	NFM	Benson	A Cabs
166.88750	171.68750	NFM	Birmingham	Taxi Company
166.88750	171.68750	NFM	Blackpool	Council Transport
166.88750	171.68750	NFM	Bolton	Express Taxis
166.88750	171.68750	NFM	Dorset	Nightguard Security
166.88750	171.68750	NFM	Fleetwood	Works Department
166.88750	171.68750	NFM	Flintwick	Airlink
166.88750	171.68750	NFM	Gateshead	Taxi Company
166.88750	171.68750	NFM	Halifax	Whitehill Taxis
166.88750	171.68750	NFM	Haworth	Leam Taxis
166.88750	171.68750	NFM	Lancaster	Council
166.88750	171.68750	NFM	Letchworth	Mick's Taxis (94.8)
166.88750	171.68750	NFM	London	Blackheath Car Services
166.88750	171.68750	NFM	Morecambe	Council
166.88750	171.68750	NFM	Poole	Repeater
166.88750	171.68750	NFM	West Suffolk	Cambridge & East Coast Cable
166.90000	171.70000	NFM	Aberdeen	Aberdeen Vets
166.90000	171.70000	NFM	Blackpool	Taxi Company (77)
166.90000	171.70000	NFM	Colchester	AE Arnold
166.90000	171.70000	NFM	Doncaster	Fone-A-Car
166.90000	171.70000	NFM	Ely	Vets
166.90000	171.70000	NFM	London	Skip Hire Company (173.8)
166.90000	171.70000	NFM	Oldham	Council
166.91250	171.71250	NFM	Bolton	Zodiac Taxis
166.91250	171.71250	NFM	Coleraine	Fifers Taxis (131.8)
166.91250	171.71250	NFM	Holyhead	Taxi Company
166.91250	171.71250	NFM	Maidenhead	Taxi Company
166.91250	171.71250	NFM	Newark	Taxi Company
166.91250	171.71250	NFM	Norwich	Canary Cars
166.91250	171.71250	NFM	Nottingham	Taxi Company
166.91250	171.71250	NFM	Peterborough	Peterborough Cars (250.3)
166.91250	171.71250	NFM	Sheffield	Tri-Star Security Ltd. (Bulldog)
166.91250	171.71250	NFM	St Austell	Star Cars
166.91250	171.71250	NFM	Stevenage	Ace Taxis (218.1)
166.92500	171.72500	NFM	Belfast	Cedarcabs, Antrim Road
166.92500	171.72500	NFM	Bootle	Taxi Company
166.92500	171.72500	NFM	Canterbury	City Cars
166.92500	171.72500	NFM	Frome	ABC Taxis
166.92500	171.72500	NFM	Gt Yarmouth	Birds Eye Vans
166.92500	171.72500	NFM	London	Taxi Company, Enfield
166.92500	171.72500	NFM	London	Taxi Company, Finchley
166.92500	171.72500	NFM	Lowestoft	Birds Eye
166.92500	171.72500	NFM	Manchester	Lion Private Hire
166.92500	171.72500	NFM	Neath	Swallow /Mel's Cabs
166.92500	171.72500	NFM	Newcastle	Taxi Company
166.92500	171.72500	NFM	Oldham	Roller's Private Hire
166.92500	171.72500	NFM	Penarth	Taxi Company (110.9)
166.92500	171.72500	NFM	Peterborough	3 Star Taxis (192.8)
166.92500	171.72500	NFM	Shipley	Eagle Kars
166.92500	171.72500	NFM	Slough	Viking Radio Cars
166.93750	171.73750	NFM	Corby	Rockingham Speedway Contractor Ch.2
166.93750	171.73750	NFM	Edinburgh	Parking Enforcement (APCOA) (107.2)
166.93750	171.73750	NFM	Hindley	Anrich Vets
166.93750	171.73750	NFM	London	Winter's Ship Hire

Base	Mobile	Mode	Location	User and Notes
166.93750	171.73750	NFM	Newcastle	Highway Maintenance
166.93750	171.73750	NFM	Portsmouth	Harbour Security
166.93750	171.73750	NFM	South Glamorgan	Doctors' Service
166.93750	171.73750	NFM	Sunderland	Royal Hospital Security
166.93750	171.73750	NFM	Trowbridge	Alpha Taxis
166.95000	171.75000	NFM	Accrington	Doctors' Service
166.95000	171.75000	NFM	Blackburn	Doctors' Service (173)
166.95000	171.75000	NFM	Canterbury	Doctors' Service
166.95000	171.75000	NFM	Coventry	Euroguard Security
166.95000	171.75000	NFM	East Dereham	Taxi Company
166.95000	171.75000	NFM	Hampshire	Doctors' Service
166.95000	171.75000	NFM	Holderness	Farmwatch
166.95000	171.75000	NFM	Kent	Community Recycling
166.95000	171.75000	NFM	Leeds	Bell Cable Engineers Ch.14
166.95000	171.75000	NFM	London	Amey Roadstone
166.95000	171.75000	NFM	Pembroke	Taxi Company (118.8)
166.95000	171.75000	NFM	Sheffield	Vending Machine Company
166.95000	171.75000	NFM	Southampton	Doctors' Service
166.95000	171.75000	NFM	Surrey	Amey Roadstone M3 Maintenance
166.96250	171.76250	NFM	Ashford	Invicta Taxis
166.96250	171.76250	NFM	Bradford	Broadway Taxis
166.96250	171.76250	NFM	Glasgow	Taxi Company
166.96250	171.76250	NFM	Hull	Taxi Company
166.96250	171.76250	NFM	Irvine	Taxi Company
166.96250	171.76250	NFM	Letchworth	Gary's Taxis (67)
166.96250	171.76250	NFM	London	Fleetcabs, Camden
166.96250	171.76250	NFM	Newtownabbey	Carnmoney Taxis, Woodford Road
166.96250	171.76250	NFM	Norwich	Readicrete Concrete (67)
166.96250	171.76250	NFM	Prestwich	Taxi Company
166.96250	171.76250	NFM	Salford	Taxi Company
166.96250	171.76250	NFM	Whitefield	Blueline Private Hire
166.96250	171.76250	NFM	Winchester	Taxi Company
166.96250	171.76250	NFM	Worthing	Taxi Company
166.97500	171.77500	NFM	Barnsley	Taxi Company
166.97500	171.77500	NFM	Dyfed	Crane Hire Company
166.97500	171.77500	NFM	Harwich	Dave's Taxis
166.97500	171.77500	NFM	Haverfordwest	Crane Hire Company
166.97500	171.77500	NFM	London	Parking Enforcement, Enfield (192.8)
166.97500	171.77500	NFM	Manchester	Taxi Company
166.97500	171.77500	NFM	Oxford	001 Cars
166.97500	171.77500	NFM	Peterborough	Associated Adams Taxis
166.97500	171.77500	NFM	Peterborough	Peterborough City Cars
166.97500	171.77500	NFM	Portsmouth	Taxi Company
166.97500	171.77500	NFM	Sheffield	A1 Cars
166.97500	171.77500	NFM	Sheffield	Toby Cars
166.97500	171.77500	NFM	Southampton	Taxi Company
166.97500	171.77500	NFM	Wolverhampton	Associated Taxis
166.98750	171.78750	NFM	Banbridge	Q Cabs
166.98750	171.78750	NFM	Bedford	A to B Cars
166.98750	171.87500	NFM	Bradford	Elvis Taxis
166.98750	171.78750	NFM	Broadstairs	Smileys Cabs
166.98750	171.78750	NFM	Cambridgeshire	Haulage Co
166.98750	171.78750	NFM	Dunstable	Jim & Jock's Taxis
166.98750	171.78750	NFM	Felixstowe	Road Haulage Company
166.98750	171.78750	NFM	Fleetwood	Wyre Borough Council
166.98750	171.78750	NFM	Glasgow	Taxi Company

Base	Mobile	Mode	Location	User and Notes
166.98750	171.78750	NFM	Littleport	Sallis Bros
166.98750	171.78750	NFM	Luton	Silverline Taxis
166.98750	171.78750	NFM	Newmarket	EF Saltmarsh
166.98750	171.78750	NFM	Poole	Council
167.00000	171.80000	NFM	Anglesey	Anglesey Security Company
167.00000	171.80000	NFM	Bedfordshire	Vet Service
167.00000	171.80000	NFM	Cambridge	Skip Hire Company (107.2)
167.00000	171.80000	NFM	Cambridge	Community Repeater Taxi Company (206.5)
167.00000	171.80000	NFM	Ellerker	FS & EM Wood Haulage
167.00000	171.80000	NFM	Hampshire	Dickson Bros.
167.00000	171.80000	NFM	Leicester	Taxi Company
167.00000	171.80000	NFM	Newcastle	Breakdown Recovery Company
167.00000	171.80000	NFM	Newcastle	Delivery Company
167.00000	171.80000	NFM	Newcastle	Road Maintenance Company
167.00000	171.80000	NFM	Norwich	Doctors' Service
167.01250	171.81250	NFM	Binbrook	Nickerson's Farm
167.01250	171.81250	NFM	Burnley	General Hospital Security
167.01250	171.81250	NFM	Cardiff	Council Community Transport
167.01250	171.81250	NFM	Cardiff	Fraser Security
167.01250	171.81250	NFM	Coventry	BFI Waste
167.01250	171.81250	NFM	Humberside	Birds Eye Foods
167.01250	171.81250	NFM	Ipswich	Yellow Taxis
167.01250	171.81250	NFM	Kenilworth	Brookline Taxis
167.01250	171.81250	NFM	Northampton	Taxi Company
167.01250	171.81250	NFM	Wales	Council Contractors
167.01250	171.81250	NFM	Wigan	Wigan Dairy (123)
167.02500	171.82500	NFM	Benfleet	Vehicle Recovery Company
167.02500	171.82500	NFM	Birmingham	Taxi Company, Chelmsley Wood
167.02500	171.82500	NFM	Bolton	Lyma Taxis
167.02500	171.82500	NFM	Burnley	Whites Taxis
167.02500	171.82500	NFM	East Dereham	Fransham Farm
167.02500	171.82500	NFM	Ely	Stopps Taxis
167.02500	171.82500	NFM	Essex	Mobile Garage (67)
167.02500	171.82500	NFM	Glasgow	Taxi Company
167.02500	171.82500	NFM	Hull	Taxi Company
167.02500	171.82500	NFM	Leicester	Taxi Company
167.02500	171.82500	NFM	London	Kerri Cars
167.02500	171.82500	NFM	London	Enter Minicabs, Willesden Green
167.02500	171.82500	NFM	Mapperton	Hooke Park Estate
167.02500	171.82500	NFM	Menston	Ride Away Private Hire
167.02500	171.82500	NFM	Merry Hill	Centre Traffic
167.02500	171.82500	NFM	Poulton	Poulton Cabs
167.02500	171.82500	NFM	Whiston	Britannia Taxis
167.02500	171.82500	NFM	Whitley Bay	Taxi Company
167.03750	171.83750	NFM	Alton Towers	Ch.4 Retail (88.5)
167.03750	171.83750	NFM	Bristol	Hospital Security (241.8)
167.03750	171.83750	NFM	Cambridge	City Tours Buses
167.03750	171.83750	NFM	Cardiff	National Sports Centre of Wales (67)
167.03750	171.83750	NFM	Carlisle	Tullie House Museum
167.03750	171.83750	NFM	Chessington	World of Adventures Ch.8 (241.8)
167.03750	171.83750	NFM	Coventry	Security Company (NHP Base)
167.03750	171.83750	NFM	Edinburgh	Shopwatch, Musselborough
167.03750	171.83750	NFM	Elverdon	Centre Parcs, Reception & Admin (107.2)
167.03750	171.83750	NFM	Gaydon	MG Rover Test Track Circuit Control
167.03750	171.83750	NFM	Glasgow	Securiguard
167.03750	171.83750	NFM	Gravesend	St Georges Shopping Centre Security

Base	Mobile	Mode	Location	User and Notes
167.03750	171.83750	NFM	Hatfield	Hatfield House Staff & Security (103.5)
167.03750	171.83750	NFM	Heathrow	Heathrow Express Station Staff (107.2)
167.03750	171.83750	NFM	Hull	East Yorkshire Motor Services
167.03750	171.83750	NFM	Ingleton	Hanson Quarry Trucks
167.03750	171.83750	NFM	Ipswich	Ipswich Town Football Club Stewards (107.2)
167.03750	171.83750	NFM	Isle of Man	Manx Transport Services
167.03750	171.83750	NFM	Kingston Lacy	National Trust House
167.03750	171.83750	NFM	London	Burns Security
167.03750	171.83750	NFM	London	Leyton Orient Football Club
167.03750	171.83750	NFM	London	London Underground Museum Depot Acton (82.5)
167.03750	171.83750	NFM	London	Natwest Tower
167.03750	171.83750	NFM	Longleat	Longleat House and Safari Park
167.03750	171.83750	NFM	Lowestoft	Birds Eye
167.03750	171.83750	NFM	Minsmere	Bird Reserve/Trust Ch.1 (123)
167.03750		NFM	Minsmere	Bird Reserve/Trust Ch.2 (123) If Repeater Fails
167.03750	171.83750	NFM	Nationwide	National Trust Properties
167.03750	171.83750	NFM	Newport	Hales TV Repairs
167.03750	171.83750	NFM	Newquay	Hendra Holiday Park Staff/Security/Bars
167.03750	171.83750	NFM	Norwich	Council Car Parks
167.03750	171.83750	NFM	Pontefract	Shopwatch
167.03750	171.83750	NFM	Prestatyn	Pontins Holiday Camp Housekeepers
167.03750	171.83750	NFM	Sheffield	Sheffield Further Education College Staff
167.03750	171.83750	NFM	Shefford	Beadlow Manor Golf Course (67)
167.03750	171.83750	NFM	Shepperton	Shepperton Studios Admin/Staff (DCS131)
167.03750	171.83750	NFM	Stockport	Shopwatch
167.03750	171.83750	NFM	Swanage	Purbeck Beach Patrols (110.9)
167.03750	171.83750	NFM	Tannington	Pea Harvesting
167.03750	171.83750	NFM	Wentworth	Wentworth Golf Club Staff
167.03750	171.83750	NFM	West Yorkshire	St Aidans Opencast Coal Mine Ch2
167.05000	171.85000	NFM	London	Onyx Council Cleaning/Refuse (118.8)
167.05000	171.85000	NFM	Nottingham	TV Repair Company
167.06250	171.86250	NFM	Abbeywood	Taxi Company
167.06250	171.86250	NFM	Bedford	Taxi Company (167.9)
167.06250	171.86250	NFM	Belfast	Enterprise Taxis, Ormeau Road
167.06250	171.86250	NFM	Bolton	Private Hire Company
167.06250	171.86250	NFM	Cardiff	Taxi Company, East Cardiff (136.5)
167.06250	171.86250	NFM	Chelmsford	Car Recovery Company
167.06250	171.86250	NFM	Gorsginon	Kestral Cabs
167.06250	171.86250	NFM	Halifax	Ziggy's Taxis
167.06250	171.86250	NFM	Hemel Hempstead	United Kabs (203.5)
167.06250	171.86250	NFM	Humberside	Haulage Company
167.06250	171.86250	NFM	Kirkcaldy	Ellis Taxis
167.06250	171.86250	NFM	Leeds	Headingley & Quickline
167.06250	171.86250	NFM	Leicester	University Security
167.06250	171.86250	NFM	Newark	Taxi Company
167.06250	171.86250	NFM	Nottingham	Diamond Cable
167.06250	171.86250	NFM	Retford	You & Me Parcels
167.06250	171.86250	NFM	Salford	Pubwatch
167.06250	171.86250	NFM	Sharnbrook	Associated Asphalt
167.06250	171.86250	NFM	Sheffield	A1 Cars Ch.2
167.06250	171.86250	NFM	Sheffield	KC Cars
167.06250	171.86250	NFM	Yorkshire	Hargreaves Quarries
167.07500	171.87500	NFM	Belfast	Network Taxis, Andersontown Road
167.07500	171.87500	NFM	Bradford	Jenny's Private Hire
167.07500	171.87500	NFM	Chorley	Taxi Company
167.07500	171.87500	NFM	Cleveland	Peter's Taxis

Base	Mobile	Mode	Location	User and Notes
167.07500	171.87500	NFM	Denton	Village Cars
167.07500	171.87500	NFM	Didcot	Bob's Taxis (94.8)
167.07500	171.87500	NFM	Forrest Hill	Taxi Company
167.07500	171.87500	NFM	Glasgow	Taxi Company
167.07500	171.87500	NFM	Humberside	Haulage Company
167.07500	171.87500	NFM	Manchester	Taxi Company
167.07500	171.87500	NFM	Motherwell	Redline Cabs
167.07500	171.87500	NFM	Newport	Reliance Taxis
167.07500	171.87500	NFM	North Walsham	Norfolk Canneries
167.08750	171.88750	NFM	Birmingham	Taxi Company
167.08750	171.88750	NFM	Cwmbran	Aerial Riggers
167.08750	171.88750	NFM	Elgin	Clover Cabs
167.08750	171.88750	NFM	Glamorgan	Council Works Department
167.08750	171.88750	NFM	Gt Yarmouth	Botton Bros, Yarmouth Pleasure Beach (186.2)
167.08750	171.88750	NFM	Lincolnshire	Ross Foods
167.08750	171.88750	NFM	Hull	Hotham Cars
167.08750	171.88750	NFM	Kent	Dutton Forshaw Breakdown Recovery
167.08750	171.88750	NFM	Perth	Taxi Company
167.08750	171.88750	NFM	Poole	Repeater
167.08750	171.88750	NFM	Portsmouth	Council
167.08750	171.88750	NFM	Somerset	Council
167.08750	171.88750	NFM	Suffolk	Business Post
167.08750	171.88750	NFM	Swansea	Civic Rescue Breakdown Recovery (210.7)
167.08750	171.88750	NFM	Torpoint	Taxi Company
167.08750	171.88750	NFM	Walsall	Metro Taxis
167.10000	171.90000	NFM	Birmingham	Taxi Company, 4 Oaks
167.10000	171.90000	NFM	Brandon	F Hiam Farms
167.10000	171.90000	NFM	Cambridge	Ace Taxis
167.10000	171.90000	NFM	Cardiff	Capital Taxis
167.10000	171.90000	NFM	Cardiff	Castle Taxis
167.10000	171.90000	NFM	Carlisle	Caveys Security
167.10000	171.90000	NFM	Eltham	Taxi Company
167.10000	171.90000	NFM	Glasgow	Taxi Company
167.10000	171.90000	NFM	Guernsey	Bluebird Taxis
167.10000	171.90000	NFM	Hampshire	Council
167.10000	171.90000	NFM	Hemel Hempstead	Minicab Company
167.10000	171.90000	NFM	Hull	Arrow/Atlas Cars
167.10000	171.90000	NFM	Isle of Man	Taxi Company (77)
167.10000	171.90000	NFM	Londonderry	Doe Water Treatment Plant, Carnmoney Hill
167.10000	171.90000	NFM	Manchester	Taxi Company
167.10000	171.90000	NFM	Newcastle	Taxi Company
167.10000	171.90000	NFM	Perth	Taxi Company
167.10000	171.90000	NFM	Stockton-on-Tees	Taxi Service
167.10000	171.90000	NFM	Swansea	Viv's Cabs, Ystradgynlais
167.10000	171.90000	NFM	Wolverhampton	City Cars
167.11250	171.91250	NFM	Bradford	Douglas Private Hire
167.11250	171.91250	NFM	Bristol	Peters Taxis
167.11250	171.91250	NFM	Coventry	Central Taxis
167.11250	171.91250	NFM	Dover	Invicta Cars
167.11250	171.91250	NFM	Farnham	Minicab Co
167.11250	171.91250	NFM	Glasgow	Taxi Company
167.11250	171.91250	NFM	Gt Yarmouth	J & H Bunn
167.11250	171.91250	NFM	Kempston	AAA Taxis
167.11250	171.91250	NFM	Manchester	Taxi Company
167.11250	172.91250	NFM	Mansfield	123 Taxis
167.11250	171.91250	NFM	Rotherham	Crown Taxis

Base	Mobile	Mode	Location	User and Notes
167.11250	171.91250	NFM	Strood	Medway Cabs
167.11250	171.91250	NFM	Swansea	Taxl Company
167.12500	171.92500	NFM	Antrim	Bridge Taxis (Data/Voice)
167.12500	171.92500	NFM	Burnley	Bus Station Taxi Rank
167.12500	171.92500	NFM	Buxton	Allied Taxis
167.12500	171.92500	NFM	Castle Donington	Racing (Rescue)
167.12500	171.92500	NFM	Dudley	Skip Hire Company
167.12500	171.92500	NFM	Edinburgh	Taxi Company
167.12500	171.92500	NFM	Folkestone	Folkestone Cabs
167.12500	171.92500	NFM	Hawick	Buccleugh Estates
167.12500	171.92500	NFM	Hemel Hempstead	Lynx Cars (110.9)
167.12500	171.92500	NFM	Kings Lynn	Watlington Plant
167.12500	171.92500	NFM	Liverpool	Taxi Company
167.12500	171.92500	NFM	Llantrisant	Taxi Company
167.12500	171.92500	NFM	London	Marquis Express Cabs
167.12500	171.92500	NFM	March	Ross Produce
167.12500	171.92500	NFM	Medway	Star Taxis
167.12500	171.92500	NFM	Melton	Atlas Cars (67)
167.12500	171.92500	NFM	Milton Keynes	Pursell Taxis
167.12500	171.92500	NFM	Norwich	Allstar Cars
167.12500	171.92500	NFM	Scunthorpe	Transport Firm
167.12500	171.92500	NFM	Shoreham by Sea	Shoreham Taxis
167.12500	171.92500	NFM	Swansea	Brynamman Taxis
167.12500	171.92500	NFM	Wolverhampton	West Side Radio Cars
167.13750	171.93750	NFM	Barry	Taxi Company
167.13750	171.93750	NFM	Belfast	Sunningdale Taxis, Ballysillan
167.13750	171.93750	NFM	Blackburn	Golden Line Private Hire
167.13750	171.93750	NFM	Bournemouth	Station Taxis
167.13750	171.93750	NFM	Eastbourne	Taxi Company
167.13750	171.93750	NFM	Edinburgh	Eagle Couriers
167.13750	171.93750	NFM	Jersey	Skip Company
167.13750	171.93750	NFM	Kings Lynn	Wheelers TV Services
167.13750	171.93750	NFM	Lancashire	Bulkers Commercial Refuse
167.13750	171.93750	NFM	Leicester	Taxi Company
167.13750	171.93750	NFM	London	Chepstow 007 Car Service
167.13750	171.93750	NFM	Oxford	Streamline Taxis
167.13750	171.93750	NFM	Preston	South Ribble School Bus
167.13750	171.93750	NFM	Scunthorpe	Taxi Company
167.13750	171.93750	NFM	Tynemouth	Taxi Company
167.15000	171.95000	NFM	Aberdeen	Taxi Company
167.15000	171.95000	NFM	Aberystwyth	University Security
167.15000	171.95000	NFM	Barrow in Furness	JC Taxis
167.15000	171.95000	NFM	Bury	Bury Taxi Rank
167.15000	171.95000	NFM	Cambridge	Regency Taxi Company
167.15000	171.95000	NFM	Carlisle	Radio Taxis
167.15000	171.95000	NFM	Crewe	Taxi Company
167.15000	171.95000	NFM	Lancashire	South Ribble Refuse
167.15000	171.95000	NFM	Langholm	Buccleugh Estates, Gamekeepers
167.15000	171.95000	NFM	Lincoln	Imp Taxis
167.15000	171.95000	NFM	Manchester	Taxi Company
167.15000	171.95000	NFM	Newport, Gwent	Servu Taxis
167.15000	171.95000	NFM	Norwich	Taxi Company
167.15000	171.95000	NFM	Nottingham	Taxi Company
167.15000	171.95000	NFM	Oldham	Startex Cabs
167.15000	171.95000	NFM	Shipley	Shipley Private Hire
167.15000	171.95000	NFM	St. Neots	T & R Taxis

Base	Mobile	Mode	Location	User and Notes
167.15000	171.95000	NFM	West Midlands	ABS Taxis
167.15000	171.95000	NFM	Wolverhampton	Central Taxis
167.16250	171.96250	NFM	Coventry	Skyline Taxis
167.16250	171.96250	NFM	Darlington	Darlington Car & Commercial Recovery
167.16250	171.96250	NFM	Dover	Victory Cars
167.16250	171.96250	NFM	Gorseinon	Gem Cabs
167.16250	171.96250	NFM	Iken	Stanny House Farm
167.16250	171.96250	NFM	Ipswich	Taxi Company
167.16250	171.96250	NFM	Newport, Gwent	Servu Taxis
167.16250	171.96250	NFM	Sheffield	City Taxis
167.16250	171.96250	NFM	Shillington	New Farm (186.2)
167.16250		NFM	Stevenage	Sovereign Bus & Coach Ch.2 (151.4)
167.16250	171.96250	NFM	Swindon	Starlight Taxis
167.16250	171.96250	NFM	Wrexham	Prostigo Taxis
167.17500	171.97500	NFM	Bexleyheath	Taxi Company
167.17500	171.97500	NFM	Cambridge	Sawston Taxis (131.8)
167.17500	171.97500	NFM	Cheshire	Choice Taxis
167.17500	171.97500	NFM	Glasgow	Taxi Company
167.17500	171.97500	NFM	Manchester	Taxi Company
167.17500	171.97500	NFM	Norwich	Canary Cars Taxis
167.17500	171.97500	NFM	Rochdale	Tiger Cars
167.17500	171.97500	NFM	Salisbury	District Taxis
167.17500	171.97500	NFM	Sidcup	Taxi Company
167.18750	171.98750	NFM	Bolton	North West Cars
167.18750	171.98750	NFM	Brownhills	Bee-Jays Taxis
167.18750	171.98750	NFM	Bury St Edmunds	Goldline Taxis
167.18750	171.98750	NFM	Colchester	A1 Taxis
167.18750	171.98750	NFM	Coventry	Taxi Company
167.18750	171.98750	NFM	Glasgow	Mac Cars
167.18750	171.98750	NFM	Great Yarmouth	Taxi Company
167.18750	171.98750	NFM	Immingham	Oaklands Taxis
167.18750	171.98750	NFM	Lancaster	Council Highways Department
167.18750	171.98750	NFM	Lisburn	Five Star Taxis
167.18750	171.98750	NFM	Macclesfield	Taxi Company
167.18750	171.98750	NFM	Manchester	Midway Taxis
167.18750	171.98750	NFM	Middleton	Swan Cars
167.18750	171.98750	NFM	Milton Keynes	Raffles Taxis
167.18750	171.98750	NFM	Scarborough	Taxi Company
167.18750	171.98750	NFM	Sheffield	A2B Car Hire
167.20000	172.00000	NFM	Ashford	United Taxis
167.20000	172.00000	NFM	Barrow	Mobile Community Watch
167.20000	172.00000	NFM	Dunstable	Glider Taxis
167.20000	172.00000	NFM	Edinburgh	Burtons Security
167.20000	172.00000	NFM	Fleetwood	Taxi Company
167.20000	172.00000	NFM	Leicester	Taxi Company
167.20000	172.00000	NFM	London	Skip Hire Company (77)
167.20000	172.00000	NFM	Morecambe	Security Company
167.20000	172.00000	NFM	Nottingham	Parking Enforcement
167.20000	172.00000	NFM	Thetford	Abbey Taxis
167.21250	172.01250	NFM	Belfast	City Cabs
167.21250	172.01250	NFM	Bradford	Idleway Private Hire
167.21250	172.01250	NFM	Bradford	M1 Cruisers
167.21250	172.01250	NFM	Chelmsford	A1 Demolition
167.21250	172.01250	NFM	Chelmsford	Crest Dairies
167.21250	172.01250	NFM	Chester	Dee Cars
167.21250	172.01250	NFM	Cumbernauld	Yellow Star Taxis

Base	Mobile	Mode	Location	User and Notes
167.21250	172.01250	NFM	Edinburgh Airport	Stock Control
167.21250	172.01250	NFM	Glasgow	Taxi Company
167.21250	172.01250	NFM	Hemel Hempstead	Hemel Cars
167.21250	172.01250	NFM	Hull	A1 Taxis
167.21250	172.01250	NFM	Maidstone	Intacabs
167.21250	172.01250	NFM	Manchester	Taxi Company
167.21250	172.01250	NFM	Newcastle	Silver Cars
167.21250	172.01250	NFM	Oldham	Home James Taxis
167.21250	172.01250	NFM	Rayleigh	Taxi Company
167.22500	172.02500	NFM	Belfast	Quarry Cabs
167.22500	172.02500	NFM	Coventry	Taxi Company
167.22500	172.02500	NFM	Doncaster	Cadeby Quarry
167.22500	172.02500	NFM	Hull	Salthouse Taxis
167.22500	172.02500	NFM	Humberside	Haulage Company
167.22500	172.02500	NFM	Jersey	Waverley Coaches
167.22500	172.02500	NFM	London	Business Post, Harrow
167.22500	172.02500	NFM	London	Minicab Company, Wimbledon
167.22500	172.02500	NFM	Mendips	Business Post
167.22500	172.02500	NFM	Midlands	Yellow Cabs
167.22500	172.02500	NFM	Spalding	Royal Taxis (94.8)
167.22500	172.02500	NFM	Stockton on Tees	Taxi Service
167.22500	172.02500	NFM	Thetford	Chips Taxis
167.22500	172.02500	NFM	Worksop	Bee Line Taxis
167.22500	172.02500	NFM	Yeadon	Westfield Private Hire
167.23750	172.03750	NFM	Aberdeen	Taxi Company
167.23750	172.03750	NFM	Ashton	Taxi Company
167.23750	172.03750	NFM	Bridlington	Promenade Taxis
167.23750	172.03750	NFM	Cardiff	Taxi Company (67)
167.23750	172.03750	NFM	Chadderton	Chadderton Cars
167.23750	172.03750	NFM	Chepstow	Taxi Company
167.23750	172.03750	NFM	Dartford	Black Cabs
167.23750	172.03750	NFM	Faversham	A1 Taxis
167.23750	172.03750	NFM	Glasgow	Taxi Company
167.23750	172.03750	NFM	Guernsey	Total Oil
167.23750	172.03750	NFM	Halifax	AA Taxis
167.23750	172.03750	NFM	Hampshire	Vets
167.23750	172.03750	NFM	Haverhill	Chequer Cabs
167.23750	172.03750	NFM	Hornchurch	A1 Taxis
167.23750	172.03750	NFM	Huntingdon	Pete's Taxis
167.23750	172.03750	NFM	Leicester	Asda Security
167.23750	172.03750	NFM	Liverpool	City Centre Taxis
167.23750	172.03750	NFM	Oxford	Black Cabs
167.23750	172.03750	NFM	Portrush	North West Taxis
167.23750	172.03750	NFM	Swansea	Diamond Cabs
167.23750	172.03750	NFM	Swansea	Oyster Cabs, Mumbles
167.25000	172.05000	NFM	Aberdeen	Taxi Company
167.25000	172.05000	NFM	Bolton	Pal Cars Taxis
167.25000	172.05000	NFM	Chelmsford	Taxi Company
167.25000	172.05000	NFM	Elvington	Garrowby Estate Farms
167.25000	172.05000	NFM	Hull	Goldstar Taxis
167.25000	172.05000	NFM	Hull	Wallis Taxis
167.25000	172.05000	NFM	London	Alan Car Service
167.25000	172.05000	NFM	Newtown	Taxi Company
167.25000	172.05000	NFM	Plymouth	Armada Taxis
167.25000	172.05000	NFM	Plymouth	Tamar Taxis
167.25000	172.05000	NFM	Powys	Thomas Jones (Vet)

Base	Mobile	Mode	Location	User and Notes
167.25000	172.05000	NFM	Slough	Interpoint Taxis
167.25000	172.05000	NFM	Swansea	Fishwicks Taxis
167.25000	172.05000	NFM	Upton	Road Runner Taxis
167.25000	172.05000	NFM	Whiston	Diamond Taxis
167.25000	172.05000	NFM	Whiston	Sapphire Taxis
167.26250	172.02500	NFM	Blackpool	J Cabs
167.26250	172.06250	NFM	Blantyre	Mac Cars
167.26250	172.06250	NFM	Coventry	DJS Security
167.26250	172.06250	NFM	Cwmbran	Taxi Company
167.26250	172.06250	NFM	Debach	Debach Enterprises
167.26250	172.06250	NFM	Hastings	Taybar Radio Taxis
167.26250	172.06250	NFM	Haverhill	Havtaxi
167.26250	172.06250	NFM	Lowestoft	Peeks Driving School
167.26250	172.06250	NFM	Milton Keynes	Embassy Cars
167.26250	172.06250	NFM	Portsmouth	Blue Light Cabs
167.26250	172.06250	NFM	Reading	1st City Cars
167.26250	172.06250	NFM	Sheffield	Paymaster Ltd.
167.26250	172.06250	NFM	Symonds Yat	Symonds Yat Boat Hire (107.2)
167.26250	172.06250	NFM	West Midlands	Fruit Machine Repairs
167.26250	172.06250	NFM	Worcester	Central Taxis
167.27500	172.07500	NFM	Alloa	Taxi Company
167.27500	172.07500	NFM	Belfast	Leaf Taxis
167.27500	172.07500	NFM	Birmingham	Taxi Company, Moseley
167.27500	172.07500	NFM	Blackpool	Bus Company
167.27500	172.07500	NFM	Bolton	Red Rose Taxis
167.27500	172.07500	NFM	Brighton	Southern Taxis
167.27500	172.07500	NFM	Gt. Stokely	H. Raby & Sons
167.27500	172.07500	NFM	Hockwold Cum Wilton	J Denney Taxis
167.27500	172.07500	NFM	Hull	Taxi Company
167.27500	172.07500	NFM	Huntingdon	H. Raby & Sons
167.27500	172.07500	NFM	Ipswich	Dave Rogers Cabs
167.27500	172.07500	NFM	Liverpool	Croxteth Park
167.27500	172.07500	NFM	London	Rentowers Ltd
167.27500	172.07500	NFM	Portsmouth	Taxi Company
167.27500	172.07500	NFM	Rhondda Valley	Taxi Company
167.27500	172.07500	NFM	Sheffield	Foundry Maintenance
167.27500	172.07500	NFM	Southend on Sea	Associated Radio Cars
167.27500	172.07500	NFM	Sunderland	Star Taxis
167.27500	172.07500	NFM	Sutton	Darby Plant
167.27500	172.07500	NFM	Weymouth	Taxi Company
167.28750	172.08750	NFM	Abingdon	Autotaxis
167.28750	172.08750	NFM	Aylesbury	Kindell Motors
167.28750	172.08750	NFM	Beaconsfield	Fleet Cabs
167.28750	172.08750	NFM	Bradford	Manningham Private Hire
167.28750	172.08750	NFM	Burnley	AK Taxis
167.28750	172.08750	NFM	Cardiff	Sports Centre (88.5)
167.28750	172.08750	NFM	Chesterfield	Central Taxis
167.28750	172.08750	NFM	Dalton in Furness	Club Cars
167.28750	172.08750	NFM	East Dereham	Breckland Taxis
167.28750	172.08750	NFM	Eastleigh	Taxi Company
167.28750	172.08750	NFM	Felixstowe	AB Line Taxis
167.28750	172.08750	NFM	Glasgow	Taxi Company
167.28750	172.08750	NFM	Hampshire	Taxi Company
167.28750	172.08750	NFM	Haverfordwest	Rocky's Taxis
167.28750	172.08750	NFM	Hawick	AH Taxis
167.28750	172.08750	NFM	Leicester	Taxi Company

Base	Mobile	Mode	Location	User and Notes
167.28750	172.08750	NFM	Hull	Cream Cabs
167.28750	172.08750	NFM	Montrose	Taxi Company
167.28750	172.08750	NFM	Plymouth	Chequers Cabs
167.28750	172.08750	NFM	Thetford	Breakland Taxis (94.8)
167.28750	172.08750	NFM	Trimley St Martin	Roselea Garden Centre (110.9)
167.28750	172.08750	NFM	Wrexham	Ace Taxis
167.30000	172.10000	NFM	Aberystwyth	Taxi Company, Llanbadarn
167.30000	172.10000	NFM	Belfast	Blue Star Taxis, Donegall Rd
167.30000	172.10000	NFM	Blackburn	Super Line Private Hire
167.30000	172.10000	NFM	Glasgow	Glasgow Fruit Centre
167.30000	172.10000	NFM	Harrogate	Blue Line Taxis
167.30000	172.10000	NFM	London	Grove Cars, W12
167.30000	172.10000	NFM	Luton	Black Cabs
167.30000	172.10000	NFM	Oxford	Radiotaxis
167.30000	172.10000	NFM	Sheffield	Toby Taxis
167.30000	172.10000	NFM	Swindon	Taxi Company
167.31250	172.11250	NFM	Brownhills	Taxi Company
167.31250	172.11250	NFM	Doncaster	Race Course
167.31250	172.11250	NFM	Felixstowe	Coastal Cabs
167.31250	172.11250	NFM	Glasgow	Taxi Company
167.31250	172.11250	NFM	Gt Cornard	ABA Taxis
167.31250	172.11250	NFM	Newark	Taxi Company
167.31250	172.11250	NFM	Retford	Golf course
167.31250	172.11250	NFM	Southampton	Taxi Company
167.32500	172.12500	NFM	Astley	Astley Van Hire
167.32500	172.12500	NFM	Barrow in Furness	Coastline Taxis
167.32500	172.12500	NFM	Bedford	Bedfordia Farms
167.32500	172.12500	NFM	Blaenavon	Taxi Company (151.4)
167.32500	172.12500	NFM	Chatteris	Graves & Graves
167.32500	172.12500	NFM	Chester	Radio Cars
167.32500	172.12500	NFM	Cramlington	Parkside Taxis
167.32500	172.12500	NFM	Dartford	Taxi Company
167.32500	172.12500	NFM	Forest Hill	Taxi Company
167.32500	172.12500	NFM	Glasgow	Taxi Company
167.32500	172.12500	NFM	Horsforth	Universal-5 Star
167.32500	172.12500	NFM	Hull	Five O Taxis
167.32500	172.12500	NFM	Ipswich	Robin Hood Taxis
167.32500	172.12500	NFM	London	Taxi Company/Couriers
167.32500	172.12500	NFM	Medway	ABC Cabs
167.32500	172.12500	NFM	Manchester	Astley Van Hire
167.32500	172.12500	NFM	Shoreham by Sea	Southern Taxis (141.3)
167.32500	172.12500	NFM	Southend on Sea	Doctors' Service (123)
167.32500	172.12500	NFM	Swansea	A & M Taxis
167.33750	172.13750	NFM	Biggleswade	Whitbread Farms
167.33750	172.13750	NFM	Bradford	Wrose Village Taxis
167.33750	172.13750	NFM	Bromsgrove	Golden Black Cabs
167.33750	172.13750	NFM	Cambridge	Parking Enforcement Ch.2 (225.7)
167.33750	172.13750	NFM	Cardiff	Taxi Company
167.33750	172.13750	NFM	Glasgow	Taxi Company
167.33750	172.13750	NFM	Greenisland	Taxi Company
167.33750	172.13750	NFM	Heywood	Eagle Cars
167.33750	172.13750	NFM	Norwich	Enterprise Private Hire
167.33750	172.13750	NFM	Stowmarket	Stow Taxis
167.33750	172.13750	NFM	Stretford	New Moon Private Hire
167.33750	172.13750	NFM	Weston Super Mare	Apple Central Taxis
167.33750	172.13750	NFM	Windsor	Council

Base	Mobile	Mode	Location	User and Notes
167.35000	170.15000	NFM	Aberdeen	Taxi Company
167.35000	170.15000	NFM	Blackpool	R Walker & Co
167.35000	170.15000	NFM	Burnham	Burnham Radio Cabs
167.35000	172.15000	NFM	Caernarfonshire	Taxi Company
167.35000	170.15000	NFM	Cornwall	English China Clay
167.35000	170.15000	NFM	Coventry	Coventry Aerial Services
167.35000	170.15000	NFM	Eccles	Taxi Company
167.35000	170.15000	NFM	Fareham	Taxi Company
167.35000	170.15000	NFM	Hull	Taxi Company
167.35000	170.15000	NFM	Jersey	Regal Construction
167.35000	172.15000	NFM	Llantrisant	Taxi Company
167.35000	170.15000	NFM	Luton	Super Anglia Cars
167.35000	170.15000	NFM	Manchester	Taxi Company
167.35000	170.15000	NFM	Newport, Gwent	Caxton Taxis
167.35000	170.15000	NFM	Preston	Taxi Company
167.35000	170.15000	NFM	Rochdale	Central Taxis
167.35000	170.15000	NFM	Salford	Taxi Company
167.35000	170.15000	NFM	Stockport	Taxi Company
167.35000	170.15000	NFM	Stoke on Trent	Taxi Company
167.35000	172.15000	NFM	Symonds Yat	Symonds Yat Farming (127.3)
167.35000	170.15000	NFM	Tamworth	Bennett's Taxis
167.35000	170.15000	NFM	Whiston	Diamond Taxis
167.35000	170.15000	NFM	Whittlesey	Luxicabs
167.36250	172.16250	NFM	Bolton	Murtax Taxis
167.36250	172.16250	NFM	Bradford	Kelly's Private Hire
167.36250	172.16250	NFM	Coventry	City Centre Store Detectives
167.36250	172.16250	NFM	Halifax	Beeline Taxis
167.36250	172.16250	NFM	Hull	Taxi Company
167.36250	172.16250	NFM	London	Oakwood Cars
167.36250	172.16250	NFM	Neath	Taxi Company
167.36250	172.16250	NFM	Plymouth	Oakwood Cars
167.36250	172.16250	NFM	Sheerness Docks	Sheppey Taxis
167.36250	172.16250	NFM	Soham	Greens of Soham
167.36250	172.16250	NFM	Stansted	Stansted Airport Cars
167.36250	172.16250	NFM	Worthing	Wortax Taxis
167.36250	172.16250	NFM	Yeadon	A1 Cars
167.37500	172.17500	NFM	Aberdeen	Tyre Service
167.37500	172.17500	NFM	Chippenham	Taxi Company
167.37500	172.17500	NFM	Eastbourne	Taxi Company
167.37500	172.17500	NFM	Hertford	CJ Taxis
167.37500	172.17500	NFM	Kings Lynn	Gaywood Taxis
167.37500	172.17500	NFM	Maidstone	Cavalier Cabs
167.37500	172.17500	NFM	Manchester	Taxifone Taxis
167.37500	172.17500	NFM	New Malden	Allways Ltd
167.37500	172.17500	NFM	Poole	Repeater
167.37500	172.17500	NFM	Southampton	Taxi Company
167.37500	172.17500	NFM	Winchester	Council
167.37500	172.17500	NFM	Wrexham	Regal Taxis
167.38750	172.18750	NFM	Aberdeen	Taxi Company
167.38750	172.18750	NFM	Cardiff	Council Park Rangers (141.3)
167.38750	172.18750	NFM	Derby	Taxi Company
167.38750	172.18750	NFM	Devizes	Devizes Taxis
167.38750	172.18750	NFM	Glasgow	Taxi Company
167.38750	172.18750	NFM	Hull	Sutton Cars
167.38750	172.18750	NFM	Kettering	KLM Taxis
167.38750	172.18750	NFM	Lincoln	City Cars

Base	Mobile	Mode	Location	User and Notes
167.38750	172.18750	NFM	London	ADC Despatch Couriers
167.38750	172.18750	NFM	London	Paul's Plumbers, Hammersmith
167.38750	172.18750	NFM	Manchester	Taxi Company
167.38750	172.18750	NFM	Pontypool	Red Dragon Taxis
167.38750	172.18750	NFM	Salford	Swan Private Hire
167.38750	172.18750	NFM	Sheffield	TCS Taxis
167.38750	172.18750	NFM	Skegness	North Shore Taxis
167.38750	172.18750	NFM	Swansea	Amber Taxis
167.40000	172.20000	NFM	Bedford	Associated Leisure Ltd
167.40000	172.20000	NFM	Birmingham	Taxi Company, Erdington
167.40000	172.20000	NFM	Burnley	Burnley Taxis
167.40000	172.20000	NFM	Colchester	Paxmans Diesels
167.40000	172.20000	NFM	Crowborough	Associated Leisure Ltd
167.40000	172.20000	NFM	Hampshire	Cascade Cars
167.40000	172.20000	NFM	Ipswich	Quinto Cranes
167.40000	172.20000	AM	Lakenheath	Air Base Taxis
167.40000	172.20000	NFM	Leeds	Associated Leisure Ltd
167.40000	172.20000	NFM	Leicester	Taxi Company
167.40000	172.20000	NFM	Leigh on Sea	Kelly's Radio
167.40000	172.20000	NFM	Manchester	Taxi Company
167.40000	172.20000	NFM	Norfolk	Associated Leisure Ltd.
167.40000	172.20000	NFM	Oldham	Bluebird Private Hire
167.40000	172.20000	NFM	Perth	Taxi Company
167.41250	172.21250	NFM	Bury	Harvey's Taxis
167.41250	172.21250	NFM	Dalton	Marj's Cars
167.41250	172.21250	NFM	Edinburgh	Doctors' Service
167.41250	172.21250	NFM	Glasgow	Taxi Company
167.41250	172.21250	NFM	Grimsby	MD Cars
167.41250	172.21250	NFM	Ipswich	Anglia Taxis
167.41250	172.21250	NFM	Leicester	Taxi Company
167.41250	172.21250	NFM	Manchester	Taxi Company
167.41250	172.21250	NFM	Newark	Taxi Company
167.41250	172.21250	NFM	Oxford	City Taxis
167.41250	172.21250	NFM	Portsmouth	Taxi Company
167.41250	172.21250	NFM	Sheffield	Direct Taxis
167.41250	172.21250	NFM	Sittingbourne	Ace Taxis
167.41250	172.21250	NFM	Skegness	4000 Taxis
167.41250	172.21250	NFM	Stoke on Trent	Haulage Company
167.42500	172.22500	NFM	Aberdeen	Taxi Company
167.42500	172.22500	AM	Barnet	Metro Cars
167.42500	172.22500	NFM	Coventry	Trinity Street Taxis
167.42500	177.22500	NFM	Barnet	Metro Cars
167.42500	177.22500	NFM	Bedford	JS Cars
167.42500	177.22500	NFM	Bloxwich	Abba Taxis
167.42500	177.22500	NFM	Glasgow	Taxi Company
167.42500	172.22500	NFM	Cambridge	Regional College Site Maintenance
167.42500	177.22500	NFM	Jersey	Lucas Bros. Farm Shop
167.42500	177.22500	NFM	Jersey	Ransom Garden Centre
167.42500	177.22500	NFM	Larbert	Plough Taxis
167.42500	177.22500	NFM	Lowestoft	Atlas Cars
167.42500	177.22500	NFM	Maidstone	WJF Motors
167.42500	177.22500	NFM	Nottingham	Jubilee Cars
167.42500	177.22500	NFM	Plymouth	Cotton's Taxis
167.42500	177.22500	NFM	Swansea	Glamtax Taxis
167.43750	172.23750	NFM	Airdrie	Taxi Company
167.43750	172.23750	NFM	Bristol	Taxi Company (210.7)

Base	Mobile	Mode	Location	User and Notes
167.43750	172.23750	NFM	Cardiff Airport	Alpha Flight Catering (162.2)
167.43750	172.23750	NFM	Cleveland	City Taxis
167.43750	172.23750	NFM	Coventry	BFI Waste
167.43750	172.23750	NFM	Ebbw Vale	Taxi Company
167.43750	172.23750	NFM	Glasgow	Taxi Company
167.43750	172.23750	NFM	Hemblington	C Wace Ltd
167.43750	172.23750	NFM	Hitchin	Taxi Company (151.4)
167.43750	172.23750	NFM	Manchester	Biffa Waste Services
167.43750	172.23750	NFM	Montrose	Taxi Company
167.43750	172.23750	NFM	Newport	French's TV Repairs
167.43750	172.23750	NFM	Sheppey	Angie's Taxis
167.43750	172.23750	NFM	Steeple Bumpstead	Shore Hall Estates
167.43750	172.23750	NFM	Tywyn,	Taxi Company
167.45000	172.25000	NFM	Abingdon	Newtop Taxis
167.45000	172.25000	NFM	Belfast	Peter Pan Taxis, Springvale Rd
167.45000	172.25000	NFM	Bradford	ABC Radio Cars
167.45000	172.25000	NFM	Canterbury	Lynx Taxis
167.45000	172.25000	NFM	Edinburgh	Taxi Company
167.45000	172.25000	NFM	Knebworth	Vendustrial Ltd
167.45000	172.25000	NFM	London	Olympia Cars, Talgarth Road (146.2)
167.45000	172.25000	NFM	Manchester	White Line Taxis
167.45000	172.25000	NFM	Musselburgh	Taxi Company
167.45000	172.25000	NFM	Newmarket	Chilcotts Taxis
167.45000	172.25000	NFM	Nuneaton	JK Taxis
167.45000	172.25000	NFM	Retford	A2B Taxis
167.45000	172.25000	NFM	Sheffield	Alpha Taxis
167.45000	172.25000	NFM	Southsea	Pier Security
167.45000	172.25000	NFM	Warwickshire	Skip Company
167.45000	172.25000	NFM	Wolverhampton	Albro Taxis
167.46250	172.26250	NFM	Aberdeen	Crane Hire Company
167.46250	172.26250	NFM	Bristol	Works Dispatch
167.46250	172.26250	NFM	Broklesby	Pea Harvesters
167.46250	172.26250	NFM	Eastbourne	Taxi Company
167.46250	172.26250	NFM	Gt Yarmouth	Birds Eye Vans
167.46250	172.26250	NFM	London	Taxi Company/Couriers
167.46250	172.26250	NFM	Lowestoft	Birds Eye
167.46250	172.26250	NFM	Oldham	Security Company
167.46250	172.26250	NFM	Sheffield	Alpha Cars Ch.1
167.46250	172.26250	NFM	Southampton	Taxi Company
167.46250	172.26250	NFM	Stevenage	Community Patrols (131.8)
167.46250	172.26250	NFM	Warminster	Taxi Company
167.47500	172.27500	NFM	Belfast	Laurel Hill Taxis
167.47500	172.27500	NFM	Bradford	Tyersal Cars
167.47500	172.27500	NFM	Bristol	Shell Gas Bottle Delivery
167.47500	172.27500	NFM	Burton	Taxi Company
167.47500	172.27500	NFM	Liverpool	Car Breakdown Recovery
167.47500	172.27500	NFM	London	National Radio Cars, New Barnet
167.47500	172.27500	NFM	Nottingham	TC Taxis, Hucknall
167.47500	172.27500	NFM	Poole	Repeater
167.47500	172.27500	NFM	Preston	Preston Trucks (103.5)
167.47500	172.27500	NFM	Sheffield	Mercury Cars Ch.2
167.48750	172.28750	NFM	Aberdeen	Taxi Company
167.48750	172.28750	NFM	Edinburgh	Taxi Company
167.48750	172.28750	NFM	Glasgow	Forge Shopping Mall Security
167.48750	172.28750	NFM	Isle of Man	Community Repeater, Snaefell
167.48750	172.28750	NFM	Leeds	Taxi Company, Seacroft

Base	Mobile	Mode	Location	User and Notes
167.48750	172.28750	NFM	Leicester	Taxi Company
167.48750	172.28750	NFM	Newport	Red Base Taxis
167.48750	172.28750	NFM	Portsmouth	Council
167.48750	172.28750	NFM	Ryton	A1 Taxis
167.50000	172.30000	NFM	Barway	Shropshire Produce
167.50000	172.30000	NFM	Blackpool	Streamline Taxis
167.50000	172.30000	NFM	Bradford	Girlington Taxis
167.50000	172.30000	NFM	Brighton	John Jug Ltd
167.50000	172.30000	NFM	Bristol	Council City Centre Refuse Collectors
167.50000	172.30000	NFM	Charminster	Bee Cabs
167.50000	172.30000	NFM	Hemingbrough	AIS Brown Butlin Chemicals
167.50000	172.45000	NFM	Lincoln	Swan Taxis
167.50000	172.30000	NFM	Nottingham	Parking Enforcement
167.50000	172.30000	NFM	Rochford	Taxi Company
167.50000	172.30000	NFM	Saltdean	Taxi Company
167.50000	172.30000	NFM	Swindon	Link Taxis
167.51250	172.31250	NFM	Blackley	Avenue Cars
167.51250	172.31250	NFM	Bradford	Prune Park Private Hire
167.51250	172.31250	NFM	Comber	Castle Taxis
167.51250	172.31250	NFM	Cwmbran	Chauffeur Taxis
167.51250	172.31250	NFM	Guildford	A3 Cars
167.51250	172.31250	NFM	Humberside	East Yorkshire Motor Service Buses
167.51250	172.31250	NFM	Ipswich	Cambridge & East Coast Cable
167.51250	172.31250	NFM	Manchester	Taxi Company
167.51250	172.31250	NFM	Newcastle	Taxi Company
167.51250	172.31250	NFM	Romsey	Broadlands Farm (67)
167.51250	172.31250	NFM	Swansea	Taxi Company
167.52500	172.32500	NFM	Bargoed	Taxi Company (110.9)
167.52500	172.32500	NFM	Birkenhead	Cavalier Taxis
167.52500	172.32500	NFM	Bolsover	Bolsover Castle Staff
167.52500	172.32500	NFM	Bradford	Blackcabs
167.52500	172.32500	NFM	Cambridge	Able Taxis
167.52500	172.32500	NFM	Irvine	C-Cars
167.52500	172.32500	NFM	Jersey	Fort Regent Leisure Complex Ch.2
167.52500	172.32500	NFM	Leeds	Streamline Taxis
167.52500	172.32500	NFM	Letchworth	A-B Taxis
167.52500	172.32500	NFM	Letchworth	Mick's Taxis
167.52500	172.32500	NFM	Maidstone	Leeds Castle Stewards Ch.2 (156.7)
167.52500	172.32500	NFM	Normanton	Taxi Company
167.52500	172.32500	NFM	Norwich	Five Star Taxis
167.52500	172.32500	NFM	Nottingham	Taxi Company
167.52500	172.32500	NFM	Salford	Taxi Company
167.52500	172.32500	NFM	Westbourne	Taxi Company
167.53750	172.33750	NFM	Bradford	Cosy Cars
167.53750	172.33750	NFM	Bury	Peel Cars
167.53750	172.33750	NFM	Cornwall	English China Clay
167.53750	172.33750	NFM	Humberside	Elan Transport
167.53750	172.33750	NFM	Pembrokeshire	Taxi Company (DCS 125)
167.53750	172.33750	NFM	Rendlesham	Naunton Hall Farms
167.53750	172.33750	NFM	Sheffield	Taxi Company (88.5)
167.53750	172.33750	NFM	Stamford	Silver Cabs (82.5)
167.53750	172.33750	NFM	Stoke On Trent	Taxi Company
167.53750	172.33750	NFM	Walsall Wood	Barons Taxis
167.55000	172.35000	NFM	Biggleswade	AI CARS
167.55000	172.35000	NFM	Bradford on Avon	Taxi Company
167.55000	172.35000	NFM	Colchester	Abbeygate Taxis

Base	Mobile	Mode	Location	User and Notes
167.55000	172.35000	NFM	Colindale	Chequers Cars
167.55000	172.35000	NFM	Jersey	Fort Regent Leisure Complex Ch.1
167.55000	172.35000	NFM	London	Chequers Cars, Colindale
167.55000	172.35000	NFM	Portsmouth	City Wide Taxis
167.55000	172.35000	NFM	Salford	Briffin Cars
167.55000	172.35000	NFM	Weymouth	Taxi Company
167.56250	172.36250	NFM	Blackburn	Super B Private Hire
167.56250	172.36250	NFM	Cheshire	Station Cars
167.56250	172.36250	NFM	Gillingham	Taxi Company
167.56250	172.36250	NFM	Glasgow	Taxi Company
167.56250	172.36250	NFM	Grangemouth	Taxi Owners Association
167.56250	172.36250	NFM	Guernsey	Sunshine Cabs
167.56250	172.36250	NFM	Ipswich	Wilmot Dixon Builders
167.56250	172.36250	NFM	Isle of Wight	Taxi Company
167.56250	172.36250	NFM	Newmarket	Sound City Cabs & Style Cars
167.56250	172.36250	NFM	Norwich	Goldstar Taxis
167.56250	172.36250	AM	Nottingham	Taxi Company
167.56250	172.36250	NFM	Plymouth	Key Cab Taxis
167.56250	172.36250	NFM	Salford	Dolphin Cars
167.56250	172.36250	NFM	Swansea	Taxi Company
167.56250	172.36250	NFM	Worthing	Taxi Company
167.57500	172.37500	NFM	Bradford	New B-Line Taxis
167.57500	172.37500	NFM	Cambridge	Housing Repairs (241.8)
167.57500	172.37500	NFM	Coventry	Sky Blue Radio Taxis
167.57500	172.37500	NFM	Dumfries	Taxi Company
167.57500	172.37500	NFM	Erith	Taxi Company
167.57500	172.37500	NFM	Essex	Taxi Company
167.57500	172.37500	NFM	Faversham	Starlight Taxis
167.57500	172.37500	NFM	Felixstowe	Aero Taxis (94.8)
167.57500	172.37500	NFM	London	Courier Company
167.57500	172.37500	NFM	Manchester	Mantax (173.8)
167.57500	172.37500	NFM	March	David Johnson Farms
167.57500	172.37500	NFM	Newcastle	Taxi Company
167.57500	172.37500	NFM	Salford	Taxi Company
167.57500	172.37500	NFM	Southampton	Taxi Company
167.57500	172.37500	NFM	Worthing	Taxi Company
167.58750	172.38750	NFM	Bedford	Anglia Cars
167.58750	172.38750	NFM	Bedford	Riverside Taxis
167.58750	172.38750	NFM	Bedworh	Autoway Taxis
167.58750	172.38750	NFM	Elvington	Inturf
167.58750	172.38750	NFM	Glasgow	Taxi Company
167.58750	172.38750	NFM	Hertfordshire	Taxi Company
167.58750	172.38750	NFM	Leicester	Taxi Company
167.58750	172.38750	NFM	Maldon	Taxi Company
167.58750	172.38750	NFM	Newtownards	Fab Cabs
167.58750	172.38750	NFM	Swinton	Swintax
167.58750	172.38750	NFM	Tarrant Keynston	Ashley Wood Garage (67)
167.58750	172.38750	NFM	Templepatrick	Templepatrick Taxis
167.60000	172.40000	NFM	Bingley	Bingley Taxis
167.60000	172.40000	NFM	Caernarfonshire	Taxi Company
167.60000	172.40000	NFM	Cumbernauld	Central Cabs
167.60000	172.40000	NFM	East Dereham	Venture Taxis
167.60000	172.40000	NFM	Glasgow	Taxi Company
167.60000	172.40000	NFM	Hemel Hempstead	Choice Cars
167.60000	172.40000	NFM	Hitchin	Boxhall Taxis
167.60000	172.40000	NFM	Manchester	Taxi Company

Base	Mobile	Mode	Location	User and Notes
167.60000	172.40000	NFM	Penarth	Taxi Company (71.9)
167.60000	172.40000	NFM	Salford	Central Private Hire
167.60000	172.40000	NFM	Swansea	Cabletel
167.60000	172.40000	NFM	Telford	Car Repairs
167.61250	172.41250	NFM	Bedford	Windshield Enterprises
167.61250	172.41250	NFM	Belfast	Taxi Company
167.61250	172.41250	NFM	Blantyre	Mac Cars
167.61250	172.41250	NFM	Cheltenham	Astra Taxis (151.4)
167.61250	172.41250	NFM	Glasgow	Taxi Company
167.61250	172.41250	NFM	Grimsby	Skip Company
167.61250	172.41250	NFM	London	Taxi Company
167.61250	172.41250	NFM	Lowestoft	Lowestoft Cab Company
167.61250	172.41250	NFM	Portsmouth	University Security (71.9)
167.61250	172.41250	NFM	Stevenage	Amber Cars
167.61250	172.41250	NFM	Stevenage	Goldstar Taxi
167.61250	172.41250	NFM	Warwickshire	Farm (Acorn)
167.62500	172.42500	NFM	Aberdeen	Deeside Shop Fitters
167.62500	172.42500	NFM	Barnstaple	K & J Refrigeration
167.62500	172.42500	NFM	Barway	Shropshire Produce
167.62500	172.42500	NFM	Blackburn	Blackburn's Taxi Ranks
167.62500	172.42500	NFM	Bolsover	Hospital Patient Transport
167.62500	172.42500	NFM	Burton	Taxi Company
167.62500	172.42500	NFM	Glasgow	Taxi Company
167.62500	172.42500	NFM	Ipswich	Borough Council
167.62500	172.42500	NFM	Isle of Wight	Newport Council
167.62500	172.42500	NFM	Jersey	Hospital Patient Transport
167.62500	172.42500	NFM	Kings Lynn	Ken's Cars
167.62500	172.42500	NFM	Llandudno	Station Taxis
167.62500	172.42500	NFM	Llantrisant	Taxi Company (173.8)
167.62500	172.42500	NFM	Perth	Tayside Shopper Fitters
167.62500	172.42500	NFM	Pudsey	Rodley & Pudsey Private Hire
167.62500	172.42500	NFM	Rochford	Andrews Taxis
167.62500	172.42500	NFM	Shropshire	Shropshire Produce
167.62500	172.42500	NFM	Walton	Taxi Company
167.62500	172.42500	NFM	Warwickshire	Farm (Acorn)
167.62500	172.42500	NFM	Wolverhampton	Excel Cars
167.63750	172.43750	NFM	Breckland	Council House Repairs
167.63750	172.43750	NFM	Glasgow	Taxi Company
167.63750	172.43750	NFM	Hitchin	Cabstar Taxis (151.4)
167.63750	172.43750	NFM	Lees	Cartax
167.63750	172.43750	NFM	Manchester	Taxi Company
167.63750	172.43750	NFM	Nottingham	Taxi Company
167.63750	172.43750	NFM	Trowbridge	Ace's Taxis
167.65000	172.45000	NFM	Aldershot	Taxi Company
167.65000	172.45000	NFM	Belfast	Apple Taxis, Antrim Road
167.65000	172.45000	NFM	Bradford	Greengates Private Hire
167.65000	172.45000	NFM	Bristol	Hemmings Waste
167.65000	172.45000	NFM	Edinburgh	Airport Taxis
167.65000	172.45000	NFM	Glasgow	Taxi Company
167.65000	172.45000	NFM	Lincoln	Swan Taxis
167.65000	172.45000	NFM	London	Comet Cars, Kensal Town
167.65000	172.45000	NFM	Preston	VIP Cabs
167.65000	172.45000	NFM	Southampton	Randal's Taxis
167.65000	172.45000	NFM	Welwyn	Target Cars
167.65000	172.45000	NFM	Wirral	Eastham Cabs
167.66250	172.46250	NFM	Bristol	Council Maintenance (103.5)

Base	Mobile	Mode	Location	User and Notes
167.66250	172.46250	NFM	Colchester	Smythe Motors
167.66250	172.46250	NFM	Edinburgh	Parking Enforcement (107.2)
167.66250	172.46250	NFM	Glasgow	Taxi Company
167.66250	172.46250	NFM	Ipswich	Cambridge & East Coast Cable
167.66250	172.46250	NFM	Leicester	Taxi Company
167.66250	172.46250	NFM	Ramsgate	Taxi Company
167.66250	172.46250	NFM	Swilland	Stennett & Sons Farms
167.66250	172.46250	NFM	Widnes	Taxi Company
167.66250	172.46250	NFM	Wolverhampton	Rainbow Taxis
167.67500	172.47500	NFM	Aylesbury	Arrowtax Taxis
167.67500	172.47500	NFM	Glasgow	Glasgow Zoo
167.67500	172.47500	NFM	Guernsey	Central Cabs
167.67500	172.47500	NFM	Ipswich	Avenue Taxis Data (67)
167.67500	172.47500	NFM	Larbert	Taxi Company
167.67500	172.47500	NFM	Perth	Perth & Kinross Council
167.67500	172.47500	NFM	Pontypool	Real Gwent Taxis
167.67500	172.47500	NFM	Portsmouth	Taxi Company
167.67500	172.47500	NFM	Rochdale	Cozy Cars
167.67500	172.47500	NFM	Stevenage	Rowleys Taxis
167.68750	172.48750	NFM	Bedford	County Cars
167.68750	172.48750	NFM	Belfast	Park Taxis, Falls Road
167.68750	172.48750	NFM	Buxton	Taxi Company
167.68750	172.48750	NFM	Cardiff	Taxi Company (88.2)
167.68750	172.48750	NFM	Dovercourt	Station Taxis
167.68750	172.48750	NFM	Dunstable	Threeways Taxis
167.68750	172.48750	NFM	Hull	Kingston Cars
167.68750	172.48750	NFM	Leeds	Pegasus Private Hire
167.68750	172.48750	NFM	Medway	Taxi Company
167.68750	172.48750	NFM	Sale	Trafford Private Hire
167.68750	172.48750	NFM	Trowbridge	Taxi Company
167.70000	172.50000	AM	Aberdeen	Security Company
167.70000	172.50000	NFM	Ancoats	Town Cars
167.70000	172.50000	NFM	Belfast	D Cabs, King Street
167.70000	172.50000	NFM	Glasgow	East Kilbride Taxis
167.70000	172.50000	NFM	Hull	Willingham's Vehicle Recovery
167.70000	172.50000	NFM	London	Olympia Cars, Talgarth Road
167.70000	172.50000	NFM	London	Red Caps Radio Cars, W5
167.70000	172.50000	NFM	London	Tally Ho Cars, Finchley
167.70000	172.50000	NFM	Manchester	Taxi Company
167.70000	172.50000	NFM	Norwich	Z Cars
167.70000	172.50000	NFM	Peacehaven	Taxi Company
167.70000	172.50000	NFM	Portsmouth	Taxi Company
167.70000	172.50000	NFM	Ramsgate	Doctors' Service
167.70000	172.50000	NFM	Sheffield	Regency Valley Cars
167.70000	172.50000	NFM	Southampton	Taxi Company
167.71250	172.51250	NFM	Attlebridge	Hales Containers
167.71250	172.51250	NFM	Bristol	Council Maintenance (103.5)
167.71250	172.51250	NFM	Chester	Doctors
167.71250	172.51250	NFM	Felixstowe	Felixstowe & Harwich Haulage (103.5)
167.71250	172.51250	NFM	Hayes	Roundabout Cars
167.71250	172.51250	NFM	Heathrow	Heathrow Luxury Cars
167.71250	172.51250	NFM	Ipswich	Hawk Express Cabs
167.71250	172.51250	NFM	London	Direct Cars, NW6
167.71250	172.51250	NFM	Nuneaton	Taxi Company
167.71250	172.51250	NFM	Prestwich	Magnum Private Hire
167.71250	172.51250	NFM	Scunthorpe	Corus Steel Transport

Base	Mobile	Mode	Location	User and Notes
167.72500	172.52500	NFM	Barton	Booth Transport
167.72500	172.52500	NFM	Gt. Yarmouth	Birds Eye
167.72500	172.52500	NFM	Hastings	Thomas Taxis
167.72500	172.52500	NFM	Kilburn	Taxi Company
167.72500	172.52500	NFM	Kirkcaldy	Taxi Company
167.72500	172.52500	NFM	Leicester	Taxi Company
167.72500	172.52500	NFM	Lowestoft	Birds Eye
167.72500	172.52500	NFM	Newport	Town Taxis
167.72500	172.52500	NFM	Poole	Repeater
167.72500	172.52500	NFM	Reading	ABC Taxis
167.72500	172.52500	NFM	Stockport	Taxi Company
167.72500	172.52500	NFM	Stourbridge	Taxi Company
167.72500	172.52500	NFM	Tamworth	Taxi Company
167.72740	172.53750	NFM	Seaford	Taxi Company
167.73500	172.73500	NFM	Ayr	Taxi Company
167.73750	172.53750	NFM	Ashford	Refuse Collection (EF)
167 73750	172.53750	NFM	Bournemouth	Council Electricians
167.73750	172.53750	NFM	Brighton	NCP Car Parks
167.73750	171.53750	NFM	Cheshire	Vet
167.73750	172.53750	NFM	Crewe	Doctors' Service (114.8)
167.73750	172.53750	NFM	Dorchester	Mill Farm, Stratton (127.3)
167.73750	172.53750	NFM	Dover	Skip Company
167.73750	172.53750	NFM	Essex	Cleanaway
167.73750	172.53750	NFM	Gloucester	Associated Taxis
167.73750	172.53750	NFM	Gt Yarmouth	Shopwatch /Pubwatch/Street Patrol/TVEye
167.73750	172.53750	NFM	Hull	Taxi Company
167.73750	172.53750	NFM	Kilmarnock	Thistle Taxis
167.73750	172.53750	NFM	Lincoln	Sam's Taxis
167.73750	172.53750	NFM	Manchester	Veterinary Surgeon
167.73750	172.53750	NFM	Sheffield	Leigh Environmental
167.73750	172.53750	NFM	Silverstone	St John Ambulance at Race Track
167.73750	172.53750	NFM	Skegness	Fred's Taxis
167.73750	172.53750	NFM	Wolverhampton	A1 Abbey Cars
167.75000	172.55000	NFM	Bangor	Galaxy Cabs (71.9)
167.75000	172.55000	NFM	Dundee	Taxi Company
167.75000	172.55000	NFM	Hull	Belmont/Langham Cars
167.75000	172.55000	NFM	Lowestoft	Oulton Radio Taxis
167.75000	172.55000	NFM	Newcastle	Grosvenor Taxis
167.75000	172.55000	NFM	Norfolk	South Norfolk District Council (192.8)
167.75000	172.55000	NFM	Norwich	Haulage Company
167.75000	172.55000	NFM	Nottingham	Yellow Cabs
167.75000	172.55000	NFM	Redcar	Redcarz
167.75000	172.55000	NFM	Southampton	University Estates Department.
167.75000	172.55000	NFM	West Midlands	Wheelchair Cabs
167.75000	172.55000	NFM	Wirral	New Brighton Cabs
167.76250	172.56250	NFM	Ashwell	Bluegate Farm (114.8)
167.76250	172.56250	NFM	Ballyclare	Ballyclare Taxis (71.9)
167.76250	172.56250	NFM	Birmingham	Taxi Company
167.76250	172.56250	NFM	Bolton	Manor Taxis
167.76250	172.56250	NFM	Bromley	Cannon Cars
167.76250		NFM	Chalgrove	Martin Baker Ejector Seat Test Channel
167.76250	172.56250	NFM	Cumbernauld	Cita Taxis (Cita)
167.76250	172.56250	NFM	Dunstable	Cannon Cars
167.76250	172.56250	NFM	Felixstowe	Wizard Taxis Ch.1 (67)
167.76250	172.56250	NFM	Glasgow	Taxi Company
167.76250	172.56250	NFM	Gloucester	Central Taxis

Base	Mobile	Mode	Location	User and Notes
167.76250	172.56250	NFM	Halifax	Pennine Taxis
167.76250	172.56250	NFM	Newhaven	Tate's Garden Paradise (71.9)
167.76250	172.56250	NFM	Walsall	Taxi Company
167.77500	172.57500	NFM	Boston	Star Taxis
167.77500	172.57500	NFM	Brentwood	Taxi Company
167.77500	172.57500	NFM	Exmouth	Discount Cars
167.77500	172.57500	NFM	Hull	Ken Cars
167.77500	172.57500	NFM	Manchester	Taxi Company
167.77500	172.57500	NFM	Norwich	Cablevision
167.77500	172.57500	NFM	Shaftesbury	Alfords Taxis
167.77500	172.57500	NFM	Taplow	Burnham Couriers
167.77500	172.57500	NFM	Welwyn Garden City	Industrial Services
167.77500	172.57500	NFM	Woburn	Speedwell Farms
167.77500	172.57500	NFM	Wolverhampton	Ace Radio Cars
167.77500	172.57500	NFM	York	Taxi Company
167.78750	172.58750	NFM	Basildon	Ace Taxi Group
167.78750	172.58750	NFM	Belfast	Taxi Company, Andersonstown
167.78750	172.58750	NFM	Birmingham	Taxi Company
167.78750	172.58750	NFM	Eccles	New Lyle Cars
167.78750	172.58750	NFM	Edinburgh	Falcon Delivery
167.78750	172.58750	NFM	Lincoln	Taxi Company
167.78750	172.58750	NFM	London	Swiss Cottage Radio Cars
167.78750	172.58750	NFM	Manchester	Taxi Company
167.78750	172.58750	NFM	Peterborough	ABBA Taxis
167.78750	172.58750	NFM	Rochdale	Town Cars
167.78750	172.58750	NFM	Saddleworth	Taxi Company
167.78750	172.58750	NFM	St Andrews	Jay's Taxis
167.80000	172.60000	NFM	Aberdeen	Security Company
167.80000	172.60000	NFM	Barry	Taxi Company
167.80000	172.60000	NFM	Blackburn	Lancs Private Hire
167.80000	172.60000	NFM	Burnley	Taxi Company
167.80000	172.60000	NFM	Cambridge	H Collins Communications
167.80000	172.60000	NFM	Cambridge	United Taxis
167.80000	172.60000	NFM	Coventry	T White Skips
167.80000	172.60000	NFM	Cumbernauld	Taxi Company
167.80000	172.60000	NFM	Dovercourt	Starling Taxis
167.80000	172.60000	NFM	Droitwich	MY Taxis
167.80000	172.60000	NFM	Glasgow	Taxi Company
167.80000	172.60000	NFM	Grimsby	Revels Taxis
167.80000	172.60000	NFM	Leicester	Slot Machine Company
167.80000	172.60000	NFM	Manchester	Cresta Cars
167.80000	172.60000	NFM	Nottingham	Amusement Machine Servicing
167.80000	172.60000	NFM	Oldham	Britannia Cars
167.80000	172.60000	NFM	Sheffield	Eagle Cars
167.80000	172.60000	NFM	Weymouth	Taxi Company
167.80000	172.60000	NFM	Wirral	50-50 Cabs
167.81250	172.61250	NFM	Alloa	Taxi Company
167.81250	172.61250	NFM	Bath	Abbey Taxis
167.81250	172.61250	NFM	Bedford	M.W. Ward
167.81250	172.61250	NFM	Belfast	Spring Taxis, Springvale Road
167.81250	172.61250	NFM	Bootle	Taxi Company
167.81250	172.61250	NFM	Cwmbran	Gwent Taxis
167.81250	172.61250	NFM	Glasgow	Taxi Company
167.81250	172.61250	NFM	Jersey	CSL Repeater, Westmount
167.81250	172.61250	NFM	Jersey	De La Haye Plant, Westmount Ltd
167.81250	172.61250	NFM	Jersey	Fuel Supplies Ltd, Westmount

Base	Mobile	Mode	Location	User and Notes
167.81250	172.61250	NFM	Jersey	Keith Prowse Tours, Westmount
167.81250	172.61250	NFM	Jersey	MacLead & Allan, Westmount
167.81250	172.61250	NFM	Jersey	Ronez Ltd, Westmount
167.81250	172.61250	NFM	Portsmouth	Portsmouth University Security (71.9)
167.81250	172.61250	NFM	Manchester	Kings Private Hire, Leverhulme
167.81250	172.61250	NFM	Stoke on Trent	Magnum Taxis
167.81250	172.61250	NFM	Watlington	Watlington Plant Hire
167.82500	172.62500	NFM	Bolton	Tele Taxis
167.82500	172.62500	NFM	Bristol	Downend Taxis
167.82500	172.62500	NFM	Burseldon	Angela Coaches
167.82500	172.62500	NFM	Cheltenham	Starline Taxis (136.5)
167.82500	172.62500	NFM	Edinburgh	Taxi Company
167.82500	172.62500	NFM	Grangemouth	Tartan Line Radio Cabs (Tartan)
167.82500	172.62500	NFM	Ipswich	ABC Couriers/Parcels
167.82500	172.62500	NFM	Ipswich	Robin Hood Taxis
167.82500	172.62500	NFM	Liverpool	Cavalier Taxis
167.82500	172.62500	NFM	Tamworth	Polesworth Cars
167.83700	172.63700	NFM	Atherstone	AJ's Taxis
167.83750	172.63750	NFM	Canterbury	Longport Taxi
167.83750	172.63700	NFM	Coventry	Security Company
167.83750	172.63750	NFM	Kings Lynn	House Plant Growers
167.83750	172.63750	NFM	Manchester	Taxi Company
167.83750	172.63700	NFM	Merthyr Tydfil	Scottie's Cabs
167.83750	172.63700	NFM	Polesworth	Polesworth Cabs
167.83750	172.63750	NFM	Portsmouth	Fruit/Vegetable/Food Packing Plant (131.8)
167.83750	172.63700	NFM	Rochdale	Milnrow Cars
167.83750	172.63750	NFM	Swansea	Taxis Company
167.83750	172.63700	NFM	Tattingstone	Collins Skip Hire
167.83750	172.68750	NFM	Tynemouth	Taxi Company
167.85000	172.65000	NFM	Bexleyheath	Taxi Company
167.85000	172.65000	NFM	Blackpool	Ace Cabs
167.85000	172.65000	NFM	Bridlington	Q Cars
167.85000	172.65000	NFM	Cambridge	Cleanaway
167.85000	172.65000	NFM	Cardiff	Amber Taxis
167.85000	172.65000	NFM	Cardiff	Capital Taxis Ch.2 (218.1)
167.85000	172.65000	NFM	Cleveleys	Ace Cabs
167.85000	172.65000	NFM	Gloucester	First Association Taxis
167.85000	172.65000	NFM	Ipswich	Taxi Company
167.85000	172.65000	NFM	London	Alpine Radio Cars, NW2
167.85000	172.65000	NFM	Milford Haven	Taxi Company (127.3)
167.85000	172.65000	NFM	Nottinghamshire	Clumber Park
167.85000	172.65000	NFM	Pembroke	Taxi Company
167.86250	172.66250	NFM	Leicester	Taxi Company
167.86250	172.66250	NFM	London	Challenger Couriers
167.86250	172.66250	NFM	London	Taxi Company, NW6
167.86250	172.66250	NFM	Manchester	Taxi Company
167.86250	172.66250	NFM	Middleton	Star Taxis
167.86250	172.66250	NFM	Milton Keynes	Metrobus MK Control (123)
167.86250	172.66250	NFM	Ormskirk	Ormskirk Taxis
167.86250	172.66250	NFM	Sheerness	Sheppey Taxis
167.86250	172.66250	NFM	Sheffield	Mercury Cars Ch 1
167.86250	172.66250	NFM	Swansea	E & G Taxis
167.86250	172.66250	NFM	Worthing	Taxi Company
167.87500	172.67500	NFM	Bedworth	MGM Taxis
167.87500	172.67500	NFM	Plymouth	Taxi Company

Base	Mobile	Mode	Location	User and Notes
167.87500	172.67500	NFM	Romford	A1 Cars
167.87500	172.67500	NFM	Scunthorpe	Taxi Company
167.87500	172.67500	NFM	Sheffield	DB Radio Cars
167.88750	172.68750	NFM	Atherton	J & K Taxis
167.88750	172.68750	NFM	Bangor	Shoreline Taxis
167.88750	172.68750	NFM	Caerphilly	Taxi Company
167.88750	172.68750	NFM	Cheshire	Whites Taxis
167.88750	172.68750	NFM	Congleton	Taxi Company
167.88750	172.68750	NFM	Eastleigh	Taxi Company
167.88750	172.68750	NFM	Glasgow	Taxi Company
167.88750	172.68750	NFM	Ipswich	Taxi Company
167.88750	172.68750	NFM	Liverpool	Dock Taxis
167.88750	172.68750	NFM	Oldham	Radio Cars
167.88750	172.68750	NFM	Sheffield	Airport Express Cars
167.88750	172.68750	NFM	Woburn	Farm (146.2)
167.90000	172.70000	NFM	Brighton	Auto Windscreens
167.90000	172.70000	NFM	Caerphilly	Taxi Company
167.90000	172.70000	NFM	Carrickfergus	Taxi Company
167.90000	172.70000	NFM	Chesterfield	Auto Windscreens
167.90000	172.70000	NFM	Coventry	Mercia Taxis
167.90000	172.70000	NFM	Falkirk	Auto Windscreens
167.90000	172.70000	NFM	Heywood	Heywood Cars
167.90000	172.70000	NFM	Hull	Auto Windscreens
167.90000	172.70000	NFM	Leicester	Auto Windscreens
167.90000	172.70000	NFM	Lincoln	Handsome Cabs
167.90000	172.70000	NFM	Mansfield	Auto Windscreens
167.90000	172.70000	NFM	Newark	Auto Windscreens
167.90000	172.70000	NFM	Northampton	Taxi Company
167.90000	172.70000	NFM	Nottingham	Auto Windscreens
167.90000	172.70000	NFM	Port Talbot	Taxi Company
167.90000	172.70000	NFM	Prescot	All Black Cabs Ltd
167.90000	172.70000	NFM	Scunthorpe	Auto Windscreens
167.90000	172.70000	NFM	Wells	Wookey Taxi Consortium (67)
167.90000	172.70000	NFM	Welwyn	Garden City Taxis
167.90000	172.70000	NFM	Winton	Taxi Company
167.91250	172.71250	NFM	Dalton in Furness	Taxi Company
167.91250	172.71250	NFM	Faversham	Reeves Taxis
167.91250	172.71250	NFM	Felixstowe	Normans Shipping
167.91250	172.71250	NFM	Grain	Geoffrey Clark
167.91250	172.71250	NFM	Hitchin	Tiny's Taxis (136.5)
167.91250	172.71250	NFM	Ipswich	Taxi Company
167.91250	172.71250	NFM	Leeds	Bell Cable engineers
167.91250	172.71250	NFM	London	Skip Hire Company
167.91250	172.71250	NFM	Medway	Withers Concrete
167.91250	172.71250	NFM	Newport, Gwent	Dragon Taxis Ch.1
167.91250	172.71250	NFM	Sheffield	Blue Star Security
167.91250	172.71250	NFM	Woodbridge	Normans Transport
167.91250	172.71250	NFM	Wrexham	Cresta Taxis
167.92500	172.72500	NFM	Cambridge	RBLA Security
167.92500	172.72500	NFM	Chelmsford	Ace Mini Cabs
167.92500	172.72500	NFM	Cheltenham	Taxi Company
167.92500	172.72500	NFM	Cheshunt	Martini Cars
167.92500	172.72500	NFM	Leeds	Taxi Company
167.92500	172.72500	NFM	Lincoln	Yellow Cabs
167.92500	172.72500	NFM	Newmarket	Sound City Cars

Base	Mobile	Mode	Location	User and Notes
167.92500	172.72500	NFM	Northfleet	Scorpio Taxis
167.92500	172.72500	NFM	Penarth	B-Line Taxis (88.5)
167.92500	172.72500	NFM	Radcliffe	United Private Hire
167.92500	172.72500	NFM	Sheffield	Sita (GB) Ltd., Plant & Skips
167.92500	172.72500	NFM	Stevenage	Sierra Taxis
167.92500	172.72500	NFM	Swansea	Taxi Company
167.93750	172.73750	NFM	Amersham	Taxi Company (162.2)
167.93750	172.73750	NFM	Belfast	Cable Cabs, Grosvenor Road
167.93750	172.73750	NFM	Bracknell	Bracknell Radio Cars
167.93750	172.73750	NFM	Cambridge	Doctors' Service
167.93750	172.73750	NFM	Coatbridge	Town Taxis
167.93750	172.73750	NFM	Cumbernauld	Taxi Company
167.93750	172.73750	NFM	Greenisland	Greenisland Taxis
167.93750	172.73750	NFM	Glasgow	Taxi Company
167.93750	172.73750	NFM	Hemel Hempstead	Minicab Company
167.93750	172.73750	NFM	London	Bow Taxis
167.93750	172.73750	NFM	London	Mile End Radio Cars
167.93750	172.73750	NFM	Luton	Harvey Plant Hire
167.93750	172.73750	NFM	Oldham	Red Cars
167.93750	172.73750	NFM	St Andrews	R & BA Taxis
167.93750	172.73750	NFM	Tamworth	Taxi Company
167.93750	172.73750	NFM	Taunton	Ace Taxis
167.95000	172.72500	NFM	Cwmbran	Taxi Company
167.95000	172.75000	NFM	Glasgow	Taxi Company
167.95000	172.75000	NFM	Ipswich	Taxi Company
167.95000	172.75000	NFM	Jersey	Clarendon Cabs
167.95000	172.75000	NFM	Lichfield	Taxi Company
167.95000	172.75000	NFM	Rochdale	Kings Private Hire
167.95000	172.75000	NFM	Southend on Sea	Deck Chair Attendants
167.95000	172.75000	NFM	Swinton	Clifton Cars
167.96250	172.76250	NFM	Belfast	Call-A-Cab, Crumlin Road
167.96250	172.76250	NFM	Birkenhead	Robo's Taxis
167.96250	172.76250	NFM	Bootle	Taxi Company
167.96250	172.76250	NFM	Brighton	Taxi Company
167.96250	172.76250	NFM	Cambridge	Scudamores Boat Yard
167.96250	172.76250	NFM	Coventry	JK Lynch Construction
167.96250	172.76250	NFM	Jersey	Falles Hire Cars
167.96250	172.76250	NFM	Nottingham	Central Cars, Bulwell
167.96250	172.76250	NFM	Peterborough	Clover Cars
167.96250	172.76250	NFM	Peterborough	Horrells Dairies
167.96250	172.76250	NFM	Pocklington	Central Taxis
167.96250	172.76250	NFM	Sheffield	KC Cars
167.96250	172.76250	NFM	Sheffield	Moss Cabs
167.96250	172.76250	NFM	Wells	A Taxis
167.97500	172.77500	NFM	Belfast	Taxi Company
167.97500	172.77500	NFM	Cardiff	St John Ambulance (88.5)
167.97500	172.77500	NFM	Edinburgh	Taxi Company
167.97500	172.77500	NFM	Glasgow	Croft Radio Cars
167.97500	172.77500	NFM	Ipswich	Hawk Express/Premier Cars Data
167.97500	172.77500	NFM	Lincoln	Taxi Company
167.97500	172.77500	NFM	Liverpool	Taxi Company
167.97500	172.77500	NFM	London	Taxi Company
167.97500	172.77500	NFM	March	Coy & Manchett
167.97500	172.77500	NFM	Neath	Abbey Cabs
167.97500	172.77500	NFM	Peterborough	Crown Taxis

Base	Mobile	Mode	Location	User and Notes
167.97500	172.77500	NFM	Portsmouth	Taxi Company
167.97500	172.77500	NFM	Royton	Royton Private Hire
167.97500	172.77500	NFM	Silverstone	Silverstone Race Track Marshals (173.8)
167.98750	172.78750	NFM	Airdrie	M. Moffat Cars
167.98750	172.78750	NFM	Belfast	Taxi Company
167.98750	172.78750	NFM	Devon	Imerys China Clay MPT1327 Sysid 4129
167.98750	172.78750	NFM	Exeter	Capital Taxis
167.98750	172.78750	NFM	Glasgow	Taxi Company
167.98750	172.78750	NFM	Halifax	Railway Taxis
167.98750	172.78750	NFM	Hull	Streamline Taxis
167.98750	172.78750	NFM	Leicester	Taxi Company
167.98750	172.78750	NFM	London	Star Cars, Whitechapel
167.98750	172.78750	NFM	Manchester	Taxi Company
167.98750	172.78750	NFM	Salford	Shopping City Security
167.98750	172.78750	NFM	Seaford	Taxi Company
167.98750	172.78750	NFM	Sheffield	Hallam University Porters
167.98750	172.78750	NFM	Sussex	Brighton Marina Security
167.98750	172.78750	NFM	Swansea Docks	Crane Crews
167.98750	172.78750	NFM	Thanet	BC Taxis
167.98750	172.78750	NFM	Walkden	Star Private Hire
167.98750	172.78750	NFM	Wrexham	Gold Star Taxis
168.00000	172.80000	NFM	Belfast	Standard Taxi Company, Shankhill Road
168.00000	172.80000	NFM	Beverley	Westholme Cars
168.00000	172.80000	NFM	Bristol	Dial A Cab
168.00000	172.80000	NFM	Burnley	Day Rider Couriers
168.00000	172.80000	NFM	Cambridge	Camtax Taxis (110.9)
168.00000	172.80000	NFM	Falkirk	Express Taxis (Express)
168.00000	172.80000	NFM	Glasgow	Eastwood Taxis
168.00000	172.80000	NFM	Jersey	Pioneer Holiday Coaches
168.00000	172.80000	NFM	Manchester	Taxi Company
168.00000	172.80000	NFM	Salford	Taxi Company
168.00000	172.80000	NFM	Stoke on Trent	Abbey Taxis
168.00000	172.80000	NFM	Weymouth	Brewers Quay Exhibition
168.01250	172.81250	NFM	Brighton	Taxi Company
168.01250	172.81250	NFM	Clacton	Onyx Council Refuse Collectors
168.01250	172.81250	NFM	Devon	Imerys China Clay MPT1327 Sysid 4129
168.01250	172.81250	NFM	Doncaster	A1 Taxis
168.01250	172.81250	NFM	Edinburgh	Capital Cabs Ch 1
168.01250	172.81250	NFM	Letchworth	KP Cars (186.2)
168.01250	172.81250	NFM	Letchworth	Martini Cars (110.9)
168.01250	172.81250	NFM	London	Speed Couriers
168.01250	172.81250	NFM	Salford	Mainline Taxis
168.01250	172.81250	NFM	Sheffield	Central Cabs
168.01250		NFM	Stoke on Trent	4 Star Taxis
168.02500	172.82500	NFM	Cheltenham	Andy's Cars (136.5)
168.02500	172.82500	NFM	Glasgow	Taxi Company
168.02500	172.82500	NFM	Hitchin	Swan Garage
168.02500	172.82500	NFM	Ipswich	Robin Hood Taxis
168.02500	172.82500	NFM	Leamington	Refuse Collection
168.02500	172.82500	NFM	Newtownabbey	Taxi Company
168.02500	172.82500	NFM	Norwich	ABC Taxis
168.02500	172.82500	NFM	Swansea	ABC Cabs
168.03750	172.83750	NFM	Bangor	Taxi Company
168.03750	172.83750	NFM	Beverley	Hackney Cabs
168.03750	172.83750	NFM	Bristol	Taxi Company (203.5)

Base	Mobile	Mode	Location	User and Notes
168.03750	172.83750	NFM	Edinburgh	Capital Cabs Ch.2
168.03750	172.83750	NFM	Glasgow	Taxi Company
168.03750	172.83750	NFM	Guernsey	DJ Machan Engineering
168.03750	172.83750	NFM	London	Metrocars, Barnet
168.03750	172.83750	NFM	Peterborough	Marpol Security (67)
168.03750	172.83750	NFM	Wolverhampton	Penn Radio Cars
168.05000	172.85000	NFM	Bristol	Z Cars Taxis
168.05000	172.85000	NFM	Cambridge	A1 Taxis
168.05000	172.85000	NFM	Colchester	AA Taxis
168.05000	172.85000	NFM	Cowley	MG Rover Plant Ambulance
168.05000	173.05000	NFM	Gt Yarmouth	Docks
168.05000	172.85000	NFM	Heathrow	Airport Cars
168.05000	172.85000	NFM	Oldham	Delta Taxis
168.05000	172.85000	NFM	Port Talbot	Taxi Company (141.3)
168.05000	172.85000	NFM	St Andrews	Golf City Taxis
168.05000	172.85000	NFM	Tamworth	Alpha Cars
168.05000	172.85000	NFM	Worthing	Taxi Company
168.06250	172.86250	NFM	Bedford	Eagle Cars
168.06250	172.86250	NFM	Birmingham	Taxi Company
168.06250	172.86250	NFM	Hull	Hull Daily Mail Newspaper
168.06250	172.86250	NFM	Manchester	Taxi Company, Reddish
168.06250	172.86250	NFM	Manchester	Taxi Company, Walkden
168.06250	172.86250	NFM	Peterborough	ABC Taxis
168.06250	172.86250	NFM	Peterborough	Betta Cars (110.9)
168.06250	172.86250	NFM	Swansea	Taxi Company
168.07500	172.87500	NFM	Belfast	Sure Cabs, Antrim Road
168.07500	172.87500	NFM	Cheshunt	Atlas Cars
168.07500	172.87500	NFM	Coventry	Edwards Taxis, Bedworth
168.07500	172.87500	NFM	Devon	Imerys China Clay MPT1327 Sysid 4105
168.07500	172.87500	NFM	Heywood	New Embassy Taxis
168.07500	172.87500	NFM	Liverpool	City Centre Taxis
168.07500	172.87500	NFM	Lurgan	A1 Cabs
168.07500	172.87500	NFM	Newport	Reliance Taxis
168.07500	172.87500	NFM	Potters Bar	Potters Bar Radio Cars (94.8)
168.08750	172.88750	NFM	Ascot	Cooper 24Hr Taxis
168.08750	172.88750	NFM	Avon	Severn Bridge Contractors
168.08750	172.88750	NFM	Ballymena	Regent Taxis
168.08750	172.88750	NFM	Barrow in Furness	Taxi Company
168.08750	172.88750	NFM	Birmingham	Taxi Company
168.08750	172.88750	NFM	Cardiff	Taxi Company
168.08750	172.88750	NFM	Colchester	AA Cars
168.08750	172.88750	NFM	Colchester	Micraline Taxis
168.08750	172.88750	NFM	Dovercourt	Mathews TV & Electrical (67)
168.08750	172.88750	NFM	Glasgow	Taxi Company
168.08750	172.88750	NFM	Guernsey	Unigrow
168.08750	172.88750	NFM	Sittingbourne	Channel Taxis
168.08750	172.88750	NFM	St Athan	Valetax Taxis (151.4)
168.08750	172.88750	NFM	Walney	Avon Taxis (82.5)
168.10000	172.90000	NFM	Bristol	Streamline Taxis (118.8)
168.10000	172.90000	NFM	Burnley	Taxi Company
168.10000	172.90000	NFM	Cardiff	Taxi Company
168.10000	172.90000	NFM	Co Durham	Taxi Company
168.10000	172.90000	NFM	Cumbernauld	Taxi Company
168.10000	172.90000	NFM	Edinburgh	Taxi Company
168.10000	172.90000	NFM	Glasgow	Kingsway Taxis

Base	Mobile	Mode	Location	User and Notes
168.10000	172.90000	NFM	Hamilton	Wellman Taxis
168.10000	172.90000	NFM	Newark	Taxi Company
168.10000	172.90000	NFM	Ramsgate	Taxi Company
168.10000	172.90000	NFM	Slough	A-2-B Taxis
168.10000	172.90000	NFM	Southampton	ESSO Fawley Security (192.8)
168.10000	172.90000	NFM	Sussex	Palace Pier Security
168.10000	172.90000	NFM	Tottington	Tram Cars
168.10000	172.90000	NFM	Welwyn	752 Taxis
168.11250	172.91250	NFM	Bath	Taxi Company
168.11250	172.91250	NFM	Bromley	Taxi Company
168.11250	172.91250	NFM	Caister	Avenue Taxis
168.11250	172.91250	NFM	Cardiff	Capital Taxis Ch.1 (218.1)
168.11250	172.91250	NFM	Cardiff	Green Cabs
168.11250	172.91250	NFM	Edinburgh	Taxi Company
168.11250	172.91250	NFM	Heysham	Heysham Radio Taxis
168.11250	172.91250	NFM	London	Minicab Company, Woodford
168.11250	172.91250	NFM	Newcastle	Star Taxis
168.11250	172.91250	NFM	Radcliffe	Centre Radio Cars
168.11250	172.91250	NFM	Sunderland	Star Taxis Data
168.12500	172.92500	NFM	Bristol	Brinks Mat Security
168.12500	172.32500	NFM	Cambridgeshire	Farm (167.9)
168.12500	172.92500	NFM	Cardiff	DSS Fraud Teams (94.8)
168.12500	172.92500	NFM	Devon	Imerys China Clay MPT1327 Sysid 4153
168.12500	172.92500	NFM	Dundry	Brinks Mat Security
168.12500	172.92500	NFM	Edinburgh	Taxi Company
168.12500	172.92500	NFM	Elgin	Brinks Mat Cash in Transit
168.12500	172.92500	NFM	Emley Moor	Brinks Mat
168.12500	172.92500	NFM	Heathrow	Brinks Mat Cash/Bullion Vans Airside (141.3)
168.12500	172.92500	NFM	Ipswich	Ipswich Buses
168.12500	172.92500	NFM	London	Brinks Mat
168.12500	179.92500	NFM	London	Stratford Transport Company
168.12500	172.92500	NFM	Sheffield	Balfour Beatty Base
168.12500	172.92500	NFM	West Midlands	Blue Taxis
168.13750	172.93750	NFM	Aberdeen	Plant Hire Company
168.13750	172.93750	NFM	Arlesey	Station Cars
168.13750	172.93750	NFM	Belfast	Dundonald Taxis (67)
168.13750	172.93750	NFM	Bolton	Breightmet Taxis
168.13750	172.93750	NFM	Burton on Trent	Lift Maintenance Company
168.13750	172.93750	NFM	Cardiff	Capital Taxis Ch3 (218.1)
168.13750	172.93750	NFM	Devon	Imerys China Clay MPT1327 Sysid 4137
168.13750	172.93750	NFM	Edinburgh	Black Cabs
168.13750	172.93750	NFM	Glasgow	Taxi Company
168.13750	172.93750	NFM	Gosport	Taxi Company
168.13750	172.93750	NFM	Larne	AA Taxis
168.13750	172.93750	NFM	London	Leytonstone & Stratford Car Service
168.13750	172.93750	NFM	Manchester Airport	Taxi Company
168.13750	172.93750	NFM	Mansfield	A Line Taxis
168.13750	172.93750	NFM	Stoke on Trent	Sid's Taxis
168.15000	172.95000	NFM	Belfast	Diamond Taxis, Ormeau Road
168.15000	172.95000	NFM	Benwick	Bank Farms
168.15000	172.95000	NFM	Carrickfergus	Mahoods Taxis (71.9)
168.15000	172.95000	NFM	Devon	Imerys China Clay MPT1327 Sysid 4121
168.15000	172.95000	NFM	Didcot	Harold's Taxis
168.15000	172.95000	NFM	Dover	District Council
168.15000	172.95000	NFM	Dublin	Dublin Cablelink

Base	Mobile	Mode	Location	User and Notes
168.15000	172.95000	NFM	Ely	Evans Taxis
168.15000	172.95000	NFM	Hull	Taxi Company
168.15000	172.95000	NFM	Manchester	Town Cars
168.15000	172.95000	NFM	Newport	Taxi Company (127.3)
168.15000	172.95000	NFM	Sandy	SC Banks Grain Storage Farm (114.8)
168.15000	172.95000	NFM	Scarborough	Bee Line Taxis
168.15000	172.95000	NFM	Skegness	Seacroft Garage
168.15000	172.95000	NFM	Swansea	S & E Taxis
168.16250	172.96250	NFM	Aberdeen	Taxi Company
168.16250	172.96250	NFM	Bedford	A1 Cars
168.16250	172.96250	NFM	Birmingham	Taxi Company, 4 Oaks
168.16250	172.96250	NFM	Bognor	Home James Taxis
168.16250	172.96250	NFM	Bristol	Taxi Company
168.16250	172.96250	NFM	Cleethorpes	Taxi Company
168.16250	172.96250	NFM	Devon	Imerys China Clay MPT1327 Sysid 4137
168.16250	172.96250	NFM	Eastbourne	Community Transport (82.5)
168.16250	172.96250	NFM	Essex	Minicab Company
168.16250	172.96250	NFM	Glasgow	Taxi Company
168.16250	172.96250	NFM	Goodwood	Goodwood House Staff
168.16250	172.96250	NFM	Hull	City Cabs
168.16250	172.96250	NFM	Kent	County Council Highways Department
168.16250	172.96250	NFM	London	Capital Cars
168.16250	172.96250	NFM	Manchester	Taxi Company
168.16250	172.96250	NFM	Kent	County Council Highways
168.16250	172.96250	NFM	London	Capital Cars, Colindale
168.16250	172.96250	NFM	Sheerness	Home James Taxis
168.16250	172.96250	NFM	Wisbech	Ellis & Everard
168.17500	172.97500	NFM	Bedford	Key Cars
168.17500	172.97500	NFM	Belfast	Taxi Company
168.17500	172.97500	NFM	Birmingham	Taxi Company, Shirley
168.17500	172.97500	NFM	Devon	Imerys China Clay MPT1327 Sysid 4137
168.17500	172.97500	NFM	Grimsby	TV Repair Company
168.17500	172.97500	NFM	Humberside	A Brunton & Co Skips & Scrap
168.17500	172.97500	NFM	Newmarket	Triax
168.17500	172.97500	NFM	Oxford	001 Taxi (107.2)
168.17500	172.97500	NFM	Rochdale	Castle Private Hire
168.18750	172.98750	NFM	Abingdon	K-9 Security
168.18750	172.98750	NFM	Birmingham	Taxi Company, Shard End
168.18750	172.98750	NFM	Blackpool	Black Taxis
168.18750	172.98750	NFM	Bridgend	Radio Cabs (77)
168.18750	172.98750	NFM	Devon	Imerys China Clay MPT1327 Sysid 4137
168.18750	172.98750	NFM	Eastbourne	East College
168.18750	172.98750	NFM	Hull	Atlas Cabs
168.18750	172.98750	NFM	Long Melford	A Line Taxis
168.18750	172.98750	NFM	Manchester	White Line Private Hire, Leverhulme
168.18750	172.98750	NFM	Oxford	K-9 Security
168.18750	172.98750	NFM	Peterborough	DJ Taxis
168.18750	172.98750	NFM	Reading	Arena Security
168.18750	172.98750	NFM	Sutton	Salisbury Bros.
168.20000	173.00000	NFM	Abergavenny	Taxi Company
168.20000	173.00000	NFM	Ayr	Adairs Cabco
168.20000	173.00000	NFM	Beswick	UK Cars
168.20000	173.00000	NFM	Caerphilly	Taxi Company
168.20000	173.00000	NFM	Devon	Imerys China Clay MPT1327 Sysid 4121
168.20000	173.00000	NFM	Glasgow	Taxi Company

Base	Mobile	Mode	Location	User and Notes
168.20000	173.00000	NFM	Grimsby	Taxi Company
168.20000	173.00000	NFM	London	Junction Cars, Archway
168.20000	173.00000	NFM	London	Parking Enforcement, Enfield
168.20000	173.00000	NFM	Manchester	Taxi Company
168.20000	173.00000	NFM	Peterborough	Rivergate Security
168.20000	173.00000	NFM	Reading	1A Cars
168.20000	173.00000	NFM	Shaftesbury	Alford Taxis
168.20000	173.00000	NFM	Shaftesbury	Hilltop Taxis
168.21250	173.01250	NFM	Avon	Laing Construction, Severn Crossing (82.5)
168.21250	173.01250	NFM	Belfast	Taxi Company
168.21250	173.01250	NFM	Cambridge	Bettacars
168.21250		NFM	Chepstow	HMS Neptune Training
168.21250	173.01250	NFM	Craigavon	Sun Taxis
168.21250	173.01250	NFM	Dukinfield	Taxi Company
168.21250	173.01250	NFM	Glasgow	Taxi Company
168.21250	173.01250	NFM	Knowsley	Knowsley Safari Park
168.21250	173.01250	NFM	London	Fleet Cars, Camden
168.21250	173.01250	NFM	London	Roman Cars, East London
168.21250	173.01250	NFM	Manchester	Zip Dispatch
168.21250	173.01250	NFM	Norwich	Loyal Taxis
168.21250	173.01250	NFM	Sheffield	Eagle Taxis
168.21250	173.01250	NFM	Sheffield	Fleet Cars
168.21250	173.01250	NFM	Sheffield	GT Cars
168.21250	173.01250	NFM	Southminster	Denge Crops Ltd.
168.21250	173.01250	NFM	Stirling	D & M Taxis (D)
168.21250	173.01250	NFM	Swinton	Zip Dispatch
168.21250	173.01250	NFM	Trowbridge	Alpha Taxis
168.21250	173.01250	NFM	Trowbridge	A & D Taxis
168.22500	173.02500	NFM	Belfast	Taxi Company
168.22500	173.02500	NFM	Blackpool	Green Star Taxis
168.22500	173.02500	NFM	Clevedon	Taxi Company
168.22500	173.02500	NFM	Crewe	White Line Taxis (88.5)
168.22500	173.02500	NFM	Felixstowe	Compass Cars
168.22500	173.02500	NFM	Glasgow	Taxi Company
168.22500	173.02500	NFM	Lincoln	Fon-A-Car
168.22500	173.02500	NFM	London	A-Z Couriers
168.22500	173.02500	NFM	Manchester	Taxi Company
168.22500	173.02500	NFM	Medway	Countdown Cars
168.22500	173.02500	NFM	Oldham	Untied Private Hire
168.22500	173.02500	NFM	Peterborough	Rivergate Security (71.9)
168.22500	173.02500	NFM	Swindon	A2B Taxis
168.22500	173.02500	NFM	Worcester	City Taxis
168.23750	173.03750	NFM	Carlisle	City Taxis
168.23750	173.03750	NFM	Chepstow	M & R Cars
168.23750	173.03750	NFM	Corsham	Taxi Company
168.23750	173.03750	NFM	Fakenham	Woody's Haulage
168.23750	173.03750	NFM	Felling	Taxi Company
168.23750	173.03750	NFM	Gt Yarmouth	Halcyon Shipping
168.23750	173.03750	NFM	Llandudno	Taxi Company (67)
168.23750	173.03750	NFM	Luton	Amec Maintenance
168.23750	173.03750	NFM	Nottingham	Holme Pier Water Sports
168.23750	173.03750	NFM	Paddock Wood	County Council Repairs
168.23750	173.03750	NFM	Peterborough	Royal Cars (250.3)
168.23750	173.03750	NFM	Woodbridge	M & R Cars

Scanning At Formula One Grand Prix Meetings
A Guide to Race Car Monitoring

Introduction

A motorsport event can be one of the most interesting places to take your scanner and the highlight for us is the British Grand Prix at Silverstone, run in July each year. The race weekend will usually see over 100,000 people attend and with everyone from the Formula One teams, pit crews, track officials, media, sponsors, security guards, car park attendants, emergency services and air traffic controllers using radios there is an enormous amount of communications traffic to listen to.

With so much going on, tuning into the Formula One Team's communications isn't straightforward. It's made even more difficult as the teams change their radio equipment from year to year and their frequencies between races and sometimes even during the race weekend to avoid interference. To pick out the best pit-to-car communications you need to have an idea of how the radio systems work, where to look for the team communications and to take the right equipment along with you to listen in. Here are some tips on what to listen out for.

Communications Equipment

The key radio communications take place between the driver and his race engineer. Each car is fitted with a portable radio located in the nose or cockpit of the car and linked to a press to talk switch on the driver's steering wheel. The driver's helmet is fitted with a very sophisticated microphone to help cut out the enormous amount of background noise from the car and he wears earplugs fitted with earphones to listen to his engineer.

Each pit crew member has a portable radio and given the deafening background noise, the teams use industrial-style headphones to listen to the communications. Most teams use standard off-the-shelf PMR radios although these are often modified to enhance the audio output to help overcome the background noise. The most rugged versions of Kenwood and Motorola radios are common in the pitlane. Several press-to-talk switches can be mounted on the engineer's headsets with each one giving access to a different radio channel.

Most modern race circuits are several miles long with trees, buildings and crash barriers separating the cars from a direct line of sight back to the pits. To maintain a good communications link, teams use repeater systems to relay the pit-to-car signals. The aerials of these repeater stations are located on pump-up masts that are built into and then erected high above the team transporters parked in the pits. Most commercial repeater systems will be optimised to allow good communications at long ranges. Formula One repeater aerials are specially modified to allow them to be used not only at long range but also when users are in the pits directly below the aerial.

Radio Networks

In order to understand what you are listening to, it's important to realise that each team will have several different radio networks in place and a hierarchy of who can talk to whom. This enables efficient and timely communication of information and also stops unnecessary messages being relayed to the driver, allowing him to concentrate on driving.

Each car has his own specific 'race' or 'driver' channel allocated and this is used by the driver and his race engineer. One or two others in the pits, such as the team principals, may have the ability to transmit on this channel but they will rarely speak on it. Key members of the team will sit on the pitwall and they are linked via an intercom system. Drivers are not permitted to communicate with one another via the radio during the race so each of the race/driver channels is completely separate.

The engineers who support each car will often have a separate 'engineering' channel and some teams will have one 'engineering' channel per car. This allows the race engineer to communicate with the pitcrew without interrupting the driver and will be used to alert them to pitstop. This channel is often shared with the telemetry engineers but, again, some teams will chose to have separate 'telemetry' channels to provide instant feedback to the race engineer about how the car is performing. On top of all these, some top teams run 'management' channels to allow communications between the top personnel on key strategy decisions. The major engine suppliers, such as Renault and Honda, have their own radio channels, as do the tyre manufacturers.

With so many independent channels to run, and excessive demands for frequency allocations at the racetrack, Formula One teams make extensive use of CTCSS or DCS tones to create several channels from the small number of frequencies that can be assigned to them, in much the same way as a PMR community repeater will work. Almost every team is unique in the way in sets up its channels. Here are a couple of examples:

The Renault Team uses their radios in a conventional PMR repeater setup and at least five channels are available:

- Driver Channel 1: Driver #1 and his Race Engineer transmit on a mobile frequency (freq #1). This is then rebroadcast by the repeater on a single base frequency (freq #2). The driver and race engineer listen in on the base frequency (freq #2). Freq #1 and #2 use the same CTCSS tone.
- Driver Channel 2: Driver #2 and his Race Engineer transmit on a mobile frequency (freq #3). This is then rebroadcast by the repeater on a single base frequency (freq #4). The driver and race engineer listen in on the base frequency (freq #4). Freq #3 & #4 use the same CTCSS tone, which is different to that on Channel 1.
- Channel 3: This is a simplex engineering channel to allow all the engineers to talk to one another without the drivers hearing these communications. It uses yet another frequency (freq #5) and yet another CTCSS tone.
- Channel 4: This is a simplex channel used by the engine and telemetry engineers. The pitcrew and drivers don't need to hear this so it uses yet another frequency (freq #6) and CTCSS tone.
- Channel 5: This is used by the repeater system to rebroadcast both Driver channels on one frequency (freq #7). It takes its input from freq #1 and freq #3. This allows team personnel to listen into one frequency to hear both drivers. By transmitting on this channel, both drivers can be spoken to at the same time, the signal being repeated out on the respective Driver Channel base frequencies.

So, to run five channels, three of which are repeated to ensure good coverage, the Renault team needs seven different frequencies.

The Williams team does things differently, in particular for its race engineers:

- Driver #1 – Race Channel: Driver #1 and his Race Engineer transmit on a mobile frequency (freq #1) which is rebroadcast by the repeater on a single base frequency (freq #2). The driver and race engineer listen in on the base frequency (freq #2). To use this Race Channel the repeater must be accessed via the mobile freq (freq #1) with a specific CTCSS tone for the driver and DCS tone for the race engineer.
- Driver #1 – Engineering Channel: This is only used by the engineers for Driver #1. They transmit on the mobile frequency (freq #1) but with a specific DCS tone and it's rebroadcast by the repeater on freq #2, but with yet another CTCSS tone. Therefore, the driver does not hear what is being said on this channel as his radio is only set with the CTCSS tone to hear signals on the Race Channel.
- Driver #2 – Race Channel: Driver #2 and his Race Engineer transmit on a mobile frequency (freq #3), which is rebroadcast by the repeater on a single base frequency (freq #2). The driver and race engineer listen in on the base frequency (freq #4). To use this Race Channel, the repeater must be accessed via the mobile freq (freq #3) with a specific CTCSS tone for the driver and DCS tone for the race engineer.
- Driver #2 – Engineering Channel: This is only used by the engineers for Driver #2. They transmit on the mobile frequency (freq #3) but with a specific DCS tone and it's rebroadcast by the repeater on freq #4, but with yet another CTCSS tone. Therefore the driver does not hear what is being said on this channel as his radio is only set with the CTCSS tone to hear signals on the Race Channel.
- Management Channel: This is a simplex channel used by the senior team personnel. The pitcrew and drivers don't need to hear this so It uses yet another frequency (freq #5) and DCS tone. Sometimes this channel has a link to the repeater system that rebroadcasts signals from each of the two race channels and two engineering channels, all of which have separate CTCSS tones.

So Williams can run two independent engineering/telemetry channels but as they share frequencies with the race channels, engineering and driver conversations can't take place at the same time. In this case, five channels are created out of only five frequencies.

Once the demands of marketing, public relations and support team personnel are taken into account, it's easy to see how the requirement for many separate frequencies soon adds up. It has been known for one team to request up to fourteen separate frequencies for its use at one event!

Trunked networks have been used by the Formula One officials (FIA) and TV crews (FOCA) in the past but they are not favoured by the current racing teams. The now obsolete Prost Grand Prix Teamt used an MPT1327 trunked radio system from 1999 to 2001 but it is understood there were several problems with it, in particular, with the time taken to initiate a call between each radio unit given the hostile radio environment in which Formula One operates.

Recently the FIA have begun using TETRA handsets for communications at the Grand Prix around the world. It is likely that other users at Grand Prix races will move to TETRA in the future as the technology becomes more established.

To date, most teams have stayed away from digital radios given the cost and sometimes degraded voice quality associated with these systems; with signals sometimes sounding 'robotic' and unnatural. Digital radios will often fail to work if there isn't a good signal path between driver and the pits, which can sometimes happen at racetracks where the terrain is difficult, particularly when the weather is bad. Analogue radio signals will just tend to 'fade' in these conditions.

Frequencies

Over the years, Formula One teams have shared their radio equipment with conventional PMR users and their radio bands too. The most common bands in use have been VHF High band (165-173 MHz) and the UHF band (453-470 MHz). Increasingly the VHF Mid band (158-165 MHz) has been used for motorsport events but this too has become overloaded. As these bands have become more congested and the emergency services have vacated their parts of the spectrum, there has been a trend to allocate these to the Formula One teams. Half duplex links are used for driver-to-pit links and simplex links are adequate for the engineer's channels in the pitlane.

Formula One teams are also making more use of VHF frequencies for their pit-to-driver links. That's because they can use slightly higher-powered radios and VHF is more effective than UHF when genuine line-of-sight between the car and the pitlane aerials can't be achieved. Also, the VHF band tends to be less congested at a race, especially with so many (UHF) TV/media frequencies in use. UHF is still favoured for the close range communications between pit crews in the garage as these signals are more effective at penetrating buildings.

A relatively new idea for Formula One communications is the adoption of cross-band repeaters. Often found in other fields, a cross band repeater works in a similar way to a conventional PMR repeater but it differs in that it receives on one band (say UHF) and then rebroadcasts on another band (say VHF) or the other way around. This system works well for Formula One teams because it allows the team personnel to use UHF radios while the car can be fitted with a VHF radio. Drivers and engineers can still talk with one another via the repeater and subaudible tones can be used to create engineering and driver channels on the same frequency just as before. In a cross-band repeater setup, the driver transmits and receives on only one frequency (VHF) and the engineers transmit and receive on only one frequency (UHF). The subaudible tone used with each of the transmissions is used by the repeater to determine whether the signal is rebroadcast on the other band or not.

The actual frequencies used by Formula One teams can vary, sometimes considerably, from race to race. Each team will generally design its system to fit in with the band-plan used in the country where the team is based. The government will allocate a set of frequencies and the team will generally stick with these frequencies for the entire season. Before each race, each team will apply to the host nation's regulatory authority for frequencies. They tend to be allocated as requested but sometimes a frequency that's available in, for example, England might be used by a taxi company in France. It's in the interests of the teams to keep changes to a minimum. The more frequency changes a team needs to make to its radios during the season, the more work its engineers have to do to prepare and test everything to make sure it works. If new frequencies have not been tested correctly, there is an increased risk that there will be interference from the on-board telemetry radios.

In general, team frequencies do not vary by more than a few MHz between each race throughout the season. The teams will also try to keep to roughly the same frequencies from year to year as they will know what worked well at a previous event, but this can be influenced by new users at the host track or a change in the team's radio equipment. Formula One test teams will also try to maintain the same frequencies throughout the year and as they travel from track to track. However, while the frequencies will be similar, rarely do the test team and race teams use the same frequencies at a particular venue. It has been known for some very unusual frequencies to be used, including some in the ex-emergency services section and even one in the marine band!

This table shows some of the recent frequencies used by racing teams:

Team	Radio System	Recent Frequencies (MHz)	
		Repeater	Mobile
Ferrari	Ascom Linked-Radio Repeater	165.01250	170.38750
	Mobiles and Repeaters use	164.80000	152.50000
	146 - 172 MHz	153.72500	167.52500
McLaren	Kenwood Cross-Band Repeater	147.63750	450.22500
	Race Channels 147 - 157 MHz	152.37500	451.66875
	Engineers 450 - 460 MHz	153.61250	454.42500
Williams	Kenwood Repeater	164.46250	169.43750
	Mobiles 159 - 160 MHz & 168 -170 MHz	163.63750	159.13750
	Repeated on 163 -165 MHz	164.33125	169.48750
Renault	Motorola Repeater	458.13750	468.00000
	Mobiles 467 - 469 MHz	458.26250	468.25000
	Repeated on 457 - 460 MHz	459.68750	468.52500
BAR	Kenwood Repeater	457.45625	467.51250
	Mobiles 467 - 469 MHz	457.27500	467.45625
	Repeated on 452 - 459 MHz	457.43125	467.46875
Sauber	Kenwood Repeater	455.87500	460.37500
	Mobiles & Repeaters use 455 - 462 MHz	460.37500	461.27500
Red Bull	Kenwood Repeater	453.48750	459.91250
Racing	Mobiles 459 - 467 MHz	454.67500	466.01250
	Repeated on 453 - 456 MHz	454.75000	462.01250
Toyota	Kenwood Repeater	461.23750	451.61250
	Mobiles 450 - 456 MHz	464.65000	454.72500
	Repeated on 460 - 469 MHz	464.60000	454.88750
Jordan	Yaesu Cross-Band Repeater	146.18750	442.56875
	Race Channels 146 - 170 MHz	151.27500	472.73750
	Engineers 440 - 473 MHz	146.23750	440.82500
Minardi	Kenwood Repeater	164.87500	159.22500
	Mobiles 158 - 163 MHz	164.53750	160.41250
	Repeated on 163 - 165 MHz	164.03750	158.26250

Security
Given the competitive nature of the sport, Formula One teams closely guard their tactics and strategy for the races. This also means that the teams are usually very security conscious when using their radios. All teams are aware that the opposition may be listening in so

they rarely discuss car setups in detail or race tactics nor do they give much advanced warning of making a pit stop. In fact, the amount of information passed from pit to driver throughout the race can sometimes be very small indeed, increasing around pit stops or if the car has a problem. Drivers will tend to transmit very little, perhaps only calling for car changes before a pit stop.

Surprisingly, there are very few teams that use any form of scrambling or encryption to protect their voice communications. Some top teams, including Williams and McLaren, used simple voice-inversion scrambling during the late 1990's but it degraded voice quality on the radio and given the ease with which the signals could be unscrambled, it added almost no security. Also, as any CTCSS tones would also be inverted on the radio channel, these could not be used with voice inversion modules and, therefore, the repeater systems were more prone to interference.

In 2005, only three race teams protected their radio signals. The Jordan team have been successfully using an effective voice-inversion scrambling module with their radios since 2002. This system works by mixing all the voice frequencies with a single set frequency, the inversion point. The voice frequencies below the inversion point are moved higher in the voice spectrum and the ones above moved lower. This gives voices a distinctive 'Donald Duck' sound. The signal is unscrambled by mixing it with a signal at the same inversion point. Jordan uses this module with DCS tones and, therefore, their repeater systems are less prone to interference problems.

Ferrari operates the most secure radio in the pitlane. It is the only digital radio to be used by any of the Formula One teams. It's based on a system developed for the Swiss Army and uses a sophisticated 128-bit encryption algorithm to protect its communications. While it is a true digital system, the radios also have the ability to operate as a standard analogue radios transmitting on Narrowband FM.

During 2004, the McLaren team tested a digital encryption module with their analogue VHF radios and they were obviously happy with the results as they have now adopted it. For the 2005 season, the team has been using the "McLaren Special II" radio specially built for them by Kenwood. The system, which employs a digital 'white noise' module and is thought to be based on the APCO-25 standard, is installed in the VHF TK-780 car radios and TK-380 pitcrew radios.

Telemetry Signals

While there have been very few fundamental changes to the pit-to-car radio links over the years, the radio telemetry links have changed significantly. In the early years, these links would be limited to a single microwave link, which would download a burst of data each time the car passed the pits. While this helped the engineers, the data was always one or two laps old and not very useful if a major problem developed suddenly. What the teams needed was a real-time data feed, so several low data-rate transmitters were added to the cars for the most vital engine data. These would operate in the UHF (450-473 MHz) band at up to 9.6kbps.

Today, the telemetry links have advanced considerably. All teams run at least one high-speed wideband telemetry link from the car to the pit. These links can operate at up to 4 Mbps using GMSK signalling and they provide real-time or near real-time information. Near real-time links will be set up when there is not a constantly clear line-of sight link from the car to the pits and the telemetry system is then programmed to store and forward the data when the path is clear. This configuration can be set up during test runs of the car round the track to determine blind spots in the coverage. The burst transmission principle can also be used as the car passes the pits to ensure a complete download of data is achieved on every lap. Given the need for the high data rates, a large bandwidth is required and so these links are to be found in the microwave L-band and S-band.

There are three telemetry systems manufacturers in Formula One today. Most signals can be found in the 1.45 GHz or 1.65 GHz range, while the Pi system used by Red Bull Racing, BAR and Williams uses the 3 - 4.25 GHz band. As the telemetry data records every aspect of how a car is performing, it is highly likely that all teams encrypt this signal to keep its content secret from the prying eyes of rival teams.

The Future
The future for Formula One communications is very hard to predict. All teams regularly update their radio systems and are always on the look out for the tiniest of advantages over their competitors. This will include their communications too. New rules made by the governing body mean that the broadcasting of the team communications will probably become more frequent and as the public are given greater access to their communications, teams will forced to move towards systems which offer greater clarity so that it's easier for everyone to understand what is being said on the radio.

As advances in wireless technologies are made and systems like TETRA become more popular, it is probable that teams will also move in this direction. This is likely to be driven not only by the teams wanting better radio links but also by the communications companies wanting to demonstrate their latest hi-tech products to the public

---

Silverstone 2005 Grand Prix
There is an excellent group (http://sports.groups.yahoo.com/group/f1scanner) on Yahoo. It has many members who are experts at following Grand Prix communications around the world and I am grateful to member AB for allowing me to list the frequencies that he collected while he was at the Silverstone 2005 Grand Prix. It's a very good example of how much radio traffic there is at one of these meetings and it also shows just how important subaudible tones are to successful race car communications.

(R = Race Channel, RE = Race Engineer, D = Driver, E = Engineers)

Car	Driver	Team	Repeater	Tone	Mobile	Tone
1	MSC	Ferrari	164.8000	DIGITAL	170.4000	DIGITAL
2	BAR	Ferrari	153.7250	DIGITAL	159.0125	DIGITAL
3	BUT	BAR	457.3500	110.9 R	467.3250	DCS 071RE
4	SAT	BAR	457.4375	107.2 R	467.5625	118.8 D
4	SAT	BAR	457.4375	110.9 E	467.5625	DCS 446 RE
5	ALO	Renault	458.2500	97.4	467.9125	97.4
6	FIS	Renault	457.9375	85.4	467.5375	85.4
7	WEB	Williams	164.1625	77.0 R	169.4875	97.4 D
7	WEB	Williams	164.1625	88.5 E	169.4875	DCS 065 RE

Car	Driver	Team	Repeater	Tone	Mobile	Tone
7	WEB	Williams			169.4875	DCS 271E
8	HEI	Williams	163.6750	151.4 R	168.5000	114.8 D
8	HEI	Williams	163.6750	127.3 E	168.5000	DCS 152 RE
8	HEI	Williams			168.5000	DCS 115 E
9	RAI	McLaren	149.3750	DIGITAL	459.6875	DIGITAL
10	MOY	McLaren	147.6000	DIGITAL	458.4500	DIGITAL
35	DLR	McLaren	153.6375	DIGITAL	454.2000	DIGITAL
11	VIL	Sauber	457.5000	DCS 132 R	Unknown	
11	VIL	Sauber	457.5000	DCS 546 E	Unknown	
12	MAS	Sauber	460.3750	DCS 446 R	Unknown	
12	MAS	Sauber	460.3750	DCS 662 E	Unknown	
14	COU	Red Bull	454.7375	151.4 R	463.4375	110.9 D
14	COU	Red Bull	454.7375	127.3 E		
15	KLI	Red Bull	454.4875	77.0 R	461.3875	97.4 D
15	KLI	Red Bull	454.4875	88.5 E	461.3875	DCS 065 RE
15	KLI	Red Bull			461.3875	DCS 271 E
37	LIU	Red Bull	452.7500	103.5 R	463.7000	82.5 D
37	LIU	Red Bull	452.7500	103.5 R	463.7000	DCS 465 E
16	TRU	Toyota	461.2375	69.3 R	451.6625	85.4 R
16	TRU	Toyota			451.6625	71.9 E
17	RSC	Toyota	454.7250	88.5 R	462.2625	67.0 R
17	RSC	Toyota	454.7250	103.5 E		
38	ZON	Toyota	454.5500	118.8 R	464.2500	Unknown
38	ZON	Toyota	454.5500	DCS 411 E	464.2500	Unknown
18	MON	Jordan	169.6500	DCS 343 R	472.7375	DCS 364 R
19	KAR	Jordan	146.1875	DCS 114 R	442.5625	DCS 172 R
39	DOO	Jordan	156.3625	DCS 664 R	449.5125	Unknown
20	FRI	Minardi	164.5375	94.8 R	159.2500	131.8 D
20	FRI	Minardi			159.2500	DCS 074 E
21	ALB	Minardi	165.0125	103.5 R	160.4125	DCS 134 RE
21	ALB	Minardi	165.0125	135.5 E	160.4125	DCS 223 E

Some of the teams also used:

Ferrari
162.70000 Ferrari Race Engineers (DIGITAL)
165.07500 Ferrari Race Engineers (DIGITAL)
167.52500 Ferrari Race Engineers (DIGITAL)

Renault:
458.3875 Renault Common Channel (114.8)
468.5250 Renault Engineers (69.3)

McLaren
152.000 McLaren Hospitality (DCS 023)

Jordan
440.4625 Jordan Engineers (DCS 125)
470.6250 Jordan Engineers (DCS Unknown)
All Jordan channels are voice inverted.

BAR-Honda
450.0250 Honda (151.4)
450.2750 BAR Engineers (Sato) (146.2)
450.7750 BAR Engineers (Button) (210.7)

Toyota
462.3125 Toyota Engineers [DCS Unknown]
464.0500 Toyota Engineers (82.5)

Red Bull Racing
442.1500 Red Bull Engineers (110.9Hz)

Unknowns (Maybe Teams)
451.6250 F1 Team Engineers Discussing Tyres
463.13750 Unknown F1 Team and Driver
467.75625 Unknown F1 Team Radio Check

Various other frequencies AB noted at this event:

121.07500 Silverstone ATC
130.62500 Silverstone ATC
135.97500 Blue Eagles Helicopter Team
147.30000 German - Mercedes? (233.6)
152.50000 Clothing Vendor (123.0)
152.50000 Ferrari Engineers
153.35000 French (DCS 023)
153.53125 French (DCS Unknown)
153.71250 St John Ambulance (186.2)
158.78750 Marshals - Posts (173.8)
159.18750 Spectator Marshsls (82.5)
159.40000 FIA and Medical Centre (94.8)
159.45000 Silverstone User (110.9)
159.48750 Silverstone User (69.3)
159.50000 Clothing Vendor (123.0)
162.80000 Medic Callsigns (94.8)
163.28750 Marshals - Posts (173.8)
163.35000 Media? (94.8)
163.67500 Silverstone User
163.68750 Silverstone Race Control (82.5)
163.85000 Silverstone Traffic Control (151.4)
163.90000 Marshals - Posts (94.8): Bridge Callsigns
163.92500<>159.425 (77.0) Marshals - Posts
163.95000 Silvertone: Gates (110.9)
164.03750 Silverstone Traffic Control/AIR1 Helicopter (69.3)
164.08750 Silvertone: Gates (77.0)
164.15000 Silverstone Traffic Control/AIR1 Helicopter
164.23750 MPT1327 Control Channel
164.46250 Silverstone - Unknown User
164.51250 (DCS)<>162.950 (DCS 043) German User
167.18750 Silverstone User (123.0)
167.30000 German User (127.3)
167.73750 St John Ambulance (156.7)
167.97500 Silverstone Marshals (173.8)
168.95000 TV O/B Frequency
169.08750 Silverstone User (114.8)
169.10000 Silverstone User (114.8)
173.05000 Silverstone User
446.21250 Silverstone User (103.5)
446.40000 Media Frequency
446.42500 TV Director
446.47500 TV Director
446.50000 BBC Radio 5 Live O/B
446.60000 TV Director
447.40625 Silverstone User (69.3)
448.00000 Dutch TV
448.40000 MPT1327 Trunked Channel
449.31250 St John Ambulance (DCS 431)
450.47500 MPT1327 Control Channel
450.77500 Continuous Data

450.95000 Open Carrier
450.98750 Open Carrier
452.67500<>466.575 (131.8) Ofcom Radio Technicans
453.92500 Silverstone Security (156.7)
453.97500 Silverstone User (71.9)
455.00000 Media
455.18750 Media
455.77500 Media
456.07500 Media
456.16250 ITV TV Director
456.67500 Silverstone User
456.72500 Silverstone User (123.0)
457.25000 Media
457.25000 Speaking Clock - Media? (67.0)
457.30000 Open Carrier
457.31250 Silverstone TV Broadcast
457.32500 Silverstone TV Broadcast
458.60000 Silverstone User
459.96250 MPT1327 Trunked Channel
461.37500 Silverstone Car Parking (136.5)
461.46250 Silverstone Car Parking
461.46250 Paddock Security (218.1)
461.80000 MPT1327 Trunked Channel
461.85000 Silverstone User
461.86250 German User (141.3)
461.88750 Silverstone User
461.88750 Silverstone User
461.93750 MPT1327 Trunked Channel
462.02500 Silverstone User
462.17500 F1 Team Hospitality (103.5)
462.31250 French User (DCS Unknown)
462.42500 Silverstone Race Control
462.95000 BAR?
463.87500 Silverstone User
467.21250 BAR Engineers (162.2)
467.51250 Foreign Media (DCS023)
467.66250 Unknown (88.5)
469.22500 Foreign Media
485.00000 RTL
485.79000 ORF
485.95000 RTL
604.75000 ORF
1618.00000 F1 Team 6 MHz Allocation
1620.00000 Media Broadcast Allocation
1624.00000 F1 Team 6 MHz Allocation
1628.00000 F1 Team 6 MHz Allocation
1632.00000 F1 Team 6 MHz Allocation
3180.00000 Downlink Allocation
3210.00000 Downlink Allocation
15266.0000 F1 Team Allocation

AB's impressive list certainly shows that a major motor racing event such as the Silverstone Grand Prix can be a fertile hunting ground for frequency collectors and I would like to thank him once again for allowing me to reproduce it here.

Ofcom UHF Band I and Band II Channel Allocations

The channel numbers and frequencies listed here have been allocated by Ofcom and are a useful place to start when trying to find a specific user. The ones marked Transitory can be used anywhere in the UK, much like SRBR. Users have to apply for a licence to use these frequencies and they are supposed to notify the local Ofcom office of the time and place of intended use but this is often ignored. Anyone who wants more information on frequency allocations and users can write to the OFCOM Contact Centre at Riverside House, 2a Southwark Bridge Road, London SE1 9HA or phone them on 020 7981 3040. Better still, visit their web site at www.ofcom.org.uk and have a browse through the wealth of documents there.

Knowing these allocations makes finding individual users much easier. For instance, if you are looking for the frequencies used by a large car factory, the first place to look would be On Site Dual Allocations. UHF I allocations are usually only used in certain large cities, so for most parts of the UK, UHF II is used.

Let's assume you are in Luton and looking for the frequencies used by your local car manufacturer. Start your scanner searching and watch out for it stopping on frequencies in the UHF II allocation. Let's say it stops on 456.025 and 453.0625. As you can see from the list, these are On Site 15 Dual and On Site 2 Dual respectively. Now you know that, you also know it's worth listening to them as they are on site allocations, so listen to both frequencies and try to hear if they are talking about anything to do with car production. It's a bit hit and miss but there is a good chance the site you're looking at will be using one of these frequencies. If, during searching, the scanner stopped on other frequencies that are not normal on site allocations, take a note of them and check them later. Most big companies usually have a varied selection of channels available, so don't just find one frequency and think that's all there is. Check the On Site Single Allocations list as well because they will almost certainly also have at least one of these allocated to them. Then think about the users on the site. If it were a car factory, it would have frequencies used by production, maybe one for management or administration, others for security, maintenance, catering and so on. At some sites it has been found that if a large number of on site duplex channels are in use on site or in the area, other allocations such as Wide Area Shared will be given to the user even though these are usually used by taxis, couriers and council services.

Community repeaters are not listed here because these are easily identified by the number of different users on one frequency. Small shops, restaurants, clubs, factories and so on will use almost any frequency in the On Site Single Allocations, short term hire, SRBR and PMR446 bands.

There are also VHF On Site Duplex allocations. The ones shown as On Site Dual are the only official on site dual vhf frequencies but at some sites, various other frequencies do crop up. It's a good idea to check the official ones first but don't be surprised if you find they're using something totally out of band.

VHF

MHz	MHz	Radio Users
165.02500	169.82500	
165.07500	169.87500	
165.08750	169.88750	
165.16250	169.96250	On Site 32 Dual
165.18750	169.98750	On Site 33 Dual
165.21250	170.01250	On Site 34 Dual
165.23750	170.03750	
165.28750	170.08750	
166.71250	171.51250	
166.76250	171.56250	On Site 35 Dual
166.83750	171.63750	
167.03750	171.83750	On Site 35 Dual

UHF 1

MHz	MHz	Radio Users
440.02500	425.52500	On Site 1 Dual
440.17500	425.67500	On Site 2 Dual
440.20000	425.70000	On Site 3 Dual
440.22500	425.72500	On Site 4 Dual
440.27500	425.77500	On Site 5 Dual
440.30000	425.80000	On Site 6 Dual
440.32500	425.82500	On Site 7 Dual
440.35000	425.85000	On Site 8 Dual
440.37500	425.87500	On Site 9 Dual
440.47500	425.97500	On Site 10 Dual
440.50000	426.00000	On Site 11 Dual
440.52500	426.02500	On Site 12 Dual
440.55000	426.05000	On Site 13 Dual
440.86250	426.36250	On Site 14 Dual
440.88750	426.38750	On Site 15 Dual
440.90000	426.40000	On Site 16 Dual
440.91250	426.41250	On Site 17 Dual
440.93750	426.43750	Wide Area Shared Dual
440.95000	426.45000	On Site 18 Dual
441.01250	426.51250	On Site Dual
441.03750	426.53750	On Site Dual
441.07500	426.57500	On Site Dual
441.11250	426.61250	On Site 20 Dual
441.16250	426.66250	On Site Dual
441.18750	426.68750	On Site Dual
441.23750	426.73750	On Site Dual
441.26250	426.76250	On Site Dual
441.28750	426.78750	On Site Dual
441.31250	426.81250	On Site Dual

441.3375	426.8375	On Site Dual
441.7000	427.2000	On Site Dual
441.8375	427.3375	On Site Dual
441.9000	427.4000	Widearea Shared Dual
441.9125	427.4125	On Site Dual
441.9250	427.4250	On Site Dual
441.9375	427.4375	On Site Dual
441.9625	427.4625	On Site Dual
441.9875	427.4875	On Site Dual
442.0000	427.5000	On Site Dual
442.0125	427.5125	On Site Dual
442.5250	428.0250	On Site 26 Dual
442.5500	428.0500	On Site Dual
442.5625	428.0625	On Site Dual
442.6000	428.1000	On Site Dual
442.6250	428.1250	On Site 30 Dual
442.6500	428.1500	On Site 31 Dual
442.6750	428.1750	On Site Dual
442.7000	428.2000	On Site Dual
442.7250	428.2250	On Site Dual
442.7500	428.2500	On Site 34 Dual
442.7750	428.2750	On Site 39 Dual
442.8750	428.3750	Wide Area Shared 43 Dual
442.9000	428.4000	Wide Area Shared 45 Dual
442.9625	428.4625	On Site Dual
443.0000	428.5000	On Site Dual
443.0250	428.5250	On Site 41 Dual
443.0500	428.5500	On Site 43 Dual
443.0750	428.5750	On Site Dual
443.1000	428.6000	On Site Dual
443.1250	428.6250	On Site Dual
443.1625	428.6625	Wide Area Shared Dual
443.2500	428.7500	On Site Dual
443.4000	428.9000	On Site Dual
443.4125	428.9125	On Site Dual
443.4500	428.9500	On Site 61 Dual
443.4750	428.9750	On Site 53 Dual
445.6500	425.1500	On Site Dual
445.6750	425.1750	On Site Dual
445.7000	425.2000	On Site Dual
445.7250	425.2250	On Site 57 Dual
445.7500	425.2500	On Site 58 Dual
445.7750	425.2750	On Site 59 Dual
445.8750	425.3750	On Site Dual
445.8000	425.3000	On Site 60 Dual
445.9750	425.4750	Wide Area Shared 62 Dual

446.00000	On Site 1 Single
446.00625	Ch.1 PMR446
446.01250	On Site 2 Single
446.01875	Ch.2 PMR446
446.02500	On Site 3 Single
446.03125	Ch.3 PMR446
446.03750	On Site 4 Single
446.04375	Ch.4 PMR446
446.05000	On Site 5 Single
446.05625	Ch.5 PMR446
446.06250	On Site 6 Single
446.06875	Ch.6 PMR446
446.07500	On Site 7 Single
446.08125	Ch.7 PMR446
446.08750	On Site 8 Single
446.09375	Ch.8 PMR446
446.10000	On Site 9 Single
446.11250	On Site 10 Single
446.12500	On Site 11 Single
446.13750	On Site 12 Single
446.15000	On Site 13 Single
446.16250	On Site 14 Single
446.17500	On Site 15 Single
446.18750	On Site 16 Single
446.20000	On Site 17 Single
446.21250	On Site 18 Single
446.22500	On Site 19 Single
446.23750	On Site 20 Single
446.25000	On Site 21 Single
446.26250	On Site 22 Single
446.27500	On Site 23 Single
446.28750	On Site 24 Single
446.30000	On Site 25 Single
446.31250	On Site 26 Single
446.32500	On Site 27 Single
446.33750	On Site 28 Single
446.35000	On Site 29 Single
446.36250	On Site 30 Single
446.37500	On Site 31 Single
446.38750	On Site 32 Single
446.40000	On Site 33 Single
447.63750	On Site Single
447.65000	On Site 34 Single
447.66250	On Site 35 Single
447.68750	On Site 37 Single
447.71250	On Site 38 Single

447.72500		On Site 39 Single
447.78750		On Site 41 Single
447.81250		On Site 42 Single
447.82500		On Site 43 Single

UHF II

MHz	MHz	Radio Users
453.02500	459.52500	On Site 1 Dual
453.05000	459.55000	Wide Area Shared Dual
453.06250	459.56250	On Site 2 Dual
453.07500		On Site 31 Single
453.07500	459.57500	Split Dual 1
453.08750	459.58750	On Site 3 Dual
453.10000	459.60000	On Site 4 Dual
453.11250	459.61250	On Site 5 Dual
453.12500		On Site 32 Single
453.12500	459.62500	Split Dual 2
453.15000	459.65000	Wide Area Shared Dual
453.17500	459.67500	On Site 6 Dual
453.20000	459.60000	Wide Area Shared Dual
453.25000	459.75000	Wide Area Shared 4 Dual
453.35000		On Site 35 Single
453.35000	459.85000	Split Dual 5
453.45000		On Site 38 Single
453.45000	459.95000	Split Dual 8
453.47500	459.97500	On Site 7 Dual
453.50000	460.00000	On Site 8 Dual
453.52500		On Site 39 Single
453.55000	460.05000	National 4 Dual
453.55000		UK General Use
453.57500		On Site 40 Single
453.60000	460.10000	On Site 9 Dual
453.62500		On Site 41 Single
453.65000	460.15000	Split Dual 12
453.65000		On Site 42 Single
453.67500	460.17500	Split Dual 13
453.67500		On Site 43 Single
453.75000	460.25000	On Site 11 Dual
453.77500	460.27500	On Site 12 Dual
453.87500	460.37500	Split Dual 15
453.87500		On Site 45 Single
453.90000	460.40000	National 5 Dual
453.90000		UK General Use
453.92500	460.42500	On Site 14 Dual
453.97500	460.47500	Wide Area Shared 7 Dual
456.00000	461.50000	National 18 Dual Security Channel

456.02500	461.52500	On Site 15 Dual
456.05000	461.55000	Wide Area Shared 8 Dual
456.26250	461.76250	National 35 Dual
456.35000	461.85000	On Site 16 Dual
456.37500	461.87500	National 38 Dual
456.40000	461.90000	National 39 Dual
456.41250	461.91250	National 40 Dual
456.42500	461.92500	National 41 Dual
456.45000	461.95000	National 42 Dual
456.47500	461.97500	Wide Area Shared 9 Dual
456.60000	462.10000	On Site 18 Dual
456.62500		On Site 48 Single
456.62500	462.12500	Split Dual 18
456.65000	462.15000	On Site 19 Dual
456.67500	462.17500	On Site 20 Dual
456.72500	462.22500	Split Dual 19
456.72500		On Site 49 Dual
456.82500	462.32500	On Site 23 Dual
456.87500	462.37500	On Site 24 Dual
456.90000		On Site 52 Single
456.90000	462.40000	Split Dual 22
456.97500	462.47500	Split Dual 23
459.57500		On Site 1 Single
459.62500		On Site 2 Single
459.85000		On Site 5 Single
459.95000		On Site 8 Single
460.02500		On Site 9 Single
460.15000		On Site 12 Single
460.17500		On Site 13 Single
460.37500		On Site 15 Single
461.28750		UK General 1 [Transitory]
461.31250		On Site 17 Single
461.32500		On Site 18 Single
461.33750		On Site 19 Single
461.35000		On Site 20 Single
461.36250		On Site 21 Single
461.37500		UK General 2 [Transitory]
461.38750		On Site 22 Single
461.40000		On Site 23 Single
461.45000		UK General 3 [Transitory]
461.46250		On Site 24 Single
462.10000		UK General
462.12500		On Site 26 Single
462.22500		On Site 27 Single
462.40000		On Site 30 Single

More Useful Frequencies

Experienced frequency collectors know that no frequency list is ever complete and finished. Things change all the time as bands are re-allocated, new technology is introduced and users buy new equipment. A good example of this is the way most police services moved away from their analogue frequencies when they bought a new secure digital system. The latest news is that ambulance services and fire brigades are set to join them. Similarly, the RAF police are no longer to be found around 79 MHz, London buses have gone from their usual place on 440 MHz and so on.

All this makes life interesting for avid frequency collectors but it can be confusing for the newcomer to the hobby. He might think that all he has to do is buy a frequency guide and he'll have a definitive list of everything he can hear. He won't; he'll have a list that was up to date on the day it was printed and as comprehensive as the publisher could make it. What he will not have is a complete list of all the things he can hear in his area because there are just too many frequencies to fit into any book. What a good guide will do is to show the beginner where to start looking by grouping together various services and users. Beginners can also use a frequency guide to see for themselves how users tend to be grouped together. For example, if you look through this book and find that several pages contain scores of frequencies for taxi companies, there's a good chance that your local taxi company will use a similar frequency. As you become more experienced, you'll notice that there are patterns in the frequency allocations and although you might not know the spot frequency of the user you're looking for, you will know which part of the spectrum to look in. One of the first things a beginner should do is to familiarize himself with the frequencies in this section because they are in widespread use throughout the country.

Short Term Hire Frequencies

Short term hire frequencies are used by those who may need radios for a single event that's on for just one day or for few weeks or the user might hire the same radios for many months. To use these frequencies, the end user simply contacts a radio supplier who holds the licence and who should notify the local OFCOM office of the end user.

Six dual frequencies were recently allocated for on site and event trunked radio networks but those duals are often illegally used as single allocations. The most common users of those extra singles are film and television production companies.

There are also several VHF short term hire frequencies set aside for construction companies but these are often used in normal VHF short term sets as well.

72.3750		Short Term Hire Single
85.8750	72.3750	Short Term Hire Dual
85.8750		Short Term Hire Single
158.7875		Short Term Hire Single
159.1875		Short Term Hire Single Construction
159.2500		Short Term Hire Single Construction
159.3500		Short Term Hire Single Construction
159.4875		Short Term Hire Single
159.5000		Short Term Hire Single
159.5875		Short Term Hire Single
159.6250		Short Term Hire Single

159.6875		Short Term Hire Single
163.2875	158.7875	Short Term Hire Dual
163.2875		Short Term Hire Single
163.6875	159.1875	Short Term Hire Dual Construction
163.6875		Short Term Hire Single Construction
163.7500	159.250	Short Term Hire Dual Construction
163.7500		Short Term Hire Single Construction
163.8500	159.350	Short Term Hire Dual Construction
163.8500		Short Term Hire Single Construction
163.9000	159.400	Short Term Hire Dual
163.9000		Short Term Hire Single
163.9250	159.425	Short Term Hire Dual
163.9250		Short Term Hire Single
163.9875		Short Term Hire Single
164.0000		Short Term Hire Single
164.0875		Short Term Hire Single
164.1250		Short Term Hire Single
164.1875		Short Term Hire Single
169.0125		Short Term Hire Single
169.1375		Short Term Hire Single
169.1625		Short Term Hire Single
169.1875		Short Term Hire Single
456.0125		Short Term Hire
456.0125	461.5125	Short Term Hire Trunked
456.3375		Short Term Hire
456.3375	461.8375	Short Term Hire Trunked
456.3875	461.8875	Short Term Hire Dual
456.3875		Short Term Hire Single
456.4625		Short Term Hire
456.4625	461.9625	Short Term Hire Trunked
456.5625		Short Term Hire
456.5625	462.0625	Short Term Hire Trunked
456.6875		Short Term Hire
456.6875	462.1875	Short Term Hire Trunked
456.8625		Short Term Hire Single
456.9625		Short Term Hire
456.9625	462.4625	Short Term Hire Trunked
456.9875	462.4875	Short Term Hire Dual
456.9875		Short Term Hire Single
461.5125		Short Term Hire
461.8375		Short Term Hire
461.8875		Short Term Hire Single
461.9625		Short Term Hire
462.0625		Short Term Hire
462.1875		Short Term Hire
462.3625		Short Term Hire Single
462.4625		Short Term Hire
462.4750		Short Term Hire Single
462.4875		Short Term Hire Single

Parking and Demonstration

A parking and demonstration frequency is one that has been allocated to a radio supplier so that he can use it to demonstrate a radio system to a customer or as a place where he can park a customer while he is waiting for Ofcom to supply a long term frequency. Officially, this means these frequencies will only be in use for a month or so but we have found users who have been parked on these frequencies for more than 10 years.

The same six dual frequencies used for short term hire trunking are also available for parking and demonstration trunking.

68.6250		Parking & Demonstration
72.3750		Parking & Demonstration
82.1250	68.6250	Parking & Demonstration
82.1250		Parking & Demonstration
85.8750	72.3750	Parking & Demonstration
159.4500		Parking & Demonstration
163.9500	159.4500	Parking & Demonstration
163.9500		Parking & Demonstration
167.2000	172.0000	Parking & Demonstration
172.0000		Parking & Demonstration
426.0375		Parking & Demonstration
440.5375	426.0375	Parking & Demonstration
440.5375		Parking & Demonstration
456.0125	461.5125	Parking & Demonstration Trunked
456.3375	461.8375	Parking & Demonstration Trunked
456.4625	461.9625	Parking & Demonstration Trunked
456.5625	462.0625	Parking & Demonstration Trunked
456.6875	462.1875	Parking & Demonstration Trunked
456.9250	462.4250	Parking & Demonstration
456.9250		Parking & Demonstration
456.9625	462.4625	Parking & Demonstration Trunked
462.4250		Parking & Demonstration

UK General

The UK General license is nationwide and one license allows users access to all 15 frequencies although most users usually stay within one band. It also allows up to 5 watts output power and unlike other licenses, the price is the same no matter how many handhelds are used. This makes it ideal for users such as Woolworths and HMV stores as the one license will cover all their sites in the UK. Also, with this license security companies such as Showsec can travel anywhere in UK and use the same radios. For the same reason, frequencies in this section are also popular with private detective companies, DSS fraud squads, trading standards officers and various other government bodies who may need to conduct surveillance operations all over the country.

RA UK General 2002 Allocations

77.6875	86.3375	86.3500	86.3625	86.3750
164.0500	164.0625	169.0875	169.3125	173.0500
173.0625	173.0875	449.3125	449.4000	449.4750

Road Construction License

This license is very rarely used as most road projects use other frequencies in one of the previous sections or even unlicensed radios. Usually there are less than half a dozen road construction licenses allocated at any one time but if you want to check your local bypass construction, start with these frequencies.

82.5250	69.0250	Road Construction Traffic Management
163.0875	158.4875	Road Construction
163.3000	158.8000	Road Construction
163.3750	158.8750	Road Construction
163.5125	159.0125	Road Construction
163.6125	159.1125	Road Construction
165.0750	169.8750	Road Construction Resident Engineer

PMR446 and Other Common UK Frequencies

PMR446 is completely license free so there are many business and private users. Signals in this band crop up all over the country and users vary from crane operators to families shopping in Tesco. The signals don't travel very far, usually up to about 2 miles, because the output power is only 500 mw but this is a good band to start looking in because there are so many of these radios in use.

446.00625Ch.1	446.01875 Ch.2	446.03125 Ch.3	446.04375 Ch.4
446.05625 Ch.5	446.06875 Ch.6	446.08125 Ch.7	446.09375 Ch.8

In America they have several similar systems and the radios can be bought very cheaply in stores like Wal-Mart. Their frequencies make them illegal to use in the UK but because so many holidaymakers bring them back with them and also because unscrupulous dealers at car boot sales and flea markets are happy to sell them to anyone who wants a cheap walkie-talkie, they can be found in use throughout this country.

FRS

The unlicensed Family Radio Service is the most widely used public radio system in America, probably because radios can cost as little as $14.99 a pair in larger stores. It uses 14 simplex channels, some of which are also the first 7 channels of the GMRS system.

462.5625 Ch.1	462.5875 Ch.2	462.6125 Ch.3	462.6375 Ch.4
462.6625 Ch.5	462.6875 Ch.6	462.7125 Ch.7	467.5625 Ch.8
467.5875 Ch.9	467.6125 Ch.10	467.6375 Ch.11	467.6625 Ch.12
467.6875 Ch.13	467.7125 Ch.14		

GMRS

The American General Mobile Radio Service uses the above frequencies plus 16 more that are interleaved with those of FRS. Eight are for simplex and repeater outputs and eight for repeater inputs. Inputs and outputs are usually paired 5 MHz apart but any pairing of input/output frequencies is legal. An FCC license is required but this is easily obtained.

462.550	462.575	462.600	462.625
462.650	462.675	462.700	462.725
467.550	467.575	467.600	467.625
467.650	467.675	467.700	467.725

MURS

The Multi-Use Radio Service is an American VHF CB band where anyone can use the frequencies just as they can on 27 MHz.

| 151.820 | 151.880 | 151.940 | 154.570 | 154.600 |

BRS

The US Business Radio Service is a licensed radio service which was designed for the business user. It uses a system of dots and stars to identify its channels.

Red Dot	151.6250	Purple Dot	151.9550	Blue Dot	154.5700
Green Dot	154.6000	Brown Dot	464.5000	Yellow Dot	464.5500
J Dot	467.7625	K Dot	467.8125	Silver Star	467.8500
Gold Star	467.8750	Red Star	467.9000	Blue Star	467.9250

Others

In the UK, the forerunner of PMR446 was SRBR, Short Range Business Radio. This had an easy to obtain, cheap licence. Then, in December 2003, the license was withdrawn and it became illegal to use this band. Naturally, everyone who had a radio that operated on one of these frequencies just carried on using it. In fact, in recent years the number of users has been increasing so it's worth checking these three voice channels

| 461.2625 Ch.1 | 461.4750 Ch.2 | 461.4875 Ch.3 |

Before new channels were introduced to the UK General License in 2000, there were a few frequencies on the old license that were different to the current ones. The frequencies may have gone from the license but users haven't. They have been given until 2006 to move so you'll still find plenty of them using these old frequencies.

| 461.2875 | 461.3750 | 461.4500 |

Major Events Use of Radio Frequencies

If you're lucky enough to be able to attend a major event, it can be the ideal opportunity to collect some new frequencies. You'll find that at large sporting events, concerts, shows and other major events, short term hire and UK general frequencies are used a lot. At some events other frequencies will also be used. This is usually because the event is very large and there are so many people using short term hire and UK general frequencies that even with the use of subaudible tones there could still be clashes.

This is when Ofcom and a company called JFMG, the Joint Frequency Management Group, have to allocate other frequencies to be used for the organization and management of the event.

Ofcom will allocate them from a reserve pool of frequencies that are not normally licensed to any other user at the time and location of the event. They can allocate frequencies from any part of the spectrum for large events such as the Grand Prix, even from Home Office and MoD allocations.

Also, the frequencies shown in UHF I can be used, again as a mix of single/dual or trunked but they are not used as often as those in UHF II. In addition to UHF II, frequencies are occasionally drawn from a pool of reserved frequencies and sometimes on site or other allocations can be utilized if they are not already in use in the local area.

Usually UHF II is the first choice because there are quite a few 12.5 KHz channels interspersed with the main ones and they are held in reserve:

453.0125	459.6125	Single Or Dual Either Frequency
453.0375	459.5375	Single Or Dual Either Frequency
453.0500	459.5500	Single Or Dual Either Frequency
453.1875	459.6875	Single Or Dual Either Frequency
453.4125	459.9125	Single Or Dual Either Frequency
453.4625	459.9625	Single Or Dual Either Frequency
453.4875	459.9875	Single Or Dual Either Frequency
453.5125	460.0125	Single Or Dual Either Frequency
453.5375	460.0375	Single Or Dual Either Frequency
453.5875	460.0875	Single Or Dual Either Frequency
453.6375	460.1375	Single Or Dual Either Frequency
453.6625	460.1625	Single Or Dual Either Frequency
453.6875	460.1875	Single Or Dual Either Frequency
453.7375	460.2375	Single Or Dual Either Frequency
453.7875	460.2875	Single Or Dual Either Frequency
453.8375	460.3375	Single Or Dual Either Frequency
453.9375	460.4375	Single Or Dual Either Frequency
453.9500	460.4500	Single Or Dual Either Frequency
456.3000	461.8125	Single Or Dual Either Frequency
456.3125	461.8125	Single Or Dual Either Frequency
456.4875	461.9875	Single Or Dual Either Frequency
456.5875	462.0875	Single Or Dual Either Frequency
456.6375	462.1375	Single Or Dual Either Frequency
456.6625	462.1625	Single Or Dual Either Frequency
456.7125	462.2125	Single Or Dual Either Frequency
456.8125	462.3125	Single Or Dual Either Frequency
456.9125	462.4125	Single Or Dual Either Frequency
461.2750		Single
461.4125		Single
461.4250		Single
461.4375		Single

These are used at events like the London Marathon, large demonstrations and other big events across the UK.

Sometimes, for a specific event they will allow any frequency to be used, either single or as a repeater and it's not unknown for local community repeater frequencies, which are usually used by private mobile radio users, to be allocated for use as well. So a frequency on which you might normally hear a courier, a skip company or a security company could suddenly start to be used for events management.

Some events are so massive that frequencies have to be taken from a reserve in other bands. Then they usually use UHF I. Two big users of both UHF I and UHF II reserve frequencies were the Queens Golden Jubilee and the Commonwealth Games. They each used trunked networks on both bands.

Also, JFMG (www.jfmg.co.uk), whose prime responsibility is to allocate licenses for TV, radio and media outside broadcasts and studio links, will sometimes allocate frequencies from within their own bands for major events. So frequencies normally used only by the media can be used by events management/stewards/timekeepers and so on. In most cases they will use single and dual JFMG UHF short term allocations. These are known as PMSE, Programme Making and Special Event, allocations

At most events where the media are involved you will find these frequencies in use for TV and radio programme production and talkback sound gallery links although you might find other events users using them as well.

454.99375	468.36875	Short Term PMSE
455.00625	468.38125	Short Term PMSE
455.01875	468.04375	Short Term PMSE
455.03125	468.05625	Short Term PMSE
455.09375	468.39375	Short Term PMSE
455.10625	468.40625	Short Term PMSE
455.11875	468.41875	Short Term PMSE
455.13125	468.43125	Short Term PMSE
455.19375	468.01875	Short Term PMSE
455.20625	468.03125	Short Term PMSE
455.21875	468.49375	Short Term PMSE
455.23125	468.50625	Short Term PMSE
455.24375	468.16875	Short Term PMSE
455.25625	468.19375	Short Term PMSE
455.26875	468.18125	Short Term PMSE
455.28125	468.29375	Short Term PMSE
455.39375	468.33125	Short Term PMSE
455.40625	468.20625	Short Term PMSE
455.41875	468.30625	Short Term PMSE
455.43125	468.31875	Short Term PMSE
455.44375		Short Term PMSE
455.45625	468.55625	Short Term PMSE
457.25625	467.30625	Short Term PMSE
457.26875	467.31875	Short Term PMSE
457.28125	467.29375	Short Term PMSE
457.29375	467.40625	Short Term PMSE
457.30625	467.36875	Short Term PMSE
457.31875	467.48125	Short Term PMSE
457.33125	467.44375	Short Term PMSE
457.34375	467.38125	Short Term PMSE
457.35625	467.33125	Short Term PMSE
457.36875	467.35625	Short Term PMSE
457.39375	467.39375	Short Term PMSE
457.40625	467.34375	Short Term PMSE
457.41875	467.49375	Short Term PMSE
457.43125	467.46875	Short Term PMSE
457.44375	467.53125	Short Term PMSE
457.45625	467.51875	Short Term PMSE
457.46875	467.50625	Short Term PMSE
461.23750	468.52500	Short Term PMSE
461.25000	468.53750	Short Term PMSE

446.43125	PMSE Can Be Dual 467 MHz
446.44375	PMSE Can Be Dual 467 MHz
446.45625	PMSE Can Be Dual 467 MHz
446.46875	PMSE Can Be Dual 467 MHz
446.47500	PMSE Can Be Dual 467 MHz
446.48125	PMSE Can Be Dual 467 MHz
446.49375	PMSE Can Be Dual 467 MHz
446.50625	PMSE Can Be Dual 467 MHz
446.51875	PMSE Can Be Dual 467 MHz
446.53125	PMSE Can Be Dual 467 MHz
446.54375	PMSE Can Be Dual 467 MHz
446.55625	PMSE Can Be Dual 467 MHz
446.56875	PMSE Can Be Dual 467 MHz
446.58125	PMSE Can Be Dual 467 MHz
446.59375	PMSE Can Be Dual 467 MHz
446.60625	PMSE Can Be Dual 467 MHz
446.61875	PMSE Can Be Dual 467 MHz
446.63125	PMSE Can Be Dual 467 MHz
446.64375	PMSE Can Be Dual 467 MHz
446.65625	PMSE Can Be Dual 467 MHz
446.66875	PMSE Can Be Dual 467 MHz
446.68125	PMSE Can Be Dual 467 MHz
447.01875	PMSE Can Be Dual 467 MHz
447.03125	PMSE Can Be Dual 467 MHz
447.04375	PMSE Can Be Dual 467 MHz
447.05625	PMSE Can Be Dual 467 MHz
447.06875	PMSE Can Be Dual 467 MHz
447.08125	PMSE Can Be Dual 467 MHz
447.09375	PMSE Can Be Dual 467 MHz
447.10625	PMSE Can Be Dual 467 MHz
447.11875	PMSE Can Be Dual 467 MHz
447.13125	PMSE Can Be Dual 467 MHz
447.14375	PMSE Can Be Dual 467 MHz
447.15625	PMSE Can Be Dual 467 MHz
447.16875	PMSE Can Be Dual 467 MHz
447.18125	PMSE Can Be Dual 467 MHz
447.19375	PMSE Can Be Dual 467 MHz
447.20625	PMSE Can Be Dual 467 MHz
447.21875	PMSE Can Be Dual 467 MHz
447.23125	PMSE Can Be Dual 467 MHz
447.24375	PMSE Can Be Dual 467 MHz
447.25625	PMSE Can Be Dual 467 MHz
447.26875	PMSE Can Be Dual 467 MHz
447.28125	PMSE Can Be Dual 467 MHz
447.29375	PMSE Can Be Dual 467 MHz
447.30625	PMSE Can Be Dual 467 MHz
447.31875	PMSE Can Be Dual 467 MHz
447.33125	PMSE Can Be Dual 467 MHz
447.34375	PMSE Can Be Dual 467 MHz
447.35625	PMSE Can Be Dual 467 MHz
447.36875	PMSE Can Be Dual 467 MHz
447.38125	PMSE Can Be Dual 467 MHz

447.39375	PMSE Can Be Dual 467 MHz
447.40625	PMSE Can Be Dual 467 MHz
447.41875	PMSE Can Be Dual 467 MHz
447.43125	PMSE Can Be Dual 467 MHz
447.44375	PMSE Can Be Dual 467 MHz
447.45625	PMSE Can Be Dual 467 MHz
447.46875	PMSE Can Be Dual 467 MHz
447.48125	PMSE Can Be Dual 467 MHz
447.49375	PMSE Can Be Dual 467 MHz
447.50625	PMSE Can Be Dual 467 MHz
467.75625	PMSE Can Be Dual 446 MHz
467.76875	PMSE Can Be Dual 446 MHz
467.78125	PMSE Can Be Dual 446 MHz
467.79375	PMSE Can Be Dual 446 MHz
467.80625	PMSE Can Be Dual 446 MHz
467.81875	PMSE Can Be Dual 446 MHz
467.83125	PMSE Can Be Dual 446 MHz
467.84375	PMSE Can Be Dual 446 MHz
467.85625	PMSE Can Be Dual 446 MHz
467.86875	PMSE Can Be Dual 446 MHz
467.88125	PMSE Can Be Dual 446 MHz
467.89375	PMSE Can Be Dual 446 MHz
467.90625	PMSE Can Be Dual 446 MHz
467.91875	PMSE Can Be Dual 446 MHz
467.93125	PMSE Can Be Dual 446 MHz
467.94375	PMSE Can Bc Dual 446 MHz
467.95625	PMSE Can Be Dual 446 MHz
467.96875	PMSE Can Be Dual 446 MHz
467.98125	PMSE Can Be Dual 446 MHz
467.99375	PMSE Can Be Dual 446 MHz

If you're just starting out in the hobby, figuring out where to begin looking in the spectrum can be a bit daunting. We hope this section will help you to become familiar with frequencies that are either UK wide or very heavily used for specific purposes. It should also help you to understand the way frequencies are allocated and used. For example, if you come across a user on 456.8625, you should know that this is a UHF short term hire frequency. Therefore, it's likely that particular user will also have the other UHF short term hire frequencies programmed in same radio in different channel positions. Some of those channels will almost certainly be in use at same site so UHF short term hire is the band where you'd look for more frequencies.

One minor problem is that these frequencies are available to almost everyone and in busy locations you can expect to find several different users on the same frequency. This is where subaudible tones are useful. If you listen without using these tones, you'll hear all the users on that frequency but if you use a specific tone, you'll only hear radios that are using the same tone. That makes it a lot easier to identify individual users and is the reason why we've printed the known tone in brackets after the users name wherever we can. If that tone comes up on your display (assuming your radio shows subaudible tones), it's almost certain you have the user we've shown. If it's a different tone, it's probably someone else.

168.2500 - 169.39375 MHz — PMR High Band, Government Agencies & Emergency Services Simplex 12.5 kHz

Base	Mobile	Mode	Location	User and Notes
168.25000		NFM	Aberystwyth	Quay West Holiday Park, New Quay
168.25000		NFM	Ambleside	Charlotte Mason College
168.25000		NFM	Bletchley	Ready Mix Concrete
168.25000		NFM	Carlisle	Bottuby Dairy
168.25000		NFM	Carlisle	Carlisle Football Club
168.25000		NFM	Chapel Cross	Power Station Security
168.25000		NFM	Chesterfield	Chesterfield Football Club Security
168.25000		NFM	Dumfries	Chapel Cross Power Station Security
168.25000		NFM	Felixstowe	Leisure Centre
168.25000		NFM	Ferndown	EG Hoare
168.25000		NFM	Leiston	Leisure Centre
168.25000		NFM	Nationwide	Was RA Investigations, now Educational Departments
168.25000		NFM	Swindon	Cooper's Metals
168.25000		NFM	Midlands	Bass Leisure, Ashton Court
168.25000	173.05000	NFM	Moreton	Hurst Farm (77)
168.25000		NFM	W Glamorgan	Benefit Agency [MASC]
168.25000		NFM	Woodbridge	Suffolk Coastal Council Office Security
168.26250		NFM	Caerphilly	Corus Steel, Lintels (88.5)
168.26250		NFM	Nationwide	BT Cable Laying
168.27500		NFM	Hertfordshire	Post Office Investigations
168.27500	173.07500	NFM	London	Heathrow Express Terminal Staff, Paddington (110.9)
168.28750		NFM	Burnley	Taxi Company
168.28750		NFM	Felixstowe	Port Transport/Haulage (82.5)
168.28750		NFM	Nationwide	OAP Wardens
168.30000		NFM	Ascot	RaceTech Race Course Technical Services
168.30000		NFM	Ayr	RaceTech Race Course Technical Services
168.30000		NFM	Brighton	RaceTech Medical Staff (103.5)
168.30000		NFM	Chepstow	RaceTech Race Course Technical Services
168.30000		NFM	Nationwide	Post Office Investigators
168.30000		NFM	Nationwide	RaceTech (At All Jockey Club Racecourses)
168.32500	174.03750	NFM	Nationwide	UKSAR GPS Tracking & Mobile-Base Ch.100
168.34250		NFM	St. Lawrence	R Procter Farms
168.36250		NFM	Chesterfield	Government Agency (DVP)
168.38750		NFM	Melksham	Taxi Company
168.43750		NFM	Aberdeen	Security Company
168.47500		NFM	Dudley	Hospital Security
168.47500		NFM	Tamworth	Drayton Manor Park
168.53750		NFM	High Wycombe	Council Car Park Staff
168.56250		NFM	Stirling	Stirling Castle
168.77500		NFM	Bedfordshire	Government Agency (DVP)
168.77500		NFM	London	Government Agency
168.80000		NFM	Dorset	Fire Brigade Link (QD)
168.80000	173.60000	NFM	Nationwide	Police Regional Crime Squads DVP/Cougarnet Voice
168.81250		NFM	Dorset	Fire Brigade Link (QD)
168.81250		NFM	Nationwide	Police Regional Crime Squads DVP/Cougarnet Voice
168.82500		NFM	Ipswich	Royal Mail Sorting Office
168.82500		NFM	London	Royal Mail Sorting Office, Mount Pleasant
168.82500		NFM	Norwich	Royal Mail Sorting Office
168.85000		NFM	Edinburgh	Royal Mail Sorting Office
168.85000		NFM	Liverpool	Royal Mail Sorting Office
168.85000		NFM	Nationwide	Local Authority Emergency Services Link
168.85000		NFM	Weymouth	Mount Vernon Post Office
168.86250		NFM	Glasgow	Taxi Company
168.86250		NFM	London	London Underground Engineering Ch.1

Base	Mobile	Mode	Location	User and Notes
168.86250		NFM	Nationwide	DSS Fraud Teams
168.86250		NFM	Nationwide	National Seismic Studies
168.86250		NFM	Nationwide	Police Regional Crime Squads
168.86250		NFM	W Glamorgan	DSS Fraud Teams
168.87500		NFM	Crowborough	Military World Collection, Events (192.8)
168.87500		NFM	Doncaster	DSS
168.87500		NFM	Doncaster	Royal Mail
168.87500		NFM	Ipswich	DSS
168.87500		NFM	London	Royal Mail, Mount Pleasant
168.87500		NFM	Nationwide	BT Engineers (Microwave Set-Up)
168.87500		NFM	Nationwide	DSS Fraud Teams
168.87500		NFM	Nationwide	Royal Mail Cash Vans
168.88750		NFM	Nationwide	BT Engineers (Microwave Set-Up)
168.88750		NFM	Nationwide	BT Investigations
168.90000		NFM	Guernsey	Lesbirel Agricultural Services
168.90000		NFM	Nationwide	DSS Fraud Teams
168.91250		NFM	Kent	Kent Ambulance Service Ch.10
168.91250		NFM	Jersey	Kingslea Hire
168.92500		NFM	Brighton	RaceTech (103.5)
168.92500		NFM	Chepstow	RaceTech
168.92500		NFM	London	Bullion Movement Vans Security
168.92500		NFM	Nationwide	RaceTech (At All Jockey Club Racecourses)
168.92500		NFM	Wincanton	RaceTech
168.93750		NFM	Nationwide	Local Authority Alarms
168.95000		NFM	Ashford	Watling Tyre Service
168.95000		NFM	Martlesham	BT Research Laboratory Fire/Rescue/Events
168.95000		NFM	Nationwide	BT Common Channel
168.95000		NFM	RAF Cosford	Museum Staff Ch.2
168.96250		NFM	Aberdeen	Docks
168.96250		NFM	Brightwell	Mayhew AG, Sheerdrift Farm (94.8)
168.96250		NFM	Bury St Edmunds	Rushbrooke Farms
168.96250		NFM	Coventry	Coventry City Football Club
168.96250		NFM	Eastbourne	Treasure Island
168.96250		NFM	Epson	Racecourse
168.96250		NFM	Eype, Bridport	Highlands End Farm (88.5)
169.96250		NFM	Folkstone	Rotunda Pleasure Centre
169.96250		NFM	Gt Yarmouth	Haulage Company Ch.2 (107.2)
168.96250		NFM	Hopton on Sea	Hoseasons Hopton Holiday Village
168.96250		NFM	Jersey	Industrial (Motors) Ltd
168.96250		NFM	Kempton Park	Racecourse (233.6)
168.96250		NFM	Leeds	Freightliner Terminal, Stourton
168.96250		NFM	London	London Underground Engineering
168.96250		NFM	Macclesfield	Gawsworth Hall (Moss)
168.96250		NFM	Minehead	Butlins
168.96250		NFM	Newton Abbot	Trago Mills Designer Outlet Security
168.96250		NFM	Sandown	Racecourse
168.96250		NFM	Scarborough	Brunswick Pavilion Shopping Centre
168.96250		NFM	Skegness	Butlins
168.96250		NFM	Southend on Sea	Deckchair Attendants
168.97500		NFM	Belfast	Dundonald Ice Bowl
168.97500		NFM	Bury St Edmunds	Printing Works
168.97500		NFM	Caversham Park	BBC Monitoring Service
168.97500		NFM	Felixstowe	Pentlelvar Shunters, Felixstowe Docks (82.5)
168.97500		NFM	Hopton on Sea	Hoseasons, Hopton Holiday Village
168.97500		NFM	Jersey	Les Landes Racecourse
168.97500		NFM	Kilmarnock	Kilmarnock Football Club Staff

Base	Mobile	Mode	Location	User and Notes
168.97500		NFM	Leeds	Headrow Shopping Centre Security
168.97500		NFM	Melcombe Bingham	Higher Melcombe Farm (186.2)
168.97500		NFM	Middlesbrough	Hill Street Shopping Centre Security
168.97500		NFM	Nationwide	BBC TV O/B Engineers
168.97500		NFM	Nationwide	Ordinance Survey
168.97500		NFM	Oldham	Oldham Market
168.97500		NFM	Port Glasgow	Fergussons Shipyard
168.97500		NFM	Port Talbot	Corus Steelworks (71.9)
168.97500		NFM	Skegness	North Shore Hotel & Golf Course
168.97500		NFM	Tamworth	Drayton Manor Park & Zoo Staff
168.97500		NFM	Woolhampton	Athletics Park
168.98750		NFM	Aberdeen	Docks
168.98750		NFM	Cambridge	Fitzwilliam College
168.98750		NFM	Cumbria	Muncaster Castle, Ravenglass
168.98750		NFM	Felixstowe	Docks Police
168.98750		NFM	Guernsey	Condor Shipping
168.98750		NFM	Haverfordwest	Farm
168.98750		NFM	Jersey	Harbour (Condor)
168.98750		NFM	Kent	Port Lympne Zoo, Nr Hythe
168.98750		NFM	London	London Underground Engineering Ch.30
168.98750		NFM	Manchester	Government Agency
168.98750		NFM	Nationwide	BBC O/B Engineering Channel
168.98750		NFM	Nationwide	Ordnance Survey Teams
168.98750		NFM	Nationwide	St .John Ambulance
168.98750		NFM	Peterborough	Ferry Meadows Rangers
168.98750		NFM	Preston	Moathouse Hotel
168.98750		NFM	Sheffield	Concorde Sports Centre
168.98750		NFM	Sheffield	Orchard Square Shopping Centre Security
169.00000		NFM	Aberystwyth	UCW Security
169.00000		NFM	Bolton	Council Car Park Attendants
169.00000		NFM	Bournemouth	Synagogue Security
169.00000		NFM	Cambridge	Trinity College
169.00000		NFM	Cheltenham	FMR Investigations
169.00000		NFM	Crewe	Oakley Centre
169.00000		NFM	Galston	Loudoun Castle Theme Park
169.00000		NFM	Guernsey	PSS Security
169.00000		NFM	High Wycombe	Octagon Shopping Centre Security
169.00000		NFM	Kettering	Wickstead Park
169.00000		NFM	Kilwinning	Water Bailiffs
169.00000		NFM	Leicester	TNT Depot
169.00000		NFM	London	London Underground Engineering Ch.40
169.00000		NFM	New Milton	Bashley Park Campsite
169.00000		NFM	RAF Cosford	Museum Ch.1 (67)
169.00000		NFM	Sheffield	Meadowhall Passenger Transport Interchange
169.00000		NFM	Skegness	Richmond Holiday Centre
169.00000		NFM	Southampton	Docks Security
169.00000		NFM	Southampton	TNT Depot
169.00000		NFM	Stowmarket	Mid-Suffolk Leisure Centre
169.00000		NFM	Swindon	Science Museum, Wroughton
169.00000		NFM	Tilbury	Docks Freightliner Terminal
169.00000		NFM	Worthing	HM Revenue & Customs Site, Durrington (77)
169.01250		NFM	Bentwaters	Park Security
169.01250		NFM	Dundee	Tay Bridge Maintenance
169.01250		NFM	Epping	North Weald Airfield Motor Racing (136.5)
169.01250		NFM	Lakenheath	L & V Taxis
169.01250		NFM	Lancaster	Salt Ayre Sports Centre

Base	Mobile	Mode	Location	User and Notes
169.01250		NFM	Leicester	Leicester Airport Ops
169.01250		NFM	London	Lords Cricket Ground Stewards
169.01250		NFM	London	Twickenham Rugby Ground
169.01250		NFM	London	Taylor Woodrow Cranes
169.01250		NFM	Nationwide	Used By Government Agencies For Surveillance
169.01250		NFM	Newmarket	Racecourse Stewards
169.01250		NFM	Portsmouth	VT Industries Plc Shipbuilding Division (254.1)
169.01250		NFM	Sheffield	Hallam FM Arena
169.01250		NFM	Sheffield	Constant Security, Tinsley Park Estate
169.01250		NFM	Southsea	Clarendon Pier Amusements Security/Staff (123)
169.01250		NFM	Wentworth	Wentworth PGA Golf Course Admissions (141.3)
169.01250		NFM	Weymouth	Guardforce Security
169.02500		NFM	Blackpool	Pontins (Closed But Site Still Maintained) (123)
169.02500		NFM	Brighton	Pier & Front
169.02500		NFM	Boxworth	Ministry of Agriculture Food & Fisheries
169.02500		NFM	Bury St Edmunds	Leisure Centre
169.02500		NFM	Cambridge	Posthouse Forte Hotel
169.02500		NFM	Coventry	Foleshill Church of England School
169.02500		NFM	Dorset	Brownsea Castle, Brownsea Island
169.02500		NFM	Eastbourne	South Cliff Tower (71.9)
169.02500		NFM	Gt Yarmouth	Seacroft Holiday Park (123)
169.02500		NFM	Guernsey	Mainland Market Deliveries
169.02500		NFM	Hull	Sector Security
169.02500		NFM	London	Cazenove & Co.
169.02500		NFM	London	Hillingdon Council
169.02500		NFM	London	London Underground Engineering Ch.50
169.02500		NFM	Perth	Security Company
169.02500		NFM	Prestatyn Sands	Pontins Holiday Camp Security
169.02500		NFM	Ramsgate	Jentex Fuels
169.02500		NFM	Sheffield	Shirecliffe Security (Apple)
169.02500		NFM	Skegness	Embassy Centre
169.02500		NFM	Southend on Sea	Magistrates Court (127.3)
169.02500		NFM	Ufford	Anglia Activity Centre (77)
169.03750		NFM	Aberystwyth	UCW Groundsmen, Penbryn Halls
169.03750		NFM	Barking	Freightliner Terminal
169.03750		NFM	Birmingham	Freightliner Terminal, Lawley Street
169.03750		NFM	Bournemouth	International Centre Security
169.03750		NFM	Bristol	Fruit Market
169.03750		NFM	Cheltenham	FMR Investigations
169.03750		NFM	Clacton	Pier Company
169.03750		NFM	Cleethorpes	Thorpe Park Holiday Camp
169.03750		NFM	Cleveland	Freightliner Terminal
169.03750		NFM	Cumbria	Wild Animal Park, Dalton in Furness (114.8)
169.03750		NFM	Darlington	Dolphin Sports & Leisure Centre
169.03750		NFM	Doncaster	Freightliner Terminal
169.03750		NFM	Eastbourne	Treasure Island Play Centre (82.5)
169.03750		NFM	Edinburgh	Edinburgh Zoo
169.03750		NFM	Felixstowe	Freightliner Terminal
169.03750		NFM	Fort William	Nevis Range Ski Company
169.03750		NFM	Hitchin	E&S Scrap Metal
169.03750		NFM	Hull	Hull Rugby Stewards
169.03750		NFM	Ipswich	University College Suffolk
169.03750		NFM	Jersey	Jersey Zoo
169.03750		NFM	Liverpool	Britannia Adelphi Hotel
169.03750		NFM	Liverpool	Freightliner Terminal
169.03750		NFM	Lochaber	Nevis Rescue Services

Base	Mobile	Mode	Location	User and Notes
169.03750		NFM	London	London Underground Engineering Ch.60
169.03750		NFM	London	London Zoo Staff (88.5)
169.03750		NFM	Maidstone	Leeds Castle Security/Staff
169.03750		NFM	Manchester	Freightliner Terminal Yard Staff
169.03750		NFM	Nationwide	Freightliner Terminals
169.03750		NFM	Ramsgate	Ramsgate Port Operations
169.03750		NFM	Salisbury	Cathedral
169.03750		NFM	Scarborough	Core Security
169.03750		NFM	Seaforth	Freightliner Terminal
169.03750		NFM	Southampton	Freightliner Terminal
169.03750		NFM	Stourton	Freightliner Terminal
169.03750		NFM	Tendring	Tendring Hundreds Water
169.03750		NFM	Thamesport	Freightliner Terminal
169.03750		NFM	Tilbury	Freightliner Terminal
169.03750		NFM	Wentloog	Freightliner Terminal (203.5)
169.03750		NFM	Widnes	Freightliner Terminal
169.05000		NFM	Bacton	British Gas
169.05000		NFM	Nationwide	Gas & Electricity Companies, Handhelds
169.05000		NFM	Nationwide	Gas & Electricity Companies, Nature Reserve Wardens
169.05000		NFM	Nationwide	Gas & Electricity Companies, Site Security
169.05000		NFM	New Cumnock	New Cumnock Opencast Mine
169.05000		NFM	Sizewell	Power Station
169.06250		NFM	Brighton	Palace Pier Staff (94.8)
169.06250		NFM	Carlisle	Portland Centre
169.06250		NFM	Coventry	Milvers Metals, Rowley Green
169.06250		NFM	Ipswich	Co-Op In-Store Comms.
169.06250		NFM	Jersey	Commodore Shipping
169.06250		NFM	London	Trocadero Centre Security, Piccadilly
169.06250		NFM	London	Debenhams Plain Clothes Security, Oxford St (146.2)
169.06250		NFM	Lowestoft	Christian Salvesen
169.06250		NFM	Manchester	Arndale Shopping Centre Maintenance/Security
169.06250		NFM	Millom	Millom Quarry (82.5)
169.06250		NFM	Nationwide	Cable & Wireless Cabling Teams
169.06250		NFM	Norwich	Castle Museum Security/Staff
169.06250		NFM	Portsmouth	Royal Navy Museum & HMS Victory
169.06250		NFM	Waltham Cross	Pavilion Shopping Centre Security
169.06250		NFM	Woburn	Woburn Abbey Staff/Security (151.4)
169.07500		NFM	Bedfordshire	DSS
169.07500		NFM	Brands Hatch	Race Track
169.07500		NFM	Bridgend	First Cymru Buses (118.8)
169.07500		NFM	Cadwell Park	Cadwell Park Motor Racing Circuit
169.07500		NFM	Coventry	Park Surveyors
169.07500		NFM	Glen Coe	White Corries Ski Co.
169.07500		NFM	Guernsey	Balfour Beatty, Falla
169.07500		NFM	Ipswich	Eastgate Shopping Centre
169.07500		NFM	Liverpool	Albert Dock Security
169.07500		NFM	Llanelli	Pembury Country Park Rangers
169.07500		NFM	London	Arsenal Football Club Stewards
169.07500		NFM	London	Queens Park Rangers Football Club Stewards
169.07500		NFM	London	West Ham Football Club Stewards (103.5)
169.07500		NFM	Martlesham	Kingpin Bowling Centre
169.07500		NFM	Nationwide	Jaguar Motor Sport
169.07500		NFM	Newquay	Hendra Caravan Park
169.07500		NFM	Poole	Valiant Security
169.07500		NFM	Reading	Madejski Stadium (88.5)
169.07500		NFM	Sheffield	Transport Interchange

Base	Mobile	Mode	Location	User and Notes
169.07500		NFM	Troon	P & O Container Tugs
169.07500		NFM	Turbury	Nestles
169.07500		NFM	Tyneside	Five Star Security
169.07500		NFM	Warwickshire	County Council Highways Department
169.07500		NFM	Woburn	Woburn Abbey Staff/Security (141.3)
169.07500		NFM	Worthing	HM Revenue & Customs Site, Durrington (77)
169.08500		NFM	Ayr	Water Bailiff Handhelds
169.08750		NFM	Aberystwyth	Air Ambulance Air-Ground Ch.9
169.08750		NFM	Ascot	Racecourse
169.08750		NFM	Bedfordshire	Red Cross (114.8)
169.08750		NFM	Birmingham	Birmingham City Football Club
169.08750		NFM	Birmingham	Birmingham Wheels Go Karts
169.08750		NFM	Bolton	Peak Security
169.08750		NFM	Brighton	Palace Pier
169.08750		NFM	Canterbury	Howletts Zoo
169.08750		NFM	Coatbridge	Freightliner Terminal
169.08750		NFM	Guernsey	Allied Heating
169.08750		NFM	Guernsey	Louis Dekker Bulbs
169.08750		NFM	Leeds	Freightliner Terminal
169.08750		NFM	London	Beach Communications (140.2)
169.08750		NFM	London	QD Film Productions (94.8)
169.08750		NFM	Medway	In-Sewer Surveys
169.08750		NFM	Merseyside	Merseyrail
169.08750		NFM	Nationwide	Cable & Wireless Cabling Teams
169.08750		NFM	Nationwide	East Midlands Racing Association Ch.1
169.08750		NFM	Nationwide	Medicman Events Medical Service Handhelds (192.8)
169.08750		NFM	Nationwide	MG Car Club Events
169.08750		NFM	Nationwide	Often Used By Government Agencies For Surveillance
169.08750		NFM	Nationwide	Paramededico Events Medical Service Handhelds
169.08750		NFM	Nationwide	Red Cross Shared UK General
169.08750		NFM	Nationwide	Scouts Association Ch.3
169.08750		NFM	Nationwide	St John Ambulance UK General Ch.7 (186.2)
169.08750		NFM	Newmarket	Newmarket Racecourse Betting Net
169.08750		NFM	Peterborough	East of England Show Ground Medic/Ambulances
169.08750		NFM	Plymouth	Plymouth Market Security
169.08750		NFM	Sheffield	Transport Interchange
169.08750		NFM	Southampton	Docks
169.08750		NFM	Suffolk	County Council Surveyors (131.8)
169.08750		NFM	Yeadon	Securitas Security
169.10000		NFM	Cambridge	Medical Research Council
169.10000		NFM	Gt Yarmouth	Market Gates Shopping Centre (123)
169.10000		NFM	Isle of Arran	National Trust for Scotland Rangers
169.10000		NFM	Keswick	Keswick Boat Launches (123)
169.10000		NFM	Leicester	Next Shop (141.3)
169.10000		NFM	London	Next Shop, Marble Arch
169.10000		NFM	London	Next Shop, Oxford Circus (110.9)
169.10000		NFM	London	Next Shop, Piccadilly
169.10000		NFM	Norwich	Norwich City Football Club Stewards
169.10000		NFM	Ramsgate	Ramsgate Port Operations Ch.1
169.10000		NFM	Silverstone	Silverstone Race Track Hospitality (114.8)
169.10000		NFM	Skegness	Blue Anchor Leisure Ltd
169.10000		NFM	Wishaw	Belfry Golf Course
169.10000		NFM	Wookey Hole	Wookey Hole Caves & Paper Mill
169.11250		NFM	Abercravg	Amec Mining (67)
169.11250		NFM	Ayr	Taxi Company
169.11250		NFM	Bournemouth	International Centre Security

Base	Mobile	Mode	Location	User and Notes
169.11250		NFM	Canterbury	University of Kent
169.11250		NFM	Coatbridge	Freightliner Terminal
169.11250		NFM	Doncaster	Steatley Quarry
169.11250		NFM	Dymchurch	Romney, Hythe & Dymchurch Railway
169.11250		NFM	Grimsby	Shopping Centre
169.11250		NFM	Halesworth	KW Thomas
169.11250		NFM	London	Kensington Palace State Apartments
169.11250		NFM	Port Talbot	Corus Steelworks
169.11250		NFM	Rugby	Swift Valley Industrial Estate
169.11250		NFM	Sheffield	Bassets Sweet Factory
169.11250		NFM	Sheffield	Hallam FM Arena Ops
169.11250		NFM	Skegness	Freshney Place Shopping Centre
169.11250		NFM	Southend on Sea	Central Library
169.11250		NFM	St Helier	Reclamation Site
169.11250		NFM	Trowbridge	Garden Centre
169.12500		NFM	Birkenhead	Shopping Centre Security
169.12500		NFM	Birmingham	Birmingham City Football Club Turnstiles
169.12500		NFM	Brighton	Palace Pier Rides/Bars (114.8)
169.12500		NFM	Colchester	Colchester Castle
169.12500		NFM	Felixstowe	Taylor Barnards Transport (103.5)
169.12500		NFM	Gaydon	Heritage Motor Centre
169.12500		NFM	Greenock	Wilson Coaches
169.12500		NFM	Humberside	Council Highways Department Handhelds
169.12500		NFM	Isle of Man	Emerald Operations, Ronaldsway Airport
169.12500		NFM	Portsmouth	Cascades Shopping Centre
169.12500		NFM	Scarborough	Scarborough Football Club Stewards
169.12500		NFM	Sheffield	Gleadless First School
169.12500		NFM	Sheffield	Hallam FM Arena Ops
169.12500		NFM	Southend on Sea	Co-Op, Royals Shopping Centre (167.9)
169.12500		NFM	Stansted	Airport Ops
169.12500		NFM	Woburn	Woburn Abbey Staff/Security Ch.3 (210.7)
169.12500		NFM	Woodbridge	Seckford School
169.12500		NFM	Worcester	White Arrow Delivery
169.13750		NFM	Aberdeen	Bon Accord Centre Security
169.13750		NFM	Barton Mills	Middle Field Manor Autistic Society Home (71.9)
169.13750		NFM	Brighton	Brighton Racecourse Track Staff/Vets (103.5)
169.13750		NFM	Durris	National Trust for Scotland Rangers
169.13750		NFM	Hampshire	Council
169.13750		NFM	London	Camden Lock Market
169.13750		NFM	London	DSS Inspectors
169.13750		NFM	London	Twickenham Rugby Ground Caterers (131.8)
169.13750		NFM	Louth	Cadwell Park Racing Circuit Marshals
169.13750		NFM	Nationwide	East Midlands Racing Association Ch.2
169.13750		NFM	Newmarket	Racecourse, Ladbrookes
169.13750		NFM	Pontyclun	Stables
169.13750		NFM	Sheffield	Council Dry Ski Slope
169.13750		NFM	Weymouth	RSPB
169.15000		NFM	Banham	Zoo Keepers Ch.2 (77)
169.15000		NFM	Bournemouth	Beach Wardens
169.15000		NFM	Corby	Earlstrees Industrial Estate
169.15000		NFM	Jersey	Jersey Builders
169.15000		NFM	Gosport	Bridgemary Community School (77)
169.15000		NFM	Leicester	Beaumont Leys Shopping Centre Staff (218.1)
169.15000		NFM	London	Alexandra Palace Leisure Centre
169.15000		NFM	Lowestoft	Pleasurewood Hills Leisure Park
169.15000		NFM	Manchester	Civic Centre Leisure Centre

Base	Mobile	Mode	Location	User and Notes
169.15000		NFM	Nationwide	National Trust
169.15000		NFM	Nuneaton	Lynx Parcels
169.15000		NFM	Port Talbot	Corus Steelworks (67)
169.15000		NFM	Reading	Madejski Stadium Ch.5 (192.8)
169.15000		NFM	Sheerness	Sheerness Metal
169.15000		NFM	Shottisham	Deben Farms
169.15000		NFM	Stanton	East Coast Slag
169.15000		NFM	Swanage	National Trust, Corfe Castle
169.15000		NFM	Whitland	Dairy Crest
169.15000		NFM	Worksop	Bassetlaw Hospital
169.16250		NFM	Ascot	Racecourse Maintenance
169.16250		NFM	Ballachulish	Glencoe MR Team
169.16250		NFM	Bishop Stortford	Mears Construction
169.16250		NFM	Canterbury	Taxi Company
169.16250		NFM	Cardigan	Cardi Cabs
169.16250		NFM	Coventry	Mayfair Security
169.16250		NFM	Edinburgh	City Surveyors
169.16250		NFM	Essex	Top Guard International
169.16250		NFM	Grimsby	West Marsh Brick
169.16250		NFM	Ipswich	RSPCA Ch.2 Discrete
169.16250		NFM	Jersey	Keith Rogers Building Renovation
169.16250		NFM	Kings Lynn	Star Cars
169.16250		NFM	London	BBC Radio O/B Production
169.16250		NFM	London	Twickenham Rugby Ground Staff
169.16250		NFM	London	Lawn Tennis Club Groundsmen, Wimbledon
169.16250		NFM	Newmarket	Chilcots Taxis
169.16250		NFM	Queensborough	Sea King Group, Car Dealers
169.16250		NFM	Scotland	St Andrews Medical Service Ch.1 (233.6)
169.16250		NFM	Sittingbourne	Forum Shopping Centre Security
169.16250		NFM	Surrey	Council County Engineer
169.16250		NFM	Swansea	Sommervilles Scrap Metal/Car Parts
169.16250		NFM	Taplow	Cliveden House Hotel Security
169.16250		NFM	Thetford	A & S Taxis
169.17500		NFM	Barrow in Furness	VSEL Shopfloor Services
169.17500		NFM	Boston	Organic Lincolnshire Growers Association
169.17500		NFM	Cardiff	RMC Aggregates, Wenvoe Quarry (82.5)
169.17500		NFM	Guernsey	Ronez, Monmains
169.17500		NFM	Ipswich	Hospital Maintenance
169.17500		NFM	Perth	Landscape Gardens
169.17500		NFM	Peterborough	East of England Show Ground
169.17500		NFM	Scarborough	Scarborough University College Security
169.17500		NFM	Scotland	Scottish Mountain Rescue Teams
169.17500		NFM	Snowdonia	Snowdon Mountain Railway
169.17500		NFM	Southampton	Freightliner Terminal
169.17500		NFM	Stapleton	Woodland Nurseries
169.17500		NFM	Stourton	Freightliner Terminal
169.17500		NFM	Wareham	Charborough Park Estate
169.18750		NFM	Ayr	Racecourse, Sunday Market Stewards
169.18750		NFM	Bentwaters	Abbey Security (On Ex-USAF Bases)
169.18750		NFM	Brighton	Asda Supermarket, Brighton Marina
169.18750		NFM	Garston	Freightliner Terminal
169.18750		NFM	Grimsby	West Marsh Brick
169.18750		NFM	Inglestone	Market Stewards
169.18750		NFM	Ipswich	Fisons Fertz Ltd
169.18750		NFM	London	Chelsea Football Club Stewards
169.18750		NFM	London	Tennis Championships Stewards, Wimbledon

Base	Mobile	Mode	Location	User and Notes
169.18750		NFM	Morecambe	Trino's Taxis
169.18750		NFM	Newcastle	Five Star Taxis, Gosforth
169.18750		NFM	Penrith	Market Security
169.18750		NFM	Perth	Security Company
169.18750		NFM	Portsmouth	Marina Security (88.5)
169.18750		NFM	Sheffield	Hallam FM Arena Car Parking
169.18750		NFM	Wigan	Statesman Security
169.20000		NFM	Aberdeen	Aberdeen Ice Rink
169.20000		NFM	Alford	Woodthorpe Garden Centre
169.20000		NFM	Ashford	Stour Leisure Centre
169.20000		NFM	Bolton	Peak Security
169.20000		NFM	Cardiff	Indoor Market Security (118.8)
169.20000		NFM	Edinburgh	National Museum of Scotland, Chamber St.
169.20000		NFM	Fort William	BSW Sawmill
169.20000		NFM	Gateshead	Leisure Centre, Fewster Square
169.20000		NFM	Ipswich	Total Car Park Management
169.20000		NFM	Jersey	Wilson Vets & Animal Shelter
169.20000		NFM	Liverpool	Clicks Wine Bar Security
169.20000		NFM	Liverpool	Liverpool University (173.8)
169.20000		NFM	London	Arding & Hobbs, Clapham (67)
169.20000		NFM	London	Harvey Nichols Security, Knightsbridge
169.20000		NFM	London	University College, London University
169.20000		NFM	London	Westminster City Hall
169.20000		NFM	Peterborough	Peterborough Regional College
169.20000		NFM	Sheffield	Makro Car Parking
169.20000		NFM	Skegness	North Shore Holiday Centre
169.20000		NFM	Southend on Sea	Southend United Football Club (151.4)
169.20000		NFM	Suffolk	Alton Water Wardens
169.20000		NFM	Swansea	FRF Motors
169.20000		NFM	Thanet	Thanet Technical College
169.20000		NFM	York	York Minster Constabulary
169.21250		NFM	Bognor Regis	Butlins Holiday Camp
169.21250		NFM	Bournemouth	M&J Security
169.21250		NFM	Coventry	Airport
169.21250		NFM	Croydon	Water Palace
169.21250		NFM	Dover	District Council
169.21250		NFM	Eastbourne	The Grand Hotel
169.21250		NFM	Felixstowe	TDM Transport Felixstowe Docks (88.5)
169.21250		NFM	Hull	Coastal Sea Rescue
169.21250		NFM	Ipswich	Port
169.21250		NFM	Jersey	Beach Guards
169.21250		NFM	Kent	Eastgate Centre Security
169.21250		NFM	London	Barbican Centre Security
169.21250		NFM	London	London Underground Engineering Ch.70
169.21250		NFM	Port Talbot	Corus Steelworks
169.21250		NFM	Scarborough	Primrose Valley
169.21250		NFM	Southend on Sea	Essex Golf Club (94.8)
169.21250		NFM	Stoke on Trent	Stoke City Football Club Security
169.22500		NFM	Biggleswade	Shuttleworth College, Middle Farm
169.22500		NFM	Bushmills	Bushmills Distillery, Co Antrim
169.22500		NFM	Carlisle	Thomas Graham & Sons
169.22500		NFM	Coventry	Apex Trust
169.22500		NFM	Epping	North Weald Airfield Security/Fire (141.3)
169.22500		NFM	Glasgow	University Security
169.22500		NFM	Leeds	St John's Shopping Centre Security
169.22500		NFM	London	London Underground Engineering Ch.80

Base	Mobile	Mode	Location	User and Notes
169.22500		NFM	London	London Zoo Catering & Shops
169.22500		NFM	Lowestoft	Birds Eye Factory (71.9)
169.22500		NFM	Motherwell	M&D Scottish Theme Park
169.22500		NFM	Peterborough	Orton Longueville School
169.22500		NFM	Port Talbot	Corus Steelworks (82.5)
169.22500		NFM	Seaton	Warners Holiday Camp
169.22500		NFM	Shelshley Walsh	Midland Car Club High Speed Hill Climb Course
169.22500		NFM	Sible Hedingham	Sible Hedingham Farms
169.22500		NFM	Silverstone	Race Track Ops
169.22500		NFM	Southport	Leisure Lakes
169.22500		NFM	Wigan	Rugby Ground Stewards
169.23750		NFM	Aberystwyth	Water Bailiffs
169.23750		NFM	Barnet	Spires Shopping Centre Security
169.23750		NFM	Barrow in Furness	Barrow Quarry
169.23750		NFM	Blackpool	South Pier Staff/Security
169.23750		NFM	Blantyre	Forge Centre Security (114.8)
169.23750		NFM	Chatham	Pentagon Centre Security
169.23750		NFM	Grimsby	Fresney Place Shopping Centre Security
169.23750		NFM	Heathrow	Terminal 3 Car Park Control
169.23750		NFM	Ingoldmells	Fantasy Island
169.23750		NFM	Isle of Wight	Harcourt Sands Holiday Camp
169.23750		NFM	Isle of Wight	Lower Hyde Holiday Village
169.23750		NFM	Isle of Wight	Savoy Country Club Security
169.23750		NFM	Kessingland	Caravan Park Staff
169.23750		NFM	Liverpool	Cavern Club Security
169.23750		NFM	Liverpool	Dolcis Shop Ordering Department
169.23750		NFM	Liverpool	GH Lee Security
169.23750		NFM	London	Asprey & Garrards Jewellers, Bond Street (118.8)
169.23750		NFM	London	London Underground Engineering Ch.90
169.23750		NFM	Nationwide	Water Bailiffs
169.23750		NFM	Scarborough	Lifeguards
169.23750		NFM	Southend on Sea	Peter Pan's Adventure Island Security Ch.2
169.23750		NFM	Stevenage	Westgate Shopping Centre Cleaners (82.5)
169.23750		NFM	Stevenage	Westgate Shopping Centre Security (107.2)
169.23750		NFM	Stowmarket	ICI Paints
169.23750		NFM	Swansea	Water Bailiffs
169.23750		NFM	Winterbourne Whitechurch	Walston Poultry Farm
169.25000		NFM	Brecon	Mountain Railway
169.25000		NFM	Clacton	Tower Holiday Park (94.8)
169.25000		NFM	Epping	North Weald Airfield Security (141.3)
169.25000		NFM	Felixstowe	Suffolk Sands Caravan Park (118.8)
169.25000		NFM	Heysham	Norse Merchant Ferries to Belfast (DCS 114)
169.25000		NFM	Leicester	Beaumont Leys Shopping Centre Security (146.2)
169.25000		NFM	Liverpool	Reed Aviation Freight, Liverpool Airport
169.25000		NFM	London	Thames River Marina
169.25000		NFM	London	London Underground Engineering Ch.10
169.25000		NFM	Sittingbourne	Shell Research Centre Security
169.25000		NFM	Southampton	Red Funnel Ferry Ops
169.25000		NFM	Stevenage	Roger Harvey Garden Centre
169.25000		NFM	Waltham Abbey	Market Traders
169.26250		NFM	Edinburgh	John Lewis Security
169.26250		NFM	Fairbourne	Fairbourne & Barmouth Steam Railway
169.26250		NFM	Felixstowe	Docks South Freightliner Terminal
169.26250		NFM	Guernsey	Harlequin Hire Cars
169.26250		NFM	Hopton on Sea	Hopton Holiday Village
169.26250		NFM	Hull	Prospect Shopping Centre Security

Base	Mobile	Mode	Location	User and Notes
169.26250		NFM	Liverpool	Students Union
169.26250		NFM	London	John Lewis Security, Brent Cross
169.26250		NFM	London	John Lewis Security, Oxford Street
169.26250		NFM	London	London Underground Engineering Ch.11
169.26250		NFM	Newtownards	Ards Shopping Centre Security (103.5)
169.26250		NFM	Norwich	John Lewis Security
169.26250		NFM	Preston	St. Georges Shopping Centre Security
169.26250		NFM	Skegness	Pier
169.26250		NFM	Stevenage	John Lewis Warehouse Security (94.8)
169.26250		NFM	Weymouth	Holiday Camp
169.27500		NFM	Butley	Kenbell & Sons Farms
169.27500		NFM	Elvedon	Centre Parcs Holiday Village Maintenance
169.27500		NFM	Leeds	Batleys C&C Security/Reception
169.27500		NFM	London	London Transport Museum, Covent Garden
169.27500		NFM	London	London Underground Engineering Ch.12
169.27500		NFM	Malton	Flamingo Land
169.27500		NFM	Sheffield	Millennium Galleries
169.27500		NFM	Shoreham Airport	Ground Vehicles
169.27500		NFM	Shrewsbury	Shrewsbury Football Club Stewards
169.27500		NFM	Skegness	Sunnymeade Caravan Park
169.27500		NFM	Southend on Sea	Technical College (107.2)
169.27500		NFM	Stansted Airport	Pinkerton Security
169.28750		NFM	Arlesley	Waste Site Ops.
169.28750		NFM	Birmingham	Freightliner Terminal, Lawley Street
169.28750		NFM	Boscombe	Littledown Centre
169.28750		NFM	Felixstowe	Docks North Freightliner Terminal
169.28750		NFM	High Wycombe	John Lewis Security
169.28750		NFM	Kettering	Metalforce Ltd
169.28750		NFM	London	London Underground Engineering Ch.13
169.28750		NFM	Newton Abbot	Trago Mills Designer Outlet
169.28750		NFM	Rotherham	Bus Station Staff
169.28750		NFM	Sittingbourne	Sittingbourne Football Club Security
169.28750		NFM	Southampton	Dock, Stevedores
169.28750		NFM	Woburn Sands	Plysu Plc
169.28750		NFM	Worthing	HM Revenue & Customs Site, Durrington (77)
169.30000		NFM	Banham	Zoo Ch.1 (77)
169.30000		NFM	Birmingham	West Bromwich Albion Football Club Stewards
169.30000		NFM	Blackpool	Blackpool Pleasure Beach
169.30000		NFM	Brands Hatch	Brands Hatch Race Track
169.30000		NFM	Bury	Indoor Shopping Centre
169.30000		NFM	Carlisle	H&H Auction Mart
169.30000		NFM	Chesterfield	Pub Bouncers
169.30000		NFM	Felixstowe	Docks South Freightliner Terminal
169.30000		NFM	Guernsey	Sarnia Hire Cars
169.30000		NFM	Heathrow	Airline Passenger Service
169.30000		NFM	Hurn	Alice in Wonderland Theme Park
169.30000		NFM	Kessingland	Zoo Keepers Ch.1
169.30000		NFM	Ipswich	Wolsey Theatre
169.30000		NFM	Leeds	National Express, Leeds Coach Station
169.30000		NFM	London	London Underground Engineering Ch.14
169.30000		NFM	Morecambe	Frontierland
169.30000		NFM	Pimperne	Hametts Farm
169.30000		NFM	Ramsgate	Port Operations
169.31250		NFM	Bristol	Bristol City Football Club Car Parks
169.31250		NFM	Derbyshire	Derbyshire Council Rangers
169.31250		NFM	Epping	North Weald Market Car Park Stewards (67)

Base	Mobile	Mode	Location	User and Notes
169.31250		NFM	Fairburn	RSPB Wardens
169.31250		NFM	Gosport	Woolworths Staff (DCS 243)
169.31250		NFM	Ingleton	Hanson Quarry Security
169.31250		NFM	Ipswich	National Car Parks
169.31250		NFM	Jersey	Commodore Shipping
169.31250		NFM	Kidderminster	West Midlands Safari Park
169.31250		NFM	Kent	Priority Medical Service, Events (103.5)
169.31250		NFM	Letchworth	Amec Building Maintenance
169.31250		NFM	London	Abbey (National), Triton Square
169.31250		NFM	London	Amec Building, EC4
169.31250		NFM	Louth	Cadwell Park Racing Circuit
169.31250		NFM	Milton Keynes	Abbey (National) Security/Staff
169.31250		NFM	Nationwide	Andy's Loos, Events Portaloo Provider (DCS 032)
169.31250		NFM	Nationwide	Cable & Wireless Cabling Teams
169.31250		NFM	Nationwide	MG Car Club Events
169.31250		NFM	Nationwide	Used By Government Agencies For Surveillance
169.31250		NFM	Nationwide	Spedeworth International Ltd Stock Car Racing
169.31250		NFM	Nationwide	Scouts Association Ch.4
169.31250		NFM	Nationwide	St John Ambulance UK General Ch.2
169.31250		NFM	Nationwide	Titan Fire Services
169.31250		NFM	North Weald	Market Organisers and Sabre Ambulance Service
169.31250		NFM	Wellesbourne	Market Organisers
169.32500		NFM	Bath	Theatre Royal
169.32500		NFM	Cardiff	Wentloog Security, Rumney & Wentloog Ch.2
169.32500		NFM	Epping	North Weald Airfield Tower/Fire Trucks (141.3)
169.32500		NFM	Exeter	Exeter Cathedral
169.32500		NFM	Felixstowe	Container Port
169.32500		NFM	Hull	Hull City Football Club Stewards
169.32500		NFM	Ilkeston	American Adventure Theme Park
169.32500		NFM	Ipswich	Ipswich Town Football Club Stewards (107.2)
169.32500		NFM	London	London Underground Engineering Ch.15
169.32500		NFM	London	Matalan Store, Wood Green
169.32500		NFM	London	Selborne Walk Centre, Walthamstow (151.4)
169.32500		NFM	Newquay	Car Park Attendants
169.32500		NFM	Southampton	Red Funnel Ferries
169.32500		NFM	Ufford	Douglas Goldsmith Nurseries
169.32500		NFM	Worthing	HM Revenue & Customs Site, Durrington (77)
169.32500		NFM	York	Grand Opera House
169.33750		NFM	Alton Towers	Ch.5 Reserved/Special
169.33750		NFM	Brands Hatch	Race Track (Marshals & Rescue)
169.33750		NFM	Canvey Island	Knightswick Security
169.33750		NFM	Corby	Rockingham Speedway Control/Marshals/Safety
169.33750		NFM	Devon	Tamar Bridge Security
169.33750		NFM	Halifax	Websters Brewery Security
169.33750		NFM	Kirkby Mallory	Mallory Park Motor Racing Circuit
169.33750		NFM	Knockhill	Knockhill Racing (Marshals & Rescue)
169.33750		NFM	London	London Underground Engineering Ch.16
169.33750		NFM	Louth	Cadwell Park Motor Racing Circuit
169.33750		NFM	Nationwide	750 Club Rally Medical Services
169.33750		NFM	Nationwide	BRSCC Motor Rally/Racing Circuit Marshals
169.33750		NFM	Nationwide	British Automobile Racing Club
169.33750		NFM	Nationwide	National Motor Rally/Circuit Marshal/Safety
169.33750		NFM	Nationwide	RAC Rally Events Marshals/Safety
169.33750		NFM	Oldham	Town Square Shops Security
169.33750		NFM	Oulton Park	Racing (Marshals & Rescue)
169.33750		NFM	Perth	St John's Shopping Centre Security

Base	Mobile	Mode	Location	User and Notes
169.33750		NFM	Sheffield	Don Valley Sports Arena
169.33750		NFM	Sheffield	Ponds Forge Sports Centre
169.33750		NFM	Silverstone	Racing (Marshals & Rescue)
169.33750		NFM	Snetterton	Racing (Marshals & Rescue)
169.33750		NFM	Thruxton	Racing (Marshals & Rescue)
169.35000		NFM	Bournemouth	Weymouth House Security
169.35000		NFM	Doncaster	Dome Centre
169.35000		NFM	Hull	Humber Bridge Control
169.35000		NFM	Isle Of Man	MEA Manx Electricity
169.35000		NFM	London	London Underground Engineering Ch.17
169.35000		NFM	Lowestoft	Corton Classic Resort Holiday Camp
169.35000		NFM	Southend on Sea	Pier Trains (107.2)
169.35000		NFM	Swansea	Swansea Airport Maintenance
169.35000		NFM	Woodbridge	Company Of Four Musical Theatre Group
169.36250		NFM	Bolton	Bolton Football Club Stewards
169.36250		NFM	Doncaster	Tesco Warehouse Ops.
169.36250		NFM	Glasgow	Timbmet Woyka Ltd.
169.36250		NFM	London	London Underground Ch.7A Central DTM
169.36250		NFM	London	London Underground Engineering Ch.18
169.36250		NFM	London	London Underground S/Bridge Shunting
169.36250		NFM	Manchester	Manchester Polytechnic Security
169.36250		NFM	Peterborough	Scott's Skips (203.5)
169.36250		NFM	Plymouth	Plymouth Argyle Football Club
169.36250		NFM	Preston	Harris Museum
169.36250		NFM	Sheffield	Avesta Ltd.
169.36250		NFM	Sheffield	Owlerton Security
169.36250		NFM	Whiston	Hexagon (HISS) Security Ltd
169.37500		NFM	Alfriston	Drusillas Zoo
169.37500		NFM	Bath	NCP Car Park, Ham Lane
169.37500		NFM	Brands Hatch	Race Track
169.37500		NFM	Chrich	National Tramway Museum
169.37500		NFM	Croydon	Forbidden Planet Shop Security
169.37500		NFM	Elvedon	Centre Parcs Holiday Village Security
169.37500		NFM	Felixstowe	Container Port
169.37500		NFM	Langholm	Eskside Engineering
169.37500		NFM	London	Forbidden Planet Shop Security, Oxford St
169.37500		NFM	London	London Underground, Acton Town Ch.7B
169.37500		NFM	London	London Underground, Circle Line DTM
169.37500		NFM	London	London Underground Engineering Ch.19
169.37500		NFM	London	London Underground, Fulham Broadway
169.37500		NFM	London	London Underground, Hammersmith
169.37500		NFM	London	London Underground, Jubilee Line DTM
169.37500		NFM	London	London Underground, Upton Park Depot
169.37500		NFM	London	National Theatre Security, Southbank
169.37500		NFM	London	Somerset House Security
169.37500		NFM	Ramsgate	Ramsgate Port Operations
169.37500		NFM	Saffron Walden	Bell College
169.37500		NFM	Sheffield	Council Housing Department
169.37500		NFM	Skegness	Butlins Holiday Camp
169.37500		NFM	Southend n Sea	Southend United Football Club
169.37500		NFM	Sussex	Sussex Ambulance Special Use
169.37500		NFM	Warwickshire	Arable Farm, North Warwickshire
169.37500		NFM	Weston Super Mare	Council Beach/Amenities Patrol
169.37500		NFM	Weymouth	Holiday Camp (110.9)
169.38750		NFM	Blackpool	Car Park Attendants
169.38750		NFM	Cambridge	Cambridge Science Park Security

Base	Mobile	Mode	Location	User and Notes
169.38750		NFM	Cambridge	Cambridge University Rowing Club
169.38750		NFM	Cardiff	Cardiff University Students Union Security/Staff
169.38750		NFM	Coventry	Showcase Cinema Staff
169.38750		NFM	Felixstowe	Haulage Company (136.5)
169.38750		NFM	Humberside	Airport Tower-Ground
169.38750		NFM	London	London Underground Ch.7C
169.38750		NFM	London	London Underground Engineering Ch.20
169.38750		NFM	London	London Underground, Piccadilly DTM
169.38750		NFM	London	Southwark Crown Court Security
169.38750		NFM	London	Surrey Quays Shopping Centre Security (88.5)
169.38750		NFM	Lowestoft	Holiday Camp
169.38750		NFM	Preston	Council Car Parks
169.38750		NFM	Sheffield	Makro Car Park Control
169.83750		NFM	Skegness	South View Leisure Park
169.38750		NFM	Silverstone	Airfield Security & Crash Ops
169.38750		NFM	Stevenage	Roye Security, Hollywood Bowl
169.38750		NFM	Wool	Monkey World (118.8)

169.39375 - 169.84375 MHz　　　　PMR Simplex 12.5 kHz

Base	Mobile	Mode	Location	User and Notes
169.82500		NFM	Bridlington	Forum Leisure Centre
169.82500		NFM	Cambridge	Cambridge Council (233.6)
169.82500		NFM	Chesterfield	Arnold Lavers Timberyard
169.82500		NFM	Coventry	Watch Security
169.82500		NFM	Folkestone	Burstin Hotel
169.82500		NFM	Leamington Spa	The Watch Security
169.83750		NFM	London	Secure Parking, Southall
169.82500		NFM	Morecombe	Arndale Shopping Centre Security
169.82500		NFM	Peterborough	Pedigree Pet Foods
169.82500		NFM	RAF Cosford	Museum (173.8)
169.82500		NFM	Southend on Sea	The Kuursal Leisure Complex
169.82500		NFM	Welwyn Garden City	Car Park Control (186.2)
169.83750		NFM	Belfast	Yorkgate Movie House (77)
169.83750		NFM	Heysham	Isle of Man Steam Packet
169.83750		NFM	Hull	Princes Quay Car Park Security
169.83750		NFM	Oxford	Oxford United Football Club Stewards
169.83750		NFM	Sheffield	Orchard Square Shopping Centre
169.83750		NFM	Slimbridge	Bird Sanctuary
169.83750		NFM	St Austell	ECC Pits

169.84375 - 173.04375 MHz　　　　PMR Simplex (Old Bandplan)

Base	Mobile	Mode	Location	User and Notes
171.00000		NFM	London	London Ambulance/Red Cross Emergency Channel
172.01250		NFM	Thetford	Range Wardens' Handhelds, Stanford Training Area

173.04375 - 173.09375 MHz　　　　PMR Simplex 12.5 kHz NFM

Base	Mobile	Mode	Location	User and Notes
173.05000		NFM	Felixstowe	JDM Haulage (167.9)
173.05000		NFM	Nationwide	MG Car Club Events
173.05000		NFM	Nationwide	Andy's Loos, Events Portaloo Provider (DCS 446)
173.05000		NFM	Nationwide	Used By Government Agencies For Surveillance
173.05000		NFM	Nationwide	St John Ambulance UK General (186.2)
173.06250		NFM	Baldock	Taxi Company (110.9)
173.06250		NFM	Canvey Island	Abbey Investigations
173.06250		NFM	Cambridge	Ministry of Agriculture, Food & Fisheries (131.8)
173.06250		NFM	Edinburgh	Heart of Midlothian FC, Tynecastle Stadium Security
173.06250		NFM	Ipswich	B & Q Store
173.06250		NFM	Nationwide	Abbey Investigations
173.06250		NFM	Nationwide	Gerry Cottles Circus

Base	Mobile	Mode	Location	User and Notes
173.06250		NFM	Nationwide	MG Car Club Events (67)
173.06250		NFM	Nationwide	National Crime Squad DVP/Cougarnet/Voice
173.06250		NFM	Nationwide	Used By Government Agencies For Surveillance
173.06250		NFM	Nationwide	Red Cross Shared UK General
173.06250		NFM	Nationwide	St John Ambulance UK General (186.2)
173.07500		NFM	Jersey	Stolen Car Detector Systems
173.08750		NFM	Brighton	Private Detective Agency, Surveillance (107.2)
173.08750		NFM	Cambridge	Ministry of Agriculture, Food & Fisheries (131.8)
173.08750		NFM	Isle of Man	Summerland Leisure Centre
173.08750		NFM	Jersey	Surveyors
173.08750		NFM	London	Airline Check-In, Paddington Station
173.08750		NFM	Nationwide	Abbey Investigations
173.08750		NFM	Nationwide	MG Car Club Events
173.08750		NFM	Nationwide	Used By Government Agencies For Surveillance
173.08750		NFM	Nationwide	Red Cross Shared UK General
173.08750		NFM	Nationwide	St John Ambulance UK General (186.2)
173.08750		NFM	Scotland	St Andrews Medical Service (233.6)
173.08750		NFM	Torridon	National Trust for Scotland Rangers

173.09375 - 173.9875 MHz Low Power Devices, Radio Deaf Aids, Biological Telemetry & Garage Door Openers

Base	Mobile	Mode	Location	User and Notes
173.18750		NFM	Nationwide	Mobile Alarm Paging
173.18750		NFM	Nationwide	Car Tracker Systems
173.22500		NFM	Nationwide	Building Site Alarms
173.22500		NFM	Nationwide	Radio Controlled Garage Doors
173.22500		NFM	Nationwide	Short Range Security Alarms
173.35000		NFM	Jersey	School Deaf Aids
173.40000		NFM	Jersey	School Deaf Aids
173.40000		NFM	Nationwide	Deaf Aids
173.46250		NFM	Jersey	School Deaf Aids
173.46500		NFM	Nationwide	Deaf Aids
173.54500		NFM	Nationwide	Deaf Aids

173.2000 - 177.0000 Mhz PMR & Radio Microphones

Base	Mobile	Mode	Location	User and Notes
173.21250		NFM	Llanelli	BSC Tostre Works
173.22000		WFM	Scotland	Singing Kettle Entertainment Group
173.22500		NFM	Nationwide	Suma Designs Bugging Devices
173.35000		NFM	Llanelli	BSC Tostre Works
173.60000		WFM	Worthing	Radio Microphone at Social Club
173.64000		NFM	Jersey	School Deaf Aids
173.64000		NFM	Nationwide	Deaf Aids
173.77500		WFM	Cardiff	Permanent PA Link At Millennium Stadium
173.80000		WFM	Lincolnshire	Lincs FM Radio Microphones (Red)
173.80000		WFM	Nationwide	Unlicensed Radio Microphones Ch.00
173.80000		WFM	Newmarket	Aerobics Club Radio Microphone
173.80000		WFM	Perth	Church Radio Microphone
173.80000		WFM	Preston	Carey Baptist Church Radio Microphone
173.80000		WFM	Swansea	Elim Pentecostal Church Radio Microphone
173.80000		WFM	Woodbridge	Riverside Theatre Radio Microphone
173.80000		WFM	Worcester	Swan Theatre Radio Microphone
173.80000		WFM	Worthing	Community Hall Radio Microphone
173.82500		NFM	Newport	Panic Phone Alarms
173.95000		NFM	Jersey	School Deaf Aids
174.03750		NFM	Scotland	UKSAR GPS Tacking Data Ch.99
174.07500		NFM	Bristol	BBC Radio Microphones
174.08750		NFM	Nationwide	Anglia TV O/B Radio Microphones

Base	Mobile	Mode	Location	User and Notes
174.10000		NFM	Guernsey	Channel TV Radio Microphones
174.10000		WFM	Nationwide	Unlicensed Radio Microphones Ch.01
174.11000		WFM	Scotland	Singing Kettle Entertainment Group
174.11800		WFM	Scotland	Singing Kettle Entertainment Group
174.15000		WFM	Kirkby	Gala Bingo Radio Microphones
174.20000		WFM	Kirkby	Gala Bingo Radio Microphones
174.28750		NFM	Edinburgh	Edinburgh Castle Security
174.30000		WFM	Nationwide	Church Radio Microphones
174.40000		WFM	Kirkby	Gala Bingo Radio Microphones
174.41500		WFM	Kirkby	Gala Bingo Radio Microphones
174.50000		WFM	Glasgow	Baptist Church Radio Microphones
174.50000		WFM	Leicester	Church Radio Mix
174.50000		WFM	Nationwide	Unlicensed Radio Microphones Ch.02
174.50000		WFM	Lincoln	Coral Bingo Radio Microphones
174.50000		WFM	Worcester	Worcester Cathedral Radio Microphones
174.52500		WFM	Nationwide	Low Power Radio Guitar Systems
174.60000		WFM	Nationwide	Unlicensed Radio Microphones
174.66250		WFM	Scarborough	Theatre Radio Microphones
174.70000		NFM	Jersey	BBC Jersey Radio Microphones
174.77000		WFM	Nationwide	Radio Microphones Channel
174.80000		WFM	Blackpool	St Thomas Church Radio Microphones
174.80000		WFM	Nationwide	Unlicensed Radio Microphones
174.80000		WFM	Prescot	Leisure Centre Radio Microphones
174.80000		WFM	Southampton	Mecca Bingo Radio Microphones
174.97500		WFM	Dorset	2CR Radio Microphones
174.98750		WFM	Lincoln	Methodist Church Radio Microphones
175.00000		WFM	Ambleside	Methodist Church Radio Microphones
175.00000		NFM	Jersey	BBC Jersey Radio Microphones
175.00000		NFM	Lincolnshire	Lincs FM Radio Microphones
175.00000		WFM	Nationwide	Unlicensed Radio Microphones
175.00000		WFM	Scotland	Singing Kettle Entertainment Group
175.00000		WFM	St. Helier	Church Radio Microphones
175.08750		NFM	Canvey Island	Trio Radio Cars
175.20000		NFM	Kirkby	Gala Bingo Radio Microphones
175.25000		NFM	Nationwide	Anglia TV O/B Radio Microphones
175.25000		NFM	Nationwide	JFMG Radio Microphones Common Ch.7E
175.52000		NFM	Nationwide	ITV Radio Microphones
175.52500		NFM	Nationwide	Anglia TV O/B Radio Microphones
175.52500		NFM	Nationwide	JFMG Radio Microphones ITV Ch.8A
176.16250		NFM	Sheffield	City Cars
176.18750		NFM	Basildon	Taxi Company
176.40000		NFM	Nationwide	JFMG Radio Microphones Fixed Site Ch.TA
176.40000		NFM	Nationwide	Theatre Radio Microphones
176.60000		NFM	Nationwide	BBC Radio Microphones
176.60000		NFM	Nationwide	JFMG Radio Microphones BBC Ch.8B
176.80000		NFM	Nationwide	BBC News Radio Microphones
177.00000		NFM	Nationwide	JFMG Radio Microphones Fixed Site Ch.TB
177.00000		NFM	Nationwide	Theatre Radio Microphones

177.2000 - 181.7000 MHz — Trunked PMR Base Repeaters 12.5 kHz

Base	Mobile	Mode	Location	User and Notes
177.25000	185.25000	NFM	Bassetlaw	Council Trunked Network
177.25000	185.25000	NFM	Nottingham	Express Transit Trams Mpt1327 Trunked Voice
177.26250	185.26250	NFM	London	Fleetcomm Trunked Control Channel, Crystal Palace
177.28750	185.28750	NFM	London	Camden Council Refuse Team
178.28750	186.28750	NFM	London	Cash in Transit Vans Trunked
177.31250	185.31250	NFM	London	Fleetcomm Trunked Control Channel, Crystal Palace

Base	Mobile	Mode	Location	User and Notes
177.31250	185.31250	NFM	London	Ice Delivery Service
177.31250	185.31250	NFM	St Helens	St Helens Council Mpt1327 Trunk Control Channel
177.32500	185.32500	NFM	Croydon	Tramlink
177.37500	185.37500	NFM	Heathrow	T5 Construction/Security Mpt1327 Trunked Network
177.37500	184.37500	NFM	Southampton	Southampton City Council Trunk Control, Parking Enforcement/Refuse Collectors/Housing Repairs
177.38750	185.38750	NFM	Epping Green	Taxi Company, Welwyn/Hatfield Trunked
177.38750	185.38750	NFM	Hertford	Taxi Company, Fleetcomm Mpt1327 Trunked Voice
177.38750	185.38750	NFM	Nottingham	Express Transit Trams Mpt1327 Trunked Data
177.38750	185.38750	NFM	Sheffield	Sheffield University Trunked Data Control Channel
177.40000	185.40000	NFM	Bassetlaw	Council Trunked
177.40000	185.40000	NFM	Nottingham	Express Transit Trams Mpt1327 Trunked Voice
177.45000	185.45000	NFM	London	The Big Bus Company Trunked Control Channel
177.45000	185.45000	NFM	Nottingham	Express Transit Trams Mpt1327 Trunked Voice
177.45000	18445000	NFM	Southampton	Southampton City Council Parking Enforcement/Refuse Collectors/Housing Repairs Trunked Voice
177.46250	185.46250	NFM	London	Multi-Business Shared Repeater
177.46250	185.46250	NFM	Nottingham	Nottingham City Council Trunked Network
177.46250	185.46250	NFM	Yorkshire	East Riding Council Trunked
177.47500	185.47500	NFM	Croydon	Tramlink
177.47500	185.47500	NFM	Huddersfield	S&W Yorkshire Buses Trunked Network Control
177.47500	185.47500	NFM	Todmorden	S&W Yorkshire Buses Trunked Network Control
177.48750	185.48750	NFM	Heathrow	Plane Handling/Virgin Cargo Trunked
178.48750	186.48750	NFM	London	Cash in Transit Vans Trunked
177.50000	184.50000	NFM	Southampton	Southampton City Council Parking Enforcement/Refuse Collectors/Housing Repairs Trunked Voice
177.52500	18452500	NFM	Southampton	Southampton City Council Parking Enforcement/Refuse Collectors/Housing Repairs Trunked Voice
177.52500	185.52500	NFM	St Helens	St Helens Council Mpt1327 Trunked Voice
177.53750	185.53750	NFM	Epping Green	Taxi Company, Welwyn/Hatfield Trunked
177.53750	185.53750	NFM	Sheffield	Sheffield University Trunked
177.55000	185.55000	NFM	Bassetlaw	Council Trunked
177.55000	185.55000	NFM	Nottingham	Express Transit Trams Mpt1327 Trunked Voice
177.58750	185.58750	NFM	London	Camden Council Refuse Team
178.58750	186.58750	NFM	London	Cash in Transit Vans Trunked
177.60000	185.60000	NFM	London	The Big Bus Company Trunked Voice
177.60000	185.60000	NFM	Nottingham	Express Transit Trams Mpt1327 Trunked Voice
177.61250	185.61250	NFM	London	Courier Service
177.62500	185.62500	NFM	Croydon	Tramlink
177.62500	185.62500	NFM	Doncaster	S&W Yorkshire Buses Trunked Network Voice
177.62500	185.62500	NFM	Reading	Royal Berkshire & Battle Hospital Trust Trunked
177.62500	185.62500	NFM	Todmorden	S&W Yorkshire Buses Trunked Network Voice
177.63750	185.63750	NFM	Heathrow	Plane Handling/Virgin Cargo Trunked
177.63750	185.63750	NFM	Lincolnshire	N Lincolnshire Highways Department
178.63750	186.63750	NFM	London	Cash in Transit Vans Trunked
177.65000	184.65000	NFM	Southampton	Southampton City Council Parking Enforcement/Refuse Collectors/Housing Repairs Trunked Voice
177.67500	185.67500	NFM	Reading	Royal Berkshire & Battle Hospital Trust Trunked
177.67500	184.67500	NFM	Southampton	Southampton City Council Parking Enforcement/Refuse Collectors/Housing Repairs Trunked Control Channel
177.67500	185.67500	NFM	St Helens	St Helens Council Mpt1327 Trunked Voice
177.68750	185.68750	NFM	Epping Green	Taxi Company, Welwyn/Hatfield Trunked
177.68750	185.68750	NFM	Nottingham	Express Trams MPT1327 Trunked Voice
177.68750	185.68750	NFM	Sheffield	Sheffield University Trunked
177.70000	185.70000	NFM	Bassetlaw	Council Trunked
177.70000	185.70000	NFM	Nottingham	Express Trams MPT1327 Trunked Voice

Base	Mobile	Mode	Location	User and Notes
177.72500	185.72500	NFM	Bristol	Parking Enforcement Trunked Data Control
177.73750	185.73750	NFM	London	Camden Council Refuse Team
178.73750	186.73750	NFM	London	Cash in Transit Vans Trunked
177.73750	185.73750	NFM	Reading	Royal Berkshire & Battle Hospital Trust Trunked
177.76250	185.76250	NFM	London/Surrey	RSPCA Trunked
177.76250	185.76250	NFM	Nottingham	Nottingham City Council Trunked Network
177.76250	185.76250	NFM	Yorkshire	East Riding Council Trunked
177.77500	185.77500	NFM	Brighton	Brighton & Hove Buses MPT1327 Trunked
177.77500	185.77500	NFM	Doncaster	S&W Yorkshire Buses Trunked Network Data
177.77500	185.77500	NFM	Heathrow	T5 Construction & Security MPT1327 Trunked Network
177.77500		NFM	Hertford	Fleetcomm MPT1327 Trunked Taxi Data
177.77500	185.77500	NFM	Todmorden	S&W Yorkshire Buses Trunked Network Data
177.78750	185.78750	NFM	Heathrow	Plane Handling/Virgin Cargo Trunked
177.78750	185.78750	NFM	Lincolnshire	N Lincolnshire Highways Department
178.78750	186.78750	NFM	London	Cash in Transit Vans Trunked
177.80000	185.80000	NFM	Nottingham	Express Trams MPT1327 Trunked Voice
177.80000	185.80000	NFM	Reading	Royal Berkshire & Battle Hospital Trust Trunked
177.80000	184.80000	NFM	Southampton	Southampton City Council Parking Enforcement/Refuse Collectors/Housing Repairs Trunked Control Channel
177.81250	185.81250	NFM	Bassetlaw	Council Trunked
178.81250	186.81250	NFM	London	Cash in Transit Vans Trunked
177.81250	185.81250	NFM	London	Sovereign Buses, Harrow
177.85000	185.85000	NFM	Nottingham	Nottingham City Council Trunked Network
177.85000	185.85000	NFM	Sheffield	Sheffield University Trunked
177.87500	185.87500	NFM	Bristol	Parking Enforcement Trunked Voice
177.87500	185.87500	NFM	Epping Green	Taxi Company, Welwyn/Hatfield Trunked
177.88750	185.88750	NFM	London	Camden Council Refuse Team
177.91250	185.91250	NFM	London/Surrey	RSPCA Trunked
177.91250	185.91250	NFM	Nottingham	Nottingham City Council Trunked Network
177.92500	185.92500	NFM	Brighton	Brighton & Hove Buses MPT1327 Trunked
177.92500	185.92500	NFM	Heathrow	T5 Construction & Security MPT1327 Trunked Network
177.92500	185.92500	NFM	Reading	Royal Berkshire & Battle Hospital Trust Trunked
177.92500	185.92500	NFM	St Helens	St Helens Council MPT1327 Trunked Voice
177.93750	185.93750	NFM	Heathrow	Plane Handling/Virgin Cargo Trunked
177.93750	185.93750	NFM	Lincolnshire	N Lincolnshire Highways Department
177.95000	185.95000	NFM	London	The Big Bus Company Trunked Voice
178.00000	186.00000	NFM	Nottingham	Express Trams MPT1327 Trunked Voice
178.02500	186.25000	NFM	Bristol	Parking Enforcement Trunked Voice/Data Channel
178.06250	186.06250	NFM	London/Surrey	RSPCA Trunked
178.08750	186.08750	NFM	Heathrow	Plane Handling/Virgin Cargo Trunked
178.11250	186.11250	NFM	Lincolnshire	N Lincolnshire Highways Department
178.11250	186.11250	NFM	London	Camden Council Refuse Team
178.13750	186.13750	NFM	Epping Green	Taxi Company, Welwyn/Hatfield Trunked
178.15000	186.15000	NFM	Heathrow	T5 Construction & Security MPT1327 Trunked Network
178.15000	186.15000	NFM	Nottingham	Express Trams MPT1327 Trunked Voice
178.18750	186.18750	NFM	London	Sovereign Buses, Harrow
178.23750	186.23750	NFM	Heathrow	Plane Handling/Virgin Cargo Trunked
178.23750	186.23750	NFM	Nottingham	Nottingham City Council Trunked Network
178.23750	186.23750	NFM	Yorkshire	East Riding Council Trunked
178.26250	186.26250	NFM	London	Camden Council Refuse Team
178.28750	186.28750	NFM	Epping Green	Taxi Company, Welwyn/Hatfield Trunked
178.28750		NFM	Hertford	Fleetcomm MPT1327 Taxi Company Trunked Voice
178.30000	186.30000	NFM	Heathrow	T5 Construction & Security MPT1327 Trunked Network
178.32500	186.32500	NFM	London	Hammersmith & Fulham Council Trunked
178.38750	186.38750	NFM	Heathrow	Plane Handling/Virgin Cargo Trunked
178.41250	186.41250	NFM	London	Camden Council Refuse Team

Base	Mobile	Mode	Location	User and Notes
178.43750	186.43750	NFM	Epping Green	Taxi Company, Welwyn/Hatfield Trunked
178.45000	186.45000	NFM	Chapeltown	S&W Yorkshire Buses Trunked Network Control
178.45000	186.45000	NFM	Doncaster	S&W Yorkshire Buses Trunked Network Control
178.45000	186.45000	NFM	Heathrow	T5 Construction & Security MPT1327 Trunked Network
178.45000	186.45000	NFM	Todmorden	S&W Yorkshire Buses Trunked Network Control
178.51250	186.51250	NFM	Nottingham	Nottingham City Council Trunked Network
178.51250	186.51250	NFM	Yorkshire	East Riding Council Trunked Control Data Channel
178.56250	186.56250	NFM	London	Camden Council Refuse Team
178.60000	186.60000	NFM	Heathrow	T5 Construction & Security MPT1327 Trunked Network
178.61250	186.61250	NFM	London	Doctors' Service Trunked
178.61250	186.61250	NFM	London	The Big Bus Company Trunked Voice
178.63750	186.63750	NFM	Emley Moor	Fleetcomm Multi User MPT1327 Voice
178.71250	186.71250	NFM	London	Camden Council Refuse Team
178.76250	186.76250	NFM	London	Doctors' Service Trunked
178.78750	186.78750	NFM	Emley Moor	Fleetcomm Multi User MPT1327 Voice
178.80000	186.80000	NFM	Nationwide	JFMG Radio Microphones Ch 8C
178.81250	186.81250	NFM	Nottingham	Nottingham City Council Trunked Network
178.83750	186.83750	NFM	Heathrow	Plane Handling/Virgin Cargo Trunked
178.86250	186.86250	NFM	London	Camden Council Refuse Team
178.91250	186.91250	NFM	London	Doctors' Service Trunked
178.93750	186.93750	NFM	Emley Moor	Fleetcomm Multi User MPT1327 Voice
178.96250	186.96250	NFM	London/Surrey	RSPCA Trunked
178.96250	186.96250	NFM	Nottingham	Nottingham City Council Trunked Network
178.97500	186.97500	NFM	London	The Big Bus Company Trunked Voice
178.98750	186.98750	NFM	Heathrow	Plane Handling/Virgin Cargo Trunked
179.01250	187.01250	NFM	London	Barnet Council Refuse Collection
179.01250	187.01250	NFM	London	Camden Council Refuse Team
179.01250	187.01250	NFM	London	Havering Council Refuse Collection
179.03750	187.03750	NFM	London	Cash in Transit Vans Trunked
179.08750	187.08750	NFM	Emley Moor	Fleetcomm Multi User MPT1327 Voice
179.11250	187.11250	NFM	Nottingham	Nottingham City Council Trunked Network
179.13750	187.13750	NFM	Heathrow	Plane Handling/Virgin Cargo Trunked
179.16250	187.16250	NFM	London	Camden Council Refuse Team
179.20000	187.20000	NFM	Portsmouth	Council Multi User Trunked System Voice Channel
179.20000	187.20000	NFM	Portsmouth	Solent First Bus Multi User Trunked System Voice
179.27500	187.27500	NFM	Nottingham	Nottingham City Council Trunked Network
179.28750	187.28750	NFM	Heathrow	Plane Handling/Virgin Cargo Trunked
179.31250	187.31250	NFM	London	Camden Council Refuse Team
179.33750	187.33750	NFM	London	Cash in Transit Vans Trunked
179.3875	187.2875	NFM	London	Hotellink Mpt1327 Single Channel Trunked System
179.43750	187.43750	NFM	Heathrow	Plane Handling/Virgin Cargo Trunked
179.46250	187.46250	NFM	London	Camden Council Refuse Team
179.48750	187.48750	NFM	London	Cash in Transit Vans Trunked
179.50000	187.50000	NFM	London	Cash in Transit Vans Trunked
179.50000	187.50000	NFM	Portsmouth	Council Multi User Trunk System Voice Channel
179.50000	187.50000	NFM	Portsmouth	Solent First Bus Multi User Trunk System Voice
179.52500	187.52500	NFM	Huddersfield	S&W Yorkshire Buses Trunked Network Data
179.52500	187.52500	NFM	London	The Big Bus Company Trunked Voice
179.58750	187.58750	NFM	Heathrow	Plane Handling/Virgin Cargo Trunked
179.65000	187.65000	NFM	Hampshire	Hampshire Ambulance Patient Transport Service
179.65000	187.65000	NFM	Portsmouth	Council Multi User Trunk System Voice Channel
179.65000	187.65000	NFM	Portsmouth	Solent First Bus Multi User Trunk System Voice
179.66250	187.66250	NFM	Leeds	Leeds City Council Trunked System
179.66250	187.66250	NFM	London	Barnet Council Refuse Collection
179.66250	187.66250	NFM	London	Havering Council Refuse Collection
179.73750	187.73750	NFM	Heathrow	Plane Handling/Virgin Cargo Trunked

Base	Mobile	Mode	Location	User and Notes
179.75000	187.75000	NFM	London	Evening Standard Deliveries
179.80000	187.80000	NFM	Portsmouth	Council Multi User Trunk System Voice Channel
179.80000	187.80000	NFM	Portsmouth	Solent First Bus Multi User Trunk System Voice
179.81250	187.81250	NFM	Leeds	Leeds City Council Trunked System
179.86250	187.86250	NFM	Newcastle	Newcastle City Trunked
179.88750	187.88750	NFM	Heathrow	Plane Handling/Virgin Cargo Trunked
179.92500	187.92500	NFM	London	Camden Council Refuse Team
179.93750	187.93750	NFM	Birmingham	Buses/Road Sweeper/Vending Co/Taxis Trunked Voice
179.93750	187.93750	NFM	London	Cash in Transit Vans Trunked
179.95000	187.95000	NFM	Portsmouth	Council Multi User Trunk System Voice Channel
179.95000	187.95000	NFM	Portsmouth	Solent First Bus Multi User Trunk System Voice
179.96250	187.96250	NFM	Chapeltown	S&W Yorkshire Buses Trunked Network Voice
179.96250	187.96250	NFM	Leeds	Leeds City Council Trunked System
180.00000		NFM	Nationwide	Illegal Bugging Devices
180.03750	188.03750	NFM	Heathrow	Plane Handling/Virgin Cargo Trunked
180.03750	188.03750	NFM	London	Evening Standard Deliveries
180.07500	187.07500	NFM	London	Camden Council Refuse Team
180.08750	188.08750	NFM	Birmingham	Buses/Road Sweeper/Vending Co/Taxis Trunked Voice
180.10000	188.10000	NFM	Portsmouth	Council Multi User Trunk System Voice Channel
180.10000	188.10000	NFM	Portsmouth	Solent First Bus Multi User Trunk System Voice
180.11250	188.11250	NFM	Leeds	Leeds City Council Trunked System
180.15000	188.15000	NFM	Emley Moor	Fleetcomm Multi User MPT1327 Voice
180.15000	188.15000	NFM	Heathrow	Plane Handling/Virgin Cargo Trunked
180.16250	188.16250	NFM	London	Cash in Transit Vans Trunked
180.20000	188.20000	NFM	Portsmouth	Council Multi User Trunk System Data Control Channel
180.20000	188.20000	NFM	Portsmouth	Solent First Bus Multi User Trunk System Data Control
180.23750	188.23750	NFM	Birmingham	Buses/Road Sweeper/Vending Co/Taxis Trunked Voice
180.26250	188.26250	NFM	Leeds	Leeds City Council Trunked System
180.27500	188.27500	NFM	Glasgow	South Lanarkshire Council MPT1327 Trunked System
180.28750	188.28750	NFM	London	Camden Council Refuse Team
180.30000	188.30000	NFM	Berkshire	Berkshire Ambulance Patient Transport Service
180.30000	190.30000	NFM	Emley Moor	Fleetcomm Multi User MPT1327 Data Control
180.32500	187.32500	NFM	Chapeltown	S&W Yorkshire Buses Trunked Network Data
180.32500	187.32500	NFM	London	The Original Tour Bus, Arriva Buses
180.35000	188.35000	NFM	London	Banham Burglary Prevention Alarms
180.35000	188.35000	NFM	Portsmouth	Council Multi User Trunk System Voice Channel
180.35000	188.35000	NFM	Portsmouth	Solent First Bus Multi User Trunk System Voice
180.37500	188.37500	NFM	Shropshire	Multi User Fleetcom Trunked Network Control
180.40000	188.40000	NFM	Portsmouth	Fleetcomm Multi User Trunked System Data Control
180.40000	188.40000	NFM	Portsmouth	Ambulance Service Patient Transport Service Trunked
180.42500	188.42500	NFM	London	Multi-Business Shared Repeater
180.45000	188.45000	NFM	Birmingham	Buses/Road Sweeper/Vending Co/Taxis Trunked Voice
180.48750	188.48750	NFM	Glasgow	South Lanarkshire Council MPT1327 Trunked System
180.52500	188.52500	NFM	Leeds	Leeds City Council Trunked System
180.52500	188.52500	NFM	Shropshire	Multi User Fleetcom Trunked Network Voice
180.56250	188.56250	NFM	Glasgow	South Lanarkshire Council MPT1327 Trunked System
180.60000	188.60000	NFM	Portsmouth	Fleetcomm Multi User Trunked System Voice
180.60000	188.60000	NFM	Portsmouth	Ambulance Service Patient Transport Trunked
180.62500	188.62500	NFM	Chapeltown	S&W Yorkshire Buses Trunked Network Voice
180.67500	188.67500	NFM	Bedfordshire	Mid Bedfordshire Council Trunked
180.67500	188.67500	NFM	Shropshire	Multi User Fleetcom Trunked Network Voice
180.68750	188.68750	NFM	Birmingham	Buses/Road Sweeper/Vending Co/Taxis Trunked Voice
180.70000	188.70000	NFM	Portsmouth	Council Multi User Trunk System Voice Channel
180.70000	188.70000	NFM	Portsmouth	Solent First Bus Multi User Trunk System Voice
180.71250	188.71250	NFM	Glasgow	South Lanarkshire Council MPT1327 Trunked System
180.71250	188.71250	NFM	Leeds	Leeds City Council Trunked System

Base	Mobile	Mode	Location	User and Notes
180.75000	188.75000	NFM	Emley Moor	Fleetcomm Multi User MPT1327 Voice
180.75000	188.75000	NFM	Portsmouth	Fleetcomm Multi User Trunked System Voice
180.75000	188.75000	NFM	Portsmouth	Ambulance Service Patient Transport Trunked
180.78750	188.78750	NFM	Glasgow	South Lanarkshire Council MPT1327 Trunk System
180.82500	188.82500	NFM	Bedfordshire	Mid Bedfordshire Council Trunked
180.82500	188.82500	NFM	Shropshire	Multi User Fleetcom Trunked Network Voice
180.85000	188.85000	NFM	Portsmouth	Council Multi User Trunk System Voice Channel
180.85000	188.85000	NFM	Portsmouth	Solent First Bus Multi User Trunk System Voice
180.90000	188.90000	NFM	Portsmouth	Fleetcomm Multi User Trunked System Voice
180.90000	188.90000	NFM	Portsmouth	Ambulance Service Patient Transport Trunked
180.93750	189.93750	NFM	Bournemouth	Drainbusters Limited
180.93750	118.03750	NFM	Glasgow	South Lanarkshire Council MPT1327 Trunked
181.01250	189.01250	NFM	Guiseley	S&W Yorkshire Buses Trunked Network Control
181.01250	189.01250	NFM	Seacroft	S&W Yorkshire Buses Trunked Network Control
181.05000	189.05000	NFM	Portsmouth	Fleetcomm Multi User Trunked System Voice
181.05000	189.05000	NFM	Portsmouth	Ambulance Service Patient Transport Trunked
181.06250	189.66250	NFM	Newcastle	Newcastle City Trunked
181.12500	189.12500	NFM	Bedfordshire	Mid Bedfordshire Council Trunked
181.12500	189.12500	NFM	Shropshire	Multi User Fleetcom Trunked Network Voice
181.16250	189.16250	NFM	Guiseley	S&W Yorkshire Buses Trunked Network Voice
181.17500	189.17500	NFM	Heathrow	T5 Construction & Security MPT1327 Trunked
181.17500	189.17500	NFM	Milton Keynes	Skips/Waste Disposal Multi User Trunked System
181.20000	189.20000	NFM	High Hunsley	Fleetcomm National Band 111 Trunk MPT1327
181.20000	189.20000	NFM	Pocklington	Orchard Taxis
181.20000	189.20000	NFM	Portsmouth	Fleetcomm Multi User Trunked System Voice
181.20000	189.20000	NFM	Portsmouth	Ambulance Service Patient Transport Trunked
181.21250	189.21250	NFM	Newcastle	Newcastle City Trunked
181.23750	189.23750	NFM	Bassetlaw	Council Trunked
181.26250	189.26250	NFM	Berkshire	Ambulance Service Patient Transport
181.27500	189.27500	NFM	Bedfordshire	Mid Bedfordshire Council Trunked
181.28750	189.28750	NFM	Glasgow	Amey Roadstone Gritters MPT1327 Trunked
181.30000	189.30000	NFM	Leeds	Leeds City Council Trunked System
181.32500	189.32500	NFM	Bedfordshire	Mid Bedfordshire Council Trunked
181.32500	189.32500	NFM	Glasgow	South Lanarkshire Council MPT1327 Trunked
181.35000	189.35000	NFM	High Hunsley	Fleetcomm National Band III Trunked MPT1327
181.35000	189.35000	NFM	Portsmouth	Fleetcomm Multi User Trunked System Voice
181.35000	189.35000	NFM	Portsmouth	Ambulance Service Patient Transport Trunked
181.36250	189.36250	NFM	Newcastle	Newcastle City Trunked
181.42500	189.42500	NFM	Guiseley	S&W Yorkshire Buses Trunked Network Data
181.45000	189.45000	NFM	Leeds	Leeds City Council Trunked System
181.47500	189.37500	NFM	Milton Keynes	Skips/Waste Disposal Multi User Trunked System
181.50000	189.50000	NFM	High Hunsley	Fleetcomm National Band III Trunked MPT1327
181.57500	189.57500	NFM	Seacroft	S&W Yorkshire Buses Trunked Network Voice
181.58750	189.58750	NFM	Glasgow	Amey Roadstone Gritters MPT1327 Trunked
181.60000	189.60000	NFM	Portsmouth	Fleetcomm Multi User Trunked System Voice
181.60000	189.60000	NFM	Portsmouth	Ambulance Service Patient Transport Trunked
181.61250	189.61250	NFM	Glasgow	South Lanarkshire Council MPT1327 Trunked
181.61250	189.61250	NFM	Leeds	Leeds City Council Trunked System
181.62500	189.62500	NFM	Milton Keynes	Skips/Waste Disposal Multi User Trunked System
181.65000	189.65000	NFM	High Hunsley	Fleetcomm National Band III Trunked MPT1327
181.69375		NFM	Nationwide	JFMG Wide Area Camera Control Data Channel
181.72500		NFM	Nationwide	ITN Radio Microphones
181.77500		NFM	Nationwide	BBC Digital O/B Datalink
181.80625		NFM	Nationwide	JFMG Wide Area Camera Control Data Channel
181.85000	189.85000	NFM	Portsmouth	Fleetcomm Multi User Trunked System Voice
181.85000	189.85000	NFM	Portsmouth	Ambulance Service Patient Transport Trunked

Base	Mobile	Mode	Location	User and Notes
181.87500	189.87500	NFM	Seacroft	S&W Yorkshire Buses Trunked Network Data
181.88750	189.88750	NFM	Leeds	Leeds City Council Trunked System
181.90000	189.90000	NFM	Glasgow	Amey Roadstone Gritters MPT1327 Trunked
181.92500	189.92500	NFM	Bedfordshire	Mid Bedfordshire Council Trunked
182.00000	190.00000	NFM	Portsmouth	Fleetcomm Multi User Trunked System Voice
182.00000	190.00000	NFM	Portsmouth	Ambulance Service Patient Transport Trunked
182.03750	190.03750	NFM	Leeds	Leeds City Council Trunked System
182.07500	190.07500	NFM	Bedfordshire	Mid Bedfordshire Council Trunked
182.11250	190.11250	NFM	Birmingham	Ring & Ride MPT1327 Trunked Control Channel
182.16250	190.16250	NFM	High Hunsley	Fleetcomm National Band III Trunked MPT1327
182.22500	190.22500	NFM	Bedfordshire	Mid Bedfordshire Council Trunked
182.23750	190.23750	NFM	Mendip	Multi User Trunk System Data Control Channel
182.25000	190.25000	NFM	Emley Moor	Fleetcomm Multi User MPT1327 Voice
182.26250	190.26250	NFM	Birmingham	Ring & Ride MPT1327 Trunk Voice Channel
182.35000	190.35000	NFM	Bedworth	Multi User/Bus Company MPT1327 Trunked Data
182.35000	190.35000	NFM	Corley	Interlink Parcels/Abbey Taxis/Buses/Skip Hire Trunked
182.37500	190.37500	NFM	Bedfordshire	Mid Bedfordshire Council Trunked
182.37500	190.37500	NFM	Milton Keynes	Skips/Waste Disposal Multi User Trunked System
182.38750	190.38750	NFM	Mendip	Fleetcomm Multi User Trunk System
182.41250	190.41250	NFM	Birmingham	Ring & Ride MPT1327 Trunk Voice Channel
182.50000	190.50000	NFM	Bedworth	Multi User/Bus Company MPT1327 Trunked Voice
182.50000	190.50000	NFM	Corley	Interlink Parcels/Abbey Taxis/Buses/Skip Hire Trunked
182.50000	190.50000	NFM	West Midlands	Watch Security
182.52500	190.52500	NFM	Milton Keynes	Skips/Waste Disposal Multi User Trunked System
182.53750	190.53750	NFM	Mendip	Fleetcomm Multi User Trunk System
182.58750	190.58750	NFM	Birmingham	Ring & Ride MPT1327 Trunk Voice Channel
182.61250	190.61250	NFM	Heathrow	T5 Construction & Security MPT1327 Trunked
182.61250	190.61250	NFM	Nottingham	Nottingham Radio Telephones Trunked Network
182.65000	190.65000	NFM	Bedworth	Multi User/Bus Company MPT1327 Trunked Voice
182.65000	190.65000	NFM	Corley	Interlink Parcels/Abbey Taxis/Buses/Skip Hire Trunked
182.65000	190.65000	NFM	West Midlands	Watch Security
182.68750	190.68750	NFM	Mendip	Fleetcomm Multi User Trunk System
182.73750	190.73750	NFM	Birmingham	Ring & Ride MPT1327 Trunk Voice Channel
182.76250	190.76250	NFM	Nottingham	Nottingham Radio Telephones Trunked Network
182.80000	190.80000	NFM	Bedworth	Multi User/Bus Company MPT1327 Trunked Voice
182.80000	190.80000	NFM	Corley	Interlink Parcels/Abbey Taxis/Buses/Skip Hire Trunked
182.83750	190.83750	NFM	Mendip	Fleetcomm Multi User Trunk System
182.88750	190.88750	NFM	Birmingham	Ring & Ride MPT1327 Trunk Voice Channel
182.91250	190.91250	NFM	Heathrow	T5 Construction & Security MPT1327 Trunked Network
182.91250	190.91250	NFM	Nottingham	Nottingham Radio Telephones Trunked Network
183.06250	191.06250	NFM	Nottingham	Nottingham Radio Telephones Trunked Network
183.21250	191.21250	NFM	Nottingham	Nottingham Radio Telephones Trunked Network

181.8000 - 183.5000 MHz   PMR 12.5 kHz NFM Duplex

Base	Mobile	Mode	Location	User and Notes
182.05000		NFM	Hyde	Florist
182.12500		NFM	Oldham	Skip Hire Company
182.28750		NFM	Oldham	Alarm Company
182.28750		NFM	Oldham	Browns Car Factors
182.40000	190.20000	NFM	Sheffield	Fleetcomm Trunked Voice
182.50000	190.50000	NFM	West Midlands	Watch Security
182.65000	190.65000	NFM	West Midlands	Watch Security

183.5000 - 184.5000 MHz   Meter Reading

Allocated To Future Remote Meter Reading Applications - MPT1601.

Base	Mobile	Mode	Location	User and Notes

184.5000 - 185.1000 MHz   Radio Microphones

Base	Mobile	Mode	Location	User and Notes
181.69375		NFM	Nationwide	JFMG Wide Area TB/Camera CTRI Data
181.80625		NFM	Nationwide	JFMG Wide Area TB/Camera CTRI Data
184.60000		NFM	Nationwide	BBC News Radio Microphones
184.60000		NFM	Nationwide	JFMG Radio Microphones BBC News Ch.9C
184.80000		NFM	Jersey	Channel TV Radio Microphones
184.80000		NFM	Nationwide	Anglia TV O/B Radio Microphones
184.80000		NFM	Nationwide	ITV Radio Microphones
184.80000		NFM	Nationwide	JFMG Radio Microphones ITV Ch.9A
185.00000		NFM	Nationwide	ITV Radio Microphones
185.00000		NFM	Nationwide	JFMG Radio Microphones ILR Ch.11D
185.00000		NFM	Tayside	Radio Tay O/B Microphones

185.2000 - 201.0000 MHz   Broadcasting Links & Radio Microphones

Base	Mobile	Mode	Location	User and Notes
187.40000		NFM	Ipswich	SGR FM Radio O/B
189.69375		NFM	Nationwide	JFMG Wide Area TB/Camera Control Data
189.70250		NFM	Twickenham	BBC ITV Links
189.77500		NFM	London	ITN News Camera-Engineering Van (118.8)
189.79380		NFM	Twickenham	BBC ITV Links
189.80625		NFM	Nationwide	JFMG Wide Area TB/Camera Control Data
191.60000		NFM	London	Network 10 Australia Radio Microphones
191.62500		NFM	Nationwide	Sky News Radio Microphones
191.63750		NFM	Nationwide	Sky News Radio Microphones
191.70000		NFM	Nationwide	JFMG Radio Microphones
191.70000		NFM	London	Network 10 Australia Radio Microphones
191.90000		NFM	Nationwide	JFMG Radio Microphones mobile Ch.ML1
191.90000		NFM	Scarborough	Theatre Radio Microphones
191.90000		NFM	Woodbridge	Riverside Theatre Radio Microphones
192.10000		NFM	Nationwide	JFMG Radio Microphones ILR Ch.14D
192.30000		NFM	Nationwide	JFMG Radio Microphones
191.50000		NFM	London	Network 10 Australia Radio Microphones
191.52500		NFM	London	Network 10 Australia Radio Microphones
191.65000		NFM	London	Network 10 Australia Radio Microphones
191.90000	467.26880	NFM	Nationwide	Radio 5 Live Talkback Radio Microphone Ch.1
192.60000		NFM	Nationwide	JFMG Radio Microphones BBC News Ch.10C
192.60000		NFM	Nationwide	BBC News Radio Microphones
192.80000		NFM	London	Network 10 Australia Radio Microphones
192.80000		NFM	Nationwide	Anglia TV O/B Radio Microphones
192.80000		WFM	Nationwide	BBC Antiques Roadshow Radio Microphones
192.80000		NFM	Nationwide	JFMG Radio Microphones ITV Ch.10A
192.80000		NFM	Nationwide	ITV Radio Microphones
193.00000		NFM	Nationwide	JFMG Radio Microphones BBC Ch.9B
193.00000		NFM	Nationwide	BBC Radio Microphones
199.70000		WFM	Ipswich	Hospital Radio O/B Link
199.70000		NFM	Nationwide	JFMG Radio Microphones Mobile Ch.ML28
199.70000		WFM	Nationwide	JFMG Stereo Sound Link
199.70000		WFM	Nationwide	Sky Sports Engineering Radio Microphones
199.70000		WFM	Woodbridge	Riverside Theatre Radio Microphones
199.90000		WFM	Nationwide	JFMG Stereo O/B Sound Link
199.90000	467.55625	WFM	Nationwide	Radio 5 Live Talkback Radio Microphone Ch.2
200.10000		NFM	Nationwide	JFMG Radio Microphones
200.30000		NFM	Nationwide	JFMG Radio Microphones Ch.ML8
200.30000		WFM	Scarborough	Theatre Radio Microphones
200.30000		WFM	Woodbridge	Riverside Theatre Radio Microphones

Base	Mobile	Mode	Location	User and Notes

200.5000 - 201.0000 MHz — Radio Microphones

Base	Mobile	Mode	Location	User and Notes
200.50000		NFM	Nationwide	Radio Microphones
200.60000		NFM	Nationwide	JFMG Radio Microphones BBC Ch.10B
200.60000		NFM	Nationwide	BBC Radio Microphones
200.60000		NFM	Nationwide	BBC Antiques Roadshow Radio Microphones
200.80000		NFM	London	94.8 Capital Radio Microphones
200.80000		NFM	Nationwide	JFMG Radio Microphones ITN Ch.12D
200.80000		NFM	Nationwide	ITV News Radio Microphones
201.00000		NFM	Jersey	Channel TV Radio Microphones
201.00000		NFM	Nationwide	Anglia TV O/B Radio Microphones
201.00000		NFM	Nationwide	JFMG Radio Microphones ITV Ch.11A
201.00000		NFM	Nationwide	ITV Radio Microphones

201.1125 - 207.5000 MHz — Trunked Base PMR 12.5 kHz

Base	Mobile	Mode	Location	User and Notes
201.31250	193.31250	NFM	Edinburgh	Lothian Regional Transport Buses, Dunearn Farm
201.31250	193.31250	NFM	London	London Buses, Guys Hospital
201.31250	193.31250	NFM	Nationwide	National Bus Allocation
201.35000	193.85000	NFM	Perth	Stagecoach Buses
201.36250	193.36250	NFM	London	London Buses, Trellick Tower
201.36250	193.36250	NFM	Nationwide	National Bus Allocation
201.40000	193.40000	NFM	Perth	Stagecoach Buses
201.41250	193.41250	NFM	Alder Valley	Bus Company
201.41250	193.41250	NFM	London	London Buses, Streatham Bus Depot
201.41250	193.41250	NFM	Nationwide	National Bus Allocation
201.41250	193.41250	NFM	Wiltshire/Dorset	Wiltshire & Dorset Buses, Whitefields Hill
201.45000	193.45000	NFM	London	Fleetcom Trunked Net Control, Sysid 10233
201.46250	193.46250	NFM	Glasgow	Buses, Shawhill Road
201.46250	193.46250	NFM	Leeds	First Bus
201.46250	193.46250	NFM	London	London Buses, Guys Hospital
201.46250	193.46250	NFM	Nationwide	National Bus Allocation
201.51250	193.51250	NFM	Cardiff	Cardiff Buses
201.51250	193.51250	NFM	Edinburgh	Lothian Regional Transport Buses, Falside
201.51250	193.51250	NFM	London	London Buses, Trellick Tower
201.51250	193.51250	NFM	Nationwide	National Bus Allocation
201.51250	193.51250	NFM	Sheffield	Stagecoach Supertram Voice
201.52500	193.52500	NFM	Hull	Mobile Doctors' Service
201.55000	193.55000	NFM	Perth	Stagecoach Buses
201.56250	193.56250	NFM	Glasgow	Buses, Red Rocourt
201.56250	193.56250	NFM	London	London Buses
201.56250	193.56250	NFM	London	London Buses, Streatham Bus Depot
201.56250	193.56250	NFM	Manchester	Manchester Metrolink Control
201.56250	193.56250	NFM	Nationwide	National Bus Allocation
201.60000	193.60000	NFM	London	Fleetcom Trunked Net Voice, Sysid 10233
201.61250	193.61250	NFM	Cardiff	Cardiff Buses Data Control
201.61250	193.61250	NFM	Glasgow	Buses, Shawhill Road
201.61250	193.61250	NFM	London	London Buses, Guys Hospital
201.61250	193.61250	NFM	Nationwide	National Bus Allocation
201.65000	193.65000	NFM	London	Doctors' Service
201.66250	193.66250	NFM	Birmingham	West Midlands Travel, Barr Beacon Reservoir
201.66250	193.66250	NFM	Cardiff	Cardiff Buses
201.66250	193.66250	NFM	Chester	Bus Company
201.66250	193.66250	NFM	Darlington	Bus Company
201.66250	193.66250	NFM	Edinburgh	Lothian Regional Transport Buses, Dunearn Farm
201.66250	193.66250	NFM	London	London Buses, Trellick Tower

Base	Mobile	Mode	Location	User and Notes
201.66250	193.66250	NFM	Nationwide	National Bus Allocation
201.70000	193.70000	NFM	Perth	Stagecoach Buses
201.71250	193.71250	NFM	Cardiff	Cardiff Buses
201.71250	193.71250	NFM	Edinburgh	Lothian Regional Transport Buses, Falside
201.71250	193.71250	NFM	Halifax	First Bus Control/Voice
201.71250	193.71250	NFM	London	London Buses, Streatham Bus Depot
201.71250	193.71250	NFM	Nationwide	National Bus Allocation
201.71250	193.71250	NFM	Tyne & Wear	Bus Company
201.71250	193.71250	NFM	Wiltshire/Dorset	Wiltshire & Dorset Buses, Whitefields Hill
201.76250	193.76250	NFM	London	London Buses, Guys Hospital
201.76250	193.76250	NFM	Nationwide	National Bus Allocation
201.81250	193.81250	NFM	Cardiff	Cardiff Buses
201.81250	193.81250	NFM	Edinburgh	Lothian Regional Transport Buses, Edinburgh Castle
201.81250	193.81250	NFM	Liverpool	Buses, Neville House Farm
201.81250	193.81250	NFM	London	London Buses, Alexandra Palace
201.81250	193.81250	NFM	Nationwide	National Bus Allocation
201.85000	193.85000	NFM	Perth	Stagecoach Buses
201.86250	193.86250	NFM	Glasgow	Buses, Shawhill Road
201.86250	193.86250	NFM	London	London Buses, Streatham Bus Depot
201.86250	193.86250	NFM	Nationwide	National Bus Allocation
201.86250	193.86250	NFM	Wiltshire/Dorset	Wiltshire & Dorset Buses, Whitefields Hill
201.90000	193.90000	NFM	Bristol	Zycall Multi-User Trunked System Control Channel
201.90000	193.90000	NFM	London	Fleetcom Trunked Net Voice, Sysid 10233
201.91250	193.91250	NFM	Edinburgh	Lothian Regional Transport Buses, Dunearn Farm
201.91250	193.91250	NFM	Halifax	First Bus Control/Voice
201.91250	193.91250	NFM	London	London Buses
201.91250	193.91250	NFM	Lothian	First Bus
201.91250	193.91250	NFM	Nationwide	National Bus Allocation
201.91250	193.91250	NFM	Warrington	Buses
201.96250	193.96250	NFM	Bristol	Buses
201.96250	193.96250	NFM	Cardiff	Cardiff Buses
201.96250	193.96250	NFM	Edinburgh	Lothian Regional Transport Buses, Falside
201.96250	193.96250	NFM	Liverpool	Buses, Bennett Street
201.96250	193.96250	NFM	London	London Buses, Alexandra Palace
201.96250	193.96250	NFM	Nationwide	National Bus Allocation
202.00000	194.00000	NFM	Perth	Stagecoach Buses
202.01250	194.01250	NFM	Bristol	Buses
202.01250	194.01250	NFM	Derby	Buses
202.01250	194.01250	NFM	Liverpool	Buses, Neville House Farm
202.01250	194.01250	NFM	London	London Buses, Streatham Bus Depot
202.01250	194.01250	NFM	Nationwide	National Bus Allocation
202.01250	194.01250	NFM	Tyne & Wear	Buses
202.01250	194.01250	NFM	Wiltshire/Dorset	Wiltshire & Dorset Buses, Whitefields Hill
202.05000	194.05000	NFM	London	Fleetcom Trunked Net Voice, Sysid 10233
202.06250	194.06250	NFM	Edinburgh	Lothian Regional Transport Buses, Edinburgh Castle
202.06250	194.06250	NFM	London	London Buses, Guys Hospital
202.06250	194.06250	NFM	Manchester	Manchester Metrolink
202.06250	194.06250	NFM	Nationwide	National Bus Allocation
202.06250	194.06250	NFM	Sheffield	Mainline Buses Trunked, Olive Grove
202.11250	194.11250	NFM	Glasgow	Buses, Red Rocourt
202.11250	194.12250	NFM	Liverpool	Buses, Cow Lane
202.11250	194.11250	NFM	London	London Buses, Alexandra Palace
202.11250	194.11250	NFM	Nationwide	National Bus Allocation
202.11250	194.11250	NFM	Nationwide	National Express Buses
202.15000	194.15000	NFM	Perth	Stagecoach Buses

Base	Mobile	Mode	Location	User and Notes
202.16250	194.16250	NFM	Avon	Zycomm Radio Site
202.16250	194.16250	NFM	Birmingham	West Midlands Travel, Barr Beacon Reservoir
202.16250	194.16250	NFM	Glasgow	Buses, Shawhill Road
202.16250	194.16250	NFM	Liverpool	Buses, Bennett Street
202.16250	194.16250	NFM	London	London Buses, Streatham Bus Depot
202.16250	194.16250	NFM	Nationwide	National Bus Allocation
202.16250	194.16250	NFM	Nationwide	National Express Buses
202.16250	194.16250	NFM	Wiltshire/Dorset	Wiltshire & Dorset Buses, Morgans Hill
202.21250	194.21250	NFM	Birmingham	West Midlands Travel, Harts Hill Garage
202.21250	194.21250	NFM	Edinburgh	Lothian Regional Transport Buses, Falside
202.21250	194.21250	NFM	London	London Buses, Alexandra Palace
202.21250	194.21250	NFM	London	London Buses, Guys Hospital
202.21250	194.76250	NFM	London	London Buses, Trellick Tower
202.21250	194.21250	NFM	Nationwide	National Bus Allocation
202.21250	194.21250	NFM	Sheffield	Stagecoach Supertram Voice (1)
202.23750	194.23750	NFM	London	Fleetcom Trunked Net Voice, Sysid 10225
202.26250	194.26250	NFM	Glasgow	Buses, Red Rocourt
202.26250	194.26250	NFM	Liverpool	Buses, Cow Lane
202.26250	194.26250	NFM	Maidstone	Buses
202.26250	194.26250	NFM	Nationwide	National Bus Allocation
202.26250	194.26250	NFM	Oxford	Cityline Bus Company
202.28750	194.28750	NFM	London	London Buses
202.31250	194.31250	NFM	Edinburgh	Lothian Regional Transport Buses, Edinburgh Castle
202.31250	194.31250	NFM	Liverpool	Buses, Bennett Street
202.31250	194.31250	NFM	London	London Buses, Streatham Bus Depot
202.31250	194.31250	NFM	Nationwide	National Bus Allocation
202.31250	194.31250	NFM	Swindon	Stagecoach
202.31250	194.31250	NFM	Tyne & Wear	Buses
202.31750	194.31750	NFM	London	London Buses Revenue Protection Inspectors
202.36250	194.36250	NFM	Edinburgh	Lothian Regional Transport Buses, Dunearn Farm
202.36250	194.36250	NFM	Liverpool	Buses, Birtle
202.36250	194.36250	NFM	London	London Buses, Shooters Hill
202.36250	194.36250	NFM	Nationwide	National Bus Allocation
202.36250	194.36250	NFM	Tyne & Wear	Buses
202.36250	194.36250	NFM	Wiltshire/Dorset	Wiltshire & Dorset Buses, Morgans Hill
202.41250	194.41250	NFM	Nationwide	National Bus Allocation
202.46250	194.46250	NFM	Glasgow	Buses, Red Rocourt
202.46250	194.46250	NFM	Liverpool	Buses, Cow Lane
202.46250	194.46250	NFM	London	London Buses, Streatham Bus Depot
202.46250	194.46250	NFM	Nationwide	National Bus Allocation
202.51250	194.51250	NFM	East Kent	Buses
202.51250	194.51250	NFM	Edinburgh	Lothian Regional Transport Buses, Edinburgh Castle
202.51250	194.51250	NFM	London	London Buses, Radio Room
202.51250	194.51250	NFM	Nationwide	National Bus Allocation
202.51250	194.51250	NFM	Oxford	Oxford Tube Coaches (110.9)
202.60000	194.60000	NFM	Immingham	Network Rail Trunked
202.60000	194.60000	NFM	London	Eurostar Passenger Services Staff, Waterloo
202.60000	194.60000	NFM	Nationwide	National Rail Network Limited Use
202.65000	194.65000	NFM	Felixstowe	Freightliner Rail Depot
202.65000	194.65000	NFM	Immingham	Loadhaul Depot
202.65000	194.65000	NFM	London	Eurostar, Waterloo
202.65000	194.65000	NFM	London	Heathrow Express
202.65000	194.65000	NFM	Nationwide	National Rail Network Limited Use
202.66250	194.66250	NFM	London	London Buses, Guys Hospital
202.70000	194.70000	NFM	Cardiff	Aberthaw Power Station Rail Movements

Base	Mobile	Mode	Location	User and Notes
202.70000	194.70000	NFM	Didcot	Didcot Rail Shunting
202.70000	194.70000	NFM	Felixstowe	Freightliner Rail Depot
202.70000	194.70000	NFM	Immingham	Loadhaul Depot
202.70000	194.70000	NFM	Knottingley	Knottingley Rail Depot
202.70000	194.80000	NFM	London	Eurostar, Waterloo
202.70000	194.70000	NFM	London	Stratford Freight Terminal
202.70000	194.70000	NFM	London	Wembley Rail Yard
202.70000	194.70000	NFM	Nationwide	National Rail Network Limited Use
202.70000	194.70000	NFM	Paddock Wood	Paddock Wood Shunters
202.70000	194.70000	NFM	Southampton	Rail Depot
202.70000	194.70000	NFM	Wolverton	Wolverton Rail Depot
202.95000	194.95000	NFM	London	Fleetcom Trunked Net Voice, Sysid 10233
202.96250	194.96250	NFM	Devon	Buses
202.96250	194.96250	NFM	Glasgow	Buses, Red Rocourt
202.96250	194.26250	NFM	London	London Buses, Guys Hospital
202.96250	194.96250	NFM	Nationwide	National Bus Allocation
202.96250	194.96250	NFM	Sheffield	Stagecoach Supertram Data
202.96250	194.96250	NFM	Wiltshire/Dorset	Wiltshire & Dorset Buses, Morgans Hill
203.01250	195.01250	NFM	Birmingham	West Midlands Travel, Barr Beacon Reservoir
203.01250	195.01250	NFM	Bradford	First Bus Control/Voice Channel
203.01250	195.01250	NFM	Hampshire	Buses
203.01250	195.01250	NFM	London	London Buses, Trellick Tower
203.01250	195.01250	NFM	Nationwide	National Bus Allocation
203.01250	195.01250	NFM	Sheffield	Stagecoach Supertram Voice
203.01250	195.01250	NFM	Wiltshire/Dorset	Wiltshire & Dorset Buses, Mere Down
203.02500	195.02500	NFM	London	Fleetcom Trunked Net Voice, Sysid 10225
203.06250	195.06250	NFM	Devon	Buses
203.06250	195.06250	NFM	London	London Buses, Shoreditch Training College
203.06250	195.06250	NFM	Nationwide	National Bus Allocation
203.06250	195.06250	NFM	Sheffield	Stagecoach Supertram Voice
203.06250	195.06250	NFM	Tyne & Wear	Buses
203.07500	195.07500	NFM	Essex	Doctors' Service
203.11250	195.11250	NFM	Devon	Buses
203.11250	195.11250	NFM	Glasgow	Buses, Red Rocourt
203.11250	195.11250	NFM	London	London Buses, Shooters Hill
203.11250	195.11250	NFM	Maidstone	Buses
203.11250	195.11250	NFM	Nationwide	National Bus Allocation
203.11250	195.11250	NFM	Wiltshire/Dorset	Wiltshire & Dorset Buses, Morgans Hill
203.16250	195.16250	NFM	Birmingham	West Midlands Travel, Goldthorn Hill
203.16250	195.16250	NFM	Birmingham	West Midlands Travel, Samuel Vale House
203.16250	195.16250	NFM	Glasgow	Buses, Shawhill Road
203.16250	195.16250	NFM	London	London Buses, Alexandra Palace
203.16250	195.16250	NFM	Nationwide	National Bus Allocation
203.16250	195.16250	NFM	Plymouth	Buses
203.16250	195.16250	NFM	Wiltshire/Dorset	Wiltshire & Dorset Buses, Mere Down
203.16250	195.16250	NFM	Wiltshire/Dorset	Wiltshire & Dorset Buses, Newton Barrow
203.17500	195.17500	NFM	London	Fleetcom Trunked Net Voice, Sysid 10225
203.21250	195.21250	NFM	London	London Buses, Shoreditch Training College
203.21250	195.21250	NFM	Nationwide	National Bus Allocation
203.21250	195.21250	NFM	Sheffield	Mainline Buses Trunked, Olive Grove
203.26250	195.26250	NFM	Birmingham	West Midlands Travel, Harts Hill Garage
203.26250	195.26250	NFM	Chesterfield	Buses
203.26250	195.26250	NFM	Glasgow	Buses, Red Rocourt
203.26250	195.26250	NFM	Glasgow	Buses, Sergeant Law Road
203.26250	195.26250	NFM	Glasgow	Buses, South Cathkin Farm

Base	Mobile	Mode	Location	User and Notes
203.26250	195.26250	NFM	Hartlepool	Buses
203.26250	195.26250	NFM	London	London Buses, Shooters Hill
203.26250	195.26250	NFM	Nationwide	National Bus Allocation
203.28750	195.28750	NFM	Essex	Doctors Scheme
203.31250	195.31250	NFM	Bradford	First Bus Control/Voice Channel
203.31250	195.31250	NFM	London	London Buses, Alexandra Palace
203.31250	195.31250	NFM	Nationwide	National Bus Allocation
203.31250	195.31250	NFM	Wiltshire/Dorset	Wiltshire & Dorset Buses, Mere Down
203.32500	195.32500	NFM	London	Fleetcom Trunked Net Voice, Sysid 10225
203.36250	195.36250	NFM	Burnley	Buses
203.36250	195.36250	NFM	Glasgow	Buses, Sergeant Law Road
203.36250	195.36250	NFM	London	London Buses, Shoreditch Training College
203.36250	195.36250	NFM	Nationwide	National Bus Allocation
203.41250	195.41250	NFM	London	London Buses, Shooters Hill
203.42500	195.42500	NFM	London	Parking Enforcement, Hammersmith & Fulham
203.47500	195.47500	NFM	London	Fleetcom Trunked Net Voice, Sysid 10225
203.51250	194.51250	NFM	London	London Buses, Streatham Bus Depot
203.66250	195.66250	NFM	Ipswich	Ipswich Buses
203.66250	194.66250	NFM	London	London Buses, Shoreditch Training College
203.66250	195.66250	NFM	Nationwide	National Bus Allocation
203.66250	195.66250	NFM	Sheffield	Mainline Buses Trunked, Halfway Garage
203.66250	195.66250	NFM	Warrington	Borough Transport Buses MPT1327 Data
203.67500	195.67500	NFM	Croydon	Buses
203.70000	195.70000	NFM	London	Fleetcom Trunked Net Voice, Sysid 10225
203.71250	195.71250	NFM	Birmingham	West Midlands Travel, Calthrope House
203.71250	195.71250	NFM	Coventry	Coventry Buses
203.71250	195.71250	NFM	Glasgow	Buses, Red Rocourt
203.71250	195.71250	NFM	London	London Buses, Shooters Hill
203.71250	195.71250	NFM	London	London Buses, Streatham Bus Depot
203.71250	195.71250	NFM	Tyne & Wear	Buses
203.71250	195.71250	NFM	Wiltshire/Dorset	Wiltshire & Dorset Buses, Mere Down
203.76250	195.76250	NFM	Birmingham	West Midlands Travel, Vodafone Site
203.76250	195.76250	NFM	Sheffield	Don Valley Buses Trunked
203.76250	195.76250	NFM	Sheffield	Mainline Buses Data Command
203.80000	195.80000	NFM	Oxford	Witney Bus Depot
203.81250	195.81250	NFM	Birmingham	West Midlands Travel, West Bromwich Garage
203.81250	195.81250	NFM	Bradford	S&W Yorkshire Buses Trunked Network Voice
203.81250	195.81250	NFM	Cardiff	Cardiff Buses
203.81250	195.81250	NFM	London	London Buses, Streatham Bus Depot
203.81250	195.81250	NFM	Nationwide	National Bus Allocation
203.81250	195.81250	NFM	Ribble	Buses
203.81250	195.81250	NFM	Sheffield	Mainline Buses Data Command Channel
203.85000	195.85000	NFM	London	Fleetcom Trunked Net Voice, Sysid 10225
203.86250	195.86250	NFM	Sheffield	Supertram Trunked Data
203.91250	195.91250	NFM	Birmingham	West Midlands Travel, Calthrope House
203.91250	195.91250	NFM	London	Buses
203.91250	195.91250	NFM	Nationwide	National Bus Allocation
203.91250	195.91250	NFM	Reading	Buses
203.91250	195.91250	NFM	Sheffield	Supertram Trunked Data
203.91250	195.91250	NFM	Wiltshire/Dorset	Wiltshire & Dorset Buses, Newton Barrow
204.15000	196.15000	NFM	London	Fleetcom Trunked Net Voice, Sysid 10225
204.30000	196.30000	NFM	London	Fleetcom Trunked Net Voice, Sysid 10225
204.45000	196.45000	NFM	London	Fleetcom Trunked Net Voice, Sysid 10225
204.55000	196.55000	NFM	Perth	Stagecoach Buses
204.60000	196.60000	NFM	London	Fleetcom Trunked Net Voice, Sysid 10225

Base	Mobile	Mode	Location	User and Notes
204.70000	196.70000	NFM	Newcastle	Newcastle Buses Trunked
204.71250	196.71250	NFM	Birmingham	West Midlands Travel, Goldthorn Hil
204.71250	196.71250	NFM	Bradford	S&W Yorkshire Buses Trunked Network Voicel
204.71250	196.71250	NFM	Coventry	Coventry Buses
204.71250	196.71250	NFM	Glasgow	Buses, Sergeant Law Road
204.71250	196.41250	NFM	Ipswich	Ipswich Buses
204.71250	196.71250	NFM	Liverpool	Buses, Hatton Garden
204.71250	195.86250	NFM	Nationwide	National Bus Allocation
204.71250	196.71250	NFM	Oxford	Stagecoach Buses
204.76250	196.76250	NFM	Aberdeen	Buses, St Nicholas House
204.76250	196.76250	NFM	Birmingham	West Midlands Travel, Calthrope House
204.76250	196.76250	NFM	Bristol	Buses
204.76250	196.76250	NFM	Brixham	Rugby Football Buses
204.76250	196.76250	NFM	Glasgow	Buses, Cathkin Braes
204.76250	196.76250	NFM	London	London Buses, Guys Hospital
204.76250	196.76250	NFM	Nationwide	National Bus Allocation
204.76250	195.86250	NFM	Sheffield	Stagecoach Supertram Data (3)
204.76250	196.76250	NFM	Wiltshire/Dorset	Wiltshire & Dorset Buses, Newton Barrow
204.81250	196.81250	NFM	Avon	Zycomm Radio Site
204.81250	196.81250	NFM	Birmingham	West Midlands Travel, Samuel Vale House
204.81250	196.81250	NFM	Bristol	Buses
204.81250	196.81250	NFM	Liverpool	Buses, Bennett Street
204.81250	196.81250	NFM	Liverpool	Buses, Birtle
204.81250	196.81250	NFM	London	London Buses, Alexandra Palace
204.81250	196.81250	NFM	Nationwide	National Bus Allocation
204.81250	196.81250	NFM	Newcastle	Newcastle City Trunked
204.81250	196.81250	NFM	Ribble	Buses
204.82500	196.82500	NFM	Newcastle	Newcastle City Trunked
204.83750	196.83750	NFM	Blackpool	Vehicle Recovery Company
204.85000	196.85000	NFM	Baldock	Network Rail
204.85000	196.85000	NFM	Nationwide	National Rail Network 401T
204.85000	196.85000	NFM	Newport	National Rail Network
204.85000	196.85000	NFM	Tyneside	National Rail Zone 93
204.86250	196.86250	NFM	Birmingham	West Midlands Travel, Harts Hill Garage
204.86250	196.86250	NFM	Cardiff	Cardiff Buses
204.86250	196.86250	NFM	Glasgow	South Cathkin Farm
204.86250	196.86250	NFM	Liverpool	Buses, Neville House Farm
204.86250	196.86250	NFM	London	London Buses, Streatham Bus Depot
204.86250	196.86250	NFM	Nationwide	National Bus Allocation
204.86250	196.86250	NFM	Wiltshire/Dorset	Wiltshire & Dorset Buses, Newton Barrow
204.90000	196.90000	NFM	Nationwide	National Rail Network 402T
204.90000	196.90000	NFM	Nationwide	Network Rail 204.950 Control Channel
204.91250	196.91250	NFM	Brixham	Rugby Football Buses
204.91250	196.91250	NFM	Glasgow	Buses, Cathkin Braes
204.91250	196.91250	NFM	Liverpool	Buses, Werneth Low
204.91250	196.91250	NFM	London	London Buses, Guys Hospital
204.91250	196.91250	NFM	Nationwide	National Bus Allocation
204.91250	196.91250	NFM	Tyne & Wear	Buses
204.91250	196.91250	NFM	Wiltshire/Dorset	Wiltshire & Dorset Buses, Newton Barrow
204.92500	196.92500	NFM	Newcastle	Newcastle City Trunked
204.95000	196.95000	NFM	Irvine	Caledonian Paper Mill trains
204.95000	196.95000	NFM	Mauchline	Coal trains
204.95000	196.95000	NFM	Nationwide	National Rail Network 403T
204.96250	196.96250	NFM	Aberdeen	Buses, St Nicholas House
204.96250	196.96250	NFM	Birmingham	West Midlands Travel, Calthrope House

Base	Mobile	Mode	Location	User and Notes
204.96250	196.96250	NFM	Glasgow	Buses, Sergeant Law Road
204.96250	196.96250	NFM	Liverpool	Buses, Birtle
204.96250	195.91250	NFM	London	London Buses, Trellick Tower
205.00000	197.00000	NFM	Nationwide	National Rail Network 404T
205.01250	197.01250	NFM	Birmingham	West Midlands Travel, Goldthorn Hill
205.01250	197.01250	NFM	Birmingham	West Midlands Travel, Samuel Vale House
205.01250	197.01250	NFM	Coventry	Buses
205.01250	197.01250	NFM	Nationwide	National Bus Allocation
205.01250	197.01250	NFM	Sheffield	Stagecoach Supertram Data (2)
205.01250	197.01250	NFM	Wiltshire/Dorset	Wiltshire & Dorset Buses, Newton Barrow
205.05000	197.05000	NFM	Aberystwyth	British Rail Aber Area
205.05000	197.05000	NFM	Kings Cross-York	Network Rail Zone 23
205.05000	197.05000	NFM	London	Buses
205.05000	197.05000	NFM	Nationwide	National Rail Network 405T
205.06250	197.06250	NFM	London	Buses
205.06250	197.06250	NFM	Newcastle	Buses
205.06250	197.06250	NFM	Plymouth	City Buses
205.10000	197.10000	NFM	Gillingham	Network Rail Trunked
205.10000	198.10000	NFM	Inverness	Cab-Shore Train Comms
205.10000	197.10000	NFM	London	Royal Oak Rail Depot
205.10000	197.10000	NFM	Nationwide	National Rail Network 406T
205.10000	197.10000	NFM	Southampton	Network Rail
205.15000	197.15000	NFM	Nationwide	National Rail Network 407T
205.20000	197.20000	NFM	London	Wembley Freight Depot
205.20000	197.20000	NFM	Nationwide	National Rail Network 408T
205.22500	197.22500	NFM	Newcastle	Newcastle City Trunked
205.25000	197.25000	NFM	Hitchin	Network Rail Engineering
205.25000	197.25000	NFM	London	Wembley Rail Yard
205.25000	197.25000	NFM	Nationwide	National Rail Network 409T
205.30000	197.30000	NFM	London	Rail Yard Old Oak Common
205.30000	197.30000	NFM	Nationwide	National Rail Network 410T
205.35000	197.35000	NFM	Ipswich	Network Rail Ipswich Relay
205.35000	197.35000	NFM	Nationwide	National Rail Network 411T
205.37500	197.37500	NFM	Newcastle	Newcastle Buses Trunked
205.37500	197.37500	NFM	Newcastle	Newcastle City Trunked
205.40000	197.40000	NFM	Nationwide	National Rail Network 412T
205.46250	197.46250	NFM	Aberdeen	Buses, St Nicholas House
205.46250	197.46250	NFM	Bournemouth	Bournemouth Yellow Buses Data & Voice
205.46250	197.46250	NFM	Brighton	Buses
205.46250	197.46250	NFM	Glasgow	South Cathkin Farm
205.46250	197.46250	NFM	Manchester	Manchester Metrolink
205.46250	197.46250	NFM	Nationwide	National Bus Allocation
205.46250	197.46250	NFM	Newcastle	Newcastle Buses Trunked
205.46250	197.46250	NFM	Preston	Buses
205.51250	197.51250	NFM	Exeter	Buses, County Hall
205.51250	197.51250	NFM	Fareham	Buses
205.51250	197.51250	NFM	Gosport	Buses
205.51250	197.51250	NFM	Leeds	First Bus Control Channel
205.51250	197.51250	NFM	Nationwide	National Bus Allocation
205.51250	197.51250	NFM	Southend	Buses
205.51250	197.51250	NFM	Warrington	Borough Transport Buses MPT1327 Voice
205.53750	197.53750	NFM	Bournemouth	Bournemouth Yellow Buses Voice
205.55000	197.55000	NFM	Northampton	Band 3 Trunked
205.56250	197.56250	NFM	Bradford	S&W Yorkshire Buses Trunked Network Control
205.56250	197.56250	NFM	Colchester	Buses

Base	Mobile	Mode	Location	User and Notes
205.56250	197.56250	NFM	Emley Moor	S&W Yorkshire Buses Trunked Network Control
205.56250	197.56250	NFM	Glasgow	Buses, Sergeant Law Road
205.56250	197.56250	NFM	Nationwide	National Bus Allocation
205.60000	197.60000	NFM	Kings Cross-York	Network Rail Zone 23
205.60000	197.60000	NFM	Nationwide	National Rail Network 413T
205.61250	197.61250	NFM	Birmingham	Buses, Centro House
205.61250	197.61250	NFM	Bournemouth	Bournemouth Yellow Buses Data & Voice
205.61250	197.61250	NFM	Eastbourne	Buses
205.61250	197.61250	NFM	Glasgow	Buses, South Cathkin Farm
205.61250	197.61250	NFM	Ipswich	Buses
205.61250	197.61250	NFM	Liverpool	Buses, Neville House Farm
205.61250	197.61250	NFM	London	London Buses, Shoreditch Training College
205.61250	197.61250	NFM	Nationwide	National Bus Allocation
205.61250	197.61250	NFM	Ribble	Buses
205.61250	197.61250	NFM	Wigan	First Bus
205.65000	197.65000	NFM	Nationwide	National Rail Network 414T
205.65000	197.65000	NFM	Saxmundham	Network Rail Saxmundham Relay
205.66250	197.66250	NFM	Leeds	First Bus
205.66250	197.66250	NFM	London	London Buses, Shooters Hill
205.66250	197.66250	NFM	Nationwide	National Bus Allocation
205.67500		NFM	Acton London	Rail Yard Old Oak Common
205.67500		NFM	Bangor	Bangor Station Staff
205.67500		NFM	Bedford	Silverlink Staff Bedford Station
205.67500		NFM	Cardiff	Cardiff Inter City Train Movements Into Platforms
205.67500		NFM	Chester	Chester Station Staff
205.67500		NFM	Hitchin	Network Rail Engineers
205.67500		NFM	Holyhead	Holyhead Station Staff
205.67500		NFM	Immingham	Network Rail
205.67500		NFM	Lancashire	Runcorn Station Staff
205.67500		NFM	Llandudno	Station Staff Llandudno Junction
205.67500		NFM	London	Maintenance Crews Kings Cross
205.67500		NFM	London	Network Rail Maintenance Crews
205.67500		NFM	London	Old Oak Rail Depot
205.67500		NFM	London	Royal Oak Rail Depot
205.67500		NFM	London	Wembley Freight Depot
205.67500		NFM	Nationwide	National Rail Network
205.67500	197.67500	NFM	Nationwide	National Rail Network 415T
205.67500		NFM	Southend	Station Staff
205.67500		NFM	Sunderland	Sunderland Station Staff
205.70000	197.70000	NFM	Nationwide	National Rail Network 416T
205.70000	197.70000	NFM	Nationwide	Network Rail
205.70000	197.70000	NFM	South Wales	Network Rail Control Channel 205.725
205.71250	197.71250	NFM	Glasgow	Buses, Sergeant Law Road
205.71250	197.71250	NFM	Liverpool	Buses, Werneth Low
205.71250		NFM	London	London Buses, Code Red Incident Channel
205.71250	197.71250	NFM	Nationwide	National Bus Allocation
205.71250	197.71250	NFM	Portsmouth	Buses
205.71250	197.71250	NFM	Wiltshire/Dorset	Wiltshire & Dorset Buses, Rollington Hill
205.72500	197.72500	NFM	Nationwide	National Rail Network 417T
205.73750	197.73750	NFM	Hythe	Nightforce Security
205.75000	197.75000	NFM	Ely	Central Trains Guard Radio
205.75000	197.75000	NFM	Nationwide	National Rail Network 418T
205.76250	197.76250	NFM	Birmingham	Buses, Centro House
205.76250	197.76250	NFM	Glasgow	Buses, South Cathkin Farm
205.76250	197.76250	NFM	Emley Moor	S&W Yorkshire Buses Trunked Network Voice

Base	Mobile	Mode	Location	User and Notes
205.76250	197.76250	NFM	Isle of Wight	Buses
205.76250	197.76250	NFM	London	London Buses, Streatham Bus Depot
205.76250	197.76250	NFM	Nationwide	National Bus Allocation
205.80000	197.80000	NFM	Aberystwyth	British Rail Aber Area
205.80000	197.80000	NFM	Nationwide	National Rail Network 419T
205.81250	197.81250	NFM	Birmingham	West Midlands Travel, Vodafone Site
205.81250	197.81250	NFM	Bradford	S&W Yorkshire Buses Trunked Network Data
205.81250	197.81250	NFM	Glasgow	Buses, Cathkin Braes
205.81250	197.81250	NFM	Liverpool	Buses, Hatton Garden
205.81250	197.81250	NFM	Liverpool	Mersey Smart Bus
205.81250	197.81250	NFM	London	London Buses, Shooters Hill
205.81250	197.81250	NFM	Nationwide	National Bus Allocation
205.81250	197.81250	NFM	Nationwide	National Express Buses
205.81250	197.81250	NFM	Newcastle	Newcastle Buses Trunked
205.82500	197.82500	NFM	London	Thamesway Buses Trunked
205.83750	197.83750	NFM	Cardiff	Network Rail
205.83750	197.83750	NFM	Nationwide	National Rail Network 420T
205.85000	197.85000	NFM	Ipswich	Network Rail Engineering
205.85000	197.85000	NFM	Nationwide	National Rail Network 421T
205.86250	197.86250	NFM	Glasgow	Buses, Sergeant Law Road
205.86250	197.86250	NFM	Leeds	First Bus
205.86250	197.86250	NFM	London	London Buses, Trellick Tower
205.86250	197.86250	NFM	Nationwide	National Bus Allocation
205.86250	197.86250	NFM	Nationwide	National Express Buses
205.86250	197.86250	NFM	Warrington	Borough Transport Buses MPT1327 Voice
205.86250	197.86250	NFM	Wiltshire/Dorset	Wiltshire & Dorset Buses, Rollington Hill
205.90000	197.90000	NFM	Cardiff	Shunters
205.90000	197.90000	NFM	Hollesley	Network Rail Hollesley Relay
205.90000	197.90000	NFM	Nationwide	National Rail Network 422T
205.90000	197.90000	NFM	South Wales	Network Rail 204.950 Control Channel
205.91250	197.91250	NFM	Bradford	S&W Yorkshire Buses Trunked Network Voice
205.91250	197.91250	NFM	Glasgow	South Cathkin Farm
205.91250	197.91250	NFM	Gt. Yarmouth	Buses
205.91250	197.91250	NFM	London	London Buses, Streatham Bus Depot
205.91250	197.91250	NFM	Nationwide	National Bus Allocation
205.91250	197.91250	NFM	Nottingham	Nottingham City Transport Buses
205.91250	197.91250	NFM	Southampton	Buses
205.95000	197.95000	NFM	Nationwide	National Rail Network 423T
205.96250	197.96250	NFM	Liverpool	Buses, Cow Lane
205.96250	197.96250	NFM	London	London Buses, Shooters Hill
206.00000	198.00000	NFM	London	Old Oak Rail Depot
206.00000	198.00000	NFM	London	Royal Oak Rail Depot
206.00000	198.00000	NFM	Lowestoft	Network Rail Lowestoft Relay
206.00000	198.00000	NFM	Nationwide	National Rail Network 424T
206.01250	198.01250	NFM	Birmingham	West Midlands Travel, West Bromwich Garage
206.01250	198.01250	NFM	Devon	Buses, Great Haldon Hill
206.01250	198.01250	NFM	Edinburgh	First Bus Edinburgh
206.01250	198.01250	NFM	London	London Buses, Alexandra Palace
206.01250	198.01250	NFM	London	London Buses, Guys Hospital
206.01250	198.01250	NFM	Nationwide	National Bus Allocation
206.01250	198.01250	NFM	Newcastle	Newcastle Buses Trunked
206.06250	198.06250	NFM	Birmingham	West Midlands Travel, Calthrope House
206.06250	198.06250	NFM	Blackpool	Buses
206.06250	198.06250	NFM	Bradford	S&W Yorkshire Buses Trunked Network Data
206.06250	198.06250	NFM	Chester	Buses, Station Road

Base	Mobile	Mode	Location	User and Notes
206.06250	198.06250	NFM	Glasgow	Buses, Cathkin Braes
206.06250	198.06250	NFM	London	London Buses, Shoreditch Training College
206.06250	198.06250	NFM	London	London Buses, Trellick Tower
206.06250	198.06250	NFM	Nationwide	National Bus Allocation
206.06250	198.06250	NFM	Wiltshire/Dorset	Wiltshire & Dorset Buses, Rollington Hill
206.10000	198.10000	NFM	Euston-Brum	Virgin Express
206.10000	198.10000	NFM	Holyhead	National Rail Network
206.10000	198.10000	NFM	London	Old Oak Rail Depot
206.10000	198.10000	NFM	Nationwide	National Rail Network 425T
206.10000	198.10000	NFM	Plymouth	National Rail Network Trunk Control
206.11250	198.11250	NFM	Glasgow	Buses, South Cathkin Farm
206.11250	198.11250	NFM	London	London Buses, Radio Room
206.11250	198.11250	NFM	Nationwide	National Bus Allocation
206.15000	198.15000	NFM	Nationwide	National Rail Network 426T
206.15000	198.15000	NFM	Winchester	Network Rail Trunked
206.16250	198.16250	NFM	Avon	Zycomm Radio Site
206.16250	198.16250	NFM	Birmingham	West Midlands Travel, West Bromwich Garage
206.16250	198.16250	NFM	Bristol	City Line Buses
206.16250	198.16250	NFM	Glasgow	Buses, Sergeant Law Road
206.16250	198.16250	NFM	Liverpool	Buses, Birtle
206.16250	198.16250	NFM	London	London Buses, Alexandra Palace
206.16250	198.16250	NFM	London	London Buses, Streatham Bus Depot
206.16250	198.16250	NFM	Nationwide	National Bus Allocation
206.16250	198.16250	NFM	Newcastle	Newcastle Buses Trunked
206.16250	198.16250	NFM	Newcastle	Newcastle City Trunked
206.21250	198.21250	NFM	Birmingham	West Midlands Travel, Vodafone Site
206.21250	198.21250	NFM	Bristol	Zycall Multi User Trunked System
206.21250	198.21250	NFM	London	London Buses, Stanford Hill
206.21250	198.21250	NFM	Nationwide	National Bus Allocation
206.25000	198.25000	NFM	London	Eurostar Data, Waterloo
206.25000	198.25000	NFM	Nationwide	National Rail Network 427T
206.25000	198.25000	NFM	North Wales	North Wales Coast Line Cab - Shore
206.26250	198.26250	NFM	Birmingham	West Midlands Travel, Calthrope House
206.26250	198.26250	NFM	Devon	Buses, Great Haldon Hill
206.26250	198.26250	NFM	Emley Moor	S&W Yorkshire Buses Trunked Network Data
206.26250	198.26250	NFM	Exeter	Stagecoach Buses
206.26250	198.26250	NFM	Glasgow	Buses, South Cathkin Farm
206.26250	198.26250	NFM	London	London Buses, Shooters Hill
206.26250	198.26250	NFM	London	London Buses, Stockwell
206.26250	198.26250	NFM	Nationwide	National Bus Allocation
206.26250	198.26250	NFM	Wiltshire/Dorset	Wiltshire & Dorset Buses, Rollington Hill
206.30000	198.30000	NFM	Dover	Network Rail Ch.28T Voice
206.30000	198.30000	NFM	Nationwide	National Rail Network 428T
206.36250	198.36250	NFM	Nationwide	National Bus Allocation

207.5000 - 208.5000 MHz — Broadcasting Links

Base	Mobile	Mode	Location	User and Notes
207.70000		NFM	Nationwide	JFMG Radio Microphones
207.90000		NFM	Nationwide	JFMG News Gathering Radio Microphones
207.90000		NFM	Nationwide	JFMG Radio Microphones
208.10000		NFM	Nationwide	JFMG Radio Microphones
208.30000		NFM	Jersey	BBC Radio Jersey Radio Microphones
208.30000		NFM	Liverpool	Mecca Bingo Radio Microphones
208.30000		NFM	Nationwide	JFMG Radio Microphones Mobile Ch.ML2
208.30000		WFM	Woodbridge	Riverside Theatre Radio Microphones
208.40000		NFM	Liverpool	Mecca Bingo Radio Microphones

208.500 - 224.500 MHz — Outside Broadcasts & Radio Microphones

Frequency		Mode	Location	Description
208.50000		NFM	Liverpool	Mecca Bingo Radio Microphones
208.60000		NFM	Nationwide	BBC Radio 1 Roadshow Radio Microphones
208.60000		NFM	Nationwide	BBC Antiques Roadshow Radio Microphones
208.60000		NFM	Nationwide	BBC Radio Suffolk O/B Radio Microphones
208.60000		NFM	Nationwide	JFMG Radio Microphones BBC Ch.11B
208.60000		NFM	Suffolk	BBC Radio Suffolk O/B Radio Microphones
208.70000		NFM	Liverpool	Mecca Bingo Radio Microphones
208.80000		NFM	Nationwide	JFMG Radio Microphones ITV Ch.13D
208.80000		NFM	Nationwide	ITV Radio Microphones
209.00000		NFM	Nationwide	JFMG Radio Microphones BBC Ch.12B
209.00000		NFM	Nationwide	BBC Radio Microphones
211.91875		NFM	Nationwide	JFMG Wide Area Talkback Mobile
211.95000		WFM	London	BBC News link
212.10000		WFM	Cambridge	BBC Radio Cambridge O/B
212.19375		NFM	Nationwide	JFMG Wide Area Talkback Mobile
212.20000		NFM	Wolverhampton	Beacon Radio O/B
212.60000		NFM	Essex	Breeze AM Radio O/B
212.60000		NFM	London	Classic Gold Breeze Radio O/B
213.06250		NFM	Kent	Eye in the Sky O/B
213.23750	141.23125	NFM	Kent	BBC Radio Kent Talkback
213.87500		NFM	Silverstone	BBC TV O/B
213.95000		WFM	London	BBC Radio Car O/B
214.00000		WFM	Essex	Radio Essex O/B Link
214.02500		NFM	Castle Donington	Grand Prix Radio O/B Link
214.02500		NFM	London	BBC TV O/B
214.10000		WFM	London	BBC Radio Car O/B
215.26875		NFM	Nationwide	JFMG Temporary Audio Point-Point Portable
215.31250		NFM	London	BBC Helicopter O/B link
215.49375		NFM	Nationwide	JFMG Temporary Audio Point-Point Portable
216.10000		NFM	Liverpool	Mecca Bingo Radio Microphones
216.10000		NFM	Nationwide	JFMG Radio Microphones Mobile Ch.ML3
216.10000		WFM	Woodbridge	Riverside Theatre Radio Microphones
216.20000		NFM	Liverpool	Mecca Bingo Radio Microphones
216.30000		NFM	Liverpool	Mecca Bingo Radio Microphones
216.30000		NFM	Nationwide	JFMG Radio Microphones
216.40000		NFM	Liverpool	Mecca Bingo Radio Microphones
216.60000		WFM	Nationwide	Anglia TV Radio Microphones O/B
216.60000		WFM	Nationwide	JFMG Radio Microphones ITV Ch.12A
216.80000		WFM	Nationwide	BBC Antiques Roadshow Radio Microphones
216.80000		WFM	Nationwide	JFMG Radio Microphones BBC Ch.13B
217.00000		WFM	Nationwide	Anglia TV Radio Microphones O/B
217.00000		WFM	Nationwide	JFMG Radio Microphones ITV Ch.13A
224.00625		WFM	Nationwide	JFMG Portable Audio Links
224.10625		NFM	Sheffield	BBC Radio Sheffield O/B
224.16875		NFM	Coventry	CWR Radio O/B
224.21810		NFM	Scotland	BBC Studio Feed
224.23125		NFM	Bristol	BBC O/B Talkback
224.23200		NFM	Scotland	BBC Clean Feed from Glasgow
224.49375		WFM	Nationwide	JFMG Portable Audio Links

217.500 - 230.000 MHz   Digital Audio Broadcasting (DAB)

All DAB broadcasts in the UK are transmitted at around 220 MHz (Band III) but some other countries use frequencies in the L-Band (1452 – 1492 MHz).

There are very few frequencies allocated to DAB even though there are numerous stations because DAB is broadcast in blocks called multiplexes. Each multiplex carries several stations on the same frequency. So, instead of tuning to a frequency, listeners select a multiplex channel and then choose a station.

There are only two national digital radio multiplexes in the UK. One, the BBC, broadcasts all its stations on channel 12B (225. 648 MHz). The other national multiplex is a commercial one operated by Digital One. It broadcasts on channel 11D (226.064 MHz) in England and 12A (223.936 MHz) in Scotland.

There are also several smaller local companies operating multiplexes and they tend to offer local programming mixed with a some national stations. Along with those are a few regional companies which cover a wider area.

BBC National Stations

Radio 1	1 Xtra	Radio 2	Radio 3	Radio 4 FM
Radio 4 LW	6 Music	BBC 7	World Service	Asian Network
Radio 5 Live	Radio 5 Sports Extra			

BBC Regional Stations

Radio Scotland	Radio Wales Radio Cymru	Radio Ulster	Nan Gaidheal

BBC Local Radio Stations

Radio Berkshire	Radio Bristol	Radio Cambridgeshire	Radio Cleveland
Radio Cornwall	Radio Devon	BBC Essex	BBC GMR
Radio Humberside	Radio Kent	Radio Lancashire	Radio Leeds
Radio Leeds	Radio Bradford	Radio Leicester	BBC London 94.9
Radio Merseyside	Radio Newcastle	Radio Nottingham	Radio Norfolk
Radio Stoke	Radio Wiltshire	BBC WM Coventry	BBC WM
Radio Sheffield	Radio Swindon	Southern Counties Radio	Radio Shropshire
BBC Radio Solent Bournemouth		BBC Radio Solent South Hampshire	

National

Digital One England: Block 11D: 222.064 MHz   Scotland: Block 12A: 223.936 MHz

Classic FM	Core	Capital Life	Oneword
Planet Rock	PrimeTime Radio	talkSPORT	Virgin Radio

Regional

Scotland
Switch Digital: Block11D: 222.064 MHz

Beat 106	Galaxy
The Arrow	Jazz FM
Heart	Real Radio
Kerrang!	Smash Hits Radio
Saga Radio	BBC Radio Nan Gaidheal

North East England
MXR Limited: Block 12C: 227.360 MHz

Capital Disney	Century FM
DNN	Galaxy
Heart	Jazz FM
Smooth FM	The Arrow
Urban Choice	

North West England
MXR Limited: Block 12C: 227.360 MHz

Capital Disney	Century FM
DNN	Galaxy
Heart	Real Radio
Smooth FM	The Arrow
Urban Choice	

West Midlands
MXR Limited: Block 12A: 223.936 MHz

Capital Disney	DNN
Galaxy	Heart
Jazz FM	Kerrang!
Saga 105.7	Smooth FM
The Arrow	

Yorkshire
MXR Limited: Block 12A: 223.936 MHz

Capital Disney	DNN
Galaxy	Heart
Jazz FM	Real Radio!
Saga 105.7	Smooth FM
The Arrow	

S Wales & Severn Estuary
MXR Limited: Block 12C: 227.360 MHz

Capital Disney	DNN
Heart	Jazz FM
Real Radio	Smooth
The Arrow	Urban Choice
Vibe 101	

Local

Aberdeen
Switchdigital: Block 11C: 220.352 MHz

Kerrang!	KISS
Smash Hits	Waves
Northsound 1	Northsound 2
NECR	BBC Radio Scotland
BBC Radio Nan Gaidheal	

Bath
NOW Digital: Block 12D: 229.072 MHz

Capital Disney	Classic Gold
GWR Bath	KISS
Passion	The Storm
BBC Radio Wiltshire	

Bradford
TWG Digital: Block 11B: 218.640 MHz

Classic Gold	KISS
Masti	Panjab Radio
Smash Hits	Sunrise Radio
The Pulse	YARR Radio
BBC Radio Leeds	

Bristol
NOW Digital: Block 11B: 218.640 MHz

Classic Gold	Chill
Fun Radio	GWR Radio
KISS	Passion
The Storm	XFM

Central Lancashire
Emap Digital Radio: Block 12A: 223.936 MHz

Asian Sound	Classic Gold
Heat	Kerrang!
KISS	Magic 999
Rock FM	Smash Hits
XFM	3C Cool Country
BBC Radio Lancashire	

Ayr
Score Digital: Block 11B: 218.640 MHz

Smash Hits	UCA Radio
Vibe FM	West Sound
3C Cool Country	West FM
BBC Radio Scotland	
BBC Radio Nan Gaidheal	

Birmingham
CE Digital: Block 11C: 220.352 MHz

Beat 106	Capital Gold
Century	KISS
Magic	New BRMB
Radio XL	XFM
Sunrise Radio	BBC Radio WM

Bournemouth
NOW Digital: Block 11B: 218.640 MHz

2CR FM	Chill
KISS	Classic Gold
Passion	The Storm
Wave 105	BBC Radio Solent

Cambridge
NOW Digital: Block 11C: 220.352 MHz

Chill	Classic Gold
Q103	Smash Hits
The Storm	Vibe FM
Zeta	BBC Radio Bristol
BBC Radio Cambridgeshire	

Cardiff
Capital Radio Digital
Block 11C: 220.352 MHz

Capital Gold	Century
Red Dragon FM	BBC Radio Cymru
XFM	BBC Radio Wales

Cornwall
South West Digital Radio
Block 11B: 218.640 MHz

Chill	Classic Gold
KISS	Pirate FM
Plymouth Sound	The Storm
BBC Radio Cornwall	

Dundee
Score Digital: Block 11B: 218.640 MHz

Tay AM	Tay FM
Vibe FM	3C Cool Country
BBC Radio Scotland	
BBC Radio Nan Gaidheal	

Exeter
NOW Digital: Block 11C: 220.352 MHz

Chill	Classic Gold
Gemini	KISS
Passion	The Storm
BBC Radio Devon	

Humberside
Emap Digital Radio: Block 11B: 218.640 MHz

Classic Gold	Heat
Kerrang!	KISS
Lincs FM	Magic
Smash Hits	Viking
XFM	BBC Radio Humberside

Kent
Emap Digital Radio: Block 11B: 218.640 MHz

Capital Gold	Invicta FM
KISS	KM Digital
Swale Sound	XFM
BBC Radio Kent	

Leicester
Emap Digital Radio: Block 11B: 218.640 MHz

Capital Disney	Galaxy 105
A Plus	Century FM
Classic Gold	Leicester Sound
Sabras Sound	The Storm
BBC Radio Leicester	

London 1
CE Digital: Block 12C: 227.360 MHz

Capital Disney	Capital FM
Capital Gold	Century
KISS	LBC News 1152
LBC 97.3	Magic
Smash Hits	Sunrise Radio
XFM	

London 3
Digital Radio Group: Block 11B: 218.640 MHz

Chill	Choice
Classic Gold	Easy Radio
Fun Radio	Gaydar Radio
Passion	Panjab Radio
Heat The Arrow	Virgin Classic Rock

Coventry
NOW Digital: Block 12D: 229.072 MHz

Chill	Classic Gold
KISS	Kix 96.2
Mercia FM	Sunrise Radio
The Storm	YARR Radio
BBC WM (Coventry & Warwickshire)	

Edinburgh
Score Digital: Block 12D: 229.072 MHz

Forth 1	Forth 2
KISS	Saga Radio
Sunrise Radio	XFM
3C Cool Country	BBC Radio Scotland

Glasgow
Score Digital: Block 11C: 220.352 MHz

Clyde 1	Clyde 2
KISS	Q96
Saga 105.2 FM	Sunrise Radio
XFM	3C Cool Country

Inverness
Score Digital Radio
Block 11B: 218.640 MHz

MFR	BBC Radio Scotland
BBC Radio Nan Gaidheal	

Leeds
Emap Digital Radio
Block 12D: 229.072 MHz

Classic Gold	Heat
Kerrang!	KISS
Magic 828	Ridings FM
Smash Hits	XFM
Radio Aire	BBC Radio Leeds

Liverpool
Emap Digital Radio
Block 11B: 218.640 MHz

Classic Gold	Heat
Magic	Radio City
Smash Hits	3C Cool Country
XFM	BBC Radio Merseyside

London 2
Switch Digital: Block 12A: 223.936 MHz

Gakaxy	Heart
Kerrang!	Saga
Smooth FM	Spectrum Radio
The Hits	Virgin Groove
YARR Radio	BBC Radio London

Manchester
CE Digital: Block 11C: 220.352 MHz

Asian Sound	Capital Gold
Key 103	KISS
Magic	Smash Hits
XFM	
BBC Greater Manchester Radio	

Northern Ireland
Score Digital: Block 12D: 229.072 MHz

Citybeat	Classic FM
Downtown Radio	Prime Time Radio
KISS	Q102.9
3C Cool Country	BBC Radio Ulster

Nottingham
NOW Digital: Block 12C: 227.360 MHz

Capital Disney	Classic Gold
Century FM	Galaxy
Sabras Sound	Saga 106.6
The Storm	96 Trent FM
BBC Radio Nottingham	

Plymouth
NOW Digital: Block 12A: 223.936 MHz

Chill	Classic Gold
KISS	Pirate FM
Plymouth Sound	The Storm
BBC Radio Devon	

Southend on Sea
NOW Digital: Block 12D: 229.072 MHz

Breeze	Chill
Fun Radio	Essex FM
KISS	Passion
The Storm	BBC Radio Essex

South Yorkshire
Emap Digital Radio: Block 11C: 220.352 MHz

Classic Gold	Hallam FM
Heat	Kerrang!
KISS	Magic AM
Smash Hits	Trax FM
XFM	3C Cool Country
BBC Radio Sheffield	

Sussex Coast
Capital Radio Digital
Block 11B: 218.640 MHz

Capital Gold	Gaydar Radio
Juice	KISS
Southern FM	XFM
BBC Southern Counties Radio	

Swindon
NOW Digital
Block 11C: 220.352 MHz

Capital Disney	Chill
Classic Gold	GWR FM
KISS	Passion
Swindon FM	The Storm
BBC Radio Swindon	

Norwich
NOW Digital: Block 11B: 218.640 MHz

Broadland 102.4	Classic Gold Amber
Chill	Smash Hits
The Beach	The Storm
Vibe FM	3C Cool Country
BBC Radio Norfolk	

Peterborough
NOW Digital: Block 12D: 229.072 MHz

Chill	Classic Gold
Hereward FM	Passion
Smash Hits	Vibe FM
BBC Radio Cambridgeshire	

Reading
NOW Digital: Block 12D: 229.072 MHz

Chill	Classic Gold
Fun Radio	KISS
The Storm	2-TEN
BBC Radio Berkshire	

South Hampshire
Capital Radio Digital
Block 11C: 220.352 MHz

Capital Disney	Capital Gold
Ocean FM	Power FM
Saga Radio	The Saint
Wave 105	XFM
BBC Radio Solent	
Southampton Hospital Radio	

Stoke on Trent
TWG Emap Digital
Block 12D: 229.072 MHz

KISS	Signal 1
Signal 2	Smash Hits
BBC Radio Stoke	

Swansea
TWG Emap Digital
Block 12A: 223.936 MHz

KISS	Smash Hits
Swansea Sound	96.4FM The Wave
BBC Radio Cymru	BBC Radio Wales

Teesside
Emap Digital Radio
Block 11B: 218.640 MHz

Classic Gold	Heat
Kerrang!	KISS
Magic	Smash Hits
96.6TFM	3C Cool Country
XFM	BBC Radio Sheffield

Tuning in the Military Airband
by William K. Armstrong

The various recent wars have given us all an insight into the mechanics of war but for military radio enthusiasts in Europe, particularly those in Italy and Greece, it was a rare opportunity to tune into the military in action on VHF and UHF. Several listeners recorded air-to-air conversations between fighters and AWACS aircraft and made them available to the world through the Internet.

For those who heard them, there is one fact that stands out above all others; what they heard was exactly the same type of traffic as is often heard during peacetime exercises, only this time the targets were real and the weapons were hot.

What Can I Hear?
Military aviation communications on VHF and UHF can roughly be divided into two distinct groups; air traffic control and tactical communications. Even though the majority of military flights operate autonomously, they still require a degree of air traffic control when, for example, joining or crossing airways. However, by far the largest use of the VHF and UHF radio spectrum is for tactical communications. Such communications can be heard almost daily as fighters such as Tornado F3s from RAF Coningsby, Leeming and Leuchars engage in Air Combat Training exercises up and down the country. Most of these missions are co-ordinated from ground by Ground Control Intercept sites, such as those at RAF Buchan and Neatishead, or by an E3D AWACS from RAF Waddington orbiting high over the exercise area. Communications are brief, precise and filled with nail biting tension. You will actually hear fighters being vectored onto targets and ultimately the code word "Splash" will be passed as the interception results in a kill.

Tuning into an AWACS is the ambition of many listeners because it is the AWACS aircraft that usually co-ordinates the entire exercise, arranging frequency changes, controlling the Link-11 tactical digital information link and vectoring missions to their tasked patrol areas.

Probably the most visible form of military aviation is Low Level Flying. As their altitude is so low, pilots on these missions rarely talk to anyone simply because no one can hear them. Instead, they talk to each other on discrete air-to-air frequencies where they discuss bombing runs and scores, tactics and the maintenance states of each aircraft. Many of these missions focus on the half dozen or so bombing ranges around the country and their frequencies can be found later in this book. Once the aircraft pulls up from its Low Level run, it generally checks in only on the air traffic control frequency for a radar service back to base.

Unfortunately, not all military communications are as interesting. You might just as easily pick up a flight of USAF F16s looking for a tanker to carry out an air-to-air refuelling exercise or a lone Netherlands Royal Navy P3 Orion on a navigation exercise around the UK. Of course, that might all be straightforward during the day, but the military are usually just as active at night.

Over the past few years, several Internet resources have been developed for British military enthusiasts. A quick search will soon find some very interesting web sites. Alternatively, you could search for the various groups that gather on the Internet to swap information about exercises and frequencies. A good place to start is at *http://groups.yahoo.com/group/militarycomms*.

Air Displays

Finally, let's take a quick look at Air Displays. Many enthusiasts go to airshows armed with their scanners to tune in the air-to-air commands of the display leader. Display teams do change their frequencies and it can be tricky keeping up with them but if you start with these frequencies, which they have used in the past, it shouldn't take you too long to find the current ones.

Display Team Frequencies

AAC Blue Eagles Display Team	1135.975, 136.975, 380.200, 259.100
Aero Stars Aerobatic Team	122.475 (Manual 2)
Air Display Team Frecce Tricolori	123.475
Air-Air Display Co-ordination	118.000
Aquilla Spanish Air Display Team	130.300, 130.500, 252.5
Battle of Britain Flight	120.800
Chilean Air Force Display Team	136.175
Crunchie Flight Team	118.000
Dutch F-16 Display Team	122.275, 130.900, 316.900
Green March Moroccan Display Team	135.925, 135.975
Marlboro Aerobatic Display	118.000
Navy Gazelle Duo	136.975
Patrouille Suisse Air Display Team	370.100
Patrouille de France Air Display Team	242.600, 242.650, 242.850, 243.450
RAF Falcons Parachutists	255.100
Red Arrows Air Display Team	242.050, 242.200, 243.450, 377.600
Red Star Racing Yaks Team	123.350
Sharks Helicopter Air Display Team	136.975, 248.800, 250.475, 388.000
Silver Eagles Display Team	135.975, 252.900
Swedish Tower Air Display Team	370.100
Turkish Star 5 Air Display Team	225.750, 243.000, 279.600
USAF Air Display Team	235.250, 251.500, 322.950

A final note; be sensible and be careful. Don't be blatant about your hobby and don't wave your scanner in the face of authority. Although listening to aircraft is generally accepted, it is still unlawful. Most officials will turn a blind eye but these are sensitive times and everyone is being more vigilant. You will hear a lot more if your scanner is not confiscated. But most of all, enjoy yourself. Scanning and frequency collecting are hobbies that might not be is the top-ten but they are harmless and rewarding and, ultimately, well worth the effort.

RIAT 2005

The annual Royal International Air Tattoo held at Fairford is the largest air display in Europe and always yields a wealth of frequencies for the avid collector. To give you an idea of just how much radio traffic there is at this event, here's a look at the 2005 show.

Let's start with what you couldn't hear – the police. Both the Wiltshire and Gloucestershire forces have moved over to Airwave and their communications are now digital and secure so there was no point in looking for them.

However, there was still plenty to hear at the show. A multitude of radio channels, mainly at UHF, was allocated to the event organisers' own communications team and these were used by the 850 handhelds, 16 mobiles and 20 or so repeaters they hired just for the occasion. They have an incredibly complicated job as they have to coordinate all the communications for people who look after fuels, VIP arrivals, crew buses, all the emergency services, engineering, leader vehicles, medical operations, car parking, RAF Police (who handle the main security), spectator grandstands and viewing areas, programme selling, RIAT's own traders, other trader and exhibitor booking in and movements and so on.

They have used pretty much the same system for the last 15 years - both single and dual repeaters are set up and they tend to use the same bands but often with slight differences in spot frequencies. The frequencies shown below should give you an idea of how the communications are arranged. Most are from 2005 with a few from 2004 added just to give you the overall picture. A few users and repeater inputs were not found, but there is enough to illustrate how a typical arrangement is set up.

The bands used were the CAA airport users band at 455 MHz paired with 460/461 MHz and the military 444 MHz band paired with 449.500 and above.

449.5750		Friends of RIAT/Park & View
449.6250		Site Ops
449.8000		Leader Vehicles
455.4750		Medical Ops
455.6375	460.9375	Engineering Operations
444.0375		Hunter Ops Crew
444.1000		Speedbird Ops
444.1250		
444.1375		Trader Ops
444.2000		RIAT Tower
444.2500		Medical Ops
444.2750		Fuels Ops
444.2875		Friends of RIAT/Park & View
444.3000		Site Ops
444.5000		Embassy (VIP)
444.5375		Transport
444.5875	449.7375	Media And Press Office

444.6125		Leaders Vehicles
444.6875		Friends of RIAT
449.1375		
449.3500		
449.4500		
449.5000		RIAT Tower
449.5625		
449.5750		Friends of RIAT/Park & View
449.6250		Site Ops.
449.6375		
449.8000		Leader Vehicles
449.8375		
449.8625		
455.4750		Medical Ops
455.5000		
455.6375	460.9375	Engineering Ops
455.7250	461.025	Site Office
455.7500		Mover/Hunter
455.7875	461.0875	Car Park/Trader Ops
460.7750		Crash Ops/Tower
460.8000		RAF Police Tasker Channel
461.0500		

These frequencies were all allocated channel numbers and users could switch between channels to talk to other users. It was quite tricky finding the corresponding frequencies because there are two channel plans. One plan is for the main users, both airside and the administration/emergency services and the other is for people selling programmes, park & view, emptying the lavatories and so on. The second plan does not include the tower and emergency frequencies because the users might accidentally change to one of those channels and a confusing transmission at a hectic event such as this could cause chaos.

Here's how the second group of channels was set up in 2004. Some were single frequencies and some were repeater inputs.

Ch.1	449.8375	Ch.2	449.6375	Ch.3	461.0875	Ch.4	449.8625
Ch.5	461.1500	Ch.6	449.4500	Ch.7	461.1500	Ch.8	444.1250
Ch.9	460.8000	Ch.10	449.7375	Ch.11	449.7250	Ch.12	449.5750
Ch.13	444.1000	Ch.14	449.4500	Ch.15	461.0250	Ch.16	432.3750

Here's what was found in 2005:

Base	Mobile	User If Known
444.1375	???.????	Checklist/Programmes
444.2000	???.????	
444.2500	449.5625	Ch.13 Fuels
444.2875	449.5750	Medical Ops
444.3000	449.6250	FRIAT Park & View
444.5000	449.6375	
444.5375	449.7250	Leader Vehicles/Airfield Manager
444.6125	449.8000	Hunter Ops Aircrew Reception

444.6375	449.8375	Information Centre/Administration
444.6875	449.8625	RAFPOL Silver Control
449.3500		
455.4750	460.7750	Engineering Ops
455.5000	460.8000	Movers/Loaders
455.6250	???.????	
455.6375	460.9375	
455.7250	461.0250	
455.7005	461.0500	Trader and Exhibitions Ops
455.7875	461.0875	Admissions Control/Car Parks
455.8500	461.1500	Tower and Incident Control

As you can see, some channel frequencies were used twice. This probably means that they were either using two different subaudible tones for different users or one was dual on one tone and the other was single for a different user with a different tone. This could have been because there were some users at the event who didn't need to use their radios a lot so they didn't need a completely independent channel of their own.

Many visitors will only be interested in aircraft arriving and departing and will ignore the above bank of channels but they can be a good source of information about what's happening in the background.

When it comes to keeping track of aircraft, it's a good idea to be aware of the frequencies for RAF Brize Norton as they control the local airspace around the show while Fairford controls tower and ground movements. Also, each year a mix of UHF/VHF base and CAA temporary allocations are added to help Brize filter Fairford show traffic and then Fairford uses its own UHF/VHF base frequencies.

In 2004 they used:

123.550	Brize Radar		119.150	Ground
124.550	Delivery (Departure Clearance)		277.350	Arrival via Brize
126.225	Reserved/Special		337.575	Tower
134.550	Arrival via Brize		120.375	Tower
257.750	Metro USAFE on Request Weather		338.650	Arrival via Brize
257.800	NATO Tower		379.475	Fairford Operations
259.975	Ground		240.225	Dragon Operations U2s

In 2005 the official basic RIAT Arrivals and departure frequency list was:

Fairford Director (at Brize) 123.55 / 277.35
Fairford Tower 130.675 / 337.575
Fairford Ground 119.15 / 259.975
Fairford Clearance Delivery (Monday 18th only) 124.55
Fairford Weather (from Brize) 254.475
132.900 was allocated for use by the SCAN EAGLE UAV team
134.550 was added in as an extra radar frequency for Brize Norton
The visiting hot air balloons were on 122.475

Display Teams

Teams that display with more than one aircraft will use either an air to air or squadron and base ops frequency, so check airband lists for these. Here's a selection of ones that were used and should give you an idea of where to start looking:

259.100	AAC Blue Eagles
135.975	AAC Historics/Blue Eagles
380.200	AAC Historics
255.125	Albert Formation RAF Hercules 4 SHIP
130.000	Aquilla
130.300	Aquilla
130.500	Aquilla
141.275	Aquilla
252.500	Aquilla Used for Display 2005
337.975	Aquilla Used for Arrival 2005
307.175	Dutch PC-7 Air-Ground Static 2005 Used for Arrival
140.600	Frecce Tricolori 2005 Radio Checks Only
307.800	Frecce Tricolori
440.450	Frecce Tricolori Ground Crew (NFM)
267.850	Harrier 4 Ship
118.000	Honda Dream Team Air To PA Ground
243.450	Red Arrows
375.450	RN Lynx Duo Black Cats

The following are based on RN FRADU (Fleet Requirements And Distribution Unit) and FSATO (Fleet Support Air Tasking Organisation) frequencies:

FRADU Black Sea Hawks

249.725	312.575	364.650	369.925
375.750	384.025	388.425	240.650
238.000	275.800	307.200	359.200
367.500	385.200	389.125	390.800

FR Aviation Falcon 20s

123.650	358.925	369.925	337.950

Falcon 20s and Sea Hawks used UHF tower 337.575

These are some of the frequencies used by visiting aircraft in 2005:

377.000	B1/Omega Tanker Departure
139.325	Danish Air Force F15s
361.900	Danish Air Force F15s
251.400	French Air Force Mirage 2000
242.400	German Air Force Phantoms Departure
364.750	RNLAF Apaches
136.575	USAF East Coast Demo Team
142.175	USAF East Coast Demo Team Departure
384.550	USAF East Coast Demo Team
143.475	USAFE A10s
254.575	USAF F15s Lakenheath 494FS

Apart from the air display teams, if any air force sends more than a single aircraft from a squadron, air to air or ops frequencies might be used, if only for arrival and departure.

Here are some examples of overseas squadrons from 2004:

139.800	Belgian Air Force 31 Squadron F-16s
141.075	Belgian Air Force 31 Squadron F-16s
232.300	Belgian Air Force 31 Squadron F-16s
251.400	French Air Force EC2/5 Ops Mirage 2000
396.750	German Air Force MFG2 Tornado
299.950	Norwegian Air Force
140.125	Royal Netherlands AF 322 Squadron F-16s
255.775	USAFE Aviano 555 Squadron Ops F16

And some squadrons from 2005:

31.3750	RNAF 301 Squadron AH-64 (NFM)
41.1250	RNAF 301 Squadron AH-64 (NFM)
48.9500	RNAF 301 Squadron AH-64 (NFM)
55.6750	RNAF 301 Squadron AH-64 (NFM)
58.5500	RNAF 301 Squadron AH-64 (NFM)
60.6250	RNAF 301 Squadron AH-64 (NFM)
70.6875	RNAF 301 Squadron AH-64 (NFM)
81.4750	RNAF 301 Squadron AH-64 (NFM)
139.425	RNAF 301 Squadron AH-64
142.750	RNAF 301 Squadron DN AH-64
338.675	RNAF 301 Squadron AH-64
364.750	RNAF 301 Squadron DN AH-64
367.825	RNAF 301 Squadron AH-64

31 Squadron Belgian Air Force F-16s

367.025	313.100	399.825	240.700	140.275	122.650
142.925	140.225	142.675	139.500	141.025	

Danish Army ESK 724 Fennec

300.175	340.150	340.250

French Air Force Mirage 2000 EC1/12

344.200	247.200	374.575	387.150	266.125

French Air Force Mirage 2000 EC2/5

373.850	365.325

Royal Netherlands Air Force F-16 313 Squadron

232.775	265.125	367.400	142.125	139.075	142.425
139.175	141.450	138.700	140.575	126.125	137.375

RNAF F-16 311 Squadron

231.925	251.800	142.975	140.175	143.275	130.900
138.550	140.300	141.250	140.100		

RNAF F-16 323 Squadron

| 387.175 | 245.350 | 140.875 | 140.625 | 142.025 | 129.275 |
| 143.175 | 143.375 | 143.775 | 143.975 | 140.975 | |

USAF F-15 48FW 492FS

| 231.225 | 231.825 | 232.075 | 242.450 | 246.900 | 254.575 |
| 369.575 | | | | | |

USAF F-15 48FW 493FS

| 244.450 | 248.275 | 263.300 | 264.600 | 276.925 | 279.175 |
| 279.475 | 284.900 | 290.375 | 299.875 | 338.575 | |

USAF F-15 48FW 494FS

| 269.075 | 337.575 | 341.675 | 343.550 | 345.175 | 358.350 |
| 358.950 | 359.225 | 362.125 | | | |

USAFE 555FS 31FW

| 355.500 | 255.775 | 344.250 | 139.150 | 140.350 | 141.300 |
| 142.200 | 129.300 | | | | |

Fire Brigade command usually uses:

457.03750	
457.08750	462.58750
457.13750	462.63750

NHS Ambulance Control:

462.4000		453.3750	459.875
453.2750	459.775	453.2750	Single
453.3250	459.825	165.5750	170.3750 Major Incident Control

Air Training Corps
The Air Training Corps is usually at RIAT and they can use any of their normal frequencies:

36.80000		153.8000	149.2750
37.30000		153.8000	
38.10000		153.8250	
40.20000		153.8250	
78.10000		271.5000	
78.10000		273.0000	
79.35000		434.4125	439.5500
149.2750	153.8000	435.6250	
149.2750		435.6250	
149.3375		435.7250	
149.4000		435.7500	
149.4125		435.7500	
153.6875		439.5500	434.4125
153.8000			

And finally, working away in the background were:

163.2875	158.7875	EP Events Car Parking
461.2875		Rock Steady Security
173.0500		Andy's Loos

225.000 - 400.000 MHz   NATO Communications 25 kHz

Base	Mobile	Mode	Location	User and Notes
225.275		AM	Nationwide	USAF AMC Air-Air
226.600		AM	Nationwide	Royal Navy TAC Common
228.275		AM	USAF Mildenhall	B2 Command Post
230.650		AM	Nationwide	AWACS Overland Cap TAD 512
230.650		AM	RAF Waddington	NATO 30 - 47 / Magic 80 - 97
231.100		AM	RAF Lyneham	Interplane
231.100		AM	Yeovilton	ASW X (S)
231.150		AM	Nationwide	Royal Navy ASW Net
231.225		AM	USAFE Lakenheath	Maintenance
231.375		AM	RAF Valley	4FTS Air-to-Air
231.425		AM	USAFE Lakenheath	Ground
231.425		AM	RAF Lossiemouth	Talkdown
231.450		AM	RAF Leeming	100 Squadron TAC 1 Stud 16
231.550		AM	Yeovilton	Interplane/Ops
231.600		AM	RAF Marham	2 Squadron "Cropper"
231.625		AM	Nationwide	Scottish ACC Primary
231.825		AM	USAFE Lakenheath	Interplane
231.850		AM	Dorset	RN Ship-Air Thursday War
231.850		AM	Lyme Bay	RN Primary Live Firing
232.025		AM	Nationwide	Swanwick ACC Primary
232.075		AM	USAFE Lakenheath	Interplane
232.300		AM	Nationwide	RAF Hercules Air-Air
233.000		AM	RAF Waddington	AWACS TAD
233.100		AM	RAF Lyneham	Interplane
233.125		AM	Nationwide	AWACS Tactical TAD
233.150		AM	Dorset	RN Ship-Air Thursday War
233.150		AM	HMS Ark Royal	Fly Co
233.150		AM	HMS Illustrious	Fly Co
233.450		AM	USAF AMC	Air-Air
233.700		AM	RAF Brize Norton	Air-Air
233.700		AM	RAF Coltishall	6 Squadron Interplane Ops (S)
233.725		AM	RAF Kinloss	Ground Standby
233.925		AM	Yeovilton	ASW Z (P)
235.000		AM	Nationwide	FAC Fortune Control
236.075		AM	USAF AMC	Air-Air
237.850		AM	HMS Illustrious	Fly Co
237.850		AM	HMS Invincible	Air-Deck
238.000		AM	Nationwide	FRADU/FSATO Ship-Air

232.000 - 236.000 MHz   Radio Astronomy

Darnhall, Defford, Jodrell Bank, Knockin, Pickmere and Wardle

240.0000 - 243.9450 MHz   Tactical Military Exercise Communications

Base	Mobile	Mode	Location	User and Notes
240.000		AM	Wattisham	AAC Interplane
240.225		AM	RAF Fairford	Dragon Ops. U2
240.300		AM	Nationwide	AWACS Tactical TAD
240.500		AM	Nationwide	Europe Aircent Offensive Air Support/FAC
240.650		AM	Nationwide	FRADU/FSATO Ship-Air
240.700		AM	Nationwide	USAF Air-Air Refuelling
240.900		AM	Yeovilton	Interplane
241.000		AM	RAF Coningsby	Fast Jet Operational Evaluation Unit
241.100		AM	Nationwide	Europe Aircent Offensive Air Support/FAC
241.175		AM	Cowden	Range Primary
241.275		AM	Nationwide	AWACS Tactical TAD
241.600		AM	Castlemartin	Range Air-Ground
241.625		AM	RAF Benson	DATIS

Base	Mobile	Mode	Location	User and Notes
241.650		AM	RAF Linton on Ouse	ATIS
241.700		AM	Nationwide	Europe Aircent Offensive Air Support/FAC
241.775		AM	Cowden	Range
241.825		AM	RAF Aldergrove	RAF Ops.
241.825		AM	RAF St Mawgan	Tower
241.875		AM	RAF Valley	Interplane
241.950		AM	RNAS Culdrose	Approach/Radar
241.950		AM	RNAS Predannack	Approach
242.050		AM	RAF Leuchars	TAC 2
242.075		AM	USAF Lakenheath	Departure
242.075		AM	USAF Mildenhall	Departure
242.100		AM	RAF Conigsby	17 Squadron Operations Laser Ops.
242.100		AM	RAF Cottesmore	Interplane
242.175		AM	HMS Ocean	Homer
242.275		AM	Nationwide	AWACS Tactical TAD
242.325		AM	RAF Cottesmore	DATIS
242.375		AM	USAF Lakenheath	492FS Air to Air Auxiliary
242.400		AM	RAF Leuchars	TAC 4
242.400		AM	USAF Mildenhall	100 ARW/AAR
242.400		AM	RAF Warton	Special Task Cell
242.450		AM	USAF Lakenheath	Interplane
242.450		AM	RAF Wittering	1 Sqn Ops (Willard Ops)
242.475		AM	Nationwide	RAF Air-Air
242.500		AM	RAF Leeming	11 Squadron TAC 1
242.550		AM	RAF Leuchars	5 Squadron Interplane
242.550		AM	RAF Lyneham	Interplane
242.600		AM	RAF Leeming	11 Squadron TAC 2
242.600		AM	RAF Warton	Test Flights Air-Ground
242.650		AM	Nationwide	Patrouille de France Air Display Team
242.850		AM	Nationwide	Patrouille de France Air Display Team (Rarely Used)
243.000		AM	International	Air Distress Frequency TAD 008
243.000		AM	International	Maritime Emergency Position Indicating Beacons
243.200		AM	RAF Aldergrove	TAC
243.275		AM	RAF Leeming	11 Squadron TAC 3
243.300		AM	RAF Warton	Discrete Emergency Frequency
243.325		AM	RAF Coningsby	29 Squadron Buzzard Ops
243.400		AM	Nationwide	NATO Common Standby
243.450		AM	Nationwide	Red Arrows Air Display Team
243.500		AM	International	Personal Locator Beacons (Rarely Used in the UK)
243.500		AM	Middle Wallop	ATIS
243.800		AM	RAF Leuchars	Interplane
243.850		AM	Nationwide	Patrouille de France Air Display Team Transit

243.9450 - 244.2500 MHz   US AFSATCOM Down Links

Base	Mobile	Mode	Location	User and Notes
243.945		NFM	AFSATCOM F2	NB Channel 11
243.955		NFM	AFSATCOM F2	NB Channel 12
243.960		NFM	AFSATCOM F2	NB Channel 13
243.965		NFM	AFSATCOM F2	NB Channel 14
243.970		NFM	AFSATCOM F2	NB Channel 15
243.975		NFM	AFSATCOM F2	NB Channel 16
243.980		NFM	AFSATCOM F2	NB Channel 17
243.985		NFM	AFSATCOM F2	NB Channel 18
243.990		NFM	AFSATCOM F2	NB Channel 19
243.995		NFM	AFSATCOM F2	NB Channel 20
244.000		NFM	AFSATCOM F2	NB Channel 21
244.010		NFM	AFSATCOM F2	NB Channel 22

Base	Mobile	Mode	Location	User and Notes
244.045		NFM	AFSATCOM F3	NB Channel 11
244.055		NFM	AFSATCOM F3	NB Channel 12
244.060		NFM	AFSATCOM F3	NB Channel 13
244.065		NFM	AFSATCOM F3	NB Channel 14
244.070		NFM	AFSATCOM F3	NB Channel 15
244.075		NFM	AFSATCOM F3	NB Channel 16
244.080		NFM	AFSATCOM F3	NB Channel 17
244.085		NFM	AFSATCOM F3	NB Channel 18
244.090		NFM	AFSATCOM F3	NB Channel 19
244.095		NFM	AFSATCOM F3	NB Channel 20
244.100		NFM	AFSATCOM F3	NB Channel 21
244.110		NFM	AFSATCOM F3	NB Channel 22
244.145		NFM	AFSATCOM F1	NB Channel 11
244.155		NFM	AFSATCOM F1	NB Channel 12
244.160		NFM	AFSATCOM F1	NB Channel 13
244.165		NFM	AFSATCOM F1	NB Channel 14
244.170		NFM	AFSATCOM F1	NB Channel 15
244.175		NFM	AFSATCOM F1	NB Channel 16
244.180		NFM	AFSATCOM F1	NB Channel 17
244.185		NFM	AFSATCOM F1	NB Channel 18
244.190		NFM	AFSATCOM F1	NB Channel 19
244.195		NFM	AFSATCOM F1	NB Channel 20
244.200		NFM	AFSATCOM F1	NB Channel 21
244.210		NFM	AFSATCOM F1	NB Channel 22

244.21000 - 248.8000 MHz   Tactical Military Exercise Communications 25 kHz

Base	Mobile	Mode	Location	User and Notes
244.300		AM	RAF Valley	Interplane
244.325		AM	Nationwide	AWACS Tactical TAD
244.375		AM	Nationwide	Swanwick ACC Berry Head Special Tasks
244.425		AM	RAF Northolt	Ops
244.450		AM	USAF Lakenheath	Squadron Ops.
244.600		AM	St Mawgan	SAR
244.600		AM	RAF Wattisham	Scene of SAR Control
244.650		AM	AARA 6 (S North Sea)	Refuelling
244.825		AM	RAF Leeming	25 Squadron TAC 1
244.875		AM	RAF Leconfield	Air-Ground
244.900		AM	RAF Leeming	11 Squadron Air-Air
244.925		AM	Nationwide	AWACS Tactical TAD
245.100		AM	Nationwide	Personal Locator Beacons (Rarely Used in the UK)
245.100		AM	Nationwide	Swanwick ACC
245.175		AM	Nationwide	Swanwick ACC Primary
245.250		AM	Nationwide	Swanwick ACC Special Tasks
245.375		AM	RAF Wyton	Tower
246.700		AM	Nationwide	Forward Air Controllers
246.700		AM	RAF Lyneham	Drop Zone
246.900		AM	USAF Lakenheath	Interplane
247.000		AM	RAF Wattisham	AAC Interplane
247.025		AM	RAF Cottesmore	Interplane
247.025		AM	USAF Mildenhall	Interplane
247.175		AM	RAF Cranwell	DATIS
247.225		AM	USAF Mildenhall	Blackhat Interplane
247.275		AM	Nationwide	Swanwick Military West
247.300		AM	Nationwide	Swanwick ACC Emergency
248.200		AM	Nationwide	Swanwick ACC Emergency

Base	Mobile	Mode	Location	User and Notes
248.275		AM	USAF Lakenheath	Interplane
248.300		AM	Nationwide	Forward Air Controllers
248.425		AM	USAF Mildenhall	Talon Ops.
248.625		AM	RAF Lyneham	Air-Air
248.700		AM	RAF Waddington	Ops.

248.8500 - 249.3500 MHz — US AFSATCOM Down Links

Base	Mobile	Mode	Location	User and Notes
248.850	302.450	NFM	MARISAT	Channel 1
248.875	302.475	NFM	MARISAT	Channel 2
248.900	302.500	NFM	MARISAT	Channel 3
248.925	302.525	NFM	MARISAT	Channel 4
248.950	302.550	NFM	MARISAT	Channel 5
248.975	302.575	NFM	MARISAT	Channel 6
249.000	302.700	NFM	MARISAT	Channel 7
249.025	302.725	NFM	MARISAT	Channel 8
249.050	302.750	NFM	MARISAT	Channel 9
249.075	302.775	NFM	MARISAT	Channel 10
249.100	302.800	NFM	MARISAT	Channel 11
249.125	302.825	NFM	MARISAT	Channel 12
249.150	302.850	NFM	MARISAT	Channel 13
249.175	302.875	NFM	MARISAT	Channel 14
249.200	302.900	NFM	MARISAT	Channel 15
249.225	302.925	NFM	MARISAT	Channel 16
249.250	302.950	NFM	MARISAT	Channel 17
249.275	302.975	NFM	MARISAT	Channel 18
249.300	303.000	NFM	MARISAT	Channel 19
249.325	303.025	NFM	MARISAT	Channel 20
249.350	303.050	NFM	MARISAT	Channel 21

249.350 - 269.950 MHz — US FLTSATCOM Fleet Broadcast Down Links & Tactical Military Communications

Base	Mobile	Mode	Location	User and Notes
249.400		AM	RAF Wyton	Ground
249.425		AM	Prestwick	Scottish ACC Low Level Climbout
249.425		AM	Prestwick	Scottish Military
249.450		AM	RAF Valley	Ops
249.475		AM	Swanwick Military	Middle Airspace (Scottish)
249.475		AM	Swanwick Military	Upper Airspace (Scottish)
249.500		AM	RAF Boscombe Down	Interplane
249.525		AM	RAF Leeming	AFIS
249.550		AM	Nationwide	849 Squadron AEW Ops.
249.575		AM	RAF Leuchars	DATIS
249.600		AM	Dorset	RN FOST Thursday War
249.625		AM	Nationwide	Scottish ACC Standby
249.650		AM	RAF Linton on Ouse	ATIS
249.675		AM	Nationwide	Scottish ACC Special Tasks
249.700		NFM	USAY Lakenheath	ATIS
249.700		NFM	USAY Lakenheath	Information
249.725		AM	RNAS Culdrose	D School
249.750		AM	USAF Fairford	B-1B/B-52 SOF Ops
249.750		AM	USAF Mildenhall	ACC Ops
249.775		AM	USAF Mildenhall	Air-Air Refuelling
249.800		NFM	Nationwide	Dynamic Sciences Surveys
249.850		AM	RAF Waddington	Radar
249.900		AM	RAF Wattisham	AAC Interplane
249.975		AM	USAF Fairford	B-52 Fortress Ops.

Base	Mobile	Mode	Location	User and Notes
250.050		AM	RAF Cranwell	Radar
250.050		AM	RAF Lossiemouth	Talkdown
250.125		AM	Nationwide	AWACS Tactical TAD
250.150		AM	Nationwide	Forward Air Controllers (Fortune)
250.175		AM	Nationwide	AWACS Tactical TAD
250.175		AM	RNAS Culdrose	Plymouth Military Radar
250.275		AM	Nationwide	Royal Navy Helicopter-Ship
250.350	291.350	NFM	FLTSATCOM	Channel W1
250.450	291.450	NFM	FLTSATCOM F1	Channel X1
250.550	291.550	NFM	FLTSATCOM F3	Channel Y1
250.650	291.650	NFM	FLTSATCOM F2	Channel Z1
250.900		AM	Dorset	Royal Navy Thursday War
250.900		AM	RAF Wattisham	AAC Ops.
251.175		AM	Nationwide	AWACS Tactical TAD
251.200		AM	RNAS Culdrose	Kilderkin Ops
251.225		AM	Swanwick Military	Lower Airspace (South East)
251.300		AM	RAF Odiham	7 Squadron Interplane
251.375		AM	Nationwide	AWACS Tactical TAD
251.650		AM	Nationwide	AWACS Tactical TAD
251.700		AM	Nationwide	AWACS Tactical TAD
251.750		AM	Nationwide	AWACS Tactical TAD
251.750		AM	RAF Brize Norton	UK ASACS ICF
251.750		AM	RAF Leeming	UK ASACS ICF
251.850	292.850	NFM	FLTSATCOM	Channel W 2
251.900		AM	RAF Aldergrove	AAC Ops.
251.900		AM	RAF Wattisham	AAC Interplane
251.950	292.950	NFM	FLTSATCOM F1	Channel X 2
252.000		AM	Nationwide	AWACS Tactical TAD
252.000		AM	Nationwide	Primary UK ASACS
252.050	293.050	NFM	FLTSATCOM F3	Channel Y 2
252.100		AM	RFA Argus	ATC
252.150	293.150	NFM	FLTSATCOM F2	Channel Z 2
252.400		AM	Nationwide	AWACS Tactical TAD
252.425		AM	RAF Valley	Interplane
252.500		AM	Nationwide	Aquilla Spanish Air Display Team
252.525		AM	Nationwide	USAF Common Interplane Triple 25
252.525		AM	RAF St Mawgan	DATIS
252.800		AM	Nationwide	Helicopter SAR Training TAD 017
252.800		AM	RAF Chivenor	Air-Ground
252.800		AM	RAF St Mawgan	SAR Training
252.800		AM	RAF Valley	SAR
252.800		AM	RAF Wattisham	NATO SAR Training
252.800		AM	USAF Mildenhall	Dust Off Ops.
252.900		AM	Dishforth	Ops.
252.900		AM	Nationwide	AAC Common Air-Air/Air-Ground
252.900		AM	RNAS Culdrose	Interplane
252.900		AM	RAF Middle Wallop	Ops.
252.900		AM	RAF Shawbury	Aviation Common
252.900		AM	RAF Wattisham	AAC Ops
252.900		AM	RAF Yeovilton	Interplane
253.350		AM	RAF Waddington	Maintenance Ops
253.550	294.550	NFM	FLTSATCOM	Channel W 3
253.650	294.650	NFM	FLTSATCOM F1	Channel X 3
253.750	294.750	NFM	FLTSATCOM F3	Channel Y 3
253.800		AM	RAF Wattisham	SAR Standby
253.850	294.850	NFM	FLTSATCOM F2	Channel Z 3

Base	Mobile	Mode	Location	User and Notes
253.900		AM	Nationwide	Magic AWACS Air-Ground
253.900		AM	RAF Middle Wallop	Duty Instructor Ops
253.900		AM	RAF Wattisham	AAC Interplane
254.075		AM	RAF Marham	2 Sqn Air-to-Air
254.200		AM	RAF Shawbury	Director
254.250		AM	RAF Coltishall	Ground
254.275		AM	Swanwick Military	Lower Airspace (North West)
254.275		AM	Swanwick Military	Upper Airspace (North West)
254.400		AM	RAF Leuchars	Radar
254.425		AM	Nationwide	AWACS Tactical TAD
254.475		AM	RAF Brize Norton	ATIS
254.500		AM	Aberporth	Range
254.525		AM	Church Fenton	Approach
254.575		AM	USAF Lakenheath	Interplane
254.600		AM	Nationwide	AWACS FAC/Overland Cap
254.625		AM	USAF Mildenhall	Maintenance
254.650		AM	RAF Lyneham	Wing Ops
254.800		AM	RAF Wattisham	Interplane
254.875		AM	RAF Honington	Radar
255.100		AM	Nationwide	RAF Falcons Parachute Team Primary
255.100		AM	RAF Aldergrove	Interplane/Flight Safety
255.125		AM	Nationwide	Hercules Air-Air
255.250	296.250	NFM	FLTSATCOM	Channel W 4
255.275		AM	USAF Lakenheath	Interplane
255.350	296.350	NFM	FLTSATCOM F1	Channel X 4
255.400		AM	RAF Leuchars	Radar
255.450	296.450	NFM	FLTSATCOM F3	Channel Y 4
255.550	296.550	NFM	FLTSATCOM F2	Channel Z 4
255.600		AM	RAF Topcliffe	Director
255.700		AM	RAF Valley	Interplane
255.750		AM	RAF Coltishall	41 Squadron Ops.
255.775		AM	Nationwide	AWACS Tactical TAD
255.825		AM	Nationwide	AWACS Tactical TAD
255.850		AM	RAF Cottesmore	Skeleton Ops.
255.950		AM	Nationwide	Royal Navy ASW Primary
256.000		AM	Royal Navy	Ship-Air
256.100		AM	Royal Navy	Ship-Air
256.200		AM	RAF St Mawgan	Ops.
256.275		AM	RAF Wittering	Interplane
256.850	297.850	NFM	FLTSATCOM	Channel W 5
256.900		AM	Nationwide	RAF Falcons Parachute Team Secondary
256.950	297.950	NFM	FLTSATCOM F1	Channel X 5
257.050	298.050	NFM	FLTSATCOM F3	Channel Y 5
257.100		AM	USAF Fairford	CAC (Brize)
257.150	298.150	NFM	FLTSATCOM F2	Channel Z 5
257.750		AM	USAF Mildenhall	Weather
257.750		AM	USAF Lakenheath	Weather
257.750		AM	USAF Lakenheath	Metro
257.800		AM	RAF Brize Norton	Tower
257.800		AM	RAF Cottesmore	Tower
257.800		AM	RAF Cranwell	Tower
257.800		AM	RAF Kinloss	Tower
257.800		AM	RAF Leuchars	Tower
257.800		AM	RAF Linton on Ouse	Tower
257.800		AM	RAF Marham	Tower
257.800		AM	RAF Northolt	Tower
257.800		AM	RAF Odiham	Tower

Base	Mobile	Mode	Location	User and Notes
257.800		AM	RAF St Athan	Tower
257.800		AM	RAF Topcliffe	Tower
257.800		AM	RAF Valley	Tower
257.800		AM	RAF Waddington	Tower
257.800		AM	RAF Wittering	Tower
258.350	299.350	NFM	FLTSATCOM	Channel W 6
258.450	299.450	NFM	FLTSATCOM F1	Channel X 6
258.500		AM	RAF Scampton	Ground
258.550	299.550	NFM	FLTSATCOM F3	Channel Y 6
258.650	299.650	NFM	FLTSATCOM F2	Channel Z 6
258.725		AM	Nationwide	RAF Air Refuelling UK
258.800		AM	Nationwide	British Army Air-Air
258.800		AM	RAF Benson	33 Squadron Air-Air
258.825		AM	RAF Mona	Radar
258.825		AM	RAF Valley	Radar
258.850		AM	RAF Kinloss	Departure
258.850		AM	RAF Lossiemouth	Departure
258.950		AM	Nationwide	AWACS Tactical TAD
258.975		AM	RAF Colerne	Tower
259.000		AM	Aberporth	AFIS
259.000		AM	MoD West Freugh	Radar
259.050		AM	USAF Lakenheath	Radar
259.125		AM	RAF Leuchars	Tower
259.600		AM	Nationwide	AAC Blue Eagles Display Team
259.675		AM	Nationwide	Air-Air Refuelling 2 TAD 091
259.700		AM	International	Space Shuttle Downlink
259.750		AM	RNAS Culdrose	Talkdown
259.825		AM	Dishforth	Tower
259.875		AM	RAF Linton on Ouse	Talkdown
259.925		AM	RAF Leuchars	Talkdown
259.950		AM	RAF Woodvale	Tower
259.975		AM	RAF Kinloss	Director
259.975		AM	RAF Lossiemouth	Director
259.975		AM	USAF Fairford	Ground
260.000		AM	RAF St Mawgan	Ops
260.025		AM	MoD West Freugh	Approach
260.150		AM	Nationwide	AWACS Tactical TAD
260.350	293.950	NFM	FLTSATCOM F1	WB Channel A/X 1
260.375	293.975	NFM	FLTSATCOM F1	WB Channel A/X 2
260.400	294.000	NFM	FLTSATCOM F1	WB Channel A/X 3
260.425	294.025	NFM	FLTSATCOM F1	WB Channel A/X 4
260.450	294.050	NFM	FLTSATCOM F1	WB Channel A/X 5
260.475	294.075	NFM	FLTSATCOM F1	WB Channel A/X 6
260.500	294.100	NFM	FLTSATCOM F1	WB Channel A/X 7
260.525	294.125	NFM	FLTSATCOM F1	WB Channel A/X 8
260.550	294.150	NFM	FLTSATCOM F1	WB Channel A/X 9
260.575	294.175	NFM	FLTSATCOM F1	WB Channel A/X 10
260.600	294.200	NFM	FLTSATCOM F1	WB Channel A/X 11
260.625	294.225	NFM	FLTSATCOM F1	WB Channel A/X 12
260.650	294.250	NFM	FLTSATCOM F1	WB Channel A/X 13
260.675	294.275	NFM	FLTSATCOM F1	WB Channel A/X 14
260.700	294.300	NFM	FLTSATCOM F1	WB Channel A/X 15
260.725	294.325	NFM	FLTSATCOM F1	WB Channel A/X 16
260.750	294.350	NFM	FLTSATCOM F1	WB Channel A/X 17
260.775	294.375	NFM	FLTSATCOM F1	WB Channel A/X 18
260.800	294.400	NFM	FLTSATCOM F1	WB Channel A/X 19
260.825	294.425	NFM	FLTSATCOM F1	WB Channel A/X 20

Base	Mobile	Mode	Location	User and Notes
260.850	294.450	NFM	FLTSATCOM F1	WB Channel A/X 21
260.950		AM	RAF Cottesmore	Air-to-Air
261.075		AM	RAF Leeming	100 Squadron Ops
261.200		AM	RAF Marham	ATIS
261.450	295.050	NFM	FLTSATCOM F3	WB Channel B/Y 1
261.475	295.075	NFM	FLTSATCOM F3	WB Channel B/Y 2
261.500	295.100	NFM	FLTSATCOM F3	WB Channel B/Y 3
261.525	295.125	NFM	FLTSATCOM F3	WB Channel B/Y 4
261.550	295.150	NFM	FLTSATCOM F3	WB Channel B/Y 5
261.575	295.175	NFM	FLTSATCOM F3	WB Channel B/Y 6
261.600	295.200	NFM	FLTSATCOM F3	WB Channel B/Y 7
261.625	295.225	NFM	FLTSATCOM F3	WB Channel B/Y 8
261.650	295.250	NFM	FLTSATCOM F3	WB Channel B/Y 9
261.675	295.275	NFM	FLTSATCOM F3	WB Channel B/Y 10
261.700	295.300	NFM	FLTSATCOM F3	WB Channel B/Y 11
261.725	295.325	NFM	FLTSATCOM F3	WB Channel B/Y 12
261.750	295.350	NFM	FLTSATCOM F3	WB Channel B/Y 13
261.775	295.375	NFM	FLTSATCOM F3	WB Channel B/Y 14
261.800	295.400	NFM	FLTSATCOM F3	WB Channel B/Y 15
261.825	295.425	NFM	FLTSATCOM F3	WB Channel B/Y 16
261.850	295.450	NFM	FLTSATCOM F3	WB Channel B/Y 17
261.875	295.475	NFM	FLTSATCOM F3	WB Channel B/Y 18
261.900	295.500	NFM	FLTSATCOM F3	WB Channel B/Y 19
261.925	295.525	NFM	FLTSATCOM F3	WB Channel B/Y 20
261.950	295.550	NFM	FLTSATCOM F3	WB Channel B/Y 21
262.050	295.650	NFM	FLTSATCOM F2	WB Channel C/Z 1
262.075	295.675	NFM	FLTSATCOM F2	WB Channel C/Z 2
262.100	295.700	NFM	FLTSATCOM F2	WB Channel C/Z 3
262.125	295.725	NFM	FLTSATCOM F2	WB Channel C/Z 4
262.150	295.750	NFM	FLTSATCOM F2	WB Channel C/Z 5
262.175	295.775	NFM	FLTSATCOM F2	WB Channel C/Z 6
262.200	295.800	NFM	FLTSATCOM F2	WB Channel C/Z 7
262.225	295.825	NFM	FLTSATCOM F2	WB Channel C/Z 8
262.250	295.850	NFM	FLTSATCOM F2	WB Channel C/Z 9
262.275	295.875	NFM	FLTSATCOM F2	WB Channel C/Z 10
262.300	295.900	NFM	FLTSATCOM F2	WB Channel C/Z 11
262.325	295.925	NFM	FLTSATCOM F2	WB Channel C/Z 12
262.350	295.950	NFM	FLTSATCOM F2	WB Channel C/Z 13
262.375	295.975	NFM	FLTSATCOM F2	WB Channel C/Z 14
262.400	296.000	NFM	FLTSATCOM F2	WB Channel C/Z 15
262.425	296.025	NFM	FLTSATCOM F2	WB Channel C/Z 16
262.450	296.050	NFM	FLTSATCOM F2	WB Channel C/Z 17
262.475	296.075	NFM	FLTSATCOM F2	WB Channel C/Z 18
262.500	296.100	NFM	FLTSATCOM F2	WB Channel C/Z 19
262.525	296.125	NFM	FLTSATCOM F2	WB Channel C/Z 20
262.550	296.150	NFM	FLTSATCOM F2	WB Channel C/Z 21
262.625		AM	Nationwide	AWACS Tactical TAD
262.650		AM	RAF Valley	4FTS Air-to-Air
262.725		AM	RAF Lossiemouth	TWCU Air-to-Air
262.775		AM	RNAS Culdrose	Talkdown
262.900		AM	RAF Cottesmore	Talkdown
262.925		AM	RNAS Yeovilton	Royal Navy Ops
262.950		AM	RAF Coningsby	Radar
263.175		AM	Nationwide	AWACS Tactical TAD
263.500		AM	Boscombe Down (MoD)	DATIS
263.550	297.150	NFM	FLTSATCOM	WB Channel W 1

Base	Mobile	Mode	Location	User and Notes
263.575	297.175	NFM	FLTSATCOM	WB Channel W 2
263.600	297.200	NFM	FLTSATCOM	WB Channel W 3
263.625	297.225	NFM	FLTSATCOM	WB Channel W 4
263.650	297.250	NFM	FLTSATCOM	WB Channel W 5
263.675	297.275	NFM	FLTSATCOM	WB Channel W 6
263.700	297.300	NFM	FLTSATCOM	WB Channel W 7
263.725	297.325	NFM	FLTSATCOM	WB Channel W 8
263.750	297.350	NFM	FLTSATCOM	WB Channel W 9
263.775	297.375	NFM	FLTSATCOM	WB Channel W 10
263.800	297.400	NFM	FLTSATCOM	WB Channel W 11
263.825	297.425	NFM	FLTSATCOM	WB Channel W 12
263.850	297.450	NFM	FLTSATCOM	WB Channel W 13
263.875	297.475	NFM	FLTSATCOM	WB Channel W 14
263.900	297.500	NFM	FLTSATCOM	WB Channel W 15
263.925	297.525	NFM	FLTSATCOM	WB Channel W 16
263.950	297.550	NFM	FLTSATCOM	WB Channel W 17
263.975	297.575	NFM	FLTSATCOM	WB Channel W 18
264.000	297.600	NFM	FLTSATCOM	WB Channel W 19
264.025	297.625	NFM	FLTSATCOM	WB Channel W 20
264.050	297.650	NFM	FLTSATCOM	WB Channel W 21
264.325		AM	Nationwide	Airborne Alert/Aircraft Hijack TAD 141
264.675		AM	USAF Lakenheath	Radar
265.250	306.250	NFM	FLTSATCOM	Channel W 7
265.350	306.350	NFM	FLTSATCOM F1	Channel X 7
265.450	306.450	NFM	FLTSATCOM F3	Channel Y 7
265.550	306.550	NFM	FLTSATCOM F2	Channel Z 7
265.850		AM	Nationwide	AWACS Tactical TAD
265.900		AM	Nationwide	AWACS Tactical TAD
266.500		AM	Nationwide	USAF Air-Air Refuelling
266.750	307.750	NFM	FLTSATCOM	Channel W 8
266.775		NFM	Nationwide	Patrouille Suisse Display Team
266.850	307.850	NFM	FLTSATCOM F1	Channel X 8
266.950	307.950	NFM	FLTSATCOM F3	Channel Y 8
267.050	308.050	NFM	FLTSATCOM F2	Channel Z 8
267.475		NFM	Nationwide	AWACS Tactical TAD
268.150	309.150	NFM	FLTSATCOM	Channel W 9
268.250	309.250	NFM	FLTSATCOM F1	Channel X 9
268.250		AM	Nationwide	USAF Air-Air Refuelling
268.350	309.350	NFM	FLTSATCOM F3	Channel Y 9
268.450	309.450	NFM	FLTSATCOM F2	Channel Z 9
268.500		AM	RAF Brize Norton	Radar
268.525		AM	Dorset	RN Ship-Air Thursday War
268.600		AM	Nationwide	AWACS Tactical TAD
268.650		AM	RAF Valley	4FTS Air-to-Air
268.700		AM	RAF Coningsby	Ops
268.800		AM	Nationwide	Air - Air Refuelling
268.825		AM	RAF Benson	Approach
268.875		AM	RAF Marham	Approach
269.025		AM	RAF Lossiemouth	DATIS
269.075		AM	USAF Lakenheath	Ops (Command Post)
269.650	310.650	NFM	FLTSATCOM	Channel W 10
269.700		AM	RAF Cosford	Ground
269.750	310.750	NFM	FLTSATCOM F1	Channel X 10
269.850	310.850	NFM	FLTSATCOM F3	Channel Y 10
269.900		AM	RAF Barkston Heath	DATIS
269.950	310.950	NFM	FLTSATCOM F2	Channel Z 10

Base	Mobile	Mode	Location	User and Notes

270.000 - 326.900 MHz — Tactical Military Exercise Communications 25 kHz

Base	Mobile	Mode	Location	User and Notes
270.000		AM	Swanwick	London Military
270.025		AM	Nationwide	AWACS Tactical TAD
271.500		AM	Nationwide	Air Training Corps Ch.U4
272.000		AM	Nationwide	Fortune Control FAC
273.000		AM	Nationwide	Air Training Corps Ch.U3
273.450		AM	Dorset	RN Ship-Air Thursday War
273.525		AM	English Channel	Royal Navy
273.900		AM	Nationwide	NATO Low-Level Flying
274.850		AM	Nationwide	Forward Air Controller
275.350		AM	Swanwick Military	Lower Airspace (Central)
275.350		AM	Swanwick Military	Upper Airspace (West)
275.400		AM	Middle Wallop	Radar
275.450		AM	Swanwick Military	Middle Airspace (West)
275.475		AM	RAF Benson	Approach (London Military)
275.475		AM	RAF Lyneham	CAC
275.475		AM	RAF Wittering	CAC (Westerly Departures)
275.500		AM	RAF Church Fenton	Tower
275.575		AM	Nationwide	AWACS Tactical TAD Air-Air UK Ch.3
275.700		AM	Nationwide	AWACS Tactical TAD Air-Air UK Ch.2
275.750		AM	Nationwide	AWACS Tactical TAD
275.800		NFM	RAF Brize Norton	HQ 1 Group
275.800		AM	Upavon (Army)	Tower
275.875		AM	RAF Coningsby	Tower
275.900		AM	RAF Leuchars	111 Squadron Ops (Sabre Ops)
275.950		AM	Nationwide	AWACS Tactical TAD
275.975		AM	RAF Coltishall	Talkdown
276.025		AM	RAF Odiham	18 Squadron Interplane
276.125		AM	RAF Cosford	Approach
276.175		AM	RAF Odiham	ATIS
276.200		AM	RAF Valley	Interplane
276.225		AM	Nationwide	AWACS Tactical TAD
276.250		AM	RNAS Yeovilton	Air-Air
276.850		AM	Boscombe Down (MoD)	Radar
276.975		AM	Nationwide	AWACS Tactical TAD
277.000		AM	Nationwide	Army Euromux Radio Relay
277.075		AM	USAF Mildenhall	ATIS
277.200		AM	Nationwide	AWACS Tactical TAD
277.225		AM	Cardiff	Approach/Radar
277.225		AM	RAF St Athan	Approach
277.250		AM	RAF Leeming	25 Squadron Ops.
277.275		AM	RAF Colerne	Approach
277.300		AM	RAF Leuchars	43 Squadron Ops (Chequers Ops)
277.350		AM	RAF Brize Norton	Radar
277.450		AM	RAF Cottesmore	4 Squadron Air-to-Air
277.500		AM	Aberporth	Range Tertiary
277.625		AM	RAF Linton on Ouse	Departure
277.750		AM	Nationwide	AWACS Tactical TAD
277.925		AM	RAF Lyneham	ATIS
278.150		AM	USAF Mildenhall	Ground
279.000		AM	Space	Space Shuttle Down Link
279.225		AM	Nationwide	AWACS Tactical TAD
279.350		AM	RAF Benson	Tower
279.475		AM	USAF Lakenheath	Interplane
279.525		AM	Nationwide	AWACS Tactical TAD

Base	Mobile	Mode	Location	User and Notes
279.725		AM	Nationwide	AWACS Tactical TAD
279.875		AM	RAF Coningsby	Fast Jet Operational Evaluation Unit Auxiliary
280.400		AM	Nationwide	Forward Air Controllers
281.100		AM	Nationwide	AWACS Tactical TAD
281.150		AM	Lyme Bay	Range Primary
281.175		AM	Nationwide	AWACS Tactical TAD
281.200		AM	Nationwide	Royal Navy Ship-Air
281.500		AM	RAF Coningsby	DATIS
281.550		AM	Nationwide	Air-Air
281.725		AM	English Channel	Naval Exercises
281.800		AM	Nationwide	Forward Air Controllers
282.000		AM	RAF Cranwell	Radar
282.050		AM	RAF Marham	13 Squadron Dagger Ops.
282.075		AM	Nationwide	AWACS Tactical TAD
282.100		AM	RNAS Culdrose	ATIS
282.200		AM	Nationwide	AWACS Tactical TAD
282.250		AM	Netheravon (Army)	Air-Ground, Salisbury Plain
282.275		AM	RAF Honington	Tower
282.450		AM	Nationwide	AWACS Tactical TAD
282.800		AM	Nationwide	NATO SAR Helicopters
282.800		AM	RAF Boulmer	SAR Air/Ground
282.800		AM	RAF Leconfield	SAR Air/Ground
282.975		AM	Nationwide	AWACS Tactical TAD
283.050		AM	Nationwide	USAF Air-Air Refuelling
283.450		AM	Nationwide	9 Sqn Air-Air
283.575		AM	Wattisham (Army Airfield)	Director
283.600		AM	Nationwide	17 Squadron Air-Air
283.650		AM	Nationwide	AWACS Tactical TAD
283.900		AM	RAF Lossiemouth	Safety Officer
284.100		AM	RAF Aldergrove	Interplane/Flight Safety
284.600		AM	Newcastle	Approach/Radar
284.900		AM	USAF Lakenheath	Maintenance
284.925		AM	RAF St Athan	ATIS
284.950		AM	RAF Lyneham	Air-Air
284.975		AM	Nationwide	AWACS Tactical TAD
285.025		AM	RAF Leuchars	Wing Ops.
285.075		AM	RAF Valley	Interplane
285.100		AM	Nationwide	FRADU Discrete
285.150		AM	RAF Cranwell	Talkdown
286.600		AM	Nationwide	Air - Air Refuelling
287.000		AM	Nationwide	Army Euromux Radio Relay
287.250		AM	Nationwide	RAF Air-Air Tanker Ops.
287.650		AM	Royal Navy	Ship-Air
288.850		AM	Nationwide	Patrouille Suisse Display Team
288.950		AM	Eskmeals Range	MoD Range
289.100		AM	Nationwide	USAF Air-Air Refuelling
289.250		AM	RAF Lossiemouth	16 Squadron Air-Air
289.600		AM	Nationwide	USAF Air-Air Refuelling
290.050		AM	RAF Coningsby	29 Squadron Air-Air
290.675		AM	Nationwide	AWACS Tactical TAD
290.800		AM	RAF Coningsby	Air-Air
290.850		AM	RAF Coningsby	29 Squadron Ops (Triplex Ops)
290.950		AM	Netheravon (Army)	AFIS
291.125		AM	Wattisham (Army Airfield)	Approach
291.225		AM	RAF Lossiemouth	TAC 1
291.650		AM	Boscombe Down (MoD)	Approach/Director

Base	Mobile	Mode	Location	User and Notes
291.675		AM	RAF Waddington	DATIS
291.700		AM	RAF Barkston Heath	Departure
292.450		AM	RAF Coltishall	54 Squadron Interplane Ops
292.475		AM	RAF Leuchars	Approach
292.550		AM	Nationwide	AWACS Tactical TAD
292.575		AM	RAF Shawbury	DATIS
292.700		AM	RAF Leeming	Director
292.800		AM	Aberystwyth	MoD/RAF Marine Craft
292.800		AM	RAF Linton on Ouse	Approach/Departure/Radar
292.900		AM	Nationwide	Air-Air
293.425		AM	RAF Coltishall	FIS/Radar
293.525		AM	Nationwide	RAF Air Refuelling UK
293.700		AM	Nationwide	Air-Air UK Common Ch.1
293.775		AM	RAF Marham	Radar
294.700		AM	Nationwide	AWACS Tactical TAD
296.400		AM	RAF Lossiemouth	15 Squadron Air-Air
296.725		AM	RAF Kinloss	Ground
296.725		AM	RNAS Culdrose	705 Squadron Air-Air
296.775		AM	Nationwide	Air-Air Refuelling 5 TAD 076
296.800		AM	International	Space Shuttle Downlink
296.825		AM	Nationwide	Air-Air Refuelling 3 TAD 057
297.100		AM	RAF Valley	Interplane
297.900		AM	RAF Cranwell	Ground
297.900		AM	RAF Leuchars	Ground
298.650		AM	Nationwide	AWACS Tactical TAD
299.100		AM	RAF Boulmer	Air/Ground
299.400		AM	Boscombe Down (MoD)	Ground
299.400		AM	RAF Lossiemouth	Ground
299.400		AM	RNAS Culdrose	Ground
299.500		AM	Nationwide	AWACS Tactical TAD
299.700		AM	Nationwide	USAF Air Refuelling
299.925		AM	Nationwide	AWACS Tactical TAD
299.975		AM	RAF Coltishall	CAC (London Military)
299.975		AM	RAF Coningsby	CAC (London Military)
299.975		AM	RAF Cottesmore	CAC (London Military)
299.975		AM	RAF Waddington	CAC
299.975		AM	RAF Wittering	CAC (Easterly Departures)
299.975		AM	Swanwick Military	Middle Airspace (East)
299.975		AM	Swanwick Military	Upper Airspace (East)
299.975		AM	USAF Lakenheath	CAC (London Military)
299.975		AM	USAF Mildenhall	CAC
300.025		AM	Nationwide	French Jaguar Display Team
300.050		AM	Portland Exercise Area	Ops
300.100		AM	Nationwide	Air-Air Refuelling 1 TAD 041
300.175		AM	Plymouth	Plymouth Military Radar RN
300.250		AM	Boscombe Down (MoD)	ETPS Tester Ops
300.350		AM	RAF Northolt	ATIS
300.425		AM	RAF Linton on Ouse	Tower
300.450		AM	RAF Odiham	Talkdown
300.475		AM	RAF Lyneham	Radar
300.575		AM	RAF Waddington	Director
300.625		AM	RAF Cranwell	3FTS Air-to-Air
300.675		AM	Yeovil (Westland)	Radar (Judwin)
300.700		AM	Nationwide	AWACS Tactical TAD
300.800		AM	Nationwide	NATO Low Level
300.825		AM	Lilstock Range (D119)	Range Control

Base	Mobile	Mode	Location	User and Notes
300.825		AM	USAF Lakenheath	Dispatcher
300.875		AM	RAF Leeming	11 Squadron Black Ops.
300.925		AM	RAF Coningsby	Talkdown
301.075		AM	Nationwide	AWACS Tactical TAD
304.000		NFM	Worldwide	USAF Satcom Downlink
305.900		AM	RNAS Culdrose	Squadron Ops
306.500		AM	Southern North Sea	Air-Air Refuelling, AARA 6
306.650		AM	SW Scotland	Combat Air Patrol Area
307.800		AM	Nationwide	Frecce Tricolori Display Team
307.800		AM	Stanford	Air/Ground (Army)
308.000		AM	Northern North Sea	Air-Air Refuelling, AARA 3
309.525		AM	Nationwide	Air-Air Common UK Ch.4
309.550		AM	RAF Chetwynd	Ternhill Tower
309.625		AM	RAF Odiham	Tower
309.650		AM	RAF Valley	4FTS Air-to-Air
309.675		AM	RAF Waddington	Talkdown
309.725		AM	RAF Topcliffe	Tower
309.825		AM	RAF Scampton	Talkdown
309.875		AM	RAF Leeming	Talkdown
310.000		AM	Northern North Sea	Air-Air Refuelling, AARA 2
310.000		AM	RAF Aldergrove	Approach/Radar
311.000		AM	Nationwide	RN Movements Primary
311.00		AM	RAF Shawbury	Approach
311.200		AM	RAF Valley	4FTS Air-to-Air
311.300		AM	Warton (BAe)	Approach/Radar/Tower
311.325		AM	RAF Lossiemouth	Approach
311.325		AM	RNAS Yeovilton	Ground
311.825		AM	USAF Fairford	CAC (Brize)
311.950		AM	RAF Wittering	Ground
312.000		AM	Benbecular	Qinitiq Range
312.000		AM	Middle Wallop (Army)	Approach
312.075		AM	RAF Cottesmore	Director
312.225		AM	RAF Coningsby	Approach
312.350		AM	RAF Northolt	Tower
312.400		AM	RAF Lossiemouth	Talkdown
312.450		AM	RAF Mildenhall	Ops (Command Post)
312.500		AM	RAF Waddington	Approach
312.550		AM	RAF Marham	Wing Ops
312.675		AM	Middle Wallop (Army)	Tower
312.700		AM	RNAS Merryfield	Tower
312.800		AM	RAF Woodvale	Approach
313.100		AM	RAF Valley	4FTS Air-to-Air
314.400		AM	Benbecular	Qinetiq Range
315.325		AM	RAF Coltishall	Approach
315.375		AM	USAF Mildenhall	Navy Ops
315.575		AM	USAF Lakenheath	Radar
315.700		AM	RAF Wyton	ATIS
315.750		AM	RAF Benson	Director/Radar
315.975		AM	RAF Odiham	Flight Information
316.350		AM	Northern North Sea	Air-Air Refuelling, AARA 8
316.600		AM	Northern North Sea	Air-Air Refuelling, AARA 4
317.850		AM	Nationwide	AWACS Tactical TAD
318.050		AM	Nationwide	AWACS Tactical TAD
319.600		AM	Nationwide	Royal Navy Ship-Air
319.700		AM	Nationwide	Army Euromux Radio Relay
322.950		AM	Nationwide	AWACS Tactical TAD

325.0000 - 325.4875 MHz — Short Range Radio Service, Simplex
Philippines/Brunei/Singapore
Often Used Illegally in the UK

Base	Mode	Location	User and Notes
325.0125	NFM	Nationwide	Philippines/Brunei/Singapore SRRS Ch.1
325.0250	NFM	Nationwide	Philippines/Brunei/Singapore SRRS Ch.2
325.0375	NFM	Nationwide	Philippines/Brunei/Singapore SRRS Ch.3
325.0500	NFM	Nationwide	Philippines/Brunei/Singapore SRRS Ch.4
325.0625	NFM	Nationwide	Philippines/Brunei/Singapore SRRS Ch.5
325.0750	NFM	Nationwide	Philippines/Brunei/Singapore SRRS Ch.6
325.0875	NFM	Nationwide	Philippines/Brunei/Singapore SRRS Ch.7
325.1000	NFM	Nationwide	Philippines/Brunei/Singapore SRRS Ch.8
325.1125	NFM	Nationwide	Philippines/Brunei/Singapore SRRS Ch.9
325.1250	NFM	Nationwide	Philippines/Brunei/Singapore SRRS Ch.10
325.1375	NFM	Nationwide	Philippines/Brunei/Singapore SRRS Ch.11
325.1500	NFM	Nationwide	Philippines/Brunei/Singapore SRRS Ch.12
325.1625	NFM	Nationwide	Philippines/Brunei/Singapore SRRS Ch.13
325.1750	NFM	Nationwide	Philippines/Brunei/Singapore SRRS Ch.14
325.1875	NFM	Nationwide	Philippines/Brunei/Singapore SRRS Ch.15
325.2000	NFM	Nationwide	Philippines/Brunei/Singapore SRRS Ch.16
325.2125	NFM	Nationwide	Philippines/Brunei/Singapore SRRS Ch.17
325.2250	NFM	Nationwide	Philippines/Brunei/Singapore SRRS Ch.18
325.2375	NFM	Nationwide	Philippines/Brunei/Singapore SRRS Ch.19
325.2500	NFM	Nationwide	Philippines/Brunei/Singapore SRRS Ch.20
325.2625	NFM	Nationwide	Philippines/Brunei/Singapore SRRS Ch.22
325.2750	NFM	Nationwide	Philippines/Brunei/Singapore SRRS Ch.23
325.2875	NFM	Nationwide	Philippines/Brunei/Singapore SRRS Ch.24
325.3000	NFM	Nationwide	Philippines/Brunei/Singapore SRRS Ch.25
325.3125	NFM	Nationwide	Philippines/Brunei/Singapore SRRS Ch.26
325.3250	NFM	Nationwide	Philippines/Brunei/Singapore SRRS Ch.27
325.3375	NFM	Nationwide	Philippines/Brunei/Singapore SRRS Ch.28
325.3500	NFM	Nationwide	Philippines/Brunei/Singapore SRRS Ch.29
325.3625	NFM	Nationwide	Philippines/Brunei/Singapore SRRS Ch.30
325.3750	NFM	Nationwide	Philippines/Brunei/Singapore SRRS Ch.31
325.3875	NFM	Nationwide	Philippines/Brunei/Singapore SRRS Ch.32
325.4000	NFM	Nationwide	Philippines/Brunei/Singapore SRRS Ch.33
325.4125	NFM	Nationwide	Philippines/Brunei/Singapore SRRS Ch.34
325.4250	NFM	Nationwide	Philippines/Brunei/Singapore SRRS Ch.35
325.4375	NFM	Nationwide	Philippines/Brunei/Singapore SRRS Ch.36
325.4500	NFM	Nationwide	Philippines/Brunei/Singapore SRRS Ch.37
325.4625	NFM	Nationwide	Philippines/Brunei/Singapore SRRS Ch.38
325.4750	NFM	Nationwide	Philippines/Brunei/Singapore SRRS Ch.39
325.4875	NFM	Nationwide	Philippines/Brunei/Singapore SRRS Ch.40

326.500 - 328.500 MHz — Radio Astronomy, Jodrell Bank

328.600 - 335.400 MHz — Aeronautical ILS (Glideslope Component)

Base	Mode	Location	User and Notes
329.150	AM	Nationwide	Glideslope (Localiser 108.95 MHz)
329.150	AM	Woodford	Runway 25
329.300	AM	Nationwide	Glideslope (Localiser 108.90 MHz)
329.450	AM	Filton (BAe), Bristol	Runway 10/28
329.450	AM	Nationwide	Glideslope (Localiser 110.55 MHz)
329.600	AM	Bournemouth	Runway 08/26
329.600	AM	London/Stansted	Runway 05/23
329.600	AM	Nationwide	Glideslope (Localiser 110.50 MHz)
329.750	AM	Nationwide	Glideslope (Localiser 108.55 MHz)

Base	Mobile	Mode	Location	User and Notes
329.900		AM	Nationwide	Glideslope (Localiser 108.50 MHz)
329.900		AM	RAF Benson	Runway 19
330.050		AM	Nationwide	Glideslope (Localiser 110.75 MHz)
330.200		AM	Cardiff	Runway 12/30
330.200		AM	Connaught	Runway 27
330.200		AM	London/Heathrow	Runway 23
330.200		AM	Nationwide	Glideslope (Localiser 110.70 MHz)
330.200		AM	RAF Coningsby	Runway 26
330.350		AM	Humberside	Runway 21
330.350		AM	Nationwide	Glideslope (Localiser 108.75 MHz)
330.500		AM	Nationwide	Glideslope (Localiser 108.70 MHz)
330.500		AM	RAF Leuchars	Runway 27
330.500		AM	RAF Shawbury	Runway 19
330.500		AM	RAF St Mawgan	Runway 31
330.650		AM	Nationwide	Glideslope (Localiser 110.95 MHz)
330.800		AM	Belfast (Aldergrove)	Runway 17
330.800		AM	Jersey	Runway 09
330.800		AM	Leeds & Bradford	Runway 32/14
330.800		AM	London/Gatwick	Runway 08R/26L
330.800		AM	Nationwide	Glideslope (Localiser 110.90 MHz)
330.800		AM	Norwich	Runway 27
330.800		AM	Ronaldsway, Isle of Man	Runway 27
330.950		AM	Nationwide	Glideslope (Localiser 111.95 MHz)
331.250		AM	Luton	Runway 08/28
331.250		AM	Nationwide	Glideslope (Localiser 109.15 MHz)
331.300		AM	Nationwide	Glideslope (Localiser 111.90 MHz)
331.300		AM	RAF Brize Norton	Runway 08/26
331.400		AM	Nationwide	Glideslope (Localiser 109.10 MHz)
331.550		AM	Nationwide	Glideslope (Localiser 111.15 MHz)
331.700		AM	Nationwide	Glideslope (Localiser 111.10 MHz)
331.700		AM	RAF Fairford	Runway 09/27
331.700		AM	RAF Lossiemouth	Runway 23
331.700		AM	RAF Waddington	Runway 21
331.700		AM	Wattisham (Army Airfield)	Runway 23
331.850		AM	Nationwide	Glideslope (Localiser 109.35 MHz)
332.000		AM	Glasgow Airport	Runway 23
332.000		AM	Nationwide	Glideslope (Localiser 109.30 MHz)
332.000		AM	RAF Church Fenton	Runway 24
332.150		AM	Nationwide	Glideslope (Localiser 111.35 MHz)
332.300		AM	Hatfield	Runway 24
332.300		AM	Nationwide	Glideslope (Localiser 111.30 MHz)
332.300		AM	Teesside	Runway 23
332.450		AM	Nationwide	Glideslope (Localiser 109.55 MHz)
332.600		AM	London/Heathrow	Runway 09R/27L
332.600		AM	Manchester	Runway 06/24
332.600		AM	Nationwide	Glideslope (Localiser 109.50 MHz)
332.600		AM	Plymouth	Runway 31
332.600		AM	Shannon	Runway 24
332.750		AM	Nationwide	Glideslope (Localiser 111.55 MHz)
332.750		AM	Newcastle	Runway 07/25
332.900		AM	Nationwide	Glideslope (Localiser 111.50 MHz)
332.900		AM	RAF Coltishall	Runway 22
333.050		AM	Coventry	Runway 23
333.050		AM	Nationwide	Glideslope (Localiser 109.75 MHz)
333.200		AM	Beauvais	Runway 31
333.200		AM	Belfast (Aldergrove)	Runway 25

Base	Mobile	Mode	Location	User and Notes
333.200		AM	Dinard	Runway 36
333.200		AM	Nationwide	Glideslope (Localiser 109.70 MHz)
333.200		AM	RAF Cranwell	Runway 27
333.200		AM	RAF Kinloss	Runway 26
333.200		AM	RAF Lyneham	Runway 25
333.200		AM	RAF Valley	Runway 14
333.350		AM	Liverpool	Runway 09/27
333.350		AM	Nationwide	Glideslope (Localiser 111.75 MHz)
333.500		AM	Nationwide	Glideslope (Localiser 111.70 MHz)
333.500		AM	RAE Boscombe Down	Runway 24
333.650		AM	Nationwide	Glideslope (Localiser 109.95 MHz)
333.800		AM	Aberdeen/Dyce	Runway 16/34
333.800		AM	Cherbourg	Runway 29
333.800		AM	Cork	Runway 17/35
333.800		AM	East Midlands	Runway 09/27
333.800		AM	Exeter	Runway 26
333.800		AM	Nationwide	Glideslope (Localiser 109.90 MHz)
333.800		AM	Stornoway	Runway 18
333.800		AM	Warton	Runway 26
333.950		AM	Nationwide	Glideslope (Localiser 108.35 MHz)
334.100		AM	Bedford	Runway 27
334.100		AM	Nationwide	Glideslope (Localiser 108.30 MHz)
334.100		AM	RAF Lakenheath	Runway 24
334.250		AM	Bristol	Runway 09/27
334.250		AM	Nationwide	Glideslope (Localiser 110.15 MHz)
334.400		AM	Birmingham	Runway 15/33
334.400		AM	Glasgow Airport	Runway 05
334.400		AM	Nationwide	Glideslope (Localiser 110.10 MHz)
334.400		AM	RAF Marham	ILS Runway 24
334.550		AM	Blackpool	Runway 28
334.550		AM	Lydd	Runway 22
334.550		AM	Nationwide	Glideslope (Localiser 108.15 MHz)
334.700		AM	Guernsey	Runway 09/27
334.700		AM	Nationwide	Glideslope (Localiser 108.10 MHz)
334.700		AM	RAF Chivenor	Runway 28
334.700		AM	RAF Mildenhall	Runway 11/29
334.750		AM	RAF Neatishead	MRSA
334.850		AM	Nationwide	Glideslope (Localiser 110.35 MHz)
335.000		AM	Jersey	Runway 27
335.000		AM	London/Heathrow	Runway 09L/27R
335.000		AM	Nationwide	Glideslope (Localiser 110.30 MHz)
335.000		AM	Prestwick	Runway 13/31
335.000		AM	RAF Cottesmore	Runway 23
335.000		AM	RAF Leeming	Runway 16

335.400 - 338.000 MHz   UHF Military Aviation 25 kHz

Base	Mobile	Mode	Location	User and Notes
335.900		AM	Nationwide	31 Squadron Air-Air
335.975		AM	RAF Lossiemouth	15 Squadron Air-Air
336.150		AM	Boscombe Down (MoD)	Talkdown
336.225		AM	Manorbier	Range
336.225		AM	RAF Lossiemouth	617 Squadron Ops
336.325		AM	Hawarden	Tower
336.350		AM	RAF Kinloss	Tower
336.350		AM	RAF Leeming	Talkdown
336.350		AM	RAF Marham	Ground
336.375		AM	RAF Cottesmore	Ground

Base	Mobile	Mode	Location	User and Notes
336.475		AM	Filton (BAe)	Director
336.475		AM	Warton (BAe)	Approach/Radar
336.525		AM	RAF St Athan	Tower
337.575		AM	USAF Fairford	Tower
337.575		AM	USAF Lakenheath	Maintenance
337.600		AM	RAF Tain Range	Range
337.600		AM	USAF Lakenheath	Approach/RAPCon
337.600		AM	USAF Mildenhall	Approach
337.725		AM	RAF Valley	Director
337.750		AM	Prestwick	HMS Gannet Air-Ground Ops
337.750		AM	RAF Lossiemouth	Tower
337.750		AM	RNAS Prestwick	Navy Ops
337.825		AM	RAF Leeming	Approach
337.875		AM	RAF Cottesmore	Talkdown
337.900		AM	RAF Marham	Tower
337.900		AM	RAF Shawbury	Ground
337.925		AM	MoD West Freugh	Tower
337.950		AM	RAF Wittering	Talkdown
337.975		AM	Nationwide	Aquilla Spanish Display Team
337.975		AM	RAF Coningsby	Talkdown

338.000 - 390.000 MHz   Tactical Military Communications 25 kHz

Base	Mobile	Mode	Location	User and Notes
338.650		AM	RAF Brize Norton	Talkdown
338.825		AM	RAF Ternhill	Tower
338.875		AM	RNAS Yeovilton	Director
338.975		AM	RNAS Predannack	Tower
339.950		AM	RAF Coltishall	Tower
339.950		AM	RNAS Culdrose	Radar
339.975		AM	RNAS Yeovilton	Talkdown
340.025		AM	RAF Linton on Ouse	Ground
340.050		AM	Wainfleet	Range Primary
340.100		AM	RAF St Athan	Talkdown
340.175		AM	RAF Lyneham	Ground
340.175		AM	RAF Valley	Tower
340.200		AM	RAF Church Fenton	Ground
340.250		AM	Warton	Special Tasks/Test Flights
340.300		AM	RAF Spadeadam	Secondary
340.325		AM	RAF Benson	Ground
340.350		AM	RAF Shawbury	Tower
340.475		AM	RAF Barkston Heath	Approach (Cranwell)
340.475		AM	RAF Cranwell	Approach
340.525		AM	RAF Barkston Heath	Ground
340.575		AM	RAF Cottesmore	Radar
340.900		AM	Nationwide	AWACS Tactical TAD
342.075		AM	RAF Barkston Heath	Tower
342.000		AM	RAF Marham	2 Squadron Cropper Ops.
342.100		AM	RAF Valley	4FTS Air-to-Air
342.125		AM	RAF Waddington	Ground
342.175		AM	Donna Nook Range	Control
342.250		AM	RAF Coltishall	Approach/Radar
342.450		AM	RAF Brize Norton	Approach
342.450		AM	USAF Fairford	Approach/B52 Fortress Ops (118.8)
342.650		AM	Nationwide	AWACS Overland CAP TAD 508
342.925		AM	RAF Coningsby	Discrete
343.325		AM	RAF Marham	39 Squadron Ops
343.375		AM	Holbeach Range	Range

Base	Mobile	Mode	Location	User and Notes
343.500		AM	Nationwide	Forward Air Controllers
343.600		AM	USAF Croughton	Air/Ground
343.600		AM	USAF Lakenheath	493FS
343.675		AM	RAF Leeming	Auxiliary Ops
343.675		AM	RNAS Yeovilton	Squadron Ops
343.700		AM	Warton (BAe)	Director
344.000		AM	RAF Brize Norton	Radar
344.000		AM	RAF Church Fenton	Radar
344.000		AM	RAF Coningsby	Radar
344.000		AM	RAF Cranwell	Radar
344.000		AM	RAF Leeming	Director
344.000		AM	RAF Linton on Ouse	Radar
344.000		AM	RAF Lyneham	Radar
344.000		AM	RAF Marham	Director
344.000		AM	RAF St Mawgan	Radar
344.000		AM	RAF Valley	Director
344.000		AM	RAF Waddington	Director
344.000		AM	RAF Wittering	Departure
344.100		AM	Nationwide	USAF Air-Air Refuelling
344.350		AM	RAF Topcliffe	Talkdown
344.350		AM	RNAS Yeovilton	Talkdown
344.475		AM	RAF Linton on Ouse	Radar
344.500		AM	Warton (BAe)	Operations (Boffin Ops)
344.575		AM	RAF Leeming	Tower
344.625		AM	RAF Coningsby	Approach
344.850		AM	Nationwide	AWACS Tactical TAD
344.900		AM	RAF Marham	Talkdown
344.975		AM	RAF Northolt	Approach
345.025		AM	RAF Lyneham	MATZ
345.100		AM	RAF Wittering	Interplane
345.200		AM	Larkhill	Range Primary
345.450		AM	Dorset	RN Ship-Air Thursday War
352.475		AM	Nationwide	AWACS Tactical TAD
353.550		AM	Boscombe Down (MoD)	Ops
354.450		AM	Kyle of Lochalsh	British Underwater Test & Evaluation Centre
355.025		AM	Nationwide	Forward Air Controllers
355.725		AM	Nationwide	AWACS Tactical TAD
356.175		AM	Wattisham (Army Airfield)	Talkdown
356.200		AM	Aberporth	Range Primary
356.275		AM	Nationwide	Swiss Air Force PC7 Display Team
356.325		AM	Nesscliffe Army Camp	Air/Ground
356.325		AM	RAF Chetwynd	Approach
356.325		AM	RAF Shawbury	Radar (Low Level)
356.325		AM	RAF Ternhill	Approach
356.400		AM	RAF Valley	4FTS Air-to-Air
356.425		AM	Nationwide	AWACS Tactical TAD
356.450		AM	Nationwide	USAF Air-Air Refuelling
356.725		AM	RAF Leeming	Wing Ops
356.750		AM	RAF Valley	Ground
356.775		AM	RAF Marham	2 Squadron
356.800		AM	RAF Wainfleet	Range
356.875		AM	RAF Brize Norton	Radar
356.925		AM	RAF Cranwell	Talkdown
356.975		AM	RAF Shawbury	Talkdown
357.125		AM	RAF Cosford	Tower

Base	Mobile	Mode	Location	User and Notes
357.150		AM	RAF Wittering	Tower
357.175		AM	RAF St Athan	Approach
357.200		AM	RAF St Mawgan	Approach
357.375		AM	Dishforth	Approach
357.375		AM	RAF Topcliffe	Approach
357.475		AM	RAF Brize Norton	Brize Ops.
357.700		AM	Nationwide	AWACS Tactical TAD
358.200		AM	Dorset	RN Ship-Air Thursday War
358.475		AM	RAF Kinloss	Ops
358.525		AM	RAF Linton on Ouse	Talkdown
358.550		AM	RAF Coningsby	Ground
358.600		AM	Wattisham (Army Airfield)	Tower
358.650		AM	RAF Leeming	Approach
358.675		AM	RAF Tain Range	Range
358.675		AM	RAF Valley	Talkdown
358.675		AM	USAF Lakenheath	Tower
358.725		AM	RAF Cottesmore	Approach
358.750		AM	RAF Mona	Tower
358.800		AM	RAF Benson	Ground
359.500		AM	RAF Lyneham	Approach
359.625		AM	Nationwide	AWACS Tactical TAD
359.775		AM	Boscombe Down (MoD)	Director
359.800		AM	Nationwide	Air-Air Common UK Ch.5
359.825		AM	Wattisham (Army Airfield)	Talkdown
360.450		AM	Holbeach	Range
360.550		AM	RAF St Mawgan	Radar
360.725		AM	RAF Barkston Heath	Talkdown
360.750		AM	RAF Colerne	Ground
361.100		AM	RAF Leeming	11 Squadron Air-Air
361.825		AM	Nationwide	AWACS Tactical TAD
361.875		AM	RAF Benson	Talkdown
362.050		AM	Salisbury Plain	Range
362.100		AM	Nationwide	AWACS Tactical TAD
362.175		AM	RAF Lossiemouth	15 Squadron Air-Air
362.250		AM	Dorsett	RN Ship-Air Thursday War
362.300		AM	Dishforth	Approach
362.300		AM	RAF Benson	Approach/Radar
362.300		AM	RAF Brize Norton	Approach
362.300		AM	RAF Church Fenton	Approach/Radar
362.300		AM	RAF Colerne	Approach
362.300		AM	RAF Coningsby	Approach
362.300		AM	RAF Cranwell	Approach
362.300		AM	RAF Kinloss	Approach
362.300		AM	RAF Leeming	Approach
362.300		AM	RAF Leuchars	Approach
362.300		AM	RAF Linton on Ouse	Approach
362.300		AM	RAF Lossiemouth	Approach
362.300		AM	RAF Lyneham	Approach
362.300		AM	RAF Marham	Approach
362.300		AM	RAF Northolt	Approach
362.300		AM	RAF St Athan	Approach
362.300		AM	RAF Topcliffe	Approach
362.300		AM	RAF Valley	Approach
362.300		AM	RAF Waddington	Approach
362.300		AM	RAF Wittering	Approach/Director

Base	Mobile	Mode	Location	User and Notes
362.300		AM	RNAS Yeovilton	Approach/Director
362.300		AM	USAF Fairford	Approach
362.375		AM	Nationwide	AWACS Tactical TAD
362.475		AM	RAF Shawbury	Radar
362.525		AM	RAF Valley	4FTS Air-to-Air
362.650		AM	Boscombe Down (MoD)	MATZ
362.675		AM	RAF Linton on Ouse	Approach
362.750		AM	RAF Marham	Approach
362.900		AM	RAF Wittering	Pegasus Ops.
363.025		AM	Nationwide	AWACS Tactical TAD
363.675		AM	Nationwide	AWACS Tactical TAD
364.200		AM	Nationwide	NATO AWACS ICF TAD 014
364.275		AM	Nationwide	AWACS Tactical TAD
364.450		AM	Nationwide	AWACS Tactical TAD
364.800		AM	RAF Coltishall	Ops.
364.825		AM	Middle Wallop (Army)	Talkdown
364.850		AM	RAF Valley	4FTS Air-Air
364.900		AM	Nationwide	AWACS Tactical TAD
365.025		AM	RAF Valley	Duty Instructor
365.100		AM	RAF Mildenhall	Ops. (Dispatcher)
365.975		AM	USAF Lakenheath	MATZ Crossing
367.250		AM	Nationwide	AWACS Tactical TAD
367.325		AM	Nationwide	AWACS Tactical TAD
367.350		AM	Nationwide	AWACS Tactical TAD
367.475		AM	Nationwide	AWACS Tactical TAD
368.000		AM	Nationwide	AWACS Tactical TAD
368.275		AM	RAF Cottesmore	Interplane
368.425		AM	Nationwide	AWACS Tactical TAD
369.000		AM	Nationwide	AWACS Tactical TAD
369.025		AM	Nationwide	AWACS Tactical TAD
369.075		AM	USAF Lakenheath	Approach/Radar
369.100		AM	Faslane	Royal Navy Fly Co Ship-Air
369.125		AM	Nationwide	AWACS Tactical TAD
369.150		AM	RAF Spadeadam	Radar
369.875		AM	RNAS Yeovilton	Approach/Radar
369.975		AM	Yeovil (Westland)	Approach
370.000		AM	RNAS Predannack	Tower
370.050		AM	RAF Cottesmore	Tower
370.050		AM	RAF Kinloss	Talkdown
370.075		AM	RAF Leuchars	Talkdown
370.075		AM	RAF Odiham	Director
370.125		AM	RAF Waddington	Tower
370.250		AM	RAF Mildenhall	Tower
370.300		AM	RAF Brize Norton	Ground
370.325		AM	Plymouth	RN Military Radar
370.900		AM	Nationwide	AWACS Tactical TAD
371.200		AM	USAF Fairford	Flight Ops.
372.300		AM	Nationwide	Forward Air Controllers
372.350		AM	Nationwide	Forward Air Controllers
371.600		AM	Nationwide	AWACS Tactical TAD
372.250		AM	Nationwide	AWACS Tactical TAD
372.325		AM	RAF Mona	Radar
372.325		AM	RAF Valley	Approach
372.350		AM	RAF Coltishall	54 Squadron Ops (Lion Ops)
372.375		AM	RAF St Athan	Talkdown

Base	Mobile	Mode	Location	User and Notes
372.425		AM	Cambridge Airport	Tower/Radar
372.425		AM	HMS Cambridge	Royal Navy
372.425		AM	Yeovil (Westland)	Tower
372.500		AM	RAF Odiham	Ground
372.625		AM	Middle Wallop (Army)	Tower
372.650		AM	RAF Lossiemouth	617 Squadron Air-Air
372.650		AM	RNAS Yeovilton	Tower
372.825		AM	RAF Leeming	25 Squadron TAC 2
373.100		AM	Nationwide	AWACS Tactical TAD
373.350		AM	Nationwide	AWACS Tactical TAD
373.700		AM	Nationwide	Fisheries Protection
373.700		AM	RAF Kinloss	Maritime Patrol
373.700		AM	RAF Leuchars	Maritime Patrol
374.400		AM	Nationwide	AWACS Tactical TAD
374.500		AM	RAF Waddington	Ops
374.500		AM	Benbecular	Qinetiq Range
374.750		AM	Nationwide	AWACS Tactical TAD
374.850		AM	Nationwide	AWACS Overland CAP TAD 501
374.925		AM	RAF Wittering	Approach/Director
375.000		AM	USAF Lakenheath	Radar
375.125		AM	RAF Wyton	Approach
375.200		AM	RAF Lyneham	Talkdown
375.275		AM	Nationwide	AWACS Tactical TAD
375.325		AM	RAF Church Fenton	Radar
375.500		AM	RAF Northolt	Radar/Talkdown
375.550		AM	Nationwide	AWACS Tactical TAD
375.750		AM	Dorset	RN Ship-Ship Thursday war
376.075		AM	Nationwide	AWACS Tactical TAD
376.525		AM	RAF Kinloss	Talkdown
376.550		AM	Plymouth	RN Military Radar
376.575		AM	RAF Cottesmore	Radar
376.575		AM	RAF Wittering	Departure
376.625		AM	RAF St Mawgan	Ground
376.650		AM	RAF Kinloss	Approach
376.650		AM	RAF Lossiemouth	Approach
376.675		AM	RAF Shawbury	Talkdown
378.150		AM	RAF Wittering	Interplane
378.200		AM	Nationwide	USAF Air-Air Refuelling
378.675		AM	Nationwide	AWACS Tactical TAD
379.100		AM	RAF Leeming	100 Squadron Air-Air
379.200		AM	Aberporth	Range Secondary
379.250		AM	RAF Scampton	Talkdown
379.375		AM	RAF Coningsby	Air-to-Air
379.400		AM	Aberporth	Range Secondary
379.425		AM	RAF Northolt	Director
379.475		AM	USAF Fairford	Ops
379.500		AM	RN Culdrose	Falmouth Bay Radar
379.525		AM	RAF Barkston Heath	Radar
379.650		AM	RAF Marham	Talkdown
379.675		AM	Dishforth	Ground
379.700		AM	RAF Mona	Approach
379.750		AM	RNAS Yeovilton	ATIS
379.850		AM	Plymouth	Plymouth Military Radar
379.875		AM	Pembrey	Range Primary
379.900		AM	Nationwide	AWACS Tactical TAD

Base	Mobile	Mode	Location	User and Notes
380.200		AM	Nationwide	AAC Blue Eagles Display Team
380.200		AM	Nationwide	AAC Historic Flights
380.925		AM	Nationwide	Air-Air Refuelling 6 TAD 071
380.975		AM	Nationwide	Air-Air Refuelling 4 TAD 064
381.100		AM	RAF Waddington	Raven Ops
382.000		AM	Nationwide	AAC Blue Eagles Display Team
382.900		AM	HMS Drake (Plymouth)	Royal Navy
383.600		AM	RAF Valley	4FTS Air-to-Air
384.750		AM	Nationwide	Forward Air Controllers
385.400		AM	RAF Brize Norton	Talkdown
385.400		AM	RAF Church Fenton	Talkdown
385.400		AM	RAF Leeming	Talkdown
385.400		AM	RAF Leuchars	Talkdown
385.400		AM	RAF Lyneham	Talkdown
385.400		AM	RAF Marham	Talkdown
385.400		AM	RAF Northolt	Talkdown
385.400		AM	RAF Odiham	Talkdown
385.400		AM	RAF St Mawgan	Talkdown
385.400		AM	RAF Topcliffe	Talkdown
385.400		AM	RAF Valley	Talkdown
385.400		AM	RAF Waddington	Talkdown
386.500		AM	Benbecular	Qinetiq Range
386.500		AM	RAF St Athan	Ground
386.525		AM	RAF Leeming	Ground
386.525		AM	RNAS Culdrose	Tower
386.625		AM	RAF Leuchars	Director
386.675		AM	MoD Llanbedr	Approach
386.700		AM	Boscombe Down (MoD)	Tower
386.725		AM	Dartmouth	Military Helipad
386.725		AM	RAF Church Fenton	Talkdown
386.775		AM	RAF Odiham	Approach/Radar
386.825		AM	RAF Lyneham	Tower
387.125		AM	Nationwide	AWACS Tactical TAD
387.450		AM	RAF St Mawgan	Talkdown
387.450		AM	RAF Topcliffe	Ground
387.675		AM	Donna Nook	Range Control
387.750		AM	MoD Llanbedr	Tower
387.775		AM	RAF Coltishall	Talkdown (Secondary)
388.075		AM	Nationwide	Patrouille Suisse Display Team
388.300		AM	Nationwide	AWACS Tactical TAD
388.725		AM	Nationwide	AWACS Tactical TAD
388.775		AM	Nationwide	AWACS Tactical TAD
389.600		AM	Nationwide	RAF Personal Locator Beacons
389.650		AM	RAF Leeming	100 Squadron Air-Air
389.875		AM	Nationwide	AWACS Tactical TAD

390.0125 - 390.1375 MHz   **TETRA Airwave Direct Mode (Input -10 MHz)
CID, Incidents & Events Ch.1-6 250 kHz**

390.1625 - 394.7875 MHz   **TETRA Airwave Trunk Mode (Input -10 MHz)
Standard Use Ch.7-192 250 kHz**

394.8125 - 394.9875 MHz   **TETRA Airwave AGA Mode (Input -10 MHz)
Air to Ground Use Ch.193-200 250 kHz**

390.000 - 399.900 MHz — Tactical Military Communications 25 kHz

Base	Mobile	Mode	Location	User and Notes
390.9750		AM	USAF Fairford	B52 Interplane
391.4625		AM	Nationwide	Military Bomb Disposal Telemetry
391.5250		AM	Nationwide	Military Bomb Disposal Telemetry
392.2000		AM	USAF Fairford	B52 Interplane
394.3500		AM	RAF Kinloss	Sonar Buoy
396.4500		AM	USAF Mildenhall	AMC Ops.
396.4750		AM	Nationwide	AWACS Tactical TAD
396.7000		AM	RAF Brize Norton	Tower
396.8500		AM	RAF Wittering	Talkdown
398.60625		NFM	Nationwide	Bugging Devices Ch.1
398.62500		AM	Nationwide	Forward Air Controllers
399.45625		NFM	Nationwide	Bugging Devices Ch.2

399.9000 - 401.100 MHz — Satellite Downlinks & Telemetry

Base	Mobile	Mode	Location	User and Notes
400.100		NFM	Nationwide	Satellite Standard Frequency
401.000		NFM	Nationwide	RAF Target Telemetry

401.0000 - 406.1000 MHz — Military Land Mobile

Base	Mobile	Mode	Location	User and Notes
403.3250		NFM	Aldermaston	UKAEA Fire Channel

406.000 - 406.100 MHz — Low Power Satellites for Emergency Position-Indicating Radio Beacons and North Sea Radio Position Beacons

Base	Mobile	Mode	Location	User and Notes
406.00000		AM	International	Distress Frequency
406.00000		NFM	Nationwide	Ship's EPIRB
406.02500		AM	Nationwide	RAF Locator Beacons
406.10000		AM	International	Distress Frequency Monitored by UK, USA & Japan

406.100 - 410.000 MHz — Radio Astronomy

Cambridge, Chilbolton, Darnhall, Defford, Jodrell Bank, Knoockin, Pickmere and Wardle

402.450 - 425.000 MHz — MoD, USAF, US Navy & PMR 25 kHz

Base	Mobile	Mode	Location	User and Notes
403.32500		NFM	Aldermaston	UKAEA Fire Channel
405.68750		NFM	Scotland	Meteorological Office
406.12500	415.45000	NFM	Nationwide	USS Truman On Board Trunked Network
406.15000		NFM	Nationwide	US Navy On-Board Comms
406.17500		NFM	Nationwide	US Navy On-Board Comms
406.47500		NFM	Nationwide	US Navy On-Board Comms
406.51250		NFM	Nationwide	US Navy On-Board Comms
406.55000		NFM	Nationwide	US Navy On-Board Comms
406.65000	415.92500	NFM	Nationwide	USS Truman On Board Trunked Network
406.67500		NFM	USAF Fairford	USAF Fairford Ground Ops. (118.8)
406.77500	414.67500	NFM	Channel Tunnel	Tactical Ch.10 French Ch.8
406.85000		NFM	Nationwide	USS Truman On Board Trunked Network
406.87500		NFM	Nationwide	USS Enterprise On Board Comms Encrypted
406.87500	416.07500	NFM	Nationwide	USS Truman On Board Trunked Network
406.87500		NFM	USAF Fairford	Dragon Ops (118.8)
406.95000		NFM	Nationwide	US Navy On-Board Comms
407.07500		NFM	Nationwide	USS Truman On Board Trunked Network
407.20000		NFM	Nationwide	USS Enterprise On Board Comms Phone Patch
407.35000		NFM	Nationwide	US Navy On-Board Comms
407.42500		NFM	London	US Embassy London Marines Security (173.8)
407.65000		NFM	Nationwide	USS Truman On Board Trunked Network
407.75000		NFM	Aldermaston	Atomic Weapons Establishment Services
407.75000		NFM	USAF Welford	Armaments Store

Base	Mobile	Mode	Location	User and Notes
407.95000		NFM	USAF Welford	Armaments Store
407.97500		NFM	USAF Fairford	F117 Squadron Ch.18
407.97500		NFM	USAF Welford	Armaments Store
408.00000	410.00000	NFM	Nationwide	RAF Base Management/Security/Ops (192.8)
408.12500	416.60000	NFM	Nationwide	USS Truman On Board Trunked Network
408.27500		NFM	London	US Embassy
408.30000		NFM	Jersey	Data Link
408.32500		NFM	RAF Valley	RAF Valley (192.8)
408.32500		NFM	RAF Leeming	RAF Leeming (192.8)
408.32500		NFM	RAF Woodvale	RAF Woodvale (192.8)
408.37500		NFM	RAF Benson	RAF Benson (192.8)
408.40000		NFM	RAF Coningsby	RAF Coningsby (192.8)
408.40000		NFM	RAF Leuchars	RAF Police Escort Motorcycles (192.8)
408.45000		NFM	Nationwide	USS Enterprise On Board Comms Phone Patch
408.45000	416.67500	NFM	Nationwide	USS Truman On Board Trunked Network
408.52500	421.17500	NFM	Channel Tunnel	Tactical Ch.7 Kent Ambulance Trust
408.52500		NFM	RAF Leuchars	RAF Leuchars Control Maintenance (192.8)
408.60000		NFM	RAF Leuchars	RAF Leuchars (192.8)
408.62500		NFM	London	US Embassy Marines
408.67500		NFM	London	US Embassy Marines
408.62500		NFM	RAF Leuchars	RAF Leuchars (192.8)
408.67500		NFM	RAF Valley	Medics/Doctors (192.8)
408.70000	416.27500	NFM	Nationwide	USS Truman On Board Trunked Network
408.70000		NFM	RAF Cosford	RAF Cosford (192.8)
408.70000		NFM	USAF Fairford	USAF Fairford
408.72500		NFM	RAF Waddington	Medical Control (192.8)
408.75000		NFM	RAF Leuchars	RAF Leuchars (192.8)
408.82500		NFM	RAF Leeming	RAF Leeming (192.8)
408.82500		NFM	Yeovilton	Royal Navy Yeovilton 800 Squadron
408.85000		NFM	RAF Honington	RAF Regiment (192.8)
408.90000		NFM	RAF Odiham	Tower (192.8)
408.92500		NFM	RAF Coningsby	Tower (192.8)
408.95000		NFM	RAF Leeming	Maintenance (192.8)
408.97500	418.02500	NFM	Nationwide	USS Truman On Board Trunked Network
409.00000		NFM	Wattisham	AAC Wattisham Tower
409.02500		NFM	RAF Leuchars	43 Squadron Ground Crew (192.8)
409.02500		NFM	RAF Valley	RAF Valley (192.8)
409.02500		NFM	USAF Lakenheath	Base Operations Security
409.07500		NFM	London	US Secret Service
409.15000		NFM	RAF Henlow	RAF Henlow Ch.6 (192.8)
409.17500		NFM	RAF Wittering	Police (192.8)
409.17500		NFM	RAF Waddington	Fuels (192.8)
409.20000	418.12500	NFM	Nationwide	USS Truman On Board Trunked Network
409.20000		NFM	RAF Brize Norton	RAF Police (192.8)
409.20000		NFM	RAF Henlow	RAF Henlow (192.8)
409.20000	417.22500	NFM	Wattisham	Army Air Corps Crash Operations
409.22500		NFM	RAF Leeming	Refuelling (192.8)
409.25000		NFM	RAF Leuchars	111 Squadron Ground Crew (192.8)
409.25000		NFM	RAF Marham	Operations (192.8)
409.27500		NFM	RAF Cosford	RAF Police Ch.3 (192.8)
409.27500		NFM	RAF Henlow	RAF Henlow Ch.5 (192.8)
409.27500		NFM	RAF Marham	Operations (192.8)
409.32500		NFM	RAF Marham	Operations (192.8)
409.35000		NFM	RAF Cosford	RAF Cosford (192.8)
409.37500		NFM	RAF Leuchars	RAF Leuchars (192.8)
409.40000		NFM	RAF Valley	RAF Police (192.8)
409.42500		NFM	Menwith Hill	US NSA Monitoring Station
409.45000		NFM	RAF Henlow	RAF Henlow On Test (192.8)

Base	Mobile	Mode	Location	User and Notes
409.45000		NFM	RAF Marham	Operations (192.8)
409.45000		NFM	RAF Waddington	RAF Police (192.8)
409.47500		NFM	RAF Leeming	Tower (192.8)
409.50000		NFM	RAF Leuchars	Tower (192.8)
409.50000		NFM	RAF Lyneham	RAF Police (192.8)
409.52500		NFM	RAF Henlow	Airfield Ops Ch.4 (192.8)
409.52500		NFM	RAF Marham	Tower (192.8)
409.52500		NFM	RAF Halton	RAF Police (192.8)
409.53750		NFM	Aldermaston	Royal Ordnance Factory
409.55000		NFM	RAF Cosford	RAF Cosford (192.8)
409.55000		NFM	RAF Henlow	RAF Henlow (192.8)
409.55000		NFM	RAF Leuchars	RAF Leuchars (192.8)
409.55000		NFM	Nationwide	RAF Police Close Protection Team
409.57500		NFM	Aldermaston	UKAEA
409.57500		NFM	RAF Leuchars	RAF Leuchars
409.58750	422.20000	NFM	Channel Tunnel	Tactical Ch.6 Kent Police Firearms Unit
409.60000		NFM	RAF Leuchars	RAF Leuchars (192.8)
409.62500		NFM	RAF Leuchars	RAF Leuchars (192.8)
409.67500		NFM	RAF Leuchars	RAF Leuchars (192.8)
409.68750	418.91250	NFM	Aldermaston	Royal Ordnance Factory Security Ch.1
409.68750		NFM	Reading	Royal Ordnance Factory, Burghfield,
409.70000		NFM	RAF Leuchars	RAF Police (192.8)
409.71250		NFM	Aldermaston	Royal Ordnance Factory Ch.2 Fire
409.72500		NFM	RAF Henlow	RAF Henlow (192.8)
409.75000		NFM	Nationwide	China Public Radio Often Used Illegally In UK Ch.1
409.75000		NFM	RAF Benson	Tower (192.8)
409.75000		NFM	RAF Coningsby	RAF Police (192.8)
409.75000		NFM	RAF Cranwell	RAF Cranwell (192.8)
409.75000		NFM	RAF Leuchars	Fuel/Maintenance (192.8)
409.75000		NFM	RAF Valley	Tower (192.8)
409.76250		NFM	Nationwide	China Public Radio Often Used Illegally In UK Ch.2
409.77500		NFM	Nationwide	China Public Radio Often Used Illegally In UK Ch.3
409.77500		NFM	RAF Henlow	RAF Henlow Security Back Up (192.8)
409.77500		NFM	RAF Leuchars	RAF Police (192.8)
409.77500		NFM	RAF Wittering	Maintenance (192.8)
409.78750		NFM	Nationwide	China Public Radio Often Used Illegally In UK Ch.4
409.80000		NFM	RAF Northolt	RAF Northolt (192.8)
409.80000		NFM	RAF Waddington	Tower (192.8)
409.80000		NFM	RAF Wittering	RAF Service Control (192.8)
409.80000		NFM	Nationwide	China Public Radio Often Used Illegally In UK Ch.5
409.81250		NFM	Nationwide	China Public Radio Often Used Illegally In UK Ch.6
409.82500		NFM	RAF Cosford	Refuelling (192.8)
409.82500		NFM	RAF Henlow	RAF Henlow Ch2 (192.8)
409.82500		NFM	RAF Northolt	RAF Northolt (192.8)
409.82500		NFM	RAF Wittering	Refuelling (192.8)
409.85000		NFM	RAF Lyneham	Tower (192.8)
409.85000		NFM	RAF Wittering	Tower (192.8)
409.87500		NFM	Nationwide	China Public Radio Often Used Illegally In UK Ch.11
409.87500		NFM	RAF Brize Norton	Tower (192.8)
409.87500		NFM	RAF Cosford	RAF Police (192.8)
409.87500		NFM	RAF Henlow	RAF Henlow Ch3 (192.8)
409.88750		NFM	Nationwide	China Public Radio Often Used Illegally In UK Ch.12
409.90000		NFM	Nationwide	China Public Radio Often Used Illegally In UK Ch.13
409.90000		NFM	RAF Cosford	Tower (192.8)
409.90000		NFM	RAF Henlow	RAF Security (192.8)
409.90000		NFM	RAF North Luffenham	RAF North Luffenham (192.8)
409.90000		NFM	RAF Northolt	RAF Police (192.8)
409.91250		NFM	Nationwide	China Public Radio Often Used Illegally In UK Ch.14

Base	Mobile	Mode	Location	User and Notes
409.92500		NFM	Nationwide	China Public Radio Often Used Illegally In UK Ch.15
409.93750		NFM	Nationwide	China Public Radio Often Used Illegally In UK Ch.16
409.95000		NFM	Nationwide	China Public Radio Often Used Illegally In UK Ch.17
409.95000		NFM	RAF Henlow	Crash Ops "Antacid" (192.8)
409.95000		NFM	RAF Northolt	Tower (192.8)
409.95000		NFM	RAF Waddington	RAF Waddington (192.8)
409.96250		NFM	Nationwide	China Public Radio Often Used Illegally In UK Ch.18
409.97500		NFM	Nationwide	China Public Radio Often Used Illegally In UK Ch.19
409.97500		NFM	RAF Henlow	RAF Henlow Ch1 (192.8)
409.97500		NFM	RAF Waddington	RAF Waddington (192.8)
409.98750		NFM	Nationwide	China Public Radio Often Used Illegally In UK Ch.20
410.02500		NFM	Nationwide	USS Truman On Board Trunked Network
410.05000		NFM	Nationwide	RAFASUPU Convoy
410.05000		NFM	RAF Cottesmore	RAF Police
410.05000		NFM	RAF St Mawgan	RAF St Mawgan Ch.1
410.07500		NFM	Menwith Hill	US NSA Monitoring Station
410.12500		NFM	RAF Cottesmore	Tower
410.12500		NFM	RAF Coltishall	RAF Police
410.12500	410.05000	NFM	RAF St Mawgan	RAF St Mawgan Ch.2
410.13750		NFM	Channel Tunnel	Tactical Ch.11 UK & French Fire Brigade Teams
410.13750	420.53750	NFM	Channel Tunnel	Tactical Ch.8 Channel Tunnel All Services
410.15000		NFM	Menwith Hill	US NSA Monitoring Station
410.20000		NFM	RAF St Mawgan	RAF St Mawgan Ch.3
410.25000	417.17500	NFM	USAF Lakenheath	Police/Fire/Crash/Command Trunked
410.25000	417.17500	NFM	USAF Mildenhall	Police/Fire/Crash/Command Trunked
410.35000		NFM	Menwith Hill	US NSA Monitoring Station
410.42500		NFM	USAF Mildenhall	USAF Command Phone Patch Channel
410.47500		NFM	RAF Northolt	RAF Northolt
410.52500		NFM	Portsmouth	Navy Provosts
410.57500		NFM	RAF St Mawgan	RAF St Mawgan Ch.4
410.70000		NFM	RAF Donna Nook	Range Wardens
410.77500	417.55000	NFM	USAF Lakenheath	Police/Fire/Crash/Command Trunked
410.77500	417.55000	NFM	USAF Mildenhall	Police/Fire/Crash/Command Trunked
410.80000		NFM	USAF Mildenhall	Fuel Tankers Ch 5
410.85000		NFM	RAF Waddington	RAF Waddington
410.87500		NFM	RAF Donna Nook	RAF Air Defence
410.90000		NFM	USAF Mildenhall	Command Network
410.92500		NFM	RAF Coltishall	RAF Police
410.92500		NFM	RAF St Mawgan	RAF St Mawgan Ch.5
411.00000		NFM	USAF Fairford	Tanker Ops. Ch.5
411.05000		NFM	RAF Odiham	RAF Police
411.07500	423.46250	NFM	Channel Tunnel	Fire Brigade Ch.5 Breathing Apparatus
411.07500		NFM	Channel Tunnel	Tactical Ch.16 Kent Fire Service
411.15000		NFM	USAF Mildenhall	USAF Police
411.25000		NFM	London	NATO Command Centre, Northwood
411.25000		NFM	Nationwide	RAFASUPU Convoys
411.27500		NFM	RAF Odiham	Refuellers
411.40000		NFM	Nationwide	RAFASUPU Convoys
411.40000		NFM	RAF Coltishall	Fuel Ops
411.40000		NFM	RAF Linton on Ouse	RAF Linton on Ouse
411.40000	422.15000	NFM	RAF St Mawgan	Security Ch.8
411.41250		NFM	Nationwide	Transportable Intruder Detection Devices
411.42500		NFM	USAF Lakenheath	Trunked Voice
411.42500		NFM	USAF Mildenhall	Trunked Voice
411.51250		NFM	Nationwide	Transportable Intruder Detection Devices
411.58750		NFM	London	NATO Command Centre, Northwood
411.61250		NFM	Nationwide	Transportable Intruder Detection Devices

Base	Mobile	Mode	Location	User and Notes
411.62500		NFM	USAF Mildenhall	Base Operations
411.67500		NFM	USAF Lakenheath	Police/Fire/Crash/Command
411.67500		NFM	USAF Mildenhall	Police/Fire/Crash/Command
411.71250		NFM	Nationwide	Transportable Intruder Detection Devices
411.72500		NFM	USAF Lakenheath	Trunked Voice
411.72500		NFM	USAF Mildenhall	Trunked Voice (Bandit)
411.75000		NFM	RAF Coltishall	Tower - Ground Vehicles
411.75000		NFM	RAF Henlow	Fire Brigade Fire Truck
411.77500		NFM	RAF Linton on Ouse	RAF Linton on Ouse
411.85000		NFM	RAF Lossiemouth	Tower
411.87500		NFM	RAF Chivenor	Ground Crews
411.87500		NFM	RAF St Mawgan	Tower Ch.6
411.87500		NFM	RAF Topcliffe	Tower
411.92500		NFM	RAF Brampton	RAF Police
411.92500		NFM	RAF St Mawgan	RAF St Mawgan Ch.7
411.95000		NFM	USAF Lakenheath	Police/Fire/Crash/Command Trunked
411.95000		NFM	USAF Mildenhall	Police/Fire/Crash/Command Trunked
411.97500	419.60000	NFM	Nationwide	USS Truman On Board Trunked Network
412.02500		NFM	Nationwide	Royal Signals
412.10000		NFM	RAF Cottesmore	RAF Cottesmore
412.10000		NFM	RAF St Mawgan	RAF St Mawgan Ch.9
412.15000		NFM	RAF Cottesmore	Fuel Trucks
412.27500		NFM	Nationwide	British Army Motorcycle Training
412.27500	418.50000	NFM	USAF Lakenheath	Police/Fire/Crash/Command Trunked
412.27500	418.50000	NFM	USAF Mildenhall	Police/Fire/Crash/Command Trunked
412.37500		NFM	USAF Mildenhall	Services Squadron
412.47500		NFM	Nationwide	USS Truman On Board Trunked Network
412.85000		NFM	RAF Cottesmore	RAF Cottesmore
412.92500	418.75000	NFM	USAF Lakenheath	Police/Fire/Crash/Command Trunked
412.92500	418.75000	NFM	USAF Mildenhall	Police/Fire/Crash/Command Trunked
413.00000		NFM	USAF Mildenhall	USAF Police
413.02500		NFM	USAF Croughton	Operations
413.07500	419.27500	NFM	Suffolk	Transient Alert Trunked
413.18750		NFM	Fort Halsted	Qinetiq Armaments Research Centre
413.37500	418.65000	NFM	USAF Lakenheath	Police/Crash/Fire/Command Trunked
413.37500	418.65000	NFM	USAF Mildenhall	Police/Crash/Fire/Command Trunked
413.50000		NFM	USAF Mildenhall	Secure Digital Data-Link
413.66250		NFM	Nationwide	Royal Signals
413.80000		NFM	London	US Embassy (103.5)
414.15000	419.47500	NFM	USAF Mildenhall	Transient Alert
414.27500		NFM	London	NATO Command Centre, Northwood
414.37500		NFM	USAF Croughton	USAF Security
415.10000		NFM	Windsor	Windsor Castle Security (127.3)
415.55000		NFM	USAF Mildenhall	Base Operations
415.56250		NFM	Belfast	British Military Data Link
415.73750		NFM	Bicester	MoD Military Railway Trains
416.17500		NFM	London	NATO Command Centre, Northwood
416.47500		NFM	Nationwide	USS Truman On Board Trunked Network
416.47500	413.00000	NFM	USAF Lakenheath	Police/Fire/Crash/Command Trunked
416.47500	413.00000	NFM	USAF Mildenhall	Police/Fire/Crash/Command Trunked
417.15000		NFM	RAF West Ruislip	Mod Police Defence Juliet/US Navy Control
417.47500	432.47500	NFM	RAF West Ruislip	Mod Police Defence Juliet/US Navy Control
417.52500		NFM	USAF Mildenhall	Aircrew Reception Ch.2
417.73750		NFM	Newbury	Mod Guard Services
417.87500	413.30000	NFM	USAF Lakenheath	Police/Fire/Crash/Command Trunked
417.87500	413.30000	NFM	USAF Mildenhall	Police/Fire/Crash/Command Trunked
418.00000		NFM	Newport	Moss House Alarms

Base	Mobile	Mode	Location	User and Notes
418.20000		NFM	Normandy	French Marine Ch 16 Link
418.25000		NFM	London	US Embassy Marines, Simple Scrambling
418.77500		NFM	Devonport	MoD Police
418.83750		NFM	Nationwide	MoD Fire
419.07500		NFM	Nationwide	USS Truman On Board Trunked Network
419.62500		NFM	Yeovilton	RNAS Yeovilton Marshallers
419.72500		NFM	Yeovilton	RNAS Yeovilton Marshallers
419.82500		NFM	Yeovilton	RNAS Yeovilton
422.07500	422.10000	NFM	RAF St Mawgan	RAF St Mawgan Ch.10
422.13750		NFM	Nationwide	MoD Police
422.25000		NFM	Nationwide	RAF Bomb Disposal (192.8)
422.25000		NFM	RAF Waddington	Bomb Disposal
422.95000	411.95000	FM	Lakenheath	RAF Motor Pool Ops
423.66250	436.76250	NFM	Channel Tunnel	Tactical Ch.9 French Ch.4
424.25000		NFM	Belfast	Police Mobile Data Link

425.1125 - 429.9750 MHz   Broadcasting Links, MoD & PMR

Base	Mobile	Mode	Location	User and Notes
425.11250	445.61250	NFM	London	London Underground Northern Line Trunked Control
425.13750	445.63750	NFM	London	London Underground Northern Line Trunked Control
425.13750		NFM	Nationwide	Independent Local Radio Ch.H1
425.15000	445.65000	NFM	London	London Underground Stations Ch.4 (67)
425.16250	445.66250	NFM	London	London Underground Northern Line Trunked Control
425.18750	425.18750	NFM	London	London Underground Northern Line Trunked Voice
425.21250	445.71250	NFM	London	London Underground Northern Line Trunked Voice
425.22500	445.72500	NFM	London	London Underground Kings Cross (67)
425.22500	445.72500	NFM	London	London Underground Northern Line Trunked Voice
425.22500	445.72500	NFM	London	London Underground Stations Ch.1 (67)
425.22500	445.72500	NFM	London	London Underground Oxford Circus (67)
425.22500	445.72500	NFM	London	London Underground Piccadilly Circus (67)
425.22500	445.72500	NFM	London	London Underground Westminster (67)
425.23750	445.73750	NFM	London	London Underground Northern Line Trunked Voice
425.23750		NFM	Nationwide	Independent Local Radio Ch.H2
425.25000	445.75000	NFM	London	London Underground
425.27500	445.77500	NFM	London	London Underground Embankment (67)
425.27500	445.77500	NFM	London	London Underground London Bridge (67)
425.27500	445.77500	NFM	London	London Underground Northern Line Trunked Voice
425.27500	445.77500	NFM	London	London Underground Stations Ch.2 (67)
425.30000	445.80000	NFM	London	London Underground Northern Line Trunked Voice
425.30000	445.80000	NFM	London	London Underground Stations Ch.3 (67)
425.31250		NFM	Nationwide	JFMG Temp Point-Point Audio Links Sth/Sth West UK
425.33750		NFM	Nationwide	Independent Local Radio Ch.H3
425.43750		NFM	Nationwide	Independent Local Radio Ch.H4
425.48750		NFM	Dorset	2CR Radio Microphones
425.53750		NFM	Nationwide	Independent Local Radio Ch.H5
425.56250		NFM	Nationwide	JFMG Temp Point-Point Audio Links Sth/Sth West UK
426.03750		NFM	Cardiff	Millennium Plaza
427.76250		NFM	Nationwide	JFMG Wide Area Talkback
427.81250		NFM	Manchester	ITN O/B Studio Link
428.00000		NFM	Birmingham	Xtra AM Radio 0/B Link
428.01250		NFM	Nationwide	JFMG Wide Area Talkback
428.23750		NFM	Edinburgh	St Andrews Coach Station Staff
429.00000	439.98750	NFM	Nationwide	MoD Radio Branch, Army/Navy/High Security Locations
429.72500		AM	Nationwide	Sea Cadet Corps Ch.SV1
429.83750		NFM	Channel Tunnel	Tactical Ch.15 Kent Ambulance Trust
429.83750	439.26250	NFM	Channel Tunnel	Tactical Ch.4 Kent Police Command
429.91250		NFM	London	Mould

Base	Mobile	Mode	Location	User and Notes

430.0000 - 440.0000 MHz   70cm Amateur Radio Band

Base	Mobile	Mode	Location	User and Notes
430.00000		SSB	Nationwide	Digital communications
430.01250		NFM	Nationwide	Internet Voice Gateway
430.02500		NFM	Nationwide	Internet Voice Gateway
430.03750		NFM	Nationwide	Internet Voice Gateway
430.05000		NFM	Nationwide	Internet Voice Gateway
430.06250		NFM	Nationwide	Internet Voice Gateway
430.07500		NFM	Nationwide	Internet Voice Gateway
430.80000		NFM	Nationwide	Raynet
430.85000	438.45000	NFM	Braintree	Repeater (GB3BZ) (110.9)
430.85000	438.45000	NFM	Mansfield	Repeater (GB3MD) (71.9)
430.85000	438.45000	NFM	Plymouth	Repeater (GB3IE) (77)
430.90000	438.50000	NFM	Dunkinfield	Repeater (GB3PZ) (82.5)
430.92500	438.52500	NFM	Worksop	Repeater (GB3XN) (71.9)
430.95000	438.55000	NFM	Winceby	Repeater (GB3FJ) (71.9)
430.99000		SSB	Nationwide	Digital communications
431.07500		NFM	Nationwide	Internet Voice Gateway
431.12500		NFM	Nationwide	Internet Voice Gateway
431.15000		NFM	Nationwide	Internet Voice Gateway
431.17500		NFM	Nationwide	Internet Voice Gateway
432.00000		CW	Nationwide	Moonbounce
432.02500		CW	Nationwide	Moonbounce
432.05000		CW	Nationwide	CW Centre of Activity
432.08800		NFM	Nationwide	PSK31 Centre of Activity
432.08800		SSB	Nationwide	SSB Centre of Activity
432.35000		SSB	Nationwide	Microwave Talkback Calling
432.37000		SSB	Nationwide	FSK441 Calling
432.60000		SSB	Nationwide	RTTY (FSK) Centre of Activity
432.62500		NFM	Nationwide	Packet radio
432.65000		NFM	Nationwide	Packet radio
432.67500		NFM	Nationwide	Packet radio
432.70000		NFM	Nationwide	Fax Centre of Activity
432.77500		NFM	Nationwide	Raynet
432.89000		CW	Sutton Coldfield	Beacon (GB3SUT)
432.91000		CW	Emley Moor	Beacon (GB3MLY)
432.93400		CW	Bristol	Beacon (GB3BSL)
432.96500		CW	Lerwick	Beacon (GB3LER)
432.97000		CW	St Austell	Beacon (GB3MCB)
432.98000		CW	Dundee	Beacon (GB3ANG)
433.00000	434.60000	NFM	Ashford	Repeater (GB3CK) (103.5)
433.00000	434.60000	NFM	Bishop Stortford	Repeater (GB3SV) (110.9)
433.00000	434.60000	NFM	Blackburn	Repeater (GB3PF) (82.5)
433.00000	434.60000	NFM	Blandford Forum	Repeater (GB3DT) (71.9)
433.00000	434.60000	NFM	Boston	Repeater (GB3SO) (71.9)
433.00000	434.60000	NFM	Bracknell	Repeater (GB3BN) (118.8)
433.00000	434.60000	NFM	Exeter	Repeater (GB3EX) (94.8)
433.00000	434.60000	NFM	Llandudno	Repeater (GB3LL) (110.9)
433.00000	434.60000	NFM	Milton Keynes	Repeater (GB3MK) (77)
433.00000	434.60000	NFM	Newcastle	Repeater (GB3NT) (118.8)
433.00000	434.60000	NFM	Norwich	Repeater (GB3NR) (94.8)
433.00000	434.60000	NFM	Perth	Repeater (GB3PU) (94.8)
433.00000	434.60000	NFM	Scarborough	Repeater (GB3NY) (118.8)
433.00000	434.60000	NFM	Sheffield	Repeater (GB3US) (103.5)
433.00000	434.60000	NFM	Wolverhampton	Repeater (GB3WN) (67)
433.02500	434.62500	NFM	Bury	Repeater (GB3MA) (82.5)

Base	Mobile	Mode	Location	User and Notes
433.02500	434.62500	NFM	Doncaster	Repeater (GB3DV) (71.9)
433.02500	434.62500	NFM	Harrogate	Repeater (GB3HJ) (118.8)
433.02500	434.62500	NFM	Hemel Hempstead	Repeater (GB3BV) (82.5)
433.02500	434.62500	NFM	Melton Mowbray	Repeater (GB3EM) (77)
433.02500	434.62500	NFM	Stonehaven	Repeater (GB3BA) (67.1)
433.02500	434.62500	NFM	Warminster	Repeater (GB3WA) (None)
433.05000	434.65000	NFM	Aylesbury	Repeater (GB3AV) (82.5)
433.05000	434.65000	NFM	Belfast	Repeater (GB3UL) (110.9)
433.05000	434.65000	NFM	Blackpool	Repeater (GB3FC) (82.5)
433.05000	434.65000	NFM	Corby	Repeater (GB3CI) (77)
433.05000	434.65000	NFM	Crawley	Repeater (GB3NX) (88.5)
433.05000	434.65000	NFM	Enfield Town Centre	Repeater (GB3LV) (82.5)
433.05000	434.65000	NFM	Hawick	Repeater (GB3HK) (118.8)
433.05000	434.65000	NFM	Lincoln	Repeater (GB3LS) (71.9)
433.05000	434.65000	NFM	Liskeard	Repeater (GB3CH) (77)
433.05000	434.65000	NFM	Margate	Repeater (GB3EK) (103.5)
433.05000	434.65000	NFM	Portsmouth	Repeater (GB3PH) (71.9)
433.05000	434.65000	NFM	Stoke on Trent	Repeater (GB3ST) (103.5)
433.05000	434.65000	NFM	Wells	Repeater (GB3NN) (94.8)
433.05000	434.65000	NFM	Yeovil	Repeater (GB3YS) (94.8)
433.07500	434.67500	NFM	Chelmsford	Repeater (GB3ER) (110.9)
433.07500	434.67500	NFM	Chichester	Repeater (GB3CC) (88.5)
433.07500	434.67500	NFM	Hull	Repeater (GB3HU) (88.5)
433.07500	434.67500	NFM	Kidderminster	Repeater (GB3KR) (67)
433.07500	434.67500	NFM	Kilmarnock	Repeater (GB3KA) (103.5)
433.07500	434.67500	NFM	Northampton	Repeater (GB3NH) (77)
433.07500	434.67500	NFM	Swindon	Repeater (GB3TD) (118.8)
433.07500	434.67500	NFM	Taunton	Repeater (GB3VS) (94.8)
433.07500	434.67500	NFM	Uxbridge	Repeater (GB3HL) (82.5)
433.10000	434.70000	NFM	Appleby, Cumbria	Repeater (GB3VE) (77)
433.10000	434.70000	NFM	Bath	Repeater (GB3UB) (118.8)
433.10000	434.70000	NFM	Bo'ness	Repeater (GB3OH) (94.8)
433.10000	434.70000	NFM	Erith	Repeater (GB3NK) (103.5)
433.10000	434.70000	NFM	Ipswich	Repeater (GB3IH) (110.9)
433.10000	434.70000	NFM	Isle of Wight	Repeater (GB3IW) (71.9)
433.10000	434.70000	NFM	Kings Lynn	Repeater (GB3KL) (94.8)
433.10000	434.70000	NFM	Leicester	Repeater (GB3LE) (77)
433.10000	434.70000	NFM	Pembroke	Repeater (GB3SP) (94.8)
433.12500	434.72500	NFM	Cheltenham	Repeater (GB3GH) (118.8)
433.12500	434.72500	NFM	Douglas	Repeater (GB3IM) (110.9)
433.12500	434.72500	NFM	Haywards Heath	Repeater (GB3HY) (88.5)
433.12500	434.72500	NFM	Huntingdon	Repeater (GB3OV) (94.8)
433.12500	434.72500	NFM	Scunthorpe	Repeater (GB3WJ) (88.5)
433.15000	434.75000	NFM	Ampthill	Repeater (GB3BD) (77)
433.15000	434.75000	NFM	Barnsley	Repeater (GB3SY) (71.9)
433.15000	434.75000	NFM	Brighton	Repeater (GB3BR) (88.5)
433.15000	434.75000	NFM	Canterbury	Repeater (GB3SK) (103.5)
433.15000	434.75000	NFM	Didcot	Repeater (GB3DI) (118.8)
433.15000	434.75000	NFM	Hereford	Repeater (GB3HC) (118.8)
433.15000	434.75000	NFM	London, Central	Repeater (GB3LW) (82.5)
433.15000	434.75000	NFM	Mold, Clwyd	Repeater (GB3CR) (118.8)
433.15000	434.75000	NFM	Newtown, Powys	Repeater (GB3CW) (103.5)
433.15000	434.75000	NFM	Rugby	Repeater (GB3ME) (67)
433.17500	434.77500	NFM	Amersham	Repeater (GB3HZ) (82.5)
433.17500	434.77500	NFM	Bedford	Repeater (GB3BL) (77)

Base	Mobile	Mode	Location	User and Notes
433.17500	434.77500	NFM	Halifax	Repeater (GB3WY) (82.5)
433.17500	434.77500	NFM	Mendlesham	Repeater (GB3DE) (110.9)
433.17500	434.77500	NFM	Nottingham	Repeater (GB3NM) (71.9)
433.17500	434.77500	NFM	Worcester	Repeater (GB3MS) (118.8)
433.20000	434.80000	NFM	Anglesey	Repeater (GB3AN) (110.9)
433.20000	434.80000	NFM	Banbury	Repeater (GB3EH) (67)
433.20000	434.80000	NFM	Bolsover	Repeater (GB3RB) (71.9)
433.20000	434.80000	NFM	Cambridge	Repeater (GB3PY) (77)
433.20000	434.80000	NFM	Carmarthen	Repeater (GB3CM) (94.8)
433.20000	434.80000	NFM	Leeds	Repeater (GB3LA) (82.5)
433.20000	434.80000	NFM	Telford	Repeater (GB3TF) (103.5)
433.22500	434.82500	NFM	Coventry	Repeater (GB3CV) (67)
433.22500	434.82500	NFM	Dumbarton	Repeater (GB3DM) (None)
433.22500	434.82500	NFM	Huddersfield	Repeater (GB3HD) (82.5)
433.25000	434.85000	NFM	Bristol	Repeater (GB3BS) (118.8)
433.25000	434.85000	NFM	Dundee	Repeater (GB3DD) (94.8)
433.25000	434.85000	NFM	Leamington Spa	Repeater (GB3MW) (67)
433.25000	434.85000	NFM	Liverpool	Repeater (GB3LI) (82.5)
433.25000	434.85000	NFM	Luton	Repeater (GB3LT) (77)
433.25000	434.85000	NFM	Newbury	Repeater (GB3AW) (71.9)
433.25000	434.85000	NFM	Peterborough	Repeater (GB3PB) (94.8)
433.25000	434.85000	NFM	Wirksworth	Repeater (GB3DY) (71.9)
433.25000	434.85000	NFM	Witney	Repeater (GB3WO) (118.8)
433.27500	434.87500	NFM	Axminster	Repeater (GB3RH) (None)
433.27500	434.87500	NFM	East Dereham	Repeater (GB3AH) (94.8)
433.27500	434.87500	NFM	Grantham	Repeater (GB3GR) (71.9)
433.27500	434.87500	NFM	Grimsby	Repeater (GB3GY) (88.5)
433.27500	434.87500	NFM	Hinckley	Repeater (GB3HT) (77)
433.27500	434.87500	NFM	Hitchin	Repeater (GB3HN) (82.5)
433.27500	434.87500	NFM	Maidstone	Repeater (GB3RE) (103.5)
433.27500	434.87500	NFM	Newhaven	Repeater (GB3LR) (88.5)
433.27500	434.87500	NFM	Stalybridge	Repeater (GB3WP) (82.5)
433.30000	434.90000	NFM	Birmingham	Repeater (GB3GB) (67)
433.30000	434.90000	NFM	Boroughbridge	Repeater (GB3HM) (118.8)
433.30000	434.90000	NFM	Chesterfield	Repeater (GB3EE) (71.9)
433.30000	434.90000	NFM	Guildford	Repeater (GB3GF) (88.5)
433.30000	434.90000	NFM	Oxford	Repeater (GB3OX) (118.8)
433.32500	434.92500	NFM	Carlisle	Repeater (GB3CA) (77)
433.32500	434.92500	NFM	Daventry	Repeater (GB3XX) (77)
433.32500	434.92500	NFM	Leek	Repeater (GB3SM) (103.5)
433.32500	434.92500	NFM	Louth	Repeater (GB3LC) (71.9)
433.32500	434.92500	NFM	Romford	Repeater (GB3HW) (71.9)
433.32500	434.92500	NFM	St Peter Port	Repeater (GB3GU) (77)
433.32500	434.92500	NFM	Welwyn Garden City	Repeater (GB3VH) (82.5)
433.32500	434.92500	NFM	Winchester	Repeater (GB3ET) (None)
433.32500	434.92500	NFM	Worksop	Repeater (GB3DS) (71.9)
433.32500	434.92500	NFM	York	Repeater (GB3CY) (88.5)
433.35000	434.95000	NFM	Bideford	Repeater (GB3ND) (77)
433.35000	434.95000	NFM	Birmingham	Repeater (GB3CB) (67)
433.35000	434.95000	NFM	Colchester	Repeater (GB3CE) (110.9)
433.35000	434.95000	NFM	Edinburgh	Repeater (GB3ED) (94.8)
433.35000	434.95000	NFM	Glasgow	Repeater (GB3GL) (103.5)
433.35000	434.95000	NFM	Harrow	Repeater (GB3HR) (82.5)
433.35000	434.95000	NFM	Hastings	Repeater (GB3HE) (103.5)
433.35000	434.95000	NFM	Lancaster	Repeater (GB3LF) (110.9)

Base	Mobile	Mode	Location	User and Notes
433.35000	434.95000	NFM	Leeds	Repeater (GB3WF) (82.5)
433.35000	434.95000	NFM	Lowestoft	Repeater (GB3YL) (94.8)
433.35000	434.95000	NFM	Spalding	Repeater (GB3TL) (71.9
433.35000	434.95000	NFM	Stockport	Repeater (GB3MR) (82.5)
433.35000	434.95000	NFM	Weymouth	Repeater (GB3SD) (71.9)
433.37500	434.97500	NFM	Bournemouth	Repeater (GB3SZ) (71.9)
433.37500	434.97500	NFM	Cardiff	Repeater (GB3SG) (94.8)
433.37500	434.97500	NFM	Farnham	Repeater (GB3FN) (82.5)
433.37500	434.97500	NFM	Omagh	Repeater (GB3OM) (110.9)
433.37500	434.97500	NFM	Preston	Repeater (GB3PP) (82.5)
433.37500	434.97500	NFM	Shrewsbury	Repeater (GB3LH) (103.5)
433.37500	434.97500	NFM	St Austell	Repeater (GB3HB) (77)
433.37500	434.97500	NFM	Tamworth	Repeater (GB3TH) (67)
433.37500	434.97500	NFM	Wisbech	Repeater (GB3WI) (94.8)
433.40000		NFM	Nationwide	Channel 16
433.42500		NFM	Nationwide	Channel 17
433.45000		NFM	Nationwide	Channel 18
433.47500		NFM	Nationwide	Channel 19
433.50000		NFM	Nationwide	Channel 20 Calling
433.52500		NFM	Nationwide	Channel 21
433.55000		NFM	Nationwide	Channel 22 Rally Talk-In
433.57500		NFM	Nationwide	Channel 23
433.60000		NFM	Nationwide	Channel 24 RTTY (AFSK)
433.70000		NFM	Nationwide	Raynet
433.72500		NFM	Nationwide	Raynet
433.75000		NFM	Nationwide	Raynet
433.77500		NFM	Nationwide	Raynet
434.47500		NFM	Nationwide	Internet Voice Gateway
434.50000		NFM	Nationwide	Internet Voice Gateway
434.52500		NFM	Nationwide	Internet Voice Gateway
435.02500	145.82500	NFM	Space	Oscar 11
435.07500	145.92500	NFM	Space	PO-28 POSAT-1
435.12000	145.90000	NFM	Space	Oscar 22
435.12000	145.97500	NFM	Space	Oscar 22
435.27500	145.97500	NFM	Space	PO-28 POSAT-1
435.79500	145.87000	NFM	Space	Oscar 20
435.86700	145.92500	NFM	Space	Oscar 26
436.77500	145.85000	NFM	Space	Oscar 41
436.80000	145.85000	NFM	Space	Oscar 50
437.12500	145.84000	NFM	Space	Oscar 19
437.15300	145.88000	NFM	Space	Oscar 19
437.32500	145.85000	NFM	Space	Oscar 46
437.32500	145.92500	NFM	Space	Oscar 46
435.91000	145.89000	NFM	Space	Oscar 20
436.79600	145.85000	NFM	Space	Oscar 27
437.02600	145.92000	NFM	Space	Oscar 16
437.05100	145.96000	NFM	Space	Oscar 16
437.12700		CW	Space	Oscar 19 Beacon
437.82200	145.87500	NFM	Space	Oscar 26
438.00000		NFM	Nationwide	Fast Scan TV
438.02500		NFM	Nationwide	Fast Scan TV
438.17500		NFM	Nationwide	Fast Scan TV
438.40000		NFM	Nationwide	Raynet
438.42500		NFM	Nationwide	Fast Scan TV

Base	Mobile	Mode	Location	User and Notes

433.7200 - 434.1200 MHz   **Vehicle Radio Keys**

430.0000 - 439.9500 MHz   **MoD, Utilities & Some PMR**

Base	Mobile	Mode	Location	User and Notes
430.00000		NFM	London	Chuen Cheng Ku Chinese Restaurant, Soho
430.00000	435.85000	NFM	London	Royal Military Police Special Use Repeater
430.07500		NFM	Hampshire	Royal Engineers, Gibraltar Barracks
430.07500		NFM	South Cerney	Army Fire/Crash (107.2)
430.10000		NFM	USAF Welford	Armaments Store
430.12500		NFM	London	US Embassy, Relay Of 407.425
430.25000		NFM	London	Military Repeater
430.40000		NFM	Plymouth	Royal Navy Trunked Network, Devonport
430.50000		NFM	London	Royal Military Police Special Use Repeater
430.52500		NFM	Plymouth	Royal Navy Trunked Network, Devonport
430.60000		NFM	USAF Fairford	Ground Ops (118.8)
430.62500	439.62500	NFM	Portsmouth	RN Dockyard Trunked Network
430.65000		NFM	Plymouth	Royal Navy Trunked Network, Devonport
430.70000		NFM	Plymouth	Royal Navy Trunked Network, Devonport
430.72500		NFM	USAF Fairford	Ground Ops (118.8)
430.75000	439.75000	NFM	Portsmouth	RN Dockyard Trunked Network
430.77500		NFM	USAF Fairford	Fuel (118.8)
430.80000	439.80000	NFM	Portsmouth	RN Dockyard Trunked Network
430.82500	439.82500	NFM	Portsmouth	RN Dockyard Trunked Network
430.85000		NFM	USAF Fairford	MoD Police/USAF Police (118.8)
430.85000	435.85000	NFM	London	Royal Military Police Special Use Repeater
430.87500	439.87500	NFM	Portsmouth	RN Dockyard Trunked Network
430.92500		NFM	Hampshire	Army, South Hampshire
430.08750		NFM	Channel Tunnel	Tactical Ch.3 Kent Police Incident
430.85000	439.98750	NFM	Channel Tunnel	Tactical Ch.14 Kent Police
431.25000	407.47500	NFM	USAF Fairford	424 Airbase Squadron (118.8)
431.42500		NFM	USAF Fairford	Crash/Fire Operations (118.8)
432.07500		NFM	London	RAF Uxbridge Public Address System
432.30000		NFM	USAF Fairford	MoD Police (118.8)
432.30000	407.75000	NFM	USAF Welford	Armaments Store
432.47500		NFM	London	Ruislip MoD Police Mobile Patrols
432.51250	439.53750	NFM	Channel Tunnel	Tactical Ch.2 Kent Fire Service Command
432.51250		NFM	Channel Tunnel	Tactical Ch.13 Kent Fire Service
432.65000		NFM	USAF Fairford	Transient Alert (118.8)
432.90000	406.62500	NFM	USAF Fairford	Tower Air Ground Environment (118.8)
432.95000	406.-25000	NFM	USAF Fairford	Comms Engineers (118.8)
433.21250		NFM	London	Mould Link
433.30000		NFM	London	Mango Fashion Store Staff, Regent Street
433.31250		NFM	London	Mould Link
433.36250		NFM	London	Mould Link
433.47500		NFM	Abingdon	Army, Dalton Barracks
433.55000		NFM	London	Mango Fashion Store Staff, Regent Street
433.57500		NFM	London	Mango Fashion Store Staff, Regent Street
433.71250		NFM	Tidworth	Army Barracks
433.75000		NFM	London	MoD Ch.1, Whitehall
433.80000		NFM	London	Mango Fashion Store Staff, Regent Street
433.82500		NFM	London	MoD Ch.2, Whitehall
433.85000		NFM	Hampshire	Gibraltar Barracks Base Security
433.87500		NFM	London	MoD Ch.3, Whitehall
433.92500		NFM	Bulford	Army Barracks
433.92500		NFM	Southampton	Marchwood Military Port Security

Base	Mobile	Mode	Location	User and Notes
433.97500		NFM	London	MoD Ch.4, Whitehall
434.00000		NFM	London	MoD Ch.5, Whitehall
434.02500	439.77500	NFM	Nationwide	British Energy Generation Trunked Network
434.05000	439.55000	NFM	London	MoD Ch.6 (Relays 443.575 MoD Police), Whitehall
434.17500	439.50000	NFM	London	MoD Ch.7, Whitehall
434.41250	439.50000	NFM	Nationwide	Air Training Corps Ch.U8-U9 Paired
434.55000		NFM	London	Mango Fashion Store Staff, Regent Street
434.57500		NFM	London	Mango Fashion Store Staff, Regent Street
434.67500	439.63750	NFM	Channel Tunnel	Tactical Ch.1 Kent Fire Service Commander
434.67500		NFM	Channel Tunnel	Kent Fire Service Ch.12
434.67500		NFM	London	Mango Fashion Store Staff, Regent Street
434.70000		NFM	London	Mango Fashion Store Staff, Regent Street
434.72500		NFM	London	Mango Fashion Store Staff, Regent Street
435.07500		NFM	Nationwide	Army Cadet Force
435.62500		NFM	Nationwide	Air Training Corps Ch.U5
435.62500		NFM	Nationwide	Army Cadet Force
435.62500		NFM	Nationwide	Sea Cadet Corps Ch.SV2
435.72500		NFM	Nationwide	Air Training Corps Ch.U2
435.75000		NFM	Nationwide	Air Training Corps Ch.U1
435.77500		NFM	Nationwide	Sea Cadet Corps Ch.SV3
435.85000		NFM	Bovington	Army Camp
436.02500	443.65000	NFM	Nationwide	British Energy Generation Trunked Network
436.30000		NFM	Aldershot	Army Base Security (88.5)
436.72500		NFM	Kineton	MoD Kineton Trunked Control Channel
437.02500	443.77500	NFM	Nationwide	British Energy Generation Trunked Network
437.06250	444.15000	NFM	Nationwide	British Energy Generation Trunked Network
437.57500		NFM	Aldershot	Keogh Barracks (167.9)
437.65000	432.50000	NFM	London	Downing Street Staff/Security (DCS 031)
437.80000		NFM	Chicksands	Intelligence Centre, Civil & Military
438.02500		NFM	Aldermaston	UKAEA
438.02500		NFM	Chicksands	Intelligence Centre, Civil & Military
438.06250	444.75000	NFM	Nationwide	British Energy Generation Trunked Network
438.45000		NFM	Plymouth	Navy Trunked Network, Devonport
438.47500		NFM	Aldermaston	AWE Sample Checking (Bantam Control)
438.50000		NFM	Plymouth	Navy Trunked Network, Devonport
438.57500		NFM	Aldermaston	AWE Sample Checking (Bantam Control)
438.67500		NFM	Aldershot	Keogh Barracks
438.72500		NFM	Bracknell	Fujitsu Defence Technology
438.72500		NFM	London	Royal Military Police, Wellington Barracks
438.72500		NFM	Pirbright	Barracks
438.98750		NFM	Aldershot	Keogh Barracks
439.00000		NFM	Chicksands	Intelligence Centre, Civil & Military
439.06250	445.06250	NFM	Nationwide	British Energy Generation Trunked Network
439.10000		NFM	Wattisham	Army Base Security
439.17500		NFM	Chicksands	Intelligence Centre, Royal Marines
439.23750		NFM	London	Royal Military Police
439.25000		NFM	Aldershot	Army Base Security
439.25000		NFM	Leicestershire	North Luffenham Intelligence Training Base
439.25000		NFM	London	Royal Military Police
439.35000		NFM	Plymouth	Navy Trunked Network, Devonport
439.40000		NFM	Plymouth	Navy Trunked Network, Devonport
439.51250	433.71250	NFM	Blandford Forum	Royal Signals, Blandford Army Camp (82.5)
439.55000	434.41250	NFM	Nationwide	Air Training Corps Ch.V10
439.60000		NFM	Nationwide	Army Cadet Force

Base	Mobile	Mode	Location	User and Notes

440.00625 - 442.25625 MHz — PMR Base Repeaters 12.5 kHz

Base	Mobile	Mode	Location	User and Notes
440.02500	425.52500	NFM	Birmingham	Airport Multi User Trunked Net Control Channel
440.02500	425.52500	NFM	Cardiff	Millennium Stadium Security Trunked Voice
440.02500	425.52500	NFM	Dagenham	Ford Motors
440.02500	425.52500	NFM	Dudley	Merryhill Shopping Centre Trunked Control Channel
440.02500	425.52500	NFM	Gatwick	Trunked Network
440.02500	425.52500	NFM	London	Brent Cross Shopping Centre
440.02500	425.52500	NFM	London	Dorchester Hotel Security, Park Lane (77)
440.02500	425.52500	NFM	London	Homerton Hospital, Clapton
440.02500	425.52500	NFM	London	Port of London Authority (S)
440.05000	425.55000	NFM	Billericay	Council Social Services
440.05000	425.55000	NFM	Coventry	Council Highways Dept (94.8)
440.05000	425.55000	NFM	Lanarkshire	Monklands Direct Works
440.05000	425.55000	NFM	Leicester	City Council Housing Maintenance
440.05000	425.55000	NFM	London	Lambeth Council
440.05000	425.55000	NFM	London	Parking Enforcement, Camden
440.05000	425.55000	NFM	London	Parking Enforcement, Hounslow
440.05000	425.55000	NFM	Preston	Preston Council Trunked
440.07500	425.57500	NFM	Harlow	Council Telephone Interconnect (192.8)
440.07500	425.57500	NFM	Liverpool	Liverpool Ranger Service
440.07500	425.57500	NFM	London	Council Noise Abatement Patrols, Kensington (103.5)
440.07500	425.57500	NFM	London	Parking Enforcement, Islington
440.07500	425.57500	NFM	London	Parking Enforcement N1/N17 (141.3)
440.07500	425.57500	NFM	London	Strand Palace Hotel Security
440.07500	425.57500	NFM	London	Wandsworth Council Parks Constabulary Ch.1
440.07500	425.57500	NFM	Newcastle	Council Highways Department
440.07500	425.57500	NFM	Tamworth	Tamworth Council Trunked
440.10000	425.60000	NFM	Barrow	VSEL Submarine Guards
440.10000	425.60000	NFM	Coventry	Community Patrols, Willenhall/Ernsford
440.10000	425.60000	NFM	Harlow	Council Telephone Interconnect (156.7)
440.10000	425.60000	NFM	Leicester	City Council 24hr Repairs
440.10000	425.60000	NFM	Liverpool	Police, Mersey Tunnel Ch 1
440.10000	425.60000	NFM	London	Wandsworth Council
440.10000	425.60000	NFM	London	Parking Enforcement, Hackney
440.10000	425.60000	NFM	Middlesbrough	Parking Enforcement
440.11250	425.61250	NFM	Blackpool	Doctors on Call
440.12500	425.62500	NFM	Birmingham	Fort Retail Park Security
440.12500	425.62500	NFM	London	Parkwest Cars
440.12500	425.62500	NFM	London	Quickfinder Ltd
440.12500	425.62500	NFM	Ripley	Zycomm Radio Engineers (Service)
440.15000	425.67500	NFM	Birmingham	Parking Enforcement Trunked
440.15000	425.65000	NFM	Watford	Council (71.9)
440.17500	425.67500	NFM	Cardiff	Companies House Security (88.5)
440.17500	425.67500	NFM	Egham	Royal Holloway Library Engineering/Maintenance (82.5)
440.17500	425.67500	NFM	Ellesmere Port	Shopwatch
440.17500	425.67500	NFM	Heathrow	Olympic Airways, T2 (103.5)
440.17500	425.67500	NFM	Leith	Ocean Terminal Centre Security/Admin (82.5)
440.17500	425.67500	NFM	Liverpool	Police, Mersey Tunnel Ch 2
440.17500	425.67500	NFM	London	British Museum (118.8)
440.17500	425.67500	NFM	London	Strand Palace Hotel Emergency Channel (77)
440.17500	425.67500	NFM	London	Thames Flood Barrier (94.8)
440.20000	425.70000	NFM	Cardiff	Celsa Steelworks Trunked Control Channel
440.20000	425.70000	NFM	Dagenham	Ford Motors
440.20000	425.70000	NFM	Leith	Ocean Terminal Centre Cleaners/Staff (82.5)
440.20000	425.70000	NFM	Liverpool	Police, Mersey Tunnel Ch.3
440.20000	425.70000	NFM	London	Centre Court Shopping Centre, Wimbledon

Base	Mobile	Mode	Location	User and Notes
440.20000	425.70000	NFM	London	GlaxoSmithKline Fire and Security, Greenford
440.20000	425.70000	NFM	London	North Pole Rail Depot
440.20000	425.70000	NFM	London	Shopwatch, Oxford Street (77)
440.20000	425.70000	NFM	Thurrock	Lakeside Shopping Centre Trunked Network Voice
440.22500	425.72500	NFM	Birmingham	NEC Security & Maintenance (156.7)
440.22500	425.72500	NFM	Cardiff	Millennium Stadium Ticket Office (88.5)
440.22500	425.72500	NFM	Glasgow	Regional Council Trunked
440.22500	425.72500	NFM	Heathrow	Metro Business Aviation
440.22500	425.72500	NFM	London	Centre Court Shopping Centre, Wimbledon
440.22500	425.72500	NFM	London	Westminster Security Patrols/CCTV (67)
440.22500	425.72500	NFM	Luton	Airport Ops
440.22500	425.72500	NFM	Manchester	Airport Trunked Network
440.25000	425.75000	NFM	Dartford	Elderly Care Service (71.9)
440.25000	425.75000	NFM	Leicester	Council
440.25000	425.75000	NFM	London	Lambeth Borough Council
440.25000	425.75000	NFM	London	Newham Borough Council (C)
440.25000	425.75000	NFM	Newcastle	OAP Care Alarm Service
440.25000	425.72500	NFM	Rotherham	Council
440.25000	425.72500	NFM	Sinnington	Council
440.27500	425.77500	NFM	Birmingham	Airport Multi User Trunked Net Control Channel
440.27500	425.77500	NFM	Birmingham	International Convention Centre Trunked
440.27500	425.77500	NFM	Dartford	Bluewater Shopping Centre Car Parks Ch.3 (88.5)
440.27500	425.77500	NFM	Hartlepool	Port Control
440.27500	425.77500	NFM	Heathrow	AirRadio Trunked British Airways/Multi User
440.27500	425.77500	NFM	London	Britannic House Investments (67)
440.27500	425.77500	NFM	London	Guys Hospital Maintenance (103.5)
440.27500	425.77500	NFM	London	Inns of Court/Lord Chancellor's Office Security (114.8)
440.27500	425.77500	NFM	Manchester	International Airport Trunked
440.27500	425.77500	NFM	Merseyside	Merseyside Docks & Harbour Police
440.27500	425.77500	NFM	Solihull	Council
440.27500	425.77500	NFM	Wigan	Shopwatch, Galleries Shopping Centre (82.5)
440.28750	425.78750	NFM	Birmingham	International Convention Centre Trunked Net
440.30000	425.80000	NFM	Cardiff	Companies House Maintenance (110.9)
440.30000	425.80000	NFM	Coventry	Parcelforce Central UK Hub Transport/Bays (88.5)
440.30000	425.80000	NFM	Gatwick	Trunked Network
440.30000	425.80000	NFM	London	Kenwood Car Service, Finchley
440.30000	425.80000	NFM	Manchester	Manchester Airport Trunked Net
440.32500	425.82500	NFM	Cardiff	Millennium Stadium Security/Stewards Trunked
440.32500	425.82500	NFM	Dartford	Bluewater Shopping Centre Maintenance Ch.4 (107.2)
440.32500	425.82500	NFM	Dudley	Merryhill Shopping Centre Trunked
440.32500	425.82500	NFM	London	Hays Galleria Shops Security, Tower Bridge
440.32500	425.82500	NFM	Redditch	Kingfisher Shopping Centre Trunked Control Channel
440.35000	425.85000	NFM	Gatwick	Airport Trunked Network
440.35000	425.85000	NFM	Heathrow	AirRadio Trunked British Airways/Multi User
440.35000	425.85000	NFM	Leeds	Royal Armouries Museum Security
440.35000	425.85000	NFM	London	Middlesex Hospital Security
440.35000	425.85000	NFM	Redbridge	Council
440.37500	425.87500	NFM	Cardiff	Ikea Furniture Store (107.2)
440.37500	428.57500	NFM	Liverpool	Liverpool City Football Club Staff, Anfield (88.5)
440.37500	428.57500	NFM	London	City of Westminster Council
440.37500	425.87500	NFM	Manchester	International Airport Trunked
440.37500	425.87500	NFM	Redbridge	Council (Unity Base)
440.37500	425.87500	NFM	Wigan	Pubwatch
440.40000	425.90000	NFM	Co. Durham	Taxi Company
440.40000	425.90000	NFM	London	Dunmedic (Base)
440.40000	425.90000	NFM	Nationwide	Ambulance Incident Channel

Base	Mobile	Mode	Location	User and Notes
440.40000	425.90000	NFM	Surrey	Ambulance Mobile Repeater at Incidents
440.42500	425.92500	NFM	Heathrow	Northside Medics (186.2)
440.45000	425.95000	NFM	London	St. Bartholomew's Hospital
440.45000	425.95000	NFM	London	Whittington Hospital Security
440.45000	425.95000	NFM	Nationwide	Ambulance Incident Channel
440.45000		NFM	Nationwide	Frecce Tricolori Display Team Ground Crew
440.47500	425.97500	NFM	Birmingham	Airport Multi User Trunked Network
440.47500	425.97500	NFM	Birmingham	Shopwatch, City Centre Trunked
440.47500	425.97500	NFM	Cardiff	Celsa Steelworks Trunked
440.47500	425.97500	NFM	Chester	Shopwatch & Council Trunked
440.47500	425.97500	NFM	London	Shopwatch, Oxford Street (77)
440.50000	426.00000	NFM	Cardiff	Companies House Security (162.2)
440.50000	426.00000	NFM	Heathrow	Aer Lingus T1/Swissport T2 (146.2)
440.50000	426.00000	NFM	Liverpool	John Lewis Security
440.50000	426.00000	NFM	London	Canary Wharf Security, Cabot Square
440.50000	426.00000	NFM	Manchester	Manchester Evening News Arena Security (88.5)
440.50000	426.00000	NFM	Slough	Reading Numbers
440.52500	426.02500	NFM	Birmingham	International Convention Centre Trunked
440.52500	426.02500	NFM	Cardiff	Millennium Centre Security (82.5)
440.52500	426.02500	NFM	Heathrow	AirRadio Trunked British Airways/Multi User
440.52500	426.02500	NFM	Dartford	Bluewater Shopping Centre Command Centre (67)
440.52500	426.02500	NFM	London	Royal Mail Depot, Bromley By Bow
440.52500	426.02500	NFM	London	Royal Mail Depot, Islington
440.52500	426.02500	NFM	London	Royal Mail Depot, King Edwards Post Office
440.52500	426.02500	NFM	London	Royal Mail Depot, Lisson Grove
440.52500	426.02500	NFM	London	Royal Mail Depot, Mount Pleasant
440.52500	426.02500	NFM	London	Royal Mail Depot, Nine Elms
440.52500	426.02500	NFM	London	Royal Mail Depot, Peckham
440.52500	426.02500	NFM	London	Royal Mail Depot, Stonebridge Park
440.53750		NFM	Cardiff	Millennium Plaza Bar
440.53750		NFM	Coventry	Magistrates Court Security
440.53750		NFM	Liverpool	Burtons Staff Net
440.53750		NFM	London	East India Dock Company Security (79)
440.53750	426.03750	NFM	London	GlaxoSmithKline Security, Euston Rd (77)
440.53750		NFM	London	JJB Sports Security, Plaza Shopping Centre (103.5)
440.53750		NFM	London	London Bus Inspectors, Goldtops (167.9)
440.53750		NFM	Stevenage	British Aerospace Ch 3
440.53750		NFM	Stevenage	Lytton Catering, Knebworth House
440.53750		NFM	Stevenage	Midas Security, Kings Leisure Park (71.9)
440.55000	426.05000	NFM	Chester	Shopwatch & Council Trunked
440.55000	426.05000	NFM	Heathrow	Virgin Atlantic Cleaners (77)
440.55000	426.05000	NFM	London	Regus Business Centre Security, Chiswick High Rd
440.55000	426.05000	NFM	London	Strand Palace Hotel (67)
440.55000	426.05000	NFM	Manchester	Manchester Evening News Arena
440.55000	426.05000	NFM	Thurrock	Lakeside Shopping Centre Trunked Network Voice
440.57500	426.07500	NFM	Gateshead	Metro Centre Security (110.9)
440.57500	426.07500	NFM	Glasgow	TOA Taxis Ch.1 Data
440.57500	426.07500	NFM	London	London Taxis North/Central
440.57500	426.07500	NFM	Wigan	Parking Enforcement
440.58750	426.08750	NFM	Dudley	Council Housing Repairs Trunked
440.58750	426.08750	NFM	London	London Taxis, N1/N7
440.60000	426.10000	NFM	Glasgow	TOA Taxis Ch.2 (Data)
440.60000	426.10000	NFM	Knowsley	Council Security
440.60000	426.10000	NFM	London	London Taxis, WC/SW1
440.62500	426.12500	NFM	Glasgow	TOA Taxis Ch.3 Voice
440.62500	426.12500	NFM	London	London Taxis, Greater London

Base	Mobile	Mode	Location	User and Notes
440.63750	426.13750	NFM	W Bromwich	Shopwatch (103.5)
440.65000	426.15000	NFM	Birmingham	NEC Catering
440.65000	426.15000	NFM	Chester	464 Taxis
440.65000	426.15000	NFM	Edinburgh	Radio Cabs
440.65000	426.15000	NFM	London	London Taxis, Greater London
440.66250	426.16250	NFM	Edinburgh	Radio Cabs
440.67500	426.17500	NFM	Birmingham	NEC Car Park Control (156.7)
440.67500	426.17500	NFM	Edinburgh	Radio Cabs
440.70000	426.20000	NFM	Stoke on Trent	Plant Hire (Star Base)
440.71250	426.21250	NFM	Edinburgh	City Council Housing Department Trunked
440.72500	426.22500	NFM	Birmingham	NEC Maintenance (192.8)
440.72500	426.22500	NFM	Edinburgh	Accolade Cars
440.73750	426.23750	NFM	Birmingham	Council/Parking Enforcement/Tow Away Trunked
440.73750	426.23750	NFM	Edinburgh	City Council Housing Department Trunked
440.75000	426.25000	NFM	Gatwick	Parking Express Courtesy Bus
440.75000	426.25000	NFM	Heathrow	Passenger Transport Service (210.7)
440.75000	426.25000	NFM	Heathrow	Parking Express Courtesy Bus
440.75000		NFM	London	Chequers Cabs, Sainsbury W10
440.75000	426.25000	NFM	Romford/Ilford	Parking Enforcement (94.8)
440.75000	426.25000	NFM	Solihull	Refuse Collectors
440.76250	426.26250	NFM	London	Hammersmith & Fulham Parks Police (123)
440.77500	426.27500	NFM	Dover	HM Revenue & Customs, Docks
440.77500		NFM	Felixstowe	HM Revenue & Customs, Port
440.77500	426.27500	NFM	Heathrow	HM Revenue & Customs
440.77500	426.27500	NFM	Luton Airport	HM Revenue & Customs
440.77500	426.27500	NFM	Manchester Airport	HM Revenue & Customs
440.77500		NFM	Nationwide	HM Revenue & Customs Ch.1
440.77500	426.27500	NFM	Nationwide	HM Revenue & Customs Ch.4
440.77500	426.27500	NFM	Ramsgate	HM Revenue & Customs, Port
440.77500	426.27500	NFM	Stansted Airport	HM Revenue & Customs
440.78750	426.28750	NFM	London	Links Courier Service
440.80000	426.30000	NFM	Leeds	Council, Environmental
440.82500	426.32500	NFM	Dorset	HM Revenue & Customs
440.82500	426.32500	NFM	Felixstowe	HM Revenue & Customs, Docks
440.82500	426.32500	NFM	Heathrow	HM Revenue & Customs Surveillance
440.82500		NFM	Nationwide	HM Revenue & Customs Ch.2
440.82500	426.32500	NFM	Nationwide	HM Revenue & Customs Ch.5
440.82500	426.32500	NFM	Portsmouth	HM Revenue & Customs
440.82500	426.32500	NFM	Shoreham by Sea	HM Revenue & Customs
440.83750		NFM	Heathrow	HM Revenue & Customs
440.85000	426.35000	NFM	Felixstowe	HM Revenue & Customs
440.85000	426.35000	NFM	Heathrow	HM Revenue & Customs
440.85000	426.35000	NFM	Harwich	HM Revenue & Customs
440.85000	426.35000	NFM	Nationwide	HM Revenue & CustomsCh.6
440.85000		NFM	Nationwide	HM Revenue & Customs Ch.3
440.85000	426.35000	NFM	Newhaven	HM Revenue & Customs
440.85000	426.35000	NFM	Poole	HM Revenue & Customs
440.85000	426.35000	NFM	Southampton	HM Revenue & Customs, Docks (Aztec)
440.85000		NFM	Stansted Airport	HM Revenue & Customs
440.86250	426.36250	NFM	Birmingham	Airport Multi User Trunked Network
440.86250	426.36250	NFM	Cardiff	Millennium Stadium Stewards Trunked
440.86250	426.36250	NFM	Dudley	Merryhill Shopping Centre Trunked
440.86250	426.36250	NFM	Glasgow Airport	AirRadio Trunked British Airways/Multi User
440.86250	426.36250	NFM	London	Security, 137 Grays Inn Road
440.86250	426.36250	NFM	London	Selfridges Maintenance (123)
440.86250	426.36250	NFM	London	St Thomas Hospital Security (103.5)

Base	Mobile	Mode	Location	User and Notes
440.86250	426.36250	NFM	London	Tate & Lyle Sugar, Silvertown
440.86250	426.36250	NFM	Romford	Harold Wood Hospital
440.86250	426.36250	NFM	Wallasey	Shopwatch, Cherry Tree Shopping Centre (88.5)
440.87500	426.37500	NFM	Nationwide	HM Revenue & Customs Ch.7
440.88750	426.38750	NFM	Birmingham	Shopwatch, City Centre Trunked
440.88750	426.38750	NFM	Glasgow	Shopwatch, Argyle/Buchanan Street
440.88750	426.38750	NFM	Heathrow	BAA Trunked Network
440.88750	426.38750	NFM	London	St Thomas Hospital Security (103.5)
440.88750	426.38750	NFM	London	Transport Operator, Chelsea Wharf SW10
440.88750	426.38750	NFM	London	University College
440.88750	426.38750	NFM	South Wirral	Shopwatch, Cheshire Oaks Shopping Centre
440.90000	426.40000	NFM	Birmingham	Rackhams Security (103.5)
440.90000	426.40000	NFM	Coventry	Community Wardens
440.90000	426.40000	NFM	Edinburgh	Hotel
440.90000	426.40000	NFM	Gillingham	Sainsbury Savacentre Security
440.90000	426.40000	NFM	Heathrow	BAA Trunked Network
440.90000	426.40000	NFM	Liverpool	Lime Street Station Staff
440.90000	426.40000	NFM	London	Goldsmiths College Security, Greenwich
440.90000	426.40000	NFM	London	Street Patrols/CCTV, Regent Street, Piccadilly (71.9)
440.90000	426.40000	NFM	London	University College Staff/Security, Gower St (94.8)
440.91250	426.41250	NFM	Coventry	Lower Precinct
440.91250	426.41250	NFM	Edinburgh	Shopwatch, Kinnaird Park
440.91250	426.41250	NFM	Glasgow Airport	AirRadio Trunked British Airways/Multi User
440.91250	426.41250	NFM	Heathrow	Aircraft Security T1/T4 (118.8)
440.91250	426.41250	NFM	London	BBC TV Centre Security, Shepherds Bush
440.91250	426.41250	NFM	London	Gillette Plc Security, Brentford
440.91250	426.41250	NFM	London	ITN Security Grays Inn Road
440.91250	426.41250	NFM	Manchester	Manchester Airport Trunked Network
440.92500	426.42500	NFM	Croydon	Parking Enforcement (71.9)
440.92500	426.42500	NFM	Harlow	Harlow Council Telephone Interconnect (233.6)
440.92500	426.42500	NFM	Liverpool	Parking Enforcement Citilink Inner Zone
440.92500	426.42500	NFM	London	Parking Enforcement, Kensington & Chelsea (103.5)
440.92500	426.42500	NFM	London	St Bartholomew's Hospital
440.92500	426.42500	NFM	Newcastle	Newcastle Council Trunked
440.92500	426.42500	NFM	Rotherham	Council
440.92500	426.42500	NFM	Stockport	Shopwatch
440.93750	426.43750	NFM	Dudley	Dudley Council Housing Repairs Trunked
440.93750	426.43750	NFM	London	Parking Enforcement, Lambeth (107.2)
440.92500	426.42500	NFM	Rotherham	Council
440.95000	426.45000	NFM	Birkenhead	Twelve Quays Ferry Terminal Ch.1
440.95000	426.45000	NFM	Birmingham	International Convention Centre
440.95000	426.45000	NFM	Bolton	Shopwatch
440.95000	426.45000	NFM	Liverpool	Arndale Shopping Centre Security
440.95000	426.45000	NFM	London	Canary Wharf Security Ch.1
440.95000	426.45000	NFM	Heathrow	Scandinavian Airlines T3 (136.5)
440.95000	426.45000	NFM	London	Marks & Spencer, Baker Street
440.95000	426.45000	NFM	London	Marks & Spencer, Marble Arch (82.5)
440.95000	426.45000	NFM	South Wirral	Cheshire Oaks Shopping Centre Security
440.96250	426.46250	NFM	Tamworth	Tamworth Council Trunked
440.97500	426.47500	NFM	London	Parking Enforcement, SW12 (77)
440.98750	426.48750	NFM	Birmingham	Parking Enforcement/Tow Away Trunked
440.98750	426.48750	NFM	London	Green Cars
441.00000	426.50000	NFM	Birmingham	NEC Maintenance (156.7)
441.00000	426.50000	NFM	London	Traffic Wardens, City of Westminster
441.00000	426.50000	NFM	London	Premiere Cars, Kings Cross
441.00000	426.50000	NFM	Plumstead	Taxi Company

Base	Mobile	Mode	Location	User and Notes
441.01250	426.51250	NFM	Heathrow	AirRadio Trunked British Airways/Multi User
441.01250	426.51250	NFM	London	Excel Conference Building Security/Staff Trunked
441.02500	426.52500	NFM	Heathrow	AirRadio Trunked British Airways/Multi User
441.02500	426.52500	NFM	Ellesmere Port	Shopwatch
441.02500	426.52500	NFM	Leicester	Leicester Buses
441.02500	426.52500	NFM	Redditch	Kingfisher Shopping Centre Trunked
441.03750	426.53750	NFM	Birmingham Airport	AirRadio Trunked British Airways/Multi User
441.03750	426.53750	NFM	Glasgow Airport	AirRadio Trunked British Airways/Multi User
441.03750	426.53750	NFM	Heathrow	JAL Cargo Ops (114.8)
441.03750	426.53750	NFM	Barking	Shopwatch (107.2)
441.03750	426.53750	NFM	Bootle	Shopwatch
441.03750	426.53750	NFM	Chester	Council & Shopwatch Trunked
441.03750	426.53750	NFM	Heathrow	AirRadio Trunked British Airways/Multi User
441.03750	426.53750	NFM	London	Shopwatch, Edgware
441.03750	426.53750	NFM	Manchester	The Print Works Retail/Leisure Site Security (110.9)
441.05000	426.55000	NFM	Heathrow	AirRadio Trunked British Airways/Multi User
441.06250	426.57500	NFM	Coventry	Council
441.06250	426.56250	NFM	London	KJS Recovery (Kilo)
441.07500	426.57500	NFM	Chesterfield	Saracen Security
441.07500	426.57500	NFM	Gatwick	Trunked Network
441.07500	426.57500	NFM	Heathrow	AirRadio Trunked British Airways/Multi User
441.08750	426.58750	NFM	Liverpool	Merseytravel Buses
441.08750	426.58750	NFM	Preston	Doctors' Service
441.10000	426.60000	NFM	London	Doctors' Service
441.10000	426.60000	NFM	Manchester	Stagecoach Buses
441.10000	426.60000	NFM	West Midlands	Bus Company
441.11250	426.61250	NFM	Dagenham	Rhone Poulenc Chemicals
441.11250	426.61260	NFM	Dartford	Dartford Tunnel Ch.1
441.11250	426.61250	NFM	London	Channel Tunnel Rail Link Trunked, N1
441.11250	426.61250	NFM	London	St Thomas Hospital (114.8)
441.11250	426.61250	NFM	London	Whittington Hospital Security, NW5
441.11250	426.61250	NFM	Heathrow	British Airways T1 Passenger Transfer Buses (103.5)
441.12500	426.62500	NFM	Birmingham	Community Repeater, Ambulance
441.12500	426.62500	NFM	Birmingham	Community Repeater, Security Company
441.12500	426.62500	NFM	Birmingham	Community Repeater, Skip Hire Company
441.12500	426.62500	NFM	Gatwick	Trunked Network
441.12500	426.62500	NFM	Heathrow	AirRadio Trunked British Airways/Multi User
441.13750	426.63750	NFM	Dudley	Merryhill Shopping Centre Trunked
441.13750	426.63750	NFM	Heathrow	Malev, Uzbekistan Airways & Alitalia T2 Cleaners (67)
441.13750	426.63750	NFM	London	Wardens/CCTV, Church Street, Lisson Grove (71.9)
441.13750	426.63750	NFM	Manchester	Airport Trunked Network
441.15000	426.65000	NFM	Edinburgh	Doormen Caledonian/Allied Security Pubs (77)
441.15000	426.65000	NFM	Edinburgh	Parking Enforcement (151.4)
441.15000	426.65000	NFM	London	Parking Enforcement, W11 (82.5)
441.16250	426.66250	NFM	Birkenhead	Twelve Quays Ferry Terminal Ch.2
441.16250	426.66250	NFM	Coventry	Airport Handling (94.8)
441.16250	426.66250	NFM	Dartford	Bluewater Shopping Centre Staff (146.2)
441.16250	426.66250	NFM	Heathrow	Malev, Uzbekistan Airways & Alitalia T2 Cleaners (67)
441.16250	426.66250	NFM	London	Eurostar North Pole Depot (77)
441.16250	426.66250	NFM	London	Eurostar Passenger Service, Waterloo Station (103.5)
441.16250	426.66250	NFM	London	Middle Schools, Wimbledon
441.16250	426.66250	NFM	London	Thames Barrier Control, Woolwich
441.17500	426.67500	NFM	Birmingham	Eagle Car Clampers, City Centre
441.17500	426.67500	NFM	Denton	FMR Investigations
441.17500	426.67500	NFM	Glasgow	Vehicle Removal Unit
441.17500	426.67500	NFM	Middlesbrough	Pritchard Security

Base	Mobile	Mode	Location	User and Notes
441.17500	441.17500	NFM	Tamworth	Pubwatch
441.18750	426.68750	NFM	Dartford	Bluewater Shopping Centre Staff (146.2)
441.18750	426.68750	NFM	Heathrow	Scandinavian Airlines T3 (136.5)
441.20000	426.70000	NFM	Dorking	Silver Cars (77)
441.21250	426.72500	NFM	Leicestershire	Community Repeater, Car Valeters
441.21250	426.72500	NFM	Leicestershire	Community Repeater, Courier Company
441.21250	426.72500	NFM	Leicestershire	Community Repeater, Security Company Encrypted
441.21250	426.72500	NFM	Leicestershire	Community Repeater, Taxi Company
441.22500	426.72500	NFM	Coventry	Shopwatch/Pubwatch/Car Parks Trunked
441.22500	426.72500	NFM	Dorking	Apollo Taxis
441.22500	426.72500	NFM	London	Newham Borough Parks Constabulary (127.3)
441.22500	426.72500	NFM	London	Parking Enforcement, Greenwich (203.5)
441.22500	426.72500	NFM	London	Parking Enforcement, Plumstead
441.23750	426.73750	NFM	Chester	Shopwatch & Council
441.23750	426.73750	NFM	London	Channel Rail Link Security Trunked, St Pancras
441.25000	426.75000	NFM	Gatwick	Trunked Network
441.26250	426.76250	NFM	Birmingham	The Mailbox Leisure/BBC Studio Complex Trunked
441.26250	426.76250	NFM	Heathrow	Aircraft Engineers (131.8)
441.26250	426.76250	NFM	London	West End Security Patrols (67)
441.26250	426.76250	NFM	Manchester	Airport Trunked Network
441.27500	426.77500	NFM	Gatwick	Trunked Network
441.27500	426.77500	NFM	Heathrow	AirRadio Trunked British Airways/Multi User
441.28750	426.78750	NFM	Birmingham	University of Central England Trunked Control
441.28750	426.78750	NFM	Edinburgh	Council Housing Department Trunked
441.28750	426.78750	NFM	Heathrow	AirRadio Trunked British Airways/Multi User
441.28750	426.78750	NFM	London	Excel Conference Building Security/Staff Trunked
441.30000	426.80000	NFM	Heathrow	AirRadio Trunked British Airways/Multi User
441.30000	426.80000	NFM	London	Security Patrols Trunked, Oxford Street
441.30000	426.80000	NFM	London	Shopwatch Trunked, Regent St
441.30000	426.80000	NFM	Newcastle	Community Repeater, Security Company
441.31250	426.81250	NFM	Birmingham	University of Central England Trunked Voice
441.31250	426.81250	NFM	Heathrow	AirRadio Trunked British Airways/Multi User
441.31250	426.81250	NFM	Liverpool Airport	AirRadio Trunked British Airways/Multi User
441.31250	426.81250	NFM	London	West End Security Patrols/ CCTV (67)
441.32500	426.82500	NFM	Gatwick	Trunked Network
441.32500	426.82500	NFM	Heathrow	AirRadio Trunked British Airways/Multi User
441.33750	426.83750	NFM	Birmingham	Shopwatch City Centre Trunked
441.33750	426.83750	NFM	Heathrow	AirRadio Trunked British Airways/Multi User
441.33750	426.83750	NFM	Liverpool Airport	AirRadio Trunked British Airways/Multi User
441.35000	426.85000	NFM	Gatwick	Trunked Network
441.35000	426.85000	NFM	Heathrow	AirRadio Trunked British Airways/Multi User
441.35000	426.85000	NFM	Newcastle	Community Repeater, Security Company
441.36250	426.86250	NFM	Edinburgh	Council Housing Department Trunked
441.37500	426.87500	NFM	Newcastle	Community Repeater, Security Company
441.37500	426.87500	NFM	Wigan	Pubwatch
441.38750	426.88750	NFM	Epsom	Top Cars
441.40000	426.90000	NFM	Glasgow	B & Q Store, Drumchapel
441.40000	426.90000	NFM	Sheffield	A1 Security
441.41250	426.92500	NFM	Coventry	Shopwatch/Pubwatch/Car Parks Trunked
441.43750	426.93750	NFM	London	Courier Company
441.45000	426.95000	NFM	Glasgow	Paramedics
441.45000	426.95000	NFM	London	APCOA Parking Enforcement/Vehicle Removals (131.8)
441.47500	426.97500	NFM	Coventry	Shopwatch/Pubwatch/Car Parks Trunked
441.48750	426.98750	NFM	Edinburgh	Council Housing Department Trunked
441.50000	427.00000	NFM	London	Parking Enforcement, Hackney
441.51250	427.01250	NFM	Edinburgh	Council Housing Department Trunked

Base	Mobile	Mode	Location	User and Notes
441.52500	427.02500	NFM	Newcastle	Community Repeater, Security Company
441.53750	427.03750	NFM	Edinburgh	Council Housing Department Trunked
441.55000	427.05000	NFM	Heathrow	AirRadio Trunked British Airways/Multi User
441.56250	427.56250	NFM	Edinburgh	Council Housing Department Trunked
441.57500	427.07500	NFM	Cannock	Taxi Company
441.57500	427.07500	NFM	Manchester	Harcross Building Supplies
441.58750	427.08750	NFM	Edinburgh	Council Housing Department Trunked
441.60000	427.10000	NFM	London	Chase Couriers (Chase)
441.61250	427.11250	NFM	Edinburgh	Council Housing Department Trunked
441.62500	427.12500	NFM	London	Parking Enforcement, Newham
441.63750	427.13750	NFM	Edinburgh	Council Housing Department Trunked
441.65000	427.15000	NFM	Birmingham	Shopwatch, Bearwood
441.65000	427.15000	NFM	Chalfont St Peter	OAP Transport Service
441.66250	427.17500	NFM	Blackpool	Community Repeater, Delivery Company (67)
441.67500	427.17500	NFM	London	Premier Motorbike Couriers
441.68750	427.18750	NFM	London	Diamond Taxis
441.70000	427.20000	NFM	Gatwick	Trunked Network
441.70000	427.20000	NFM	Heathrow	AirRadio Trunked British Airways/Multi User
441.70000	427.20000	NFM	London	Excel Conference Building Security/Staff Trunked
441.71250	427.21250	NFM	London	Apollo Bike Couriers
441.72500	427.22500	NFM	Doncaster	Browns Farm
441.72500	427.22500	NFM	Glasgow	Medicall
441.72500	427.72500	NFM	Nottingham	Medicall Couriers
441.73750	427.23750	NFM	High Bradfield	Zycomm Community Repeater
441.75000	427.25000	NFM	London	VIP Dining Services (67)
441.76250	427.26250	NFM	Edinburgh	Council Housing Department Trunked
441.77500	427.27500	NFM	Coventry	Community Repeater, Niall Bailley
441.77500	427.27500	NFM	Doncaster	Robin Hood Airport Taxi Co-ordination/Flight Arrivals
441.77500	427.27500	NFM	Manchester	Pubwatch
441.78750	427.28750	NFM	Coventry	Shopwatch/Pubwatch/Car Parks Trunked
441.80000	427.30000	NFM	Heathrow	AirRadio Trunked British Airways/Multi User
441.81250	427.31250	NFM	Essex	Community Repeater, Tyre Fitters (186.2)
441.82500	427.32500	NFM	London	Minicabs, Victoria
441.83750	427.33750	NFM	Heathrow	AirRadio Trunked British Airways/Multi User
441.83750	427.33750	NFM	London	Excel Conference Building Security/Staff Trunked
441.85000	427.35000	NFM	Essex	Skip Hire Company (94.8)
441.85000	427.35000	NFM	Liverpool	Expo Boarding-Up Service
441.86250	427.36250	NFM	Heathrow	AirRadio Trunked British Airways/Multi User
441.87500	427.37500	NFM	London	Globe & City Bikes Couriers
441.88750	427.38750	NFM	London	Dining In Meals Delivery, Ealing (67)
441.88750	427.38750	NFM	London	Parks Police, Holland Park
441.90000	427.40000	NFM	Leicester	Community Repeater, Merrimans Machinery
441.90000	427.40000	NFM	Leicester	Community Repeater, Security Company
441.90000	427.40000	NFM	London	Aysialfield Cars (67)
441.90000	427.40000	NFM	London	RS Hill Community Repeater
441.90000	427.40000	NFM	London	Security Patrols Trunked, Oxford Street
441.91250	427.41250	NFM	Birmingham	University Sport, Birmingham University (115)
441.91250	427.41250	NFM	Heathrow	AirRadio Trunked British Airways/Multi User
441.91250	427.41250	NFM	London	Excel Conference Building Security/Staff Trunked
441.92500	427.42500	NFM	London	Froebel Institute & College Security, Roehampton
441.93750	427.43750	NFM	Heathrow	AirRadio Trunked British Airways/Multi User
441.93750	427.43750	NFM	London	Canary Wharf Security Trunked
441.95000	427.45000	NFM	Gatwick	Trunked network
441.95000	427.45000	NFM	Heathrow	AirRadio Trunked British Airways/Multi User
441.96250	427.46250	NFM	Heathrow	AirRadio Trunked British Airways/Multi User
441.96250	427.46250	NFM	London	Canary Wharf Security Trunked

Base	Mobile	Mode	Location	User and Notes
441.97500	427.47500	NFM	Glasgow	Doctors' Service
441.98750	427.48750	NFM	Heathrow	AirRadio Trunked British Airways/Multi User
442.00000	427.70000	NFM	Heathrow	AirRadio Trunked British Airways/Multi User
442.01250	427.51250	NFM	Birmingham	Shopwatch, City Centre Trunked Network
442.01250	427.51250	NFM	Heathrow	AirRadio Trunked British Airways/Multi User
442.01250	427.51250	NFM	London	Excel Conference Building Security/Staff Trunked
442.02500	427.52500	NFM	Coventry	Community Repeater, Building Merchant
442.02500	427.52500	NFM	Coventry	Community Repeater, DCE Ltd.
442.02500	427.52500	NFM	Coventry	Community Repeater, Nyanza Car Spares
442.02500	427.52500	NFM	London	Lewisham Council
442.05000	427.55000	NFM	London	Animal Rescue Centre
442.05000	427.55000	NFM	London	KJ Bike Couriers
442.07500	427.77500	NFM	Liverpool	Albert Docks Complex Security
442.07500	427.57500	NFM	London	Lewisham Council
442.10000	427.60000	NFM	Dartford	Bluewater Shopping Centre Staff
442.10000	427.60000	NFM	Ilford	TW Communications
442.10000	427.60000	NFM	London	Apollo Dispatch
442.10000	427.60000	NFM	London	Grovefair Security, Highgate
442.10000	427.60000	NFM	Walsall	Mercia Lifting Gear
442.10000	427.60000	NFM	West Midlands	Security Company
442.12500	427.82500	NFM	Bournemouth	Lynx Couriers
442.12500	427.82500	NFM	London	Ircheck Security Services, Islington
442.12500	427.82500	NFM	Warrington	Ineos Silicas
442.15000	427.65000	NFM	Chelmsford	Boreham Tyre Services
442.17500	427.67500	NFM	London	Parking Enforcement, Fulham (71.9)
442.17500	427.67500	NFM	London	Parking Enforcement, Westminster (77)
442.17500	427.67500	NFM	London	Pronto Bikes
442.17500	427.67500	NFM	Stoke on Trent	Doctors' Service
442.20000	427.70000	NFM	Hertsmere	Council Refuse Collectors (67)
442.20000	427.70000	NFM	London	Blackheath Cleansing Department
442.22500	427.72500	NFM	London	Ambulance Incident Repeaters
442.22500	427.72500	NFM	Nationwide	Ambulance Incident Repeaters
442.22500	427.72500	NFM	Worcestershire	Ambulance Incident Repeaters

442.2625 - 442.5125 MHz   Broadcasting Links

Base	Mobile	Mode	Location	User and Notes
442.26250		NFM	Nationwide	JFMG Wide Area Talkback
442.27500		NFM	London	BBC TV Talkback
442.27500		NFM	London	BBC Breakfast TV Link
442.28750		NFM	London	BBC Radio 5 Talkback
442.28750		NFM	London	BBC TV & Radio O/B
442.32500		NFM	London	BBC TV Talkback & Studio Links
442.33750		NFM	London	BBC TV Talkback
442.36250		NFM	London	BBC TV Talkback & Studio Links
442.38750		NFM	London	BBC TV News Feed, White City
442.38750		NFM	London	Reuters TV News Audio Feed
442.42500		NFM	London	ITN Link
442.43125		NFM	Birmingham	ITN Talkback
442.43750		NFM	London	ITN Studio Link 2
442.45000		NFM	London	ITN Studio
442.46250		NFM	London	ITN News Director
442.47500		NFM	Grays	ITN MCR
442.48125		NFM	London	ITN Studio Link
442.48750		NFM	London	ITN Talkback
442.49375		NFM	London	ITN Studio Link
442.50000		NFM	London	ITN News Talkback
442.51250		NFM	London	ITN Circuit Feed
442.51250		NFM	Nationwide	JFMG Wide Area Talkback

442.51875 - 443.49375 MHz   PMR Mobile 12.5 kHz

Base	Mobile	Mode	Location	User and Notes
442.52500	428.02500	NFM	Birmingham	Airport BAA Multi User Trunked Network
442.52500	428.02500	NFM	Borehamwood	BBC Security, Elstree Studio (94.8)
442.52500	428.02500	NFM	Cardiff	Millennium Stadium Security/Stewards Trunked
442.52500	428.02500	NFM	Enfield	Enfield Council, Trent Valley Park
442.52500	428.02500	NFM	Heathrow	Qatar Airways T3 (118.8)
442.52500	428.02500	NFM	Liverpool	OMBC Security
442.52500	428.02500	NFM	London	Hackney Council
442.52500	428.02500	NFM	London	Lambeth Council
442.52500	428.02500	NFM	London	BBC Security, Acton
442.52500	428.02500	NFM	London	BBC Security, Ealing
442.52500	428.02500	NFM	London	BBC Security, Park Royal
442.52500	428.02500	NFM	London	BBC Security, White City (127.3)
442.52500	428.02500	NFM	Tilbury	Container Port (94.8)
442.53750	428.03750	NFM	Surrey	Kingswood Cars
442.55000	428.05000	NFM	Ellesmere Port	Shell Thornton Research Centre Ch.1
442.55000	428.05000	NFM	Gateshead	Metro Centre Staff (110.9)
442.55000	428.05000	NFM	Heathrow	Iran Air T3 Ramp Ops (167.9)
442.55000	428.05000	NFM	London	Leyton Council
442.55000	428.05000	NFM	London	Police, Billingsgate Market (192.8)
442.55000	428.05000	NFM	London	Police, Leadenhall Market
442.55000	428.05000	NFM	London	Police, Smithfield Market (114.8)
442.55000	428.05000	NFM	London	Police, Spitalfields Market
442.55000	428.05000	NFM	London	Shopwatch, Oxford Street (77)
442.55000	428.05000	NFM	London	Watneys Brewery, Mortlake (118.8)
442.56250	428.06250	NFM	Coventry	Shopwatch/Pubwatch/Car Parks Trunked
442.57500	428.07500	NFM	Glasgow	Council Landlord Services/Concierge/Cleansing Teams
442.57500	428.07500	NFM	Heathrow	Asterix Control Security KUA/QTR/UAE/UAL (71.9)
442.57500	428.07500	NFM	Tilbury	Container Port (94.8)
442.58750	428.08750	NFM	Basildon	Integrated Security Group
442.58750	428.08750	NFM	London	Integrated Security Group
442.58750	428.08750	NFM	Manchester	Skip Company
442.60000	428.10000	NFM	Birmingham	The Mailbox Centre/BBC Studio Complex Trunked
442.60000	428.10000	NFM	London	Brunel University Security, Uxbridge
442.60000	428.10000	NFM	London	Chelsea & Westminster Hospital Porters, Chelsea
442.60000	428.10000	NFM	Manchester	Trafford Park Security
442.60000	428.10000	NFM	Redditch	Kingfisher Shopping Centre Trunked
442.60000	428.10000	NFM	Tilbury	Container Port (94.8)
442.61250	428.11250	NFM	Coventry	Shopwatch/Pubwatch/Car Parks Trunked
442.61250	428.11250	NFM	London	Hammersmith & Fulham Parks Police (123)
442.61250	428.11250	NFM	London	Hounslow Car Spares
442.61250	428.11250	NFM	London	Parking Enforcement WC1
442.62500	428.12500	NFM	Birmingham	Airport Multi User Trunked Network
442.62500	428.17500	NFM	Glasgow	Maryhill Shopping Centre
442.62500	428.12500	NFM	Heathrow	Singapore Airlines T3 (186.2)
442.62500	428.12500	NFM	London	Baltic Exchange, City of London
442.62500	428.12500	NFM	London	National Maritime Museum, Greenwich
442.62500	428.12500	NFM	London	Royal Festival Hall Security, Waterloo (107.2)
442.62500	428.12500	NFM	London	Whitechapel Hospital Security (88.5)
442.62500	428.12500	NFM	Maidstone	Chequers Shopping Centre (94.8)
442.62500	428.12500	NFM	Manchester	Airport, Servisair/GlobeGround
442.63750	428.13750	NFM	London	Hackney Council Cleansing Department
442.63750	428.13750	NFM	London	Doctors' Service
442.63750	428.13750	NFM	London	Parking Enforcement, Greenwich (67)
442.63750	428.13750	NFM	London	Waltham Forest Council
442.65000	428.15000	NFM	Bolton	Shopwatch, Farnworth
442.65000	428.15000	NFM	Heathrow	Air Fayre Catering (DCS 212)

Base	Mobile	Mode	Location	User and Notes
442.65000	428.15000	NFM	Heathrow	Egyptair Ramp Ops (82.5)
442.65000	428.15000	NFM	Liverpool	Merseyside Maritime Museum
442.65000	428.15000	NFM	London	British Museum Security (67)
442.65000	428.15000	NFM	London	National Maritime Museum, Greenwich
442.66250	428.16250	NFM	Birmingham	NEC Stores & Warehouse (156.7)
442.67500	428.17500	NFM	Clydebank	Clyde Shopping Centre Security
442.67500	428.17500	NFM	Glenrothes	Kingdom Shopping Centre Security
442.67500	428.17500	NFM	Heathrow	BP Aviation Fuel (71.9)
442.67500	428.17500	NFM	Wirral	Wirral Beach Guards (82.5)
442.68750	428.18750	NFM	Birmingham	Council/Parking Enforcement/Tow Away
442.68750	428.18750	NFM	London	Parking Enforcement, Wandsworth (94.8)
442.70000	428.20000	NFM	Birmingham	Selfridges Departments Store
442.70000	428.20000	NFM	Coventry	Parcelforce Central UK Hub Conveyor Belts (88.5)
442.70000	428.20000	NFM	Dudley	Merryhill Shopping Centre Trunked
442.70000	428.20000	NFM	Ellesmere Port	Shell Thornton Research Centre (94.8)
442.70000	428.20000	NFM	Heathrow	Loaders (173)
442.71250	428.21250	NFM	Edinburgh	Council Housing Department Trunked
442.71250	428.21250	NFM	Glasgow	Council Roads & Lighting Services Trunked
442.71250	428.21250	NFM	London	Johns Delivery Ltd
442.71250	428.21250	NFM	Birmingham	Multi User Trunked Network, Chubb Security
442.72500	428.22500	NFM	Capenhurst	UKAEA
442.72500	428.22500	NFM	Heathrow	Saudi Airlines (118.8)
442.72500	428.22500	NFM	London	Liberty Store Security, Regent Street (67)
442.72500	428.22500	NFM	Manchester	Airport Baggage Handlers
442.72500	428.22500	NFM	Tilbury	Container Port (94.8)
442.73750	428.23750	NFM	Dudley	Council Housing Repairs Trunked
442.73750	428.23750	NFM	Glasgow	Council Trunked
442.73750	428.23750	NFM	London	Wandsworth Parks Constabulary
442.75000	428.25000	NFM	Birmingham	Market Police (67)
442.75000	428.25000	NFM	Edinburgh	BAA Airport Trunked Network
442.75000	428.25000	NFM	Heathrow	BAA Security Airside (107.2)
442.76250	428.26250	NFM	Glasgow	Council Trunked
442.77500	428.27500	NFM	Capenhurst	UKAEA
442.77500	428.27500	NFM	Croydon	Whitgift Centre Security (107.2)
442.77500	428.27500	NFM	Heathrow	Servisair/GlobeGround T2/T3 (123)
442.77500	428.27500	NFM	London	Centre Court Shopping Centre, Wimbledon
442.77500	428.27500	NFM	London	Lloyds of London Security, City of London
442.77500	428.27500	NFM	London	Riverdale Shopping Centre Security, Lewisham.
442.77500	428.27500	NFM	London	West Middlesex Hospital
442.78750	428.28750	NFM	Glasgow	Council Services Parking/Tow Away/Cleansing
442.80000	428.30000	NFM	Glasgow	Council Phone Patches
442.80000	428.30000	NFM	London	Prestige Courier Bike Service
442.81250	428.31250	NFM	Glasgow	Council Trunked
442.81250	428.31250	NFM	London	Parking Enforcement, Hillingdon (110.9)
442.82500	428.32500	NFM	London	Borough of Hackney Housing
442.83750	428.33750	NFM	Glasgow	Council Services Parking/Tow Away/Cleansing
442.85000	428.35000	NFM	Glasgow	Trojan Security
442.85000	428.35000	NFM	Gatwick	Handling (131.8)
442.85000	428.35000	NFM	London	Addison Lee Couriers
442.86250	428.36250	NFM	Glasgow	Council Trunked
442.87500	428.37500	NFM	Bexley	Parking Enforcement
442.87500	428.37500	NFM	Heathrow	Sigma Aircraft Services (146.2)
442.88750	428.38750	NFM	Glasgow	Council Roads & Lighting
442.90000	428.40000	NFM	Bexley	Parking Enforcement
442.90000	428.40000	NFM	Liverpool	Parking Enforcement (156.7)
442.90000	428.40000	NFM	London	Guys Hospital Porters/Security (103.5)
442.90000	428.40000	NFM	Redbridge	Parking Enforcement, Sureway Parking
442.91250	428.41250	NFM	Dudley	Council Housing Repairs Trunked

Base	Mobile	Mode	Location	User and Notes
442.91250	428.41250	NFM	Glasgow	Council Environmental Dept/Pest Control/Needle Removals
442.91250	428.41250	NFM	London	Courier Company, Central London
442.92500	428.42500	NFM	Glasgow	TOA Taxis
442.93750	428.43750	NFM	Birmingham	Council/Parking Enforcement/Tow Away Trunked
442.93750	428.43750	NFM	Glasgow	Council Land Services Cleansing Trunked
442.95000		NFM	Lowestoft	HM Revenue & Customs, Docks
442.96250	428.46250	NFM	Birmingham	Airport BAA Multi User Trunked Network
442.96250	428.46250	NFM	Bootle	Shopwatch, Strand Shopping Centre
442.96250	428.46250	NFM	Edinburgh	Airport BAA Trunked Network
442.96250	428.46250	NFM	Heathrow	Budget Rent A Car/Courtlands (67)
442.97500	428.47500	NFM	Glasgow	Council Trunked
442.97500	428.47500	NFM	London	Checker Cabs
442.97500	428.47500	NFM	London	Supreme Cabs
442.98750	428.48750	NFM	London	Hornet Bike Couriers
443.00000	428.50000	NFM	Altrincham	Shopwatch (67)
443.00000	428.50000	NFM	Crewe	Wellcome Foundation
443.00000	428.50000	NFM	Heathrow	Thai Airways T3 (103.5)
443.00000	428.50000	NFM	London	Centre Court Shopping Centre Security, Wimbledon (110.9)
443.00000	428.50000	NFM	London	Chelsea & Westminster Hospital Porters, Chelsea
443.00000	428.50000	NFM	London	Lloyds Building
443.00000	428.50000	NFM	London	Middlesex Hospital Security (94.8)
443.00000	428.50000	NFM	London	Shopwatch, Newham/Plaistow
443.00000	428.50000	NFM	London	Shopwatch, Wimbledon (151.4)
443.00000	428.50000	NFM	Thurrock	Lakeside Shopping Centre Trunked Network Voice
443.01250	428.51250	NFM	Birmingham	Airport BAA Multi User Trunked Network
443.01250	428.51250	NFM	London	Olympic Couriers
443.02500	428.52500	NFM	Heathrow	Kuwaiti Airways T3 (71.9)
443.02500	428.52500	NFM	London	Channel Rail Link Security Trunked, St Pancras
443.02500	428.52500	NFM	Thurrock	Lakeside Shopping Centre Trunked Network Control
443.02500	428.52500	NFM	Tilbury	Container Port (94.8)
443.03750	428.53750	NFM	Edinburgh	Council Housing Department Trunked
443.05000	428.55000	NFM	Dartford	Shopwatch
443.05000	428.55000	NFM	Gatwick	Airport Ops. (103.5)
443.05000	428.55000	NFM	Heathrow	Malaysian Airlines T3 Ops. (114.8)
443.05000	428.55000	NFM	London	Hostel, Shipton Street, Shoreditch
443.05000	428.55000	NFM	London	LIFFE, EC4 (67)
443.06250	428.56250	NFM	Coalville	Shopwatch
443.06250	428.56250	NFM	Coventry	Walsgrave Hospital Security Trunked
443.06250	428.56250	NFM	Edinburgh	Council Housing Department Trunked
443.06250	428.56250	NFM	Redditch	Kingfisher Shopping Centre Trunked
443.07500	428.57500	NFM	Birmingham	International Arena
443.07500	428.57500	NFM	Heathrow	Finnair T2 (118.8)
443.07500	428.57500	NFM	London	West 1 Cars
443.08750	428.58750	NFM	Birmingham	Airport BAA Multi User Trunked Network
443.10000	428.60000	NFM	Coventry	Parcelforce Central UK Hub (88.5)
443.10000	428.60000	NFM	Heathrow	Swissport Cargo Service Centre (67)
443.10000	428.60000	NFM	London	Shopwatch, Clapham Junction (141.3)
443.10000	428.60000	NFM	London	Shopwatch, Tooting (103.5)
443.10000	428.60000	NFM	London	Shopwatch, Wandsworth (179.9)
443.11250	428.61250	NFM	Edinburgh	Airport BAA Trunked Network
443.12500	428.62500	NFM	Cardiff	Shopwatch, Cardiff Bay Retail Park (88.5)
443.12500	428.62500	NFM	Dartford	Dartford Tunnel Ch.2
443.13750	428.63750	NFM	Coventry	Shopwatch/Pubwatch/Car Parks Trunked
443.13750	428.63750	NFM	London	Network Rail Contractors
443.15000	428.65000	NFM	Heathrow	AirRadio Trunked Net British Airways/Multi User
443.16250	428.66250	NFM	London	Security Patrols Trunked, Oxford Street
443.16250	428.66250	NFM	London	Shopwatch Security Trunked, Regent St

Base	Mobile	Mode	Location	User and Notes
443.18750	428.68750	NFM	Banstead	Home James Cars
443.22500	428.72500	NFM	Edinburgh	Council Housing Department Trunked
443.25000	428.75000	NFM	Heathrow	Swissair T2 (82.5)
443.26250	428.66250	NFM	Manchester	Shaw Radio Cars
443.27500	428.77500	NFM	St Helens	Kingdom Security
443.32500	428.82500	NFM	Liverpool	AirRadio Trunked British Airways/Multi User
443.38700	428.88700	NFM	Birmingham	Aerial Company
443.38750	428.88750	NFM	Dorking	Apollo Cars
443.38750	428.88750	NFM	London	Lewisham Council
443.00000	428.90000	NFM	Heathrow	AirRadio Trunked Network British Airways/Multi User
443.00000	428.90000	NFM	London	Ralph Lauren Store Security, New Bond Street (210.7)
443.41250	428.91250	NFM	Coventry	Shopwatch/Pubwatch/Car Parks Trunked
443.42500	428.92500	NFM	London	Camden Council Community Wardens (DCS 212)
443.42500	428.92500	NFM	London	Parking Enforcement, Poplar (77)
443.45000	428.95000	NFM	Cardiff	Cardiff Bay Retail Park Security
443.45000	428.95000	NFM	Falkirk	BP Fire And Security
443.45000	428.95000	NFM	Gatwick	Gatwick Airport Handling (103.5)
443.45000	428.95000	NFM	Heathrow	Gulf Air T3 Ops (110.9)
443.45000	428.95000	NFM	London	Bentalls Shopping Centre, Kingston upon Thames
443.45000	428.95000	NFM	London	Riverdale Shopping Centre Security, Lewisham Council
443.46250	428.96250	NFM	Banstead	Courtesy Cars (67)
443.46250	428.96250	NFM	Caterham	Shopwatch/Pubwatch (77)
443.47500	428.97500	NFM	Bromsgrove	Parks Police (107.2)
443.47500	428.97500	NFM	Dartford	Royal Holloway University (110.9)
443.47500	428.97500	NFM	Egham	Car Parking/Car Rental (118.8)
443.47500	428.97500	NFM	Heathrow	Lewisham Council
443.47500	428.97500	NFM	London	Police, Kenwood House & Hampstead Heath (127.3)
443.47500	428.97500	NFM	London	Kensington & Chelsea Parks Police, Holland Park
443.47500	428.97500	NFM	London	Shopwatch, N1 (151.4)
443.47500	428.97500	NFM	Watford	Borough Council

443.5000 - 445.3000 MHz   MoD Radiolocation & Base Comms 25 kHz

Base	Mobile	Mode	Location	User and Notes
443.50000	445.40000	NFM	Nationwide	MoD Radio Branch, High Security/Navy/Army
443.51250		NFM	London	MoD Police, Mill Hill Barracks
443.55000		NFM	Wiltshire	Dean Hill Munitions Store
443.57500	449.77500	NFM	London	MoD Police
443.58750		NFM	London	MoD Police
443.58750		NFM	Netheravon	Military Parachute Comms
443.67500		NFM	London	MoD Police
443.76250	429.53750	NFM	USAF Mildenhall	MoD Police, Airshow 2001 (131.8)
443.76250		NFM	Oxfordshire	MoD Police Bicester Barracks
443.80000		NFM	Portsmouth	Royal Naval Provosts (123)
443.82500		NFM	Nationwide	MoD Police Nuclear Convoy Escorts
443.83750		NFM	Boscombe Down	RAE Transport
443.88750		NFM	Boscombe Down	MoD Police (BD)
443.90000		NFM	London	Foreign & Commonwealth Office (94.8)
443.90000		NFM	London	Lancaster House (94.8)
443.91250		NFM	Boscombe Down	Qinetiq
443.93750	434.41250	NFM	Boscombe Down	Army Transport & Escorts
443.98750		NFM	Boscombe Down	Tower To Relay/MoD Police/Security
443.98750		NFM	Boscombe Down	Qinetiq Security, Bustard
444.03750	454.03750	NFM	Coquelles	Eurotunnel Concessions
444.05000		NFM	Aldermaston	MoD Police
444.05000		NFM	Pirbright	Mod Police
444.05000		NFM	Kirkudbright	Qinetiq Training Range Ch.1

Base	Mobile	Mode	Location	User and Notes
444.05000		NFM	USAF Mildenhall	MoD Police Airshow 2001 (131.8)
444.06250	454.06250	NFM	Eurotunnel	Eurotunnel Shuttle Internal Channel
444.07500	454.07500	NFM	Coquelles	Eurotunnel Concessions
444.10000		NFM	London	Royal Horse Artillery Grooms
444.13750	454.13750	NFM	Coquelles	Eurotunnel Concessions
444.13750	454.13750	NFM	Sangatte	Eurotunnel Concessions
444.22500	454.22500	NFM	Coquelles	Eurotunnel Concessions
444.23750	454.23750	NFM	Coquelles	Eurotunnel Concessions
444.23750	454.23750	NFM	Sangatte	Eurotunnel Concessions
444.25000		NFM	Gosport	RN Guard Services HMS Daedalus (192.8)
444.25000		NFM	Gosport	RN Guard Services HMS Sultan (192.8)
444.28750	454.28750	NFM	Eurotunnel	Eurotunnel Shuttle Internal Radio
444.30000	454.30000	NFM	Coquelles	Eurotunnel Concessions
444.30000	454.30000	NFM	Sangatte	Eurotunnel Concessions
444.31250	454.31250	NFM	Eurotunnel	Eurotunnel Shuttle Internal Radio
444.32500	454.32500	NFM	Sangatte	Eurotunnel Concessions
444.33750	454.33750	NFM	Coquelles	Eurotunnel Concessions
444.33750	449.72500	NFM	Farnborough	Tower-Ground Vehicles
444.33750		NFM	Kirkudbright	Qinetiq Training Range Ch.3
444.35000	449.72500	NFM	London	Admiralty Security, Whitehall (94.8)
444.35000	429.65000	NFM	USAF Mildenhall	MoD Police
444.37500	454.37500	NFM	Coquelles	Eurotunnel Concessions
444.43750	454.43750	NFM	Coquelles	Eurotunnel Concessions
444.43750	454.43750	NFM	Sangatte	Eurotunnel Concessions
444.45000		NFM	Aldershot	MoD Police
444.45000	454.45000	NFM	Coquelles	Eurotunnel Concessions
444.45000	431.85000	NFM	Larkhill	MoD Police Ch.158 Larkhill Range (131.8/103.5)
444.45000		NFM	USAF Mildenhall	MoD Police
444.45000		NFM	Uxbridge	MoD Police (RI)
444.46250	454.46250	NFM	Eurotunnel	Eurotunnel Shuttle Internal Radio
444.46250		NFM	Kirkudbright	Qinetiq Training Range Ch.2
444.48750	454.48750	NFM	Coquelles	Eurotunnel Concessions
444.48750	454.48750	NFM	Sangatte	Eurotunnel Concessions
444.52500		NFM	Reading	Group 4 Prisoner Van & Police Escorts, M4 J12
444.55000		NFM	Portsmouth	RN Portsmouth
444.56250	454.28750	NFM	Eurotunnel	Eurotunnel Shuttle Internal Radio
444.58750	454.31250	NFM	Eurotunnel	Eurotunnel Shuttle Internal Radio
444.66250	454.46250	NFM	Eurotunnel	Eurotunnel Shuttle Internal Radio
444.71250	454.06250	NFM	Eurotunnel	Eurotunnel Shuttle Internal Radio
444.83750		NFM	Boscombe Down	Qinetiq Transport

445.0000 - 445.9750 MHz — PMR Base 12.5 kHz NFM

Base	Mobile	Mode	Location	User and Notes
445.12500		NFM	Newhaven	Hoverspeed
445.15000	424.65000	NFM	Birmingham	British Rail Post Office
445.18750	424.68750	NFM	Portsmouth	Marine Re-fuelling
445.21875		NFM	Nationwide	Sky TV Talkback (DCS 306)
445.22500		NFM	Portsmouth	Commodore/Condor Ferries (186.2)
445.25000		NFM	Dover	Seafrance Ferries Non UK Licensed Radios
445.33750		NFM	Nationwide	RAF Falcons Parachute DZ
445.43750		NFM	Dover	Seafrance Ferries Non UK Licensed Radios
445.51250		NFM	Crayford	Interlink Couriers
445.51250	425.01250	NFM	Medway	Nu-Venture Buses, Maidstone/Aylesford (88.5)
445.52500		NFM	Preston	Deepdale Retail Park Security (110.9)
445.53750	425.03750	NFM	London	Securitas Express Cash Delivery
445.56250	425.06250	NFM	London	Parking Enforcement, Camden
445.56250	425.06250	NFM	Manchester	Mobile Mechanic

Base	Mobile	Mode	Location	User and Notes
445.57500		NFM	Dover	Hoverspeed Ch.2
445.57500	425.07500	NFM	London	West Hendon Cars
445.57500		NFM	Newhaven	Hoverspeed
445.58750	425.08750	NFM	Bootle	Security Company
445.58750	425.08750	NFM	London	Metro Taxis
445.60000	425.10000	NFM	Birmingham	City Waste Ltd
445.60000	425.10000	NFM	London	Parking Enforcement, Kensington
445.60000	425.10000	NFM	London	Parking Enforcement, Richmond
445.60000	425.10000	NFM	London	Parking Enforcement, Twickenham
445.60000	425.10000	NFM	London	Warden Patrols, Eltham
445.61350	425.11250	NFM	Birmingham	The Mailbox Centre/BBC Studio Complex Trunked
445.62500	425.12500	NFM	Leicester	Environmental Health Officers' Handhelds
445.65000	425.15000	NFM	Coventry	University Security
445.65000	425.15000	NFM	London	London Underground, All Stations Ch.4
445.65000	425.15000	NFM	Heathrow	Cathay Pacific T3 Ops. (103.5)
445.66250	425.26250	NFM	Coventry	Walsgrave Hospital Security Trunked
445.67500	425.17500	NFM	Birmingham	Midwives
445.67500	425.17500	NFM	Gatwick	Virgin Ops Control Centre (67)
445.67500	425.17500	NFM	London	High Court Security (S)
445.70000	425.20000	NFM	Blantyre	Shopwatch
445.70000	425.20000	NFM	Gatwick	Airline Ops (82.5)
445.70000	425.20000	NFM	London	Doctors' Service (67)
445.72500	425.22500	NFM	London	London Underground, All Stations Ch.1
445.72500	425.32500	NFM	London	Westinghouse Cubic Ch.1
445.75000	425.25000	NFM	Heathrow	Catering
445.75000	425.25000	NFM	London	BBC TV Centre Security, Wood Lane
445.75000	425.25000	NFM	London	Bloomberg Bank Security, Finsbury Square (123)
445.75000	425.25000	NFM	London	Legal & General Sports Ground, Kingswood
445.75000	425.25000	NFM	London	London Underground, Liverpool Street (123)
445.75000	425.25000	NFM	London	Doctors' Service (67)
445.75000	425.25000	NFM	London	University College, Gower Street
445.75000	425.25000	NFM	London	University of East London
445.75000	425.25000	NFM	London	St Georges Hospital, Tooting (Mednet) (67)
445.75000	425.35000	NFM	London	Westinghouse Cubic Ch.2
445.76250	425.26250	NFM	London	Doctors' Service (67)
445.77500	425.27500	NFM	London	London Underground, All Stations Ch.2
445.77500	425.37500	NFM	London	Westinghouse Cubic Ch.3
445.77500	445.77500	NFM	Warton	BAe
445.78750	425.28750	NFM	London	Doctors' Service (67)
445.80000	425.30000	NFM	Heathrow	Aviation Defence International Security (67)
445.80000	425.40000	NFM	London	Borough of Hackney Cleansing (167.9)
445.80000	425.30000	NFM	London	Legal And General Sports Ground, Kingswood
445.80000	425.30000	NFM	London	London Underground All Stations Ch.3
445.80000	425.30000	NFM	London	Doctors' Service (67)
445.80000	425.30000	NFM	London	Westinghouse Cubic Ch.4
445.80000	425.40000	NFM	Newcastle	Pubwatch (67)
445.82500	425.42500	NFM	Kent	Doctors' Service
445.82500	425.42500	NFM	London	Borough of Hackney Housing
445.82500	425.32500	NFM	London	Shopwatch, Woolwich (94.8)
445.85000	425.35000	NFM	London,	Parking Enforcement, E2 (136.5)
445.87500	425.37500	NFM	London	Shopwatch, Kingston (77)
445.92500	425.52500	NFM	London	Wings Couriers Ltd
445.95000	425.45000	NFM	Edenbridge	Edenbridge Cars
445.97500	425.47500	NFM	London	Parking Enforcement, Kensington & Chelsea
445.97500	425.47500	NFM	London	Parking Enforcement, Westminster
445.97500	425.47500	NFM	Tyneside	Fencing Contractors

446.00625 - 446.09375 MHz   PMR 446 Simplex 12.5 kHz

Base	Mode	Location	User and Notes
446.00625	NFM	Nationwide	Channel 1
446.01875	NFM	Nationwide	Channel 2
446.03125	NFM	Nationwide	Channel 3
446.04375	NFM	Nationwide	Channel 4
446.05625	NFM	Nationwide	Channel 5
446.06875	NFM	Nationwide	Channel 6
446.08125	NFM	Nationwide	Channel 7
446.09375	NFM	Nationwide	Channel 8

446.000 - 446.475 MHz   PMR Simplex 12.5 kHz

Base	Mode	Location	User and Notes
446.00000	NFM	London	Alexandra Palace Security
446.00000	NFM	London	Brixton Town Hall
446.00000	NFM	London	City of London Girls School
446.00000	NFM	London	Harbour Exchange Security
446.00000	NFM	London	Ouse Cafe, Covent Garden
446.00000	NFM	London	Roadhouse Restaurant, Covent Garden
446.00000	NFM	London	Royal Albert Hall Security
446.00000	NFM	London	Selfridges, Oxford Street
446.00000	NFM	London	Showsec Security
446.00000	NFM	London	Tate Gallery Security
446.00000	NFM	London	Waterfront Leisure Centre, Woolwich
446.00000	NFM	Manchester	Manchester Hospital Casualty Department
446.00625	NFM	Bristol	City Inn Staff
446.00625	NFM	Cardiff	University Hospital of Wales Fire Marshals (67)
446.00625	NFM	Carlisle	Woolworths Staff (67)
446.00625	NFM	Chichester	Sainsbury Security (DCS 225)
446.00625	NFM	Clacton	Bishop's Park School (94.8)
446.00625	NFM	Coatbridge	Summerlee Heritage Museum
446.00625	NFM	Cornwall	Eden Project (All 8 Channels in Use)
446.00625	NFM	Nationwide	PMR 446 Ch.1
446.00625	NFM	Paddock Wood	The Hop Farm Country Park
446.00625	NFM	Stevenage	Cromwell Hotel Staff
446.00625	NFM	Stevenage	Stevenage Rail Station Staff (94.8)
446.01250	NFM	Buckhurst Hill	Nature Reserve
446.01250	NFM	Edinburgh	Premier Beverages, Kinnaird Park
446.01250	NFM	London	Elephant & Castle Shopping Centre Security
446.01250	NFM	London	Buckingham Palace Security
446.01250	NFM	London	Wimbledon Common Security
446.01250	NFM	London	Royal Hospital Security, Chelsea
446.01250	NFM	London	MoD security, Thames House
446.01250	NFM	London	News International Newspapers, Wapping
446.01250	NFM	Manchester	Hospital (Alpha)
446.01875	NFM	Gower	Motorcycle Training School
446.01875	NFM	Hitchin	Hitchin Railway Station Staff
446.01875	NFM	Ipswich	Crown Swimming Pool
446.01875	NFM	Ipswich	Fire & Ice Bar
446.01875	NFM	Lancaster	Lancaster Railway Station Staff
446.01875	NFM	London	Top Shop Staff, Oxford Street (67)
446.01875	NFM	London	Tottenham Hotspur Football Club Staff
446.01875	NFM	London	Travelodge Staff, Covent Garden (67)
446.01875	NFM	Martlesham Heath	Martlesham Go Kart Racing (107.2)
446.01875	NFM	Nationwide	PMR 446 Ch.2
446.01875	NFM	Peterborough	College Arms bar
446.01875	NFM	Peterborough	Solstice Bar
446.01875	NFM	Paddock Wood	The Hop Farm Country Park

Base	Mobile	Mode	Location	User and Notes
446.01875		NFM	Whitby	Whitby Holiday Park Security, Saltley Bay
446.02500		NFM	Birmingham	Go Kart Track
446.02500		NFM	Chesterfield	Car Park Attendants
446.02500		NFM	Harlow	GlaxoSmithKline Security
446.02500		NFM	Heathrow	Airport Taxi Service
446.02500		NFM	London	British Medical Association, Tavistock Square
446.02500		NFM	London	Ikea, Neasden
446.02500		NFM	London	InterContinental Hotel, Mayfair
446.02500		NFM	London	London Underground Ch.1-3, Docklands
446.02500		NFM	London	Long Island Ice Tea Bar, Covent Garden
446.02500		NFM	London	New Covent Garden Market, Nine Elms
446.02500		NFM	London	Putney Hospital
446.02500		NFM	London	Royal Albert Hall Back of House
446.02500		NFM	Tadworth	Walton Oaks Experimental Farm Security
446.03125		NFM	Baldock	Tesco Staff
446.03125		NFM	Fairbourne	Fairbourne & Barmouth Steam Railway
446.03125		NFM	Hitchin	Hitchin Railway Station Staff
446.03125		NFM	Hull	RSJ Motorcycle Training School
446.03125		NFM	Ipswich	Fire & Ice Bar (103.5)
446.03125		NFM	Ipswich	Hare & Hound Pub
446.03125		NFM	Ipswich	St Clement's (Mental) Hospital
446.03125		NFM	London	JD Sports, Oxford Circus (103.5)
446.03125		NFM	London	Rail Gourmet Train Catering, Kings Cross
446.03125		NFM	Lowestoft	Notley's Bar
446.03125		NFM	Nationwide	Express Caterers Events Catering
446.03125		NFM	Nationwide	Freefire Zone Airsoft Clubs
446.03125		NFM	Nationwide	PMR 446 Ch.3
446.03125		NFM	Paddock Wood	The Hop Farm Country Park
446.03125		NFM	Southport	Premier Travel Inn, Ocean Plaza
446.03750		NFM	Beckenham	Beckenham Place Park
446.03750		NFM	Blackpool	Pleasure Beach Staff
446.03750		NFM	Chatham	PC World Security
446.03750		NFM	Coventry	PC World Security
446.03750		NFM	London	PC World Security, Staples Corner
446.03750		NFM	London	Royal Albert Hall Staff
446.03750		NFM	Nationwide	PC World Security
446.03750		NFM	Stockport	PC World Security
446.04375		NFM	Cambridge	WH Smith
446.04375		NFM	Cardiff	Channel View Leisure Centre
446.04375		NFM	Evesham	Vale School
446.04375		NFM	Hitchin	Wyevale Garden Centre (186.2)
446.04375		NFM	Ipswich	Fire & Ice Bar
446.04375		NFM	London	Top Shop Staff, Oxford Circus (67)
446.04375		NFM	London	Waterstones Book Shop, Piccadilly
446.04375		NFM	Nationwide	PMR 446 Ch.4
446.04375		NFM	Paddock Wood	The Hop Farm Country Park
446.04375		NFM	Stratford upon Avon	Safeway Staff
446.05000		NFM	Edinburgh	Stevenson College Janitors
446.05000		NFM	Hull	Orchard Park Shopping Centre
446.05000		NFM	London	Lords Cricket Ground Staff (186.2)
446.05000		NFM	London	Harrods Security, Knightsbridge
446.05000		NFM	London	Watneys Brewery, Mortlake
446.05000		NFM	London	Berners Park Plaza Hotel, Oxford Street
446.05000		NFM	London	Imax Cinema Staff, Piccadilly
446.05000		NFM	London	American Airlines, Victoria Station
446.05000		NFM	Manchester	MoD Ordnance Factory

Base	Mobile	Mode	Location	User and Notes
446.05000		NFM	Manchester	Rain Forest Cafe, Trafford Centre
446.05625		NFM	Carlisle	Scotts Menswear
446.05625		NFM	Bishops Stortford	Railway Station Staff
446.05625		NFM	Brighton	Volks Railway, Madeira Drive
446.05625		NFM	Fareham	Fareham College
446.05625		NFM	London	City Cruises, Waterloo Pier
446.05625		NFM	London	London Eye Cleaners
446.05625		NFM	London	Mothercare Staff, Marble Arch
446.05625		NFM	London	Pizza Hut Staff, Duke Street
446.05625		NFM	London	The Link Store, Marble Arch
446.05625		NFM	Nationwide	Express Caterers Events Catering
446.05625		NFM	Nationwide	PMR 446 Ch.5
446.05625		NFM	Paddock Wood	The Hop Farm Country Park
446.05625		NFM	Portsmouth	The White Swan Pub/Club, Southsea (110.9)
446.06250		NFM	Heathrow	Airport Taxi Service
446.06250		NFM	London	Britannia Hotel, Canary Wharf
446.06250		NFM	London	Government Offices, Tadworth
446.06250		NFM	London	Southfields Mosque
446.06250		NFM	London	Southfields School
446.06250		NFM	London	West Middlesex University Hospital, Isleworth
446.06875		NFM	Evesham	Woodlands Generators
446.06875		NFM	London	Dixons, Brent Cross
446.06875		NFM	London	JD Sports, Oxford Circus
446.06875		NFM	London	Hard Rock Cafe, Piccadilly
446.06875		NFM	London	Metropolis Motorcycle Training
446.06875		NFM	London	National Portrait Gallery
446.06875		NFM	Nationwide	PMR 466 Ch.6
446.06875		NFM	Nationwide	PROMA Scanning Group Calling Channel (250)
446.06875		NFM	Paddock Wood	The Hop Farm Country Park (67)
446.07500		NFM	Epsom	RAC Golf and Country Club
446.07500		NFM	London	Masterpark Car Park Attendants, Gerrard Street
446.07500		NFM	London	News International Security, Wapping
446.07500		NFM	London	Watneys Brewery, Mortlake
446.07500		NFM	Nationwide	Baldwin Crane Hire
446.07500		NFM	Newcastle	Hebburn Swimming Pool
446.07500		NFM	Redbridge	Technical College
446.08125		NFM	Baldock	Tesco Security
446.08125		NFM	Birmingham	Indoor Market
446.08125		NFM	Carlisle	Virgin Records Security
446.08125		NFM	Evesham	Abbey Gates Security
446.08125		NFM	Immingham	Pauls Sports Centre, Kingswood
446.08125		NFM	London	Dorothy Perkins Security/Staff, W1
446.08125		NFM	London	Royal Hospital, Chelsea
446.08125		NFM	Nationwide	PMR 446 Ch.7
446.08125		NFM	Paddock Wood	The Hop Farm Country Park
446.08750		NFM	Croydon	Woodside School
446.08750		NFM	London	Lancaster House, St. James's Palace
446.08750		NFM	London	Marks & Spencer, Marble Arch
446.08750		NFM	London	Park School, Richmond
446.08750		NFM	London	St Marks Hospital, Harrow
446.08750		NFM	London	Tate Gallery Security
446.08750		NFM	London	University College Hospital
446.08750		NFM	Manchester	Prague 5 (Praha V) Gay Club, Chorlton St.
446.09375		NFM	Cardiff	Capital Shopping Centre Cleaners
446.09375		NFM	Cardiff	Cardiff Castle Staff
446.09375		NFM	Ipswich	Fire & Ice Bar

Base	Mobile	Mode	Location	User and Notes
446.09375		NFM	London	Benetton Staff/Security, Oxford Circus
446.09375		NFM	London	JD Sports, Oxford Circus (88.5)
446.09375		NFM	London	Rail Gourmet Train Catering, Kings Cross (107.2)
446.09375		NFM	Nationwide	PMR 446 Ch.8
446.09375		NFM	Oxford	Dixons
446.09375		NFM	Paddock Wood	The Hop Farm Country Park
446.09375		NFM	Stevenage	N Herts College Staff/Security
446.10000		NFM	Cheam	St. Anthony's Hospital
446.10000		NFM	Chessington	Gascoigne Ltd., Computer Services
446.10000		NFM	Downe	West Kent Golf Course
446.10000		NFM	London	A La Kart Indoor Go Kart Racing, Battersea
446.10000		NFM	London	Erith Food Mill
446.10000		NFM	London	Thames Flood Barrier, Woolwich
446.10000		NFM	Manchester	Hospital Maintenance
446.10000		NFM	Thorpe Park	Theme Park Ch.1
446.11250		NFM	Bangor	Boom Boom Room Bouncers
446.11250		NFM	Biggin Hill	Airport Ops
446.11250		NFM	Birmingham Airport	British Airways Ops
446.11250		NFM	Braintree	George Yard Centre Security (250.3)
446.11250		NFM	Bridgend	McArthur Glen Designer Outlet Security (88.5)
446.11250		NFM	Cardiff	Cardiff LDV Truck Centre
446.11250		NFM	Cheltenham	Town Hall (123)
446.11250		NFM	Felixstowe	Docks Haulage Cranes Data
446.11250		NFM	Gloucester	Eastgate Shopping Mall Security (250.3)
446.11250		NFM	Heathrow	Car Rentals/Parking (151.4)
446.11250		NFM	London	BBC Radio Security, Bush House
446.11250		NFM	London	BBC Radio Security, Langham Place
446.11250		NFM	London	Docklands Light Railway, Greenwich
446.11250		NFM	London	London Underground West Ham
446.11250		NFM	London	London Underground All Stations Ch.5
446.11250		NFM	London	Tate Gallery Security/Staff (127.3)
446.11250		NFM	London	Underground Stations Ch.5 (94.8)
446.11250		NFM	Manchester	Shopwatch, Swinton Shopping Centre
446.11250		NFM	Morden	Merton Technical College Security
446.11250		NFM	Peterborough	Liquid Nightclub Security (118.8)
446.11250		NFM	Southend on Sea	TK Maxx Store (241.8)
446.11250		NFM	Suffolk	Snape Maltings (94.8)
446.12500		NFM	Birmingham	Shopwatch, Grosvenor Centre, Northfield
446.12500		NFM	Cardiff	Cardiff City Football Club Security (110.9)
446.12500		NFM	Croydon	Debenhams Department Store Security
446.12500		NFM	Edinburgh	Comet, Kinnaird Park
446.12500		NFM	Epping	North Weald Airfield Runway Control (103.5)
446.12500		NFM	Guildford	Debenhams Department Store Security
446.12500		NFM	London	Elephant & Castle Shopping Centre Security
446.12500		NFM	London	Rosslyn Park Rugby Club
446.12500		NFM	London	Royal Festival Hall, Waterloo (156.7)
446.12500		NFM	London	Rupert Street Gay Bar, NCS Security
446.12500		NFM	London	Thames Valley University, Ealing
446.12500		NFM	London	Twickenham Rugby Ground Security
446.12500		NFM	London	Victoria & Albert Museum Security
446.12500		NFM	Manchester	Debenhams Department Store Security
446.12500		NFM	Middlesbrough	Middlesbrough FC Riverside Stadium Catering
446.12500		NFM	Mitcham	Aquatreat Chemical Services Ltd.
446.12500		NFM	Nationwide	Debenhams Department Store Security
446.12500		NFM	Nottingham	Debenhams Department Store Security
446.12500		NFM	Romford	Shopping Centre Security

Base	Mobile	Mode	Location	User and Notes
446.12500		NFM	Romford	Debenhams Department Store Security
446.12500		NFM	Sheffield	B&Q Superstore, Queens Road
446.12500		NFM	Stapeley	Stapeley Water Gardens
446.12500		NFM	Stirling	Debenhams Department Store Security
446.13750		NFM	Belfast	Makro Security
446.13750		NFM	Birmingham	Digbeth Coach Station (67)
446.13750		NFM	London	City Airport Security/Crash/Ops. Ch.5 (218.1)
446.13750		NFM	London	Ecco Cold Store Ltd., Hornsey
446.13750		NFM	London	Funland Amusements Trocadero Centre, Piccadilly (127.3)
446.13750		NFM	London	Institute for Medical Research, Mill Hill
446.13750		NFM	London	Saw Mill, Hither Green
446.13750		NFM	London	Securiplan Security, Buckingham Palace Road (67)
446.13750		NFM	London	St. Mary's Hospital, Paddington
446.13750		NFM	Norbiton	Coombe Hill Golf Course
446.13750		NFM	Peterborough	Faith Nightclub (114.8)
446.13750		NFM	Peterborough	Quo Vadis Nightclub (114.8)
446.13750		NFM	Stevenage	Lister Hospital Security
446.15000		NFM	Duxford	Imperial War Museum Military Vehicle Collection (118.8)
446.15000		NFM	Guildford	Woolworths (156.7)
446.15000		NFM	London	British Medical Association, Tavistock Square
446.15000		NFM	London	Gap Clothes Store, Brompton Road (123)
446.15000		NFM	London	Gap Kids Clothes Store, Regent Street (114.8)
446.15000		NFM	London	Hilton Hotel Security, Park Lane
446.15000		NFM	London	Home Office, SW1
446.15000		NFM	London	Northern Trust Ltd. Security/Staff, City of London
446.15000		NFM	London	Sports Ground, Bethnal Green
446.15000		NFM	London	The Terrence Macmillan Stadium, Newham
446.15000		NFM	London	Wellington Hospital, NW8 (192.8)
446.15000		NFM	Romford	Old Church Hospital
446.16250		NFM	Cambridge	Magistrates Court Security
446.16250		NFM	Dagenham	Becontree Heath School
446.16250		NFM	Felixstowe	Docks
446.16250		NFM	Ipswich	Regent Theatre (103.5)
446.16250		NFM	London	Chelsea Football Club, Fulham
446.16250		NFM	London	Clarence House
446.16250		NFM	London	Gap Clothes Store, Notting Hill
446.16250		NFM	London	Gap Clothes Store, Plaza Centre, Oxford Street (110.9)
446.16250		NFM	Warrington	Ineos Silicas (67)
446.17500		NFM	Birmingham	Shenley Court Art College & Sixth Form Centre
446.17500		NFM	Carlisle	TK Maxx Security
446.17500		NFM	Denham	Broadwater Park, North Orbital Road
446.17500		NFM	Eastbourne	TJ Hughes Discount Store (88.5)
446.17500		NFM	Hull	Riverside Shopping Centre Security
446.17500		NFM	Liverpool	Rapid DIY Store (103.5)
446.17500		NFM	London	Australia House Staff/Security, Aldwych
446.17500		NFM	London	Bacons College, SE16
446.17500		NFM	London	HM Revenue & Customs, Aldwych
446.17500		NFM	London	Lewisham Hospital
446.17500		NFM	London	Marlborough House
446.17500		NFM	London	St. Andrews Hospital, Bromley by Bow
446.17500		NFM	London	St. Thomas Hospital, Waterloo
446.17500		NFM	Neath	B & Q Store (114.8)
446.17500		NFM	Redcar	British Steel
446.17500		NFM	Surbiton	Golf Club
446.17500		NFM	Uxbridge	Brunel University
446.18750		NFM	Belfast	Kennedy Shopping Centre (88.5)

Base	Mobile	Mode	Location	User and Notes
446.18750		NFM	Blackpool	B & Q Superstore, M55 J4
446.18750		NFM	Bromley	Church House Gardens
446.18750		NFM	Dagenham	Becontree School
446.18750		NFM	Limavady	Raddison Roe Park Hotel & Golf Resort
446.18750		NFM	London	Barnet College Security, Russell Lane
446.18750		NFM	London	Chelsea Football Club Stewards, Fulham
446.18750		NFM	London	Halfords Superstore, Catford
446.18750		NFM	London	Securiplan Security, Buckingham Palace Road (67)
446.18750		NFM	London	Sports Ground, Greenhithe
446.18750		NFM	London	Thames Valley University, Ealing
446.18750		NFM	London	Victoria Park, E2
446.18750		NFM	Norwich	Airport Ops.
446.18750		NFM	Thorpe Park	Theme Park Ops. (250)
446.20000		NFM	Beckenham	Bethlem Royal Hospital (Originally Bedlam)
446.20000		NFM	Bristol	Avonmouth Docks (107.2)
446.20000		NFM	Cardiff	B & Q Store, Hadfield Road
446.20000		NFM	Dartford	Joyce Green Hospital
446.20000		NFM	Edinburgh	Virgin Record Shop Security
446.20000		NFM	London	BBC Ealing Studios Security
446.20000		NFM	London	Commonwealth Institute, Kensington
446.20000		NFM	London	Gap Clothes Store, Putney
446.20000		NFM	London	Marks & Spencer, Oxford Street
446.20000		NFM	London	Maudsley Hospital Security, SE5
446.20000		NFM	London	Rail Depot Security, Battersea
446.21250		NFM	Birmingham	Go Karting Track
446.21250		NFM	Cardiff	UGC Cinema (77)
446.21250		NFM	Carshalton	Sutton Hospital
446.21250		NFM	Dagenham	Old Park School
446.21250		NFM	Edinburgh	Virgin Rail Customer Service Staff
446.21250		NFM	Felixstowe	Docks Haulage Cranes Data
446.21250		NFM	Gosport	Campers & Nicholsons Boat Yard
446.21250		NFM	London	Centre Court Shopping Centre, Wimbledon
446.21250		NFM	London	Charlton Athletic Football Ground
446.21250		NFM	London	Gap Clothes Store, Notting Hill
446.21250		NFM	London	St. Katherines Dock Services, Wapping
446.21250		NFM	London	St. Paul's School, SW13
446.21250		NFM	Manchester	The Triangle, Hanging Ditch Retail Park Security(167.9)
446.21250		NFM	Silverstone	Daytona Karting
446.22500		NFM	Cardiff	Millennium Stadium Security/Maintenance (94.8)
446.22500		NFM	Coventry	Council Offices (67)
446.22500		NFM	Croydon	Woodcote Green School
446.22500		NFM	Heathrow	Transfer Buses (DCS 072)
446.22500		NFM	London	Gap Clothes Store Security, Oxford Street (156.7)
446.22500		NFM	London	Hendon Town Hall
446.22500		NFM	London	Kingston University School
446.22500		NFM	London	Lambeth Sportsman Hostel, Vauxhall
446.22500		NFM	London	Lewisham Shopping Centre
446.22500		NFM	London	Moorfield's Eye Hospital, Old Street
446.22500		NFM	London	Natural History Museum, South Kensington
446.22500		NFM	London	Rayners Lane Sports Ground
446.22500		NFM	London	Royal Festival Hall, Southbank (210.7)
446.22500		NFM	Manchester	Airport Ops
446.22500		NFM	Northwich	Anderton Boat Lift (118.8)
446.22500		NFM	Southend on Sea	Top Shop (131.8)
446.23750		NFM	Brentford	T Holloway & Sons
446.23750		NFM	Coventry	City Sports Centre

Base	Mobile	Mode	Location	User and Notes
446.23750		NFM	London	Apollo Theatre, Victoria
446.23750		NFM	London	Buckingham Palace Staff Trunked Network
446.23750		NFM	London	Burlington Arcade Security, Piccadilly
446.23750		NFM	London	Carling Apollo Theatre Front of House, Hammersmith
446.23750		NFM	London	Central London Mosque, Regents Park (225)
446.23750		NFM	London	Dickens & Jones Staff Net
446.23750		NFM	London	Marble Arch Hotel
446.23750		NFM	London	Royal Academy of Dramatic Arts Security, Gower Street
446.23750		NFM	London	Sterling Food Vendors, Hyde Park (179.9)
446.23750		NFM	London	Sterling Food Vendors, St James Park (179.9)
446.25000		NFM	Dagenham	Becontree Heath Park
446.25000		NFM	Enfield	Palace Garden Shopping Centre
446.25000		NFM	Erith	Erith College of Technology
446.25000		NFM	Felixstowe	Docks
446.25000		NFM	Gatwick	Thomas Cook
446.25000		NFM	Heathrow	Holiday Inn Hotel
446.25000		NFM	Leicestershire	Council Park Rangers Ch.1 (156.7)
446.25000		NFM	Leicestershire	Council Park Rangers Ch.2 (DCS 122)
446.25000		NFM	London	Boots, Wood Green Shopping Centre
446.25000		NFM	London	Central Middlesex Hospital, Acton
446.25000		NFM	London	Greenwich District Hospital
446.25000		NFM	London	Marks & Spencer, Marble Arch
446.25000		NFM	London	Royal Albert Hall Catering
446.25000		NFM	London	Trinity Hospice, Clapham
446.25000		NFM	London	Virgin Megastore, Oxford St
446.25000		NFM	London	Whipps Cross Hospital, Walthamstow
446.25000		NFM	Manchester	UCI Cinema, Trafford
446.26250		NFM	Cardiff	Millennium Stadium Catering
446.26250		NFM	Dagenham	Ford Motors
446.26250		NFM	Dartford	River Crossing
446.26250		NFM	Edinburgh	Shopwatch, Craigleith
446.26250		NFM	Felixstowe	Docks Haulage Cranes Data
446.26250		NFM	London	Gloucester Hotel Security, SW5
446.26250		NFM	London	Hilton Hotel Staff, Park Lane
446.26250		NFM	London	Hither Green Saw Mill
446.26250		NFM	London	Royal Albert Hall Front of House
446.26250		NFM	London	University College Hospital
446.26250		NFM	Norwich	Norwich Airport
446.26250		NFM	Rickmansworth	Mount Vernon Hospital
446.27500		NFM	Carshalton	Biological Research Labs.
446.27500		NFM	Croydon	Shirley Oaks Hospital
446.27500		NFM	Liverpool	Lime Street Station Staff
446.27500		NFM	London	Buckingham Palace Gardeners
446.27500		NFM	London	Charlton Athletic Football Club, Woolwich
446.27500		NFM	London	Gloucester Hotel, SW5
446.27500		NFM	London	Kentish Town School
446.27500		NFM	London	Tate Gallery Security (127.3)
446.27500		NFM	London	Teikoku Oil Co. Ltd., Piccadilly
446.27500		NFM	Newcastle	Ikon Nightclub Security (88.5)
446.27500		NFM	Norbiton	Kingston Hospital Engineering
446.28750		NFM	Birmingham	Gap Clothes Store
446.28750		NFM	Croydon	Home Office Immigration, Lunar House
446.28750		NFM	Dartford	Dart Ferries
446.28750		NFM	Felixstowe	Docks (192.8)
446.28750		NFM	Gloucester	Eastgate Shopping Centre Cleaners
446.28750		NFM	Heathrow	Car Rental/Parking

Base	Mobile	Mode	Location	User and Notes
446.28750		NFM	Ipswich	Boots
446.28750		NFM	London	Copthall Sports Centre, NW4
446.28750		NFM	London	Enfield Council
446.28750		NFM	London	Gap Clothes Store, Covent Garden (103.5)
446.28750		NFM	London	Home Office Security, Queen Anne's Gate
446.28750		NFM	London	Rainforest Cafe Ch.2, Piccadilly (173)
446.28750		NFM	London	The Mall Galleries, The Mall SW1
446.28750		NFM	London	Tower Bridge Security (251.4)
446.28750		NFM	London	West Middlesex University Hospital, Isleworth
446.28750		NFM	Staines	Elmsleigh Shopping Centre Security
446.30000		NFM	Brentford	T Holloway & Sons
446.30000		NFM	Epson	Mounthill Gardens
446.30000		NFM	Felixstowe	Docks
446.30000		NFM	London	Central Criminal Court, Old Bailey
446.30000		NFM	London	Harris City Technology College, Norwood
446.30000		NFM	London	Royal Festival Hall, Southbank (241.8)
446.30000		NFM	London	University College, Gower Street
446.30000		NFM	London	Wormholt Park Swimming Pool Security, W12
446.31250		NFM	London	Fenwicks Store Security/Staff, Bond Street (162.2)
446.31250		NFM	London	Gap Clothes Store Staff, Regent Street (151.4)
446.31250		NFM	London	Government Transport Depot, SW8
446.31250		NFM	London	Southside Shopping Centre Security, Wandsworth
446.31250		NFM	London	Waltham Forest College, Walthamstow
446.32500		NFM	Birmingham	Bhs Store
446.32500		NFM	Erith	Europa Trading Estate Security
446.32500		NFM	Ipswich	Docks Ch.6 Engineering (94.8)
446.32500		NFM	London	Bloomsbury Crest Hotel, WCl
446.32500		NFM	London	London Underground Arnos Grove
446.32500		NFM	London	London Underground Oakwood
446.32500		NFM	London	London Underground All Stations Ch.6
446.32500		NFM	London	Southfields School, SW13
446.32500		NFM	London	Tate Gallery Security
446.33700		NFM	Barnet	Ravenscroft School
446.33750		NFM	Hounslow	Brinks Mat Cash in Transit Base
446.33750		NFM	London	25 Cannon Bridge Securiplan Security/Staff
446.33750		NFM	London	BBC TV Centre, White City
446.33750		NFM	London	Buckingham Palace Staff Trunked Network
446.33750		NFM	London	London Underground White City Stores
446.33750		NFM	London	London University, New Kent Road
446.33750		NFM	London	Nags Head Shopping Centre, Holloway
446.33750		NFM	London	Rainforest Cafe Ch.1, Piccadilly (172)
446.33750		NFM	London	Rothschilds Bank Security, EC4
446.33750		NFM	London	Royal College of Physicians, NW1
446.33750		NFM	London	Standard Bank Security, EC4
446.33750		NFM	Sevenoaks	Highlands Farm, Hextable
446.35000		NFM	Byfleet	Brooklands Museum of Transport
446.35000		NFM	Carshalton	Westcroft Leisure
446.35000		NFM	London	Club Caterers, City of London EC3
446.35000		NFM	London	Gap Clothes Store, Oxford Street (146.2)
446.35000		NFM	London	University of Greenwich, Avery Hill
446.35000		NFM	North Cheam	Sports Centre
446.35000		NFM	Redbridge	Sports Centre
446.35000		NFM	West Drayton	Car Park Attendants
446.36250		NFM	Felixstowe	Docks (173.8)
446.36250		NFM	Guildford	Friary Shopping Centre Security
446.36250		NFM	London	Public Health Labs (Defender), Colindale

Base	Mobile	Mode	Location	User and Notes
446.36250		NFM	London	Globe Theatre Staff/Security, Southwark
446.36250		NFM	London	Capel Manor Gardens, Enfield
446.36250		NFM	London	Equinox Discotheque, Leicester Square
446.36250		NFM	Sunderland	Winter Gardens
446.37500		NFM	Addington	Addington Court Golf Club
446.37500		NFM	London	BBC Radio Security, Langham Place
446.37500		NFM	London	Bern Shopping Centre, Gt. Russell Street
446.37500		NFM	London	Brunswick Shopping Centre
446.37500		NFM	London	Museum of London Security, Barbican
446.37500		NFM	London	N1 Shopping Centre Security (241.8)
446.37500		NFM	London	National Institute for Medical Research, Mill Hill
446.37500		NFM	London	Parking Enforcement, Walthamstow
446.37500		NFM	London	Shopwatch, Hounslow
446.37500		NFM	London	St. Michael Convent School, Streatham
446.37500		NFM	London	Woolwich Arsenal Education
446.37500		NFM	Sheffield	TK Maxx, Orchard Square Shopping Centre
446.37500		NFM	Sutton	Civic Centre
446.37500		NFM	Uxbridge	Civic Centre
446.37500		NFM	Weybridge	Warren Pond Engineering
446.38750		NFM	Derbyshire, NE	Council Ranger Service (Ranger)
446.38750		NFM	London	Buckingham Palace Staff Trunked Network
446.38750		NFM	London	Crown Estates Office, Carlton House Terrace
446.38750		NFM	London	Gap Clothes Store, Piccadilly Circus (156.7)
446.38750		NFM	London	Gt. Ormond Street Hospital for Sick Children
446.38750		NFM	Newport, Gwent	DSS Staff/Security, Kingsway Centre (94.8)
446.38750		NFM	Northampton	Royal Mail Distribution Centre (110.9)
446.38750		NFM	Purfleet	Vopak Gas Works (71.9)
446.38750		NFM	Stoke	Midland Storage Security
446.40000		NFM	Coventry	Ikea Furniture Security & Car Parking
446.40000		NFM	Coventry	West Orchard Shopping Centre Security
446.40000		NFM	Fairlop	Barnardos Village Security
446.40000		NFM	Hartlepool	Port Control
446.40000		NFM	London	Chelsea College of Art & Design (233)
446.40000		NFM	London	Gap Clothes Store Staff, Marble Arch
446.40000		NFM	London	Islington Conference Centre
446.40000		NFM	London	Lords Cricket Ground
446.40000		NFM	London	London Underground Cockfosters
446.40000		NFM	London	London Underground Northfields
446.40000		NFM	London	London Underground All Stations Ch.7
446.40000		NFM	London	Sugar Reef Nightclub, Windmill Street (127.3)
446.40000		NFM	London	Queens Club Tennis Security
446.40000		NFM	London	Thames Flood Barrier, Woolwich

446.4250 - 447.5500 MHz   Broadcasting Links

Base	Mobile	Mode	Location	User and Notes
446.42500		NFM	Nationwide	JFMG O/B Links Within M25 Area
446.43125		NFM	Nationwide	JFMG Programme Making/Special Events
446.44375		NFM	Nationwide	JFMG Programme Making/Special Events
446.45625		NFM	Nationwide	JFMG Programme Making/Special Events
446.45625		NFM	Rockingham	ASCAR (2004) Colin White CWS Car 78
446.46875		NFM	Nationwide	JFMG Programme Making/Special Events
446.47500		NFM	Nationwide	JFMG Programme Making/Special Events
446.47500		NFM	Nationwide	Sky TV O/B
446.48125		NFM	Nationwide	JFMG Programme Making/Special Events
446.49375		NFM	Nationwide	JFMG Programme Making/Special Events
446.50625		NFM	Nationwide	JFMG Programme Making/Special Events
446.51250		NFM	Nationwide	JFMG O/B Links Within M25 Area
446.51250		NFM	Nationwide	JFMG Temp Point-Point/Simplex/Talkback

Base	Mobile	Mode	Location	User and Notes
446.51875		NFM	Nationwide	JFMG Programme Making/Special Events
446.52500		NFM	Suffolk	BBC Radio Suffolk O/B
446.53125		NFM	Nationwide	JFMG Programme Making/Special Events
446.54375		NFM	Nationwide	JFMG Programme Making/Special Events
446.55625		NFM	Nationwide	JFMG Programme Making/Special Events
446.56250		NFM	Essex	BBC Radio Essex Links
446.56250		NFM	London	BBC Grandstand Sound Gallery
446.56875		NFM	Nationwide	JFMG Programme Making/Special Events
446.58125		NFM	Nationwide	JFMG Programme Making/Special Events
446.59375		NFM	Nationwide	JFMG Programme Making/Special Events
446.60625		NFM	Nationwide	JFMG Programme Making/Special Events
446.60625		NFM	Nationwide	JFMG Programme Making/Special Events
446.60625		NFM	Nationwide	Sky TV O/B
446.61250		NFM	Nationwide	Sky TV O/B
446.61875		NFM	Nationwide	JFMG Programme Making/Special Events
446.63125		NFM	Nationwide	JFMG Programme Making/Special Events
446.63750		NFM	Dover	Seafrance Ferries Non UK Licensed Radios
446.63750		WFM	Lincolnshire	BBC Radio Lincs O/B Car to Studio
446.63750		NFM	Nationwide	BBC Local Radio Talkback
446.63750		NFM	Nottinghamshire	Radio Nottingham O/B
446.63750		NFM	Stoke on Trent	Radio Stoke O/B
446.64375		NFM	Nationwide	JFMG Programme Making/Special Events
446.65625		NFM	Nationwide	JFMG Programme Making/Special Events
446.66875		NFM	Nationwide	JFMG Programme Making/Special Events
446.68125		NFM	Nationwide	JFMG Programme Making/Special Events
446.68750		NFM	Essex	BBC Radio Essex O/B
446.68750		NFM	Nationwide	BBC Radio Five Live
446.68750		NFM	Nationwide	BBC TV O/B
446.68750		NFM	Nationwide	BBC TV O/B For Grandstand
446.73750		NFM	Gloucestershire	BBC Radio Gloucestershire
446.73750		NFM	London	Greater London Radio Talkback
446.73750		NFM	Manchester	BBC GMR O/B
446.73750		NFM	Nationwide	BBC Local Radio Talkback
446.78750		NFM	Belfry	BBC Radio 5 Live (Ryder Cup)
446.78750		NFM	Cambridgeshire	BBC Radio Cambridgeshire O/B
446.78750		NFM	Kent	BBC Radio Kent O/B
446.78750		NFM	Kent	BBC Radio O/B
446.78750		NFM	London	BBC Radio 5 Live Talkback
446.83750		NFM	Derbyshire	Radio Derby O/B
446.83750		NFM	Nationwide	BBC Local Radio Talkback
446.85000		NFM	Kent	BBC Radio O/B
446.90000		NFM	London	Post Office (Euston)
446.93750		NFM	Essex	BBC Radio Essex O/B
446.93750		NFM	Leicester	BBC Radio Leicester Link
446.93750		NFM	Nationwide	BBC Local Radio O/B Use
446.93750		NFM	Sheffield	BBC Radio Sheffield
446.95000		NFM	London	London Underground, Holborn Station
446.95000		NFM	Nationwide	French RPS Ch.1 - Often Used Illegally in UK
446.97500		NFM	Nationwide	French RPS Ch.2 - Often Used Illegally in UK
446.98750		NFM	Nationwide	French RPS Ch.3 - Often Used Illegally in UK
447.00000		NFM	Silverstone	Japanese TV Talkback
447.01875		NFM	Nationwide	JFMG Programme Making/Special Events
447.01875		NFM	Nationwide	JFMG TV News Assignment
447.02500		NFM	London	LWT Engineering, Southbank
447.03125		NFM	Nationwide	JFMG Programme Making/Special Events
447.03125		NFM	Nationwide	JFMG TV News Assignment
447.04375		NFM	Nationwide	JFMG Programme Making/Special Events

Base	Mobile	Mode	Location	User and Notes
447.04375		NFM	Nationwide	JFMG TV News Assignment
447.05000		NFM	London	LWT Studio (This Morning), Southbank
447.05625		NFM	Nationwide	JFMG Programme Making/Special Events
447.05625		NFM	Nationwide	JFMG TV News Assignment
447.06875		NFM	Nationwide	JFMG Programme Making/Special Events
447.08125		NFM	Nationwide	JFMG Programme Making/Special Events
447.08750		NFM	Birmingham	96.4 FM BRMB/Xtra O/B
447.08750		NFM	Hull	Viking Radio O/B
447.08750		NFM	London	Capital Radio Gold O/B
447.08750		NFM	Nationwide	Independent Local Radio Ch.E1
447.08750		NFM	Peterborough	Hereward Radio O/B Car
447.08750		NFM	Stoke on Trent	Signal Radio O/B
447.08920		NFM	London	Independent Radio Talkback
447.09375		NFM	Nationwide	JFMG Programme Making/Special Events
447.10625		NFM	Nationwide	JFMG Programme Making/Special Events
447.11875		NFM	Nationwide	JFMG Programme Making/Special Events
447.12500		NFM	London	LWT Engineering, Southbank
447.13125		NFM	Nationwide	JFMG Programme Making/Special Events
447.13750		NFM	Nationwide	Independent Local Radio Ch.E2
447.14375		NFM	Nationwide	JFMG Programme Making/Special Events
447.15625		NFM	Nationwide	JFMG Programme Making/Special Events
447.16875		NFM	Nationwide	JFMG Programme Making/Special Events
447.17500		NFM	Midlands	BRMB Radio O/B
447.18750		NFM	Blackpool	Radio Wave O/B
447.18750		NFM	Hull	Viking Radio O/B
447.18750		NFM	London	Capital FM O/B & Studio Link
447.18750		NFM	Manchester	Piccadilly Radio Talkback
447.18750		NFM	Nationwide	Independent Local Radio Ch.E3
447.18750		NFM	Stoke on Trent	Signal Radio O/B
447.19375		NFM	Nationwide	JFMG Programme Making/Special Events
447.20000		NFM	Blackpool	Radio Wave O/B
447.20000		NFM	London	Capital FM O/B
447.20625		NFM	London	ITN News Feed
447.21875		NFM	Nationwide	JFMG Programme Making/Special Events
447.22500		NFM	Nationwide	JFMG Programme Making/Special Events
447.23125		NFM	Nationwide	JFMG Programme Making/Special Events
447.23750		NFM	Coventry	Mercia Radio O/B Car
447.23750		NFM	Manchester	Piccadilly Radio Studio Link
447.23750		NFM	Nationwide	Independent Local Radio Ch.E4
447.23750		NFM	Salisbury	Spire FM
447.24375		NFM	Nationwide	JFMG Programme Making/Special Events
447.25625		NFM	London	Capital FM O/B
447.25625		NFM	Nationwide	JFMG Programme Making/Special Events
447.26875		NFM	Nationwide	JFMG Programme Making/Special Events
447.28125		NFM	Nationwide	JFMG Programme Making/Special Events
447.28750		NFM	Nationwide	Independent Local Radio Ch.E5
447.28750		NFM	Preston	Red Rose Talkback
447.29375		NFM	Nationwide	JFMG Programme Making/Special Events
447.30625		NFM	Nationwide	JFMG Programme Making/Special Events
447.31875		NFM	Nationwide	JFMG Programme Making/Special Events
447.33125		NFM	Nationwide	JFMG Programme Making/Special Events
447.33125		NFM	Newmarket	Q103 Radio O/B
447.33125		NFM	Winchester	Win FM Link
447.33750		NFM	Birmingham	Buzz FM O/B
447.33750		NFM	Liverpool	Radio City Talkback
447.33750		NFM	Nationwide	Independent Local Radio Ch.E6

Base	Mobile	Mode	Location	User and Notes
447.34375		NFM	Nationwide	JFMG Programme Making/Special Events
447.35625		NFM	Nationwide	JFMG Programme Making/Special Events
447.36875		NFM	Nationwide	JFMG Programme Making/Special Events
447.36875		NFM	Nationwide	JFMG TV News Assignment
447.38125		NFM	Nationwide	JFMG Programme Making/Special Events
447.38125		NFM	Nationwide	JFMG TV News Assignment
447.38750		NFM	Nationwide	JFMG Programme Making/Special Events
447.39375		NFM	London	LWT Engineering, Southbank
447.39375		NFM	London	LWT Studio, Southbank
447.39375		NFM	Nationwide	JFMG Programme Making/Special Events
447.39375		NFM	Nationwide	JFMG TV News Assignment
447.40625		NFM	Nationwide	JFMG Programme Making/Special Events
447.40625		NFM	Nationwide	JFMG TV News Assignment
447.40625		NFM	Nationwide	Samuelson Film Productions (186.2)
447.40625		NFM	Rockingham	ASCAR (2004) John Steward Steward Racing Car 75
447.41875		NFM	London	ITN
447.41875		NFM	Nationwide	JFMG Programme Making/Special Events
447.41875		NFM	Nationwide	JFMG TV News Assignment
447.41875		NFM	Nationwide	Sky TV O/B
447.42500		NFM	London	ITV Camera Link
447.42500		NFM	London	LWT O/B Link
447.42500		NFM	Yorkshire	Yorkshire Television
447.43125		NFM	Nationwide	JFMG Programme Making/Special Events
447.43125		NFM	Nationwide	JFMG TV News Assignment
447.43125		NFM	Rockingham	ASCAR (2004) John Mickel Torquespeed Car 66
447.43750		NFM	Leeds	Yorkshire TV O/B
447.44375		NFM	Nationwide	JFMG Programme Making/Special Events
447.44375		NFM	Nationwide	JFMG TV News Assignment
447.45625		NFM	Nationwide	JFMG Programme Making/Special Events
447.45625		NFM	Nationwide	JFMG TV News Assignment
447.46875		NFM	Nationwide	JFMG Programme Making/Special Events
447.46875		NFM	Nationwide	JFMG TV News Assignment
447.47500		NFM	London	LWT O/B Link
447.47500		NFM	Nationwide	JFMG Programme Making/Special Events
447.48125		NFM	Liverpool	Mersey Television Talkback
447.48125		NFM	Nationwide	JFMG Programme Making/Special Events
447.48125		NFM	Nationwide	JFMG TV News Assignment
447.48125		NFM	Nationwide	Sky TV O/B (88.5)
447.49375		NFM	Nationwide	JFMG Programme Making/Special Events
447.49375		NFM	Nationwide	JFMG TV News Assignment
447.49375		NFM	Rockingham	ASCAR (2004) Mike Luck Team 24/7 Car 7
447.50000		NFM	London	Independent Radio Talkback
447.50000		NFM	London	ITV Camera Link
447.50625		NFM	London	ITV Camera Link
447.50625		NFM	Nationwide	JFMG Programme Making/Special Events
447.50625		NFM	Nationwide	JFMG TV News Assignment
447.50625		NFM	Rockingham	ASCAR (2004) Ian McKellar Jnr Torquespeed Car 25
447.51250		NFM	Nationwide	JFMG Temporary Point-Point/Simplex/Talkback
447.52500		NFM	Merseyside	Ambulance Repeater (97.4)

447.600 - 449.975 Mhz   PMR Simplex

Base	Mobile	Mode	Location	User and Notes
447.63750		NFM	Borehamwood	Elstree Film And TV Studio Security (88.5)
447.63750		NFM	Cardiff	Ikea Furniture (118.8)
447.63750		NFM	London	Warner Bros Cinema, Kensington Court (225)
447.65000		NFM	Cardiff	Hilton Hotel Staff
447.65000		NFM	London	Footlocker Shoe Shop Security, Oxford Street

Base	Mobile	Mode	Location	User and Notes
447.65000		NFM	London	London Eye Staff (146.2)
447.65000		NFM	London	Waxy O'Connors Bar/Club Security (250)
447.65000		NFM	London	Waxy's Little Sister (250)
447.65000		NFM	Newcastle	Odeon Cinema Staff
447.65000		NFM	Torquay	Coastal Life Aviary Centre (DCS025)
447.66250		NFM	Cardiff	B&Q Store, Culverhouse Cross
447.66250		NFM	Dagenham	Ford Motor Plant
447.66250		NFM	Edinburgh	Fountain Park
447.66250		NFM	Glasgow	Buchanan Coach/Bus Station Staff (67)
447.66250		NFM	London	Habitat and Heals Security
447.66250		NFM	London	Lilywhites Sports Store, Piccadilly
447.66250		NFM	London	Warner Bros Cinema, Kensington Church Street
447.66250		NFM	Middlesbrough	Middlesbrough Football Club Car Parking
447.68750		NFM	Birmingham	New Look Shop Security
447.68750		NFM	Croydon	Home Office Immigration, Lunar House
447.68750		NFM	Hull	Hull Stadium Stewards Ch.1
447.68750		NFM	London	B&B Building Merchants, Southall
447.68750		NFM	London	Kensington Palace
447.68750		NFM	London	Keyline Building Merchants, E16
447.68750		NFM	London	Keyline Building Merchants, N13
447.68750		NFM	London	Royal Garden Hotel, Kensington (71.9)
447.68750		NFM	London	School, Catford
447.68750		NFM	London	School, Hackney
447.68750		NFM	London	School, Holloway
447.68750		NFM	London	Woolwich Council Offices
447.68750		NFM	Manchester	New Look Shop Security
447.68750		NFM	Surrey	Thorpe Leisure Park Ch.2 (179.9)
447.68750		NFM	Woodford	Woodford Trading Estate Engineering
447.71250		NFM	Brighton	Edward Street Court Security
447.71250		NFM	Bristol	Passenger Services, International Airport
447.71250		NFM	Carshalton	College
447.71250		NFM	Didcot	Tesco Distribution Depot (210.7)
447.71250		NFM	Heathrow	Car Rental/Parking (107.2)
447.71250		NFM	London	Arsenal Football Club
447.71250		NFM	London	Eltham Palace
447.71250		NFM	London	Earls Court Security (173.8)
447.71250		NFM	London	Kings College Security
447.71250		NFM	London	London Eye Customer Services (114.8)
447.71250		NFM	London	Whipps Cross Hospital, Leytonstone
447.71250		NFM	Newport	Shopwatch, Newport Retail Park
447.72500		NFM	Birmingham	Goodyear Dunlop (123)
447.72500		NFM	Heathrow	Avis Rent-A-Car Buses Ch.1 (141.3)
447.72500		NFM	London	Alfresco Catering, St. James Park
447.72500		NFM	London	Atlantis Oil & Chemical Ltd, Silvertown
447.72500		NFM	London	Camberwell Town Hall
447.72500		NFM	London	Chelsea Football Club, Fulham (77)
447.72500		NFM	London	Hilton International Hotel, NW8
447.72500		NFM	London	JD Sports Security, Oxford Circus
447.72500		NFM	London	Richmond upon Thames Athletic Grounds
447.72500		NFM	London	Royal Academy Exhibition Staff (225)
447.72500		NFM	London	Top Shop Security, Brent Cross Shopping Centre
447.72500		NFM	London	Victoria Embankment Gardens
447.72500		NFM	London	Waste Disposal Company, Wandsworth
447.72500		NFM	London	Whitechapel Hospital
447.72500		NFM	Portsmouth	P & O Pride of Portsmouth Handhelds Ch.6
447.72500		NFM	Staines	Two Rivers Retail Park Security

Base	Mobile	Mode	Location	User and Notes
447.73750		NFM	London	JD Sports Security, Oxford Circus
447.78750		NFM	Epping	North Weald Airfield Crash Net Ch.4 (210.7)
447.78750		NFM	London	Alexandra Palace
447.78750		NFM	London	Cranford Community School, Hounslow
447.78750		NFM	London	Hilton International Hotel, NW8
447.78750		NFM	London	London Underground Ch.4, Canary Wharf
447.78750		NFM	London	London Underground Engineering
447.78750		NFM	London	New Look Shop Security, Oxford Circus
447.78750		NFM.	London	Palace Gardens Estate Management, Knightsbridge
447.78750		NFM	London	Roehampton Golf Club
447.78750		NFM	London	Royal Academy
447.78750		NFM	London	School, Dartford
447.78750		NFM	London	Trocadero Centre, Piccadilly
447.78750		NFM	London	Twickenham Rugby Ground Safety/Cleaners/Parking (82.5)
447.78750		NFM	London	Victoria & Albert Museum Security
447.78750		NFM	Sheffield	Hill End Dry Ski Slope
447.78750		NFM	Surrey	Thorpe Leisure Park Ch.3 (82.5)
447.78750		NFM	Wigan	Royal Albert Edward Infirmary Car Parks Security (186.2)
447.81250		NFM	London	Baltic Exchange Security
447.81250		NFM	London	Madame Tussaud's Security
447.81250		NFM	Newport	Sovereign Arcade/Kingsway Centre Security (71.9)
447.81250		NFM	Surrey	Thorpe Park Leisure Park Ch.1 (179.9)
447.82500		NFM	Chichester	Chicago Rock Cafe Security (167.9)
447.82500		NFM	Hull	Hull Stadium Stewards Ch.2
447.82500		NFM	London	Namco Amusements, Waterloo
447.82500		NFM	Thurrock	Warner Bros, Leisure Lakeside Shopping Centre
447.87500		NFM	London	Namco Amusements
448.02500	431.02500	NFM	London	Meadway Taxi Group
448.04375	431.04375	NFM	London	London Pride Guided Tours
448.10000	431.10000	NFM	London	Meadway Taxi Group
448.12500	431.12500	NFM	Kent	PJM Vehicle Recovery
448.16875	431.16875	NFM	London	London Pride Buses
448.25625	431.25625	NFM	London	London Hilton Trunked System
448.25630	431.25630	NFM	London	Atlas Cars
448.29375	431.29375	NFM	London	The Original Bus Tour
448.31825	431.31825	NFM	London	Froebel Institute, Roehampton (206.3)
448.31880	431.31880	NFM	London	BBC Radio, Alexander Palace
448.33750	141.20000	NFM	Yorkshire	BBC Radio Yorkshire O/B Link
448.48125	431.48125	NFM	London	Parking Enforcement, Canary Wharf
448.51250		NFM	Blackpool	Grand Metropolitan Hotel
448.51250	431.51250	NFM	London	Parking Enforcement, Victoria
448.57500	431.57500	NFM	London	Rotherhithe Couriers
448.60000	431.60000	NFM	London	Parking Enforcement, Westminster
448.60625	431.60625	NFM	London	Parking Enforcement, EC (77)
448.60625	431.60625	NFM	London	Parking Enforcement, W2 (151.4)
448.68750	431.68750	NFM	London	Churchill Cars, Acton
448.78750	431.78750	NFM	London	K Cars, East Finchley
448.75000		NFM	Nationwide	Korean FRS - Often Used Illegally in the UK
448.76250		NFM	Nationwide	Korean FRS - Often Used Illegally in the UK
448.77500		NFM	Nationwide	Korean FRS - Often Used Illegally in the UK
448.78750		NFM	Nationwide	Korean FRS - Often Used Illegally in the UK
448.79375	431.79375	NFM	London	The Original Bus Tour (118.8)
448.80000		NFM	Nationwide	Korean FRS - Often Used Illegally in the UK
448.81250		NFM	Nationwide	Korean FRS - Often Used Illegally in the UK
448.82500	431.82500	NFM	London	Absolute Despatch Ltd.
448.82500		NFM	Nationwide	Korean FRS - Often Used Illegally in the UK

Base	Mobile	Mode	Location	User and Notes
448.83750		NFM	Nationwide	Korean FRS - Often Used Illegally in the UK
448.85000		NFM	Nationwide	Korean FRS - Often Used Illegally in the UK
448.86250	431.86250	NFM	London	Zebra Cars
448.86250		NFM	Nationwide	Korean FRS - Often Used Illegally in the UK
448.87500		NFM	Nationwide	Korean FRS - Often Used Illegally in the UK
448.87500	431.87500	NFM	Tunbridge	The Wells
448.88125	441.88125	NFM	Maidstone	Addington Vehicle Recovery
448.88750	431.88750	NFM	Dartford	Vehicle Recovery Garage
448.88750		NFM	Nationwide	Korean FRS - Often Used Illegally in the UK)
448.90000		NFM	Nationwide	Korean FRS - Often Used Illegally in the UK)
448.91250		NFM	Nationwide	Korean FRS - Often Used Illegally in the UK)
448.92500		NFM	Nationwide	Korean FRS - Often Used Illegally in the UK)
448.93750		NFM	Aldermaston	AWE Support Services
448.98750		NFM	Aldermaston	AWE Support Services
449.12500		NFM	Ayr	EWS Traincare Depot
449.12500		NFM	Cardiff	EWS Canton Rail Depot (107.2/82.5)
449.12500		NFM	Coventry	EWS Traincare Murcho
449.12500		NFM	Nationwide	EWS Common Channel
449.15000		NFM	Nationwide	Korean FRS - Often Used Illegally in the UK
449.16250		NFM	Nationwide	Korean FRS - Often Used Illegally in the UK
449.17500		NFM	Nationwide	Korean FRS - Often Used Illegally in the UK
449.18750		NFM	Nationwide	Korean FRS - Often Used Illegally in the UK
449.20000		NFM	Nationwide	Korean FRS - Often Used Illegally in the UK
449.21250		NFM	Nationwide	Korean FRS - Often Used Illegally in the UK
449.22500		NFM	Nationwide	Korean FRS - Often Used Illegally in the UK
449.23750	431.56875	NFM	London	Onyx Refuse, Westminster (88.5)
449.23750		NFM	Nationwide	Korean FRS - Often Used Illegally in the UK
449.25000		NFM	Nationwide	Korean FRS - Often Used Illegally in the UK
449.26250		NFM	Nationwide	Korean FRS - Often Used Illegally in the UK
449.28750		NFM	Peterborough	EWS
449.31250		NFM	Brampton	Wm Morrisons Supermarket, Cortonwood Retail Park
449.31250		NFM	Burnley	Tesco
449.31250		NFM	Cardiff	Star Cinema Complex, Millennium Plaza (74)
449.31250		NFM	Coventry	Tesco Extra
449.31250		NFM	Coventry	Wm Morrisons Supermarket Ch.1 (179.9)
449.31250		NFM	Ebbw Vale	Wm Morrisons Supermarket Ch.1
449.31250		NFM	Grimsby	Wm Morrisons Supermarket Ch.1
449.31250		NFM	Heathrow	Hotel (67)
449.31250		NFM	Hindley	Tesco, Security (123)
449.31250		NFM	Hounslow	Woolworths Staff Ch.1 (DCS 212)
449.31250		NFM	Letchworth	Woolworths Staff Ch.1 (DCS 212)
449.31250		NFM	Lichfield	TJ Hughes Discount Store
449.31250		NFM	London	HMV Security, Oxford Circus (123)
449.31250		NFM	London	HMV Security, Piccadilly (123)
449.31250		NFM	Lowestoft	Woolworths Staff Ch.1 (DCS 212)
449.31250		NFM	Morecombe	Wm Morrisons Supermarket Ch.1
449.31250		NFM	Nationwide	HMV Security
449.31250		NFM	Nationwide	Often Used By Government Agencies For Surveillance
449.31250		NFM	Nationwide	Scout Association Ch.1
449.31250		NFM	Nationwide	St John Ambulance UK General
449.31250		NFM	Nationwide	Wm Morrisons Supermarket Ch.1
449.31250		NFM	Nationwide	Woolworths In-Store Radio Ch.1 (DCS 212)
449.31250		NFM	Nelson	Wm Morrisons Supermarket Ch.1
449.31250		NFM	Newport	Baltica Bar, Stow Hill, Gwent (67)
449.31250		NFM	Northwich	Wm Morrisons Distribution Maintenance Ch.1 (179.9)
449.31250		NFM	Northwich	Wm Morrisons Distribution Management Ch.1 (DCS 565)

Base	Mobile	Mode	Location	User and Notes
449.31250		NFM	Peterborough	Bar Royal/The Park/Verve/Genevas Security Ch.1 (DCS 114)
449.31250		NFM	Peterborough	Bar Royal/The Park/Verve/Genevas Security Ch.4 (DCS 115)
449.31250		NFM	Peterborough	Bar Royal/The Park/Verve/Genevas Security Ch.7 (DCS 116)
449.31250		NFM	Stansted	Airport Customer Assistance Staff (103.5)
449.31250		NFM	Stevenage	Woolworths Staff Ch.1 (DCS 212)
449.31250		NFM	Tamworth	Wm Morrisons Supermarket Ch.1
449.31250		NFM	Watford	Woolworths Staff Ch.1 (DCS 212)
449.31250		NFM	Wattisham	Cleaners
449.31250		NFM	Wentworth	Wentworth Estate Security (218.1)
449.31250		NFM	Yeadon	Wm Morrisons Supermarket Ch.1
449.40000		NFM	Cardiff	Jurys Hotel Staff (233)
449.40000		NFM	Edinburgh	Asda, Chesser Avenue (DCS 263)
449.40000		NFM	Hounslow	Woolworths Ch.2 (DCS 243)
449.40000		NFM	Letchworth	Woolworths Management/Security Ch.2 (DCS 243)
449.40000		NFM	Lowestoft	Woolworths Management/Security Ch.2 (DCS 243)
449.40000		NFM	Nationwide	Scout Association Ch.2
449.40000		NFM	Nationwide	St John Ambulance UK General
449.40000		NFM	Nationwide	Wm Morrisons Supermarket Ch.2
449.40000		NFM	Nationwide	Woolworths In-Store RadioCh.2 (DCS 243)
449.40000		NFM	Newport	Walkabout Club, Gwent
446.40000		NFM	Northampton	Royal Mail Distribution Centre Yard Marshall (192.8)
449.40000		NFM	Northwich	Wm Morrisons Depot Maintenance Ch.2, Rudheath (177.3)
449.40000		NFM	Peterborough	Bar Royal/The Park/Verve/Genevas Security Ch.2 (DCS 114)
449.40000		NFM	Peterborough	Bar Royal/The Park/Verve/Genevas Security Ch.5 (DCS 115)
449.40000		NFM	Peterborough	Bar Royal/The Park/Verve/Genevas Security Ch.8 (DCS 116)
449.40000		NFM	Stevenage	Woolworths Management/Security Ch.2 (DCS 243)
449.40000		NFM	Watford	Woolworths Management/Security Ch.2 (DCS 243)
449.40000		NFM	Wentworth	Wentworth Estate Security (218.1)
449.47500		NFM	Aldermaston	AWE Site Bus/Escorts
449.47500		NFM	Bordon	Tesco Security/Staff
449.47500		NFM	Cardiff	Bob Martin Pet Products Warehouse Ch.2 (127.3)
449.47500		NFM	Corley	Motorway Services Staff M6
449.47500		NFM	Hounslow	Woolworths Ch.3
449.47500		NFM	Letchworth	Woolworths Ch.3
449.47500		NFM	Lowestoft	Woolworths Ch.3
449.47500		NFM	London	HMV Security, Marble Arch (123)
449.47500		NFM	Nationwide	NSR Communications Setting Up Channel
449.47500		NFM	Nationwide	St John Ambulance UK General
449.47500		NFM	Nationwide	Wm Morrisons Supermarket Ch.3
449.47500		NFM	Nationwide	Woolworths In-Store Radio Ch.3
446.47500		NFM	Northampton	Royal Mail Distribution Centre Tug Shunter (192.8)
449.47500		NFM	Northwich	Wm Morrisons Distribution Maintenance Ch.3, Rudheath
449.47500		NFM	Oxford	John Radcliffe Hospital Porters Ch.1 (110.9)
449.47500		NFM	Peterborough	Bar Royal/The Park/Verve/Genevas Security Ch.3 (DCS 114)
449.47500		NFM	Peterborough	Bar Royal/The Park/Verve/Genevas Security Ch.6 (DCS 115)
449.47500		NFM	Peterborough	Showsec Security at Events Nationwide
449.47500		NFM	Stevenage	Asda Staff Price Checking
449.47500		NFM	Stevenage	Hollywood Bowl Staff (186.2)
449.47500		NFM	Stevenage	Woolworths Ch.3
449.47500		NFM	Tamworth	Tamworth Football Club Stewards
449.47500		NFM	Watford	Woolworths Ch.3
449.47500		NFM	Yeadon	Wm Morrisons Supermarket
449.65000		NFM	Lydd	MoD Police, Lydd Army Camp
449.65000		NFM	Aldermaston	AWE Site Bus/Escorts
449.75000		NFM	Aldermaston	AWE Support Services
449.77500		NFM	Aldermaston	AWE Security Ch.4

London Metropolitan Police

This force, in common with most others, intends to change over to a secure digital TETRA system. We had thought that it would have changed by now but the new system seems to have been delayed and it looks as though the current Motorola Smartzone System will stay in use for a while longer. Smartzone is an analogue trunked radio system that uses the frequencies shown in the lists below. In normal operation, whenever an officer presses his PTT, the radio changes frequency and uses any one of the ten or so frequencies allocated to that area. Although transmissions on these frequencies can be monitored with a normal scanner, it gets a little confusing because only parts of each conversation can be heard as the transmitting radios keep changing frequency. The full conversation can only be followed by using a computer and decoder software or a dedicated trunking scanner. For more information on trunking systems see *Scanner Busters 3* or take a look at a very good web site at http://www.ukmidlandscanner.co.uk/trunked.htm.

DIVISIONS

Area 1 – Central
Belgravia (AB)
Notting Hill (BH)
Brompton (BS)
West End Central (CD)
Charing Cross (CX)
Marylebone (DM)
Paddington (DP)
Fulham (FF)
Hammersmith (FH)

Area 2 – North West
Hampstead (EH)
Kentish Town (EK)
Holburn (EO)
Holloway (NH)
Islington (NI)
Kilburn (OK)
Harrow (QA)
Wembley (QD)
Barnet & Hertsmere (SA)

Colders Green (SG)
West Hendon (SV)
Ealing (XD)
Southall (XS)
Hornsey (YR)
Tottenham (YT)

Area 3 – North East
Shoreditch & Hackney (GD)
Stoke Newington (GN)
Limehouse (HH)
Whitechapel (HT)
Barkingside (JB)
Chingford (JC)
Redbridge (JI)
Ilford (JL)
Havering (KD)
Forest Gate (KF)
Dagenham (KG)
Plaistow (KO)
Edmonton (YE)
Enfield (YF)
Ponders End (YP)

Area 4 – South East
Southwark (MD)
Peckham (MM)
Walworth (MS)
Catford (PD)
Lewisham (PL)
Bromley (PY)
Plumstead (RA)
Grenwich (RG)
Bexleyheath (RY)
Croydon (ZD)
South Norwood (ZN)
Epsom (ZP)

Area 5 – South West
Thames (CO52)
Brixton (LD)
Streatham (LS)
Vauxhall (LX)
Chiswick (TC)
Hounslow (TD)
Spelthorne (TG)
Twickenham (TW)
Kingston (VK)
Wimbledon (VW)
Battersea (WA)
Wandsworth (WW)
Hillingdon (XH)

Cell 01 East London (Inner)
Shoreditch, Stoke Newington, Limehouse, Whitechapel, Leyton, Barkingside, Chingford, Forest Gate, Plaistow

450.6500	450.2375	450.2750	450.5125	450.5875
451.7375	451.3625	451.8375	451.9375	452.8625

Cell 02 South East London (Inner)
Walworth, South Norwood, Plumstead, Bromley, Catford, Peckham, Bexleyheath, Greenwich, Southwark, Lewisham

450.1000	450.3000	450.4500	450.9875	450.3625
450.8625	451.8875	451.5875	451.8625	451.9625
452.6625	452.7125	452.8875		

Cell 03 South West London (Inner)

Streatham, Battersea, Kingston, Vauxhall, Wandsworth, Chiswick, Wimbledon, Hounslow, Peckham, Twickenham, Brixton

450.7500	450.8375	450.5750	451.7875	452.2875
452.7625	450.5375	450.6375	451.7625	450.2625
450.1875	452.5375			

Cell 04 Central London

Belgravia, Brompton, Paddington, West End Central, Hammersmith, Marylebone, Fulham, Charing Cross, Notting Hill

450.0250	450.3250	450.9250	450.0625	450.1625
451.2375	451.4375	451.4625	451.7125	452.2375
452.9125	452.9625			

Cell 05 North West London (Inner)

West Hendon, Kentish Town, Tottenham, Hornsey, Hampstead, Ealing, Wembley, Holborn, Islington, Southall, Holloway, Kilburn

450.9750	450.7000	450.8000	450.0875	450.1375
450.2125	451.0375	451.6125	451.9125	452.2625
452.4625	452.6875	452.9375		

Cell 06 North East London (Outer)

Edmonton, Enfield

450.4875	450.2375	450.3750	450.8500	450.8750
451.1500				

Cell 7 East London (Middle)

Dagenham, Barking, Ilford, Barkingside, Walthamstow

450.9000	451.0000	451.0750	450.3375	450.7750
452.3500	451.3875	452.3125		

Cell 08 East London (Outer)

Havering

451.0500	451.0250	450.7250	450.9375	450.4125

Cell 09 South East London (Outer)

Bromley, Lewisham, Bexleyheath, Greenwich

450.5500	450.6000	451.1250	452.6375	452.7375
452.4375				

Cell 10 South London (Outer)

Croydon, Epsom, South Norwood

450.4250	450.3875	450.7875	451.4500	452.6125
452.7875				

Cell 11 South West London (Outer)

Kingston

450.7250	451.0250	451.0500	450.2875	450.9375

Cell 12 West London (Outer)

Harrow, Hillingdon, Southall, Spelthrone, Twickenham, Chiswick, Hounslow, Heathrow

451.0750	451.0000	450.9000	450.7750	450.3375
452.3500	452.3125	451.1625		

Cell 13 North West London (Outer)

West Hendon, Harrow

451.1250	450.5500	450.6000	450.8250	451.0250
452.4375	452.6375			

450.0000 - 452.9750 MHz   Police Mobile & Personal Radio System (England & Wales)

The police radio system across all of the UK has changed a lot in the last few years and now most forces are in the process of moving over to Airwave, a secure digital TETRA system. Some forces make the change almost overnight and others spread it over a year or more. Most keep their UHF analogue system in place until the rollout is complete and sometimes they keep a few of their previous discrete VHF and UHF frequencies as backup even after the changeover is complete. The frequencies listed here are correct at the time of writing but are subject to change as the new system comes in. They might remain active for just a few more months but they could still be in use for several more years.

Base	Mobile	Mode	Location	User and Notes
450.02500	464.02500	NFM	Dorset	Police (QC) Ch.4 Link to 155.925
450.02500	464.02500	NFM	London	Police Smartzone Control Channel Cell 04
450.02500	464.02500	NFM	Nationwide	Police Ch.4 (Divisional)
450.02500	464.02500	NFM	Portsmouth	Police Ch.4 Special Events
450.02500	464.02500	NFM	West Midlands	Police Ch.4
450.05000	464.05000	NFM	Birmingham	Police
450.05000	450.05000	NFM	Bournemouth	Police Bournemouth Football Club
450.05000	464.05000	NFM	Coventry	Police Coventry City Football Club
450.05000	450.05000	NFM	London	Police Arsenal Football Club
450.05000	464.05000	NFM	London	Police Chelsea Football Club
450.05000	464.05000	NFM	London	Police Public Order Control Smartzone
450.05000		NFM	London	Police City of London Divisional Support Units
450.05000		NFM	Nationwide	Police Special Use Ch.77
450.05000	450.05000	NFM	Nationwide	Police CID/Special Events/Major Incidents Ch.61
450.05000		NFM	Nationwide	Special Escort Group (SEG1) (131.8)
450.05000	450.05000	NFM	Sheffield	Police Sheffield Wednesday Football Club
450.05000	464.05000	NFM	West Midlands	Police Special Use
450.05000	464.05000	NFM	Wolverhampton	Police Wolverhampton Football Club
450.06250	464.06250	NFM	London	Police Belgravia (AB) Smartzone Cell 04
450.06250	464.06250	NFM	London	Police Brompton (BS) Smartzone Cell 04
450.06250	464.06250	NFM	London	Police Charing Cross (CX) Smartzone Cell 04
450.06250	450.06250	NFM	London	Police Hammersmith (FH) Smartzone Cell 04
450.06250	464.06250	NFM	London	Police Fulham (FF) Smartzone Cell 04
450.06250	464.06250	NFM	London	Police Marylebone (DM) Smartzone Cell 04
450.06250	464.06250	NFM	London	Police Notting Hill (BH) Smartzone Cell 04
450.06250	464.06250	NFM	London	Police Paddington (DP) Smartzone Cell 04
450.06250	464.06250	NFM	London	Police West End Central (CD) Smartzone Cell 04
450.07500		NFM	Aberystwyth	Police PR Secondary
450.07500	450.07500	NFM	Birmingham	Police Aston Villa Football Club
450.07500	464.07500	NFM	Birmingham	Police Birmingham City Football Club
450.07500	450.07500	NFM	Brighton	Police Brighton & Hove Albion Football Club
450.07500	450.07500	NFM	Goodwood	Police Racecourse Security
450.07500	464.07500	NFM	London	Police Chelsea Football Club
450.07500	450.07500	NFM	London	Police Millwall Football Club
450.07500	450.07500	NFM	London	Police Tottenham Football Club
450.07500	464.07500	NFM	London	Police, Charlton Football Club
450.07500	464.07500	NFM	London	Police, Twickenham Rugby (110.9)
450.07500	464.07500	NFM	London	Police, Wimbledon Football Club (82.5)
450.07500		NFM	London	Police City of London, Special Use
450.07500	464.07500	NFM	Nationwide	Police Ch.62 CID/Special Events/Major Incidents
450.07500		NFM	Nationwide	Police Ch.78 Special Use
450.07500	450.07500	NFM	West Midlands	Police Motorway Accidents
450.08750	464.08750	NFM	London	Police Ealing (XD) Smartzone Cell 05
450.08750	464.08750	NFM	London	Police Hampstead (EH) Smartzone Cell 05
450.08750	464.08750	NFM	London	Police Holborn (EO) Smartzone Cell 05
450.08750	464.08750	NFM	London	Police Holloway (NH) Smartzone Cell 05
450.08750	464.08750	NFM	London	Police Hornsey (YR) Smartzone Cell 05

Base	Mobile	Mode	Location	User and Notes
450.08750	464.08750	NFM	London	Police Islington (NI) Smartzone Cell 05
450.08750	464.08750	NFM	London	Police Kentish Town (EK) Smartzone Cell 05
450.08750	464.08750	NFM	London	Police Kilburn (QK) Smartzone Cell 05
450.08750	464.08750	NFM	London	Police Southall (XS) Smartzone Cell 05
450.08750	464.08750	NFM	London	Police Tottenham (YT) Smartzone Cell 05
450.08750	464.08750	NFM	London	Police Wembley (QD) Smartzone Cell 05
450.08750	464.08750	NFM	London	Police West Hendon (SV) Smartzone Cell 05
450.10000	464.10000	NFM	London	Smartzone Control Channel Cell 02
450.12500	450.12500	NFM	London	Police Barnet Football Club
450.12500	464.12500	NFM	London	Police Notting Hill Carnival
450.12500	450.12500	NFM	London	Police Queens Park Rangers Football Club
450.12500		NFM	London	Police Special Escort Group (SEG2) (131.8)
450.12500	450.12500	NFM	London	Police West Ham Football Club
450.12500	464.12500	NFM	London	Police Special Use (Hotel Raids, Kensington)
450.12500	464.12500	NFM	Maidstone	Crown Court
450.12500	464.12500	NFM	Nationwide	Police CID/ Special Events/Major Incidents Ch.63
450.12500		NFM	Nationwide	Police Special Use Ch.79
450.13750	464.13750	NFM	London	Police Ealing (XD) Smartzone Cell 05
450.13750	464.13750	NFM	London	Police Hampstead (EH) Smartzone Cell 05
450.13750	464.13750	NFM	London	Police Holborn (EO) Smartzone Cell 05
450.13750	464.13750	NFM	London	Police Holloway (NH) Smartzone Cell 05
450.13750	464.13750	NFM	London	Police Hornsey (YR) Smartzone Cell 05
450.13750	464.13750	NFM	London	Police Islington (NI) Smartzone Cell 05
450.13750	464.13750	NFM	London	Police Kentish Town (EK) Smartzone Cell 05
450.13750	464.13750	NFM	London	Police Kilburn (QK) Smartzone Cell 05
450.13750	464.13750	NFM	London	Police Southall (XS) Smartzone Cell 05
450.13750	464.13750	NFM	London	Police Tottenham (YT) Smartzone Cell 05
450.13750	464.13750	NFM	London	Police Wembley (QD) Smartzone Cell 05
450.13750	464.13750	NFM	London	Police West Hendon (SV) Smartzone Cell 05
450.15000	464.15000	NFM	Goodwood	Racecourse Secondary Channel
450.15000	464.15000	NFM	London	Police Charlton Football Club
450.15000	464.15000	NFM	London	Police Crystal Palace Football Club
450.15000	464.15000	NFM	Nationwide	Police CID/Special Events/Major Incidents Ch.64
450.15000		NFM	Nationwide	Police Special Use Ch.80
450.16250	464.16250	NFM	London	Police Belgravia (AB) Smartzone Cell 04
450.16250	464.16250	NFM	London	Police Brompton (BS) Smartzone Cell 04
450.16250	464.16250	NFM	London	Police Charing Cross (CX) Smartzone Cell 04
450.16250	464.16250	NFM	London	Police Fulham (FF) Smartzone Cell 04
450.16250	464.16250	NFM	London	Police Hammersmith (FH) Smartzone Cell 04
450.16250	464.16250	NFM	London	Police Marylebone (DM) Smartzone Cell 04
450.16250	464.16250	NFM	London	Police Notting Hill (BH) Smartzone Cell 04
450.16250	464.16250	NFM	London	Police Paddington (DP) Smartzone Cell 04
450.16250	464.16250	NFM	London	Police West End Central (CD) Smartzone Cell 04
450.17500	464.17500	NFM	London	Police Barnett Football Club
450.17500	464.17500	NFM	London	Police Arsenal Football Club
450.17500	464.17500	NFM	London	Police Chelsea Football Club
450.17500	464.17500	NFM	London	Police Fulham Football Club
450.17500	464.17500	NFM	London	Mounted Police
450.17500		NFM	London	Special Escort Group (SEG3) (131.8)
450.17500	464.17500	NFM	London	Police Notting Hill Carnival
450.17500	464.17500	NFM	Nationwide	Police CID/ Special Events/Major Incidents Ch.65
450.17500		NFM	Nationwide	Police Special Use Ch.81
450.17500	464.17500	NFM	Manchester	Police, Ordsall
450.17500	464.17500	NFM	West Midlands	Police Ch.65 (Firearms Use)
450.18750	464.18750	NFM	London	Police Brixton (LD) Smartzone Cell 03
450.18750	464.18750	NFM	London	Police Battersea (WA) Smartzone Cell 03

Base	Mobile	Mode	Location	User and Notes
450.18750	464.18750	NFM	London	Police Chiswick (TC) Smartzone Cell 03
450.18750	464.18750	NFM	London	Police Hounslow (TD) Smartzone Cell 03
450.18750	464.18750	NFM	London	Police Kingston (VK) Smartzone Cell 03
450.18750	464.18750	NFM	London	Police Peckham (MM) Smartzone Cell 03
450.18750	464.18750	NFM	London	Police Streatham (LS) Smartzone Cell 03
450.18750	464.18750	NFM	London	Police Twickenham (TW) Smartzone Cell 03
450.18750	464.18750	NFM	London	Police Vauxhall (LX) Smartzone Cell 03
450.18750	464.18750	NFM	London	Police Wandsworth (WW) Smartzone Cell 03
450.18750	464.18750	NFM	London	Police Wimbledon (VW) Smartzone Cell 03
450.20000	464.20000	NFM	Gillingham	Police Gillingham Football Club
450.20000	464.20000	NFM	Ipswich	Police Ipswich Football Club
450.20000	464.20000	NFM	London	Police Millwall Football Club
450.20000	464.20000	NFM	London	Police Tottenham Hotspur Football Club
450.20000	464.20000	NFM	Nationwide	Police CID/Special Events/Major Incidents Ch.66
450.20000		NFM	Nationwide	Police Special Use Ch.82
450.20000	464.20000	NFM	Portsmouth	Police Portsmouth Football Club
450.20000	464.20000	NFM	Windsor	Police Windsor Castle Daily Parades
450.21250	464.21250	NFM	London	Police Ealing (XD) Smartzone Cell 05
450.21250	464.21250	NFM	London	Police Hampstead (EH) Smartzone Cell 05
450.21250	464.21250	NFM	London	Police Holborn (EO) Smartzone Cell 05
450.21250	464.21250	NFM	London	Police Holloway (NH) Smartzone Cell 05
450.21250	464.21250	NFM	London	Police Hornsey (YR) Smartzone Cell 05
450.21250	464.21250	NFM	London	Police Islington (NI) Smartzone Cell 05
450.21250	464.21250	NFM	London	Police Kentish Town (EK) Smartzone Cell 05
450.21250	464.21250	NFM	London	Police Kilburn (QK) Smartzone Cell 05
450.21250	464.21250	NFM	London	Police Southall (XS) Smartzone Cell 05
450.21250	464.21250	NFM	London	Police Tottenham (YT) Smartzone Cell 05
450.21250	464.21250	NFM	London	Police Wembley (QD) Smartzone Cell 05
450.21250	464.21250	NFM	London	Police West Hendon (SV) Smartzone Cell 05
450.22500	464.22500	NFM	London	Police Chelsea Football Club
450.22500	464.22500	NFM	London	Police Crystal Palace Football Club
450.22500	464.22500	NFM	London	Police West Ham Football Club
450.22500	464.22500	NFM	Nationwide	Police CID/Special Events/Major Incidents Ch.67
450.22500		NFM	Nationwide	Police Special Use Ch.83
450.22500	464.22500	NFM	Southampton	Police Southampton Football Club
450.22500	464.22500	NFM	West Midlands	Police Aston Villa Football Club
450.23750	464.23750	NFM	London	Police Edmonton (YE) Smartzone Cell 06
450.23750	464.23750	NFM	London	Police Enfield (YF) Smartzone Cell 06
450.25000	464.25000	NFM	Halifax	Police (FA)
450.25000	464.25000	NFM	London	Police Crystal Palace Football Club
450.25000	464.25000	NFM	London	Police Special Use
450.25000	464.25000	NFM	Nationwide	Police CID/Special Events/Major Incidents Ch.68
450.25000		NFM	Nationwide	Police Special Use Ch.84
450.25000	464.25000	NFM	Norwich	Police Norwich City Football Club
450.25000	464.25000	NFM	Plymouth	Police Football Control
450.26250	464.26250	NFM	London	Police Brixton (LD) Smartzone Cell 03
450.26250	464.26250	NFM	London	Police Battersea (WA) Smartzone Cell 03
450.26250	464.26250	NFM	London	Police Chiswick (TC) Smartzone Cell 03
450.26250	464.26250	NFM	London	Police Hounslow (TD) Smartzone Cell 03
450.26250	464.26250	NFM	London	Police Kingston (VK) Smartzone Cell 03
450.26250	464.26250	NFM	London	Police Peckham (MM) Smartzone Cell 03
450.26250	464.26250	NFM	London	Police Streatham (LS) Smartzone Cell 03
450.26250	464.26250	NFM	London	Police Twickenham (TW) Smartzone Cell 03
450.26250	464.26250	NFM	London	Police Vauxhall (LX) Smartzone Cell 03
450.26250	464.26250	NFM	London	Police Wandsworth (WW) Smartzone Cell 03
450.26250	464.26250	NFM	London	Police Wimbledon (VW) Smartzone Cell 03

Base	Mobile	Mode	Location	User and Notes
450.27500	464.27500	NFM	London	Police Barkingside (JB) Smartzone Cell 01
450.27500	464.27500	NFM	London	Police Chingford (JC) Smartzone Cell 01
450.27500	464.27500	NFM	London	Police Forest Gate (KF) Smartzone Cell 01
450.27500	464.27500	NFM	London	Police Plaistow (KO) Smartzone Cell 01
450.27500	464.27500	NFM	London	Police Leyton (JL) Smartzone Cell 01
450.27500	464.27500	NFM	London	Police Limehouse (HH) Smartzone Cell 01
450.27500	464.27500	NFM	London	Police Shoreditch (GD) Smartzone Cell 01
450.27500	464.27500	NFM	London	Police Stoke Newington (GN) Smartzone Cell 01
450.27500	464.27500	NFM	London	Police Whitechapel (HT) Smartzone Cell 01
450.28750	464.28750	NFM	London	Police Kingston (VK) Smartzone Cell 11
450.28750	464.28750	NFM	Wallasey	A2 Division Ch.97
450.30000	464.30000	NFM	Liverpool	HM Prison Ashworth
450.30000	464.30000	NFM	London	Police Bexleyheath (RY) Smartzone Cell 02
450.30000	464.30000	NFM	London	Police Bromley (PY) Smartzone Cell 02
450.30000	464.30000	NFM	London	Police Catford (PD) Smartzone Cell 02
450.30000	464.30000	NFM	London	Police Greenwich (RG) Smartzone Cell 02
450.30000	464.30000	NFM	London	Police Lewisham (PL) Smartzone Cell 02
450.30000	464.30000	NFM	London	Police Peckham (MM) Smartzone Cell 02
450.30000	464.30000	NFM	London	Police Plumstead (RA) Smartzone Cell 02
450.30000	464.30000	NFM	London	Police South Norwood (ZN) Smartzone Cell 02
450.30000	464.30000	NFM	London	Police Southwark (MD) Smartzone Cell 02
450.30000	464.30000	NFM	London	Police Walworth (MS) Smartzone Cell 02
450.32500	464.32500	NFM	London	Police Smartzone Cell 04 Control Channel
450.33750	464.33750	NFM	London	Police Overload Channel (GT) Smartzone
450.33750	464.33750	NFM	London	Police Barking (KB) Smartzone Cell 07
450.33750	464.33750	NFM	London	Police Barkingside (JB) Smartzone Cell 07
450.33750	464.33750	NFM	London	Police Dagenham (KG) Smartzone Cell 07
450.33750	464.33750	NFM	London	Police Ilford (JI) Smartzone Cell 07
450.33750	464.33750	NFM	London	Police Walthamstow (JW) Smartzone Cell 07
450.33750	464.33750	NFM	London	Police Chiswick (TC) Smartzone Cell 12
450.33750	464.33750	NFM	London	Police Harrow (QA) Smartzone Cell 12
450.33750	464.33750	NFM	London	Police Heathrow (ID) Smartzone Cell 12
450.33750	464.33750	NFM	London	Police Hillingdon (XH) Smartzone Cell 12
450.33750	464.33750	NFM	London	Police Hounslow (TD) Smartzone Cell 12
450.33750	464.33750	NFM	London	Police Spelthorne (TG) Smartzone Cell 12
450.33750	464.33750	NFM	London	Police Southall (XS) Smartzone Cell 12
450.33750	464.33750	NFM	London	Police Twickenham (TW) Smartzone Cell 12
450.33750	464.33750	NFM	Merseyside	Police Vice Squad/Special Use
450.35000	464.35000	NFM	Far Moor	Young Offender Institution (M2BL)
450.35000	464.35000	NFM	Milton Keynes	HM Prison, Secure Training Centre, Oakhill (136.5)
450.36250	464.36250	NFM	London	Police Bexleyheath (RY) Smartzone Cell 02
450.36250	464.36250	NFM	London	Police Bromley (PY) Smartzone Cell 02
450.36250	464.36250	NFM	London	Police Catford (PD) Smartzone Cell 02
450.36250	464.36250	NFM	London	Police Greenwich (RG) Smartzone Cell 02
450.36250	464.36250	NFM	London	Police Lewisham (PL) Smartzone Cell 02
450.36250	464.36250	NFM	London	Police Peckham (MM) Smartzone Cell 02
450.36250	464.36250	NFM	London	Police Plumstead (RA) Smartzone Cell 02
450.36250	464.36250	NFM	London	Police South Norwood (ZN) Smartzone Cell 02
450.36250	464.36250	NFM	London	Police Southwark (MD) Smartzone Cell 02
450.36250	464.36250	NFM	London	Police Walworth (MS) Smartzone Cell 02
450.37500	464.37500	NFM	London	Police Trunked Overload Channel (GT)
450.37500	464.37500	NFM	London	Police Edmonton (YE) Smartzone Cell 06
450.37500	464.37500	NFM	London	Police Enfield (YF) Smartzone Cell 06
450.37500	464.37500	NFM	Wednesfield	Police Ch.14
450.38750	464.38750	NFM	Coventry	Police Divisional Operations (MX) Ch.5
450.38750	464.38750	NFM	London	Police Smartzone Cell 10 Control Channel

Base	Mobile	Mode	Location	User and Notes
450.40000	464.44000	NFM	London	Police Barkingside (JB) Smartzone Cell 01
450.40000	464.44000	NFM	London	Police Chingford (JC) Smartzone Cell 01
450.40000	464.44000	NFM	London	Police Forest Gate (KF) Smartzone Cell 01
450.40000	464.44000	NFM	London	Police Plaistow (KO) Smartzone Cell 01
450.40000	464.44000	NFM	London	Police Leyton (JL) Smartzone Cell 01
450.40000	464.44000	NFM	London	Police Limehouse (HH) Smartzone Cell 01
450.40000	464.44000	NFM	London	Police Shoreditch (GD) Smartzone Cell 01
450.40000	464.44000	NFM	London	Police Stoke Newington (GN) Smartzone Cell 01
450.40000	464.44000	NFM	London	Police Whitechapel (HT) Smartzone Cell 01
450.41250	464.41250	NFM	London	Police Havering (KD) Smartzone Cell 08
450.42500	464.42500	NFM	London	Police Smartzone Cell 10 Control Channel
450.45000	464.45000	NFM	London	Police Bexleyheath (RY) Smartzone Cell 02
450.45000	464.45000	NFM	London	Police Bromley (PY) Smartzone Cell 02
450.45000	464.45000	NFM	London	Police Catford (PD) Smartzone Cell 02
450.45000	464.45000	NFM	London	Police Greenwich (RG) Smartzone Cell 02
450.45000	464.45000	NFM	London	Police Lewisham (PL) Smartzone Cell 02
450.45000	464.45000	NFM	London	Police Peckham (MM) Smartzone Cell 02
450.45000	464.45000	NFM	London	Police Plumstead (RA) Smartzone Cell 02
450.45000	464.45000	NFM	London	Police South Norwood (ZN) Smartzone Cell 02
450.45000	464.45000	NFM	London	Police Southwark (MD) Smartzone Cell 02
450.45000	464.45000	NFM	London	Police Walworth (MS) Smartzone Cell 02
450.47500	464.47500	NFM	Dorset	Police (QC) linked to 155.925
450.47500	464.47500	NFM	Liverpool	HM Prison Ashworth
450.47500	464.47500	NFM	London	HM Prison Brixton (JX)
450.48750	464.48750	NFM	London	Police Smartzone Cell 06 Control Channel
450.51250	464.51250	NFM	London	Police Barkingside (JB) Smartzone Cell 01
450.51250	464.51250	NFM	London	Police Chingford (JC) Smartzone Cell 01
450.51250	464.51250	NFM	London	Police Forest Gate (KF) Smartzone Cell 01
450.51250	464.51250	NFM	London	Police Plaistow (KO) Smartzone Cell 01
450.51250	464.51250	NFM	London	Police Leyton (JL) Smartzone Cell 01
450.51250	464.51250	NFM	London	Police Limehouse (HH) Smartzone Cell 01
450.51250	464.51250	NFM	London	Police Shoreditch (GD) Smartzone Cell 01
450.51250	464.51250	NFM	London	Police Stoke Newington (GN) Smartzone Cell 01
450.51250	464.51250	NFM	London	Police Whitechapel (HT) Smartzone Cell 01
450.52500	464.52500	NFM	Canterbury	Police (FZ) Ch.1
450.52500	464.52500	NFM	Nationwide	Police Divisional Ch.1
450.52500	464.52500	NFM	Poole	Police Ch.1
450.52500	464.52500	NFM	Stratford upon Avon	Police Ch.1 relays 155.1625 AM
450.52500	464.52500	NFM	York City	Police Ch.1
450.53750	464.53750	NFM	London	Police Brixton (LD) Smartzone Cell 03
450.53750	464.53750	NFM	London	Police Battersea (WA) Smartzone Cell 03
450.53750	464.53750	NFM	London	Police Chiswick (TC) Smartzone Cell 03
450.53750	464.53750	NFM	London	Police Hounslow (TD) Smartzone Cell 03
450.53750	464.53750	NFM	London	Police Kingston (VK) Smartzone Cell 03
450.53750	464.53750	NFM	London	Police Peckham (MM) Smartzone Cell 03
450.53750	464.53750	NFM	London	Police Streatham (LS) Smartzone Cell 03
450.53750	464.53750	NFM	London	Police Twickenham (TW) Smartzone Cell 03
450.53750	464.53750	NFM	London	Police Vauxhall (LX) Smartzone Cell 03
450.53750	464.53750	NFM	London	Police Wandsworth (WW) Smartzone Cell 03
450.53750	464.53750	NFM	London	Police Wimbledon (VW) Smartzone Cell 03
450.55000	464.55000	NFM	London	Police Smartzone Cell 09 Control Channel
450.55000	464.55000	NFM	London	Police Smartzone Cell 13 Control Channel
450.55000	464.55000	NFM	Nationwide	Police Divisional Ch.2
450.55000	464.55000	NFM	Solihull S	Police (LX) Ch.2
450.57500	464.57500	NFM	Aldermaston	UKAEA Ch.3
450.57500	464.57500	NFM	Colwyn Bay	Police (WA) Ch.3

Base	Mobile	Mode	Location	User and Notes
450.57500	464.57500	NFM	Coventry	Police Little Park Street (M1X) Ch.3
450.57500	464.57500	NFM	Dorset	Police Ch.3
450.57500	464.57500	NFM	London	Police Smartzone Cell 03 Control Channel
450.57500	464.57500	NFM	Nationwide	Police Divisional Ch.3
450.58750	464.58750	NFM	London	Police Barkingside (JB) Smartzone Cell 01
450.58750	464.58750	NFM	London	Police Chingford (JC) Smartzone Cell 01
450.58750	464.58750	NFM	London	Police Forest Gate (KF) Smartzone Cell 01
450.58750	464.58750	NFM	London	Police Plaistow (KO) Smartzone Cell 01
450.58750	464.58750	NFM	London	Police Leyton (JL) Smartzone Cell 01
450.58750	464.58750	NFM	London	Police Limehouse (HH) Smartzone Cell 01
450.58750	464.58750	NFM	London	Police Shoreditch (GD) Smartzone Cell 01
450.58750	464.58750	NFM	London	Police Stoke Newington (GN) Smartzone Cell 01
450.58750	464.58750	NFM	London	Police Whitechapel (HT) Smartzone Cell 01
450.60000	464.60000	NFM	London	HM Prison Belmarsh (MB)
450.60000	464.60000	NFM	London	Police Smartzone Cell 09 Control Channel
450.60000	464.60000	NFM	London	Police Smartzone Cell 13 Control Channel
450.60000	464.60000	NFM	Lowestoft	HM Revenue & Customs
450.62500		NFM	Nationwide	Police Ch.88 Air Support Units Air-to-Ground
450.62500		NFM	Strathclyde	Police Air Support and CID Ch.51
450.63750	464.63750	NFM	London	Police Brixton (LD) Smartzone Cell 03
450.63750	464.63750	NFM	London	Police Battersea (WA) Smartzone Cell 03
450.63750	464.63750	NFM	London	Police Chiswick (TC) Smartzone Cell 03
450.63750	464.63750	NFM	London	Police Hounslow (TD) Smartzone Cell 03
450.63750	464.63750	NFM	London	Police Kingston (VK) Smartzone Cell 03
450.63750	464.63750	NFM	London	Police Peckham (MM) Smartzone Cell 03
450.63750	464.63750	NFM	London	Police Streatham (LS) Smartzone Cell 03
450.63750	464.63750	NFM	London	Police Twickenham (TW) Smartzone Cell 03
450.63750	464.63750	NFM	London	Police Vauxhall (LX) Smartzone Cell 03
450.63750	464.63750	NFM	London	Police Wandsworth (WW) Smartzone Cell 03
450.63750	464.63750	NFM	London	Police Wimbledon (VW) Smartzone Cell 03
450.65000	464.65000	NFM	London	Police Smartzone Cell 01 Control Channel
450.65000	464.65000	NFM	West Midlands	Police Special Use Ch.97
450.67500		NFM	Gwent	Fire Brigade Ch.15/Police Air Support
450.67500		NFM	London	Police City of London Special Use Ch.09
450.67500		NFM	Nationwide	Police Ch.89 Air Support Units Air-to-Ground
450.67500		NFM	Strathclyde	Police Air Support and CID Ch.52
450.70000	464.70000	NFM	London	Police Smartzone Cell 05 Control Channel
450.72500	464.72500	NFM	London	Police Smartzone Cell 11Control Channel
450.72500	464.72500	NFM	London	Police Havering (KD) Smartzone Cell 08
450.73750	464.73750	NFM	London	Police Barkingside (JB) Smartzone Cell 01
450.73750	464.73750	NFM	London	Police Chingford (JC) Smartzone Cell 01
450.73750	464.73750	NFM	London	Police Forest Gate (KF) Smartzone Cell 01
450.73750	464.73750	NFM	London	Police Plaistow (KO) Smartzone Cell 01
450.73750	464.73750	NFM	London	Police Leyton (JL) Smartzone Cell 01
450.73750	464.73750	NFM	London	Police Limehouse (HH) Smartzone Cell 01
450.73750	464.73750	NFM	London	Police Shoreditch (GD) Smartzone Cell 01
450.73750	464.73750	NFM	London	Police Stoke Newington (GN) Smartzone Cell 01
450.73750	464.73750	NFM	London	Police Whitechapel (HT) Smartzone Cell 01
450.75000	464.75000	NFM	London	Police Smartzone Cell 03 Control Channel
450.77500	464.77500	NFM	London	Police Barking (KB) Smartzone Cell 07
450.77500	464.77500	NFM	London	Police Barkingside (JB) Smartzone Cell 07
450.77500	464.77500	NFM	London	Police Dagenham (KG) Smartzone Cell 07
450.77500	464.77500	NFM	London	Police Ilford (JI) Smartzone Cell 07
450.77500	464.77500	NFM	London	Police Walthamstow (JW) Smartzone Cell 07
450.77500	464.77500	NFM	London	Police Chiswick (TC) Smartzone Cell 12
450.77500	464.77500	NFM	London	Police Harrow (QA) Smartzone Cell 12

Base	Mobile	Mode	Location	User and Notes
450.77500	464.77500	NFM	London	Police Heathrow (ID) Smartzone Cell 12
450.77500	464.77500	NFM	London	Police Hillingdon (XH) Smartzone Cell 12
450.77500	464.77500	NFM	London	Police Hounslow (TD) Smartzone Cell 12
450.77500	464.77500	NFM	London	Police Spelthorne (TG) Smartzone Cell 12
450.77500	464.77500	NFM	London	Police Southall (XS) Smartzone Cell 12
450.77500	464.77500	NFM	London	Police Twickenham (TW) Smartzone Cell 12
450.78750	464.78750	NFM	London	Police Croydon (ZD) Smartzone Cell 10
450.78750	464.78750	NFM	London	Police Epsom (ZP) Smartzone Cell 10
450.78750	464.78750	NFM	London	Police South Norwood (ZN) Smartzone Cell 10
450.80000	464.80000	NFM	Gwynedd	Police Wide Area Special Use Ch.50
450.80000	464.80000	NFM	London	Police Wide Area Special Use Ch.50
450.80000	464.80000	NFM	London	Police Smartzone Cell 05 Control Channel
450.80000	464.80000	NFM	Nationwide	Police Divisional Ch.50
450.80000	464.80000	NFM	Rampton	HM Prison Rampton (OX)
450.80000	464.80000	NFM	West Midlands	Police Motorway Incident Unit Ch.50
450.82500	464.82500	NFM	Leamington Spa	Police Ch.72
450.82500	464.82500	NFM	London	Police Harrow (QA) Smartzone Cell 13
450.82500	464.82500	NFM	London	Police West Hendon (SV) Smartzone Cell 13
450.82500	464.82500	NFM	Nationwide	Police Divisional Ch.72
450.82500	464.82500	NFM	Portsmouth	MoD Police (PD)
450.82500	464.82500	NFM	Rhyl	Police (WA) Ch.72
450.82500	464.82500	NFM	Southam	Police Ch.72
450.82500	464.82500	NFM	Warwickshire	Police Ch.72
450.82500	464.82500	NFM	Wiltshire	Fire Brigade VHF-UHF Repeater (QF)
450.83750	464.83750	NFM	London	Police Smartzone Cell 03 Control Channel
450.85000	464.85000	NFM	Chelmsley Wood	Police (LX) Ch.38
450.85000	464.85000	NFM	London	Police Edmonton (YE) Smartzone Cell 06
450.85000	464.85000	NFM	London	Police Enfield (YF) Smartzone Cell 06
450.85000	464.85000	NFM	Nationwide	Police Divisional Ch.38
450.85000	464.85000	NFM	Poole	Police Ch.38
450.86250	464.86250	NFM	London	Police Bexleyheath (RY) Smartzone Cell 02
450.86250	464.86250	NFM	London	Police Bromley (PY) Smartzone Cell 02
450.86250	464.86250	NFM	London	Police Catford (PD) Smartzone Cell 02
450.86250	464.86250	NFM	London	Police Greenwich (RG) Smartzone Cell 02
450.86250	464.86250	NFM	London	Police Lewisham (PL) Smartzone Cell 02
450.86250	464.86250	NFM	London	Police Peckham (MM) Smartzone Cell 02
450.86250	464.86250	NFM	London	Police Plumstead (RA) Smartzone Cell 02
450.86250	464.86250	NFM	London	Police South Norwood (ZN) Smartzone Cell 02
450.86250	464.86250	NFM	London	Police Southwark (MD) Smartzone Cell 02
450.86250	464.86250	NFM	London	Police Walworth (MS) Smartzone Cell 02
450.87500	464.87500	NFM	London	Police Edmonton (YE) Smartzone Cell 06
450.87500	464.87500	NFM	London	Police Enfield (YF) Smartzone Cell 06
450.88750		NFM	Fife	Police Traffic Motorcycles
450.90000	464.90000	NFM	London	Police Smartzone Cell 07 Control Channel
450.90000	464.90000	NFM	London	Police Smartzone Cell 12 Control Channel
450.92500	464.92500	NFM	London	Police Smartzone Cell 04 Control Channel
450.92500	464.92500	NFM	West Midlands	Police Stretchford Division (D3X)
450.93750	464.93750	NFM	Holyhead	Police Link for 146.6625 to 155.0500
450.93750	464.93750	NFM	London	Police Havering (KD) Smartzone Cell 08
450.93750	464.93750	NFM	London	Police Smartzone Cell 11 Control Channel
450.97500	464.97500	NFM	London	Police Smartzone Cell 05 Control Channel
450.98750	464.98750	NFM	London	Police Bexleyheath (RY) Smartzone Cell 02
450.98750	464.98750	NFM	London	Police Bromley (PY) Smartzone Cell 02
450.98750	464.98750	NFM	London	Police Catford (PD) Smartzone Cell 02
450.98750	464.98750	NFM	London	Police Greenwich (RG) Smartzone Cell 02
450.98750	464.98750	NFM	London	Police Lewisham (PL) Smartzone Cell 02

Base	Mobile	Mode	Location	User and Notes
450.98750	464.98750	NFM	London	Police Peckham (MM) Smartzone Cell 02
450.98750	464.98750	NFM	London	Police Plumstead (RA) Smartzone Cell 02
450.98750	464.98750	NFM	London	Police South Norwood (ZN) Smartzone Cell 02
450.98750	464.98750	NFM	London	Police Southwark (MD) Smartzone Cell 02
450.98750	464.98750	NFM	London	Police Walworth (MS) Smartzone Cell 02
451.00000	465.00000	NFM	London	Police Smartzone Cell 07 Control Channel
451.00000	465.00000	NFM	London	Police Smartzone Cell 12 Control Channel
451.00000	465.00000	NFM	Pendlebury	HM Prison Forest Bank (CD)
451.01250	465.01250	NFM	London	Police Harrow (QA) Smartzone Cell 13
451.01250	465.01250	NFM	London	Police West Hendon (SV) Smartzone Cell 13
451.02500	465.02500	NFM	London	Police Smartzone Cell 11 Control Channel
451.02500	465.02500	NFM	London	Police Havering (KD) Smartzone Cell 08
451.02500	465.02500	NFM	West Midlands	Police
451.03750	465.03750	NFM	Bloxwich	Police Ch.16 (H2X)
451.03750	465.03750	NFM	London	Police Ealing (XD) Smartzone Cell 05
451.03750	465.03750	NFM	London	Police Hampstead (EH) Smartzone Cell 05
451.03750	465.03750	NFM	London	Police Holborn (EO) Smartzone Cell 05
451.03750	465.03750	NFM	London	Police Holloway (NH) Smartzone Cell 05
451.03750	465.03750	NFM	London	Police Hornsey (YR) Smartzone Cell 05
451.03750	465.03750	NFM	London	Police Islington (NI) Smartzone Cell 05
451.03750	465.03750	NFM	London	Police Kentish Town (EK) Smartzone Cell 05
451.03750	465.03750	NFM	London	Police Kilburn (QK) Smartzone Cell 05
451.03750	465.03750	NFM	London	Police Southall (XS) Smartzone Cell 05
451.03750	465.03750	NFM	London	Police Tottenham (YT) Smartzone Cell 05
451.03750	465.03750	NFM	London	Police Wembley (QD) Smartzone Cell 05
451.03750	465.03750	NFM	London	Police West Hendon (SV) Smartzone Cell 05
451.05000	465.05000	NFM	London	Police Smartzone Cell 11 Control Channel
451.05000	465.05000	NFM	London	Police Havering (KD) Smartzone Cell 08
451.07500	465.07500	NFM	Coleraine	Traffic Wardens (118.8)
451.07500	465.07500	NFM	London	Police Smartzone Cell 07 Control Channel
451.07500	465.07500	NFM	London	Police Smartzone Cell 12 Control Channel
451.12500	465.12500	NFM	London	Police Smartzone Cell 09 Control Channel
451.12500	465.12500	NFM	London	Police Smartzone Cell 13 Control Channel
451.15000	465.15000	NFM	London	Police Edmonton (YE) Smartzone Cell 06
451.15000	465.15000	NFM	London	Police Enfield (YF) Smartzone Cell 06
451.15000	465.15000	NFM	Nationwide	Police Air Support Air-Ground Ch.92
451.17500	465.17500	NFM	Colwyn Bay	Police (WA)
451.17500	465.17500	NFM	Halesowen	Police (J2X)
451.17500	465.17500	NFM	Nationwide	Police Divisional Ch.87
451.17500	465.17500	NFM	Worksop	Police
451.20000	465.10000	NFM	Nationwide	Police Divisional Ch.86
451.20000	465.10000	NFM	West Midlands	Police Wide Area Special Use (HX) Ch.86
451.21250	465.11250	NFM	Kent	Police Ch.10
451.22500	465.12500	NFM	Ashford	Police (JZ)
451.22500	465.12500	NFM	Nationwide	Police Divisional Ch.85
451.22500	465.12500	NFM	Rampton	HM Prison Rampton (OX)
451.22500	465.12500	NFM	Reading	HM Prison Broadmoor (PD)
451.22500	465.12500	NFM	Retford	HM Prison Ranby (OY)
451.23750	465.13750	NFM	London	Police Belgravia (AB) Smartzone Cell 04
451.23750	465.13750	NFM	London	Police Brompton (BS) Smartzone Cell 04
451.23750	465.13750	NFM	London	Police Charing Cross (CX) Smartzone Cell 04
451.23750	465.13750	NFM	London	Police Hammersmith (FH) Smartzone Cell 04
451.23750	465.13750	NFM	London	Police Fulham (FF) Smartzone Cell 04
451.23750	465.13750	NFM	London	Police Marylebone (DM) Smartzone Cell 04
451.23750	465.13750	NFM	London	Police Notting Hill (BH) Smartzone Cell 04
451.23750	465.13750	NFM	London	Police Paddington (DP) Smartzone Cell 04

Base	Mobile	Mode	Location	User and Notes
451.23750	465.13750	NFM	London	Police West End Central (CD) Smartzone Cell 04
451.25000	465.15000	NFM	Nationwide	Police Divisional Ch.84
451.27500	465.87500	NFM	Birmingham	Police (M2EA), International Airport
451.27500	465.87500	NFM	Gravesend	Police (AZ)
451.27500	465.87500	NFM	Nationwide	Police Divisional Ch.58
451.27500	465.87500	NFM	West Midlands	Police (MASC)
451.30000	465.20000	NFM	Nationwide	Police Motorcycle Training Ch.71
451.30000	465.20000	NFM	Nationwide	Police Air-Ground Ch.6 (Usually Ch.88 & 89 Used)
451.30000	465.20000	NFM	Nationwide	Police S. Branch/Royalty Protection (Rarely Used)
451.32500		NFM	London	Police Traffic Motorcycles Bike-Bike Ch.7
451.32500	465.22500	NFM	Nationwide	Police Back to Back Ch.7 (WO)
451.32500	465.22500	NFM	Nationwide	Police Back-Back National Allocation Ch.90
451.32500		NFM	Nationwide	Police CID/VASCAR Speed Traps Ch.7
451.32500		NFM	Nationwide	Police Special Branch/Royalty Protection Ch.7
451.32500	465.22500	NFM	Nationwide	Police Underwater Search Teams Ch.90
451.32500	465.22500	NFM	Norwich	Police Relay of 452.550 Ch.90
451.35000	465.25000	NFM	Birmingham	Immigration, International Airport
451.35000	465.25000	NFM	Dover	Immigration
451.35000	465.25000	NFM	Gatwick	Immigration Ch.8 (AO)
451.35000	465.25000	NFM	Heathrow	Immigration Ch.8
451.35000	465.25000	NFM	Liverpool	Immigration Ch.8, Port
451.35000	465.25000	NFM	London	Police London Port Authority
451.35000	465.25000	NFM	Nationwide	Airport/Docks Immigration Ch.8
451.35000	465.25000	NFM	Newhaven	Immigration
451.35000	465.25000	NFM	Stansted	Immigration
451.36250	465.26250	NFM	London	Police Barkingside (JB) Smartzone Cell 01
451.36250	465.26250	NFM	London	Police Chingford (JC) Smartzone Cell 01
451.36250	465.26250	NFM	London	Police Forest Gate (KF) Smartzone Cell 01
451.36250	465.26250	NFM	London	Police Plaistow (KO) Smartzone Cell 01
451.36250	465.26250	NFM	London	Police Leyton (JL) Smartzone Cell 01
451.36250	465.26250	NFM	London	Police Limehouse (HH) Smartzone Cell 01
451.36250	465.26250	NFM	London	Police Shoreditch (GD) Smartzone Cell 01
451.36250	465.26250	NFM	London	Police Stoke Newington (GN) Smartzone Cell 01
451.36250	465.26250	NFM	London	Police Whitechapel (HT) Smartzone Cell 01
451.37500	465.27500	NFM	Acklington	HM Prison (M2MU)
451.37500	465.27500	NFM	Andover	Police Ch.9
451.37500	465.27500	NFM	Birmingham	HM Prison Winson Green
451.37500	465.27500	NFM	Brighton	Police (SO) Ch.9
451.37500	465.27500	NFM	Durham	HM Female Prison Low Newton (JJ)
451.37500	465.27500	NFM	Feltham	Young Offenders Institution
451.37500	465.27500	NFM	Huntingdon	HM Prison Littlehey (KL)
451.37500	465.27500	NFM	London	HM Prison Pentonville
451.37500	465.27500	NFM	London	HM Prison Holloway (JH)
451.37500	465.27500	NFM	Nationwide	Police Divisional Ch.9
451.37500	465.27500	NFM	Nottingham	Police City Centre Ch.9
451.37500	465.27500	NFM	Oakham	HM Prison Ashwell (JA)
451.37500	465.27500	NFM	Preston	HM Prison Garth
451.37500	465.27500	NFM	Preston	HM Prison Kirkham (OK)
451.37500	456.27500	NFM	Rugby	Newbold Revel Prison Training College (XQ)
451.37500	465.27500	NFM	Stoke on Trent	HM Prison Werrington (WT)
451.37500	465.27500	NFM	Stockton on Tees	HM Prison Holme House (LH)
451.37500	465.27500	NFM	Thetford	HM Prison Wayland
451.37500	465.27500	NFM	York	HM Prison Full Sutton (FL)
451.40000	465.30000	NFM	Nationwide	Police Divisional Ch.11
451.40000		NFM	Nationwide	SAS Air Mobile Unit (Encrypted)
451.40000		NFM	Nationwide	Voluntary & Industrial Fire Brigades Ch.10

Base	Mobile	Mode	Location	User and Notes
451.40000		NFM	Guernsey	Fire Brigade
451.40000		NFM	Wittering	Old Civil/RAF Liaison Channel
451.42500	465.32500	NFM	Gwynedd S	Police Linked to 450.800/464.800
451.42500	465.32500	NFM	Maidstone	HM Female Prison East Sutton Park (NR)
451.42500	465.32500	NFM	Millom	HM Prison Haverigg
451.42500	465.32500	NFM	Nationwide	Police Divisional Ch.11
451.42500	465.32500	NFM	Northampton	Police Olney Ch.11
451.42500	465.32500	NFM	Portsmouth	Police Port Unit Ch.11
451.42500	465.32500	NFM	Shaftesbury	HM Prison Guys Marsh (M2BB)
451.42500	465.32500	NFM	Southampton	Airport Police Ch.11
451.42500	465.32500	NFM	West Midlands	Police Wide Area Special Use (GX)
451.42500	465.32500	NFM	Woodbridge	Young Offender Institution Hollesley Bay (PW)
451.43750	465.33750	NFM	London	Police Belgravia (AB) Smartzone Cell 04
451.43750	465.33750	NFM	London	Police Brompton (BS) Smartzone Cell 04
451.43750	465.33750	NFM	London	Police Charing Cross (CX) Smartzone Cell 04
451.43750	465.33750	NFM	London	Police Fulham (FF) Smartzone Cell 04
451.43750	465.33750	NFM	London	Police Hammersmith (FH) Smartzone Cell 04
451.43750	465.33750	NFM	London	Police Marylebone (DM) Smartzone Cell 04
451.43750	465.33750	NFM	London	Police Notting Hill (BH) Smartzone Cell 04
451.43750	465.33750	NFM	London	Police Paddington (DP) Smartzone Cell 04
451.43750	465.33750	NFM	London	Police West End Central (CD) Smartzone Cell 04
451.45000	465.35000	NFM	London	Police Croydon (ZD) Smartzone Cell 10
451.45000	465.35000	NFM	London	Police Epsom (ZP) Smartzone Cell 10
451.45000	465.35000	NFM	London	Police South Norwood (ZN) Smartzone Cell 10
451.45000	465.35000	NFM	London	Police Hendon College Training Cell
451.45000	465.35000	NFM	Nationwide	Police Divisional Ch.12
451.45000	465.35000	NFM	Pudsey	Police (CB) Ch.12
451.45000		NFM	Wittering	Old Civil/RAF Liaison Channel
451.46250	465.36250	NFM	London	Police Belgravia (AB) Smartzone Cell 04
451.46250	465.36250	NFM	London	Police Brompton (BS) Smartzone Cell 04
451.46250	465.36250	NFM	London	Police Charing Cross (CX) Smartzone Cell 04
451.46250	465.36250	NFM	London	Police Fulham (FF) Smartzone Cell 04
451.46250	465.36250	NFM	London	Police Hammersmith (FH) Smartzone Cell 04
451.46250	465.36250	NFM	London	Police Marylebone (DM) Smartzone Cell 04
451.46250	465.36250	NFM	London	Police Notting Hill (BH) Smartzone Cell 04
451.46250	465.36250	NFM	London	Police Paddington (DP) Smartzone Cell 04
451.46250	465.36250	NFM	London	Police West End Central (CD) Smartzone Cell 04
451.47500	465.37500	NFM	Alton	Police Ch.13
451.47500	465.37500	NFM	Basingstoke	Police Ch.13
451.47500	465.37500	NFM	Devizes	HM Prison Erlestoke (JM)
451.47500	465.37500	NFM	Keighley	Police Ch.13
451.47500	465.37500	NFM	Ilkley	Police Ch.13
451.47500	465.37500	NFM	London	HM Prison Wandsworth (JW)
451.47500	465.37500	NFM	Market Harborough	HM Prison Gartree (OG)
451.47500	465.37500	NFM	Nationwide	Police Divisional Ch.13
451.47500	465.37500	NFM	Petersfield	Police (Oscar 1) Ch.13
451.47500	465.37500	NFM	West Midlands	Police Green Lane Ch.13
451.50000	465.40000	NFM	Nationwide	Police Divisional Ch.14 (Old Allocation)
451.52500	465.42500	NFM	Cleveland	HM Prison Kirklevington Grange (LK)
451.52500	465.42500	NFM	Exeter	Police Ch.15 (EV)
451.52500	465.42500	NFM	Lincolnshire	Police, Special Operations
451.52500	465.42500	NFM	Milton Keynes	HM Prison Woodhill (HM)
451.52500	465.42500	NFM	Nationwide	Police Divisional Ch.15
451.52500	465.42500	NFM	Nottingham	Police Ch.14 Trent
451.52500	465.42500	NFM	Southampton	Police (Whisky 1) Ch.15
451.52500	465.42500	NFM	West Midlands	Police, Bislton Street Ch.15 (GX)

Base	Mobile	Mode	Location	User and Notes
451.55000	465.45000	NFM	Dover	Detention Centre
451.55000	465.45000	NFM	London	Police Buckingham Palace Ch.1 (Rapier Bravo)
451.55000	465.45000	NFM	Nationwide	Police Divisional Ch.15
451.55000	465.45000	NFM	Sandringham	Police Royalty Protection
451.55000	465.45000	NFM	Tetbury	Police Royalty Protection Highgrove House
451.55000	465.45000	NFM	Windsor	Police Royalty Protection (Rapier Charlie)
451.57500	465.47500	NFM	Bradford	Police (GA) Ch.17
451.57500	465.47500	NFM	Castleford	Police (DC) Ch.17
451.57500	465.47500	NFM	Cleveland	HM Prison Kirklevington Grange (LK)
451.57500	465.47500	NFM	Eastleigh	Police Ch.17
451.57500	465.47500	NFM	Evesham	HM Prison Long Lartin (JZ)
451.57500	465.47500	NFM	Goudhurst	HM Prison Blantyre House (QT)
451.57500	465.47500	NFM	Ham Common	HM Prison Latchmere House (OZ)
451.57500	465.47500	NFM	London	HM Prison Pentonville
451.57500	465.47500	NFM	Market Drayton	Young Offender Institution Stoke Heath (YH)
451.57500	465.47500	NFM	Milton Keynes	HM Prison Woodhill (HN)
451.57500	465.47500	NFM	Nationwide	Police Divisional Ch.17
451.57500	465.47500	NFM	Nottingham	HM Prison Whatton (YI)
451.57500	465.47500	NFM	Ossett	Police Ch.17 (DC)
451.57500	465.47500	NFM	Reading	HM Prison (M2AY)
451.57500	465.47500	NFM	Retford	HM Prison Ranby (M2OY)
451.57500	465.47500	NFM	Torbay	Police Ch.17
451.57500	465.47500	NFM	Wigston	Young Offender Institution Glen Parva (NX)
451.57500	465.47500	NFM	West Midlands	Police, Brierley Hill (J1X)
451.58750	465.48750	NFM	Holyhead	Police
451.58750	465.48750	NFM	London	Police Bexleyheath (RY) Smartzone Cell 02
451.58750	465.48750	NFM	London	Police Bromley (PY) Smartzone Cell 02
451.58750	465.48750	NFM	London	Police Catford (PD) Smartzone Cell 02
451.58750	465.48750	NFM	London	Police Greenwich (RG) Smartzone Cell 02
451.58750	465.48750	NFM	London	Police Lewisham (PL) Smartzone Cell 02
451.58750	465.48750	NFM	London	Police Peckham (MM) Smartzone Cell 02
451.58750	465.48750	NFM	London	Police Plumstead (RA) Smartzone Cell 02
451.58750	465.48750	NFM	London	Police South Norwood (ZN) Smartzone Cell 02
451.58750	465.48750	NFM	London	Police Southwark (MD) Smartzone Cell 02
451.58750	465.48750	NFM	London	Police Walworth (MS) Smartzone Cell 02
451.60000	465.50000	NFM	Boston	HM Prison North Sea Camp (XK)
451.60000	465.50000	NFM	Doncaster	HM Prison Lindholme (XL)
451.60000	465.50000	NFM	Maidstone	Police (CZ) Ch.18
451.60000	465.50000	NFM	Nationwide	Police Divisional Ch.18
451.60000	465.50000	NFM	Preston	HM Prison Garth (KG)
451.60000	465.50000	NFM	Rushden	Police Ch.18
451.60000	465.50000	NFM	Stretton	HM Prison Stocken (XK)
451.60000	465.50000	NFM	Wakefield	HM Prison (JK)
451.60000	465.50000	NFM	Wetherby	HM Prison Wealstun
451.60000	465.50000	NFM	West Midlands	Police Steelhouse Lane (F1X) Ch.18
451.60000	465.50000	NFM	West Yorkshire	Police Bradford Street (FI) Ch.18
451.61250	465.51250	NFM	London	Police Ealing (XD) Smartzone Cell 05
451.61250	465.51250	NFM	London	Police Hampstead (EH) Smartzone Cell 05
451.61250	465.51250	NFM	London	Police Holborn (EO) Smartzone Cell 05
451.61250	465.51250	NFM	London	Police Holloway (NH) Smartzone Cell 05
451.61250	465.51250	NFM	London	Police Hornsey (YR) Smartzone Cell 05
451.61250	465.51250	NFM	London	Police Islington (NI) Smartzone Cell 05
451.61250	465.51250	NFM	London	Police Kentish Town (EK) Smartzone Cell 05
451.61250	465.51250	NFM	London	Police Kilburn (QK) Smartzone Cell 05
451.61250	465.51250	NFM	London	Police Southall (XS) Smartzone Cell 05
451.61250	465.51250	NFM	London	Police Tottenham (YT) Smartzone Cell 05

Base	Mobile	Mode	Location	User and Notes
451.61250	465.51250	NFM	London	Police Wembley (QD) Smartzone Cell 05
451.61250	465.51250	NFM	London	Police West Hendon (SV) Smartzone Cell 05
451.62500	465.52500	NFM	London	Police Royalty Protection/Special Branch
451.62500	465.52500	NFM	London	Police City of London Special Use Ch.04
451.62500	465.52500	NFM	Nationwide	Police CID/Special Events/Major Incidents Ch.19
451.65000	465.55000	NFM	London	Police City of London Ch.08
451.65000	465.55000	NFM	Nationwide	Police VHF-UHF Repeaters Ch.20
451.67500	465.57500	NFM	Kettering	Police (CV) Ch.21
451.67500	465.57500	NFM	London	Police City of London (AJ) Ch.2
451.67500	465.57500	NFM	Nationwide	Police Divisional Ch.21
451.67500	465.57500	NFM	Waterlooville	Police (Charlie 1) Ch.21
451.68750	465.58750	NFM	Kent	Police Ch.14
451.70000	465.60000	NFM	Arnold, Notts.	Police
451.70000	465.60000	NFM	Folkestone	Police (HZ) Ch.22
451.70000	465.60000	NFM	Gillingham	Police (BB) Ch.22
451.70000	465.60000	NFM	London	HM Prison Belmarsh (MB)
451.70000	465.60000	NFM	Manchester	Police Ch.22, International Airport
451.70000	465.60000	NFM	Nationwide	Police Divisional Ch.22
451.70000	465.60000	NFM	Southampton	Police Ch.22, East
451.70000	465.60000	NFM	West Midlands	Police Wide Area Special Use (EX)
451.71250	465.61250	NFM	London	Police Belgravia (AB) Smartzone Cell 04
451.71250	465.61250	NFM	London	Police Brompton (BS) Smartzone Cell 04
451.71250	465.61250	NFM	London	Police Charing Cross (CX) Smartzone Cell 04
451.71250	465.61250	NFM	London	Police Hammersmith (FH) Smartzone Cell 04
451.71250	465.61250	NFM	London	Police Fulham (FF) Smartzone Cell 04
451.71250	465.61250	NFM	London	Police Marylebone (DM) Smartzone Cell 04
451.71250	465.61250	NFM	London	Police Notting Hill (BH) Smartzone Cell 04
451.71250	465.61250	NFM	London	Police Paddington (DP) Smartzone Cell 04
451.71250	465.61250	NFM	London	Police West End Central (CD) Smartzone Cell 04
451.72500	465.62500	NFM	Cromer	Police (N) Ch.23
451.72500	465.62500	NFM	Nationwide	Police CID/Special Events/Major Incidents Ch.23
451.75000	465.65000	NFM	Boscombe	Police
451.75000	465.65000	NFM	Bournemouth	Police
451.75000	465.65000	NFM	Gosport	Immigration Centre (HH)
451.75000	465.65000	NFM	Kinson	Police Ch.24
451.75000	465.65000	NFM	London	Police Royalty/Diplomatic Protection Ch.24
451.75000	465.65000	NFM	Nationwide	Police Divisional Ch.24
451.75000	465.65000	NFM	Retford	Police (MASC) Ch.24
451.75000	465.65000	NFM	Wakefield	HM Prison College (NP)
451.75000	465.65000	NFM	Winton	Police Ch.24
451.76250	465.66250	NFM	London	Police Brixton (LD) Smartzone Cell 03
451.76250	465.66250	NFM	London	Police Battersea (WA) Smartzone Cell 03
451.76250	465.66250	NFM	London	Police Chiswick (TC) Smartzone Cell 03
451.76250	465.66250	NFM	London	Police Hounslow (TD) Smartzone Cell 03
451.76250	465.66250	NFM	London	Police Kingston (VK) Smartzone Cell 03
451.76250	465.66250	NFM	London	Police Peckham (MM) Smartzone Cell 03
451.76250	465.66250	NFM	London	Police Streatham (LS) Smartzone Cell 03
451.76250	465.66250	NFM	London	Police Twickenham (TW) Smartzone Cell 03
451.76250	465.66250	NFM	London	Police Vauxhall (LX) Smartzone Cell 03
451.76250	465.66250	NFM	London	Police Wandsworth (WW) Smartzone Cell 03
451.76250	465.66250	NFM	London	Police Wimbledon (VW) Smartzone Cell 03
451.77500	465.67500	NFM	Brighton	Brighton Crown Court
451.77500	465.67500	NFM	London	Police City of London Special Use Ch.7
451.77500	465.67500	NFM	London	Police Notting Hill Carnival
451.77500	465.67500	NFM	Nationwide	Police CID/Special Events/Major Incidents Ch.25
451.78750	465.68750	NFM	London	Police Brixton (LD) Smartzone Cell 03

Base	Mobile	Mode	Location	User and Notes
451.78750	465.68750	NFM	London	Police Battersea (WA) Smartzone Cell 03
451.78750	465.68750	NFM	London	Police Chiswick (TC) Smartzone Cell 03
451.78750	465.68750	NFM	London	Police Hounslow (TD) Smartzone Cell 03
451.78750	465.68750	NFM	London	Police Kingston (VK) Smartzone Cell 03
451.78750	465.68750	NFM	London	Police Peckham (MM) Smartzone Cell 03
451.78750	465.68750	NFM	London	Police Streatham (LS) Smartzone Cell 03
451.78750	465.68750	NFM	London	Police Twickenham (TW) Smartzone Cell 03
451.78750	465.68750	NFM	London	Police Vauxhall (LX) Smartzone Cell 03
451.78750	465.68750	NFM	London	Police Wandsworth (WW) Smartzone Cell 03
451.78750	465.68750	NFM	London	Police Wimbledon (VW) Smartzone Cell 03
451.80000	465.70000	NFM	Burton on Trent	Police Ch.26
451.80000	465.70000	NFM	Doncaster	HM Closed Prison Moorland (XP)
451.80000	465.70000	NFM	Formby	Police Ch.26
451.80000	465.70000	NFM	Gipton	Police Ch.26
451.80000	465.70000	NFM	London	Police Kensington Palace (Rapier Kilo)
451.80000	465.70000	NFM	Lyndhurst	Police (Whisky 1) Ch.26
451.80000	465.70000	NFM	Nationwide	Police Divisional Ch.26
451.80000	465.70000	NFM	New Forest	Police Ch.26
451.80000	465.70000	NFM	Rampton	HM Prison Rampton (OX)
451.80000	465.70000	NFM	Ringwood	Police Ch.26
451.80000	465.70000	NFM	Salisbury	Police Ch.26
451.80000	465.70000	NFM	Southport	Police Ch.26
451.80000	465.70000	NFM	Telford	Police Ch.26
451.80000	465.70000	NFM	Totton	Police Ch.26
451.80000	465.70000	NFM	Wetherby	Young Offender Institution
451.80000	465.70000	NFM	Windsor	Police Windsor Castle (Rapier Lima)
451.80000	465.70000	NFM	Wisbech	Police
451.80000	466.70000	NFM	Eastbourne	Police PR (EE)
451.81250	465.71250	NFM	Kent	Police Ch.16
451.82500	465.72500	NFM	Canning	Police
451.82500	465.72500	NFM	Isle of Wight	HM Prison Parkhurst (PZ)
451.82500	465.72500	NFM	Kenilworth	Police Ch.27
451.82500	465.72500	NFM	Lincoln	HM Prison Morton Hall (NB)
451.82500	465.72500	NFM	Nationwide	Police Divisional Ch.27
451.83750	465.73750	NFM	Kent	Police Ch.51
451.83750	465.73750	NFM	London	Police Barkingside (JB) Smartzone Cell 01
451.83750	465.73750	NFM	London	Police Chingford (JC) Smartzone Cell 01
451.83750	465.73750	NFM	London	Police Forest Gate (KF) Smartzone Cell 01
451.83750	465.73750	NFM	London	Police Plaistow (KO) Smartzone Cell 01
451.83750	465.73750	NFM	London	Police Leyton (JL) Smartzone Cell 01
451.83750	465.73750	NFM	London	Police Limehouse (HH) Smartzone Cell 01
451.83750	465.73750	NFM	London	Police Shoreditch (GD) Smartzone Cell 01
451.83750	465.73750	NFM	London	Police Stoke Newington (GN) Smartzone Cell 01
451.83750	465.73750	NFM	London	Police Whitechapel (HT) Smartzone Cell 01
451.85000	465.75000	NFM	Doncaster	HM Open Prison Moorland (OF)
451.85000	465.75000	NFM	Havant	Police (Charlie 1) Ch.28
451.85000	465.75000	NFM	Leeds	HM Prison Armley (JL)
451.85000	465.75000	NFM	Nationwide	Police Divisional Ch.28
451.85000	466.75000	NFM	Nottinghamshire	Police MASC Ch.27
451.85000	465.75000	NFM	Sherwood	HM Prison Nottingham (ON)
451.85000	465.75000	NFM	Smethwick	Police Ch.28 (K2X)
451.85000	465.75000	NFM	York	HM Female Prison Askham Grange (XA)
451.86250	465.76250	NFM	London	Police Bexleyheath (RY) Smartzone Cell 02
451.86250	465.76250	NFM	London	Police Bromley (PY) Smartzone Cell 02
451.86250	465.76250	NFM	London	Police Catford (PD) Smartzone Cell 02
451.86250	465.76250	NFM	London	Police Greenwich (RG) Smartzone Cell 02

Base	Mobile	Mode	Location	User and Notes
451.86250	465.76250	NFM	London	Police Lewisham (PL) Smartzone Cell 02
451.86250	465.76250	NFM	London	Police Peckham (MM) Smartzone Cell 02
451.86250	465.76250	NFM	London	Police Plumstead (RA) Smartzone Cell 02
451.86250	465.76250	NFM	London	Police South Norwood (ZN) Smartzone Cell 02
451.86250	465.76250	NFM	London	Police Southwark (MD) Smartzone Cell 02
451.86250	465.76250	NFM	London	Police Walworth (MS) Smartzone Cell 02
451.87500	465.77500	NFM	Bournemouth	Police Football Security
451.87500	465.77500	NFM	Dartford	Police Bluewater Shopping Centre (AR) Ch.29
451.87500	465.77500	NFM	Liverpool	Police Hooligan Van
451.87500	465.77500	NFM	London	Police City of London
451.87500	465.77500	NFM	Nationwide	Police CID/Special Events/Major Incidents Ch.29
451.90000	465.80000	NFM	Coventry	Police Chase Avenue (M2X)
451.90000	465.80000	NFM	Cwmbran	Police Bravo 3 Section
451.90000	465.80000	NFM	Dover	Police Special Branch (Oscar) Ch.30
451.90000	465.80000	NFM	Nationwide	Police Divisional Ch.30
451.90000	465.80000	NFM	Folkestone	Police Special Branch
451.90000	465.80000	NFM	Fratton	Police Ch.30
451.90000	465.80000	NFM	Horsforth	Police (AB)
451.90000	465.80000	NFM	Medway	Police (DZ/ BA/ BC) Ch.30
451.90000	465.80000	NFM	Otley	Police
451.90000	465.80000	NFM	Portsmouth	Police Ch.30
451.90000	465.80000	NFM	Rochester	Police Ch.30
451.90000	465.80000	NFM	Southsea	Police Ch.30
451.91250	465.81250	NFM	London	Police Ealing (XD) Smartzone Cell 05
451.91250	465.81250	NFM	London	Police Hampstead (EH) Smartzone Cell 05
451.91250	465.81250	NFM	London	Police Holborn (EO) Smartzone Cell 05
451.91250	465.81250	NFM	London	Police Holloway (NH) Smartzone Cell 05
451.91250	465.81250	NFM	London	Police Hornsey (YR) Smartzone Cell 05
451.91250	465.81250	NFM	London	Police Islington (NI) Smartzone Cell 05
451.91250	465.81250	NFM	London	Police Kentish Town (EK) Smartzone Cell 05
451.91250	465.81250	NFM	London	Police Kilburn (QK) Smartzone Cell 05
451.91250	465.81250	NFM	London	Police Southall (XS) Smartzone Cell 05
451.91250	465.81250	NFM	London	Police Tottenham (YT) Smartzone Cell 05
451.91250	465.81250	NFM	London	Police Wembley (QD) Smartzone Cell 05
451.91250	465.81250	NFM	London	Police West Hendon (SV) Smartzone Cell 05
451.92500	465.82500	NFM	Dorchester	Police
451.92500	465.82500	NFM	Morley	Police (CC) Ch.31
451.92500	465.82500	NFM	Nationwide	Police Divisional Ch.31
451.92500	465.82500	NFM	Portsmouth	HM Prison Kingston (PZ)
451.92500	465.82500	NFM	Wiltshire	Police Gatcombe Park
451.93750	465.83750	NFM	London	Police Barkingside (JB) Smartzone Cell 01
451.93750	465.83750	NFM	London	Police Chingford (JC) Smartzone Cell 01
451.93750	465.83750	NFM	London	Police Forest Gate (KF) Smartzone Cell 01
451.93750	465.83750	NFM	London	Police Plaistow (KO) Smartzone Cell 01
451.93750	465.83750	NFM	London	Police Leyton (JL) Smartzone Cell 01
451.93750	465.83750	NFM	London	Police Limehouse (HH) Smartzone Cell 01
451.93750	465.83750	NFM	London	Police Shoreditch (GD) Smartzone Cell 01
451.93750	465.83750	NFM	London	Police Stoke Newington (GN) Smartzone Cell 01
451.93750	465.83750	NFM	London	Police Whitechapel (HT) Smartzone Cell 01
451.95000	465.85000	NFM	Bournemouth	Police
451.95000	465.85000	NFM	Garforth	Police Ch.32
451.95000	465.85000	NFM	Hastings	Police (SO)
451.95000	465.85000	NFM	Kings Heath	Police (E2X) Ch.32
451.95000	465.85000	NFM	Nationwide	Police Divisional Ch.32
451.95000	465.85000	NFM	Newark	Police MASC Ch.32
451.95000	465.85000	NFM	Plymouth	Police Response Team (Juliet) Ch.32

Base	Mobile	Mode	Location	User and Notes
451.95000	465.85000	NFM	Rye	Police Ch.32
451.95000	465.85000	NFM	Wetherby	Police Ch.32
451.96250	465.86200	NFM	London	Police Bexleyheath (RY) Smartzone Cell 02
451.96250	465.86200	NFM	London	Police Bromley (PY) Smartzone Cell 02
451.96250	465.86200	NFM	London	Police Catford (PD) Smartzone Cell 02
451.96250	465.86200	NFM	London	Police Greenwich (RG) Smartzone Cell 02
451.96250	465.86200	NFM	London	Police Lewisham (PL) Smartzone Cell 02
451.96250	465.86200	NFM	London	Police Peckham (MM) Smartzone Cell 02
451.96250	465.86200	NFM	London	Police Plumstead (RA) Smartzone Cell 02
451.96250	465.86200	NFM	London	Police South Norwood (ZN) Smartzone Cell 02
451.96250	465.86200	NFM	London	Police Southwark (MD) Smartzone Cell 02
451.96250	465.86200	NFM	London	Police Walworth (MS) Smartzone Cell 02
451.97500		NFM	Nationwide	Close Support Royalty Protection (Prot 1)
452.00000		NFM	Dorset	Police Air Support Unit (O99) Ch.95
452.00000		NFM	Derbyshire	Police Air Support Unit (HO88) Ch.95
452.00000		NFM	Nationwide	Police Air Support Units Ch.95
452.00000		NFM	Nottinghamshire	Police air support unit (HO88) Ch.95
452.00000		NFM	Sussex	Police Air Support Unit (H900) Ch.95
452.02500	466.80000	NFM	Sussex W	Fire Brigade Hilltop Link
452.02500	466.87500	NFM	Sussex W	Fire Brigade Hilltop Link
452.05000		NFM	Avon	Police Air Support Unit (QP99) Ch.96
452.05000		NFM	Derbyshire	Police Air Support Unit (HO88) Ch.96
452.05000		NFM	Dorset	Police Air Support Unit (O99) Ch.96
452.05000		NFM	Nationwide	Police Air Support Units Ch.96
452.05000		NFM	Nottinghamshire	Police Air Support Unit (HO88) Ch.96
452.07500		NFM	London	Police Air Support Link to India 98/99
452.07500		NFM	Wiltshire	Fire Brigade VHF-UHF Repeater (M2QF)
452.10000		NFM	Hampshire	Police Air Support Unit (Boxer 10)
452.10000		NFM	Nationwide	Police Air Support Units Ch.94
452.15000		NFM	London	Police Air Support Unit (India 98/99)
452.15000		NFM	Nationwide	Police Air Support Units Ch.93
452.15000		NFM	Warwickshire	Police Air Support Unit (X55)
452.16250	466.06250	NFM	Hendon	Police Training College Smartzone Cell
452.17500		NFM	London	Police Air Support Unit (India 98/99)
452.22500	466.12500	NFM	Hendon	Police Training College Smartzone Cell
452.22500	445.72500	NFM	London	London Underground Finchley Road
452.23750	466.13750	NFM	London	Police Brixton (LD) Smartzone Cell 03
452.23750	466.13750	NFM	London	Police Battersea (WA) Smartzone Cell 03
452.23750	466.13750	NFM	London	Police Chiswick (TC) Smartzone Cell 03
452.23750	466.13750	NFM	London	Police Hounslow (TD) Smartzone Cell 03
452.23750	466.13750	NFM	London	Police Kingston (VK) Smartzone Cell 03
452.23750	466.13750	NFM	London	Police Peckham (MM) Smartzone Cell 03
452.23750	466.13750	NFM	London	Police Streatham (LS) Smartzone Cell 03
452.23750	466.13750	NFM	London	Police Twickenham (TW) Smartzone Cell 03
452.23750	466.13750	NFM	London	Police Vauxhall (LX) Smartzone Cell 03
452.23750	466.13750	NFM	London	Police Wandsworth (WW) Smartzone Cell 03
452.23750	466.13750	NFM	London	Police Wimbledon (VW) Smartzone Cell 03
452.23750	466.13750	NFM	London	Police Belgravia (AB) Smartzone Cell 04
452.23750	466.13750	NFM	London	Police Brompton (BS) Smartzone Cell 04
452.23750	466.13750	NFM	London	Police Charing Cross (CX) Smartzone Cell 04
452.23750	466.13750	NFM	London	Police Hammersmith (FH) Smartzone Cell 04
452.23750	466.13750	NFM	London	Police Fulham (FF) Smartzone Cell 04
452.23750	466.13750	NFM	London	Police Marylebone (DM) Smartzone Cell 04
452.23750	466.13750	NFM	London	Police Notting Hill (BH) Smartzone Cell 04
452.23750	466.13750	NFM	London	Police Paddington (DP) Smartzone Cell 04
452.23750	466.13750	NFM	London	Police West End Central (CD) Smartzone Cell 04

Base	Mobile	Mode	Location	User and Notes
452.25000	466.15000	NFM	Reading	Remand Centre & Young Offenders Institution
452.26250	465.93750	NFM	London	Police Ealing (XD) Smartzone Cell 05
452.26250	465.93750	NFM	London	Police Hampstead (EH) Smartzone Cell 05
452.26250	465.93750	NFM	London	Police Holborn (EO) Smartzone Cell 05
452.26250	465.93750	NFM	London	Police Holloway (NH) Smartzone Cell 05
452.26250	465.93750	NFM	London	Police Hornsey (YR) Smartzone Cell 05
452.26250	465.93750	NFM	London	Police Islington (NI) Smartzone Cell 05
452.26250	465.93750	NFM	London	Police Kentish Town (EK) Smartzone Cell 05
452.26250	465.93750	NFM	London	Police Kilburn (QK) Smartzone Cell 05
452.26250	465.93750	NFM	London	Police Southall (XS) Smartzone Cell 05
452.26250	465.93750	NFM	London	Police Tottenham (YT) Smartzone Cell 05
452.26250	465.93750	NFM	London	Police Wembley (QD) Smartzone Cell 05
452.26250	465.93750	NFM	London	Police West Hendon (SV) Smartzone Cell 05
452.27500	465.92500	NFM	Nationwide	Police Divisional Ch.57
452.27500	465.92500	NFM	Nationwide	Police Reserve Channel A
452.28750	466.18750	NFM	London	Police Brixton (LD) Smartzone Cell 03
452.28750	466.18750	NFM	London	Police Battersea (WA) Smartzone Cell 03
452.28750	466.18750	NFM	London	Police Chiswick (TC) Smartzone Cell 03
452.28750	466.18750	NFM	London	Police Hounslow (TD) Smartzone Cell 03
452.28750	466.18750	NFM	London	Police Kingston (VK) Smartzone Cell 03
452.28750	466.18750	NFM	London	Police Peckham (MM) Smartzone Cell 03
452.28750	466.18750	NFM	London	Police Streatham (LS) Smartzone Cell 03
452.28750	466.18750	NFM	London	Police Twickenham (TW) Smartzone Cell 03
452.28750	466.18750	NFM	London	Police Vauxhall (LX) Smartzone Cell 03
452.28750	466.18750	NFM	London	Police Wandsworth (WW) Smartzone Cell 03
452.28750	466.18750	NFM	London	Police Wimbledon (VW) Smartzone Cell 03
452.30000	465.90000	NFM	Eastleigh	Police Special Use
452.30000	465.90000	NFM	Nationwide	Police Divisional Ch.60
452.30000	465.90000	NFM	Portsmouth	Police Diplomatic Protection & RN Docks
452.30000	465.90000	NFM	Romsey	Police Special Use
452.30000	465.90000	NFM	Southampton	Police Special Use
452.31250	465.88750	NFM	London	Police Barking (KB) Smartzone Cell 07
452.31250	465.88750	NFM	London	Police Barkingside (JB) Smartzone Cell 07
452.31250	465.88750	NFM	London	Police Dagenham (KG) Smartzone Cell 07
452.31250	465.88750	NFM	London	Police Ilford (JL) Smartzone Cell 07
452.31250	465.88750	NFM	London	Police Walthamstow (JW) Smartzone Cell 07
452.31250	465.88750	NFM	London	Police Chiswick (TC) Smartzone Cell 12
452.31250	465.88750	NFM	London	Police Harrow (QA) Smartzone Cell 12
452.31250	465.88750	NFM	London	Police Heathrow (ID) Smartzone Cell 12
452.31250	465.88750	NFM	London	Police Hillingdon (XH) Smartzone Cell 12
452.31250	465.88750	NFM	London	Police Hounslow (TD) Smartzone Cell 12
452.31250	465.88750	NFM	London	Police Spelthorne (TG) Smartzone Cell 12
452.31250	465.88750	NFM	London	Police Southall (XS) Smartzone Cell 12
452.31250	465.88750	NFM	London	Police Twickenham (TW) Smartzone Cell 12
452.32500	466.22500	NFM	Nationwide	Police Radio Engineers
452.33750	466.23750	NFM	Kent	Police Ch.16
452.35000	466.25000	NFM	Goodwood	Police, The Trundle (NO) Ch.59
452.35000	466.25000	NFM	Hastings	Police (SO) Ch.59
452.35000	466.25000	NFM	London	Police Barking (KB) Smartzone Cell 07
452.35000	466.25000	NFM	London	Police Barkingside (JB) Smartzone Cell 07
452.35000	466.25000	NFM	London	Police Dagenham (KG) Smartzone Cell 07
452.35000	466.25000	NFM	London	Police Ilford (JL) Smartzone Cell 07
452.35000	466.25000	NFM	London	Police Walthamstow (JW) Smartzone Cell 07
452.35000	466.25000	NFM	London	Police Chiswick (TC) Smartzone Cell 12
452.35000	466.25000	NFM	London	Police Harrow (QA) Smartzone Cell 12
452.35000	466.25000	NFM	London	Police Heathrow (ID) Smartzone Cell 12

Base	Mobile	Mode	Location	User and Notes
452.35000	466.25000	NFM	London	Police Hillingdon (XH) Smartzone Cell 12
452.35000	466.25000	NFM	London	Police Hounslow (TD) Smartzone Cell 12
452.35000	466.25000	NFM	London	Police Spelthorne (TG) Smartzone Cell 12
452.35000	466.25000	NFM	London	Police Southall (XS) Smartzone Cell 12
452.35000	466.25000	NFM	London	Police Twickenham (TW) Smartzone Cell 12
452.35000	466.25000	NFM	Midhurst	Police (NO) Ch.59
452.35000	466.25000	NFM	Nationwide	Police Divisional Ch.59
452.35000	466.25000	NFM	Newhaven	Police Ch.59
452.35000	466.25000	NFM	Petworth	Police (NO) Ch.59
452.35000	466.25000	NFM	Rye	Police (SO)
452.35000	466.25000	NFM	Selsey	Police (NO) Ch.59
452.37500		NFM	Dorset	Police Tactical Firearms Unit Ch.75
452.37500		NFM	Jersey	Police Tactical Firearms Unit
452.37500	466.27500	NFM	London	Police Tactical Firearms Unit Ch.76
452.37500		NFM	London	Police Tactical Firearms Unit Ch.75
452.37500	466.27500	NFM	London	City of London Special Use/Firearms Unit Ch.19
452.37500		NFM	Nationwide	Police Tactical Firearms Unit Ch.75
452.37500	466.27500	NFM	Nationwide	Police Tactical Firearms Unit Ch.76
452.40000	466.30000	NFM	Arundel	HM Prison Ford (PF)
452.40000	466.30000	NFM	Bedford	HM Prison (PI)
452.40000	466.30000	NFM	Canterbury	HM Prison (PK)
452.40000	466.30000	NFM	Dereham	Police (M) Ch.33
452.40000	466.30000	NFM	Gt Yarmouth	Police Ch.33
452.40000	466.30000	NFM	Heburn	Police (L4)
452.40000	466.30000	NFM	Holmfirth	Police Ch.33
452.40000	466.30000	NFM	Huddersfield	Police (EA) Ch.33
452.40000	466.30000	NFM	Hunstanton	Police (India) Ch.33
452.40000	466.30000	NFM	Lancaster	HM Prison (OL)
452.40000	466.30000	NFM	Leicester	HM Prison (OU)
452.40000	466.30000	NFM	London	Police House of Commons (Patriot)
452.40000	466.30000	NFM	Nationwide	Police Divisional Ch.33
452.40000	466.30000	NFM	Portsmouth	Police Special Use (Encrypted)
452.40000	466.30000	NFM	Shipley	Police
452.40000	466.30000	NFM	Stafford	HM Prison (JF)
452.40000	466.30000	NFM	Swansea	HM Prison (PQ)
452.40000	466.30000	NFM	Thetford	Police Ch.33
452.40000	466.30000	NFM	West Midlands	Police Special Use/Football Spotters (FX)
452.40000	466.30000	NFM	York	Police (AY) & Traffic Wardens Ch.33
452.42500	466.32500	NFM	Bedhampton	Police
452.42500	466.32500	NFM	Fareham	Police (CH) Ch.34
452.42500	466.32500	NFM	Gosport	Police (Charlie 1)
452.42500	466.32500	NFM	London	HM Prison Wormwood Scrubs (JS)
452.42500	466.32500	NFM	Nationwide	Police Divisional Ch.34
452.42500	466.32500	NFM	Portchester	Police
452.42500	466.32500	NFM	Portsmouth	Police
452.42500	466.32500	NFM	Reading	HM Prison Broadmoor (PD)
452.42500	466.32500	NFM	Redditch	HM Prison Brockhill (MZ)
452.42500	466.32500	NFM	Scarborough	Police (DS) Ch.34
452.42500	466.32500	NFM	Wolverhampton	HM Prison Featherstone (NJ)
452.43750	466.33750	NFM	London	Police Bexleyheath (RY) Smartzone Cell 09
452.43750	466.33750	NFM	London	Police Bromley (PR) Smartzone Cell 09
452.43750	466.33750	NFM	London	Police Greenwich (RG) Smartzone Cell 09
452.43750	466.33750	NFM	London	Police Lewisham (PL) Smartzone Cell 09
452.43750	466.33750	NFM	London	Police Harrow (QA) Smartzone Cell 13
452.43750	466.33750	NFM	London	Police West Hendon (SV) Smartzone Cell 13
452.45000	466.35000	NFM	Ashbourne	HM Prison Sudbury (JQ)

Base	Mobile	Mode	Location	User and Notes
452.45000	466.35000	NFM	Bournville	Police (E1X) Ch.35
452.45000	466.35000	NFM	Eastbourne	Police (SO) Ch.35
452.45000	466.35000	NFM	Eccleshall	HM Female Prison Drake Hall (JD)
452.45000	466.35000	NFM	Isle of Grain	Police (BA) Ch.35
452.45000	466.35000	NFM	Knutsford	Police
452.45000	466.35000	NFM	Medway	Police
452.45000	466.35000	NFM	Nationwide	Police Divisional Ch.35
452.45000	466.35000	NFM	Nottingham	Police Radford Road
452.45000	466.35000	NFM	Princes Risborough	Police Chequers, PM's Country Retreat
452.45000	466.35000	NFM	Rochester	Police (BA) Ch.35
452.45000	466.35000	NFM	Wigan	Young Offender Institution Hindley (OH)
452.45000	466.35000	NFM	Wisbech	Police Ch.35
452.45000	466.35000	NFM	Wolverhampton	Young Offender Institution Brinsford (MZ)
452.46250	466.36250	NFM	London	Police Ealing (XD) Smartzone Cell 05
452.46250	466.36250	NFM	London	Police Hampstead (EH) Smartzone Cell 05
452.46250	466.36250	NFM	London	Police Holborn (EO) Smartzone Cell 05
452.46250	466.36250	NFM	London	Police Holloway (NH) Smartzone Cell 05
452.46250	466.36250	NFM	London	Police Hornsey (YR) Smartzone Cell 05
452.46250	466.36250	NFM	London	Police Islington (NI) Smartzone Cell 05
452.46250	466.36250	NFM	London	Police Kentish Town (EK) Smartzone Cell 05
452.46250	466.36250	NFM	London	Police Kilburn (QK) Smartzone Cell 05
452.46250	466.36250	NFM	London	Police Southall (XS) Smartzone Cell 05
452.46250	466.36250	NFM	London	Police Tottenham (YT) Smartzone Cell 05
452.46250	466.36250	NFM	London	Police Wembley (QD) Smartzone Cell 05
452.46250	466.36250	NFM	London	Police West Hendon (SV) Smartzone Cell 05
452.47500	466.37500	NFM	Durham	HM Prison Frankland (M2NE)
452.47500	466.37500	NFM	Hockley	HM Female Prison Bullwood Hall (KH)
452.47500	466.37500	NFM	Nationwide	Police Divisional Ch.36
452.47500	466.37500	NFM	New Forest	Police D Division Reserve
452.47500	466.37500	NFM	West Midlands	Police Wide Area Special Use (JX)
452.50000	446.40000	NFM	Aldershot	Police (Oscar 1) Ch.37
452.50000	466.40000	NFM	Barnard Castle	Young Offenders Institution Deerbolt (PA)
452.50000	466.40000	NFM	Blandford	Police Ch.37
452.50000	466.40000	NFM	Cardiff	HM Prison (PP)
452.50000	466.40000	NFM	East Grinstead	Police (NO) Ch.37
452.50000	466.40000	NFM	Fareham	Police Special Use Ch.37
452.50000	466.40000	NFM	Farnborough	Police (Oscar 1) Ch.37
452.50000	466.40000	NFM	Fleet	Police (Oscar 1) Ch.37
452.50000	466.40000	NFM	Framlingham	Police (J8F) Ch.37
452.50000	466.40000	NFM	Gosport	Police Special Use Ch.37
452.50000	466.40000	NFM	Gt Yarmouth	Police Ch.37
452.50000	466.40000	NFM	Hailsham	Police Ch.37
452.50000	466.40000	NFM	Hove	Police Ch.37
452.50000	466.40000	NFM	Kent	Police Chevening Country Retreat
452.50000	466.40000	NFM	Kent SE	Police North Sector Ash (HZ)
452.50000	466.40000	NFM	Nationwide	Police Divisional Ch.37
452.50000	466.40000	NFM	Portland	Police Ch.37
452.50000	466.40000	NFM	Preston	HM Prison Wymott (JR)
452.50000	466.40000	NFM	Ross on Wye	Police
452.50000	466.40000	NFM	Shaftesbury	Police Ch.37
452.50000	466.40000	NFM	Todmorden	Police (FD) Ch.37
452.50000	466.40000	NFM	West Midlands	Police, Belgrave Road (E3X)
452.50000	466.40000	NFM	Weymouth	Police Ch.37
452.50000	466.40000	NFM	Worcester	Police (CA)
452.53750	466.43750	NFM	London	Police Battersea (WA) Smartzone Cell 03
452.53750	466.43750	NFM	London	Police Brixton (LD) Smartzone Cell 03

Base	Mobile	Mode	Location	User and Notes
452.53750	466.43750	NFM	London	Police Chiswick (TC) Smartzone Cell 03
452.53750	466.43750	NFM	London	Police Hounslow (TD) Smartzone Cell 03
452.53750	466.43750	NFM	London	Police Kingston (VK) Smartzone Cell 03
452.53750	466.43750	NFM	London	Police Peckham (MM) Smartzone Cell 03
452.53750	466.43750	NFM	London	Police Streatham (LS) Smartzone Cell 03
452.53750	466.43750	NFM	London	Police Twickenham (TW) Smartzone Cell 03
452.53750	466.43750	NFM	London	Police Vauxhall (LX) Smartzone Cell 03
452.53750	466.43750	NFM	London	Police Wandsworth (WW) Smartzone Cell 03
452.53750	466.43750	NFM	London	Police Wimbledon (VW) Smartzone Cell 03
452.55000	466.45000	NFM	Barnstable	Police
452.55000	466.45000	NFM	Kings Lynn	Police (D) Ch.39
452.55000	466.45000	NFM	Leeds	Police, Millgarth (BA) Ch.39
452.55000	466.45000	NFM	Nationwide	Police Divisional Ch.39
452.55000	466.45000	NFM	Newton Abbot	Police (TV) Ch.39
452.55000	466.45000	NFM	Norwich	Police (B) Ch.39
452.55000	466.45000	NFM	Nottingham	Police, Carlton MASC Ch.39
452.55000	466.45000	NFM	Ryton	Police Training College Ch.39
452.55000	466.45000	NFM	Smethwick	Police Ch.39
452.55000	466.45000	NFM	Southampton	Police Special Reserve Use
452.55000	466.45000	NFM	Uckfield	Police (SO) Ch.39
452.55000	466.45000	NFM	Westbury	Police, Ditton Marsh Ch.39
452.55000	466.45000	NFM	West Midlands	Police, Rose Road (F2X)
452.56250	466.46250	NFM	Kent	Police Ch.8
452.57500	466.47500	NFM	Basingstoke	Police (Oscar 1) Ch.40
452.57500	466.47500	NFM	Feltham	Young Offender Institution (NS)
452.57500	466.47500	NFM	Gosport	Police
452.57500	466.47500	NFM	Nationwide	Police Divisional Ch.40
452.57500	466.47500	NFM	Newhaven	Police Special Branch Ch.40
452.57500	466.47500	NFM	Portsmouth	MoD Police RN Docks & Launches
452.57500	466.47500	NFM	Redditch	HM Prison Hewell Grange (BM)
452.57500	466.47500	NFM	Wickham	Police (Charlie 1) Ch.40
452.60000	466.50000	NFM	Leiston	Police (G8A) Ch.41
452.60000	466.50000	NFM	London	Police Clarence House (Rapier Sierra)
452.60000	466.50000	NFM	London	Police St James Palace (Rapier Sierra)
452.60000	466.50000	NFM	Nationwide	Police Divisional Ch.41
452.60000	466.50000	NFM	Petworth	Police (WP) Ch.41
452.60000	466.50000	NFM	Sherborne	Police Ch.41
452.60000	466.50000	NFM	Wareham	Police Ch.41
452.60000	466.50000	NFM	West Bromwich	Police (K1X) Ch.41
452.61250	466.51250	NFM	London	Police Croydon (ZD) Smartzone Cell 10
452.61250	466.51250	NFM	London	Police Epsom (ZP) Smartzone Cell 10
452.61250	466.51250	NFM	London	Police South Norwood (ZN) Smartzone Cell 10
452.62500	466.52500	NFM	Brighton	Police (SO) Ch.42
452.62500	466.52500	NFM	Hove	Police (SO) Ch.42
452.62500	466.52500	NFM	Merseyside	Police Special Use
452.62500	466.52500	NFM	Nationwide	Police Divisional Ch.42
452.62500	466.52500	NFM	Shoreham by Sea	Police (SO) Ch.42
452.62500	466.52500	NFM	West Midlands	Police Wide Area Special Use (DX)
452.62500	466.52500	NFM	Woking	HM Female Prison Send (BN)
452.63750	466.53750	NFM	London	Police Bexleyheath (RY) Smartzone Cell 09
452.63750	466.53750	NFM	London	Police Bromley (PR) Smartzone Cell 09
452.63750	466.53750	NFM	London	Police Greenwich (RG) Smartzone Cell 09
452.63750	466.53750	NFM	London	Police Lewisham (PL) Smartzone Cell 09
452.63750	466.53750	NFM	London	Police Harrow (QA) Smartzone Cell 13
452.63750	466.53750	NFM	London	Police West Hendon (SV) Smartzone Cell 13
452.65000	466.55000	NFM	Arundel	Police (BO) Ch.43

Base	Mobile	Mode	Location	User and Notes
452.65000	466.55000	NFM	Bagshot	Police Royalty Protection
452.65000	466.55000	NFM	Bexhill	Police (EB) Ch.43
452.65000	466.55000	NFM	Bognor Regis	Police (NO) Ch.43
452.65000	466.55000	NFM	Chapeltown	Police (AC) Ch.43
452.65000	466.55000	NFM	Christchurch	Police Ch.43
452.65000	466.55000	NFM	Crowborough	Police (SO) Ch.43
452.65000	466.55000	NFM	Dorchester	HM Prison (OT)
452.65000	466.55000	NFM	Exeter	HM Prison (OE)
452.65000	466.55000	NFM	Kidderminster	Police Ch.43
452.65000	466.55000	NFM	Lewes	Police HQ
452.65000	466.55000	NFM	Littlehampton	Police (NO) Ch.43
452.65000	466.55000	NFM	Nationwide	Police Divisional Ch.43
452.65000	466.55000	NFM	Northallerton	Young Offender Institution (NM)
452.65000	466.55000	NFM	Norwich	Police, Rural Ch.43
452.65000	466.55000	NFM	Norwich	HM Prison (PO)
452.65000	466.55000	NFM	Portland	HM Prison Verne (NN)
452.65000	466.55000	NFM	Rugby	HM Prison College Newbold Revel (XQ)
452.65000	466.55000	NFM	Stratford	Police Ch.43
452.65000	466.55000	NFM	Shrewsbury	HM Prison (JY) (218.1)
452.65000	466.55000	NFM	Telford	Police
452.65000	466.55000	NFM	Weston Super Mare	Police (Mike Control) Ch.43
452.65000	466.55000	NFM	Wilmslow	HM Female Prison Styal (OB)
452.65000	466.55000	NFM	Winchester	HM Prison (PV)
452.65000	466.55000	NFM	Yelverton	HM Prison Dartmoor (LD)
452.66250	466.56250	NFM	London	Police Bexleyheath (RY) Smartzone Cell 02
452.66250	466.56250	NFM	London	Police Bromley (PY) Smartzone Cell 02
452.66250	466.56250	NFM	London	Police Catford (PD) Smartzone Cell 02
452.66250	466.56250	NFM	London	Police Greenwich (RG) Smartzone Cell 02
452.66250	466.56250	NFM	London	Police Lewisham (PL) Smartzone Cell 02
452.66250	466.56250	NFM	London	Police Peckham (MM) Smartzone Cell 02
452.66250	466.56250	NFM	London	Police Plumstead (RA) Smartzone Cell 02
452.66250	466.56250	NFM	London	Police South Norwood (ZN) Smartzone Cell 02
452.66250	466.56250	NFM	London	Police Southwark (MD) Smartzone Cell 02
452.66250	466.56250	NFM	London	Police Walworth (MS) Smartzone Cell 02
452.67500	466.57500	NFM	Aston	Police (DI) Ch.44
452.67500	466.57500	NFM	England & Wales	Prison Emergency Reserve Channel
452.67500	466.57500	NFM	Nationwide	Police Divisional Ch.44
452.67500	466.57500	NFM	Rochester	HM Female Prison Cookham Wood (JI)
452.67500	466.57500	NFM	Shipley	Police (HC) Ch.44
452.67500	466.57500	NFM	Wotton under Edge	HM Prison Eastwood Park (TW)
452.68750	466.58750	NFM	London	Police Ealing (XD) Smartzone Cell 05
452.68750	466.58750	NFM	London	Police Hampstead (EH) Smartzone Cell 05
452.68750	466.58750	NFM	London	Police Holborn (EO) Smartzone Cell 05
452.68750	466.58750	NFM	London	Police Holloway (NH) Smartzone Cell 05
452.68750	466.58750	NFM	London	Police Hornsey (YR) Smartzone Cell 05
452.68750	466.58750	NFM	London	Police Islington (NI) Smartzone Cell 05
452.68750	466.58750	NFM	London	Police Kentish Town (EK) Smartzone Cell 05
452.68750	466.58750	NFM	London	Police Kilburn (QK) Smartzone Cell 05
452.68750	466.58750	NFM	London	Police Southall (XS) Smartzone Cell 05
452.68750	466.58750	NFM	London	Police Tottenham (YT) Smartzone Cell 05
452.68750	466.58750	NFM	London	Police Wembley (QD) Smartzone Cell 05
452.68750	466.58750	NFM	London	Police West Hendon (SV) Smartzone Cell 05
452.70000	466.60000	NFM	Holyhead	Police Docks
452.70000	466.60000	NFM	Battle	Police (ET) Ch.45
452.70000	466.60000	NFM	Bognor Regis	Police (NO) Ch.45
452.70000	466.60000	NFM	Burgess Hill	Police (NB) Ch.45

Base	Mobile	Mode	Location	User and Notes
452.70000	466.60000	NFM	Halifax	Police (FA) Ch.45
452.70000	466.60000	NFM	Haywards Heath	Police (NA) Ch.45
452.70000	466.60000	NFM	Hucknall	Police MASC Ch.45
452.70000	466.60000	NFM	Lancing	Police Ch.45
452.70000	466.60000	NFM	Louth	Police Ch.45
452.70000	466.60000	NFM	Nationwide	Police Divisional Ch.45
452.70000	466.60000	NFM	Rugby	Police Ch.45
452.70000	466.60000	NFM	Seaford	Police (SO)
452.70000	466.60000	NFM	Shoreham by Sea	Police Ch.45
452.70000	466.60000	NFM	Worthing	Police Ch.45
452.71250	466.61250	NFM	London	Police Bexleyheath (RY) Smartzone Cell 02
452.71250	466.61250	NFM	London	Police Bromley (PY) Smartzone Cell 02
452.71250	466.61250	NFM	London	Police Catford (PD) Smartzone Cell 02
452.71250	466.61250	NFM	London	Police Greenwich (RG) Smartzone Cell 02
452.71250	466.61250	NFM	London	Police Lewisham (PL) Smartzone Cell 02
452.71250	466.61250	NFM	London	Police Peckham (MM) Smartzone Cell 02
452.71250	466.61250	NFM	London	Police Plumstead (RA) Smartzone Cell 02
452.71250	466.61250	NFM	London	Police South Norwood (ZN) Smartzone Cell 02
452.71250	466.61250	NFM	London	Police Southwark (MD) Smartzone Cell 02
452.71250	466.61250	NFM	London	Police Walworth (MS) Smartzone Cell 02
452.72500	466.62500	NFM	Batley	Police (EB) Ch.46
452.72500	446.62500	NFM	Heckmondwike	Police (EB) Ch.46
452.72500	466.62500	NFM	Horsham	Police (NO) Ch.46
452.72500	466.62500	NFM	Nationwide	Police Divisional Ch.46
452.72500	466.62500	NFM	Pulborough	Police (NP) Ch.46
452.72500	466.62500	NFM	Sittingbourne	Police, Swale (EZ) Ch.46
452.72500	466.62500	NFM	Steyning	Police (NO)
452.72500	466.62500	NFM	Storrington	Police (NS) Ch.46
452.72500	466.62500	NFM	Warrington	HM Prison Risley (OR)
452.72500	466.62500	NFM	West Midlands	Police, Stanton Road (M3X)
452.73750	466.63750	NFM	London	Police Bexleyheath (RY) Smartzone Cell 09
452.73750	466.63750	NFM	London	Police Bromley (PR) Smartzone Cell 09
452.73750	466.63750	NFM	London	Police Greenwich (RG) Smartzone Cell 09
452.73750	466.63750	NFM	London	Police Lewisham (PL) Smartzone Cell 09
452.75000	466.65000	NFM	Arundel	Police Ch.47
452.75000	466.65000	NFM	Bangor	Police Ch.47
452.75000	466.65000	NFM	Billingshurst	Police (NO)
452.75000	466.65000	NFM	Bridport	Police Ch.47
452.75000	466.65000	NFM	Caernarfon	Police Ch.47
452.75000	466.65000	NFM	Castleford	Police Ch.47
452.75000	466.65000	NFM	Gatwick	Police Gatpol (GB)
452.75000	466.65000	NFM	Haywards Heath	Police Ch.47
452.75000	466.65000	NFM	Ilkley	Police Ch.47
452.75000	466.65000	NFM	Keighley	Police Ch.47
452.75000	466.65000	NFM	Lancing	Police Ch.47
452.75000	466.65000	NFM	Lewes	Police Ch.47
452.75000	466.65000	NFM	Littlehampton	Police Ch.47
452.75000	466.65000	NFM	Llandudno	Police Ch.47
452.75000	466.65000	NFM	Nationwide	Police Divisional Ch.47 (Special Use)
452.75000	466.65000	NFM	Ossett	Police (DC) Ch.47
452.75000	466.65000	NFM	Shoreham by Sea	Police Ch.47
452.75000	466.65000	NFM	Wakefield	Police MASC (DA) Ch.47
452.75000	466.65000	NFM	Worthing	Police (WO, WW) Ch.47
452.76250	466.66250	NFM	London	Police Battersea (WA) Smartzone Cell 03
452.76250	466.66250	NFM	London	Police Brixton (LD) Smartzone Cell 03
452.76250	466.66250	NFM	London	Police Chiswick (TC) Smartzone Cell 03

Base	Mobile	Mode	Location	User and Notes
452.76250	466.66250	NFM	London	Police Hounslow (TD) Smartzone Cell 03
452.76250	466.66250	NFM	London	Police Kingston (VK) Smartzone Cell 03
452.76250	466.66250	NFM	London	Police Peckham (MM) Smartzone Cell 03
452.76250	466.66250	NFM	London	Police Streatham (LS) Smartzone Cell 03
452.76250	466.66250	NFM	London	Police Twickenham (TW) Smartzone Cell 03
452.76250	466.66250	NFM	London	Police Vauxhall (LX) Smartzone Cell 03
452.76250	466.66250	NFM	London	Police Wandsworth (WW) Smartzone Cell 03
452.76250	466.66250	NFM	London	Police Wimbledon (VW) Smartzone Cell 03
452.77500	466.67500	NFM	Beeston	Police Ch.48
452.77500	466.67500	NFM	Bisley	HM Prison Coldingley (JE)
452.77500	466.67500	NFM	Brighouse	Police (FB) Ch.48
452.77500	466.67500	NFM	Nationwide	Police Divisional Ch.48
452.77500	466.67500	NFM	West Midlands	Police Thornhill Road Ch.48
452.78750	452.68750	NFM	London	Police Croydon (ZD) Smartzone Cell 10
452.78750	452.68750	NFM	London	Police Epsom (ZP) Smartzone Cell 10
452.78750	452.68750	NFM	London	Police South Norwood (ZN) Smartzone Cell 10
452.80000	466.70000	NFM	Aberystwyth	Police Ch.49
452.80000	466.70000	NFM	Abingdon	Police Ch.49
452.80000	466.70000	NFM	Brighouse	Police (FB) Ch.49
452.80000	466.70000	NFM	Crawley	Police (NO/ NC) Ch.49
452.80000	466.70000	NFM	Daventry	Police Ch.49
452.80000	466.70000	NFM	Eastbourne	Police (EO/EE)
452.80000	466.70000	NFM	Hastings	Police PR (EH)
452.80000	466.70000	NFM	Horsham	Police
452.80000	466.70000	NFM	Hull	HM Prison (JU)
452.80000	466.70000	NFM	Isle of Wight	HM Prison Albany (PY)
452.80000	466.70000	NFM	Lewes	Police (CO/EL)
452.80000	466.70000	NFM	Llanelli	Police Control Ch.49
452.80000	466.70000	NFM	London	Police City of London Ch.1
452.80000	466.70000	NFM	Lowestoft	HM Prison Blundeston (PN)
452.80000	466.70000	NFM	Maidstone	HM Prison (PM)
452.80000	466.70000	NFM	Nationwide	Police Divisional Ch.49
452.80000	466.70000	NFM	Newhaven	Police (EO/ EN) Ch.49
452.80000	466.70000	NFM	Newmarket	HM Prison Highpoint (NT)
452.80000	466.70000	NFM	Newton Abbot	HM Prison Channings Wood (QR)
452.80000	466.70000	NFM	North Shields	Police (M2LBC1)
452.80000	466.70000	NFM	Plymouth	Police Ch.49
452.80000	466.70000	NFM	Polegate	Police Traffic (TP)
452.80000	466.70000	NFM	Seaford	Police (ES) Ch.49
452.80000	466.70000	NFM	Shepton Mallet	HM Prison (OM)
452.82500	466.72500	NFM	Nationwide	Police Ch.50
452.82500	466.72500	NFM	Nationwide	Police Vehicle Trackers
452.85000	466.75000	NFM	Nationwide	Police Ch.51
452.85000	466.75000	NFM	Nationwide	Police Vehicle Trackers
452.86250	466.76250	NFM	London	Police Barkingside (JB) Smartzone Cell 01
452.86250	466.76250	NFM	London	Police Chingford (JC) Smartzone Cell 01
452.86250	466.76250	NFM	London	Police Forest Gate (KF) Smartzone Cell 01
452.86250	466.76250	NFM	London	Police Plaistow (KO) Smartzone Cell 01
452.86250	466.76250	NFM	London	Police Leyton (JL) Smartzone Cell 01
452.86250	466.76250	NFM	London	Police Limehouse (HH) Smartzone Cell 01
452.86250	466.76250	NFM	London	Police Shoreditch (GD) Smartzone Cell 01
452.86250	466.76250	NFM	London	Police Stoke Newington (GN) Smartzone Cell 01
452.86250	466.76250	NFM	London	Police Whitechapel (HT) Smartzone Cell 01
452.87500	466.77500	NFM	Gloucester	Police Air Support Unit - HQ & Force Link.
452.87500	466.80000	NFM	Nationwide	Fire Brigade VHF-UHF Repeaters Ch.52
452.87500	466.77500	NFM	Nationwide	Police Divisional Ch.52

Base	Mobile	Mode	Location	User and Notes
452.87500	466.77500	NFM	Winchester	Police (Oscar 1) Ch.52
452.87500	466.77500	NFM	West Midlands	Police, Solihull North (LX)
452.88750	466.78750	NFM	London	Police Bexleyheath (RY) Smartzone Cell 02
452.88750	466.78750	NFM	London	Police Bromley (PY) Smartzone Cell 02
452.88750	466.78750	NFM	London	Police Catford (PD) Smartzone Cell 02
452.88750	466.78750	NFM	London	Police Greenwich (RG) Smartzone Cell 02
452.88750	466.78750	NFM	London	Police Lewisham (PL) Smartzone Cell 02
452.88750	466.78750	NFM	London	Police Peckham (MM) Smartzone Cell 02
452.88750	466.78750	NFM	London	Police Plumstead (RA) Smartzone Cell 02
452.88750	466.78750	NFM	London	Police South Norwood (ZN) Smartzone Cell 02
452.88750	466.78750	NFM	London	Police Southwark (MD) Smartzone Cell 02
452.88750	466.78750	NFM	London	Police Walworth (MS) Smartzone Cell 02
452.90000	466.80000	NFM	Birmingham	HM Prison Winson Green (M2JG)
452.90000	466.80000	NFM	Gloucester	Police Ch.53
452.90000	466.80000	NFM	Heathrow	Police Special Branch (SV/SB) Ch.53
452.90000	466.80000	NFM	Nationwide	Fire Brigade VHF-UHF Repeaters Ch.53
452.90000	466.80000	NFM	Nationwide	Police Divisional Ch.53
452.90000	466.80000	NFM	Sevenoaks	Police (BZ) Ch.53
452.91250	466.81250	NFM	London	Police Belgravia (AB) Smartzone Cell 04
452.91250	466.81250	NFM	London	Police Brompton (BS) Smartzone Cell 04
452.91250	466.81250	NFM	London	Police Charing Cross (CX) Smartzone Cell 04
452.91250	466.81250	NFM	London	Police Hammersmith (FH) Smartzone Cell 04
452.91250	466.81250	NFM	London	Police Fulham (FF) Smartzone Cell 04
452.91250	466.81250	NFM	London	Police Marylebone (DM) Smartzone Cell 04
452.91250	466.81250	NFM	London	Police Notting Hill (BH) Smartzone Cell 04
452.91250	466.81250	NFM	London	Police Paddington (DP) Smartzone Cell 04
452.91250	466.81250	NFM	London	Police West End Central (CD) Smartzone Cell 04
452.92500	466.82500	NFM	Nationwide	Police VHF-UHF Repeaters Ch.54
452.93750	466.83750	NFM	London	Police Ealing (XD) Smartzone Cell 05
452.93750	466.83750	NFM	London	Police Hampstead (EH) Smartzone Cell 05
452.93750	466.83750	NFM	London	Police Holborn (EO) Smartzone Cell 05
452.93750	466.83750	NFM	London	Police Holloway (NH) Smartzone Cell 05
452.93750	466.83750	NFM	London	Police Hornsey (YR) Smartzone Cell 05
452.93750	466.83750	NFM	London	Police Islington (NI) Smartzone Cell 05
452.93750	466.83750	NFM	London	Police Kentish Town (EK) Smartzone Cell 05
452.93750	466.83750	NFM	London	Police Kilburn (QK) Smartzone Cell 05
452.93750	466.83750	NFM	London	Police Southall (XS) Smartzone Cell 05
452.93750	466.83750	NFM	London	Police Tottenham (YT) Smartzone Cell 05
452.93750	466.83750	NFM	London	Police Wembley (QD) Smartzone Cell 05
452.93750	466.83750	NFM	London	Police West Hendon (SV) Smartzone Cell 05
452.95000	466.85000	NFM	Nationwide	Police Divisional Ch.55
452.95000	466.85000	NFM	Wiltshire	Fire Brigade VHF-UHF Repeater (QM) Ch.55
452.96250	466.86250	NFM	London	Police Belgravia (AB) Smartzone Cell 04
452.96250	466.86250	NFM	London	Police Brompton (BS) Smartzone Cell 04
452.96250	466.86250	NFM	London	Police Charing Cross (CX) Smartzone Cell 04
452.96250	466.86250	NFM	London	Police Hammersmith (FH) Smartzone Cell 04
452.96250	466.86250	NFM	London	Police Fulham (FF) Smartzone Cell 04
452.96250	466.86250	NFM	London	Police Marylebone (DM) Smartzone Cell 04
452.96250	466.86250	NFM	London	Police Notting Hill (BH) Smartzone Cell 04
452.96250	466.86250	NFM	London	Police Paddington (DP) Smartzone Cell 04
452.96250	466.86250	NFM	London	Police West End Central (CD) Smartzone Cell 04
452.97500	466.87500	NFM	Broadstairs	Police (GZ) Ch.56
452.97500	466.87500	NFM	Margate	Police Ch.56
452.97500	466.87500	NFM	Nationwide	Police Divisional Ch.56
452.97500	466.87500	NFM	Ramsgate	Police Ch.56
452.97500	466.87500	NFM	Thanet	Police, Swale (GZ) Ch.56

Base	Mobile	Mode	Location	User and Notes

453.0000 - 454.0000 MHz **PMR Mobile Band 12.5 kHz**

Base	Mobile	Mode	Location	User and Notes
453.02500	459.52500	NFM	Aberavon	Shopwatch
453.02500	459.52500	NFM	Aberystwyth	National Library of Wales Security/Staff
453.02500	459.52500	NFM	Bath	National Car Parks Maintenance
453.02500	459.52500	NFM	Birmingham	Shopwatch (110.9)
453.02500	459.52500	NFM	Blackpool	Blackpool Hospital (156.7)
453.02500	459.52500	NFM	Bolton	Shopping Centre Security
453.02500	459.52500	NFM	Brighton	Debenhams Store, Churchill Square (233)
453.02500	459.52500	NFM	Bristol	City CCTV System
453.02500	459.52500	NFM	Brockworth	Intavista Limited (71.9)
453.02500	459.52500	NFM	Bromley	Shopwatch, Bromley Glades (DCS 032)
453.02500	459.52500	NFM	Bournemouth	JP Morgan Security (136.5)
453.02500	459.52500	NFM	Cardiff	Barry Docks (179.9)
453.02500	459.52500	NFM	Cardiff	HM Customs & Revenue Tax Office Security
453.02500	459.52500	NFM	Carlisle	Lanes Shopping Centre Security
453.02500	459.52500	NFM	Coventry	Burger King Drive-Thru Central 6
453.02500	459.52500	NFM	Coventry	Coombe Abbey Park Rangers
453.02500	459.52500	NFM	Croydon	Shopwatch (123)
453.02500	459.52500	NFM	Dagenham	Ford Motor Plant
453.02500	459.52500	NFM	Dover	Hoverspeed
453.02500	459.52500	NFM	Dumfries	Lorebourne Shopping Centre Security
453.02500	459.52500	NFM	Eastbourne	Sainsbury Supermarket (94.8)
453.02500	459.52500	NFM	Edinburgh	Waverley Market & Westerhails Centre
453.02500	459.52500	NFM	Felixstowe	Harbour Channel
453.02500	459.52500	NFM	Gorlestone	Shopwatch
453.02500	459.52500	NFM	Gosport	Shopwatch/Pubwatch (156.7)
453.02500	459.52500	NFM	Guernsey	Harbour Channel
453.02500	459.52500	NFM	Guildford	Council Litter Wardens
453.02500	459.52500	NFM	Gwynedd	Ysbyty Hospital
453.02500	459.52500	NFM	Harrogate	Victoria Shopping Centre Security
453.02500	459.52500	NFM	Harwich	Harbour Channel
453.02500	459.52500	NFM	Heathrow	Edwardian International Hotel
453.02500	459.52500	NFM	Heathrow	Skyline Hotel
453.02500	459.52500	NFM	Heathrow	Virgin Atlantic Engineering Stores (192.8)
453.02500	459.52500	NFM	Immingham	Conoco
453.02500	459.52500	NFM	Isle of Man	Ronaldsway Airport Police (67)
453.02500	459.52500	NFM	Jersey	Shell Aviation Fuel Supplies
453.02500	459.52500	NFM	Leatherhead	Esso Oil Company HQ
453.02500	459.52500	NFM	Leicester	Shopwatch Ch.1 (110.9)
453.02500	459.52500	NFM	Lisburn	Sprucefield Shopping Centre Security
453.02500	459.52500	NFM	Llanelli	Corus Tostre Steelworks
453.02500	459.52500	NFM	London	Borough of Croydon Repeater
453.02500	459.52500	NFM	London	Covent Garden Piazza Security (77)
453.02500	459.52500	NFM	London	Houses of Parliament (123)
453.02500	459.52500	NFM	London	Harrods Staff, Knightsbridge
453.02500	459.52500	NFM	London	Putney Exchange Security (162.2)
453.02500	459.52500	NFM	London	Shopwatch, Brentford (225.7)
453.02500	459.52500	NFM	London	Shopwatch, Wembley (136.5)
453.02500	459.52500	NFM	London	Shopwatch, Wood Green Ch.2
453.02500	459.52500	NFM	Londonderry	Hospital Porters/Security
453.02500	459.52500	NFM	Manchester	International Airport Bus Service
453.02500	459.52500	NFM	Mansfield	Shopwatch, Four Seasons Shopping Centre
453.02500	459.52500	NFM	Newcastle	Metro Net - Emergency Use Only
453.02500	459.52500	NFM	Newcastle	Shopwatch, Eldon Square (186.2)
453.02500	459.52500	NFM	Pembroke	Texaco Oil Refinery
453.02500	459.52500	NFM	Port Talbot	Shopwatch

Base	Mobile	Mode	Location	User and Notes
453.02500	459.52500	NFM	Reading	KFC Drive-Thru, Reading Gate M4 Junction 12
453.02500	459.52500	NFM	Sheffield	Corus Steel Rail Movements
453.02500	459.52500	NFM	Sheffield	Pennine Foods
453.02500	459.52500	NFM	Sittingbourne	Kemsley Paper Mill
453.02500	459.52500	NFM	Southend on Sea	Sainsbury Supermarket (141.3)
453.02500	459.52500	NFM	Stansted Airport	BAA Trunked Network
453.02500	459.52500	NFM	Stevenage	Sainsbury Supermarket, Coreys Mills (162.2)
453.02500	459.52500	NFM	St Peter Port	Marina Operations
453.02500	459.52500	NFM	Sunderland	Debenhams Department Store
453.02500	459.52500	NFM	Swansea	Council Depot
453.02500	459.52500	NFM	Thame	Burger King Drive-Thru (131.8)
453.02500	459.52500	NFM	Warrington	Shopwatch (233.6)
453.02500	459.52500	NFM	Warwick	Castle Staff Ch.2
453.03750	459.53750	NFM	Nationwide	Reserved Channel Special Use
453.05000	459.55000	NFM	Abingdon	Milton Park Security (186.2)
453.05000	459.55000	NFM	Blackpool	Trams (Mobile Data)
453.05000	459.55000	NFM	Bournemouth	Winfaith Security
453.05000	459.55000	NFM	Bridport	Shopwatch
453.05000	459.55000	NFM	Brighton	American Express Ch.2 Maintenance (114.8)
453.05000	459.55000	NFM	Bristol	BAe Filton Security
453.05000	459.55000	NFM	Broadstone	Dolphin Taxis
453.05000	459.55000	NFM	Carnforth	Holme/Back Lane Quarry Bardon Aggregates Ch.1
453.05000	459.55000	NFM	Cheltenham	GCHQ Cleaners/Security Trunked Voice
453.05000	459.55000	NFM	Chinnor	Rail Operator (Romeo Base) (151.4)
453.05000	459.55000	NFM	Edinburgh	Western General Hospital Porters
453.05000	459.55000	NFM	Guernsey	Princess Elizabeth Hospital
453.05000	459.55000	NFM	Hartlepool	Port Control
453.05000	459.55000	NFM	Halewood	Ford Motor Cars
453.05000	459.55000	NFM	Hull	Royal Infirmary Porters Ch.4
453.05000	459.55000	NFM	Ilkeston	Shopwatch
453.05000	459.55000	NFM	Immingham	Coal Products Docking
453.05000	459.55000	NFM	Kent	Channel Tunnel Trains Along Route To St Pancras
453.05000	459.55000	NFM	Kings Lynn	Shopwatch (77)
453.05000	459.55000	NFM	Llanwern	Corus Steelworks (110.9)
453.05000	459.55000	NFM	London	Channel Tunnel Trains, St Pancras
453.05000	459.55000	NFM	London	Parking Enforcement, Enfield (123)
453.05000	459.55000	NFM	London	Parking Enforcement, Leytonstone (123)
453.05000	459.55000	NFM	London	Parking Enforcement, Westminster (71.9)
453.05000	459.55000	NFM	Luton Airport	Alpha Catering
453.05000	459.55000	NFM	Newcastle under Lyme	Roebuck Shopping Centre Security
453.05000	459.55000	NFM	North Shields	Pubwatch
453.05000	459.55000	NFM	Oxford	University Security (77 & 94.8)
453.05000	459.55000	NFM	Sheffield	Shopwatch
453.05000	459.55000	NFM	Shrewsbury	Shopwatch
453.05000	459.55000	NFM	Southampton	University Computer Department (67)
453.05000	459.55000	NFM	Stevenage	GlaxoSmithKline Security
453.05000	459.55000	NFM	Stoke on Trent	Roebuck Centre
453.05000	459.55000	NFM	Worksop	Pubwatch
453.06250	459.56250	NFM	Aldershot	Shopwatch
453.06250	459.56250	NFM	Barnet	Community Wardens Ch.1 (192.8)
453.06250	459.56250	NFM	Barrow	Debenhams, Portland Walk Shopping Centre
453.06250	459.56250	NFM	Boscombe	Shopwatch (114.8)
453.06250	459.56250	NFM	Brighton	Sussex University Security/Maintenance Ch.1 (210.7)
453.06250	459.56250	NFM	Cambridge	Shopwatch, Grafton Centre Ch.2
453.06250	459.56250	NFM	Cardiff	David Morgan Department Store Security (123)
453.06250	459.56250	NFM	Cardiff	Dow Corning, Barry Docks (141.3)

Base	Mobile	Mode	Location	User and Notes
453.06250	459.56250	NFM	Chatham	Shopwatch, Pentagon Shopping Centre
453.06250	459.56250	NFM	Cheltenham	GCHQ Security, Oakley
456.06250	459.56250	NFM	Chesterfield	Shopwatch
456.06250	459.56250	NFM	Chorlton Cum Hardy	Shopwatch
456.06250	459.56250	NFM	Clacton on Sea	Pubwatch
456.06250	459.56250	NFM	Cleveland	Shopping Centre Security
456.06250	459.56250	NFM	Coventry	Jaguar Cars Staff MPT1327 Voice Channel
456.06250	459.56250	NFM	Cribbs Causeway	McDonalds Drive-Thru (136.5)
453.06250	459.56250	NFM	Croyde	Ruda Holiday Park
453.06250	459.56250	NFM	Croydon	Goodenough Bryans Foods
456.06250	459.56250	NFM	Cwmbran	Shopping Centre Security
453.06250	459.56250	NFM	Eastbourne	Sainsbury Supermarket (67)
453.06250	459.56250	NFM	Edinburgh	Shopwatch/Pubwatch (179.9)
453.06250	459.56250	NFM	Gt Yarmouth	Seashore Holiday Centre (107.2)
453.06250	459.56250	NFM	Harwell	UKAEA Police
453.06250	459.56250	NFM	Heathrow	United Airlines/United Arab Emirates T3 Ramp Ops.
453.06250	459.56250	NFM	Hereford	Shopwatch
453.06250	459.56250	NFM	Holyhead	Tesco Checkout (103.5)
453.06250	459.56250	NFM	Hull	Shopwatch
453.06250	459.56250	NFM	Immingham	Princes Quay Shopping Centre
453.06250	459.56250	NFM	Inverness	Debenhams Department Store Security
453.06250	459.56250	NFM	Isle of Wight	Shopwatch, Newport (94.8)
453.06250	459.56250	NFM	Kendal	Shopwatch Westmorland Shopping Centre
453.06250	459.56250	NFM	Kent	Medway Shop Security
453.06250	459.56250	NFM	Lincoln	Shopwatch, City Centre
453.06250	459.56250	NFM	Liverpool	St. John's Shopping Centre Security
453.06250	459.56250	NFM	Llanwern	Corus Steelworks (179.9)
453.06250	459.56250	NFM	London	BBC Security, Langham Place
453.06250	459.56250	NFM	London	Buckingham Palace Maintenance/Ground Staff
453.06250	459.56250	NFM	London	Chelsea & Westminster Hospital (67)
453.06250	459.56250	NFM	London	Fortnum & Mason, Piccadilly
453.06250	459.56250	NFM	London	Science Museum Staff
453.06250	459.56250	NFM	London	Shopwatch, Walthamstow
453.06250	459.56250	NFM	London	Tate Modern Gallery, Southbank (103.5)
453.06250	459.56250	NFM	Luton	Car Assembly Plant
453.06250	459.56250	NFM	Manchester	Springfield Hospital Porters
453.06250	459.56250	NFM	Middlesbrough	Shopwatch
453.06250	459.56250	NFM	Neath	Burger King Drive-Thru (114.8)
453.06250	459.56250	NFM	Oxford	Lady Margaret Hall (94.8)
453.06250	459.56250	NFM	Portslade	Sainsbury Supermarket (151.8)
453.06250	459.56250	NFM	Prestwick	Airport Car Parks & Security (151.8)
453.06250	459.56250	NFM	Reading	Microsoft Corporation Security
453.06250	459.56250	NFM	Romford	Shopwatch, Liberty 2 Shopping Centre
453.06250	459.56250	NFM	Swansea	Singleton Hospital Porters
453.06250	459.56250	NFM	Whitby	Shopwatch
453.06250	459.56250	NFM	York	Shopwatch
453.07500		NFM	Barnet	Barnet General Hospital
453.07500	459.57500	NFM	Barnet	Queen Elizabeth Girls School
453.07500	459.57500	NFM	Billingham	ICI
453.07500	459.57500	NFM	Bristol	Portland Dock Control
453.07500	459.57500	NFM	Cardiff	Bob Martin Pet Products Warehouse Ch.1 (71.9)
453.07500	459.57500	NFM	Carnforth	Wimpey Quarry
453.07500	459.57500	NFM	Corby	McAlpine Plant Hire
453.07500	459.57500	NFM	Coryton	Shell Haven Oil Refinery
453.07500	459.57500	NFM	Dover	Docks Security
453.07500		NFM	Edinburgh	Dynamic Earth Exhibition

Base	Mobile	Mode	Location	User and Notes
453.07500	459.57500	NFM	Felixstowe	Quay Shipping
453.07500	459.57500	NFM	Harwich	Quay Shipping
453.07500	459.57500	NFM	Heathrow	Air China T3 (146.2)
453.07500	459.57500	NFM	Heathrow	El Al Ops. T1 (127.3)
453.07500	459.57500	NFM	Ipswich	Liquid Nightclub Security
453.07500	459.57500	NFM	Jersey	Harbour/Marina Ch.2
453.07500		NFM	London	Earls Court Olympia Ch.9 Electricians
453.07500	459.57500	NFM	London	London Underground, Neasden Shunters (186.2)
453.07500		NFM	London	Mount Royal Hotel, Oxford Street
453.07500		NFM	London	National Physical Laboratory, Teddington
453.07500	459.57500	NFM	London	Royal Festival Hall
453.07500	459.57500	NFM	London	Savoy Hotel
453.07500	459.57500	NFM	Manchester	Airport, Aircraft Fitters
453.07500	459.57500	NFM	Manchester	Airport, Motor Pool Maintenance
453.07500	459.57500	NFM	March	March Ground Services
453.07500	459.57500	NFM	Middlesbrough	ICI Ammonia Base
453.07500	459.57500	NFM	Oxford	University Science Area Security
453.07500	459.57500	NFM	Pembroke	Texaco Oil Refinery
453.07500		NFM	Stansted Airport	Continental Airlines Despatch
453.07500		NFM	St Helier	Harbour Department
453.07500		NFM	Tilbury	Container Port.
453.07500		NFM	Waltham Abbey	Government Research Laboratory
453.07500	459.57500	NFM	Welwyn Garden City	Roche Pharmaceuticals Security
453.07500		NFM	Weymouth	Brewers Quay Centre
453.08750		NFM	Aberystwyth	Shopwatch
453.08750	459.58750	NFM	Bedford	Pubwatch
453.08750	459.58750	NFM	Bournemouth	Shopwatch
453.08750	459.68750	NFM	Braintree	Freeport Shopping Centre Security (136.5)
453.08750	459.58750	NFM	Brighton	Churchill Square Shopping Centre Security (94.8)
453.08750	459.58750	NFM	Bristol	The Galleries Security (88.5)
453.08750	459.58750	NFM	Cambridge	Shopwatch, Grafton Centre Ch.1 (156.7)
453.08750	459.58750	NFM	Carlisle	Lanes Shopping Centre Security Ch.2
453.08750	459.58750	NFM	Carshalton	Sutton Hospital
453.08750	459.58750	NFM	Chatham	World Naval Base Admin/Security Ch.1 (131.8)
453.08750	459.58750	NFM	Cirencester	Shopwatch
453.08750	459.58750	NFM	Cowley	MG Rover Factory (118.8)
453.08750	459.58750	NFM	Crawley	Shopwatch (110.9)
453.08750	459.58750	NFM	Crewe	Shopwatch (141.3)
453.08750	459.58750	NFM	Derbyshire	Royal Infirmary Porters
453.08750	459.58750	NFM	Guildford	Shopwatch
453.08750	459.58750	NFM	Hayes	Heinz Foods
453.08750	459.58750	NFM	Heathrow	El Al Security (114.8)
453.08750	459.58750	NFM	Hemel Hempstead	Gist International Foods ((71.9)
453.08750	459.58750	NFM	Hull	Royal Infirmary Security
453.08750	459.58750	NFM	Irvine	Shopwatch
453.08750	459.58750	NFM	Liverpool	Liverpool Aviation Services, Liverpool Airport
453.08750	459.58750	NFM	Liverpool	Whiston Hospital Security Ch.1
453.08750	459.58750	NFM	London	Courtaulds Coatings Security, Silvertown
453.08750	459.58750	NFM	London	D H Evans Security, Oxford Street
453.08750	459.58750	NFM	London	European Passenger Services, Waterloo
453.08750	459.58750	NFM	London	Rugby Stadium, Twickenham (192.8)
453.08750	459.58750	NFM	London	Selfridges Security, Oxford Street
453.08750	459.58750	NFM	London	Shopwatch, Kensington
453.08750	459.58750	NFM	Luton	Arndale Centre Car Park Security (167.9)
453.08750	459.58750	NFM	Manchester	Proctor & Gamble Factory, Trafford Park (250)
453.08750	459.58750	NFM	Newark	Shopwatch

Base	Mobile	Mode	Location	User and Notes
453.08750	459.68750	NFM	Newcastle	Marks & Spencer Security (71.9)
453.08750	459.58750	NFM	Norwich	Norwich Football Club
453.08750	459.58750	NFM	Reading	Shopwatch
453.08750	459.58750	NFM	Scunthorpe	Shopwatch
453.08750	459.58750	NFM	Solihull	Touchwood Shopping Centre (241.8)
453.08750	459.58750	NFM	Southampton Airport	AirRadio Trunked Network Control Channel
453.08750	459.58750	NFM	South Shields	Shopwatch (127.3)
453.08750	459.58750	NFM	Stansted Airport	Refuelling Company (82.5)
453.08750	459.58750	NFM	Swindon	Sainsbury Supermarket
453.08750	459.58750	NFM	Watford	Shopwatch Ch.3 (233.6)
453.08750	459.58750	NFM	Weston Super Mare	Shopwatch
453.10000	459.60000	NFM	Barking	Power Station Security
453.10000	459.60000	NFM	Barnsley	Alhambra Shopping Centre Security
453.10000	459.60000	NFM	Beeston	Boots
453.10000	459.60000	NFM	Belfast	Castle Mount Shopping Centre Security
453.10000	459.60000	NFM	Belfast	Odyssey Centre
453.10000	459.60000	NFM	Belfast	Queen's University Security
453.10000	459.60000	NFM	Birmingham	Palisades Cleaners Ch.2
453.10000	459.60000	NFM	Blackpool	Shopwatch (107.2)
453.10000	459.60000	NFM	Blackpool	Tram Inspectors
453.10000	459.60000	NFM	Brighton	Metropole Hotel (127.3)
453.10000	459.60000	NFM	Bury St Edmunds	Shopwatch (DCS 145)
453.10000	459.60000	NFM	Buxton	Pubwatch
453.10000	459.60000	NFM	Caerphilly	Shopwatch (88.5)
453.10000	459.60000	NFM	Cambridgeshire	Oakington Refugee Reception Centre (110.9)
453.10000	459.60000	NFM	Cardiff Docks	Celsa Steel Site Security (146.2)
453.10000	459.60000	NFM	Carlisle	Debenhams Department Store Security
453.10000	459.60000	NFM	Cowley	MG Rover Plant Ch.1
453.10000	459.60000	NFM	Cwmbran	Shopping Centre Security
453.10000	459.60000	NFM	Fleetwood	Tram Inspectors
453.10000	459.60000	NFM	Glasgow	Ibrox Stadium Security Ch.5
453.10000	459.60000	NFM	Hatfield	Galleria Shopping Centre Security
453.10000	459.60000	NFM	Havant	Shopwatch, Meridian Shopping Centre (156.7)
453.10000	459.60000	NFM	Heathrow	Turkish Airlines (94.8)
453.10000		NFM	Isle of Man	Ronaldsway ATC Telecomms Engineers
453.10000	459.60000	NFM	Iver	Pinewood Studios
453.10000	459.60000	NFM	Keynsham	Fry's Chocolate
453.10000	459.60000	NFM	Leeds Airport	Refuelling (103.5)
453.10000	459.60000	NFM	Leicester	Council
453.10000	459.60000	NFM	Leicester	Haymarket Shopping Centre Security
453.10000	459.60000	NFM	Llanelli	Shopwatch
453.10000	459.60000	NFM	London	Canadian High Commission Security, W1 (107.2)
453.10000	459.60000	NFM	London	Lawn Tennis Association, Wimbledon
453.10000	459.60000	NFM	London	London Underground Depot, Cockfosters
453.10000	459.60000	NFM	London	Olympia Exhibition Centre
453.10000	459.60000	NFM	London	Shopwatch, Knightsbridge (136.5)
453.10000	459.60000	NFM	London	Stock Exchange Security, City of London (71.9)
453.10000	459.60000	NFM	London	Victoria and Albert Museum, South Kensington
453.10000	459.60000	NFM	Londonderry	Debenhams Department Store Security
453.10000	459.60000	NFM	Manchester	Shopwatch, Piccadilly Ch.1
453.10000	459.60000	NFM	Manchester Airport	Loading Staff (103.5)
453.10000	459.60000	NFM	Maltby	Butlers Roadstone
453.10000	459.60000	NFM	Newcastle	Metro Maintenance Trunked
453.10000	459.60000	NFM	Northampton	Carlsberg Brewery
453.10000	459.60000	NFM	Peterborough	Queensgate Shopping Centre Security.
453.10000	459.60000	NFM	Poole	Shopwatch, Dolphin Shopping Centre (94.8)

Base	Mobile	Mode	Location	User and Notes
453.10000	459.60000	NFM	Portsmouth	Gun Wharf Leisure Complex Security (110.9)
453.10000	459.60000	NFM	Prestatyn Sands	Caravan Park Maintenance/Security (167.9)
453.10000	459.60000	NFM	Sheffield	Stockbridge Steel
453.10000	459.60000	NFM	Sittingbourne	Kemsley Paper Mill Fitters/Electricians
453.10000	459.60000	NFM	South Walden	Schering Agrochemicals
453.10000	459.60000	NFM	Southampton	Hospital Transport Ch.1 (146.2)
453.10000	459.60000	NFM	Telford	Shopping Centre Security/Cleaners (118.8)
453.10000	459.60000	NFM	Warrington	Shopwatch, Cockhedge Centre
453.10000	459.60000	NFM	Watford	John Lewis Department Store Security (127.3)
453.11250	459.61250	NFM	Bridgend	Princess of Wales Hospital
453.11250	459.61250	NFM	Cardiff	NCP Car Parks (123)
453.11250	459.61250	NFM	Chelmsford	High Chelmer Shopping Centre Security (114.8)
453.11250	459.61250	NFM	Chesterfield	Chesterfield Hospital Trunked Voice Channel
453.11250	459.61250	NFM	Coventry	Jaguar Plant Security MPT1327 Voice Channel
453.11250	459.61250	NFM	Cowley	MG Rover Factory
453.11250	459.61250	NFM	Dorchester	Shopwatch/Pubwatch (131.8)
453.11250	459.61250	NFM	Gatwick Airport	ICS Cleaning (88.5)
453.11250	459.61250	NFM	Guildford	Royal Victoria Shopping Centre Security
453.11250	459.61250	NFM	Hartlepool	Shopping Centre Security
453.11250	459.61250	NFM	Heathrow	Air Canada T3 Ramp Ops. (210.7)
453.11250	459.61250	NFM	Hemel Hempstead	Hemel Hempstead Hospital (107.2)
453.11250	459.61250	NFM	Ipswich	Action For Community in Rural England
453.11250	459.58750	NFM	Kent	Eurotunnel Concession Tunnel Control
453.11250	459.61250	NFM	Leicester	Leicester Royal Infirmary Porters
453.11250	459.61250	NFM	Lichfield	Three Spires Shopping Centre Security
453.11250	459.61250	NFM	Liverpool	MTL Asset Protection Teams
453.11250	459.61250	NFM	Liverpool Airport	Liverpool Airport Services
453.11250	459.61250	NFM	London	Brent Cross Shopping Centre Security Control
453.11250	459.61250	NFM	London	Earls Court Exhibition Centre
453.11250	459.61250	NFM	London	Harrods Staff, Knightsbridge (162.2)
453.11250	459.61250	NFM	London	Kingston on Thames College
453.11250	459.61250	NFM	London	Parking Enforcement W1 Area (136.5)
453.11250	459.61250	NFM	London	Shopwatch, Harrow (77)
453.11250	459.61250	NFM	London	Southside Shopping Centre Security, Wandsworth
453.11250	459.61250	NFM	London	Waterloo Station Cleaners Ch.3 (131.8)
453.11250	459.61250	NFM	Manchester	Council Boarding Up Service & Locksmiths (77)
453.11250	459.61250	NFM	Manchester	Manchester Royal Infirmary Security (179.9)
453.11250	459.61250	NFM	Manchester	Selfridges Security, Trafford Centre
453.11250	459.61250	NFM	Manchester	Shopwatch, Piccadilly Ch.2
453.11250	459.61250	NFM	Manchester	St Marys Hospital Security (123)
453.11250	459.61250	NFM	Newbury	Vodaphone Head Office Site Security
453.11250	459.61250	NFM	Newcastle	Shopwatch, Shields Road
453.11250	459.61250	NFM	Newhaven	Sainsbury Supermarket (88.5)
453.11250	459.61250	NFM	Oldham	Council Emergency Channel (77)
453.11250	459.61250	NFM	Peterborough	Hampton Shopping Centre Security Ch.1 (203.5)
453.11250	459.61250	NFM	Sandhurst	Marks & Spencer, The Meadows
453.11250	459.61250	NFM	Sandown	Shopwatch (94.8)
453.11250	459.61250	NFM	Sheffield	Magna Centre
453.11250	459.61250	NFM	Sittingbourne	Kemsley Paper Mill Stock Staff
453.11250	459.61250	NFM	Skelmersdale	Shopwatch
453.11250	459.61250	NFM	Skipton	Shopwatch
453.11250	459.61250	NFM	Solihull	Shopwatch/Pubwatch (146.2)
453.11250	459.61250	NFM	Southampton	Esso Fawley Oil Refinery (192.8)
453.11250	459.61250	NFM	Southend on Sea	Shopwatch (88.5)
453.11250	459.61250	NFM	South Shields	Shopwatch
453.11250	459.61250	NFM	Tunbridge Wells	Royal Victoria Place Shops Security (233)

Base	Mobile	Mode	Location	User and Notes
453.11250	459.61250	NFM	Waterlooville	Shopwatch (77)
453.11250	459.61250	NFM	Watford	Marks & Spencer Security (123)
453.11250	459.61250	NFM	Welwyn Garden City	Shopwatch (186.2)
453.12500	459.62500	NFM	Belfast	Royal Victoria Hospital Porters/Staff (67/107.2)
453.12500	459.62500	NFM	Birmingham	Birmingham University Security (98.4)
453.12500	459.62500	NFM	Bristol	Avonmouth Docks (82.5)
453.12500	459.62500	NFM	Cardiff	Allied Steel & Wire Train Movements
453.12500	459.62500	NFM	Carnforth	Bardon Aggregates, Back Lane Quarry Ch.2
453.12500	459.62500	NFM	Coventry	Orchards Security
453.12500	459.62500	NFM	Cowley	MG Rover Plant Ch.4
453.12500	459.62500	NFM	Dover	Western Docks Jetfoil & Railway
453.12500	459.62500	NFM	East Midlands Airport	British Midland Airways
453.12500	459.62500	NFM	Edinburgh Airport	British Midland Airways Ops (94.8)
453.12500	459.62500	NFM	Felixstowe	Docks
453.12500	459.62500	NFM	Glasgow Airport	British Midland Airways
453.12500	459.62500	NFM	Guernsey	St. Sampson's Harbour
453.12500		NFM	Harwich	Port Loaders
453.12500	459.62500	NFM	Heathrow	British Midland Airways T1 Tugs (94.8)
453.12500	459.62500	NFM	Immingham	Conoco Oil Refinery
453.12500	459.62500	NFM	Jersey Airport	British Midland Airways Handling
453.12500	459.62500	NFM	Langley	Iveco Ford
453.12500		NFM	London	Hammersmith & Fulham Council
453.12500		NFM	London	Regent Palace Hotel (192.8)
453.12500		NFM	London	Spearmint Rhino Club (127.3)
453.12500	459.62500	NFM	London	Teddington Studios Security
453.12500	459.62500	NFM	Manchester	International Airport
453.12500		NFM	Manchester	Marks & Spencer Security, Arndale Centre
453.12500	459.62500	NFM	Middlesbrough	BASF Fibres Raw Materials
453.12500	459.62500	NFM	Newhaven	Port & Property Services
453.12500	459.62500	NFM	Norwich	Colmans Foods
453.12500	459.62500	NFM	Oldham	Garforth Glass
453.12500	459.62500	NFM	Oxted	Surrey Leisure Site.
453.12500	459.62500	NFM	Sheffield	Stockbridge Steel Engineering
453.12500	459.62500	NFM	Speke	Halewood Ford Plant Security
453.12500	459.62500	NFM	Stafford	Stafford College Security
453.12500		NFM	Stevenage	ICL/Logicom Computers Security Ch.2 (110.9)
453.12500	459.62500	NFM	Wolverhampton	Mander Shopping Centre Security (71.9)
453.12500	459.62500	NFM	Woodbridge	Tannington Pea Harvesting
453.15000	459.65000	NFM	Bedford	Hospital Engineers
453.15000	459.65000	NFM	Belfast	Zip Taxis
453.15000	459.65000	NFM	Birmingham	Midland Airport Services, International Airport (123)
453.15000	459.65000	NFM	Bolton	Parking Enforcement (71.9)
453.15000	459.65000	NFM	Bradford	Kirkgate Shopping Centre Security
453.15000	459.65000	NFM	Coventry	Hillfields Flats Security
453.15000	459.65000	NFM	Doncaster	Frenchgate Shopping Centre Security
453.15000	459.65000	NFM	Edinburgh	City Centre Couriers
453.15000	459.65000	NFM	Fleetwood	P & O Ferries Security
453.15000	459.65000	NFM	Ipswich	Shopwatch
453.15000	459.65000	NFM	Leyland	Parking Enforcement/Clampers (71.9)
453.15000	459.65000	NFM	London	Metro Bus, Orpington
453.15000	459.65000	NFM	London	Parking Enforcement, Bermondsey
453.15000	459.65000	NFM	London	Parking Enforcement/Clampers WC1/WC2 (167.9)
453.15000	459.65000	NFM	London	Pavilion Shopping Centre, Uxbridge
453.15000	459.65000	NFM	Northwich	Brunner-Mond Alkaline Chemicals
453.15000	459.65000	NFM	Nottingham	Shopwatch, Broadmarsh Shopping Centre
453.15000	459.65000	NFM	Oxford	University Halls of Residence

Base	Mobile	Mode	Location	User and Notes
453.15000	459.65000	NFM	Reading	Prudential Assurance
453.15000	459.65000	NFM	Sheffield	Council Cleansing Dept.
453.15000	459.65000	NFM	Sittingbourne	Kemsley Paper Mill Stock Plant
453.15000	459.65000	NFM	Southampton	Fawley Oil Refinery Emergency Response Team
453.15000		NFM	Stansted Airport	El-Al Security/Sky Marshals
453.15000	459.65000	NFM	Stockport	Shopwatch
453.15000	459.65000	NFM	Sunderland	University (127.3)
453.15000	459.65000	NFM	Swansea	Shopwatch (94.8)
453.15000	459.65000	NFM	Swindon	Council Maintenance
453.15000	459.65000	NFM	Whittlesey	McCain International
453.17500	459.67500	NFM	Brighton	Sainsbury Supermarket, Lewes Road (151.4)
453.17500	459.67500	NFM	Brighton	Trafalgar Place Security (77)
453.17500	459.67500	NFM	Bristol	Pubwatch
453.17500	459.67500	NFM	Carmarthen	Shopwatch
453.17500	459.67500	NFM	Cardiff	Boots Store Security
453.17500	459.67500	NFM	Cardiff	Dow Corning Manufacturing, Barry Docks
453.17500	459.67500	NFM	Chelmsford	McDonalds Drive-Thru, A12
453.17500	459.67500	NFM	Coventry	Courtaulds Security
453.17500	459.67500	NFM	Croydon	Drummonds Shopping Centre Security
453.17500	459.67500	NFM	Dagenham	Ford Motor Plant Repeater
453.17500	459.67500	NFM	Edinburgh	Royal Infirmary Security
453.17500	459.67500	NFM	Edinburgh Airport	Airline Ops.
453.17500	459.67500	NFM	Grimsby	Tioxide UK Chemical Plant
453.17500	459.67500	NFM	Harwich	Car Park
453.17500	459.67500	NFM	Hastings	Sainsbury Supermarket, Hastings Road
453.17500	459.67500	NFM	Hemel Hempstead	Shopwatch (167.9)
453.17500	459.67500	NFM	Ipswich	Burger King Drive-Thru, Codpock
453.17500	459.67500	NFM	Leeds Airport	Catering Operations, Yeadon
453.17500	459.67500	NFM	London	Container Terminal, Stratford
453.17500	459.67500	NFM	London	District Hospital, Greenwich
453.17500	459.67500	NFM	London	Harrods Security, Knightsbridge
453.17500	459.67500	NFM	London	Old Bailey Central Criminal Court
453.17500	459.67500	NFM	London	Property Management Company, Regent Street
453.17500	459.67500	NFM	London	Queen Mary's Hospital, Putney
453.17500	459.67500	NFM	Luton	Airport Station Coach Service (67)
453.17500	459.67500	NFM	Lutterworth	Asda Distribution Depot Trunk Data
453.17500	459.67500	NFM	Newcastle	Tyne & Wear Metro
453.17500	459.67500	NFM	Plymouth	Shopwatch
453.17500	459.67500	NFM	Reading	Oracle Shopping Centre (114.8)
453.17500	459.67500	NFM	Sheffield	City Parks Security
453.17500	459.67500	NFM	Southampton	Shopwatch (71.9)
453.17500	459.67500	NFM	Stansted Airport	Aviance
453.17500	459.67500	NFM	Stevenage	Knebworth House Security/Staff
453.17500	459.67500	NFM	Stevenage	MDBA (BAe Systems) Security Ch.1
453.17500	459.67500	NFM	Stoke on Trent	Potteries Shopping Centre Security, Hanley (210.7)
453.17500	459.67500	NFM	Tendring	District Council
453.17500	459.67500	NFM	Watford	Harlequin Shopping Centre Security (167.9)
453.17500	459.67500	NFM	Weybridge	Warren Pond Tennis Club
453.20000	459.70000	NFM	Birmingham	Taxi Company
453.20000	459.70000	NFM	Boston	Acorn Cabs
453.20000	459.70000	NFM	Brighton	Theobald House Security (114.8)
453.20000	459.70000	NFM	Cleveleys	ICI Polymers
453.20000	459.70000	NFM	Dartford	Borough Council Parking Enforcement (210.7)
453.20000	459.70000	NFM	Dorset	BP, Wytch Farm Ch.2 (110.9)
453.20000	459.70000	NFM	Felixstowe	Docks South Freightliner Terminal
453.20000	459.70000	NFM	Fleetwood	Plumbing Company

Base	Mobile	Mode	Location	User and Notes
453.20000	459.70000	NFM	Glasgow	City Tourist Guides
453.20000	459.70000	NFM	Hampshire	Sewage Works (V)
453.20000	459.70000	NFM	Heathrow	Budget Rent A Car (162.2)
453.20000	459.70000	NFM	Hull	Hull Royal Infirmary Security
453.20000	459.70000	NFM	Jersey Harbour	Shell Fuel Supplies
453.20000	459.70000	NFM	Liverpool	Parking Enforcement, Bootle/Sefton
453.20000		NFM	Loch Ness	Walter Scott Steamer
453.20000	459.70000	NFM	London	Linkcars, Belsize Park (77)
453.20000	459.70000	NFM	Portsmouth	Taxi Company
453.20000	459.70000	NFM	Ramsbottom	Civic Private Hire
453.20000	459.70000	NFM	Reading	Broad Street Shopping Centre Security (151.4)
453.20000	459.70000	NFM	Scunthorpe	Corus Steelworks
453.20000	459.70000	NFM	Sheffield	First Mainline Buses Inspectors
453.20000	459.70000	NFM	Silverstone	Silverstone Driving School (210.7)
453.20000	459.70000	NFM	Snodland	Smurfitt, Townsend Hook Paper Mill Security
453.20000	459.70000	NFM	Southampton	Esso Fawley Oil Refinery (192.8)
453.20000	459.70000	NFM	Southend on Sea	Shopwatch
453.20000	459.70000	NFM	Stevenage	GlaxoSmithKline Security Ch.1
453.20000	459.70000	NFM	Sunderland	Bridges Shopping Centre (88.5)
453.20000	459.70000	NFM	Wigston	Shopwatch (141.3)
453.20000	459.70000	NFM	Wisbech	Shopwatch
453.22500	459.72500	NFM	Belfast Docks	West Twin Silos Ltd (192.8)
453.22500		NFM	Brighton	Brighton Football Club (94.8)
453.22500	459.72500	NFM	Cardiff	Shopwatch, Whitchurch
453.22500	459.72500	NFM	Cleveleys	ICI Polymers
453.22500		NFM	Felixstowe	Docks
453.22500	459.72500	NFM	Heathrow	American Airlines T3 (127.3)
453.22500		NFM	Jersey	St Helier Harbour Ch.1
453.22500	459.72500	NFM	Pembroke	Texaco Oil Refinery
453.22500		NFM	Poole	Dolphin Shopping Centre Security
453.22500	459.72500	NFM	Swindon	Great West Factory Outlet
453.22500		NFM	West Thurrock	House of Fraser Security (71.9)
453.23750	459.58750	NFM	Kent	Eurotunnel Control
453.25000	459.75000	NFM	Belfast	Ulster Folk & Transport Museum Security
453.25000	459.75000	NFM	Cambridge	Westbrook Research Centre
453.25000	459.75000	NFM	Cardiff	The Edge Nightclub (123)
453.25000	459.75000	NFM	Felixstowe	Shopwatch
453.25000	459.75000	NFM	Fleetwood	Council
453.25000	459.75000	NFM	Heathrow	National Car Rental Buses (103.5)
453.25000	459.75000	NFM	Hull	Docks
453.25000	459.75000	NFM	Lee on Solent	Cols Cars
453.25000	459.75000	NFM	Leeds	Parking Enforcement
453.25000	459.75000	NFM	Leicester	Council
453.25000	459.75000	NFM	Llanwern	Corus Steelworks
453.25000	459.75000	NFM	London	Central Middlesex Hospital, Acton
453.25000	459.75000	NFM	London	Kingston University
453.25000	459.75000	NFM	London	Parking Enforcement, Enfield
453.25000	459.75000	NFM	London	Parking Enforcement, Lambeth
453.25000	459.75000	NFM	London	Parking Enforcement, Merton
453.25000	459.75000	NFM	Middlesbrough	BASF Fibres Raw Materials Ch.3
453.25000	459.75000	NFM	Norwich	Shopwatch
453.25000	459.75000	NFM	Reading	Council (RC) (156.7)
453.25000	459.75000	NFM	Stevenage	GlaxoSmithKline Ch.3 Emergency Use
453.25000	459.75000	NFM	Swansea	Pubwatch, Oxford Street
453.25000	459.75000	NFM	Whiston	Whiston Hospital Security
453.27500	459.77500	NFM	Boston	Pilgrim Hospital Porters

Base	Mobile	Mode	Location	User and Notes
453.27500		NFM	Cambridgeshire	Ambulance Service Handhelds (203.5)
453.27500	459.77500	NFM	Dorset	Ambulance Service (94.8 Input Only)
453.27500		NFM	Essex	Ambulance Service Handhelds
453.27500	459.77500	NFM	Herts/Beds	Ambulance Service (88.5)
453.27500	459.77500	NFM	Humberside	Ambulance Service Handhelds
453.27500	459.77500	NFM	Lincolnshire	Council
453.27500	459.77500	NFM	London	Ambulance Service Ch.1
453.27500		NFM	London	Ambulance Service Emergency Handhelds (107.2)
453.27500	459.77500	NFM	Nationwide	Ambulance Ch.1 (VHF/UHF Repeater for Handhelds)
453.27500	459.77500	NFM	N Ireland	Ambulance Service (Mobile Repeater)
453.30000	459.80000	NFM	Brighton	Golf Club
453.30000	459.80000	NFM	Gatwick	Airline Ops. (114.8)
453.30000	459.80000	NFM	Harwich	Port Authority Ch.1
453.30000	459.80000	NFM	Heathrow	United Airlines T3 (192.8).
453.30000	459.80000	NFM	Humberside	Lindsey Oil Refinery
453.30000	459.80000	NFM	Liverpool	MTL Buses In-Cab Radio Ch.1
453.30000		NFM	London	Chevron Oil International HQ Security (146.2)
453.30000	459.80000	NFM	London	London Eye Staff (103.5 & 88.5)
453.30000	459.80000	NFM	Nationwide	Securiplan Security at Transco Sites
453.30000	459.80000	NFM	Manchester	Piccadilly Station Staff (123)
453.30000	459.80000	NFM	Sheffield	Council Staff, Derwent House/Howden House
453.30000		NFM	Stevenage	Pulse Discotheque & Vogue Nightclub
453.31250	459.81250	NFM	N Ireland	Ambulance Service Ch.3
453.32500	459.82500	NFM	Avon	Ambulance Service Ch.2
453.32500	459.82500	NFM	Cardiff	University Hospital of Wales Security (118.8)
453.32500	459.82500	NFM	Cheltenham	Cheltenham General Hospital (136.5)
453.32500	459.82500	NFM	East Sussex	Ambulance Service Ch.2 Incident Vehicle
453.32500	459.82500	NFM	Gloucester	Royal General Hospital Porters (110.9)
453.32500	459.82500	NFM	Herts/Beds	Ambulance Service (141.3)
453.32500	459.82500	NFM	Kent	Ambulance Ch.2 Bluewater VHF-UHF Repeater
453.32500	459.82500	NFM	Lincolnshire	Ambulance Service Mobile Link
453.32500	459.82500	NFM	London	Ambulance Service Ch.2
453.32500	459.82500	NFM	London	Charring Cross Hospital Handhelds
453.32500	459.82500	NFM	Lytham	Health Centre
453.32500	459.82500	NFM	Manchester	Midwife Service
453.32500	459.82500	NFM	March	St Mary's Hospital Security
453.32500	459.82500	NFM	Merseyside	Mersey Docks & Harbour Board
453.32500	459.82500	NFM	Nationwide	Ambulance Service Handhelds
453.32500	459.82500	NFM	Northern Ireland	Ambulance Service Ch.2
453.32500	459.82500	NFM	Sussex	Ambulance Service Ch.2
453.35000	459.85000	NFM	Cowley	MG Rover Factory
453.35000	459.85000	NFM	Hartlepool	Teesside Docks Operations
453.35000	459.85000	NFM	Harwell	UKAEA
453.35000		NFM	Heathrow	Esso Fuel, Wessex Road
453.35000	459.85000	NFM	Humberside	Ambulance Handhelds UHF-VHF Link
453.35000		NFM	Humberside Airport	Bond Helicopters
453.35000	459.85000	NFM	Inverness Airport	Security
453.35000	459.85000	NFM	Langley, Bucks	Industrial Coatings
453.35000		NFM	London	Cabinet Office Security, Whitehall (103.5)
453.35000	459.85000	NFM	London	GlaxoSmithKline Security, Brentford (71.9)
453.35000		NFM	London	Masterpark, Gerrard Place
453.35000		NFM	London	Masterpark, Portland Place
453.35000	459.85000	NFM	London	Twickenham Rugby Stadium Ticket/Security(82.5)
453.35000	459.85000	NFM	Reading	Courage Brewery
453.35000		NFM	Stevenage	Town Car Park Security/Staff (67)
453.35000	459.85000	NFM	Walsall	Council Works Yard

Base	Mobile	Mode	Location	User and Notes
453.35000	459.85000	NFM	Woodford	Print Finishers
453.37500	459.87500	NFM	Ashford	William Harvey Hospital Porters
453.37500	459.87500	NFM	Brighton	Brighton General Hospital Porters (110.9)
453.37500	459.87500	NFM	Cambridge	Addenbrooke's Hospital Porters (114.8)
453.37500	459.87500	NFM	Cardiff	Millennium Stadium Medics
453.37500	459.87500	NFM	Cleveleys	ICI Polymers
453.37500	459.87500	NFM	Coventry	Walsgrave Hospital
453.37500	459.87500	NFM	Cowley	MG Rover Plant Ch.2
453.37500	459.87500	NFM	Immingham	Conoco Oil Refinery Emergency Channel
453.37500	459.87500	NFM	Immingham	Lindsey Oil Fire Service
453.37500	459.87500	NFM	Isle of Wight	St Marys Hospital Porters, Newport (110.9)
453.37500	459.87500	NFM	Leeds	Hospital Security
453.37500	459.87500	NFM	Liverpool	Mersey Docks & Harbour Board
453.37500	459.87500	NFM	London	Stock Exchange, City of London
453.37500	459.87500	NFM	London	Borough of Walthamstow Repeater
453.37500	459.87500	NFM	London	Brent Cross Shopping Centre Repeater
453.37500	459.87500	NFM	London	Charing Cross Hospital Repeater
453.37500	459.87500	NFM	London	Hammersmith Hospital Porters/Security
453.37500	459.87500	NFM	London	Kings College Hospital Porters
453.37500	459.87500	NFM	London	Richmond Park Staff Repeater
453.37500	459.87500	NFM	London	QE II Conference Centre Repeater, Westminster
453.37500	459.87500	NFM	Luton	Airport Buses Baggage Loaders (67)
453.37500	459.87500	NFM	Nationwide	Ambulance Service Ch.3
453.37500	459.87500	NFM	Port Talbot	BP Works
453.37500	459.87500	NFM	Stansted	Airport Trunked Network
453.40000	459.90000	NFM	Blackpool	Airport
453.40000		NFM	Cardiff	Brannigans/Creations Nightclub, Park Place (141.3)
453.40000		NFM	Cardiff Airport	Aviance Baggage Handlers (114.8)
453.40000	459.90000	NFM	Cliffe	Conoco Oil
453.40000		NFM	Felixstowe	Container Port
453.40000	459.90000	NFM	Glasgow	Prince's Square Shopping Mall Security
453.40000	459.90000	NFM	Heathrow	American Airlines Ramp/Cargo T3 (192.8)
453.40000	459.90000	NFM	Hull	City Council
453.40000	459.90000	NFM	Hull	Prospect Shopping Centre Security.
453.40000	459.90000	NFM	Ipswich	Port Authority
453.40000	459.90000	NFM	Jersey Airport	Esso Refuelling
453.40000	459.90000	NFM	London	Barbican Centre Staff, City of London
453.40000		NFM	London	Hippodrome Nightclub, Leicester Square
453.40000	459.90000	NFM	London	Wimbledon Common Rangers
453.40000	459.90000	NFM	Oxford	University Science Area Security
453.40000		NFM	Shannon Airport	Aer Lingus Ground Staff
453.40000	459.90000	NFM	Sittingbourne	Ridham Docks
453.40000	459.90000	NFM	Sizewell	Power Station Work Teams Ch.1
453.42500	459.92500	NFM	Ayr	Ayr Hospital Crash Teams
453.42500		NFM	Birmingham	Gap Store, Fort Retail Park
453.42500		NFM	Cardiff	Cardiff International Arena (94.8)
453.42500	459.92500	NFM	Clacton	Shopping Village (107.2)
453.42500		NFM	Eastbourne	Debenhams Department Store
453.42500	459.92500	NFM	Ellesmere Port	Shell Tranmere Oil Terminal
453.42500		NFM	Felixstowe	Docks (103.5)
453.42500	459.92500	NFM	Gatwick	Ground Repeater (141.3)
453.42500	459.92500	NFM	Heathrow	Ground Repeater
453.42500	459.92500	NFM	Immingham	Conoco Oil Refinery
453.42500	459.92500	NFM	Liverpool	Tranmere Oil Stage Operations
453.42500		NFM	London	Dominion Theatre, Tottenham Court Road
453.42500		NFM	London	Peter Jones, Chelsea (218.1)

Base	Mobile	Mode	Location	User and Notes
453.42500		NFM	London	Shopping Centre, Putney
453.42500		NFM	London	Wembley Hospital
453.42500		NFM	London	Willesden General Hospital
453.42500	459.92500	NFM	Lutterworth	Asda Distribution Depot
453.42500	459.92500	NFM	Manchester	International Airport, BP Aviation Fuel
453.42500	459.92500	NFM	Middlesbrough	British Steel Security/Medics
453.42500	459.92500	NFM	Oxford	Gap Fashion Store, Clarenden Centre
453.42500	459.92500	NFM	Swansea	DVLA Car Registration Office Security (88.5)
453.42500	459.92500	NFM	Swansea	Morriston Hospital Security
453.43750	459.93750	NFM	Blackpool	Council Trunked System
453.43750	459.93750	NFM	Luton Airport	AirRadio easyJet/Multi User Trunked Network
453.45000	459.95000	NFM	Basildon	Shopwatch
453.45000	459.95000	NFM	Cambridge	City Centre Wardens
453.45000	459.95000	NFM	Cardiff	HM Revenue & Customs Office Security
453.45000	459.95000	NFM	Cowley	MG Rover Plant Ch.3
453.45000	459.95000	NFM	Ellesmere Port	Shell Tranmere Oil Terminal Distribution
453.45000	459.95000	NFM	Felixstowe	Docks
453.45000	459.95000	NFM	Harwich	Port (173.8)
453.45000	459.95000	NFM	Kilmarnock	Shopwatch
453.45000	459.95000	NFM	Leicester	Haymarket Shopping Centre Security (103.5)
453.45000	459.95000	NFM	Leicester	University of Christian Fellowship
453.45000		NFM	Llantrisant	Royal Mint Security
453.45000	459.95000	NFM	London	Borough of Haringey Council
453.45000	459.95000	NFM	London	Hammersmith & Fulham Council
453.45000		NFM	London	School of Hygiene/Tropical Medicine, Gower Street
453.45000		NFM	London	Sky TV Studio Staff, Brentford
453.45000		NFM	London	Taylor Woodrow Security, St Katharine's Dock (67)
453.45000	459.95000	NFM	Mallory Park	Coalville Cleaning
453.45000	459.95000	NFM	Nuneaton	Mira Car Research
453.45000		NFM	Rutland	Rutland Water Duty Warden
453.45000		NFM	Salisbury	Salisbury Station Staff
453.45000	459.95000	NFM	Silverstone	Race Track
453.45000	459.95000	NFM	Sunderland	Football Stadium
453.45000	459.95000	NFM	Welwyn Garden City	Rank Xerox
453.47500	459.97500	NFM	Ashford	Ashford International Terminal
453.47500	459.97500	NFM	Ayr	Scottish Agricultural College
453.47500	459.97500	NFM	Barrow in Furness	Kimberley Clark (77)
453.47500	459.97500	NFM	Basildon	Shopwatch, Eastgate Shopping Centre
453.47500	459.97500	NFM	Birmingham	Airport Security
453.47500	459.97500	NFM	Bispham	Shopwatch
453.47500	459.97500	NFM	Burton on Trent	Shopwatch
453.47500	459.97500	NFM	Cambridge	Girton College (94.8)
453.47500	459.97500	NFM	Cardiff	University Security (88.5)
453.47500	459.97500	NFM	Chester	Grosvenor Shopping Centre Security (114.8)
453.47500	459.97500	NFM	Chorley	Shopwatch
453.47500	459.97500	NFM	Cleveleys	Shopwatch
453.47500	459.97500	NFM	Coventry	Shopwatch
453.47500	459.97500	NFM	Dorset	BP Wytch Farm Ch.3 (110.9)
453.47500	459.97500	NFM	Ellesmere Port	Shell Blends
453.47500	459.97500	NFM	Flint	CBM Security
453.47500	459.97500	NFM	Grimsby	Council
453.47500	459.97500	NFM	Guildford	House of Fraser Army & Navy Store
453.47500	459.97500	NFM	Hartlepool	Council Trunked System
453.47500	459.97500	NFM	Harwich	Stena Sealink Staff (103.5)
453.47500	459.97500	NFM	Havant	Shopwatch, Leigh Park (156.7)
453.47500	459.97500	NFM	Heathrow	BAA Baggage Handlers T3 (110.9)

Base	Mobile	Mode	Location	User and Notes
453.47500	459.97500	NFM	Huntingdon	Shopwatch
453.47500		NFM	Ipswich	Co-Op Boss Hall Security (151.4)
453.47500	459.97500	NFM	London	Channel Tunnel Control en route to St Pancras
453.47500	459.97500	NFM	London	Charring Cross Hospital Security
453.47500	459.97500	NFM	London	London School of Economics (192.8)
453.47500	459.97500	NFM	London	Royal Parks Staff, Hyde Park
453.47500	459.97500	NFM	London	Royal Parks Staff, Richmond Park
453.47500	459.97500	NFM	London	Shopwatch, Hounslow (114.8)
453.47500	459.97500	NFM	London	Tate And Lyle Sugar Refinery, Silvertown
453.47500	459.97500	NFM	London	QE II Conference Centre, Westminster (179.9)
453.47500	459.97500	NFM	London	Victoria Coach Station Staff (82.5)
453.47500	459.97500	NFM	London	Walthamstow Town Hall
453.47500	459.97500	NFM	London	Whittington Hospital Porters
453.47500	459.97500	NFM	Londonderry	Foyle Side Shopping Centre Security (94.8)
453.47500	459.97500	NFM	Maidenhead	Shopwatch (136.5)
453.47500	459.97500	NFM	Manchester	Airport Ops. (107.2)
453.47500	459.97500	NFM	Manchester	Manchester University Security
453.47500	459.97500	NFM	Mansfield	Four Seasons Shopping Centre Security
453.47500	459.97500	NFM	Newcastle	Newcastle Metro Trunked
453.47500	459.97500	NFM	North Kent	National Grid Sub Station
453.47500	459.97500	NFM	Oxford	Westgate Shopping Centre Security
453.47500	459.97500	NFM	North Sea	Conoco Murchison
453.47500	459.97500	NFM	Peterborough	Peterborough Football Club Security
453.47500	459.97500	NFM	Salford	University Security (123)
453.47500	459.97500	NFM	Shanklin	Shopwatch (94.8)
453.47500	459.97500	NFM	Sheffield	Debenhams Security, Meadowhall Centre
453.47500	459.97500	NFM	Shoreham by Sea	Power Station Engineering Ch.1 (82.5)
453.47500	459.97500	NFM	Sittingbourne	Kemsley Paper Mill Fitters/Maintenance
453.47500	459.97500	NFM	Southampton	Esso Fawley Oil Refinery (192.8)
453.47500	459.97500	NFM	Stansted Airport	Airline Ops.
453.47500	459.97500	NFM	Stevenage	ICL Computers Cleaners/Maint. Ch.3 (218.1)
453.47500	459.97500	NFM	Swindon	Parking Enforcement
453.47500	459.97500	NFM	Ulverston	GlaxoSmithKline (71.9)
453.47500	459.97500	NFM	Welham Green	Tesco Distribution Depot
453.47500	459.97500	NFM	Wolverhampton	Shopwatch (71.9)
453.50000		NFM	Ashford	Railways, Beechbrook Yard Trains Shunting
453.50000	460.00000	NFM	Belfast	Castlecourt Shopping Centre
453.50000	460.00000	NFM	Blackpool	Shopwatch (127.3)
453.50000	460.00000	NFM	Brighton	Hospital
453.50000	460.00000	NFM	Bristol	BAe Filton
453.50000	460.00000	NFM	Bromley	Glades Shopping Centre Security
453.50000	460.00000	NFM	Cardiff	Capital Shopping Centre Security (67)
453.50000	460.00000	NFM	Chatham	Pentagon Shopping Centre Security
453.50000	460.00000	NFM	Chichester	Marks & Spencer Security
453.50000	460.00000	NFM	Droylsden	Shopwatch
453.50000	460.00000	NFM	Fareham	Shopping Centre Security (123)
453.50000	460.00000	NFM	Farnborough	Society of British Aerospace Companies
453.50000	460.00000	NFM	Folkestone	Hoverspeed
453.50000	460.00000	NFM	Harwich	Dock & Port Security (107.2)
453.50000	460.00000	NFM	Heathrow	Holiday Inn Hotel Security
453.50000	460.00000	NFM	Keswick	Shopwatch/Pubwatch (88.5)
453.50000	460.00000	NFM	Lancaster	Pubwatch (173.8)
453.50000	460.00000	NFM	Lancaster	Shopwatch (151.4)
453.50000	460.00000	NFM	Liverpool	Liverpool Airport easyJet Ops. (103.5)
453.50000	460.00000	NFM	London	BBC World Service Security, Bush House
453.50000	460.00000	NFM	London	Docklands Light Railway (107.2)

Base	Mobile	Mode	Location	User and Notes
453.50000	460.00000	NFM	London	Shopwatch, Queensway, Bayswater
453.50000	460.00000	NFM	Luton Airport	AirRadio easyJet/Multi User Trunked Network
453.50000	460.00000	NFM	Manchester	Trafford Centre Security Ch.1 (Lima)
453.50000	460.00000	NFM	March	Oakington Refugee Detention Centre (151.4)
453.50000	460.00000	NFM	Margate	Shopwatch/Pubwatch
453.50000	460.00000	NFM	Newcastle	Metro, Data Command Channel
453.50000	460.00000	NFM	Northwich	Brunner-Mond Alkaline Chemicals (156.7)
453.50000	460.00000	NFM	Norwich	Castle Mall Shopping Centre Security
453.50000	460.00000	NFM	Oxford	UKAEA, Culham
453.50000	460.00000	NFM	Reading	Prudential Offices Security
453.50000	460.00000	NFM	Salford	Quays Security Company
453.50000	460.00000	NFM	Salisbury	Shopwatch
453.50000	460.00000	NFM	Sheffield	Council Markets Ops.
453.50000	460.00000	NFM	Sherborne	Shopwatch (67)
453.50000	460.00000	NFM	Southampton	General Hospital Car Parks/Porters
453.50000	460.00000	NFM	Southampton	Esso Fawley Oil Refinery (192.8)
453.50000	460.00000	NFM	St Helens	Church Square Shopping Centre Security (218.1)
453.50000	460.00000	NFM	Stansted	BAA Trunked Network
453.52500	460.02500	NFM	Bristol	BAe Filton Fire/Medics
453.52500		NFM	Edinburgh	Shopwatch, Kirkgate
453.52500	460.02500	NFM	Ellesmere Port	Shell Security
453.52500	460.02500	NFM	Felixstowe	Docks, Trinity Terminal
453.52500	460.02500	NFM	Havering	College.
453.52500	460.02500	NFM	Hull	City Council, Housing
453.52500		NFM	Jersey	St Helier Harbour Ch.2
453.52500	460.02500	NFM	Langley	Total Oil Distribution Depot
453.52500		NFM	Leeds Airport	Servisair/GlobeGround, Yeadon
453.52500	460.02500	NFM	Leicester	Leicester University Security
453.52500		NFM	London	Dickens & Jones, Oxford Street (186.2)
453.52500		NFM	London	Peter Jones, Chelsea (67)
453.52500		NFM	London	Royal Courts Of Justice/Law Courts Security (107.2)
453.52500		NFM	Milton Keynes	Dickins & Jones (82.5)
453.52500	460.02500	NFM	Sheffield	City Council Emergency Gas Fitters
453.52500		NFM	Shoreham by Sea	Goods Handling, Shoreham Docks
453.52500	460.02500	NFM	Sizewell	Power Station Work Teams Ch.2
453.52500		NFM	Swindon	Shopwatch (127.3)
453.53750	460.13750	NFM	London	London Ambulance Service Event Control
453.55000	460.05000	NFM	Aberdeen	Network Rail
453.55000	460.05000	NFM	Barrow in Furness	Network Rail
453.55000	460.05000	NFM	Bedford	Network Rail
453.55000	460.05000	NFM	Birmingham	Network Rail, New Street Station
453.55000	460.05000	NFM	Birmingham	Network Rail, Snow Hill
453.55000	460.05000	NFM	Blackpool	Network Rail
453.55000	460.05000	NFM	Bletchley	Network Rail, Bletchley Yard
453.55000	460.05000	NFM	Brentwood	Network Rail, Shenfield
453.55000	460.05000	NFM	Brighton	Network Rail, Brighton Depot (136.5)
453.55000	460.05000	NFM	Cardiff	Central Station Staff (118.8)
453.55000		NFM	Cardiff	Rail Depot Movements (110.9)
453.55000	460.05000	NFM	Carlisle	Rail Station
453.55000	460.05000	NFM	Chester	Network Rail
453.55000	460.05000	NFM	Coventry	Network Rail
453.55000	460.05000	NFM	Crewe	Rail Station (94.8)
453.55000	460.05000	NFM	Croydon	Network Rail, Selhurst Railway Depot
453.55000	460.05000	NFM	Didcot	Rail Shunters (162.2)
453.55000	460.05000	NFM	Didcot	Rail Shunters (179.9)
453.55000	460.05000	NFM	Didcot	Rail Station Staff (82.5)

Base	Mobile	Mode	Location	User and Notes
453.55000	460.05000	NFM	Doncaster	Network Rail
453.55000		NFM	East Anglia	Pest Control Company
453.55000		NFM	Eastbourne	Rail Station
453.55000	460.05000	NFM	Edinburgh	Waverley & Haymarket Rail Stations
453.55000	460.05000	NFM	Ellesmere Port	Shell Resins
453.55000		NFM	Ely	Rail Station
453.55000	460.05000	NFM	England, NW	Track Workers to Trains Ch.1
453.55000		NFM	Farnborough	Rail Station Staff
453.55000	460.05000	NFM	Farnham	Rail Station Staff
453.55000	460.05000	NFM	Glasgow	Queen Street Rail Station
453.55000		NFM	Harwich	International Rail Station Staff (94.8)
453.55000	460.05000	NFM	Harwich	Parkeston Rail Yard
453.55000	460.05000	NFM	Hull	Rail Station Staff
453.55000	460.05000	NFM	Humberside	Road Haulage Freight for Network Rail
453.55000	460.05000	NFM	Ilford	Rail Station Staff
453.55000	460.05000	NFM	Immingham	Rail Station Staff
453.55000	460.05000	NFM	Ipswich	Rail Station Staff
453.55000	460.05000	NFM	Leeds	Rail Station Staff
453.55000	460.05000	NFM	Leicester	Rail Station Staff
453.55000	460.05000	NFM	London	Network Rail Cannon Street Station
453.55000	460.05000	NFM	London	Network Rail Clapham Junction Yard
453.55000	460.05000	NFM	London	Network Rail Shunting Ops, Cricklewood
453.55000	460.05000	NFM	London	Network Rail East Croydon Station
453.55000	460.05000	NFM	London	Network Rail Fenchurch Street Station
453.55000	460.05000	NFM	London	Network Rail Ilford Car Sheds
453.55000	460.05000	NFM	London	Network Rail Liverpool Street Station
453.55000	460.05000	NFM	London	Network Rail Paddington Station (118.8)
453.55000		NFM	London	Network Rail Richmond Station (151.4)
453.55000	460.05000	NFM	London	Network Rail Slade Green Depot
453.55000	460.05000	NFM	London	Network Rail St. Pancras Station (94.8)
453.55000	460.05000	NFM	London	Network Rail Waterloo Station (136.5)
453.55000	460.05000	NFM	London	Network Rail Wimbledon Park Station
453.55000	460.05000	NFM	Manchester	Network Rail Manchester Piccadilly Station
453.55000	460.05000	NFM	Nationwide	Network Rail Stations Ch.1
453.55000	460.05000	NFM	Newcastle	Newcastle Central Station Staff
453.55000	460.05000	NFM	Norwich	Network Rail Norwich Crown Point Station
453.55000	460.05000	NFM	Penzance	Network Rail
453.55000	460.05000	NFM	Preston	Network Rail (94.8)
453.55000	460.05000	NFM	Reading	Network Rail (118.8)
453.55000		NFM	Runcorn	Network Rail
453.55000	460.05000	NFM	Salford	Network Rail
453.55000	460.05000	NFM	Selhurst Junction	Network Rail
453.55000	460.05000	NFM	Sheffield	Network Rail Midland Railway Station
453.55000	460.05000	NFM	Shrewsbury	Network Rail
453.55000	460.05000	NFM	Slade Green Depot	Network Rail
453.55000	460.05000	NFM	Slough	Rail Station (103.5)
453.55000	460.05000	NFM	Southend on Sea	Victoria Rail Station (DCS 243)
453.55000	460.05000	NFM	Stansted	Network Rail
453.55000	460.05000	NFM	Stratford upon Avon	Network Rail
453.55000	460.05000	NFM	Tunbridge Wells	Rail Station
453.55000	460.05000	NFM	Wigan	Network Rail
453.55000	460.05000	NFM	Woking	Network Rail
453.55000	460.05000	NFM	Wolverhampton	Network Rail
453.55000	460.05000	NFM	York	Network Rail
453.56250	460.06250	NFM	Bromley	Rail Maintenance Crews (67)
453.56250		NFM	Swansea	Ferry Service to Cork

Base	Mobile	Mode	Location	User and Notes
453.57500	460.07500	NFM	Dagenham	Ford Car Plant Engineering
453.57500		NFM	Debden	Debden Playing Fields
453.57500	460.07500	NFM	Ellesmere Port	Shell Gas
453.57500	460.07500	NFM	Enfield	Palace Gardens Suppliers
453.57500	460.07500	NFM	Felixstowe	Docks
453.57500	460.07500	NFM	Glasgow	Airport Refuellers
453.57500		NFM	Hatfield	TK Maxx, Galleria Shopping Centre
453.57500	460.07500	NFM	Immingham	Conoco Oil Refinery
453.57500	460.07500	NFM	Ipswich	Docks Ch.4 Management (67)
453.57500		NFM	London	Chiswick Shopping Centre
453.57500		NFM	London	Covent Garden Security
453.57500		NFM	London	Epping Forest Golf Club
453.57500		NFM	London	John Lewis, Kingston upon Thames (210.7)
453.57500		NFM	London	Kings Mall Shopping Centre Security, Hammersmith
453.57500	460.07500	NFM	Southampton	Ford Iveco Trucks
453.57500		NFM	Tonbridge	Right Guard Security (103.5)
453.57500		NFM	Whipsnade	Whipsnade Zoo
453.58750	460.08750	NFM	Nationwide	Ofcom Special Events Reserved Channel
453.60000	460.10000	NFM	Accrington	Nori Brick Works
453.60000	460.10000	NFM	Bilston	Shopwatch (94.8)
453.60000	460.10000	NFM	Bridlington	Shopwatch
453.60000	460.10000	NFM	Bristol	Avonmouth Docks (Red)(107.2)
453.60000	460.10000	NFM	Cardiff	Dow Corning Manufacturing, Barry Docks
453.60000	460.10000	NFM	Cheltenham	General Hospital Maintenance (151.4)
453.60000	460.10000	NFM	Chipping Norton	Shopwatch
453.60000	460.10000	NFM	Cowley	MG Rover Assembly
453.60000	460.10000	NFM	Dagenham	Rhone Poulenc Chemicals
453.60000	460.10000	NFM	Harwell	UKAEA
453.60000	460.10000	NFM	Hastings	Priory Meadow Shopping Centre Security
453.60000	460.10000	NFM	Heathrow	Fernley Airport Services (103.5)
453.60000	460.10000	NFM	Hove	Burger King Drive-Thru (131.8)
453.60000	460.10000	NFM	Leeds	Shopwatch, Morley
453.60000	460.10000	NFM	Liverpool	Hospital
453.60000	460.10000	NFM	London	Australian High Commission
453.60000	460.10000	NFM	London	Docklands Light Railway Depot
453.60000	460.10000	NFM	London	Earls Court Exhibition Complex
453.60000	460.10000	NFM	London	EPS Catering, Waterloo
453.60000	460.10000	NFM	London	Grosvenor House Hotel Security/Staff (103.5)
453.60000	460.10000	NFM	London	O2 Shopping Centre Security, Finchley (114.8)
453.60000	460.10000	NFM	London	Olympia Exhibition Centre Security (179.9)
453.60000	460.10000	NFM	London	Regent Palace Hotel, Piccadilly
453.60000		NFM	London	Royal Mail Depot, W1 (94.8)
453.60000	460.10000	NFM	London	Southwark Leisure Centre
453.60000	460.10000	NFM	Manchester	Sainsbury Supermarket, Regents Road
453.60000	460.10000	NFM	Manchester	Shopwatch, Droylsden
453.60000	460.10000	NFM	Morecombe	Shopwatch (218.1)
453.60000	460.10000	NFM	Newport	Godings Steel Holdings
453.60000	460.10000	NFM	Northampton	Weston Favell Shopping Centre
453.60000	460.10000	NFM	Portsmouth	Gun Wharf Retail Park
453.60000	460.10000	NFM	Preston	Shopwatch, Deepdale Retail Park
453.60000	460.10000	NFM	Reading	Shopwatch
453.60000	460.10000	NFM	Sheffield	Corus Steel Rail Movements
453.60000	460.10000	NFM	Sheffield	Hallam University
453.60000	460.10000	NFM	Southampton Airport	AirRadio MPT1327 Multi User Trunked Voice
453.60000	460.10000	NFM	Stansted	Airport Trunked Network
453.60000	460.10000	NFM	Stevenage	KFC Drive-Thru (151.4)

Base	Mobile	Mode	Location	User and Notes
453.60000	460.10000	NFM	Watford	Shopwatch (233.6)
453.60000	460.10000	NFM	Weymouth	Shopwatch/Pubwatch
453.61250	460.11250	NFM	Bristol	Rail Depot Shunting Staff
453.61250		NFM	Cambridge	Rail Station (123)
453.61250		NFM	Cardiff	Rail Depot Staff
453.61250		NFM	Heathrow	Heathrow Express Rail Depot
453.61250	460.11250	NFM	Kent	Eurotunnel Terminal
453.61250	460.11250	NFM	London	European Passenger Services, Waterloo Station (71.9)
453.61250		NFM	London	Victoria Rail Station, Southern Side (114.8)
453.61250		NFM	London	Wimbledon Rail Station (136.5)
453.61250		NFM	Manchester	Piccadilly Rail Station Staff
453.61250	460.11250	NFM	Port Talbot	Corus Steelworks (71.9)
453.61250		NFM	Teesside	Tees Railway Yard
453.62500	460.12500	NFM	Birmingham	British Airways
453.62500		NFM	Coventry	Skydome Cinema (88.5)
453.62500	460.12500	NFM	Croydon	Selhurst Rail Depot
453.62500	460.12500	NFM	Denham	Bucks Food Company
453.62500	460.12500	NFM	Ellesmere Port	Shell Alcohols Unit
453.62500	460.12500	NFM	Glasgow	British Airways, Glasgow Airport
453.62500	460.12500	NFM	Harwich	Docks, Parkestone Quay (173)
453.62500	460.12500	NFM	Heathrow	British Airways
453.62500	460.12500	NFM	Immingham	Tioxide Chemicals
453.62500	460.12500	NFM	Ipswich	Tower Ramparts Shopping Centre
453.62500	460.12500	NFM	Jersey	British Airways Handling, Jersey Airport
453.62500		NFM	London	Anthonys Metals Ltd., Stratford
453.62500		NFM	London	BBC Site Security, North Acton
453.62500		NFM	London	BP Headquarters Staff, Blackfriars
453.62500		NFM	London	CAA Headquarters, Kingsway
453.62500		NFM	London	Canons Park School, Stanmore
453.62500		NFM	London	Catford Running Track
453.62500		NFM	London	Collegiate School, Edgware
453.62500		NFM	London	Imperial War Museum Security, Lambeth (88.5)
453.62500		NFM	London	Marks & Spencer, Kensington
453.62500		NFM	London	Marks & Spencer, Oxford Circus
453.62500		NFM	London	Planner Products Ltd., Sunbury
453.62500		NFM	London	The Brewery Conference Centre, Barbican Centre
453.62500		NFM	Milford Haven	Refinery
453.62500		NFM	Pitsea	Tesco Staff/Security
453.62500		NFM	Sheerness	Sheerness Steel
453.62500		NFM	Swansea Docks	Cargo Handlers
453.63750	460.13750	NFM	London	Ambulance Service Event Control Ch.15 (218.1)
453.65000		NFM	Ayr	Golf Course
453.65000	460.15000	NFM	Belfast	Connswater Shopping Centre Security
453.65000	460.15000	NFM	Dartford	Thames Europort Car Export (82.5)
453.65000		NFM	Eastbourne	Sovereign Shuttle Nightclub (162.2)
453.65000		NFM	Enfield	Council Repairs Department (131.8)
453.65000	460.15000	NFM	Felixstowe	Walton Container Terminal Ch.2
453.65000	460.15000	NFM	Harwich	Docks
453.65000	460.15000	NFM	Heathrow	Aircraft Cleaners (114.8)
453.65000	460.15000	NFM	Inverness	British Airways Ops.
453.65000	460.15000	NFM	Ipswich	Docks (77)
453.65000	460.15000	NFM	Irvine	Gailes Golf Course
453.65000	460.15000	NFM	Leicester	Fosse Park Car Park Security (67)
453.65000	460.15000	NFM	Lincoln	Lincoln City Council
453.65000		NFM	London	Chelsea Football Club Security, Fulham (67)
453.65000	460.15000	NFM	London	LWT Security, Southbank (123)

Base	Mobile	Mode	Location	User and Notes
453.65000	460.15000	NFM	London	Port of London Authority
453.65000	460.15000	NFM	London	St James Church, Piccadilly
453.65000	460.15000	NFM	Manchester	Manchester Airport (123)
453.65000	460.15000	NFM	Matlock	Shopwatch
453.65000	460.15000	NFM	Newmarket	Racecourse Security
453.65000		NFM	Shoreham by Sea	Power Station Engineering Ch.2 (156.7)
453.65000		NFM	Stevenage	Kings Leisure Centre (162.2)
453.65000	460.15000	NFM	Warrington	Birchwood Centre/Spectrum Arena Ch.2
453.65000	460.15000	NFM	Wilby	McDonalds Drive-Thru
453.66250	460.16250	NFM	London	Ambulance Service Event Control Ch.13 (218.1)
453.67500		NFM	Ascot	Racecourse Management
453.67500		NFM	Bletchley	Leisure Centre
453.67500	460.17500	NFM	Bristol	Avonmouth Docks
453.67500	460.17500	NFM	Ellesmere Port	Shell
453.67500		NFM	Felixstowe Docks	Ralph Morton Haulage Yard
453.67500	460.17500	NFM	Kent	Eurotunnel Concession UK Terminal
453.67500	460.17500	NFM	Liverpool	Stanlow Oil Refinery
453.67500	460.17500	NFM	London	Docklands Light Railway
453.67500	460.17500	NFM	Redcar	Corus
453.67500	460.17500	NFM	Sheffield	Royal Hallamshire Hospital Security/Porters
453.67500		NFM	Warrington	Ineos Silicas (94.8)
453.68750	460.18750	NFM	Nationwide	Ofcom Special Events Reserved Channel
453.70000	460.20000	NFM	Arundel	Arundel Castle Trunked Network Control Channel
453.70000	460.20000	NFM	Barnet	General Hospital Porters/Security (136.5)
453.70000	460.20000	NFM	Barrow in Furness	Parking Enforcement (250)
453.70000	460.20000	NFM	Bedford	College Security
453.70000	460.20000	NFM	Birkenhead	Arrowe Park Hospital (173.8)
453.70000	460.20000	NFM	Birmingham	Shopwatch, Kings Heath (156.7)
453.70000	460.20000	NFM	Brighton	Metropole Hotel Function/Events
453.70000	460.20000	NFM	Bristol	Galleries Shopping Centre Cleaners
453.70000	460.20000	NFM	Bristol	University Security
453.70000	460.20000	NFM	Canvey Island	Oil Refinery
453.70000	460.20000	NFM	Cardiff	Shopwatch, Canton (88.5)
453.70000	460.20000	NFM	Cosham	Shopwatch (77)
453.70000	460.20000	NFM	Coventry	Jaguar Plant Security MPT1327 Control Channel
453.70000	460.20000	NFM	Coventry	Dunlop Security (DCS 023)
453.70000	460.20000	NFM	Dorset	BP Wytch Farm Ch.1 (110.9)
453.70000	460.20000	NFM	Dover	Port Ops.
453.70000	460.20000	NFM	Ellesmere Port	Vauxhall Car Plant
453.70000	460.20000	NFM	Felixstowe Docks	Walton Container Terminal Ch.3
453.70000	460.20000	NFM	Fleetwood	Shopwatch (77)
453.70000	460.20000	NFM	Hamble	BP Oil Jetty
453.70000	460.20000	NFM	Hastings	Shopwatch
453.70000	460.20000	NFM	Heathrow	Korean Air Lines T3 Ops. (127.3)
453.70000	460.20000	NFM	High Wycombe	Shopwatch (77)
453.70000	460.20000	NFM	Hull	Stagecoach Buses
453.70000	460.20000	NFM	Leamington Spa	Shopwatch
453.70000	460.20000	NFM	London	Barnet General Hospital Repeater
453.70000	460.20000	NFM	London	BBC Experience Staff, W1 (233)
453.70000	460.20000	NFM	London,	Hilton International Staff, W2
453.70000	460.20000	NFM	Luton Airport	AirRadio easyJet/Multi User Trunked Network
453.70000	460.20000	NFM	Manchester	Aerial Company, Shaw
453.70000	460.20000	NFM	Manchester	Trafford Centre Maintenance
453.70000	460.20000	NFM	Middlesbrough	Cleveland Centre Security
453.70000	460.20000	NFM	Middlesbrough	Middlesbrough Football Club, Riverside Stadium
453.70000	460.20000	NFM	Milton Keynes	John Lewis Store Security

Base	Mobile	Mode	Location	User and Notes
453.70000	460.20000	NFM	Newcastle	Newcastle Metro Trunked Network
453.70000	460.20000	NFM	Northwich	Brunner-Mond Alkaline Chemicals (114.8)
453.70000	460.20000	NFM	Oldham	Austin Timber Security
453.70000	460.20000	NFM	Reading	Oracle Shopping Centre Admin/Car Park (77)
453.70000	460.20000	NFM	Salford	Amec Property Management
453.70000	460.20000	NFM	Sevenoaks	Shopwatch
453.70000	460.20000	NFM	Sheffield	Sheffield Wednesday Football Club
453.70000	460.20000	NFM	Stansted Airport	Servisair/GlobeGround Handling
453.70000	460.20000	NFM	Swindon	Brunel Plaza Shopping Centre Security
453.70000	460.20000	NFM	Tamworth	Shopwatch (151.4)
453.70000	460.20000	NFM	Tostre	Corus Steelworks
453.70000	460.20000	NFM	Wakefield	Shopwatch
453.70000	460.20000	NFM	Waterlooville	Shopwatch
453.70000	460.20000	NFM	Wolverhampton	Shopwatch (141.3)
453.72500	460.22500	NFM	Belfast	Lifestyle Sports
453.72500	460.22500	NFM	Corby	Council Works Department
453.72500		NFM	Dartford	House of Fraser Security, Bluewater Centre (151.4)
453.72500	460.22500	NFM	Edinburgh	British Airways Ops (88.5)
453.72500	460.22500	NFM	Leicester	Shires Centre Surveillance
453.72500	460.22500	NFM	Middlesbrough	BASF Fibres Raw Materials Ch.2
453.72500	460.22500	NFM	Morecambe Bay	British Gas Exploration & Production
453.72500	460.22500	NFM	Oldham	Royal Oldham Hospital
453.72500	460.22500	NFM	West Midlands	Engineering/Town Planning
453.73750	460.23750	NFM	Folkestone	Eurotunnel Link
453.75000	460.25000	NFM	Aberdeen	Dyce Airport Staff
453.75000	460.25000	NFM	Bournville	Cadbury World (107.2)
453.75000	460.25000	NFM	Bridgend	Shopwatch, McArthur Glen Retail Park (94.8)
453.75000	460.25000	NFM	Brighton	American Express Security Ch.1
453.75000	460.25000	NFM	Cambridge	Addenbrookes Hospital Porters (241.8)
453.75000	460.25000	NFM	Cardiff Docks	Owen Fuel Texaco (127.3)
453.75000	460.25000	NFM	Chelmsford	Broomfield Hospital
453.75000	460.25000	NFM	Coleraine	Shopwatch (146.2)
453.75000	460.25000	NFM	Didcot	Power Station Security (71.9)
453.75000	460.25000	NFM	Gloucestershire	Debenhams Department Store Security (203.5)
453.75000	460.25000	NFM	Guiseley	Shopwatch, West Park Retail Centre (136.5)
453.75000	460.25000	NFM	Harwell	UKAEA
453.75000	460.25000	NFM	Hayes	Heinz Foods
453.75000	460.25000	NFM	Heathrow	Eva Airways (Taiwanese) T3 Ops. (173)
453.75000	460.25000	NFM	Kent	Eurotunnel Concession UK Terminal
453.75000	460.25000	NFM	London	Bank, London Wall
453.75000	460.25000	NFM	London	Grosvenor Hotel, Park Lane
453.75000	460.25000	NFM	London	Hotel, Earls Court.
453.75000	460.25000	NFM	London	Kensington Palace
453.75000	460.25000	NFM	London	Marks & Spencer Security, Brent Cross (179.9)
453.75000	460.25000	NFM	London	Marks & Spencer Security, Kingston Upon Thames (88.5)
453.75000	460.25000	NFM	London	Passport Office, SW1 (Simple Scrambling) (233)
453.75000	460.25000	NFM	London	Roans School, Greenwich Park
453.75000	460.25000	NFM	London	Sanderson Hotel, Berners Street, W1 (186.2)
453.75000	460.25000	NFM	London	Shopwatch, Golders Green
453.75000	460.25000	NFM	London	Wood Green Shopping Centre Security (71.9)
453.75000	460.25000	NFM	Manchester	Manchester United Football Club (210.7)
453.75000	460.25000	NFM	Manchester	Trafford Centre Security
453.75000	460.25000	NFM	Oldham	Spindles Shopping Centre
453.75000	460.25000	NFM	Ormskirk	Shopwatch
453.75000	460.25000	NFM	Oxford	Westgate Shopping Centre Security (118.8)
453.75000	460.25000	NFM	Plympton	Shopwatch

Base	Mobile	Mode	Location	User and Notes
453.75000	460.25000	NFM	Prestwick	Prestwick Airport Freight Warehouses
453.75000	460.25000	NFM	Royston	Shopwatch
453.75000	460.25000	NFM	Sheffield	Corus Engineering Steelworks, Coleford Road
453.75000	460.25000	NFM	Shipley	Shopwatch
453.75000	460.25000	NFM	Silverstone	Race Track
453.75000	460.25000	NFM	Sittingbourne	Shopwatch
453.75000	460.25000	NFM	Stansted Airport	Groundstar Handling
453.75000	460.25000	NFM	Stevenage	Lister Hospital
453.75000	460.25000	NFM	Stoke	Shopwatch, Festival Park (82.5)
453.75000	460.25000	NFM	Stowmarket	ICI Paints Fire/Medics (82.5)
453.75000	460.25000	NFM	Telford	Shopwatch, Telford Shopping Centre
453.75000	460.25000	NFM	Wiltshire	Great Western Security
453.77500	460.27500	NFM	Aberdeen	Pubwatch
453.77500	460.27500	NFM	Avonmouth	Dock Crane Operators & Stevedores
453.77500		NFM	Barassie	English, Welsh & Scottish Railway
453.77500	460.27500	NFM	Beds/Bucks	Shopwatch (77)
453.77500	460.27500	NFM	Belfast	Shopwatch
453.77500	460.27500	NFM	Birkenhead	Shopwatch, Pyramid Shopping Centre
453.77500	460.27500	NFM	Bournville	Cadbury World (186.2)
453.77500	460.27500	NFM	Bury	Council (179.9)
453.77500	460.27500	NFM	Bury St Edmunds	Hospital Porters (151.4)
453.77500	460.27500	NFM	Cambridge	Marks & Spencer Security (71.9)
453.77500	460.27500	NFM	Cardiff	Pubwatch (DCS 243)
453.77500	460.27500	NFM	Carlisle	Shopwatch (71.9)
453.77500	460.27500	NFM	Chelmsford	Pubwatch (107.2)
453.77500	460.27500	NFM	Coventry	Debenhams Security, W Orchards Centre (103.5)
453.77500	460.27500	NFM	Culham	UKAEA
453.77500	460.27500	NFM	Dumfries	Shopwatch
453.77500	460.27500	NFM	Farnborough	Qinetiq Transport
453.77500	460.27500	NFM	Greenock	Oak Mall Shopping Centre Security
453.77500	460.27500	NFM	Hartlepool	Shopwatch
453.77500	460.27500	NFM	Harwich	International Port Maintenance Staff (103.5)
453.77500	460.27500	NFM	Hatfield	Galleria Shopping Centre Security (82.5)
453.77500	460.27500	NFM	Heathrow	Refuellers (136.5)
453.77500	460.27500	NFM	Hemel Hempstead	Marlowes Shopping Centre Security (118.8)
453.77500	460.27500	NFM	Hull	Shopwatch, Hessle Road
453.77500	460.27500	NFM	Immingham	Conoco
453.77500	460.27500	NFM	Kent	Eurotunnel Concession UK Terminal
453.77500	460.27500	NFM	Kings Lynn	Crest Petroleum
453.77500	460.27500	NFM	Leicester	The Shires/Fosse Park Security
453.77500	460.27500	NFM	Liverpool	Shopwatch, St Johns Shopping Centre
453.77500	460.27500	NFM	London	H & M Hennes Security
453.77500	460.27500	NFM	London	John Lewis, Kingston upon Thames (123)
453.77500	460.27500	NFM	London	Meridian Hotel, Piccadilly
453.77500	460.27500	NFM	London	Piccadilly Patrollers/CCTV Trocadero Centre (186.2)
453.77500	460.27500	NFM	London	Pubwatch, West London (103.5)
453.77500	460.27500	NFM	London	Shopwatch, Regent Street (186.2)
453.77500	460.27500	NFM	Londonderry	Shopwatch (186.2)
453.77500	460.27500	NFM	Lowestoft	James Paget Hospital Porters (67)
453.77500	460.27500	NFM	Luton	Arndale Shopping Centre Security (167.9)
453.77500	460.27500	NFM	Luton Airport	AirRadio easyJet/Multi User Trunked Network
453.77500	460.27500	NFM	Manchester	Debenhams Department Store, Trafford Centre
453.77500	460.27500	NFM	Monmouth	Shopwatch
453.77500	460.27500	NFM	Newcastle Airport	Airport Ops.
453.77500	460.27500	NFM	Northampton	Shopwatch
453.77500	460.27500	NFM	Peterborough	English, Welsh & Scottish Yard Cranes (110.9)

Base	Mobile	Mode	Location	User and Notes
453.77500	460.27500	NFM	Portsmouth	Shopwatch
453.77500	460.27500	NFM	Retford	Shopwatch
453.77500	460.27500	NFM	Rugby	Clocktowers Shopping Centre Security
453.77500	460.27500	NFM	Runcorn	Halton Lea Shopping Centre Security
453.77500	460.27500	NFM	Scunthorpe	Corus Steelworks
453.77500	460.27500	NFM	Silverstone	Race Track
453.77500	460.27500	NFM	Southampton	Esso Fawley Oil Refinery (192.8)
453.77500	460.27500	NFM	Southampton	General Hospital Porters
453.77500	460.27500	NFM	Southend on Sea	Pubwatch/Shopwatch (118.8)
453.77500	460.27500	NFM	Stansted	Light Railway
453.77500	460.27500	NFM	Swindon	Car Factory
453.77500	460.27500	NFM	Whitehaven	Shopwatch
453.77500	460.27500	NFM	Wirral	Pyramids Shopping Centre Security (82.5)
453.77500	460.27500	NFM	Woking	Peacocks Shopping Centre Security
453.78750	460.28750	NFM	Nationwide	Ofcom Special Events Reserved Channel
453.80000	453.80000	NFM	Bath	Shopwatch
453.80000	453.80000	NFM	Birkenhead	Birkenhead Shopping Centre
453.80000	460.30000	NFM	Brighton	Brighton & Hove Bus and Coach Company
453.80000	460.30000	NFM	Bristol	Cribbs Causeway Shopping Centre Security
453.80000	453.80000	NFM	Bury	Millgate Shopping Centre
453.80000	460.30000	NFM	Cheltenham	Regent Arcade Security (167.9)
453.80000	460.30000	NFM	Coventry	Warwick University
453.80000	460.30000	NFM	Guildford	Debenhams Department Store Security
453.80000	460.30000	NFM	Halewood	Ford Plant (94.8)
453.80000	460.30000	NFM	Hatfield	Galleria Shopping Centre Security
453.80000	460.30000	NFM	Heathrow	American Airlines T3
453.80000	460.30000	NFM	Heathrow	Saudi Airlines T3
453.80000	460.30000	NFM	Hull	City Buses
453.80000	460.30000	NFM	Kidderminster	Shopwatch
453.80000	460.30000	NFM	Littlehampton	Shopwatch (179.9)
453.80000	460.30000	NFM	London	Cromwell Hospital Porters
453.80000	460.30000	NFM	London	Kings College Hospital, Camberwell (173.8)
453.80000	460.30000	NFM	London	Regent Palace Hotel, Piccadilly (110.9)
453.80000	460.30000	NFM	London	Royal Festival Hall
453.80000	460.30000	NFM	London	Shopwatch, South London (77)
453.80000	460.30000	NFM	London	Twickenham Rugby Stadium Caterers (241.8)
453.80000	460.30000	NFM	Loughborough	Shopwatch
453.80000	460.30000	NFM	Luton Airport	Reed Aviation (179.9)
453.80000	460.30000	NFM	Midlothian	Shopwatch, Dalkeith
453.80000	460.30000	NFM	Manchester	Trafford Park Factory Loading Bay
453.80000	460.30000	NFM	Milford Haven	Refinery
453.80000	460.30000	NFM	Newmarket	The Jockey Club
453.80000	460.30000	NFM	Northwich	Shopwatch (103.5)
453.80000	460.30000	NFM	Oxford	Shopwatch, Westgate Shopping Centre (210.7)
453.80000	460.30000	NFM	Rhyl	Ysbyty Glan Clwyd Hospital Porters
453.80000	460.30000	NFM	Salisbury	Salisbury General Hospital Porters
453.80000	460.30000	NFM	Sellafield	UKAEA
453.80000	460.30000	NFM	Sheffield	Stockbridge Steel Engineers
453.80000	460.30000	NFM	Solihull	Touchwood Shopping Centre Security (103.5)
453.80000	460.30000	NFM	Warrington	Birchwood Centre Ch.1 (141.3)
453.80000	460.30000	NFM	Weston Super Mare	Sovereign Shopping Centre Security
453.80000	460.30000	NFM	Winchester	Shopwatch
453.82500	460.32500	NFM	Brighton	Parking Enforcement, Trunked Data Channel
453.82500	460.32500	NFM	Bury	Premier Cars
453.82500	460.32500	NFM	Cheltenham	GCHQ Security/Cleaners Trunked Network
453.82500	460.32500	NFM	Clacton	Highfield Holiday Park (67)

Base	Mobile	Mode	Location	User and Notes
453.82500	460.32500	NFM	Doncaster	Shopwatch, Frenchgate Centre
453.82500	460.32500	NFM	Edinburgh	Forth Road Bridge Toll Control
453.82500	460.32500	NFM	Gatwick	Airline Ops.
453.82500	460.32500	NFM	Glasgow	Lloyds TSB Head Office
453.82500	460.32500	NFM	Heathrow	Godfrey Davis Eurocar
453.82500	460.32500	NFM	Heathrow	Passenger Transport
453.82500	460.32500	NFM	Hull	Shopwatch/Pubwatch (107.2)
453.82500	460.32500	NFM	Ipswich	Cranfield Bros. Flour Mill
453.82500	460.32500	NFM	Kent	Eurotunnel Concession UK Terminal
453.82500	460.32500	NFM	London	National Gallery
453.82500	460.32500	NFM	London	Parking Enforcement, Bethnal Green
453.82500	460.32500	NFM	London	Parking Enforcement, Victoria (71.9)
453.82500	460.32500	NFM	Manchester	Shopwatch, Arndale Centre (94.8)
453.82500	460.32500	NFM	New Holland	Howarth Timber
453.82500	460.32500	NFM	Redcar	J&P Taxis
453.82500	460.32500	NFM	Thetford	Shopwatch (94.8)
453.82500	460.32500	NFM	Troon	Shopwatch
453.82500	460.32500	NFM	Watford	P&P Security
453.85000	460.35000	NFM	Aberdeen	Hospital
453.85000	460.35000	NFM	Arundel	Arundel Castle Trunked Network Voice Channel
453.85000	460.35000	NFM	Ascot	Racecourse Network Ch.4
453.85000	460.35000	NFM	Beaulieu	Motor Museum Security
453.85000	460.35000	NFM	Belfast	Ulsterbus
453.85000	460.35000	NFM	Bellingham	ICI
453.85000	460.35000	NFM	Brighton & Hove	Bus Inspectors and Maintenance
453.85000	460.35000	NFM	Bury St. Edmunds	Shopwatch
453.85000	460.35000	NFM	Cambridge	University Security (131.8)
453.85000	460.35000	NFM	Cheltenham	Zurich Insurance Security/Maintenance
453.85000	460.35000	NFM	Coventry	Gallagher Retail Park Security
453.85000	460.35000	NFM	Dartford	Priory Shopping Centre (71.9)
453.85000	460.35000	NFM	Edinburgh	Debenhams Department Store Security (127.3)
453.85000	460.35000	NFM	Ellesmere Port	Shell Catalytic
453.85000	460.35000	NFM	Gatwick	Ground Repeater
453.85000	460.35000	NFM	Harwell	UKAEA
453.85000	460.35000	NFM	Hatfield	Hatfield Business Park (107.2)
453.85000	460.35000	NFM	Heathrow	Middle East Airlines T3 Ops.
453.85000	460.35000	NFM	Ipswich	Cranfield Bros. Flour Mill
453.85000	460.35000	NFM	Ipswich	Vopack Limited (94.8)
453.85000	460.35000	NFM	Killinholme	Lindsey Oil Refinery
453.85000	460.35000	NFM	Lancaster	University Security/Porters (94.8)
453.85000	460.35000	NFM	Liverpool	MTL Buses In-Cab Radio Ch.2
453.85000	460.35000	NFM	Liverpool	Royal Liverpool University Hospital (141.3)
453.85000	460.35000	NFM	London	Ace Radio Cars, Arnos Grove
453.85000	460.35000	NFM	London	A-Kwika Car Service, Colindale
453.85000	460.35000	NFM	London	Lloyds of London Security
453.85000	460.35000	NFM	London	Parking Enforcement, N1/N17 (203.5)
453.85000	460.35000	NFM	London	Priory Shopping Centre Security, Dartford
453.85000	460.35000	NFM	London	Sureway Parking Enforcement, SE7 (136.5)
453.85000	460.35000	NFM	Luton Airport	Car Parks Ch.6
453.85000	460.35000	NFM	Lutterworth	Asda Distribution Depot, Trunked, Voice Channel
453.85000	460.35000	NFM	Newmarket	Racecourse Security
453.85000	460.35000	NFM	Newquay	Holiday Park
453.85000	460.35000	NFM	Norfolk	Norwich & Norfolk Hospital Porters (67)
453.85000	460.35000	NFM	Northwich	Railway Trackside Crews
453.85000	460.35000	NFM	Penarth	Llandough Hospital Security (94.8)
453.85000	460.35000	NFM	Peterborough	Queensgate Shopping Centre Car Parks (225)

Base	Mobile	Mode	Location	User and Notes
453.85000	460.35000	NFM	Port Talbot	BP Oil Refinery (123)
453.85000	460.35000	NFM	Prestatyn Sands	Caravan Park Catering/Bars (103.5)
453.85000	460.35000	NFM	Preston	Shopwatch, Fishergate Shopping Centre (82.5)
453.85000	460.35000	NFM	Reading	Courage Brewery
453.85000	460.35000	NFM	Rochdale	Queensway Private Hire
453.85000	460.35000	NFM	Salford	Council Security
453.85000	460.35000	NFM	Scunthorpe	Hospital Porters
453.85000	460.35000	NFM	Sheffield	Forge Alert Security Ch.1
453.85000	460.35000	NFM	Stansted Airport	Alpha Catering (103.5)
453.85000	460.35000	NFM	Wirral	Merseybus Inspectors
453.87500	460.37500	NFM	Aberdeen	Dyce Airport Staff
453.87500		NFM	Ascot	Racecourse Network Ch.1
453.87500		NFM	Bournville	Cadbury World Security
453.87500		NFM	Cardiff Bay	NCM Security
453.87500		NFM	Harwich	Port Authority Ch.2
453.87500	460.37500	NFM	Heathrow	Air Canada Ops. T3 (210.7)
453.87500		NFM	London	Charing Cross Hotel
453.87500		NFM	London	Covent Garden Leisure
453.87500		NFM	London	Dalston Cross Centre Security (94.8)
453.87500		NFM	London	Hotel, Elephant & Castle
453.87500		NFM	London	London Pavilion Security, Piccadilly
453.87500		NFM	London	Royal Botanic Gardens, Kew
453.87500		NFM	London	School, St Johns Wood
453.87500	460.37500	NFM	Luton Airport	Monarch Airlines
453.87500		NFM	Manchester	The Triangle Security, Hanging Ditch
453.87500		NFM	Manchester	Marks & Spencer Security, Arndale Centre
453.87500	460.37500	NFM	Manchester	Trafford Container Base (67)
453.87500	460.37500	NFM	Sizewell	Power Station
453.87500	460.37500	NFM	Stansted Airport	Servisair/GlobeGround Ramp Ops.
453.90000	460.40000	NFM	Ascot	Rail Station Staff.
453.90000	460.40000	NFM	Ashford	International Rail Station
453.90000	460.40000	NFM	Bedford	Rail Depot
453.90000		NFM	Bletchley	Rail Shunting Ops.
453.90000	460.40000	NFM	Bristol	Temple Meads Rail Station Staff
453.90000	460.40000	NFM	Cardiff	Rail Shunting Ops. Steel Yard (136.5)
453.90000	460.40000	NFM	Dartford	Rail Staff (103.5)
453.90000	460.40000	NFM	Derby	Network Rail
453.90000	460.40000	NFM	Doncaster	Rail Shunting Ops.
453.90000	460.40000	NFM	Edinburgh	Haymarket Rail Depot
453.90000	460.40000	NFM	Glasgow	Glasgow Central Rail Station
453.90000	460.40000	NFM	Guildford	Guildford Rail Station
453.90000	460.40000	NFM	Hoo Junction	Network Rail Depot
453.90000	460.40000	NFM	Hull	Network Rail Paragon Signal Box
453.90000	460.40000	NFM	Ipswich	Network Rail Shunting Ops.
453.90000	460.40000	NFM	Killingholme	Network Rail /Oil Refineries
453.90000	460.40000	NFM	Leeds	Network Rail
453.90000		NFM	Leigh on Sea	Rail Station Staff
453.90000	460.40000	NFM	Lisburn	Borough Taxis
453.90000	460.40000	NFM	London	Barking Rail Station Staff
453.90000	460.40000	NFM	London	Bound Green Rail Shunting (103.5)
453.90000	460.40000	NFM	London	Charing Cross Rail Station Staff
453.90000	460.40000	NFM	London	Euston Rail Station Staff (118.8)
453.90000	460.40000	NFM	London	Kings Cross Rail Station Staff (71.9)
453.90000	460.40000	NFM	London	London Bridge Rail Station Staff (136.5)
453.90000	460.40000	NFM	London	Victoria Rail Station Security
453.90000	460.40000	NFM	London	Waterloo Rail Station Staff

Base	Mobile	Mode	Location	User and Notes
453.90000	460.40000	NFM	London	Willesden Rail Yard
453.90000	460.40000	NFM	Manchester	Network Rail, Heaton Depot
453.90000	460.40000	NFM	Nationwide	Rail Stations
453.90000	460.40000	NFM	Newport	Rail Porters
453.90000	460.40000	NFM	Norwich	Network Rail, Norwich Crown Point
453.90000	460.40000	NFM	Nottingham	Network Rail
453.90000	460.40000	NFM	Perth	Rail Station Staff
453.90000		NFM	Peterborough	Rail Station Staff
453.90000	460.40000	NFM	Ramsgate	Rail Station & Depot
453.90000	460.40000	NFM	Reading	Rail Shunting Ops. (118.8)
453.90000	460.40000	NFM	Sheffield	Tensley Hill Rail Marshalling Yard
453.90000	460.40000	NFM	Thames	Network Rail Turbo Workshop
453.90000	460.40000	NFM	Watford	Network Rail, Watford Junction
453.92500	460.42500	NFM	Barnsley	Shopwatch
453.92500	460.42500	NFM	Birmingham	Shopwatch, Grosvenor Shopping Centre (203.5)
453.92500	460.42500	NFM	Blackpool	Pubwatch
453.92500	460.42500	NFM	Borehamwood	Sainsbury Warehouse Ch.2 (103.5)
453.92500	460.42500	NFM	Bradford	Bus Inspectors
453.92500	460.42500	NFM	Brighton	Churchill Square Shopping Centre Car Parks
453.92500	460.42500	NFM	Bristol	Car Park Security (179.9)
453.92500	460.42500	NFM	Cambridge	Pubwatch (136.5)
453.92500	460.42500	NFM	Coventry	Jaguar Plant Staff MPT1327 Control Channel
453.92500	460.42500	NFM	Cowley	Templars Shopping Centre Security
453.92500	460.42500	NFM	Crewe	University Security
453.92500	460.42500	NFM	Fareham	Shopwatch/Pubwatch (103.5)
453.92500	460.42500	NFM	Felixstowe	Co-Op Store (123)
453.92500	460.42500	NFM	Heathrow	United Airlines Ramp/Cargo T3 (173)
453.92500	460.42500	NFM	Hull	Lindsey Oil Refinery
453.92500	460.42500	NFM	Kent	Eurotunnel Terminal
453.92500	460.42500	NFM	Leeds Airport	Servisair/GlobeGround Handling Operations
453.92500	460.42500	NFM	Leicester	House of Fraser, Rackhams (88.5)
453.92500	460.42500	NFM	Leicester	Shires Centre Security Ch 1
453.92500	460.42500	NFM	London	BP Oil, Finsbury Circus
453.92500	460.42500	NFM	London	Docklands Light Railway
453.92500	460.42500	NFM	London	HMSO, Nine Elms
453.92500		NFM	London	Marks & Spencer Staff, Oxford Circus (71.9)
453.92500	460.42500	NFM	London	National Gallery Security (94.8)
453.92500	460.42500	NFM	London	Shopwatch/Pubwatch/Clubwatch, Camden
453.92500	460.42500	NFM	London	St Mary's Hospital, Paddington
453.92500	460.42500	NFM	Manchester	Airport Trunked Network Control Channel
453.92500	460.42500	NFM	Mansfield	Shopwatch (110.9)
453.92500	460.42500	NFM	Middlesbrough	BASF Fibres Raw Materials Ch.1
453.92500	460.42500	NFM	Milford Haven	Oil Refinery
453.92500	460.42500	NFM	Newcastle	Newcastle University
453.92500	460.42500	NFM	Newport, Gwent	Patent Office Security
453.92500	460.42500	NFM	Nottingham	The Victoria Centre Security
453.92500	460.42500	NFM	Portsmouth	Hospital (241.8)
453.92500	460.42500	NFM	Portsmouth	Shopwatch/Pubwatch (103.5)
453.92500	460.42500	NFM	Prestwick	Prestwick Airport Check-In/Arrivals/Departures
453.92500	460.42500	NFM	Rhyl	Shopwatch/Pubwatch
453.92500	460.42500	NFM	Salisbury	Salisbury General Hospital
453.92500	460.42500	NFM	Sheerness	Shopwatch
453.92500	460.42500	NFM	Silverstone	Racetrack Security (156.7)
453.92500	460.42500	NFM	Stafford	Shopwatch, Guildhall Shopping Centre
453.92500	460.42500	NFM	Stamford	Shopwatch
453.92500	460.42500	NFM	Stansted Airport	Aviance (114.8)

Base	Mobile	Mode	Location	User and Notes
453.92500	460.42500	NFM	Thame	Shopwatch
453.92500	460.42500	NFM	Walsall	Shopwatch
453.92500	460.42500	NFM	Woking	Peacocks Shopping Centre Security
453.92500	460.42500	NFM	Worcester	Shopwatch (167.9)
453.95000	460.45000	NFM	Cheltenham	GCHQ Security/Cleaning Staff Trunked Voice
453.95000	460.45000	NFM	Dartford	Dart Ferries
453.95000	460.45000	NFM	Kent	Eurotunnel UK Terminal
453.95000	460.45000	NFM	Heathrow	Japan Airlines T3 Ops. (114.8)
453.95000	460.45000	NFM	Immingham	Conoco Oil Refinery
453.95000	460.45000	NFM	Llanwern	Corus Steelworks Security
453.95000	460.45000	NFM	London	Bromley Borough Council
453.95000	460.45000	NFM	London	Haringey Council (71.9)
453.95000		NFM	London	Peter Jones, Chelsea (67)
453.95000	460.45000	NFM	London	Waltham Forest Council
453.95000	460.45000	NFM	Manchester	Council
453.95000	460.45000	NFM	Newport	Spencer & Llanwern Docks
453.95000	460.45000	NFM	Southampton	Docks
453.96250	460.46250	NFM	Brighton	Adur District Council (94.8)
453.96250	460.46250	NFM	Brighton	Pubwatch (151.4)
453.96250	460.46250	NFM	Brighton	Shopwatch, London Road (136.5)
453.96250	460.46250	NFM	Ipswich	Pubwatch
453.96250	460.46250	NFM	Kent	Eurotunnel UK Terminal
453.96250	460.46250	NFM	London	Parking Enforcement, Westminster (67)
453.96250	460.46250	NFM	Oxford	Community Wardens (94.8)
453.96250	460.46250	NFM	Peterborough	Shopwatch/Pubwatch (192.8)
453.96250	460.46250	NFM	Portsmouth	Parking Enforcement.(118.8)
453.96250	460.46250	NFM	Sheffield	Town Hall Staff
453.96250	460.46250	NFM	Southport	Parking Enforcement.(127.3)
453.96250	460.46250	NFM	Stansted Airport	Airside Crew Coaches
453.96250	460.46250	NFM	Stevenage	Sovereign Coach & Bus Company Ch.1 (156.7)
453.96250	463.46250	NFM	Wilton	ICI Chemicals
453.97500	460.47500	NFM	Barnet	Community Wardens Ch.2 (192.8)
453.97500	460.47500	NFM	Barrow in Furness	Trident Taxis
453.97500	460.47500	NFM	Bath	University Security
453.97500	460.47500	NFM	Birmingham	Park Rangers
453.97500	460.47500	NFM	Bishop Auckland	Shopwatch
453.97500	460.47500	NFM	Bognor Regis	Shopwatch (186.2)
453.97500	460.47500	NFM	Brighton	Parking Enforcement Trunked Voice
453.97500	460.47500	NFM	Cheltenham	GCHQ Trunked Network Control Channel
453.97500	460.47500	NFM	Chichester	Shopwatch (186.2)
453.97500	460.47500	NFM	Cowley	MG Rover Security Ch.7 (156.7)
453.97500		NFM	Felixstowe	Docks North Freightliner Terminal
453.97500	460.47500	NFM	Folkestone	Eurotunnel Link
453.97500	460.47500	NFM	Heathrow	Iberia Airlines T2 (162.2)
453.97500	460.47500	NFM	Isle of Wight	Shopwatch, Newport
453.97500	460.47500	NFM	Kent	Kingsnorth Power Station
453.97500	460.47500	NFM	Liverpool	John Moore University Security (114.8)
453.97500	460.47500	NFM	London	Bromley Council (192.8)
453.97500	460.47500	NFM	London	Kodak Film Plant, Harrow
453.97500	460.47500	NFM	London	Lucky Cabs, Notting Hill
453.97500	460.47500	NFM	London	Parking Enforcement, Kingston upon Thames
453.97500	460.47500	NFM	London	Parking Enforcement, Lambeth
453.97500	460.47500	NFM	London	Shopwatch, Marble Arch
453.97500	460.47500	NFM	Lowestoft	Port of Lowestoft
453.97500	460.47500	NFM	Manchester	Airport Security
453.97500	460.47500	NFM	Morley	Black Prince Coaches

Base	Mobile	Mode	Location	User and Notes
453.97500	460.47500	NFM	Nuneaton	Motor Industry Research Association
453.97500	460.47500	NFM	Preston	Gafoor Poultry
453.97500	460.47500	NFM	Reading	University (Campus)
453.97500	460.47500	NFM	Sheffield	Stockbridge Steels Engineering
453.97500	460.47500	NFM	Silverstone	Race Control/Emergency Ambulance (71.9)
453.97500		NFM	Sizewell	Power Station Work Teams Ch.3
453.97500	460.47500	NFM	Stansted Airport	Ramp Ch.1 (127.3)
453.98750	460.48750	NFM	Chelmsford	First Bus
453.98750	460.48750	NFM	Kent	Eurotunnel UK Terminal
453.98750	460.48750	NFM	Liverpool	Liverpool City Football Club Staff
453.98750	460.48750	NFM	Liverpool	Speke Retail Park Security
453.98750	460.48750	NFM	Luton Airport	AirRadio easyJet/Multi User Trunked Network
453.98750	460.48750	NFM	Nationwide	Wide Area Dual Allocation
453.98750	460.48750	NFM	Salford	Hope Hospital Porters (88.5)
453.98750	460.48750	NFM	Warrington	Ineos Silicas Ch.1 Security/Emergency (141.3)
453.98750	460.48750	NFM	Watford	Watford General Hospital Staff

454.0125 - 454.8375 MHz — Wide Area Paging 25 kHz

Base	Mobile	Mode	Location	User and Notes
454.02500		NFM	Birmingham	Heartlands Hospital Voice Paging
454.02500		NFM	Birmingham	QE Hospital Paging
454.02500		NFM	Bury St. Edmunds	West Suffolk Hospital Paging
454.02500		NFM	Crewe	Leighton Hospital Voice Paging
454.02500		NFM	Carlisle	Hospital Paging
454.02500		NFM	Lancaster	Hospital Voice Paging
454.02500		NFM	London	Hammersmith Area Mosque
454.02500		NFM	Nationwide	Hospital Voice Paging
454.02500		NFM	Newcastle	Hospital Voice Paging
454.02500		NFM	Preston	Mosque
454.02500		NFM	Rochdale	Mosque
454.02500		NFM	Stoke on Trent	Hospital Voice Paging
454.02500		NFM	Wakefield	Clayton Hospital Voice Paging
454.05000		NFM	Coventry	Walsgrave Hospital Voice Paging
454.05000		NFM	Liverpool	Hospital Voice Paging
454.06250		NFM	Kent	Eurotunnel Trains
454.07500		NFM	Coventry	Coventry & Warwickshire Hospital Voice Paging
454.07500		NFM	Liverpool	Hospital Voice Paging
454.07500		NFM	London	Kings College Hospital Voice Paging
454.07500		NFM	North Sea	Amoco Bacton Paging System
454.08750		NFM	Kent	Eurotunnel Trains
454.10000		NFM	Birmingham	Newcross Hospital Voice Paging
454.10000		NFM	Cardiff	Mosque, Severn Road
454.10000		NFM	Leicester	Mosque
454.10000		NFM	London	Mosque, Golders Green
454.10000		NFM	London	Mosque, Wembley
454.10000		NFM	London	Mosque, Whitechapel
454.10000		NFM	London	Shree Swaminarayan Temple, Willesden
454.10000		NFM	Manchester	Hospital Voice Paging
454.10000		NFM	Norwich	Norfolk & Norwich Hospital Voice Paging
454.10000		NFM	Whiston	Hospital Voice Paging
454.10000		NFM	Wolverhampton	Hospital Voice Paging
454.12500		NFM	Bradford	Mosque
454.12500		NFM	London	Voice Paging Thames Coastguard to RNLI
454.12500		NFM	Manchester	Mosque

Base	Mobile	Mode	Location	User and Notes
454.15000		NFM	Croyton	Shell Haven Oil Refinery Voice Paging
454.15000		NFM	London	Mosque, Silvertown
454.15000		NFM	Nationwide	USS Winston Churchill On Board Trunked Network
454.16250	460.07500	NFM	Kent	Eurotunnel Traffic
454.17500		NFM	Cambridge	Addenbrooke's Hospital Voice Paging
454.17500		NFM	Cambridge	Papworth Hospital Paging
454.17500		NFM	Gorlestone	James Paget Hospital Paging
454.17500		NFM	Leeds	General Infirmary Voice Paging
454.17500		NFM	Leeds	St James (Jimmy's) Hospital Voice Paging
454.17500		NFM	Leeds	Pager Calls, Killingbeck
454.17500		NFM	Leicester	Mosque
454.17500		NFM	Nationwide	Hospital Voice Paging
454.17500		NFM	Newcastle	Hospital Voice Paging
454.17500		NFM	Norwich	Hospital Paging
454.17500		NFM	Sheffield	Royal Hallamshire Hospital Paging
454.17500		NFM	Stevenage	Lister Hospital Pagers
454.20000		NFM	Derbyshire	Centracom Doctors Paging
454.20000		NFM	Manchester	Hospital Paging
454.20000		NFM	Nationwide	Medical Paging
454.22500		NFM	Capenhurst	UKAEA Police
454.22500		NFM	Culham	UKAEA Police
454.22500		NFM	Harwell	UKAEA Police Ch.1
454.22500	460.07500	NFM	Kent	Eurotunnel Traffic
454.22500		NFM	Nationwide	UKAEA Police Common
454.22500		NFM	Preston	UKAEA Police
454.22500		NFM	Risley	UKAEA Police
454.22500		NFM	Sellafield	UKAEA Police
454.23750		NFM	Antrim	Hospital Paging
454.23750		NFM	Belfast	Royal Victoria Hospital Paging
454.23750		NFM	Coleraine	Causeway Hospital Paging
454.23750		NFM	Newtownabbey	Whiteabbey Hospital Paging
454.23750		NFM	Northern Ireland	Provincewide Hospital Paging Allocation
454.25000		NFM	Milton Keynes	Hospital Paging
454.27500		NFM	London	Mosque, Finsbury Park
454.27500		NFM	London	Mosque, Regents Park
454.28750	460.10000	NFM	Kent	Eurotunnel Traffic
454.30000		NFM	Edinburgh Airport	Paging
454.30000		NFM	Lancashire	Mosque
454.30000		NFM	Leicester	Mosque
454.30000		NFM	Merseyside	Hospital Voice Paging
454.32500		NFM	Basildon	Hospital Voice Paging
454.32500		NFM	County Durham	Hospital Voice Paging
454.32500	49.45000	NFM	Ipswich	Ipswich Hospital Paging
454.32500		NFM	Leeds	Hospital Voice Paging
454.32500		NFM	Peterborough	Peterborough District Hospital Voice Paging
454.33750	460.10000	NFM	Kent	Eurotunnel Traffic
454.35000	460.38750	NFM	Kent	Eurotunnel Control
454.35000		NFM	London	Mosque, N. London
454.39375		NFM	Nationwide	Call To Prayer Radio Service
454.40625		NFM	Nationwide	Call To Prayer Radio Service
454.41250	460.38750	NFM	Kent	Eurotunnel Control
454.46250	461.22500	NFM	Kent	Eurotunnel Traffic
454.47500		NFM	Southampton	Paging
454.50000		NFM	Nationwide	UKAEA

Base	Mobile	Mode	Location	User and Notes
454.52500	461.22500	NFM	Kent	Eurotunnel Traffic
454.58750	461.22500	NFM	Kent	Eurotunnel Traffic
454.62500		NFM	Newport	Royal Gwent Hospital Paging
454.65000	461.17500	NFM	Kent	Eurotunnel Traffic
454.70000		NFM	Bromley	Bromley Health Paging
454.70000		NFM	Lancashire	Mosque
454.70000		NFM	Leicester	Mosque
454.70000		NFM	London	Mosque, E London (254.1)
454.72500		NFM	Kent	Eurotunnel Traffic
454.75000		NFM	Kent	Eurotunnel Traffic
454.77500		NFM	Cardiff	University Hospital Of Wales Voice Paging
454.77500	461.17500	NFM	Kent	Eurotunnel Traffic
454.77500		NFM	Manchester	Mosque
454.77500		NFM	Warton	BAe
454.79375		NFM	Nationwide	Call to Prayer Radio Service
454.80625		NFM	Nationwide	Call to Prayer Radio Service
454.81250	461.38750	NFM	Kent	Eurotunnel Traffic
454.82500		NFM	Machynlleth	Hospital Paging

454.8375 - 454.9875 MHz   PMR Railways

Base	Mobile	Mode	Location	User and Notes
454.83750	461.38750	NFM	Kent	Eurotunnel Traffic
454.84375	461.34375	NFM	Essex	Rail Cab Radio, Raleigh
454.84375	448.34375	NFM	Kent	Eurotunnel Track to Terminal
454.84375	448.35375	NFM	Nationwide	Rail Cab Secure Radio Ch.1
454.85625		NFM	Nationwide	Rail Cab Radio Data Signalling Ch.2
454.86875	448.36875	NFM	London	Rail Cab Radio, Kings Cross
454.86875	448.36875	NFM	Nationwide	Rail Cab Secure Radio Ch.3
454.86875	448.36875	NFM	Welwyn	Rail Cab Radio
454.88125	448.38125	NFM	Nationwide	Rail Cab Secure Radio Ch.4
454.88125	448.38125	NFM	Scotland	ScotRail and SPT On-Board Handhelds
454.88750	448.38750	NFM	Scotland	Rail Cab Secure Radio Ch.5
454.89375	448.39375	NFM	Nationwide	Rail Cab Secure Radio Ch.5
454.89375	448.39375	NFM	Scotland	ScotRail and SPT On-Board Handhelds
454.89375	448.39375	NFM	Southampton	Rail Cab Secure Radio
454.90000	448.40000	NFM	Scotland	ScotRail and SPT On-Board Handhelds
454.90625	448.40625	NFM	Nationwide	Rail Cab Secure Radio Ch.6
454.91250	448.41250	NFM	Scotland	ScotRail and SPT On-Board Handhelds
454.91875	448.41875	NFM	London	Rail Cab Secure Radio, Kings Cross
454.91875	448.41875	NFM	London	Rail Cab Secure Radio, Waterloo
454.91875	448.41875	NFM	Nationwide	Rail Cab Secure Radio Ch7
454.91875	448.41875	NFM	Rainham	Rail Cab Secure Radio
454.91875	448.41875	NFM	Sittingbourne	Rail Cab Secure Radio
454.92500	448.42500	NFM	Scotland	ScotRail and SPT On-Board Handhelds
454.93125	448.43125	NFM	Bedford	Rail Cab Secure Radio
454.93125	448.43125	NFM	Essex	Rail Cab Secure Radio, Westhanger
454.93125	448.43125	NFM	Nationwide	Rail Cab Secure Radio Ch.8
454.94375	448.44375	NFM	Nationwide	Rail Cab Secure Radio Ch.9
454.95625	448.45625	NFM	Nationwide	Rail Cab Secure Radio Ch.10
454.96875	448.46875	NFM	Nationwide	Rail Cab Secure Radio Ch.11
454.96875	448.46875	NFM	Northampton	Rail Cab Secure Radio
454.98125	448.48125	NFM	Bournemouth	Rail Cab Secure Radio
454.98125	448.48125	NFM	Baldock	Rail Cab Secure Radio
454.98125	448.48125	NFM	Kent	Rail Cab Secure Radio, Higham Tunnel
454.98125	448.48125	NFM	Nationwide	Rail Cab Secure Radio Ch.12

Base	Mobile	Mode	Location	User and Notes

454.98750 - 455.45625 MHz   **Broadcasting Links**

Base	Mobile	Mode	Location	User and Notes
454.99250		NFM	Edinburgh	Grampian TV O/B Talkback
454.99250		NFM	Glasgow	Grampian TV O/B Talkback
454.99250		NFM	Perth	Grampian TV O/B Talkback
454.99350		NFM	East Anglia	Anglia TV Talkback
454.99350		NFM	Nationwide	ITV O/B
454.99375	468.36875	NFM	Nationwide	JFMG Short Term Talkback
454.99375	468.36875	NFM	Borehamwood	Big Brother (2003) Talkback
454.99500		NFM	Liverpool	Granada TV Talkback
455.00000		WFM	Nationwide	Central TV O/B
455.00000		NFM	Southampton	Meridian TV O/B
455.00625	468.38125	NFM	Borehamwood	BBC Elstree Regional News Talkback
455.00625		NFM	Borehamwood	Big Brother (2003) Talkback
455.00625	468.38125	NFM	Nationwide	JFMG Short Term Talkback
455.01200		NFM	Kempton Park	Channel 4 Racing Sound Link
455.01250		NFM	Nationwide	Australian TV O/B
455.01250		NFM	Wales	S4C O/B Unit
455.01250	468.05000	NFM	Jersey	Channel TV O/B
455.01875	468.04375	NFM	Nationwide	JFMG Short Term Talkback
455.02500		NFM	Lancashire	BBC TV O/B Talkback
455.02500	468.05000	NFM	Llanelli	Agenda Studio
455.02500		NFM	Midlands	BBC O/B
455.02500		WFM	Nationwide	Central TV O/B
455.03125		NFM	London	Independent TV Talkback
455.03125	468.05625	NFM	Nationwide	JFMG Short Term Talkback
455.03120	468.05625	NFM	Nationwide	Time Team Comms Ch.1
455.05000		NFM	Harwell	UKAEA Police Ch.2
455.06250		NFM	Capenhurst	UKAEA (HC/LH)
455.06250		NFM	Dorset	2CR Eye-In-The-Sky
455.06250		NFM	Edinburgh	Forth AM O/B
455.06250		NFM	Glasgow	Clyde 2 O/B link
455.06250		NFM	London	BBC South East
455.06250		NFM	Nationwide	ILR Channel D1
455.06250		NFM	Newcastle	Eye in the Sky
455.06250		NFM	Southampton	Ocean Sound Helicopter
455.06250		NFM	Stoke on Trent	Signal Radio O/B Link
455.06250		NFM	Tyne & Wear	Metro Radio O/B Helicopter
455.06250		NFM	Yorkshire	Yorkshire Gold O/B
455.07500		NFM	London	Capital Radio Flying Eye
455.09375	468.39375	NFM	Nationwide	JFMG Short Term Talkback
455.10000		NFM	Cardiff	HTV O/B
455.10000		NFM	Nottingham	BBC Radio Nottingham
455.10625	468.40625	NFM	Nationwide	JFMG Short Term Talkback
455.11875	468.41875	NFM	Nationwide	JFMG Short Term Talkback
455.12500		NFM	Liverpool	Granada TV Talkback
455.12500	468.39000	NFM	Jersey	Channel TV O/B
455.13125	468.43125	NFM	Nationwide	JFMG Short Term Talkback
455.13200		NFM	Edinburgh	Grampian TV O/B Talkback
455.13200		NFM	Glasgow	Grampian TV O/B Talkback
455.13200		WFM	Perth	Grampian TV O/B Talkback
455.13260		NFM	Nationwide	BBC TV Sports Commentary
455.13750		WFM	Nationwide	Central TV O/B
455.15000		NFM	Anglia	Anglia TV Studio Producer
455.15000		NFM	Manchester	Piccadilly Radio Eye in the Sky
455.16250		NFM	Birmingham	96.4 FM BRMB/Extra AM Flying Eye Talkback
455.16250		NFM	Dorset	2CR Outside Broadcast Feeder

Base	Mobile	Mode	Location	User and Notes
455.16250		NFM	London	BBC South East
455.16250		NFM	Milton Keynes	Chiltern Radio O/B
455.16250		NFM	Manchester	Key 103 Radio O/B
455.16250		NFM	Oxfordshire	Chiltern Radio Traffic Reports
455.16250		NFM	Peterborough	Hereward Radio O/B
455.16250		NFM	Nationwide	ILR Channel D2
455.16250		NFM	Norfolk	Radio Broadland FM O/B
455.16250		NFM	Peterborough	Hereward Radio O/B
455.16250		NFM	Stoke on Trent	Signal Radio O/B Link
455.18750		NFM	Midlands	BBC O/B
455.18750		NFM	Newmarket	Channel 4 TV Racing O/B
455.18750		NFM	Stoke on Trent	Stoke City O/B Microphones
455.19375	468.01875	NFM	Nationwide	JFMG Short Term Talkback
455.20000		NFM	Kempton Park	Channel 4 TV Racing Talkback
455.20000		WFM	Nationwide	Central TV O/B
455.20000		NFM	Newmarket	Channel 4 Racing O/B
455.20625	468.03125	NFM	Nationwide	JFMG Short Term Talkback
455.21875		NFM	Corby	ASCAR 2004 Stevie Hodgson Torquespeed Car 24
455.21875	468.49375	NFM	Nationwide	JFMG Short Term Talkback
455.22500		NFM	Burnley	Granada TV OB
455.22500		NFM	Manchester	ITN O/B Studio Link
455.22500		NFM	Nationwide	Radio Investigation Service
455.22500		WFM	Nationwide	Central TV O/B
455.22500		NFM	Newmarket	Channel 4 Racing O/B
455.23125	468.50625	NFM	Nationwide	JFMG Short Term Talkback
455.23125	468.50625	NFM	Nationwide	Time Team Comms Ch.2
455.24000		WFM	Leicester	BBC East Midlands O/B
455.24370	468.16870	NFM	Belfry	BBC TV OB (Ryder Cup)
455.24375		NFM	Aberystwyth	BBC Wales Today News Audio Feed
455.24375	468.16875	NFM	Nationwide	JFMG Short Term Talkback
455.24500		NFM	Birmingham	ITN Camera Crew
455.25620	468.19370	NFM	Nationwide	BBC TV O/B Talkback
455.25625	468.19375	NFM	Nationwide	JFMG Short Term Talkback
455.26875	468.18125	NFM	Nationwide	JFMG Short Term Talkback
455.28000		WFM	Leicester	BBC East Midlands O/B
455.28000		WFM	Portsmouth	BBC1 O/B
455.28120	468.29370	NFM	Belfry	BBC TV (Ryder Cup)
455.28125		NFM	Corby	ASCAR 2004 Shaun Richardson KR Racing Car 2
455.28125	468.29375	NFM	Nationwide	JFMG Short Term Talkback
455.28500		NFM	Edinburgh	BBC Scotland O/B
455.28500		NFM	Glasgow	BBC Scotland O/B
455.28500		WFM	Perth	BBC Scotland O/B
455.28750		NFM	Goodwood	BBC Goodwood OB
455.30625		NFM	Suffolk	BBC Radio Suffolk O/B
455.31250		NFM	Belfry (Ryder Cup)	BBC Radio 5 Live
455.31250		WFM	Jersey	BBC Jersey O/B
455.31250		NFM	Nationwide	BBC Radio 1 O/B
455.31250		WFM	Salisbury	BBC Wiltshire Sound
455.31250	141.2875	NFM	Suffolk	BBC Radio Suffolk O/B
455.36250		NFM	Belfry (Ryder Cup)	BBC Radio 5 Live
455.36250		NFM	Bristol	Radio Bristol
455.36250		NFM	Carlisle	BBC Radio Cumbria O/B
455.36250		WFM	Jersey	BBC Jersey O/B
455.36250		NFM	Nationwide	BBC Radio 1 O/B
455.36250		NFM	Nationwide	BBC Radio 5 Live Talkback
455.36250		NFM	Norfolk	BBC Radio Norfolk O/B

Base	Mobile	Mode	Location	User and Notes
455.36500		WFM	Hampshire	BBC Radio Solent Radio Car
455.37500	450.01250	NFM	Scotland	Grampian Police, Garve
455.39375	468.33125	NFM	Nationwide	JFMG Short Term Talkback
455.40625	468.20625	NFM	Nationwide	JFMG Short Term Talkback
455.41875	468.30625	NFM	Nationwide	JFMG Short Term Talkback
455.42500		NFM	Cumbria S	Data Link
455.43125	468.24375	NFM	Llanelli	Agenda Studio
455.43125	468.31875	NFM	Nationwide	JFMG Short Term Talkback
455.43125	468.31875	NFM	Nationwide	Sky News Talkback
455.43750		NFM	Lincolnshire	BBC Radio Lincs. O/B Studio Link
455.43750		NFM	Preston	Radio Lancashire O/B
455.44375		NFM	Nationwide	JFMG Short Term Talkback
455.44500		NFM	Leicester	Radio Leicester O/B Ch.2
455.45000	446.83750	NFM	Cambridge	BBC Radio Cambridgeshire
455.45000	450.02500	NFM	Scotland	Grampian Police, Applecross
455.45625	468.55625	NFM	London	JFMG Short Term Talkback

455.46875 - 455.85625 MHz   PMR Airport Security, Ground Repeaters, Railways and Limited PMR in Scotland

Base	Mobile	Mode	Location	User and Notes
455.47500	460.77500	NFM	Birmingham Airport	Ground Ch.1
455.47500	460.77500	NFM	Gatwick	Ground Services
455.47500		NFM	Lancashire	BAe Warton
455.47500	460.77500	NFM	Woodford Airfield	Crash Ops (Red Base)
455.48750	461.78750	NFM	Belfast	City Tower
455.48750	461.78750	NFM	Bournemouth (Hurn)	Tower Repeater
455.48750		NFM	Bristol	Bristol International Airport (151.4)
455.48750	461.78750	NFM	East Midlands Airport	Ground Relay
455.48750	461.78750	NFM	Heathrow	Armed Police Ch.10 (Hunter Delta)
455.48750	461.78750	NFM	Liverpool Airport	Apron Control
455.48750	461.78750	NFM	Teesside	CAA Fire School
455.50000	460.80000	NFM	Fareham	CAA Swanwick Centre Ch.3
455.50000		NFM	Guernsey, Forest	Airport Le Villiase Ground Ops
455.50000	460.80000	NFM	Manchester	Airport Trunked Network
455.51250		NFM	Cranfield Airport	Fire Services
455.51250	449.01250	NFM	London	Rail Cab Secure Radio, Paddington
455.51250	449.01250	NFM	Nationwide	Rail Cab Secure Radio Ch.13
455.52500	461.17500	NFM	Bristol Airport	Ground Ch.2
455.52500	461.17500	NFM	Cranfield Airfield	Tower/Runway (110.9 Input)
455.52500	461.17500	NFM	East Midlands	Tower Relay
455.52500	461.17500	NFM	Fareham	CAA Swanwick Centre Ch.5
455.52500	461.17500	NFM	Farnborough	Base Transport Control (131.8)
455.52500	461.17500	NFM	Heathrow	Tower Rebroadcast from 118.50MHz
455.52500	461.20000	NFM	Humberside Airport	Ground Relay
455.52500	460.82500	NFM	Manchester International	Crash Ops.
455.53750	460.53750	NFM	Birmingham International	Ground Control
455.53750	460.18750	NFM	Coventry	Airport Ground (103.5)
455.53750	460.53750	NFM	Luton Airport	Maintenance
455.53750	449.03750	NFM	Nationwide	Rail Cab Secure Radio Ch.18
455.53750	449.03750	NFM	Potters Bar	Rail Cab Secure Radio
455.55000		NFM	Gloucester	Staverton Airport Ground (254.1)
455.55000	461.85000	NFM	Heathrow	Ground Repeater (121.9 MHz Rebroadcast)
455.55000	461.85000	NFM	Leeds Airport	Tower to Ground Repeater, Yeadon
455.55000	461.85000	NFM	Manchester	Airport Tower Repeater
455.55000	461.85000	NFM	Manston	Airport Tower Repeater
455.55000	461.85000	NFM	Stansted	Tower to Ground Repeater
455.55000	461.85000	NFM	Swansea	Airport Tower Repeater

Base	Mobile	Mode	Location	User and Notes
455.55000	460.95000	NFM	Teesside	Airport Ch.1
455.56250	460.86250	NFM	Blackpool	Airport Crash/Rescue
455.56250	460.86250	NFM	Doncaster	Robin Hood Airport Tower/Ground (103.5)
455.56250	460.86250	NFM	Gatwick	Airport Data
455.57500	461.22500	NFM	Birmingham International	Fire Ch.2
455.57500	461.22500	NFM	Cranfield	Airfield Security & Fire
455.57500	461.22500	NFM	Fareham	CAA Swanwick Centre Ch.9
455.57500	460.87500	NFM	Heathrow	BAA Management/Engineers Trunked
455.57500	461.22500	NFM	Warton	BAe
455.57500	460.87500	NFM	Woodford Airfield	Tower-Ground
455.58750	449.08750	NFM	Cuxton	Rail Cab Secure Radio
455.58750	449.08750	NFM	London	Rail Cab Secure Radio, Paddington
455.58750	449.08750	NFM	London	Rail Cab Secure Radio, Greenford
455.58750	449.08750	NFM	Nationwide	Rail Cab Secure Radio Ch.14
455.60000	438.90000	NFM	Aldermaston	UKAEA
455.60000	460.90000	NFM	Blackpool	Airport
455.60000	460.90000	NFM	Bristol	Filton (BAe) Tower
455.60000	460.90000	NFM	East Midlands Airport	Terminal Security
455.60000	460.90000	NFM	Gatwick	BAA Ops (88.5)
455.60000	460.90000	NFM	Jersey Airport	Security
455.61250	460.91250	NFM	Bristol	Airport Refuelling
455.61250	461.91250	NFM	Heathrow	BAA Management/Engineering Trunked
455.61250	460.91250	NFM	Leeds Airport	Approach Link
455.61250	460.91250	NFM	Manchester	Airport Security, Trunked
455.61250	460.91250	NFM	Teesside	Airport Security Ch.3
455.62500	460.92500	NFM	Jersey	Airport Ground
455.62500	449.02500	NFM	Nationwide	Rail Cab Secure Radio Ch.19
455.62500	460.92500	NFM	Sheffield	City Airport Tower Ops.
455.62500	460.92500	NFM	Prestwick Airport	Tower to Ground
455.62500	460.92500	NFM	Warton	BAe
455.63750	460.93750	NFM	Doncaster	Robin Hood Airport Discrete Use (103.5)
455.63750	460.93750	NFM	Gatwick	Crash Ops. (88.5)
455.63750	460.93750	NFM	Liverpool	Airport Tower/Ground Movement Control
455.63750	460.93750	NFM	Luton Airport	Crash Ops. Ch.2
455.63750	460.93750	NFM	Stansted Airport	Maintenance
455.65000	460.95000	NFM	Birmingham Airport	Airway Crossing/Security
455.65000	460.95000	NFM	Bristol	BAe Filton
455.65000	460.95000	NFM	Edinburgh Airport	BAA Engineering Ch.6
455.65000	460.95000	NFM	Fareham	CAA Swanwick Centre Ch.15
455.65000	460.95000	NFM	Glasgow Airport	Tower to Ground
455.65000	460.95000	NFM	Heathrow	Crash Ops (127.3)
455.65000	460.95000	NFM	Manchester Airport	Ground Repeater
455.65000	460.95000	NFM	Stansted	Crash Ops
455.66250	449.16250	NFM	London	Rail Cab Secure Radio, Marylebone Station
455.66250	449.16250	NFM	Nationwide	Rail Cab Secure Radio Ch.15
455.66250	449.16250	NFM	Rochester	Rail Cab Secure Radio
455.67500	449.17500	NFM	Nationwide	Rail Cab Secure Radio Ch.16
455.67500	449.17500	NFM	Rainham	Rail Cab Secure Radio
455.68750	459.68750	NFM	Isle of Man	Ronaldsway Airport Tower-Ground (118.8)
455.68750	449.18750	NFM	London	Rail Cab Secure Radio, London Bridge (192.8)
455.68750	449.18750	NFM	London	Rail Cab Secure Radio, Plaistow
455.68750	449.18750	NFM	Micheldever	Rail Cab Secure Radio
455.68750	449.18750	NFM	Nationwide	Rail Cab Secure Radio Ch.17
455.68750	449.18750	NFM	Winchester	Rail Cab Secure Radio
455.70000	461.00000	NFM	Birmingham Airport	Ground/Apron Ch.4
455.70000	461.00000	NFM	Bournemouth (Hurn)	Ground Services

Base	Mobile	Mode	Location	User and Notes
455.70000	461.00000	NFM	Cardiff	Tower-Ground Vehicles
455.70000	461.00000	NFM	Edinburgh Airport	Passenger Services
455.70000	461.00000	NFM	Gatwick	Airfield Ops (88.5)
455.70000	461.00000	NFM	Hawarden Airfield	Tower Link
455.70000	461.00000	NFM	Heathrow	Tower Link
455.70000	461.00000	NFM	Prestwick	Crash Ops
455.71250	461.01250	NFM	Bristol	Douglas Cleaning Company
455.71250	461.01250	NFM	East Midlands Airport	Fire Service
455.71250	461.01250	NFM	Heathrow	Trunked BAA Management/Engineers
455.71250	461.01250	NFM	London	City Airport Tower
455.71250	461.01250	NFM	Manchester Airport	Ground Handling Trunked
455.72500	461.02500	NFM	Edinburgh Airport	Channel 3/23
455.72500	461.02500	NFM	Glasgow Airport	Security
455.72500	461.02500	NFM	Heathrow	Armed Police (Hunter Whiskey) (131.8)
455.72500	461.02500	NFM	Sheffield	Airport Tower
455.72500	461.02500	NFM	Woodford Airfield	Fuel & Maintenance
455.73750	461.03750	NFM	Bristol Airport	Security Ch.3
455.73750	461.03750	NFM	Cambridge	Ground Control
455.73750	461.03750	NFM	Coventry Airport	Ground Control (118.8)
455.73750	461.03750	NFM	Doncaster	Robin Hood Airport Operations
455.73750	461.03750	NFM	Gatwick	Airport Security (88.5)
455.73750	461.03750	NFM	London	City Airport Crash Ops. Ch.2
455.73750	461.03750	NFM	Manchester Airport	Operations Trunked
455.73750	461.03750	NFM	Newcastle Airport	Tower Repeater
455.75000	461.05000	NFM	Farnborough	Airport Fire/Rescue
455.75000	461.05000	NFM	Heathrow	Trunked BAA Management/Engineers
455.75000	461.05000	NFM	Liverpool	Airport Security (103.5)
455.75000	461.05000	NFM	Luton Airport	Tower Relay
455.75000	461.05000	NFM	Newcastle Airport	Tower Relay
455.75000	469.75000	NFM	Prestwick	Ground Ops. Ch.3
455.76250	461.06250	NFM	Birmingham International	Ground Staff
455.76250	461.06250	NFM	Liverpool	Airport Security
455.76250	461.06250	NFM	Manchester	Airport Ground Delivery Clearance
455.76250	461.06250	NFM	Teesside	Airport Ground-Tower Repeater Ch.2
455.77500	461.07500	NFM	Bristol	BAe Filton
455.77500	461.07500	NFM	Blackpool	Airport Tower-Ground
455.77500	461.07500	NFM	Edinburgh Airport	Fire Service (Handhelds) Channel 2/22
455.77500	461.07500	NFM	Gatwick	Ground Control Link
455.77500	461.07500	NFM	Glasgow	Airport Crash Ops.
455.77500	461.07500	NFM	Heathrow	Armed Police (Hunter Whisky)
455.77500	461.07500	NFM	Inverness	Airport Tower
455.77500	461.07500	NFM	Warton	BAe
455.78750	461.08750	NFM	London	City Airport Operations
455.78750	461.08750	NFM	Manchester Airport	Car Park Security Trunked
455.80000	461.10000	NFM	Birmingham International	Baggage Handlers
455.80000	461.10000	NFM	Bristol International	Tower Ch.1
455.80000	461.10000	NFM	Liverpool	Airport Ground Movements
455.81250	461.11250	NFM	Aberdeen (Dyce Airport)	Ground/Tower
455.81250	461.11250	NFM	Fareham	CAA Swanwick Centre Ch.28
455.81250	461.11250	NFM	Heathrow	Trunked BAA Management/Engineers
455.81250	461.11250	NFM	Manchester Airport	Ground Handling Trunked
455.81250	461.11250	NFM	Newcastle Airport	Baggage Handling
455.81250	461.11250	NFM	Stansted	Security Ops
455.82500	461.12500	NFM	Birmingham International	Maintenance
455.82500	461.12500	NFM	East Midlands Airport	Maintenance
455.82500		NFM	Kemble	Tower Ch.3

Base	Mobile	Mode	Location	User and Notes
455.82500	461.12500	NFM	Luton Airport	Ground Movements Ch.1
455.82500	461.12500	NFM	Stansted	Tower
455.83750	461.13750	NFM	Belfast Airport	Tower/Ground
455.83750	461.13750	NFM	Bristol Airport	Tower Relay
455.83750	461.13750	NFM	Edinburgh Airport	Tower/Ground Rebroadcasts Ch.1
455.83750	461.13750	NFM	Glasgow Airport	Tower
455.83750	461.13750	NFM	Liverpool Airport	Crash Ops
455.83750	461.13750	NFM	Lydd	Radar Repeater
455.85000	461.15000	NFM	Gatwick	Maintenance (88.5)
455.85000	461.15000	NFM	Woodford	Airfield (114.8)

455.8750 - 456.0000 MHz   Emergency Services 12.5 kHz

Base	Mobile	Mode	Location	User and Notes
455.98750		NFM	Herts/Beds	XA99 Police Helicopter
455.98750		NFM	Nationwide	Ambulance/Fire/Police Inter-Agency
455.98750		NFM	Sussex	West Sussex Fire Brigade

456.000 - 457.000 MHz   PMR

Base	Mobile	Mode	Location	User and Notes
456.00000	461.50000	NFM	Kidlington	Campsfield House Immigration Detention Centre
456.00000		NFM	London	Hillingdon Civic Centre Security, Uxbridge
456.00000	461.50000	NFM	London	Security Company, Fleet Street
456.00000		NFM	Lowestoft	Shopping Centre Security (DCS 032)
456.00000		NFM	Nationwide	Securicor Cash in Transit Handhelds
456.00000	461.50000	NFM	Poole	Tower Park Leisure Centre Security
456.01250	461.51250	NFM	Birmingham	NEC Exhibition Centre Trunked Network
456.01250	461.51250	NFM	Birmingham	Shopwatch - Relay of 441 MHz Traffic
456.01250	461.51250	NFM	Heathrow	Terminal 1
456.01250		NFM	Nationwide	Short Term Hire (Should be Trunked, often Simplex)
456.02500	461.52500	NFM	Barton	Kimberley Clark Fire Channel
456.02500	461.52500	NFM	Burton on Trent	Coopers Square Shopping Centre Security
456.02500	461.52500	NFM	Bury	Council Refuse Collection (192.8)
456.02500	461.52500	NFM	Clacton	Shopwatch
456.02500	461.52500	NFM	Cleethorpes	Shopwatch
456.02500	461.52500	NFM	Coventry	Tile Hill Shopping Centre Security
456.02500	461.52500	NFM	Cowley	MG Rover Car Factory Paint Shop (118.8)
456.02500	461.52500	NFM	Cumbernauld	Shopwatch
456.02500	461.52500	NFM	Dartford	Marks & Spencer, Bluewater (233.6)
456.02500	461.52500	NFM	Dover	Docks Police
456.02500	461.52500	NFM	Dungeness	Power Station
456.02500	461.52500	NFM	Durham	Shopwatch (110.9)
456.02500	461.52500	NFM	Gatwick	Airport Security
456.02500	461.52500	NFM	Gaydon	MG Rover Test Track
456.02500	461.52500	NFM	Glasgow Airport	Aviance
456.02500	461.52500	NFM	Guildford	Parking Enforcement
456.02500	461.52500	NFM	Havant	Xyratex Hardware Security
456.02500	461.52500	NFM	Heathrow	BP Aviation Fuels (123)
456.02500	461.52500	NFM	Hull	North Point Shopping Centre Security
456.02500	461.52500	NFM	Immingham	DFDS Transport
456.02500	461.52500	NFM	Ipswich	Buttermarket Shopping Centre (103.5)
456.02500	461.52500	NFM	Isle of Wight	Pubwatch, Ryde (71.9)
456.02500	461.52500	NFM	Isle of Wight	Shopwatch, Ryde (82.5)
456.02500	461.52500	NFM	Killinholme	Oil Refinery
456.02500	461.52500	NFM	Leicester	The Shires Shopping Centre Security
456.02500	461.52500	NFM	London	Distribution Depot, Perivale
456.02500	461.52500	NFM	London	Hamley's Toy Shop Security, Regent Street
456.02500	461.52500	NFM	London	Marks & Spencer Maintenance, Marble Arch

Base	Mobile	Mode	Location	User and Notes
456.02500	461.52500	NFM	London	Victoria Station Staff, East Side (77)
456.02500	461.52500	NFM	London	Whiteley Centre Security, Queensway (131.8)
456.02500	461.52500	NFM	Luton	Vauxhall Motors
456.02500	461.52500	NFM	Lutterworth	Asda Distribution Depot Trunked Voice
456.02500	461.52500	NFM	Manchester	Airport Boarding
456.02500	461.52500	NFM	Redcar	British Steel Security
456.02500	461.52500	NFM	Rotherham	Parkgate Shopping Centre Security
456.02500	461.52500	NFM	Shoreham by Sea	Euromin Cargo Handling (88.5)
456.02500	461.52500	NFM	Sidcup	Queens Marys Hospital
456.02500	461.52500	NFM	Stalybridge	Shopwatch
456.02500	461.52500	NFM	Swansea	Quadrant Shopping Centre Security
456.02500	461.52500	NFM	Warton	BAe
456.02500	461.52500	NFM	Windsor	Shopwatch (225.7)
456.03750	461.53750	NFM	Kent	Eurotunnel Trains en route to St Pancras
456.03750	461.53750	NFM	London	Eurotunnel Link, St Pancras
456.03750	461.53750	NFM	Stansted	Air UK Flight Despatch
456.05000	461.55000	NFM	Belfast	Metro Translink Bus Inspectors Ch.2 (67)
456.05000	461.55000	NFM	Birmingham	Airport Flightlink Coaches
456.05000	461.55000	NFM	Blackpool	Trams
456.05000	461.55000	NFM	Bristol	UKAEA Power Station Security
456.05000	461.55000	NFM	Cardiff	University Control/Security (88.5)
456.05000	461.55000	NFM	Clacton on Sea	Shopwatch
456.05000	461.55000	NFM	Crawley	Metrobus (110.9)
456.05000	461.55000	NFM	Edinburgh	Parking Enforcement
456.05000	461.55000	NFM	Gateshead	Shopwatch, Metro Centre (110.9)
456.05000	461.55000	NFM	Grays	Council Refuse Collection
456.05000	461.55000	NFM	Hull	Oil Jetty
456.05000	461.55000	NFM	Lewes	Sussex Downs College (77)
456.05000	461.55000	NFM	London	Parking Enforcement, Wandsworth
456.05000	461.55000	NFM	London	Parks Police Ch.2, Wandsworth
456.05000	461.55000	NFM	London	Southwark Council (136.5)
456.05000	461.55000	NFM	Maidstone	Shopwatch
456.05000	461.55000	NFM	Milton Keynes	Shopping Centre Cleaners
456.05000	461.55000	NFM	Newcastle	Eldon Garden Shopping Centre Security (88.5)
456.05000	461.55000	NFM	Oxford	University Security (94.8)
456.05000	461.55000	NFM	Portsmouth	Council Environmental Patrols (118.8)
456.05000	461.55000	NFM	Salford	Quays Security
456.05000	461.55000	NFM	Sheffield	Meadowhall Shopping Centre Maintenance
456.05000	461.55000	NFM	Stansted	Airport Trunked Network
456.05000	461.55000	NFM	Warton	BAe
456.05000	461.55000	NFM	Watford	Parking Enforcement (71.9)
456.05000	461.55000	NFM	York	Council Car Parks
456.06250	461.56250	NFM	Nationwide	Electricity Boards/Power & Fuel Trunked/Simplex
456.07500	461.57500	NFM	Belfast	City Hospital Security
456.07500	461.57500	NFM	Cardiff	Aberthaw Power Station
456.07500	461.57500	NFM	Middlesbrough	Power Station
456.07500	461.57500	NFM	Nationwide	Electricity Boards/Power & Fuel Trunked/Simplex
456.07500	461.57500	NFM	Warton	BAe
456.08750	461.58750	NFM	Cardiff	Aberthaw Power Station (67)
456.08750	461.58750	NFM	Nationwide	Electricity Boards/Power & Fuel Trunked/Simplex
456.08750	461.58750	NFM	Sizewell	Electricity Board/UKAEA Sizewell A Security
456.08750	461.58750	NFM	Whitehaven	Marshon Chemicals
456.10000	461.60000	NFM	Belfast	Musgrave Park Hospital Security
456.10000	461.60000	NFM	Dungeness	Power Station
456.10000	461.60000	NFM	Manchester	Manchester Velodrome (110.9)
456.10000	461.60000	NFM	Nationwide	Electricity Boards/Power & Fuel Trunked/Simplex

Base	Mobile	Mode	Location	User and Notes
456.11250	461.61250	NFM	Barrow in Furness	Gas Terminal Maintenance (71.9)
456.11250	461.61250	NFM	Nationwide	Electricity Boards/Power & Fuel Trunked/Simplex
456.12500	461.62500	NFM	Cemaes Bay	Wylfa Power Station
456.12500	461.62500	NFM	Edinburgh	Scottish Hydro Electric
456.12500	461.62500	NFM	Kent	Eurotunnel Trains en route to St Pancras
456.12500	461.62500	NFM	Nationwide	Electricity Boards/Power & Fuel Trunked/Simplex
456.12500		NFM	Nationwide	USS Winston Churchill Trunk Data Control
456.12500	461.62500	NFM	Sizewell	UKAEA
456.13750	461.63750	NFM	Nationwide	Electricity Boards/Power & Fuel Trunked/Simplex
456.13750	461.63750	NFM	Southampton	Fawley Power Station
456.15000	461.65000	NFM	Ashford	Sellindge Converter Station
456.15000	461.65000	NFM	London	London Electricity Board
456.15000	461.65000	NFM	Manchester	Sub Station Audio Alarm
456.15000	461.65000	NFM	Nationwide	Electricity Boards/Power & Fuel Trunked/Simplex
456.16250	461.66250	NFM	London	London Electricity Board
456.16250	461.66250	NFM	Nationwide	Electricity Boards/Power & Fuel Trunked/Simplex
456.16250	461.66250	NFM	Sizewell	Power Station
456.17500	461.67500	NFM	Aberystwyth	Hydro Scheme, Cwm Rheidol
456.17500	461.67500	NFM	Alwyn	Total Oil
456.17500	461.67500	NFM	Didcot	UKAEA
456.17500	461.67500	NFM	Dungeness	Power Station (110.9)
456.17500	461.67500	NFM	Hartlepool	Power Station
456.17500	461.67500	NFM	Heysham	Power Station
456.17500	461.67500	NFM	Liverpool	Jetty & Docks
456.17500	461.67500	NFM	Nationwide	Electricity Board/Power & Fuel Trunked/Simplex
456.18750	461.68750	NFM	Atwick	British Gas
456.18750	461.68750	NFM	Barrow in Furness	VSEL (118.8)
456.18750	461.68750	NFM	Isle of Grain	British Gas Depot
456.18750	461.68750	NFM	Lichfield	Intruder Alert
456.18750	461.68750	NFM	London	Electricity Engineers
456.18750	461.68750	NFM	Morecambe	Voice Alarm
456.18750	461.68750	NFM	Nationwide	Electricity Board/Power & Fuel Trunked/Simplex
456.20000	461.70000	NFM	Barry	Aberthaw Power Station (67)
456.20000	461.70000	NFM	Belfast	Metro Translink Bus Drivers Ch.1 (71.9)
456.20000	461.70000	NFM	Bristol	BNFL Command & Control, Berkeley
456.20000	461.70000	NFM	Didcot	UKAEA
456.20000	461.70000	NFM	Dungeness	Power Station
456.20000	461.70000	NFM	Heysham	Power Station Visitor Centre Guides
456.20000	461.70000	NFM	Leicester	British Gas Security
456.20000	461.70000	NFM	Nationwide	Electricity Boards/Power & Fuel Trunked/Simplex
456.20000	461.70000	NFM	Northwich	Brunner-Mond Chemicals Maintenance (171.3)
456.20000	461.70000	NFM	Sizewell	Power Station Command Channel
456.21250	461.71250	NFM	Barrow in Furness	VSEL (118.8)
456.21250	461.71250	NFM	Isle of Grain	Kingsnorth Power Station
456.21250	461.71250	NFM	London	Electricity Engineers
456.21250	461.71250	NFM	Nationwide	Electricity Board/Power & Fuel Trunked/Simplex
456.21250	461.71250	NFM	Surrey	Electricity Engineers
456.22500	461.72500	NFM	Barry	Aberthaw Power Station (67)
456.22500	461.72500	NFM	Rugeley	Power Station Staff
456.22500	461.72500	NFM	Sizewell	Power Station
456.22500	461.72500	NFM	Nationwide	Electricity Boards/Power & Fuel Trunked/Simplex
456.23750	461.73750	NFM	Bridgend	Celtic Energy Opencast Coal Mine
456.23750	461.73750	NFM	Coventry	Coventry Colliery
456.23750	461.73750	NFM	London	London Electricity Board
456.23750	461.73750	NFM	Nationwide	Electricity Boards/Power & Fuel Trunked/Simplex
456.25000	461.75000	NFM	Barrow in Furness	Gas Terminal

Base	Mobile	Mode	Location	User and Notes
456.25000	461.75000	NFM	Barry	Aberthaw Power Station (67)
456.25000	461.75000	NFM	Bristol	BNFL Command & Control, Berkeley
456.25000	461.75000	NFM	Nationwide	Electricity Board/Power & Fuel Trunked/Simplex
456.25000	461.75000	NFM	Warwick	Warwick Technology Park (CW)
456.26250	461.76250	NFM	Barrow in Furness	VSEL Test Engineers
456.26250	461.76250	NFM	Canvey Island	British Gas
456.26250	461.76250	NFM	Heathrow	Catering Company (77)
456.26250	461.76250	NFM	Nationwide	Electricity Boards/Power & Fuel Trunked/Simplex
456.27500	461.77500	NFM	Barry	Aberthaw Power Station
456.27500	461.77500	NFM	Doncaster	Power Station
456.27500	461.77500	NFM	Dungeness	Power Station
456.27500	461.77500	NFM	Heysham	Power Station
456.27500	461.77500	NFM	London	London Electricity Board
456.27500	461.77500	NFM	Nationwide	Electricity Boards/Power & Fuel Trunked/Simplex
456.27500	461.77500	NFM	Tilbury	Power Station
456.28750	461.78750	NFM	Barrow in Furness	Gas Terminal
456.28750	461.78750	NFM	Gravesend/Northfleet	Eurotunnel Trains en route to St Pancras
456.28750	461.78750	NFM	Nationwide	Electricity Boards/Power & Fuel Trunked/Simplex
456.30000	461.80000	NFM	Barrow in Furness	VSEL Security
456.30000	461.80000	NFM	Easington	British Gas Terminal
456.30000	461.80000	NFM	Gravesend/Northfleet	Eurotunnel Trains en route to St Pancras
456.30000	461.80000	NFM	London	Channel Tunnel Rail Link Trunked Network, N1
456.30000	461.80000	NFM	Nationwide	Electricity Boards/Power & Fuel Trunked/Simplex
456.31250	461.81250	NFM	Nationwide	Ofcom Special Events Reserved Channel
456.32500	461.82500	NFM	Dublin	Airport Security
456.32500	461.82500	NFM	Dungeness	Power Station
456.32500	461.82500	NFM	Nationwide	Ofcom Special Events Reserved Channel
456.33750	461.83750	NFM	Birmingham	NEC Exhibition Centre, Trunked
456.33750	461.83750	NFM	Birmingham	Shopwatch - Relay of 441 MHz Traffic
456.35000	461.85000	NFM	Aberdeen	City Buses
456.35000	461.85000	NFM	Ashton under Lyne	Shopwatch & Community Patrollers
456.35000	461.85000	NFM	Ayr	Shopwatch
456.35000	461.85000	NFM	Barrow in Furness	Gas Terminal, Trunked, Data
456.35000	461.85000	NFM	Barry	Docks (179.9)
456.35000	461.85000	NFM	Bedford	Shopwatch
456.35000	461.85000	NFM	Birmingham	Frankley Water Works (94.8)
456.35000	461.85000	NFM	Birmingham	Severn Trent Water, Coleshill (110.9)
456.35000	461.85000	NFM	Blackpool	Blackpool Airport
456.35000	461.85000	NFM	Brighton	Brighton Marina Security (118.8)
456.35000	461.85000	NFM	Brighton	Royal Pavilion Staff/Security (110.9)
456.35000	461.85000	NFM	Bristol	The Mall Shopping Centre Security (167.9)
456.35000	461.85000	NFM	Cambridge	Addenbrookes Hospital Security (210.7)
456.35000	461.85000	NFM	Cardiff	Shopwatch, Roath (146.2)
456.35000		NFM	Carlisle	Burtons Security, Arndale Centre
456.35000	461.85000	NFM	Chesterfield	Pubwatch
456.35000	461.85000	NFM	Dartford	John Lewis Security, Bluewater Centre (146.2)
456.35000	461.85000	NFM	Eastbourne	City Buses
456.35000	461.85000	NFM	Gatwick	Cleaners/Cargo Loaders/Apron Movements (107.2)
456.35000	461.85000	NFM	Heathrow	Pakistan International Airlines (82.5)
456.35000	461.85000	NFM	Holyhead	Shopwatch (82.5)
456.35000	461.85000	NFM	Isle of Grain	BP Oil Terminal
456.35000	461.85000	NFM	Liverpool	Port Operations
456.35000	461.85000	NFM	Liverpool	Shopwatch, Old Swan
456.35000	461.85000	NFM	London	Docklands Light Railway Stations (225.7)
456.35000	461.85000	NFM	London	Home Office Passport Office Security, Victoria (210.7)
456.35000		NFM	London	Mercury Asset Management Security, EC1

Base	Mobile	Mode	Location	User and Notes
456.35000	461.85000	NFM	London	National Gallery Maintenance/Engineering
456.35000	461.85000	NFM	London	Olympia Exhibition Centre
456.35000	461.85000	NFM	London	Post Office Sorting Depot, Bakers Street
456.35000	461.85000	NFM	London	Post Office Sorting Depot, Euston Station
456.35000	461.85000	NFM	London	Post Office Sorting Depot, West Ham
456.35000	461.85000	NFM	London	Science Museum Security, S Kensington
456.35000	461.85000	NFM	London	Shopwatch, Brent Cross Shopping Centre
456.35000	461.85000	NFM	London	Shopwatch, Ealing
456.35000	461.85000	NFM	London	Whipps Cross Hospital, Walthamstow
456.35000	461.85000	NFM	Londonderry	Dupont
456.35000	461.85000	NFM	Manchester	Arndale Centre Security (82.5)
456.35000	461.85000	NFM	Northwich	Morrisons Distribution Depot, Rudheath (179.9)
456.35000	461.85000	NFM	Nottingham	Shopwatch, Victoria Centre
456.35000	461.85000	NFM	Ockendon	Waste Disposal Company
456.35000	461.85000	NFM	Oxford	John Radcliffe Hospital Estates (225.7)
456.35000	461.85000	NFM	Perivale	Distribution Company
456.35000	461.85000	NFM	Reading	Courage Brewery
456.35000	461.85000	NFM	Reading	University (Campus) (250.3)
456.35000	461.85000	NFM	Romford	Security Company
456.35000	461.85000	NFM	Saltend	BP Oil Refinery
456.35000	461.85000	NFM	Selsey	Shopwatch
456.35000	461.85000	NFM	Stafford	Pubwatch
456.35000	461.85000	NFM	Stansted	BAA Airport Ops (118.8)
456.35000	461.85000	NFM	Sutton	St Nicholas Shopping Centre
456.35000	461.85000	NFM	Swanley	Shopwatch
456.35000	461.85000	NFM	Warton	BAe Security
456.35000	461.85000	NFM	Wigan	Shopwatch, Galleries Shopping Centre
456.35000	461.85000	NFM	Woodford	Print Finishers
456.36250	461.86250	NFM	Kent	Eurotunnel Trains en route to St Pancras
456.37500	461.87500	NFM	Cardiff	Council Housing Benefit Surveillance Teams (136.5)
456.37500	461.87500	NFM	Cleveland	DSS Dole Fraud Squads Ch.8
456.37500	461.87500	NFM	Felixstowe	HM Revenue & Customs Ch.7
456.37500	461.87500	NFM	London	Docklands Light Railway Ch.10
456.37500	461.87500	NFM	London	DSS Fraud Teams Aerial Site, Lewisham
456.37500	461.87500	NFM	London	DSS Fraud Teams Aerial Site, N17
456.37500	461.87500	NFM	London	Kew Gardens Constabulary
456.37500	461.87500	NFM	London	Post Office Sorting Depot, Mount Pleasant
456.37500	461.87500	NFM	London	Tower Bridge Staff
456.37500	461.87500	NFM	London	Tower of London Security/Beefeaters (131.8)
456.37500	461.87500	NFM	London	Westminster Abbey Staff, Victoria (151.4)
456.37500		NFM	Nationwide	British Transport Police (Now Mainly Airwave)
456.37500		NFM	Nottinghamshire	DSS Fraud Teams
456.37500	461.87500	NFM	Portsmouth	Astrium Space Systems/ BAe Systems
456.37500		NFM	Sellafield	UKAEA
456.37500	461.87500	NFM	Yorkshire	DSS Fraud Teams
456.38750		NFM	Alnwick	Alnwick Garden
456.38750		NFM	Ascot	Racecourse Network Ch.10
456.38750		NFM	Birmingham	Shopwatch, Fort Retail Park (67)
456.38750		NFM	Borehamwood	Big Brother (2002) Production Security (DCS 026)
456.38750		NFM	Borehamwood	Big Brother (2003) Production Security (103.5)
456.38750		NFM	Braintree	George Yard Centre Cleaners
456.38750		NFM	Canvey Island	PMR Engineers
456.38750		NFM	Cardiff	Atlantic Wharf Leisure Site Security (103.5)
456.38750		NFM	Cardiff	Caspian Point/Scott Harbour Security (77)
456.38750		NFM	Carlisle	HMV Records
456.38750	461.88750	NFM	Chelmsford	First Bus

Base	Mobile	Mode	Location	User and Notes
456.38750		NFM	Chichester	Woolworths Staff Ch.2
456.38750		NFM	Duxford	Imperial War Museum Events Net (131.8)
456.38750	461.88750	NFM	Edinburgh Airport	Servisair/GlobeGround
456.38750	461.88750	WFM	Framlingham	Richard Weston Trailers
456.38750	461.88750	NFM	Hitchin	Shopwatch
456.38750	461.88750	NFM	Ipswich	GIS Security at Docks
456.38750		NFM	Ipswich	Ipswich Tower Door Staff (146.2)
456.38750	461.88750	NFM	Ipswich	Zest Nightclub
456.38750	461.88750	NFM	Ipswich	Pubwatch
456.38750	461.88750	NFM	Kendall	Shopwatch
456.38750		NFM	London	BP Gas Headquarters Security Ch.3
456.38750		NFM	London	Cafe Royal Security (DCS 025)
456.38750		NFM	London	French Connection UK Security, Oxford Circus (77)
456.38750		NFM	London	Fulham Football Club Staff/Admin. (233.6)
456.38750		NFM	London	Funland Amusements, Trocadero Centre (127.3)
456.38750		NFM	London	Greater London Authority Heritage Wardens (192.8)
456.38750		NFM	London	Laura Ashley Staff/Security, Regent Street (67)
456.38750		NFM	London	London Eye
456.38750		NFM	London	Louis Vuitton Store Security/Staff (DCS 606)
456.38750		NFM	London	Lucky Seven Restaurant, W2
456.38750	461.88750	NFM	London	Marks & Spencer Food Hall, Oxford Street
456.38750		NFM	London	Old Bailey Crown Court
456.38750		NFM	London	Peter Jones Customer Service, Chelsea (77)
456.38750	461.88750	NFM	London	Pickets Lock Centre Security (173.8)
456.38750	461.88750	NFM	London	Planet Hollywood, Piccadilly (233.6)
456.38750		NFM	London	Riverside Studios Staff, Hammersmith (67)
456.38750		NFM	London	Shopwatch, Wood Green
456.38750		NFM	London	Westland/GKN Heliport Marshallers, Battersea (123)
456.38750	461.88750	NFM	London	Virgin Records (Tower Records Site), Piccadilly (250.3)
456.38750		NFM	London	Voodoo Lounge, Leicester Square
456.38750	461.88750	NFM	Manchester	Airport
456.38750	461.88750	NFM	Manchester	Piccadilly Rail Station (250.3)
456.38750		NFM	Meadow Bank	Shopwatch
456.38750		NFM	Nationwide	British Motorcycle Federation Events (173.8)
456.38750		NFM	Nationwide	Olympus Events Security Company (103.5)
456.38750		NFM	Nationwide	Zenith Film/TV Production Ch.1
456.38750	461.88750	NFM	Newmarket	Racecourse Stewards
456.38750		NFM	Northampton	Santa Pod Race Way Ch.3 (103.5)
456.38750		NFM	Peterborough	Woolworths Staff
456.38750		NFM	Portsmouth	Woolworths Staff
456.38750		NFM	Purfleet	Esso Oil Storage Depot.
456.38750	461.88750	NFM	Romford	Quadrant Shopping Centre Security
456.38750	461.88750	NFM	Rugby	Christian Salvesen Ch.3
456.38750	461.88750	NFM	Shoreham by Sea	Shopwatch/Pubwatch (88.5)
456.38750		NFM	Wales	Rugby Union Referees (Simple Scrambling) (218.1)
456.38750	461.88750	NFM	Weston Super Mare	Pubwatch
456.40000	461.90000	NFM	Crayford	British Telecom Site
456.40000	461.90000	NFM	Crayford	Post Office Supplies Department
456.40000	461.90000	NFM	Cleveland	DSS Fraud Teams Ch 9
456.40000	461.90000	NFM	Grays	DSS Fraud Teams (94.8)
456.40000		NFM	London	Bank of England Bullion Movements (186.2)
456.40000	461.90000	NFM	London	Bank of England Office Security (186.2)
456.40000	461.90000	NFM	London	Bank of England Sports Ground Security, Roehampton
456.40000	461.90000	NFM	London	British Telecom Satellite Station, Woolwich
456.40000	461.90000	NFM	London	DSS Fraud Teams Aerial Site, Lewisham (97.3/94.8)
456.40000	461.90000	NFM	London	DSS Fraud Teams Aerial Site, N17 (97.3/94.8)

Base	Mobile	Mode	Location	User and Notes
456.40000	461.90000	NFM	London	Marlborough House
456.40000	461.90000	NFM	London	QE II Conference Centre, Victoria
456.40000	461.90000	NFM	Martlesham	British Telecoms Research Centre Security
456.40000	461.90000	NFM	Newcastle	Royal Mail, Newcastle Central Station
456.40000	461.90000	NFM	Sheffield	City Buses
456.40000	461.90000	NFM	Sheerness	Docks Security
456.41250	461.91250	NFM	Liverpool	DSS Fraud Teams
456.41250	461.91250	NFM	London	DSS Fraud Teams Aerial Site, N17
456.41250	461.91250	NFM	Stansted	Stansted Airport Trunked Network
456.42500	461.92500	NFM	Belfast	Shorts Aircraft Security Ch.1
456.42500	461.92500	NFM	Hull	Docks Police
456.42500	461.92500	NFM	Nationwide	Transport Police (Now Mainly Airwave)
456.43750	461.94375	NFM	Blackpool	Blackpool Pleasure Beach Security
456.43750	461.94735	NFM	Kent	Channel Tunnel Trains en route to St Pancras
456.45000	461.95000	NFM	Aberdeen	City Buses
456.45000	461.95000	NFM	Aldershot	Parking Enforcement (71.9)
456.45000	461.95000	NFM	Aylesbury	Parking Enforcement
456.45000	461.95000	NFM	Brighton	Buses
456.45000	461.95000	NFM	Bury	Council
456.45000	461.95000	NFM	Cardiff	Highways Department Traffic Control (107.2)
456.45000	461.95000	NFM	Coventry	Council Security (107.2)
456.45000	461.95000	NFM	Dorchester	Parking Enforcement (88.5) (Most of W Dorset)
456.45000	461.95000	NFM	Duxford	Imperial War Museum Security Ch.1(114.8)
456.45000	461.95000	NFM	Exeter	Car Parks Control (77)
456.45000	461.95000	NFM	Farnborough	Parking Enforcement (71.9)
456.45000	461.95000	NFM	Leicester	City Council Cleansing
456.45000	461.95000	NFM	Leicester	Shopwatch, The Shires Shopping Centre (103.5)
456.45000	461.95000	NFM	London	Borough of Brent Parking Enforcement
456.45000	461.95000	NFM	London	Charring Cross Hospital Medical School (94.8)
456.45000	461.95000	NFM	London	Hammersmith Hospital
456.45000	461.95000	NFM	London	Haringey Council
456.45000	461.95000	NFM	London	Islington College
456.45000	461.95000	NFM	London	Lewisham College, Deptford
456.45000	461.95000	NFM	London	Parking Enforcement, Southwark
456.45000	461.95000	NFM	London	Parking Enforcement, Tower Hamlets (67)
456.45000	461.95000	NFM	London	Parking Enforcement, Wembley (167.9)
456.45000	461.95000	NFM	London	Property Management, Albion St, Bermondsey
456.45000	461.95000	NFM	Maidstone	Parking Enforcement (88.5)
456.45000	461.95000	NFM	Manchester	Council
456.45000	461.95000	NFM	Norwich	NCP Car Park (179.9)
456.45000	461.95000	NFM	Nottingham	Traffic Light Repairs
456.45000	461.95000	NFM	Peterborough	Town Hall Ch.2
456.45000	461.95000	NFM	Poole	Parking Enforcement (118.8)
456.45000	461.95000	NFM	Portsmouth	Beach Patrol/Wardens (88.5)
456.45000	461.95000	NFM	Rotherham	Council
456.45000	461.95000	NFM	Salford	Salford Precinct High Rise Flats Security (94.8)
456.45000	461.95000	NFM	Sheffield	Council Housing Maintenance
456.45000	461.95000	NFM	Swindon	Brunel Plaza Shopping Centre Security (67)
456.45000	461.95000	NFM	Thamesmead	Caretakers & Lift Ops.
456.45000	461.95000	NFM	Winchester	Street Wardens/Parking Enforcement (114.8)
456.46250	461.96250	NFM	Birmingham	NEC Exhibition Centre Trunked Network
456.46250	461.96250	NFM	Cleethorpes	Imperial Group Food Factory
456.46250		NFM	Nationwide	Israeli Air Force Ground Crew
456.46250		NFM	Nationwide	Jordanian RAF Falcons Display Team Ground Crew
456.47500	461.97500	NFM	Barrow in Furness	Cartmel Priory Shopping Centre Security
456.47500	461.97500	NFM	Bewdley	West Midlands Safari Park Control
456.47500	461.97500	NFM	Birmingham	University Maintenance (103.5 Input Only)

Base	Mobile	Mode	Location	User and Notes
456.47500	461.97500	NFM	Bishops Stortford	Parking Enforcement (186.2)
456.47500	461.97500	NFM	Blackpool	Council Trunked
456.47500	461.97500	NFM	Cardiff	Welsh Assembly Security (151.4)
456.47500	461.97500	NFM	Chester	Jade cars
456.47500	461.97500	NFM	Clayton	Maynes Coaches
456.47500	461.97500	NFM	Edinburgh	St James Centre Security
456.47500	461.97500	NFM	Gravesend	Eurotunnel Trains en route to St Pancras
456.47500	461.97500	NFM	Gt Yarmouth	Rosie's Bar (67)
456.47500	461.97500	NFM	Grimsby	Appleby's Coaches
456.47500	461.97500	NFM	Heathrow	BAA Inter-Terminal Transfer Buses
456.47500	461.97500	NFM	Immingham	Exxtor Shipping
456.47500	461.97500	NFM	Inverness	Council
456.47500	461.97500	NFM	Leicester	Woods Coaches Ch.2
456.47500	461.97500	NFM	Liverpool	Dockside Crane Control
456.47500	461.97500	NFM	London	Clamping Company Operating in W1
456.47500	461.97500	NFM	London	Greenwich District Hospital
456.47500	461.97500	NFM	London	Hammersmith Hospital Security
456.47500	461.97500	NFM	London	Marks & Spencer, Oxford Street (71.9)
456.47500	461.97500	NFM	London	Philips & Drew Messenger Service EC
456.47500	461.97500	NFM	London	QE II Conference Centre, Victoria
456.47500	461.97500	NFM	London	Selfridges Department Store Security
456.47500	461.97500	NFM	London	Taxi Company, Norwood
456.47500	461.97500	NFM	Luton	Vauxhall Motors
456.47500	461.97500	NFM	Middleton	Diamond Cars
456.47500	461.97500	NFM	Nationwide	Independent Coach Operators
456.47500	461.97500	NFM	Northwich	Brunner Mond Chemical Site (88.5)
456.47500	461.97500	NFM	Oxford	Classic Tour Bus
456.47500	461.97500	NFM	Oxford	Tappins Coaches Ch.2
456.47500	461.97500	NFM	Preston	Council Skips & Bottle Banks
456.47500	461.95000	NFM	Sheffield	Parking Enforcement
456.47500	461.97500	NFM	Sittingbourne	Paper Mill Fire/Security Channel
456.47500	461.97500	NFM	Stowmarket	ICI Paints Security/Staff (203.5)
456.50000	462.00000	NFM	Beamish	Open Air Museum Staff/Security
456.50000	462.00000	NFM	Blackburn	Council Base (127.3)
456.50000	462.00000	NFM	Bridgend	Shopwatch/Pubwatch
456.50000	462.00000	NFM	Bury St. Edmunds	West Suffolk Hospital Porters
456.50000	462.00000	NFM	Canterbury	Hospital Security
456.50000	462.00000	NFM	Colchester	Lion Walk Shopping Centre Security
456.50000	462.00000	NFM	Duxford	Imperial War Museum Admin/Tower/Emergency
456.50000	462.00000	NFM	Gatwick	Airline Ops.
456.50000	462.00000	NFM	Heathrow	Eurocar Car Hire Ltd. (179.9)
456.50000	462.00000	NFM	Heathrow	LSG Skychefs Airline Catering
456.50000	462.00000	NFM	Immingham	Docks
456.50000	462.00000	NFM	Leeds	Metropolitan University Security
456.50000	462.00000	NFM	Leicester	Bus Inspectors
456.50000		NFM	Liverpool	Bus Inspectors (127.3)
456.50000	462.00000	NFM	Londonderry	Ulsterbus (71.9)
456.50000		NFM	Lowestoft	HM Revenue & Customs
456.50000	462.00000	NFM	Luton Airport	Airline Ops.
456.50000	462.00000	NFM	Manchester	International Airport Catering Airside (107.2)
456.50000	462.00000	NFM	Middlesbrough	University of Teesside Security
456.50000	462.00000	NFM	Northampton	Parking Enforcement
456.50000	462.00000	NFM	Norwich	Airport
456.50000	462.00000	NFM	Peterborough	Edith Cavell Hospital Maintenance
456.50000		NFM	Sellafield	UKAEA Trunked Network
456.50000	462.00000	NFM	Sheffield	Shopwatch, City Centre
456.50000	462.00000	NFM	Stevenage	Parking Enforcement (82.5)

Base	Mobile	Mode	Location	User and Notes
456.50000	462.00000	NFM	Tilbury	Docks
456.50000	462.00000	NFM	York	Council OAP Warden Service
456.51250	462.01250	NFM	Kent	Eurotunnel Trains en route to St Pancras
456.51250	462.01250	NFM	London	Channel Tunnel Trunked Network, N1
456.52500	462.02500	NFM	Ashford	Eurostar Staff/Security
456.52500	462.02500	NFM	Bedford	Vehicle Proving Ground (141.3)
456.52500	462.02500	NFM	Birmingham	Servisair/GlobeGround (77), International Airport
456.52500	462.02500	NFM	Bradford	Shopwatch, Arndale Centre
456.52500	462.02500	NFM	Bristol	Shopwatch, Galleries Shopping Centre (173.8)
456.52500	462.02500	NFM	Cardiff	Shopwatch, Barry (88.5)
456.52500	462.02500	NFM	Chesterfield	Hospital Trunked Network Data Channel
456.52500	462.02500	NFM	Chichester	Shopwatch (114.8)
456.52500	462.02500	NFM	Coventry	West Orchards Shopping Centre Security (71.9)
456.52500	462.02500	NFM	Crawley	County Mall Shopping Centre Security (151.4)
456.52500	462.02500	NFM	Denton	Shopwatch
456.52500	462.02500	NFM	Dorking	Friends Provident Insurance Security (82.5)
456.52500		NFM	Dover	P & O Ferries Ch.1 Departures
456.52500	462.02500	NFM	Eastbourne	Shopwatch
456.52500	462.02500	NFM	Gatwick	Aircraft Tugs
456.52500	462.02500	NFM	Gillingham	Shopwatch
456.52500	462.02500	NFM	Gloucester	Royal Hospital Maintenance (146.2)
456.52500	462.02500	NFM	Gravesend	Shopwatch
456.52500	462.02500	NFM	Grimsby	Shopwatch, Freshney Place Shopping Centre
456.52500	462.02500	NFM	Heathrow	Varig (Brazilian) T3 Ops.
456.52500	462.02500	NFM	Immingham	Docks/Repairs
456.52500	462.02500	NFM	Ipswich	Docks Ch.2 Container Movements (67)
456.52500	462.02500	NFM	Kent	Eurotunnel Trains en route to St Pancras
456.52500		NFM	Leicester	Leicester City Football Club Stewards
456.52500	462.02500	NFM	Leigh	Spinning Gate Shopping Centre Security
456.52500	462.02500	NFM	Litchfield	Shopwatch
456.52500	462.02200	NFM	London	Eurostar Staff/Security, Waterloo
456.52500	462.02500	NFM	Luton	Vauxhall Motors
456.52500	462.02500	NFM	Manchester	International Airport Fire Service
456.52500	462.02500	NFM	Medway	Shopwatch
456.52500	462.02500	NFM	Newcastle U Lyme	Shopwatch (82.5)
456.52500	462.02500	NFM	Paignton	Shopwatch (67)
456.52500	462.02500	NFM	Peterborough	Marks & Spencer Internal Communications
456.52500	462.02500	NFM	Salisbury	General Hospital Emergency/Security
456.52500	462.02500	NFM	Sittingbourne	Shopwatch
456.52500	462.02500	NFM	Slough	Shopwatch
456.52500	462.02500	NFM	St Albans	Parking Enforcement (77)
456.52500	462.02500	NFM	Stansted Airport	BAA Trunked Network
456.52500	462.02500	NFM	Stevenage	Lister Hospital Porters/Maintenance (162.2)
456.52500	462.02500	NFM	Sunderland	Shopwatch
456.52500	462.02500	NFM	York	District Hospital Patient Transport
456.55000	462.05000	NFM	Boston	Shopwatch
456.55000	462.05000	NFM	Brighton	Royal Sussex County Hospital
456.55000	462.05000	NFM	Bristol	Shopwatch
456.55000	462.05000	NFM	Cambridge	Addenbrookes Hospital Car Parks
456.55000	462.05000	NFM	Carnforth	Shaw Hadwin Coaches
456.55000	462.05000	NFM	Christchurch	Council
456.55000	462.05000	NFM	Coventry	Rolls Royce Security
456.55000	462.05000	NFM	Dover	Stena Line Ch.1 Coaches/Loaders
456.55000	462.05000	NFM	Filton	BAe Security
456.55000	462.05000	NFM	Gatwick	Ground Control Link
456.55000	462.05000	NFM	Gt Yarmouth	Guardwell Security (123)

Base	Mobile	Mode	Location	User and Notes
456.55000	462.05000	NFM	Heathrow	Boker Aeroclean Aircraft Cleaners (77)
456.55000	462.05000	NFM	Heathrow	Passenger Transport
456.55000	462.05000	NFM	Hull	Docks
456.55000	462.05000	NFM	Hull	University Security
456.55000	462.05000	NFM	Immingham	Network Rail
456.55000	462.05000	NFM	Lancashire	24hr Vehicle Recovery Company
456.55000	462.05000	NFM	Leeds	Shopwatch, City Centre
456.55000	462.05000	NFM	London	Parking Enforcement, N1(71.9)
456.55000	462.05000	NFM	London	Stanmore Cars
456.55000	462.05000	NFM	Malvern	Shopwatch
456.55000	462.05000	NFM	Manchester	Community Patrols
456.55000	462.05000	NFM	Newcastle	Eldon Shopping Centre Security (210.7/192.8)
456.55000	462.05000	NFM	Poole	Council Refuse Collectors
456.55000	462.05000	NFM	Sheffield	Shopwatch, Meadowhall Shopping Centre
456.55000	462.05000	NFM	Stoke-on-Trent	Potteries Shopping Centre Cleaners (71.9)
456.55000	462.05000	NFM	Watford	Capital & Country Car Parking Services (167.9)
456.56250	462.06250	NFM	Birmingham	NEC Exhibition Centre Trunked Network
456.57500	462.07500	NFM	Beeston	Boots
456.57500	462.07500	NFM	Biggleswade	Jordan's Cereals
456.57500	462.07500	NFM	Brighton	Shopwatch (88.5)
456.57500	462.07500	NFM	Bristol	Frenchay Hospital Porters
456.57500	462.07500	NFM	Bristol	University of the West of England Security (131.8)
456.57500	462.07500	NFM	Coryton	Conoco Oil Refinery Ch.1
456.57500	462.07500	NFM	Derby	East Midlands Airport
456.57500		NFM	Felixstowe	Docks
456.57500		NFM	Gloucestershire	DoT Motorcycle Tests
456.57500	462.07500	NFM	Hull	Hull University
456.57500	462.07500	NFM	Immingham	Associated Petroleum Terminals
456.57500	462.07500	NFM	Jersey	Servisair/GlobeGround Handling
456.57500	462.07500	NFM	London	DSS Fraud Teams
456.57500		NFM	London	St. James Park Wardens Ch.1 (151.3)
456.57500		NFM	London	Walkabout Bar, Covent Garden (141.3)
456.57500	462.07500	NFM	London	Walthamstow Dog Racing Track (77)
456.57500	462.07500	NFM	Londonderry	Dupont Security
456.57500	462.07500	NFM	Luton Airport	Refuellers (67)
456.57500		NFM	Manchester	Gap Store Staff
456.57500		NFM	Nationwide	Vehicle Tests
456.57500		NFM	Nationwide	Motorcycle Tests (77)
456.57500		NFM	Neath	HGV Tests (71.9)
456.57500		NFM	Newtown	Motorcycle Tests
456.57500	462.07500	NFM	Norwich	University of East Anglia Security
456.57500	462.07500	NFM	Poole	Toys R Us Security
456.57500	462.07500	NFM	Reading	Courage Brewery
456.57500	462.07500	NFM	Sizewell	Power Station Work Teams Ch.4
456.57500	462.07500	NFM	Southampton	Esso Fawley Oil Refinery (192.8)
456.57500	462.07500	NFM	Southampton Airport	AirRadio Trunked Network Voice Channel
456.57500	462.07500	NFM	Swansea	Motorcycle Training School
456.57500	462.07500	NFM	Tilbury	Docks
456.58750	462.08750	NFM	Kent	Channel Tunnel Trains en route to St Pancras
456.58750	462.08750	NFM	Nationwide	Ofcom Special Events Reserved Channel
456.60000	462.10000	NFM	Aberdeen	Dyce Airport Loading
456.60000	462.10000	NFM	Ascot	Racecourse Network Ch.9
456.60000	462.10000	NFM	Barnstable	Pubwatch
456.60000	462.10000	NFM	Belfast Airport	Airline Ops.
456.60000	462.10000	NFM	Birmingham	Aston University Security (225.7)
456.60000	462.10000	NFM	Birmingham	Massey Ferguson Security

Base	Mobile	Mode	Location	User and Notes
456.60000	462.10000	NFM	Brighton	City College Security (118.8)
456.60000	462.10000	NFM	Brine Field	ICI Maintenance (114.8)
456.60000	462.10000	NFM	Cannock	Shopwatch
456.60000	462.10000	NFM	Cardiff	Shopwatch (DCS 131)
456.60000	462.10000	NFM	Carnforth	Holm Lane Quarry Ch.2 Emergencies/Blasting
456.60000	462.10000	NFM	Coventry	Debenhams, West Orchards Shopping Centre
456.60000	462.10000	NFM	Darlington	Shopwatch (77)
456.60000	462.10000	NFM	Derby	East Midlands Airport
456.60000	462.10000	NFM	Dover	Shopwatch
456.60000	462.10000	NFM	Edinburgh	Shopwatch (82.5)
456.60000	462.10000	NFM	Greenock	Shopwatch
456.60000	462.10000	NFM	Heathrow	Airline Catering Company
456.60000	462.10000	NFM	Heathrow	Handlers, Singapore & Japan Airlines (127.3)
456.60000	462.10000	NFM	Hull	British Petroleum, Saltend Ch.2
456.60000	462.10000	NFM	Inverness	Shopwatch/Pubwatch
456.60000	462.10000	NFM	Leeds	Bus Inspectors
456.60000	462.10000	NFM	Leicester	Shopwatch, The Shires Shopping Centre (103.5)
456.60000	462.10000	NFM	Littlehampton	Railway Station Staff (146.2)
456.60000	462.10000	NFM	Liverpool	Aintree Hospital (127.3)
456.60000	462.10000	NFM	Livingstone	McArthur Glen Retail Outlet Security
456.60000	462.10000	NFM	London	British Library Security
456.60000	462.10000	NFM	London	Docklands Light Railway Repeater
456.60000	462.10000	NFM	London	Engineering Company, Pentonville Road
456.60000	462.10000	NFM	London	Hennes & Mauritz Fashion Store, Oxford Street
456.60000	462.10000	NFM	London	New Covent Garden Market Security, Nine Elms
456.60000	462.10000	NFM	London	Newham General Hospital
456.60000	462.10000	NFM	London	Olympia Exhibition Centre Repeater
456.60000	462.10000	NFM	London	Sainsbury Savacentre, Merton
456.60000	462.10000	NFM	London	The Exchange Building, Blackfriars
456.60000	462.10000	NFM	Luton Airport	Valet Car Parking (67)
456.60000	462.10000	NFM	Manchester	Trafford Centre Maintenance Engineers (67)
456.60000	462.10000	NFM	Manchester Airport	Aircraft Cleaners (103.5)
456.60000	462.10000	NFM	Northwich	Brunner-Mond Alkaline Chemicals (114.8)
456.60000	462.10000	NFM	Norwich	Airport Departures and Arrivals
456.60000	462.10000	NFM	Paisley	Shopwatch
456.60000	462.10000	NFM	Peterborough	Hampton Shopping Centre Security Ch.1
456.60000	462.10000	NFM	Reading	Pubwatch/Clubwatch
456.60000	462.10000	NFM	Rochdale	HM Prison Buckley Hall (BW) Trunked Voice
456.60000	462.10000	NFM	Stansted	Airport Ops.
456.60000	462.10000	NFM	Southampton	Container Port Crane Ops.
456.60000	462.10000	NFM	Tamworth	Ankerside Shopping Centre Security
456.60000	462.10000	NFM	Warwick	Warwick Technology Park (CW)
456.62500	462.12500	NFM	Barrow in Furness	VSEL Traffic Department (118.8)
456.62500	462.12500	NFM	Birmingham	Birmingham University Security
456.62500	462.12500	NFM	Cardiff	Bus Company
456.62500	462.12500	NFM	Cardiff Docks	Minimet Fuel Tanks (88.5)
456.62500	462.12500	NFM	Cleethorpes	Imperial Group Food Factory
456.62500	462.12500	NFM	Coventry	Warwick University Security (88.5)
456.62500	462.12500	NFM	Croydon	Drummond Shopping Centre Security
456.62500	462.12500	NFM	Duxford	Imperial War Museum Crash/Fire Ops (94.8)
456.62500	462.12500	NFM	Felixstowe Docks	Walton Container Terminal Ch.4
456.62500	462.12500	NFM	Gatwick	Car Hire Service
456.62500	462.12500	NFM	Harwich	Docks
456.62500	462.12500	NFM	Heathrow	Terminals 1& 3
456.62500	462.12500	NFM	Ipswich	Docks Ch.1 Container Movements (67)
456.62500	462.12500	NFM	Jersey Airport	Ground

Base	Mobile	Mode	Location	User and Notes
456.62500	462.12500	NFM	Kent	Channel Tunnel Trains en route to St Pancras
456.62500	462.12500	NFM	London	BBC Worldwide Sales Ch.2, White City
456.62500	462.12500	NFM	London	Hannah Nursery, Epping Forrest, Sewardstone
456.62500	462.12500	NFM	London	Hounslow Magistrates Court Security
456.62500	462.12500	NFM	London	King George Park, Wandsworth
456.62500		NFM	London	News International Security, Wapping
456.62500	462.12500	NFM	London	Tavern Snacks, Greenwich
456.62500	462.12500	NFM	Londonderry	Dupont (82.5)
456.62500	462.12500	NFM	Manchester Airport	Airline Ops. (103.5)
456.62500	462.12500	NFM	Oxford	Clarendon Shopping Centre Security (103.5)
456.62500	462.12500	NFM	Sittingbourne	Kemsley Paper Mill Services/Security
456.62500	462.12500	NFM	Southampton	Esso Fawley Oil Refinery (192.8)
456.65000	462.15000	NFM	Aberdeen	Shopwatch
456.65000	462.15000	NFM	Barrow in Furness	Shopwatch
456.65000	462.15000	NFM	Birmingham	Aston University Maintenance (225.7)
456.65000	462.15000	NFM	Blackburn	Shopwatch
456.65000	462.15000	NFM	Brighton	Rail Station Staff (146.2)
456.65000	462.15000	NFM	Cambridge	Shopwatch & City Centre Wardens (71.9)
456.65000	462.15000	NFM	Cardiff	Legal & General (103.5)
456.65000	462.15000	NFM	Chelmsford	Shopwatch, Meadows Shopping Centre (162.2)
456.65000	462.15000	NFM	Coventry	Warwick University Conference Rooms
456.65000	462.15000	NFM	Derby	Rolls Royce Security
456.65000	462.15000	NFM	Doncaster	Robin Hood Airport Security/Ops Ch.3/2 (127.3/179.9)
456.65000	462.15000	NFM	Edinburgh Airport	PMR Ch.6
456.65000	462.15000	NFM	Farnborough	Princemead Shopping Centre Security (94.8)
456.65000		NFM	Felixstowe	Docks
456.65000	462.15000	NFM	Folkestone	Shopwatch
456.65000	462.15000	NFM	Gatwick	Aviation Fuel (103.5)
456.65000	462.15000	NFM	Heathrow	Air India T3 Ramp Ops. (103.5)
456.65000	462.15000	NFM	Hitchin	Shopwatch (156.7)
456.65000	462.15000	NFM	Hull	North Sea Ferries Ch.1
456.65000		NFM	Ipswich	Docks (67)
456.65000	462.15000	NFM	Kent	Channel Tunnel Trains en route to St Pancras
456.65000	462.15000	NFM	Kilmarnock	Burns Shopping Mall Security
456.65000	462.15000	NFM	Leeds	Council
456.65000	462.15000	NFM	Leeds	University Maintenance
456.65000	462.15000	NFM	Leek	Shopwatch
456.65000	462.15000	NFM	London	British Library Stores, Soho
456.65000	462.15000	NFM	London	British Library, St Pancras (107.2)
456.65000	462.15000	NFM	London	British Newspaper Library, Colindale
456.65000	462.15000	NFM	London	Hatzolah Jewish Paramedic Service (67)
456.65000	462.15000	NFM	London	London Electricity Company Offices
456.65000	462.15000	NFM	London	Parking Enforcement, Lewisham (67)
456.65000	462.15000	NFM	London	Price Waterhouse Coopers, Villiers Street
456.65000	462.15000	NFM	London	Property Service, West India Quay
456.65000	462.15000	NFM	London	Shopwatch, Hammersmith
456.65000	462.15000	NFM	London	Tate Modern Ch.3, Southbank (131.8)
456.65000	462.15000	NFM	Manchester	International Airport Airline Boarding (88.5)
456.65000	462.15000	NFM	Norfolk	Weasenham Farms (118.8)
456.65000	462.15000	NFM	Nuneaton	Shopwatch
456.65000	462.15000	NFM	Reading	John Lewis (103.5)
456.65000	462.15000	NFM	Salmesbury	BAe Security
456.65000	462.15000	NFM	Sheffield	Meadowhall Shopping Centre Security/Staff
456.65000	462.15000	NFM	Sidcup	Queen Mary's Hospital
456.65000	462.15000	NFM	Southampton	Esso Fawley Oil Refinery (192.8)
456.65000	462.15000	NFM	Stansted	In-Flight Cleaning Services (136.5)

Base	Mobile	Mode	Location	User and Notes
456.65000	462.15000	NFM	Stansted	Long Term Car Park
456.65000	462.15000	NFM	Warton	BAe
456.65000	462.15000	NFM	Woodbridge	Shopwatch/Pubwatch (103.5)
456.65000	462.15000	NFM	York	Council Refuse Collection
456.66250	462.16250	NFM	Newcastle Airport	Stand Services
456.67500	462.17500	NFM	Aberdeen	Dyce Airport Staff
456.67500	462.17500	NFM	Abingdon	Shopwatch
456.67500	462.17500	NFM	Ashford	Shopwatch (136.5)
456.67500	462.17500	NFM	Belfast	Castle Court Shopping Centre Security (88.5)
456.67500	462.17500	NFM	Braintree	Shopwatch (218.1)
456.67500	462.17500	NFM	Cambridge	Addenbrookes Hospital (67)
456.67500	462.17500	NFM	Chorlton	Detention Centre
456.67500	462.17500	NFM	Coventry	Arena Retail Park Security (127.3)
456.67500	462.17500	NFM	Dover	Port Of Dover Security
456.67500	462.17500	NFM	Durham	Prince Bishops Shopping Centre Security (127.3)
456.67500	462.17500	NFM	Ebbw Vale	Shopwatch
456.67500	462.17500	NFM	Feltham	Detention Centre (NS)
456.67500	462.17500	NFM	Glasgow	Shopwatch, Sauchiehall Street
456.67500	462.17500	NFM	Harlow	Shopwatch
456.67500	462.17500	NFM	Hartlepool	ICI Chemicals
456.67500	462.17500	NFM	Harwich	Shopwatch
456.67500	462.17500	NFM	Heathrow	Air France/Aeroflot/Emirates (162.2)
456.67500	462.17500	NFM	Immingham	Conoco
456.67500	462.17500	NFM	Kings Lynn	Campbell Foods
456.67500	462.17500	NFM	Larne	Port Loaders
456.67500	462.17500	NFM	London	British Library Maintenance/Security, NW1 (82.5)
456.67500	462.17500	NFM	London	Cemetery, City of London
456.67500	462.17500	NFM	London	Earls Court Exhibition Centre Catering
456.67500	462.17500	NFM	London	Foreign & Commonwealth Office
456.67500	462.17500	NFM	London	Halifax plc Offices, Broad Street (110.9)
456.67500	462.17500	NFM	London	Pubwatch/Clubwatch, WC1 (71.9)
456.67500	462.17500	NFM	London	Rail Depot, North Pole Road
456.67500	462.17500	NFM	London	Securicor at Council Offices, Tower Hamlets
456.67500	462.17500	NFM	London	Tate Modern Security Ch.4, Southbank (210.7)
456.67500	462.17500	NFM	London	The Mail Newspaper Group, Rotherhithe
456.67500	462.17500	NFM	Luton Airport	Debonair/Ryanair Arrivals & Departures (77)
456.67500	462.17500	NFM	Manchester	ICI Security
456.67500	462.17500	NFM	Manchester	Manchester United Football Club Stewards
456.67500	462.17500	NFM	Newcastle	Eldon Garden Shopping Centre Security
456.67500	462.17500	NFM	Oldham	BNFL Security
456.67500	462.17500	NFM	Oxford	John Radcliffe Hospital Porters
456.67500	462.17500	NFM	Portsmouth	Gun Wharf Retail Park
456.67500	462.17500	NFM	Salisbury	Shopwatch.
456.67500	462.17500	NFM	Silverstone	Race Track (103.5)
456.67500	462.17500	NFM	Southampton	Esso Fawley Oil Refinery (192.8)
456.67500	462.17500	NFM	St Albans	Shopwatch (77)
456.67500	462.17500	NFM	St Andrews	University Security/Staff
456.67500	462.17500	NFM	Stevenage	Astrium Space Systems/BAe Systems (186.2)
456.67500	462.17500	NFM	Stoke on Trent	Shopwatch/Pubwatch Linked to Police (241.8)
456.67500	462.17500	NFM	Sutton	Shopwatch (107.2)
456.67500	462.17500	NFM	Warton	BAe Ground Crews (110.9)
456.67500	462.17500	NFM	Windsor	Windsor Castle Wardens (WG)
456.67500	462.17500	NFM	Woburn	Woburn Abbey Wildlife Kingdom (210.7)
456.67500	462.17500	NFM	Worthing	Pubwatch (186.2)
456.67500	462.17500	NFM	Wrexham	Shopwatch
456.68750	462.18750	NFM	Birmingham	NEC Exhibition Centre Trunked Network

Base	Mobile	Mode	Location	User and Notes
456.68750	462.18750	NFM	Birmingham	Good Hope Hospital Trunked Network
456.70000	456.20000	NFM	Ashton under Lyme	Pubwatch
456.70000	462.20000	NFM	Basildon	Eastgate Shopping Centre Security
456.70000	462.20000	NFM	Burton on Trent	Coopers Square Shopping Centre
456.70000	462.20000	NFM	Cambridge	Marshalls Airport Security
456.70000	462.20000	NFM	Cheltenham	Pubwatch (94.8)
456.70000	462.20000	NFM	Darlington	Cornmill Shopping Centre (136.5)
456.70000	462.20000	NFM	Dartford	Europort (88.5)
456.70000	462.20000	NFM	Felixstowe	Docks
456.70000	462.20000	NFM	Grimsby	Courtaulds, Great Coates
456.70000	462.20000	NFM	Guilford	Friary Shopping Centre Security
456.70000	462.20000	NFM	Harwell	UKAEA
456.70000	462.20000	NFM	Heathrow	All Nippon Airways (88.5)
456.70000	462.20000	NFM	Hull	BP Oil Refinery Ch.1 Fire, Saltend
456.70000	462.20000	NFM	Ilford	Exchange Shopping Centre Security (77)
456.70000	462.20000	NFM	Killingholme	Lindsey Oil Refinery
456.70000	462.20000	NFM	Lancaster	Lancaster University Security
456.70000	462.20000	NFM	Leeds	Leeds University Security
456.70000	462.20000	NFM	London	Brent Cross Shopping Centre Security (127.3)
456.70000	462.20000	NFM	London	Network Rail Signal Engineers
456.70000	462.20000	NFM	London	Shopwatch, Wood Green (118.8)
456.70000	462.20000	NFM	London	Warburg Bank Security, Broadgate (DCS 465)
456.70000	462.20000	NFM	Lutterworth	Asda Distribution Depot Trunked Voice
456.70000	462.20000	NFM	Manchester	Manchester Airport Aircraft Refuelling (192.8)
456.70000	462.20000	NFM	Manchester	Trafford Shopping Centre Security
456.70000	462.20000	NFM	Milton Keynes	Shopping Centre Security (82.5)
456.70000	462.20000	NFM	Neath	Shopwatch
456.70000	462.20000	NFM	Perth	Car Park Security
456.70000	462.20000	NFM	Port Talbot	Corus Steelworks (82.5)
456.70000	462.20000	NFM	Port Talbot	Shopwatch, Aberavon Shopping Centre
456.70000	462.20000	NFM	Rugby	Cement Works
456.70000	462.20000	NFM	Sheffield	University Security (Campus)
456.70000	462.20000	NFM	Slough	Queensmere Shopping Centre Security (250.3)
456.70000	462.20000	NFM	Solihull	Shopwatch (141.3)
456.70000	462.20000	NFM	Southampton	Esso Fawley Oil Refinery, Fire (192.8)
456.70000	462.20000	NFM	Southport	Shopwatch (110.9)
456.70000	462.20000	NFM	Stansted	In-Flight Cleaning Services
456.70000	462.20000	NFM	Stoke Badolph	Severn Trent Water Sewage Treatment Works
456.70000	462.20000	NFM	Wishaw	Belfry Golf Course
456.70000	462.20000	NFM	Welwyn Garden City	Cereal Partners (Nabisco)
456.70000	462.20000	NFM	West Midlands	Coombe Abbey Country Park
456.70000	462.20000	NFM	Woking	Shopwatch (DCS 243)
456.70000	462.20000	NFM	York	University
456.71250	462.21250	NFM	Nationwide	Ofcom Special Events Reserved Channel
456.72500	462.22500	NFM	Belvedere	Paper Mill
456.72500	462.22500	NFM	Canvey Island	Texaco Oil Refinery
456.72500		NFM	Cobham	Heywood American Community School
456.72500	462.22500	NFM	Coventry	Peugeot Talbot
456.72500	462.22500	NFM	Cowley	MG Rover Plant Ch.5
456.72500		NFM	Doncaster	Railway Freight Yard
456.72500		NFM	Dorset	UKAEA Winfrith Technology Centre Fire Brigade
456.72500	462.22500	NFM	Edinburgh	Herriot Watt University Security
456.72500	462.22500	NFM	Gatwick	Avionics Maintenance
456.72500	462.22500	NFM	Heathrow	Crossair Swiss Engineering (71.9)
456.72500	462.22500	NFM	Harwich	Port Reception Staff.

Base	Mobile	Mode	Location	User and Notes
456.72500	462.22500	NFM	Hull	North Sea Ferries Ch.2
456.72500	462.22500	NFM	Jersey	Dock Crane Operators
456.72500	462.22500	NFM	Kent	Channel Tunnel Trains en route to St Pancras
456.72500	462.22500	NFM	Leeds	Shopwatch
456.72500		NFM	London	KFC Security/Staff, Coventry Street (94.8)
456.72500		NFM	London	Kings Walk Mall Security, Kings Road (82.5)
456.72500	462.22500	NFM	London	Merk Sharpe Dohme, Ponders End
456.72500	462.22500	NFM	London	Newham General Hospital Security
456.72500	462.22500	NFM	London	Southwark Council
456.72500	462.22500	NFM	London	St Andrews Hospital, Bromley By Bow
456.72500	462.22500	NFM	London	Tate Modern Art Gallery, Southbank
456.72500		NFM	London	Urban Outfitters, Oxford Circus (94.8)
456.72500		NFM	London	Whipps Cross Hospital, Walthamstow
456.72500	462.22500	NFM	Luton Airport	Security & Maintenance/Ops. (254.1)
456.72500	462.22500	NFM	Norwich	Lotus Motor Plant
456.72500	462.22500	NFM	Peterborough	City Council Ch.1
456.72500	462.22500	NFM	Southampton	Esso Fawley Oil Refinery (192.8)
456.72500	462.22500	NFM	Southend on Sea	Shopwatch
456.72500	462.22500	NFM	Stevenston	ICI Security and Fire Service
456.72500	462.22500	NFM	Swansea Docks	Shipping Pilots
456.72500	462.22500	NFM	Ulverston	GlaxoSmithKline
456.75000	462.25000	NFM	Aberdare	Shopwatch
456.75000	462.25000	NFM	Aberdeen	Loaders, Dyce Airport
456.75000	462.25000	NFM	Barrow	VSEL Fire & Nuclear Incidents
456.75000	462.25000	NFM	Bexleyheath	Shopping Centre Security
456.75000	462.25000	NFM	Birmingham	Palisades Shopping Centre Security Ch.1
456.75000	462.25000	NFM	Cardiff	Marks & Spencer Security, St Davids Centre (71.9)
456.75000	462.25000	NFM	Chelmsford	Meadows Shopping Centre Security (127.3)
456.75000	462.25000	NFM	Coventry	Warwick University
456.75000	462.25000	NFM	Derby	Shopwatch
456.75000	462.25000	NFM	Edinburgh	Shopwatch, St James
456.75000	462.25000	NFM	Farnborough	Shopwatch (127.3)
456.75000	462.25000	NFM	Felixstowe	Contship Ltd Ch.1 (103.5)
456.75000	462.25000	NFM	Glasgow	Airport Cargo Handlers
456.75000	462.25000	NFM	Grantham	Shopwatch
456.75000	462.25000	NFM	Hartlepool	Hartlepool Council Trunked System
456.75000	462.25000	NFM	Harwich	Port Of Harwich Admin/Reception (107.2)
456.75000	462.25000	NFM	Hastings	Pubwatch
456.75000	462.25000	NFM	Holyhead	Anglesey Aluminium Production & Process
456.75000	462.25000	NFM	Immingham	Conoco
456.75000	462.25000	NFM	London	Parking Enforcement, Mayfair (146.2)
456.75000	462.25000	NFM	London	Shopwatch, Surrey Quays Shopping Centre
456.75000	462.25000	NFM	London	Somerset House Galleries (114.8)
456.75000	462.25000	NFM	Luton Airport	Thompson/Britannia Handling Agents (203.5)
456.75000	462.25000	NFM	Manchester	Marks & Spencer Security, Arndale Centre (241.8)
456.75000	462.25000	NFM	Manston	International Airport
456.75000	462.25000	NFM	Middlesbrough	Hospital
456.75000	462.25000	NFM	Newcastle	Shopwatch, Eldon Gardens Shopping Centre
456.75000	462.25000	NFM	Newmarket	Shopwatch/Pubwatch
456.75000	462.25000	NFM	Rochdale	HM Prison Buckley Hall (BW) Trunked
456.75000	462.25000	NFM	Seaton	Seaton Tramway (103.5)
456.75000	462.25000	NFM	Skelmersdale	Concourse Shopping Centre Security
456.75000	462.25000	NFM	Staines	Shopwatch
456.75000	462.25000	NFM	Stockton on Tees	Debenhams Department Store Security
456.75000	462.25000	NFM	Tewkesbury	Shopwatch (127.3)
456.75000	462.25000	NFM	Watford	General Hospital Porters/Blood Runs/PABX

Base	Mobile	Mode	Location	User and Notes
456.75000	462.25000	NFM	Witney	Shopwatch
456.77500	462.27500	NFM	Bexleyheath	Shopping Centre Security
456.77500	462.27500	NFM	Blackpool	Blackpool Pleasure Beach Staff/Security
456.77500	462.27500	NFM	Bradford	University Security
456.77500		NFM	Cardiff	St David Concert Hall
456.77500		NFM	Dorset	UKAEA Winfrith Technology Centre
456.77500		NFM	Dover	Harbour Ops.
456.77500	462.27500	NFM	Falkirk	ICI Fire & Security
456.77500	462.27500	NFM	Gatwick	Ground Repeater (127.3)
456.77500	462.27500	NFM	Glasgow	Exececare, Glasgow Airport
456.77500	462.27500	NFM	Grangemouth	Astra/Zeneca Factory Fire/Security
456.77500	462.27500	NFM	Harwich	Trinity House
456.77500	462.27500	NFM	Heathrow	Kuwaiti Airlines
456.77500	462.27500	NFM	Hull	Docks Cranes/Loading
456.77500	462.27500	NFM	Liverpool	Manchester Ship Canal (Eastham)
456.77500	462.27500	NFM	London	Broadwalk Shopping Centre, Edgware
456.77500	462.27500	NFM	London	Parking Enforcement, Waltham Forest
456.77500	462.27500	NFM	Luton	Vauxhall Motors
456.77500	462.27500	NFM	Millbrook	Test Track
456.77500	462.27500	NFM	Nuneaton	George Elliot Hospital Security
456.77500	462.27500	NFM	Redditch	Kingfisher Shopping Centre Security
456.77500	462.27500	NFM	Southampton	Esso Fawley (Chemicals)
456.77500	462.27500	NFM	Stansted Airport	Trunked Network Data Command Channel
456.77500	462.27500	NFM	Swindon	Shopwatch, Greenbridge Retail Park
456.80000		NFM	Bath	Roman Baths & Pump House Staff/Security
456.80000	462.30000	NFM	Coryton	Conoco Oil Refinery Ch.2
456.80000	462.30000	NFM	Farnborough	Tag Aviation And Security
456.80000	462.30000	NFM	Gateshead	House of Fraser, Metro Centre (114.8)
456.80000	462.30000	NFM	Guildford	Army & Navy Stores (71.9)
456.80000	462.30000	NFM	Heathrow	Airport Security
456.80000		NFM	London	Courtaulds Gallery & Institute Security (88.5)
456.80000	462.30000	NFM	Luton Airport	Security (67)
456.80000		NFM	Manchester	Burtons Menswear, Trafford Centre
456.80000		NFM	Norwich	Norwich City Football Club
456.80000	462.30000	NFM	Peterborough	East of England Show Ground Security
456.80000	462.30000	NFM	Tilbury	Docks
456.81250	462.31250	NFM	Nationwide	Ofcom Special Events Reserved Channel
456.82500	462.32500	NFM	Barnstaple	Shopwatch
456.82500	462.32500	NFM	Bath	Hospital Security
456.82500	462.32500	NFM	Biggin Hill	Airport Management
456.82500	462.32500	NFM	Billingham	ICI Chemicals
456.82500	462.32500	NFM	Birmingham	Birmingham Airport Handling Agents (225.7)
456.82500	462.32500	NFM	Birmingham	City Plaza Shopping Centre
456.82500	462.32500	NFM	Birmingham	Kings Norton Estates Wardens (241.8)
456.82500	462.32500	NFM	Blackpool	Blackpool Winter Gardens.
456.82500	462.32500	NFM	Borehamwood	Warehouse.
456.82500	462.32500	NFM	Boscombe	Chase Manhattan Bank Security
456.82500	462.32500	NFM	Brighton	Sussex University Ch.2 Maintenance (94.8)
456.82500	462.32500	NFM	Burton on Trent	Council
456.82500	462.32500	NFM	Cardiff	Airport/Admin./Security/Maintenance (118.8)
456.82500	462.32500	NFM	Cardiff	Queens Arcade Security (88.5)
456.82500	462.32500	NFM	Cheltenham	Shopwatch (210.7)
456.82500	462.32500	NFM	Coleraine	Diamond Centre Security (136.5)
456.82500	462.32500	NFM	Coventry	Warwick University Maintenance
456.82500	462.32500	NFM	Dover	Coastguard, Cliff Rescue
456.82500	462.32500	NFM	Edinburgh	University Security

Base	Mobile	Mode	Location	User and Notes
456.82500	462.32500	NFM	Elstree	Sainsbury Distribution Centre Ch.1 (110.9)
456.82500	462.32500	NFM	Falkirk	Shopwatch, Howgate Centre
456.82500	462.32500	NFM	Guildford	University of Surrey Security
456.82500	462.32500	NFM	Heathrow	Airline & BAA Ops (123)
456.82500	462.32500	NFM	Hull	Princes Quay Shopping Centre Security
456.82500	462.32500	NFM	Littlehampton	Railway Use, Littlehampton Junction (146.2)
456.82500	462.32500	NFM	Immingham	Docks
456.82500		NFM	London	London Eye Security (67)
456.82500	462.32500	NFM	London	Marks & Spencer, Oxford Street (67)
456.82500	462.32500	NFM	London	Regents Park Mosque
456.82500	462.32500	NFM	London	Safeway Supermarket, Kings Mall
456.82500	462.32500	NFM	London	Sainsbury Supermarket, Cromwell Road
456.82500	462.32500	NFM	London	Sainsbury Supermarket, Fulham
456.82500	462.32500	NFM	Luton Airport	AirRadio easyJet/Multi User Trunked Network
456.82500	462.32500	NFM	Manchester	Manchester City FC Security/Stewards (179.9)
456.82500	462.32500	NFM	Manchester Airport	Airline Ops.
456.82500	462.32500	NFM	Port Talbot	Corus Steelworks
456.82500	462.32500	NFM	Preston	Deepdale Retail Park Security (192.8)
456.82500	462.32500	NFM	Rotherham	Shopwatch
456.82500	462.32500	NFM	Rudheath	Morrisons Distribution Depot Security
456.82500	462.32500	NFM	Sheerness	Docks Loaders/Reception
456.82500	462.32500	NFM	Southampton	Esso Fawley Oil Refinery (192.8)
456.82500	462.32500	NFM	St Albans	Parking Enforcement
456.82500	462.32500	NFM	St Helens	Pilkingtons Security
456.82500	462.32500	NFM	Stansted	Airport, Asig Refuelling
456.82500	462.32500	NFM	Sutton Coldfield	Gracechurch Shopping Centre Security
456.82500	462.32500	NFM	Swindon	Hospital Porters (71.9)
456.82500	462.32500	NFM	Tamworth	Borough Council
456.82500	462.32500	NFM	Warwick	Shopwatch
456.82500	462.32500	NFM	Wellingborough	Shopwatch
456.82500	462.32500	NFM	Woburn	Woburn Abbey Wildlife Park
456.85000	462.35000	NFM	Barrow In Furness	Shaw Hadwin Coaches
456.85000	462.35000	NFM	Blackpool	Blackpool Pleasure Beach Staff
456.85000	462.35000	NFM	Colchester	Shopwatch
456.85000	462.35000	NFM	Coventry	Social Services
456.85000	462.35000	NFM	Cowley	MG Rover Plant
456.85000	462.35000	NFM	Ely	Storeys Coaches
456.85000		NFM	Gatwick	Airport Airside Transport (141.3)
456.85000		NFM	Heathrow	Olympic Airways
456.85000	462.35000	NFM	Hove	Shopwatch (94.8)
456.85000	462.35000	NFM	Ipswich	Docks
456.85000	462.35000	NFM	Kent	Channel Tunnel Trains en route to St Pancras
456.85000	462.35000	NFM	Liverpool	Parking Enforcement, Outer Zone (167.9)
456.85000	462.35000	NFM	London	Greenford Radio Cars (114.8)
456.85000	462.35000	NFM	London	Philips & Drew, Liverpool Street
456.85000	462.35000	NFM	Manchester	Taxi Company
456.85000	462.35000	NFM	Nationwide	John Sisk & Son (Construction) Ch1
456.85000	462.35000	NFM	Nationwide	National Coach Company
456.85000	462.35000	NFM	Nottingham	Mapperly Hospital
456.85000	462.35000	NFM	Saltcoats	Shopwatch/Pubwatch
456.85000	462.35000	NFM	Skelmersdale	Taxi Company
456.85000	462.35000	NFM	Stansted	Long Term Car Park
456.85000	462.35000	NFM	Tilbury	Docks Security
456.85000	462.35000	NFM	Wansford	Nene Valley Railway (162.2)
456.85000	462.35000	NFM	Westcliffe	The Stock Exchange Second-Hand Shop
456.85000	462.35000	NFM	Wigan	Taxi Company

Base	Mobile	Mode	Location	User and Notes
456.85000	462.35000	NFM	Worthing	Taxi Company
456.86250		NFM	Ascot	Ascot Races Bookmakers
456.86250		NFM	Bury St. Edmunds	British Sugar Plant
456.86250		NFM	Canvey Island	Safeways Supermarket Maintenance
456.86250		NFM	Cardiff	Millennium Stadium Staff (131.8)
456.86250		NFM	Chatham	Rail Station Staff
456.86250		NFM	Chepstow	Chepstow Racecourse Commentary (110.9)
456.86250		NFM	Coventry	HMV Security
456.86250		NFM	Duxford	Imperial War Museum Events (131.8)
456.86250		NFM	Eastbourne	Pier
456.86250		NFM	Edinburgh	Teviot House Security
456.86250		NFM	Holyhead	Rail Station Staff
456.86250		NFM	Heathrow	Passenger Courtesy Bus
456.86250		NFM	Ipswich	Nighthawk Security
456.86250	462.36250	NFM	Kent	Kent County Showground Ch.1
456.86250	462.36250	NFM	Lakeside	Police Shoplifters Surveillance
456.86250		NFM	London	Alexandra Palace Exhibitions
456.86250		NFM	London	Arsenal Football Club Stewards (151.4)
456.86250		NFM	London	British Airways Travel Office, Regent Street
456.86250		NFM	London	Chelsea Football Club Security (103.5)
456.86250		NFM	London	Disney Store Staff/Security, Oxford St (67)
456.86250		NFM	London	Fulham Football Club Staff/Admin (218.1)
456.86250		NFM	London	Funland Amusements, Trocadero Centre (127.3)
456.86250		NFM	London	Grosvenor Hotel, Park Lane
456.86250		NFM	London	Holiday Inn Hotel, Kings Cross
456.86250		NFM	London	Israeli Embassy Security
456.86250		NFM	London	Miu Miu Fashion Store Security, Bond St
456.86250		NFM	London	Odeon Cinema Security, Leicester Square
456.86250		NFM	London	Panther Security
456.86250		NFM	London	Plaza Shopping Centre Security, Oxford St. (173.8)
456.86250		NFM	London	Royal Thames Yacht Club, 60 Knightsbridge
456.86250		NFM	London	Twickenham Rugby Ground
456.86250		NFM	London	Warner Bros Store, Regent Street (103.5)
456.86250		NFM	London	WH Smiths, Euston
456.86250		NFM	London	Wings Security
456.86250		NFM	Lowestoft	Birds/Walls Factory (82.5)
456.86250		NFM	Maidstone	Borough Council
456.86250		NFM	Nationwide	BBC O/B Production Unit
456.86250		NFM	Nationwide	British Motorcycle Federation Events (173.8)
456.86250		NFM	Nationwide	ITV 'The Bill' Production Team O/B
456.86250		NFM	Nationwide	Whitby Davies Productions
456.86250		NFM	Nationwide	Sky TV O/B
456.86250		NFM	Newmarket	Racecourse Security
456.86250	462.36250	NFM	Oxford	Nuffield Orthopaedic Hospital (123)
456.86250		NFM	Reading	Disney Store, The Oracle Centre
456.86250		NFM	Rochester	Rail Station Staff
456.86250		NFM	Rugby	Christian Salvesen Ch.7
456.86250		NFM	Sheffield	Walkabout Bar
456.86250	462.36250	NFM	Silverstone	Racetrack Maintenance
456.86250		NFM	St Helens	St Helens Rugby Club Manager/Coach
456.86250		NFM	Stevenage	Midas Security, Kings Leisure Site
456.86250		NFM	Strood	Rail Station Staff
456.86250		NFM	Warwick	Aviation Executive Bodyguards
456.86250		NFM	Woodford Airfield	BAe Security
456.87500	462.37500	NFM	Ashford	William Harvey Hospital Porters
456.87500	462.37500	NFM	Birmingham	City Centre Trunk Control

Base	Mobile	Mode	Location	User and Notes
456.87500	462.37500	NFM	Birmingham	Midland Airport Services, International Airport
456.87500	462.37500	NFM	Bristol	Esso Fuel, Avonmouth
456.87500	462.37500	NFM	Canvey Island	Oil Refinery (103.5)
456.87500	462.37500	NFM	Coventry	Tesco Maintenance, Arena Retail Park (118.8)
456.87500	462.37500	NFM	Coventry	Warwick University Security Ch.1
456.87500	462.37500	NFM	Cowley	MG Rover Factory (136.5)
456.87500	462.37500	NFM	Dagenham	Rhone Poulenc Chemicals Security
456.87500	462.37500	NFM	Derby	Eagle Shopping Centre Security/Staff/Cleaners
456.87500	462.37500	NFM	Fairlop	Leisure Site Repeater
456.87500	462.37500	NFM	Gatwick	Tinsley House (250.3)
456.87500	462.37500	NFM	Guernsey	Esso Petroleum
456.87500	462.37500	NFM	Hatfield	McDonalds Drive-Thru, Galleria Centre
456.87500	462.37500	NFM	Havant	Shopwatch (82.5)
456.87500	462.37500	NFM	Hull	Football Stewards/Rugby Stewards
456.87500	462.37500	NFM	Isle of Man	Ronaldsway Airport Operations
456.87500	462.37500	NFM	Jersey Airport	Air Commodore Ops.
456.87500	462.37500	NFM	Lancashire	Vanguard Couriers
456.87500	462.37500	NFM	London	Brent Cross Security Company
456.87500	462.37500	NFM	London	Broadway Shopping Centre, Hammersmith (107.2)
456.87500	462.37500	NFM	London	British Gas Site Repeater, S Bermondsey
456.87500	462.37500	NFM	London	Container Depot, Stratford East
456.87500	462.37500	NFM	London	Debenhams Store Security, Oxford Street (151.4)
456.87500	462.37500	NFM	London	Financial Times Security, Docklands
456.87500	462.37500	NFM	London	Gloucester Hotel, Earls Court
456.87500	462.37500	NFM	London	Hampton Court Palace Staff
456.87500	462.37500	NFM	London	House of Fraser Security, Oxford Street (151.4)
456.87500	462.37500	NFM	London	Kodak Film Plant, Harrow
456.87500	462.37500	NFM	London	London Underground, Northfields (67)
456.87500	462.37500	NFM	London	Oil Company Offices, Mayfair
456.87500	462.37500	NFM	London	Queen Mary & Westfield College, Mile End
456.87500	462.37500	NFM	London	Salvation Army Headquarters, Blackfriars
456.87500	462.37500	NFM	London	Shopwatch, Wood Green
456.87500	462.37500	NFM	London	Southbank Security (67)
456.87500	462.37500	NFM	London	Temple Construction Co
456.87500	462.37500	NFM	London	Trocadero Centre Security, Piccadilly (186.2)
456.87500	462.37500	NFM	Longbridge	MG Rover Security (127.3)
456.87500	462.37500	NFM	Luton	Airport (103.5)
456.87500	462.37500	NFM	Luton	Shopwatch (123)
456.87500	462.37500	NFM	Manchester	Airport, Catering (110.9)
456.87500	462.37500	NFM	Manchester	Airport, El Al Staff
456.87500	462.37500	NFM	Manchester	City FC Security/Match Day Hospitality (156.7)
456.87500	462.37500	NFM	Neath	BP Oil Refinery
456.87500	462.37500	NFM	Newcastle	Fenwicks Department Store Security (82.5)
456.87500	462.37500	NFM	Nottingham	Esso, Colwick
456.87500	462.37500	NFM	Purfleet	Gulf Oil UK Ltd Depot
456.87500	462.37500	NFM	Reading	University
456.87500	462.37500	NFM	Redbridge	Fairlop Waters Country Park
456.87500	462.37500	NFM	Rochdale	Shopwatch
456.87500	462.37500	NFM	Rochester	Shopwatch
456.87500	462.37500	NFM	Rustington	Shopwatch (162.2)
456.87500	462.37500	NFM	Scunthorpe	Corus Steelworks
456.87500	462.37500	NFM	Southampton	Esso Fawley Oil Refinery, Jetty (192.8)
456.87500	462.37500	NFM	Stevenston	ICI Acid Plant Maintenance
456.87500	462.37500	NFM	St Helens	Shopwatch
456.87500	462.37500	NFM	Stansted Airport	In-Flight Jet Centre
456.87500	462.37500	NFM	Swansea	Docks Security

Base	Mobile	Mode	Location	User and Notes
456.87500	462.37500	NFM	Swindon	Shopwatch, Brunel Plaza Shopping Centre (67)
456.87500	462.37500	NFM	Warwick	Castle Staff Ch.1
456.87500	462.37500	NFM	York	Marks & Spencer Security
456.90000	462.40000	NFM	Aberdeen	Servisair/GlobeGround, Dyce Airport
456.90000		NFM	Ascot	Racecourse Network Ch.3
456.90000		NFM	Ashford	Welsh School
456.90000	462.40000	NFM	Barrow in Furness	VSEL Works Security Control
456.90000	462.40000	NFM	Biggleswade	Jordans Cereals Ch.2
456.90000		NFM	Borehamwood	BBC Elstree Studios (110.9)
456.90000	462.40000	NFM	Cardiff	University Hospital Of Wales Parking (82.5)
456.90000		NFM	Dartford	Bexley Hospital
456.90000	462.40000	NFM	East Midlands Airport	Servisair/GlobeGround (107.2)
456.90000	462.40000	NFM	Edinburgh Airport	Servisair/GlobeGround
456.90000	462.40000	NFM	Gatwick	Servisair/GlobeGround (103.5)
456.90000	462.40000	NFM	Glasgow Airport	Servisair/GlobeGround
456.90000	462.40000	NFM	Heathrow	Tower Rebroadcast
456.90000	462.40000	NFM	Hull	BP Oil Terminal, Saltend
456.90000		NFM	Ipswich	Crown Swimming Pools
456.90000	462.40000	NFM	Liverpool Airport	Servisair/GlobeGround
456.90000	462.40000	NFM	London	Banking, Queen Annes Street
456.90000		NFM	London	John Lewis, Kingston upon Thames (146.2)
456.90000	462.40000	NFM	London	Tavern Snacks, Greenwich
456.90000	462.40000	NFM	Manchester	Airport Trunked Network
456.90000	462.40000	NFM	Newcastle Airport	Servisair/GlobeGround
456.90000	462.40000	NFM	Reading	Sainsbury Store, Calcot, M4 Junction 12
456.90000		NFM	Teesside Airport	Servisair/GlobeGround
456.92500	462.42500	NFM	Ayr	Shopwatch
456.92500	462.42500	NFM	Blackpool	Shopwatch
456.92500	462.42500	NFM	Boscombe	Sovereign Shopping Centre Security
456.92500		NFM	Brentwood	Retail Park Security
456.92500	462.42500	NFM	Burnley	Asda
456.92500		NFM	Coventry	Argos Warehouse
456.92500	462.42500	NFM	Cowley	MG Rover Plant Ch.6
456.92500	462.42500	NFM	Grays	Council
456.92500		NFM	Heathrow	Hertz Rent A Car
456.92500	462.42500	NFM	Inverness	Burger King Drive-Thru
456.92500	462.42500	NFM	Kent	County Showground
456.92500	462.42500	NFM	Littlehampton	Pubwatch (127.3)
456.92500		NFM	Liverpool	JD Sports Staff Net
456.92500		NFM	London	Cafe de Paris, Piccadilly
456.92500		NFM	London	Car Hire Company, Victoria (179.9)
456.92500		NFM	London	DKNY Clothes Store, Bond Street
456.92500		NFM	London	Dolcis Shoes, Brent Cross Shopping Centre
456.92500	462.42500	NFM	London	GlaxoSmithKline Security, Euston Rd (77)
456.92500		NFM	London	WAGN, Kings Cross Railway Station (123)
456.92500		NFM	London	Lea Valley Leisure Centre, Edmonton
456.92500		NFM	London	London Eye
456.92500		NFM	London	Nike Town Shop Security, Oxford Circus (79.7)
456.92500		NFM	London	Saudi Arabian Embassy Security
456.92500	462.42500	NFM	London	Shopping Centre, Ealing
456.92500		NFM	London	Shopwatch, Hornsey
456.92500		NFM	London	Urban Outfitters Security, Oxford Circus
456.92500		NFM	London	Virgin Megastore Staff, Oxford Street
456.92500		NFM	London	Warner Bros Cinema, O2 Centre Finchley (77)
456.92500	462.42500	NFM	Milton Keynes	Bowl Car Park/Staff
456.92500		NFM	Nationwide	Boys Own Band Stage Crew

Base	Mobile	Mode	Location	User and Notes
456.92500		NFM	Nationwide	Lewis Outside Catering Special Events
456.92500		NFM	Newcastle	Eldon Garden Shopping Centre Security (173.8)
456.92500		NFM	Sheffield	Magna Centre
456.92500	462.42500	NFM	Stansted	Airport
456.92500	462.42500	NFM	Stowmarket	Shopwatch
456.92500		NFM	Swindon	McDonalds Drive-Thru, Factory Retail Outlet
456.92500	462.42500	NFM	Wigan	Galleries Shopping Centre Security
456.95000	462.45000	NFM	Barrow in Furness	Roosecote Power Station
456.95000	462.45000	NFM	Barry	Aberthaw Power Station (131.8)
456.95000	462.45000	NFM	Bexleyheath	Broadway Shopping Centre
456.95000	462.45000	NFM	Brighton	Royal Sussex Hospital Porters (67)
456.95000	462.45000	NFM	Bury	The Millgate Shopping Centre
456.95000	462.45000	NFM	Cardiff	St Davids Shopping Centre Security (88.5)
456.95000	462.45000	NFM	Carlisle	Marks & Spencer Security (71.9)
456.95000	462.45000	NFM	Chester	Forum Precinct Shopping Centre Security
456.95000	462.45000	NFM	Cowley	MG Rover Factory (71.9)
456.95000	462.45000	NFM	Dudley	Shopwatch (107.2)
456.95000	462.45000	NFM	Farnham	Shopwatch
456.95000	462.45000	NFM	Gillingham	Shopwatch (103.5)
456.95000	462.45000	NFM	Guildford	Pubwatch
456.95000	462.45000	NFM	Halewood	Ford Plant Shop Stewards
456.95000	462.45000	NFM	Hartlepool	Middleton Grange Shopping Centre
456.95000	462.45000	NFM	Heathrow	Virgin Airlines (192.8)
456.95000	462.45000	NFM	Hemel Hempstead	Buncefield Oil Depot (173.8)
456.95000	462.45000	NFM	Holyhead	Anglesey Aluminium Security
456.95000	462.45000	NFM	Huddersfield	Shopwatch
456.95000	462.45000	NFM	Ilford	Shopwatch
456.95000	462.45000	NFM	Ipswich	Docks
456.95000	462.45000	NFM	Leamington	Shopwatch
456.95000	462.45000	NFM	Leeds	City Council Maintenance
456.95000	462.45000	NFM	Liverpool	Shopwatch (114.8)
456.95000	462.45000	NFM	London	Credit Suisse Bank HQ Security/Staff, Canary Wharf
456.95000	462.45000	NFM	London	London Aquarium, County Hall (114.8)
456.95000	462.45000	NFM	Luton	Vauxhall Motors
456.95000	462.45000	NFM	Manchester	National Car Parks (186.2)
456.95000	462.45000	NFM	Manchester	Selfridges Security, Trafford Centre
456.95000	462.45000	NFM	Newbury	Shopwatch
456.95000	462.45000	NFM	Norwich	Shopping Centre Security
456.95000	462.45000	NFM	Preston	Shopwatch (71.9)
456.95000	462.45000	NFM	Southampton	Esso Fawley Oil Refinery (192.8)
456.95000	462.45000	NFM	Stratford upon Avon	Shopwatch (141.3)
456.95000	462.45000	NFM	Strathclyde	Shopwatch, Kirkintilloch
456.95000	462.45000	NFM	Stretford	Kellogg Factory (203.5)
456.95000	462.45000	NFM	Sunderland	Pubwatch
456.95000	462.45000	NFM	Thanet	Hospital
456.95000	462.45000	NFM	Torquay	Shopwatch (67)
456.95000	462.45000	NFM	Uxbridge	Chimes Shopping Centre
456.95000	462.45000	NFM	Wilmslow	Taxi Company
456.96250	462.46250	NFM	Birmingham	NEC Exhibition Centre Trunked Network
456.96250		NFM	Sellafield	UKAEA Trunked Network
456.97500		NFM	Barrow In Furness	Shaw Hadwin Coaches
456.97500	462.47500	NFM	Birmingham	MG Rover Group Security & Fire, Longbridge
456.97500	462.47500	NFM	Birmingham	Shopwatch, Fort Retail Park
456.97500	462.47500	NFM	Canterbury	University of Kent Security
456.97500		NFM	Chorley	Bus Company
456.97500	462.47500	NFM	Dagenham	Shopwatch

Base	Mobile	Mode	Location	User and Notes
456.97500		NFM	Doncaster	Winifreda Coach Company
456.97500		NFM	Ely	Leroy Coaches
456.97500		NFM	Flitwick	Buffalo Bus Company
456.97500		NFM	Humberside	Appleby's Coaches
456.97500		NFM	Kent	Smith's Coaches
456.97500		NFM	Leicester	Fox Cub Buses
456.97500		NFM	Leicester	Woods' Coaches Ch.1
456.97500	462.47500	NFM	London	Kings College Hospital Security
456.97500	462.47500	NFM	London	Leadenhall Street Market Security
456.97500	462.47500	NFM	London	National Physical Laboratory, Teddington
456.97500	462.47500	NFM	Maidstone	Pubwatch/Shopwatch
456.97500		NFM	Morecombe	Battersby's Coaches
456.97500		NFM	Nationwide	National Coach Channel
456.97500		NFM	Newmarket	Miller's Coaches
456.97500	462.47500	NFM	Newport, Gwent	Newport Transport Buses (203.5)
456.97500	462.47500	NFM	North Sea	North Denes Oil Rig, East Anglia (203.5)
456.97500		NFM	Oxford	Tappin's Coaches Ch.1
456.97500		NFM	Ramsgate	G & S Travel Coaches
456.97500		NFM	Rochdale	Buses
456.97500		NFM	Scunthorpe	Burger King Drive-Thru
456.97500		NFM	Stansted	Stansted Cars
456.97500		NFM	Stevenage	Sovereign Coach & Bus Company
456.97500		NFM	Walkden	Chester's Coaches
456.97500		NFM	Weston Super Mare	Coombe's Coaches
456.97500		NFM	Wickersley	Powell's Coaches
456.98750	462.48750	NFM	Barking	Shopwatch, Vicarage Fields Shopping Centre
456.98750	462.48750	NFM	Borehamwood	Pubwatch (94.8)
456.98750	462.48750	NFM	Brighton	Royal Sussex County Hospital
456.98750	462.48750	NFM	Bristol	Pinkerton Security Services
456.98750		NFM	Cardiff	Cardiff International Arena Staff Ch.1 (127.3)
456.98750		NFM	Cardiff	Flares/Reflex Club (118.8)
456.98750		NFM	Cardiff	Millennium Stadium Maintenance (136.5)
456.98750	462.48750	NFM	Coventry	B & Q Warehouse
456.98750	462.48750	NFM	Chatham	Shopwatch (71.9)
456.98750	462.48750	NFM	Dartford	Dartford Docks Ship Loading/Unloading (67)
456.98750	462.48750	NFM	Duxford	Imperial War Museum Events Ch.8 (131.8)
456.98750	462.48750	NFM	Hull	Shopwatch
456.98750	462.48750	NFM	Huntingdon	Shopwatch
456.98750		NFM	Irvine	Burger King Drive-Thru
456.98750	462.48750	NFM	Jersey	Community Repeater
456.98750	462.48750	NFM	Kent	Kent County Showground Ch.2
456.98750	462.48750	NFM	Letchworth	Shopwatch (218.1)
456.98750		NFM	London	Brief Encounter Gay Bar, Charing Cross
456.98750		NFM	London	CAA Building Security, Holborn
456.98750	462.48750	NFM	London	CBI Security, Centrepoint Building
456.98750		NFM	London	Disney Store, Oxford Street (67)
456.98750		NFM	London	Dolcis Shoe Shop Security, Oxford Street
456.98750		NFM	London	Esprit Store Security, Regent Street
456.98750		NFM	London	Funland Amusements, Trocadero Centre (127.3)
456.98750	462.48750	NFM	London	Gap Store Staff Net, Kensington High Street
456.98750	462.48750	NFM	London	Garden Palace Hotel Security, Kensington
456.98750		NFM	London	Greater London Authority Heritage Wardens (192.8)
456.98750		NFM	London	Illegal Traders/Ticket Touts (167.9)
456.98750		NFM	London	Kings College Halls of Residence Security (110.9)
456.98750		NFM	London	Marks & Spencer Food Hall, Whitley Centre
456.98750		NFM	London	Mitzushoki Japanese Store Security Ch.3 (218.1)

Base	Mobile	Mode	Location	User and Notes
456.98750	462.48750	NFM	London	National Film Theatre, Southbank
456.98750		NFM	London	Plaza Shopping Centre Security, Oxford St (103.5)
456.98750	462.48750	NFM	London	Shopwatch, Holloway (118.8)
456.98750		NFM	London	Shopwatch, Wood Green
456.98750	462.48750	NFM	London	The 38 Club, Garrick Street
456.98750		NFM	London	Top Shop In-House TV Channel, Oxford Circus (67)
456.98750	462.48750	NFM	London	Yohan Plaza Japanese Centre, Colindale
456.98750		NFM	Nationwide	British Motorcycle Federation Events (173.8)
456.98750	462.48750	NFM	Nationwide	Christian Salvesen Ch.4
456.98750		NFM	Nationwide	Sky TV (DCS 743)
456.98750		NFM	Peterborough	Dolcis Shoe Shop Security
456.98750		NFM	Poole	Dolphin Shopping Centre Security
456.98750	462.48750	NFM	Rugby	Cement Works (203.5)
456.98750		NFM	Rugby	Christian Salvesen Ch.4
456.98750		NFM	Sellafield	UKAEA
456.98750	462.48750	NFM	Sheffield	Pubwatch
456.98750		NFM	Silverstone	Daytona Karting
456.98750	462.48750	NFM	Southend	Clubwatch/Pubwatch, Seafront
456.98750		NFM	Spelthorne	Council Car Park Inspectors (225.7)
456.98750	462.48750	NFM	Tamworth	Ankerside Car Park Security.
456.98750	462.48750	NFM	Welwyn Garden City	Shopwatch (203.5)
456.98750		NFM	Woodbridge	Old Airfield Motorcycle Time Trials (114.8)
456.98750		NFM	Worthing	Worthing Rail Station Staff

457.0000 - 457.4875 MHz — Fire Brigades Mobile Links 12.5 kHz Simplex & Duplex Base

Base	Mobile	Mode	Location	User and Notes
457.00000		NFM	Doncaster	Fire Brigade Handhelds (XS)
457.01250		NFM	Edinburgh	Fire Brigade
457.01250		NFM	Glasgow	Fire Brigade
457.01250		NFM	Hull	Fire Brigade
457.01250		NFM	London	London Fire Brigade Senior Officers Ch.3
457.01250		NFM	Nationwide	Fire Brigade Ch.3
457.01250		NFM	RAF Wittering	Fire Ch.4
457.01250		NFM	Suffolk	Fire Brigade Ch.3 (BA)
457.01250		NFM	W Sussex	Fire Brigade Ch.3
457.03750	462.53750	NFM	Cumbria	Fire Brigade Portables (BC)
457.03750	462.53750	NFM	Doncaster	Fire Brigade
457.03750	462.53750	NFM	Dyfed	Fire Brigade Ch.1
457.03750	462.53750	NFM	Halifax	Fire Brigade Ch.1 (XF)
457.03750	462.53750	NFM	Harwick	Fire Brigade
457.03750	462.53750	NFM	Humberside	Fire Brigade
457.03750	462.53750	NFM	Langholm	Fire Brigade
457.03750		NFM	London	Fire Brigade Ch.1 (Main Fire Fighters Channel) (FN)
457.03750	462.53750	NFM	Merseyside	Fire Brigade Ch.1 (FO)
457.03750		NFM	Nationwide	Fire Brigade Ch.1
457.03750		NFM	S Wales	Fire Brigade Ops. Primary Ch.1
457.03750	462.53750	NFM	W Midlands	Fire on Site Ch.1
457.03750		NFM	W Sussex	Fire Brigade
457.03750	462.53750	NFM	W Yorkshire	Fire Brigade Handhelds & Training
457.08750	462.58750	NFM	Kent	Fire Brigade Bluewater Shopping Centre Repeater
457.08750	462.58750	NFM	London	Fire Brigade Senior Officers Channel Ch.2 (FN)
457.08750	462.58750	NFM	Nationwide	Fire Brigade Ch.2
457.08750	462.58750	NFM	S Wales	Fire Brigade Mobile Incident Control Unit Ch.2
457.08750	462.58750	NFM	W Sussex	Fire Brigade Ch.2
457.11250		NFM	Fareham	CAA Swanwick Centre Air Relay/Maintenance Comms.
457.13750	462.63750	NFM	Gatwick	Fire Brigade (HF)
457.13750	462.63750	NFM	London	Fire Brigade Ch.5

Base	Mobile	Mode	Location	User and Notes
457.13750	462.63750	NFM	Moreton in the Marsh	Fire Service Training College Ch.5
457.13750	462.63750	NFM	Nationwide	Fire Brigade Ch.5
457.13750	462.63750	NFM	Peterborough	Fire Brigade VHF-UHF Repeater Fire & Rescue (118.8)
457.13750	462.63750	NFM	S Wales	Fire Brigade Fixed /Tunnel Leaky Feeder Ch.5
457.13750	462.63750	NFM	W Sussex	Fire Brigade Ch.5
457.18750		NFM	London	RAF/Civil Fire Liaison
457.18750		NFM	London	Fire Brigade Ch.4 Incident Command Channel
457.18750		NFM	Nationwide	Fire Brigade Ch.4
457.18750		NFM	Nationwide	RAF/Defence Fire Ops. Common
457.18750		NFM	RAF Valley	Fire Brigade Ch.4
457.18750		NFM	RAF Waddington	Crash Ops.
457.18750		NFM	S Wales	Fire Brigade Ops. Secondary Ch.4
457.23750		NFM	London	Fire Brigade Ch.6
457.23750		NFM	Nationwide	Fire Brigade Ch.6
457.23750		NFM	S Wales	Fire Brigade Ch.6
457.23750	462.73750	NFM	W Sussex	Fire Brigade Ch.6
457.23750		NFM	W Sussex	Fire Brigade Radio Engineers Ch.92

457.250 - 457.500 MHz — Radio Microphones, Broadcasting Links & some Fire Brigades

Base	Mobile	Mode	Location	User and Notes
457.25625	462.75625	NFM	London	National Theatre, Southbank
457.25625	467.30625	NFM	Nationwide	JFMG Short Term Talkback
457.26250		NFM	Holyhead	Irish Ferries On-Board Ship Radio Phone Patch
457.26875	467.31875	NFM	Nationwide	JFMG Short Term Talkback
457.28125	467.29375	NFM	London	Palace Theatre
457.28125	467.29375	NFM	Nationwide	JFMG Short Term Talkback
457.29375	467.40625	NFM	Nationwide	JFMG Short Term Talkback
457.30000		NFM	Nationwide	Racetech (Channel 4 Racing O/B)
457.30625	462.80625	NFM	Warwick	Racetech O/B
457.30625	467.36875	NFM	Nationwide	JFMG Short Term Talkback
467.31875		NFM	Corby	ASCAR (2004) Steve Hobday Renegade Racing Car 20
467.31875	467.48125	NFM	Nationwide	JFMG Short Term Talkback
457.32500		NFM	Nationwide	BBC TV O/B talkback
457.32500		NFM	Glasgow	Sky TV Ibrox Park
457.33125	467.44375	NFM	Nationwide	JFMG Short Term Talkback
457.34375	467.38125	NFM	Nationwide	JFMG Short Term Talkback
457.35000		NFM	Nationwide	BBC TV O/B talkback
457.35625	467.33125	NFM	Nationwide	JFMG Short Term Talkback
457.36875	467.35625	NFM	Nationwide	JFMG Short Term Talkback
457.37500		NFM	Nationwide	BBC TV O/B talkback
457.39375	467.39375	NFM	Nationwide	JFMG Short Term Talkback
457.40625	467.34375	NFM	Nationwide	JFMG Short Term Talkback
457.41875	467.49375	NFM	Nationwide	JFMG Short Term Talkback
457.42500		NFM	Manchester	Sky Sports O/B from Old Trafford
457.43125	467.46875	NFM	Nationwide	JFMG Short Term Talkback
457.44375	462.94375	NFM	Warwick	Racetech O/B
457.44375	467.53125	NFM	Nationwide	JFMG Short Term Talkback
457.45625	467.51875	NFM	Nationwide	JFMG Short Term Talkback
457.46250		NFM	Nationwide	BBC TV O/B talkback
457.46875	467.50625	NFM	Nationwide	JFMG Short Term Talkback
457.48750		NFM	Cambridgeshire	Fire & Rescue Ch.7
457.48750		NFM	Humberside	Fire Brigade Training HQ Ch.7
457.48750		NFM	London	Fire Brigade Ch.7
457.48750		NFM	Nationwide	Fire Brigade Ch.7/Ch.3
457.48750		NFM	RAF Wittering	Fire Ch.3
457.48750		NFM	S Wales	Fire Brigade Ch.3
457.48750		NFM	Suffolk	Fire Brigade Ch.7

457.50625 - 458.49375 MHz — Fixed Scan Telemetry Links

Base	Mobile	Mode	Location	User and Notes
457.55000		NFM	Glasgow	Data Link
457.55000	463.05000	NFM	Morecambe	Data Link
457.55000	463.05000	NFM	Newmarket	Scan Data Link
457.56250	463.06250	NFM	Newmarket	Data Link
457.65000		NFM	Newmarket	Digital Paging
457.66250		NFM	Newcastle	Data Link
457.67500		NFM	Newmarket	Data Link
457.76250		NFM	Stirling	Data Link
457.77500	463.27500	NFM	Fulmar FSU	Shell Telemetry
457.80000	463.30000	NFM	Birmingham	West Midlands GA Data Link
457.85000	463.35000	NFM	Viking Field	Conoco Telemetry
457.87500	463.37500	NFM	North Sea	BP Buchan
457.87500	463.37500	NFM	North Sea	BP Forties D
457.93750		NFM	Stirling	Data Link
457.95000		NFM	Newcastle	Data Link
458.00000		NFM	Lincoln	Data Link
458.02500	463.52500	NFM	Newcastle	Data Link
458.05000	463.55000	NFM	Beryl A	Mobil Telemetry
458.24375		NFM	West Cumbria	Water Telemetry
458.36250		NFM	Dundee	Data Link
458.36250		NFM	Morecambe	Data Link
458.41875		NFM	North Sea	Chevron Alba FSU Shuttle Green Line Data
458.45625		NFM	North Sea	Chevron Alba ANP Data

457.500 - 457.575 MHz — International Maritime On-Board Handheld Transceivers 12.5 kHz

Base	Mobile	Mode	Location	User and Notes
457.50000		NFM	Harwich	Stena Ferries
457.52500		NFM	Barry	Dow Corning Manufacturing Ships/Loading
457.52500		NFM	Dover	P & O On-Board Handhelds Ch.3
457.52500		NFM	Fishguard	Stena Sealink On-Board Handhelds
457.52500		NFM	North Sea	Balmoral Sun Oil Handhelds
457.52500		NFM	Portsmouth	P & O On-Board Handhelds (151.4)
457.52500		NFM	Rosslare	Stena Line On-Board Handhelds
457.52500		NFM	Worldwide	On-Board Handhelds
457.52500	467.52500	NFM	Worldwide	On-Board Handhelds Repeaters
457.52500		NFM	Worldwide	Queen Elizabeth II On-Board Handhelds
457.52500		NFM	Worldwide	Royal Fleet Auxiliary Ship to Ship
457.52500		NFM	Worldwide	USS Harry Truman US Navy Shore Patrol/Guard (103.5)
457.53750		NFM	Worldwide	On-Board Handhelds
457.55000		NFM	Dover	P & O Pride of Kent On-Board Handhelds Ch.2
457.55000	467.55000	NFM	Dover	Trans Europa Ferries
457.55000		NFM	Fishguard	Sealink On-Board Handhelds
457.55000		NFM	Holyhead	Stena Adventurer Engine Room-Bridge Radio Phone Patch
457.55000		NFM	North Sea	Balmoral Field Sun Oil Handhelds
457.55000		NFM	Rosslare	Stena Line On-Board Handhelds
457.55000		NFM	Worldwide	On-Board Handhelds
457.55000	467.55000	NFM	Worldwide	On-Board Handhelds Repeaters
457.55000	463.05000	NFM	Worldwide	P & O Cruises Aurora On-Board Handhelds (151.4)
457.55000		NFM	Worldwide	Queen Elizabeth II On-Board Handhelds
457.56250		NFM	Worldwide	On-Board Handhelds
457.57500		NFM	Dover	P & O Pride of Calais On-Board Handhelds
457.57500		NFM	Holyhead	Stena Explorer On-Board Handhelds
457.57500		NFM	Montrose Docks	Big Orange XVIII
457.57500		NFM	North Sea	BP Lolair
457.57500		NFM	North Sea	Elf Frigg Field

Base	Mobile	Mode	Location	User and Notes
457.57500		NFM	North Sea	Sun Oil Balmoral
457.57500		NFM	Portsmouth	P & O Ferries On-Board Handhelds (151.4)
457.57500		NFM	Worldwide	On-Board Handhelds
457.57500	467.57500	NFM	Worldwide	On-Board Handhelds Repeaters
457.60000		NFM	Harwich	Stena Ferries

458.500 - 459.500 MHz — Short Range Devices, Telemetry, Vehicle Paging Alarms & Radio Keys

Base	Mobile	Mode	Location	User and Notes
458.50000		NFM	Flimby	Factory Telemetry
458.50000		NFM	Nationwide	Telemetry
458.51250		NFM	Nationwide	Telemetry
458.52500		NFM	Didcot	UKAEA
458.52500		NFM	Jersey	BGS Seismic Telemetry
458.52500		NFM	Morecambe	Data Link
458.55000	458.50000	NFM	Edinburgh Airport	Telemetry Ch.8
458.60000		NFM	Glasgow	Data Link
458.62500		NFM	Stevenage	ICL Computers Telemetry
458.65000		NFM	Nationwide	Telemetry
458.67500		NFM	Jersey	BGS Seismic Telemetry
458.67500		NFM	Nationwide	Shell Geophysical
458.70000		NFM	Nationwide	Telemetry
458.72500		NFM	Jersey	BGS Seismic Telemetry
458.80000		NFM	Jersey	BGS Seismic Telemetry
458.90000		NFM	Flimby	Factory Telemetry
458.95000		NFM	Bassenthwaite	Lake Telemetry
459.02500		NFM	Jersey	BGS Seismic Telemetry

458.8375 - 459.4875 MHz — On-Site Paging & Local Communications

Base	Mobile	Mode	Location	User and Notes
458.83750		NFM	Nationwide	Transportable & Mobile Alarms
458.85000		NFM	Jersey	Paging Queens Valley Area
458.85000		NFM	Magnus	BP Paging Base
458.90000		NFM	Nationwide	Car Theft Alarm Paging
458.97500		NFM	North Sea	Mobil Statfjord A
459.00000		NFM	Nationwide	Medical & Biological Telemetry
459.00000		NFM	North Sea	Mobil Statfjord A
459.02500		NFM	North Sea	Mobil Statfjord A
459.05000		NFM	Nationwide	One Way Data Paging
459.07500		NFM	North Sea	Conoco Murchison
459.07500		NFM	North Sea	Mobil Statfjord B
459.07500	453.47500	NFM	North Sea	BP Buchan
459.10000		NFM	Lowestoft	HM Revenue & Customs
459.10000		NFM	Nationwide	One Way Data/Voice Paging
459.10000		NFM	North Sea	Mobil Statfjord B
459.12500		NFM	Gateshead	Asda Supermarket Paging, Metro Centre
459.12500		NFM	Gateshead	Marks & Spencer Paging, Metro Centre
459.12500		NFM	London	Science Museum Paging, S Kensington
459.12500		NFM	Nationwide	Two Way Data/Voice Paging
459.15000		NFM	Jersey	Paging, Fort Regent
459.15000		NFM	Montrose	GlaxoSmithKline Factory Paging
459.15000	161.02500	NFM	Nationwide	Marina Paging
459.17500		NFM	London	John Lewis Voice Paging, Oxford Street
459.17500		NFM	Nationwide	One Way Data/Voice Paging
459.17500	159.6375	NFM	Nationwide	Two Way Data/Voice Paging
459.17500		NFM	Newcastle Upon Tyne	Fenwick Department Store Voice Paging
459.17500		NFM	Perth	Paging
459.17500		NFM	Swansea	Marriott Hotel Voice Paging

Base	Mobile	Mode	Location	User and Notes
459.20000		NFM	Cardiff	Magistrates Court Voice Paging
459.20000		NFM	Gatwick	Voice Paging
459.20000		NFM	Leicester	Makro Centre Paging
459.20000		NFM	London	BBC Voice Paging, Acton
459.20000		NFM	London	Selfridges Voice Paging, Oxford Street
459.20000		NFM	Nationwide	One Way Data/Voice Paging
459.20000	159.65000	NFM	Nationwide	Two Way Data/Voice Paging
459.22500		NFM	Belfast	Royal Victoria Hospital Paging
459.22500		NFM	Biggleswade	Jordan Cereals Voice Paging
459.22500		NFM	Chesterfield	Robinsons Factory Voice Paging
459.22500		NFM	Colchester	Voice Paging
459.22500		NFM	Dudley	Marks & Spencer Voice Paging, Merryhill
459.22500		NFM	Nationwide	One Way Data/Voice Paging
459.22500	159.66250	NFM	Nationwide	Two Way Data/Voice Paging
459.22500		NFM	Newcastle	Posthouse Forte Hotel Voice Paging
459.25000		NFM	Chepstow	Voice Paging
459.25000		NFM	London	Voice Paging, Earls Court
459.25000		NFM	Nationwide	One Way Data/Voice Paging
459.25000	161.05000	NFM	Nationwide	Two Way Data/Voice Paging
459.25000		NFM	Port Talbot	BP Oil Refinery Voice Paging
459.27500	159.67500	NFM	Coventry	Hilton Hotel Voice Paging
459.27500	161.00000	NFM	High Wycombe	Tesco Voice Paging
459.27500		NFM	Nationwide	One Way Data/Voice Paging
459.27500	159.67500	NFM	Nationwide	Two Way Data/Voice Paging
459.27500	159.67500	NFM	Oxford	Littlemore Psychiatric Hospital Paging
459.27500	159.67500	NFM	Watford	Tesco Voice Paging
459.27500	159.67500	NFM	Welwyn Garden City	Queen Elizabeth II Hospital Paging
459.30000	161.07500	NFM	London	Fortnum & Mason Voice Paging
459.30000	161.00000	NFM	London	Museum of London Voice Paging
459.30000		NFM	London	Marks & Spencer Voice Paging, Oxford Circus
459.30000		NFM	Nationwide	One Way Data/Voice Paging
459.30000	159.70000	NFM	Nationwide	Two Way Data/Voice Paging
459.32500	161.01250	NFM	Birmingham	Marks & Spencer Voice Paging
459.32500	161.01250	NFM	Cambridge	Voice Paging
459.32500	161.01250	NFM	Gillingham	Marks & Spencer Voice Paging
459.32500	161.01250	NFM	Hull	Marks & Spencer Voice Paging
459.32500	161.01250	NFM	Leicester	Holiday Inn Voice Paging
459.32500	161.01250	NFM	London	Silvertown Paging
459.32500	161.01250	NFM	London	Fenwick Department Store Paging, Brent Cross
459.32500	161.01250	NFM	Nationwide	Two Way Data/Voice Paging
459.32500	161.01250	NFM	North Sea	Chevron Alba ANP Paging
459.32500	161.01250	NFM	Reading	Marks & Spencer Voice Paging
459.32500	161.01250	NFM	Romford	Tesco Staff Paging
459.32500	161.01250	NFM	Scarborough	Voice Paging
459.32500	161.01250	NFM	Swansea	Marks & Spencer Voice Paging
459.32500	161.01250	NFM	Worcester	Voice Paging
459.35000	161.02500	NFM	Cambridge	Addenbrookes Hospital Voice Paging
459.35000	161.02500	NFM	Chessington	World of Adventures Voice Paging
459.35000	161.02500	NFM	London	Voice Paging, Near Old Bailey
459.35000	161.02500	NFM	London	St Thomas Hospital Paging, Lambeth
459.35000	161.02500	NFM	Nationwide	ADT Intruder Alarms
459.35000	161.02500	NFM	Nationwide	Two Way Data/Voice Paging
459.35000	161.02500	NFM	North Sea	Marathon Brae South Paging
459.35000	161.02500	NFM	North Sea	Mobil Brett 2,1 A Paging
459.37500	161.03750	NFM	Basildon	Orsett Hospital Paging
459.37500	161.03750	NFM	Belfast	Ulster Hospital Paging

Base	Mobile	Mode	Location	User and Notes
459.37500	161.03750	NFM	Bury St Edmunds	Greene King Brewery Voice Paging, Westgate
459.37500	161.03750	NFM	Copdock	Tesco Store Voice Paging
459.37500	161.03750	NFM	Dartford	John Lewis Voice Paging, Bluewater Centre
459.37500	161.03750	NFM	Dumfries	Gates Rubber Company Paging
459.37500	161.03750	NFM	Heathrow	Heathrow Airport Voice Paging
459.37500	161.03750	NFM	Ipswich	Bhs Paging
459.37500	161.03750	NFM	Kent	Kent Hospital Paging
459.37500	161.03750	NFM	London	Bhs Paging
459.37500	161.03750	NFM	London	Littlewoods Voice Paging, Marble Arch
459.37500	161.03750	NFM	London	Peter Jones Voice Paging, Sloane Square
459.37500	161.03750	NFM	London	Selfridges Voice Paging, Oxford Street
459.37500	161.03750	NFM	Mere	Hill Brush Company
459.37500	161.03750	NFM	Nationwide	Two Way Data/Voice Paging
459.37500		NFM	Newtownabbey	Whiteabbey Hospital Paging
459.37500	161.03750	NFM	North Sea	Mobil ALP Statfjord C
459.37500	161.03750	NFM	Romford	BAC Staff Paging
459.37500	161.03750	NFM	Slough	Voice Paging
459.37500	161.03750	NFM	Stevenage	John Lewis Voice Paging
459.37500	161.03750	NFM	Thorpe Park	Voice Paging
459.37500	161.03750	NFM	Wirral	Mobil Oil Security
459.40000	161.06250	NFM	Cardiff	Cardiff Bay Hotel Voice Paging
459.40000	161.06250	NFM	Chatham	Pentagon Shopping Centre Voice Paging
459.40000	161.06250	NFM	Chesterfield	Tesco Store Voice Paging
459.40000	161.06250	NFM	Heathrow	Heathrow Airport Voice Paging
459.40000	161.06250	NFM	Lincoln	County Hospital Paging
459.40000	161.06250	NFM	London	Earls Court Paging
459.40000	161.06250	NFM	London	Wembley Conference Centre Paging
459.40000	161.06250	NFM	Nationwide	Two Way Data/Voice Paging
459.40000	161.06250	NFM	North Sea	Phillips Ekofisk Senter Paging
459.40000	161.06250	NFM	Sheffield	Meadowhall Shopping Centre Voice Paging
459.42500	161.06250	NFM	Abingdon	Tesco Supermarket Voice Paging
459.42500	161.06250	NFM	Bridgend	Ford Engine Plant Paging
459.42500	161.06250	NFM	Coventry	Paging
459.42500		NFM	Dawlish	Voice Paging /Elderly Care Alarm System
459.42500	161.06250	NFM	Leicester	Royal Infirmary Voice Paging
459.42500	161.06250	NFM	London	BBC Bush House Paging
459.42500	161.06250	NFM	London	Grosvenor House Hotel Paging
459.42500	161.06250	NFM	Nationwide	Two Way Data/Voice Paging
459.42500	161.06250	NFM	Nationwide	Tesco Stores Common Voice Paging
459.42500	161.06250	NFM	North Sea	BP Clyde A Paging
459.42500	161.06250	NFM	North Sea	Mobil Statfjord B Paging
459.42500	161.06250	NFM	Southampton	Voice Paging
459.42500	161.06250	NFM	Stevenage	Tesco Store Voice Paging
459.43750		NFM	Watford	Paging
459.45000		NFM	Blandford	Paging
459.45000		NFM	Manchester	Paging
459.45000		NFM	Nationwide	One Way Data/Voice Paging
459.45000	161.10000	NFM	Nationwide	Two Way Data/Voice Paging
459.45000		NFM	North Sea	Mobil Statfjord C Paging
459.47500	161.11250	NFM	Biggleswade	Jordans Cereals Voice Paging
459.47500	161.11250	NFM	Bury St Edmunds	Sainsbury Supermarket Voice Paging
459.47500	161.11250	NFM	Cardiff	City Centre Hotel Voice Paging
459.47500	161.11250	NFM	Coventry	Hilton Hotel Voice Paging
459.47500	161.11250	NFM	Eastbourne	Sainsbury Supermarket Voice Paging
459.47500	161.11250	NFM	Gillingham	Sainsbury Savacentre Voice Paging
459.47500	161.11250	NFM	Ipswich	Sainsbury Supermarket Voice Paging

Base	Mobile	Mode	Location	User and Notes
459.47500	161.11250	NFM	Leeds	Tetley Brewery Voice Paging
459.47500	161.11250	NFM	Luton	Arndale Shopping Centre Paging
459.47500	161.11250	NFM	Nationwide	Two Way Data/Voice Paging
459.47500	161.11250	NFM	Newcastle upon Tyne	John Lewis Voice Paging
459.47500	161.11250	NFM	Norwich	Sainsbury Supermarket Voice Paging
459.47500	161.11250	NFM	Romford	Bhs Staff Paging
459.47500	161.11250	NFM	Sittingbourne	Sainsbury Supermarket Voice Paging
459.47500	161.11250	NFM	Sleaford	Padley's Poultry
459.47500	161.11250	NFM	Weston Super Mare	Weston College Voice Paging
459.47500	161.11250	NFM	Wirral	Sainsbury Supermarket Voice Paging
459.47500	161.11250	NFM	York	National Railway Museum

459.500 - 460.500 MHz   PMR & Public Services

Base	Mobile	Mode	Location	User and Notes
459.50000		NFM	Blackpool	Tower Ascent
459.50000		NFM	London	Air Ambulance Air-Ground
459.52500		NFM	Coventry	Coombe Abbey Park
459.52500		NFM	Felixstowe	Docks Rescue/Fire
459.52500		NFM	Ipswich	Checkmate Security
459.53750		NFM	Cardiff	Air Ambulance Air-Ground
459.53750		NFM	Leeds Airport	W Yorkshire Air Ambulance, Yeadon
459.53750		NFM	London	Air Ambulance G-Hems Air-Ground (71.9)
459.53750		NFM	Northamptonshire	Two Shires Air Ambulance Air-Ground (71.9)
459.53750		NFM	Wales	Welsh Air Ambulance Air-Ground
459.55000		NFM	Glasgow	Versace Collection, The Italian Centre
459.55000		NFM	Kent	Seagas Link
459.55000		NFM	London	BBC TV Centre Staff, White City
459.55000		NFM	London	West One Shopping Centre, Oxford Street
459.55000		NFM	Luton Airport	Catering Company
459.57500		NFM	Cardiff	Crash Ops. (103.5)
459.57500		NFM	Colchester	Colchester Zoo, Stanway
459.57500		NFM	Dartford	Thamesport Containers Ch.1
459.57500		NFM	Dagenham	Ford Motor Plant
459.57500		NFM	Dover	Docks
459.57500		NFM	Eastbourne	Marks & Spencer Security (118.8)
459.57500		NFM	Fishguard	Stena Line Boarding
459.57500		NFM	Harwich	Docks
459.57500		NFM	Ipswich	Liquid Nightclub Security
459.57500		NFM	Jersey	St Helier Harbour
459.57500		NFM	London	BBC Bush House Security, Aldwych
459.57500		NFM	London	Brent Trading Estate
459.57500		NFM	London	Hammersmith Hospital
459.57500		NFM	London	London School of Economics, Aldwych
459.57500		NFM	London	Moreland School, City Road
459.57500		NFM	London	London Underground Goliath Crane (151.4)
459.57500		NFM	London	London Underground Gunnersbury Works
459.57500		NFM	London	London Underground, Neasden
459.57500		NFM	London	London Underground Welders, Ruislip
459.57500	453.07500	NFM	London	Richmond upon Thames College
459.57500		NFM	London	Southside Centre Security, Wandsworth
459.57500		NFM	London	The City University Security, Finsbury
459.57500		NFM	London	The Coliseum, English National Opera, WC2
459.57500		NFM	Manchester	House of Fraser, Kendalls (71.9)
459.57500	453.07500	NFM	Sizewell	Power Station Work Teams Ch.5
459.57500		NFM	Tadworth	BBC, Kingswood Warren
459.60000		NFM	Heathrow	Airport Ops
459.60000		NFM	Felixstowe	Docks

Base	Mobile	Mode	Location	User and Notes
459.60000		NFM	Ipswich	Corn Exchange & Film Theatre Ch.1
459.60000		NFM	Isle of Man	Ronaldsway Airport Engineers
459.62500		NFM	Brighton	Brighton Football Club, Withdean Stadium (88.5)
459.62500		NFM	Cheltenham	Racecourse (103.5)
459.62500		NFM	Dartford	Dartford Tunnel Security
459.62500		NFM	Dartford	Thamesport Containers Ch.2
459.62500		NFM	Doncaster	Robin Hood Airport Ops (107.2)
459.62500		NFM	Elstree	Haberdasher's Aske's School
459.62500		NFM	Felixstowe	Docks
459.62500		NFM	Leeds Airport	Aviance Ground Handling
459.62500		NFM	London	Guildhall Security, City of London
459.62500		NFM	Newhaven	Port Security
459.62500		NFM	Sheffield	Stockbridge Steel Engineering
459.65000		NFM	Doncaster	Arndale Centre Security Ch.1
459.65000		NFM	Ipswich	Marks & Spencer Security Ch.1
459.65000		NFM	London	Shopwatch, Pavilion Centre, Uxbridge
459.65000		NFM	Nottingham	Boots Broadmarch Shopping Centre
459.65000		NFM	Weston Super Mare	Pier Ch.1
459.67500		NFM	Dagenham	Ford Factory
459.70000		NFM	Cambridge	Cambridge Coach Services
459.70000		NFM	Felixstowe	Docks
459.70000		NFM	Gatwick	Ground Repeater
459.72500		NFM	Brighton	Brighton Crematorium
459.72500		NFM	Dartford	Thamesport Containers Ch.3
459.72500		NFM	Eastleigh	Airport
459.72500		NFM	Felixstowe	Docks
459.72500		NFM	Jersey	St Helier Harbour
459.72500		NFM	Sellafield	UKAEA
459.72500		NFM	Swansea	Grand Theatre Staff
459.75000		NFM	Chelmsford	Meadows Shopping Centre Security
459.75000		NFM	Leeds	Parking Enforcement
459.75000		NFM	London	Parking Enforcement, Enfield
459.77500	453.27500	NFM	Fife	Ambulance Handhelds Ch.1
459.77500	453.27500	NFM	Strathclyde	Ambulance Handhelds Ch.1
459.77500		NFM	Tilbury	Container Port (94.8)
459.80000		NFM	Birmingham	Pavilions Shopping Centre Security
459.80000		NFM	Cardiff	Cardiff International Arena Ch.2 (118.8)
459.80000		NFM	Cheltenham	Debenhams Department Store Security
459.80000		NFM	Dartford	Thamesport Containers Ch.4
459.80000		NFM	Eastbourne	Eastbourne Pier (107.2)
459.80000		NFM	Harwich	Docks
459.80000		NFM	Irvine	Magnum Leisure Centre
459.80000		NFM	London	London Eye Staff Ch.2 (88.5)
459.80000		NFM	London	Mango Fashion Store Staff, Oxford Circus (146.2)
459.80000		NFM	Sellafield	UKAEA
459.82500		NFM	Lincolnshire	Ambulance Service
459.82500	453.32500	NFM	Scotland	Ambulance Handhelds Ch.3
459.82500		NFM	Wales	Welsh Ambulance Trust VHF-UHF Repeaters
459.82500		NFM	West Yorkshire	Ambulance Service
459.85000		NFM	Dartford	Thamesport Containers Ch.5
459.85000		NFM	Felixstowe	Docks
459.85000		NFM	Harwich	Port Crane Loaders (107.2)
459.85000		NFM	Heathrow	Crest Hotel
459.85000		NFM	Heathrow	Excelsior Hotel
459.85000		NFM	Humberside Airport	Servisair/GlobeGround
459.85000		NFM	Jersey	Trusthouse Forte Airport Catering

Base	Mobile	Mode	Location	User and Notes
459.85000		NFM	Llandudno	Great Orme Tramway
459.85000		NFM	London	Merke Sharpe Dohme, Ponders End
459.85000		NFM	London	St Annes Centre, Harrow
459.85000		NFM	London	The Gap Fashion Store, Kensington (107.2)
459.85000		NFM	Lowestoft	Care Home Custodians (141.3)
459.85000		NFM	Morecombe Bay	British Gas Exploration & Production
459.85000		NFM	Swindon	Brunel Security
459.85000		NFM	Woking	Wolsey Place Shopping Centre Security
459.87500		NFM	Immingham	Conoco
459.87500		NFM	Salisbury	Hospital Security
459.87500	453.37500	NFM	Scotland	Ambulance Service Repeaters Ch.1
459.90000		NFM	Brighton	Brighton Football Club, Withdean Stadium (107.2)
459.90000		NFM	Felixstowe	Docks
459.90000		NFM	Sizewell	Power Stations Work Teams Ch.8
459.90000		NFM	Tilbury	Tilbury Docks (94.8)
459.90000		NFM	Welwyn Garden City	Howard Shopping Centre (107.2)
459.92500		NFM	Bristol	B & Q Store, Stoke Gifford
459.92500		NFM	Cardiff	County Hall/Nelson House/London House Security
459.92500		NFM	London	Austin Reed Store Security, Regent Street
459.92500		NFM	Sellafield	UKAEA
459.92500		NFM	Southampton Airport	MAS Air Services (77)
459.95000		NFM	Barnet	Vicarage Field Shopping Centre Security
459.95000		NFM	Dartford	Thamesport Containers Ch.6
459.95000		NFM	Felixstowe	Docks
459.95000		NFM	Harwich	Docks
459.95000		NFM	London	Gap Clothes Store, Kensington
459.95000		NFM	London	Jaeger Store Security, Regent St (146.2)
459.95000		NFM	London	Lloyds of London, City of London
459.95000		NFM	London	Twickenham Civic Centre
459.95000		NFM	London	Top Shop In-House TV Ch.1, Oxford Circus (192.8)
459.95000		NFM	Morecombe Bay	British Gas Exploration & Production
459.95000		NFM	Rochdale	Hospital Security (67)
459.95000		NFM	Southampton	Esso Fawley Oil Refinery
459.95000		NFM	Tilbury	Tilbury Docks (167.9)
459.95000		NFM	Weybridge	Brooklands Technical College
459.97500		NFM	Dorset	BP Wytch Farm
459.97500		NFM	Longleat	Centre Parcs Security
460.02500		NFM	Ascot	Racecourse Network Ch.2
460.02500		NFM	Aylesbury	Hale Leys Shopping Centre
460.02500		NFM	Felixstowe	Docks
460.02500		NFM	Jersey	St Helier Harbour
460.02500		NFM	London	Chelsea & Westminster Hospital Security (225)
460.02500		NFM	London	DH Evans Uniformed Security, Oxford Street (167.9)
460.02500		NFM	London	Edgware Council Offices, Cannons Park
460.02500		NFM	London	House of Fraser, Oxford Street (173)
460.02500		NFM	London	Pearsons Store Security, Wood Green (103.5)
460.02500		NFM	London	Royal Free Hospital, Hampstead
460.02500		NFM	London	Securiplan Security, Stockley Park
460.02500		NFM	London	Southwark Council
460.02500		NFM	London	The Body Shop, Piccadilly
460.02500		NFM	London	Voodoo Lounge, Leicester Square
460.02500		NFM	Northumberland	Geological Surveys
460.02500		NFM	Paisley	House of Fraser, Arnotts (71.9)
460.02500		NFM	Romford	Tetley Carlsberg Brewery
460.02500		NFM	Southend on Sea	Odeon Cinema Staff (94.8)
460.02500		NFM	Stevenage	Midas Security, Kings Leisure Site
460.02500		NFM	Tilbury	Docks (123)

Base	Mobile	Mode	Location	User and Notes
460.05000		NFM	Durham	Network Rail
460.05000		NFM	London	Network Rail, Ilford
460.05000		NFM	London	Network Rail, Marylebone Station (71.9)
460.05000		NFM	Tyne & Wear	Tyne Yard Ch.1
460.06250		NFM	London	Lords Cricket Ground Press Pass Allocation
460.07500		NFM	Ashford	Safeways Store
460.07500		NFM	Dartford	Thamesport Containers Ch.7
460.07500		NFM	Heathrow	Cargo Terminal Security
460.07500		NFM	London	Credit Suisse Bank Boston, Canary Wharf
460.07500		NFM	London	Elf Oil Headquarters/Office Complex, Sunbury
460.07500		NFM	Morecombe Bay	British Gas Exploration & Production
460.07500		NFM	Nationwide	Safeways Supermarkets Security
460.07500		NFM	Preston	Fishergate Shopping Centre Security (71.9)
460.07500		NFM	Swansea	Tesco Extra Security
460.07500		NFM	Watford	Watford Printers Ltd.
460.07500		NFM	Whipsnade	Wildlife Park
460.10000		NFM	Beckenham	Kent Food Manufacturing, Eden Park
460.10000		NFM	Bedford	Debenhams Department Store Security
460.10000		NFM	Birmingham	Debenhams Department Store Security
460.10000		NFM	Blackpool	Coral Island Arcade (123)
460.10000		NFM	Bridlington	Leisure World Entertainment Complex
460.10000		NFM	Camberley	Army & Navy Store Security (71.9)
460.10000		NFM	Cambridge	Debenhams Department Store Security
460.10000		NFM	Cardiff	Airport Security
460.10000		NFM	Cardiff	House of Fraser, Howells (71.9)
460.10000		NFM	Derby	Debenhams Department Store Security
460.10000		NFM	Folkestone	Debenhams Department Store Security
460.10000		NFM	Guildford	Army & Navy Store Security (173.8)
460.10000		NFM	Ipswich	Debenhams Department Store Security
460.10000		NFM	London	Army & Navy Store Security, Victoria (71.9)
460.10000		NFM	London	Australian High Commission
460.10000		NFM	London	Earls Court Centre Maintenance Ch.4
460.10000		NFM	London	Ministry Of Sound, Elephant & Castle
460.10000		NFM	London	Olympia Exhibition Centre Ch.8
460.10000		NFM	Manchester	Debenhams Department Store Security
460.10000		NFM	Norwich	Debenhams Department Store Security
460.10000		NFM	Plymouth	House of Fraser, Dingles
460.10000		NFM	Sizewell	Power Station Management Ch.10
460.11250		NFM	Doncaster	Network Rail
460.11250		NFM	London	Network Rail, Richmond
460.11250		NFM	London	Network Rail, Euston
460.11250		NFM	London	Network Rail, Waterloo
460.11250		NFM	Tyne & Wear	Tyne Yard Ch.2
460.12500		NFM	Aberdeen	House of Fraser (71.9)
460.12500		NFM	Bath	House of Fraser, Jollys (71.9)
460.12500		NFM	Bournemouth	House of Fraser, Dingles (71.9)
460.12500		NFM	Bristol	House of Fraser, Dingles (71.9)
460.12500		NFM	Bromley	Army & Navy Store Security (71.9)
460.12500		NFM	Bromley	Church House Gardens
460.12500		NFM	Cheltenham	Racecourse (67)
460.12500		NFM	Chichester	Army & Navy Store Security (71.9)
460.12500		NFM	Coventry	Bhs Security
460.12500		NFM	Coventry	Central Library
460.12500		NFM	Darlington	House of Fraser, Binns (71.9)
460.12500		NFM	Dartford	Thamesport Containers Ch.8
460.12500		NFM	Doncaster	House of Fraser, Binns (71.9)
460.12500		NFM	Dundee	House of Fraser, Arnotts (71.9)

Base	Mobile	Mode	Location	User and Notes
460.12500		NFM	Glasgow	House of Fraser, Arnotts (173.8)
460.12500		NFM	Grimsby	House of Fraser, Binns (173.8)
460.12500		NFM	Ipswich	Top Shop/Top Man Security
460.12500		NFM	Lincoln	House of Fraser, Binns (146.2)
460.12500		NFM	London	Army & Navy Store Security, Victoria (179.9)
460.12500		NFM	London	Arsenal Football Club Office Staff
460.12500		NFM	London	Barkers, Kensington (71.9)
460.12500		NFM	London	DH Evans Security, Oxford Street
460.12500		NFM	London	Harrods Security, Knightsbridge (103.5)
460.12500		NFM	London	Michael Sobell Sports Centre, Finsbury Park
460.12500		NFM	London	Top Shop (Office to Shop), Oxford Street (88.5)
460.12500		NFM	Maidstone	Army & Navy Store Security (71.9)
460.12500		NFM	Manchester	Top Shop Staff
460.12500		NFM	Middlesbrough	House of Fraser, Binns (71.9)
460.12500		NFM	Perth	House of Fraser, Frasers(71.9)
460.12500		NFM	St Helens	B & Q Store Security
460.12500		NFM	Swansea	University Warden Patrols
460.15000		NFM	Altringham	House of Fraser, Rackhams (71.9)
460.15000		NFM	Belfast	Connswater Shopping Centre Security (173.8)
460.15000		NFM	Braintree	Freeport Shopping Centre Maintenance
460.15000		NFM	Cheltenham	House of Fraser, Cavendish (71.9)
460.15000		NFM	Dartford	Dartford Engineering
460.15000		NFM	Doncaster	Robin Hood Airport Operations (107.2)
460.15000		NFM	Eastbourne	Royal Eastbourne Golf Course (162.2)
460.15000		NFM	Irvine	Fullarton Flats Concierge Station Ch.1
460.15000		NFM	Leamington Spa	House of Fraser, Rackhams (71.9)
460.15000		NFM	Leeds	House of Fraser, Schofields (71.9)
460.15000		NFM	London	Camden Council
460.15000		NFM	London	Hollywood Bowl Staff/Security, Surrey Quays (173.8)
460.15000		NFM	Newhaven	Port Services
460.15000		NFM	Norwich	Time Nightclub (88.5)
460.15000		NFM	Peterborough	Quo Vadis Club
460.15000		NFM	Sheffield	House of Fraser, Meadowhall (71.9)
460.15000		NFM	Shrewsbury	House of Fraser, Rackhams (71.9)
460.15000		NFM	Warwick	Hospital
460.17500		NFM	Cardiff	Docks (131.8)
460.17500		NFM	Cardiff Airport	Alpha Flight Catering (Cafe Staff)
460.17500		NFM	London	Harrods Security, Knightsbridge
460.17500		NFM	Poole	Tower Park Leisure Site Security
460.20000		NFM	Rugby	Christian Salvesen, Swift Valley Industrial Estate
460.20000		NFM	Tilbury	Docks (94.8)
460.22500		NFM	Cardiff	Docks
460.22500		NFM	Irvine	WH Malcolm's Lorry Depot at Rockware Glass
460.22500		NFM	London	Versace Couture, Bond St (88.5)
460.22500		NFM	Manchester	Gap Store, Trafford Centre
460.22500		NFM	Swansea	Morfa Leisure Centre
460.22500		NFM	Wareham	Tarmac
460.22500		NFM	Weston Super Mare	Pier Ch.2
460.25000		NFM	Bristol	Docks
460.25000		NFM	Cardiff	Docks (146.2)
460.25000		NFM	Immingham	Conoco
460.25000		NFM	Kettering	Newland Shopping Centre Security (114.8)
460.27500		NFM	Culham	UKAEA Laboratory Fire Team
460.27500		NFM	Farnborough	Qinetiq Escorts
460.27500		NFM	Isle of Wight	Newport Docks
460.27500		NFM	Immingham	Conoco
460.27500		NFM	Southampton	Esso Fawley Oil Refinery

Base	Mobile	Mode	Location	User and Notes
460.27500		NFM	Stafford	Guildhall Shopping Centre Staff
460.30000		NFM	London	Earls Court Ch.3 Management
460.30000		NFM	London	Callaghan's Irish Bar, Piccadilly
460.30000		NFM	London	Cromwell Hospital Porters, Kensington
460.30000		NFM	London	Royal Festival Hall, Southbank
460.32500		NFM	Bristol	House of Fraser Security
460.32500		NFM	Clacton on Sea	Highfield Holiday Park
460.32500		NFM	Ipswich	Cranfield Bros. Flour Mill
460.32500		NFM	London	Earls Court/Olympia Ch.13 Plumbers
460.32500		NFM	Sheffield	Debenhams Department Store Security
460.32500		NFM	Plymouth	Debenhams Department Store Security
460.35000		NFM	Bradford	Allied Colloids Chemicals
460.35000		NFM	Edinburgh	Debenhams Department Store Security (127.3)
460.35000		NFM	Reading	Madejski Stadium
460.37500		NFM	Ascot	Racecourse Network Ch.6
460.37500		NFM	Bournville	Cadbury World Security
460.37500		NFM	Brighton	UGC Cinema (71.9)
460.37500		NFM	Coventry	Skydome Cinema
460.37500		NFM	Dagenham	Checkers Lane Engineering
460.37500		NFM	Folkestone	Docks Security
460.37500		NFM	Ipswich	Virgin Cinema Staff
460.37500		NFM	London	Campden Hill School, Kensington
460.37500		NFM	London	Mount Charlotte Hotel, Marble Arch
460.37500		NFM	London	Hoxton School
460.37500		NFM	Southend on Sea	Chicago Rock Cafe (179.9)
460.37500		NFM	Staines	Debenhams Department Store Security (DCS 612)
460.40000		NFM	Leeds	Rail Station Staff
460.40000		NFM	London	Rail Station Staff, Upminster (110.9)
460.40000		NFM	Poole	Flight Refuelling
460.42500		NFM	London	Ikea Furniture Superstore Staff, Neasden
460.42500		NFM	Londonderry	Richmond Shopping Centre Security (94.8)
460.45000		NFM	Aldermaston	Atomic Weapons Establishment Services (WE)
460.45000		NFM	Coventry	Coventry & Warwickshire Hospital
460.45000		NFM	Glasgow	Virgin Records Security
460.45000		NFM	London	Gap Clothes Store, Whitely Centre, Bayswater
460.45000		NFM	Poole	Dolphin Packaging Security
4C0.47500		NFM	Bournville	Cadbury World Security

460.500 - 460.750 MHz — Emergency Services, UHF Point to Point & Broadcasting Links

Base	Mobile	Mode	Location	User and Notes
460.52500	467.02500	NFM	Bovingdon	Young Offender Institution The Mount (KM)
460.52500	467.02500	NFM	Bristol	HM Prison (NY)
460.52500	467.02500	NFM	Brough	HM Prison Everthorpe (NF)
460.52500	467.02500	NFM	Buckinghamshire	HM Prison, Grendon Underwood (PB)
460.52500	467.02500	NFM	Canterbury	Immigration Detention Centre (PV)
460.52500	467.02500	NFM	Carstairs	HM Prison Hospital (YX)
460.52500	467.02500	NFM	Derby	HM Female Prison Foston Hall (OJ)
460.52500	467.02500	NFM	Henley on Thames	Young Offender Institution Huntercombe (NI)
460.52500	467.02500	NFM	Huntingdon	HM Prison Littlehey (KL)
460.52500	467.02500	NFM	Lanarkshire	High Security State Hospital, Carstairs (TX)
460.52500	467.02500	NFM	Lewes	HM Prison (PS)
460.52500	467.02500	NFM	Lincoln	HM Prison (JB)
460.52500	467.02500	NFM	London	HM Prison Pentonville (JP)
460.52500	467.02500	NFM	London	HM Prison Wandsworth (JW)
460.52500	467.02500	NFM	March	HM Prison Whitemoor (VX)
460.52500	467.02500	NFM	Morpeth	HM Prison Acklington (JV)
460.52500	467.02500	NFM	Portland	Young Offender Institution Portland (PL)

Base	Mobile	Mode	Location	User and Notes
460.52500	467.02500	NFM	Rochester	Young Offender Institution (PR)
460.52500	467.02500	NFM	Rugby	HM Prison Olney (JO)
460.52500	467.02500	NFM	Shaftesbury	HM Prison Guys Marsh (BB)
460.52500	467.02500	NFM	Thetford	HM Prison Wayland (VW)
460.52500	467.02500	NFM	Wakefield	Prison Training College
460.52500	467.02500	NFM	Warrington	Young Offender Institution Thorn Cross (BO)
460.53750	467.03750	NFM	Aylesbury	Young Offender Institution (PA)
460.53750	467.03750	NFM	Banstead	HM Prison (KI)
460.53750	467.03750	NFM	Chelmsford	HM Prison (PG)
460.53750	467.03750	NFM	Gloucester	HM Prison (OQ)
460.53750	467.03750	NFM	Lichfield	Young Offender Institution Swinfen Hall (JN)
460.53750	467.03750	NFM	Liverpool	HM Prison (OW)
460.53750	467.03750	NFM	London	HM Prison Brixton (JX)
460.53750	467.03750	NFM	Manchester	HM Prison Strangeways (OS)
460.53750	467.03750	NFM	Pucklechurch	Young Offender Institution (OU)
460.53750	467.03750	NFM	Sutton	HM Female Prison Ashfield (KI)
460.53750	467.03750	NFM	Wellingborough	HM Prison (NQ)
460.55000	467.05000	NFM	Ashford	HM Female Prison Bronzefield (BZ) (218.1)
460.55000	467.05000	NFM	Bicester	HM Prison Bullingdon (HM)
460.55000	467.05000	NFM	Birmingham	HM Prison (JG)
460.55000	467.05000	NFM	Isle of Sheppey	HM Prison Swaleside (KS)
460.55000	467.05000	NFM	London	HM Female Prison Holloway (HW)
460.55000	467.05000	NFM	Preston	HM Prison (OP)
460.55000	467.05000	NFM	Reading	Young Offender Institution (OA)
460.55000	467.05000	NFM	Wakefield	HM Female Prison New Hall, Flockton (KN)
460.55000	467.05000	NFM	Wetherby	Young Offender Institution (XB)
460.55000	467.05000	NFM	Wotton under Edge	HM Open Prison (PC)
460.60000	467.10000	NFM	Usk	HM Prison (OP)
460.62500	467.12500	NFM	London	HM Prison Wormwood Scrubs (JS)
460.62500	467.12500	NFM	Sheerness	HM Prison Elmley (KE)
460.66250	467.16250	NFM	London	HM Prison Belmarsh (MB)
460.66250	467.16250	NFM	Woodbridge	Young Offender Institution Hollesey Bay (PW)
460.66250	467.16250	NFM	Woodbridge	Young Offender Institution Warren Hill (PW)
460.67500	467.17500	NFM	Bridgend	HM Prison Parc (VP)
460.67500	467.17500	NFM	Manchester	HM Prison Strangeways (OS)
460.67500	467.17500	NFM	Market Harborough	HM Prison Gartree (OG)
460.67500	467.17500	NFM	Morpeth	Young Offender Institution Castington (NU)
460.67500	467.17500	NFM	Preston	HM Prison Kirkham (OK)
460.68750	467.08750	NFM	Durham	HM Prison Frankland (NE)
460.68750	467.08750	NFM	Newport, IoW	HM Prison Camp Hill (PJ)
460.68750	467.08750	NFM	Warrington	HM Prison Risley (OR)
460.68750	467.08750	NFM	Wigston	Young Offender Institution Glen Parva (NX)
460.70000	467.20000	NFM	Portland Dock	HM Prison (Ship), The Weare (KW)
460.70000	467.20000	NFM	Sheerness	HM Prison Elmley (KE)
460.71250	467.21250	NFM	Millom	HM Prison Haverigg (HG)
460.71250	467.21250	NFM	Uttoxeter	HM Prison Dovegate (CA)
460.72500	467.22500	NFM	Doncaster	HM Prison (XD)
460.72500	467.22500	NFM	Hull	HM Prison Wolds (LW)
460.72500	467.22500	NFM	Liverpool	HM Prison Altcourse (AT)
460.72500	467.22500	NFM	Nottingham	HM Prison Lowdham Grange (LG)
460.72500	467.22500	NFM	Redditch	HM Prison Blackenhurst (YD)
460.72500	467.22500	NFM	Rochdale	HM Prison Buckley Hall (BW)
460.72500	467.22500	NFM	Sutton	HM Prison Highdown (HT)
460.72500	467.22500	NFM	Warrington	Young Offender Institution Thorn Cross (BO)
460.73750	467.23750	NFM	Isle of Sheppey	HM Prison Standford Hill (PE)
460.73750	467.23750	NFM	Willoughby	HM Training Prison Rye Hill

460.76875 - 461.23750 MHz   PMR, Airports & Broadcasting

Base	Mobile	Mode	Location	User and Notes
460.78750		NFM	Wolverhampton	Airport Refuel/Crash Operations
460.80000		NFM	London	City Airport Baggage/Apron Ops.
460.98750		NFM	Swansea	Tesco Extra Security
461.05000		NFM	Leicester	Space Centre Security
461.05000		NFM	Humberside	Airport Security
461.15000		NFM	Carlisle	Airport Ops.
461.18750		NFM	Barton	Airfield Security Ch.1
461.18750		NFM	Eastleigh	Airport Tower (Rarely Used)
461.23750	468.52500	NFM	Nationwide	JFMG Short Term Talkback
461.23750		NFM	Manchester	Manchester United Football Club O/B
461.23750		NFM	Nationwide	Goodyear Airship-Sky TV Talkback
461.23750		NFM	Nationwide	Sky Sports TV Camera Direction

461.250 - 461.500 MHz   PMR & Broadcasting

Base	Mobile	Mode	Location	User and Notes
461.25000	468.53750	NFM	Manchester	Sky Sport O/B from Old Trafford
461.25000	468.53750	NFM	Nationwide	JFMG Short Term Talkback
461.26250		NFM	Ayr	Gaiety Theatre
461.26250		NFM	Biggleswade	Old Warden/Shuttleworth Air Museum (118.8)
461.26250		NFM	Glastonbury	B & Q Store
461.26250		NFM	Letchworth	Rail Station Staff (94.8)
461.26250		NFM	Nationwide	Living History Battle Re-Enactments (118.8)
461.26250		NFM	Newcastle	Pizza Hut
461.26250		NFM	Norwich	Brannigans
461.26250		NFM	Norwich	JD Sports
461.26250		NFM	Woodbridge	Farlingaye High School Teachers
461.28750		NFM	Ascot	Racecourse Bookmaker
461.28750		NFM	Ayr	Asda Store Staff/Security
461.28750		NFM	Ayrshire	Motorcycle Instructors
461.28750		NFM	Barrow in Furness	Asda Store Staff/Security (167.9)
461.28750		NFM	Belfast	Boots, Castle Court Shopping Centre
461.28750		NFM	Birmingham	Birmingham City Football Club Car Parks
461.28750		NFM	Bournemouth	Asda Store Staff/Security, Castlepoint Centre
461.28750		NFM	Brighton	Asda Store Staff/Security, Hollingbury
461.28750		NFM	Cardiff	Asda Store Staff/Security
461.28750		NFM	Chadderton	Asda Store Staff/Security
461.28750		NFM	Cheltenham	Racecourse Car Park
461.28750		NFM	Chesterfield	Budge Arkwright Opencast Works
461.28750		NFM	Coventry	Central 6 Retail Park Security
461.28750		NFM	Edinburgh	Asda Store Staff/Security
461.28750		NFM	Edinburgh	Stones Wine Bar
461.28750		NFM	Epsom	Racecourse Staff
461.28750		NFM	Fife	Council
461.28750		NFM	Guernsey	Brock Fireworks
461.28750		NFM	Gt Yarmouth	Asda Store Staff/Security (167.9)
461.28750		NFM	Havant	Asda Store Staff/Security
461.28750		NFM	High Wycombe	Asda Store Staff/Security
461.28750		NFM	Ipswich	Anglia TV News
461.28750		NFM	Ipswich	Chicago Rock Cafe/Club Security
461.28750		NFM	Liverpool	Swan Electrical
461.28750		NFM	London	BBC Worldwide Security, White City Ch.1
461.28750		NFM	London	Brent Council Trading Standards (103.5)
461.28750		NFM	London	Chelsea Football Club Security
461.28750		NFM	London	Earls Court Olympia Ch.10 Stand Fitting
461.28750		NFM	London	European Passenger Services, Waterloo

Base	Mobile	Mode	Location	User and Notes
461.28750		NFM	London	Lords Cricket Ground Catering
461.28750		NFM	London	Motorcycle Training, Stratford
461.28750		NFM	London	Motorcycle Training, White City
461.28750		NFM	London	Walthamstow DSS
461.28750		NFM	Manchester	Asda Store Staff/Security
461.28750		NFM	Manchester	DSS Ch.1 (Manchester & North West) (71.9)
461.28750		NFM	Morecombe	Oggie's Cycles
461.28750		NFM	Nationwide	Asda Store Staff/Security
461.28750		NFM	Nationwide	BT Engineers (186.2)
461.28750		NFM	Nationwide	Used By Government Agencies For Surveillance
461.28750		NFM	Newmarket	Racecourse Bookmaker
461.28750		NFM	Peterborough	Greyhound Track Security
461.28750		NFM	Scotland	St Andrews Medical Services (146.2)
461.28750		NFM	Sheffield	Hallam FM Arena Security
461.28750		NFM	Sittingbourne	Dales Security
461.28750		NFM	Swansea	Cefn Hengoed School and Leisure Centre
461.28750		NFM	Tamworth	Asda Store Staff/Security
461.30000		NFM	Ayrshire	Motorcycle Instructors
461.30000		NFM	Borehamwood	Big Brother (2002) (DCS 431)
461.30000		NFM	Borehamwood	Big Brother (2003) Crew (DCS 431)
461.30000		NFM	Liverpool	Mecca Bingo Security Ch.2
461.30000		NFM	London	Apple Computer Shop, Regent Street
461.31250		NFM	Aldershot	Wellington Shopping Centre Security
461.31250		NFM	Ashford	County Square Shopping Centre Security
461.31250		NFM	Belfast	B&Q Store Staff
461.31250		NFM	Birmingham	Birmingham City Football Club Stewards
461.31250		NFM	Bournemouth	Tesco Supermarket, Littledown
461.31250		NFM	Carlisle	Carlisle College
461.31250		NFM	Coventry	CW Electronics
461.31250		NFM	Coventry	Geest Bananas, Walsgrave
461.31250		NFM	Cranfield	Airfield Fuelling (103.5)
461.31250		NFM	Eastbourne	Magistrates Court
461.31250		NFM	Ellesmere Port	Cheshire Oaks Outlet Village
461.31250		NFM	Elstree	Aerodrome
461.31250		NFM	Elstree	Sainsbury Distribution Transport Ch.4 (203.5)
461.31250		NFM	Falkirk	Howgate Shopping Centre Security
461.31250		NFM	Felixstowe	Spa Pavilion Theatre
461.31250		NFM	Gillingham	Sainsbury Savacentre Managers
461.31250		NFM	Ilford	Golf Course
461.31250		NFM	Ipswich	Chantry High School
461.31250		NFM	Liverpool	Top Shop/Top Man Staff Net
461.31250		NFM	London	Bhs Security, Oxford Street
461.31250		NFM	London	Brent Cross Shopping Centre Security (71.9)
461.31250		NFM	London	Carling Apollo Theatre, Hammersmith
461.31250		NFM	London	Construction Company, Edgware Road
461.31250		NFM	London	Construction Company, Park Royal
461.31250		NFM	London	Engineering Company, West India Docks
461.31250		NFM	London	Gap Store Staff, Marble Arch (203.5)
461.31250		NFM	London	Green Park Staff
461.31250		NFM	London	Hanover Square Security
461.31250		NFM	London	Kensington College
461.31250		NFM	London	Kentish Town Leisure
461.31250		NFM	London	Lewisham Centre Security (71.9)
461.31250		NFM	London	Property Management Co., St James Square
461.31250		NFM	London	Retail Outlet, Plashet Road, Upton Park
461.31250		NFM	London	Rock Circus Staff, London Pavilion (136.5)

Base	Mobile	Mode	Location	User and Notes
461.31250		NFM	London	West London Shooting Ground
461.31250		NFM	London	Whiteley Shopping Centre, Bayswater
461.31250		NFM	Londonderry	Foyle Side Shopping Centre Car Park
461.31250		NFM	Luton	Galaxy Entertainment Centre
461.31250		NFM	Martlesham	BT Laboratory Fire/Security
461.31250		NFM	Newmarket	Racecourse Bookmaker
461.31250		NFM	Oldham	Oldham 6th Form College
461.31250		NFM	Poole	Tesco Supermarket, Tower Leisure Park
461.31250		NFM	Portsmouth	Condor/Commodore Ferries
461.31250		NFM	Sheffield	Hallam FM Arena Security
461.31250		NFM	Southampton	Esso Fawley Oil Refinery
461.31250		NFM	Southport	Beach Patrols (179.9)
461.31250		NFM	Swansea	Alberto Culver Ltd.
461.31250		NFM	Tamworth	TNT Loading Bays
461.31250		NFM	Warwick	Warwick Castle Staff Ch.2
461.31250		NFM	West Thurrock	Tunnel Estate Warehouse Distribution
461.31250		NFM	Wilmslow	Top Shop Staff
461.32500		NFM	Ashington	Wansbeck General Hospital Car Park
461.32500		NFM	Belfast	Seacat
461.32500		NFM	Cardiff	Wilkinson's Store Security
461.32500		NFM	Chatham	World Naval Base Admin Ch.2 (71.9)
461.32500		NFM	Cheltenham	B&Q Store Arle Court (118.8)
461.32500		NFM	Cheltenham	Beechwood Arcade Shopping Centre Security
461.32500		NFM	Chesterfield	Chesterfield College
461.32500		NFM	Craigavon	Meadows Shopping Centre Security (71.9)
461.32500		NFM	Doncaster	DMBC Security
461.32500		NFM	Eastbourne	Langley Shopping Centre Security (250.3)
461.32500		NFM	Falkirk	Howgate Shopping Centre Admin.
461.32500		NFM	Gloucester	Eastgate Shopping Centre Security
461.32500		NFM	Gt Yarmouth	Paper Factory (71.9)
461.32500		NFM	Harwell	UKAEA
461.32500		NFM	Havant	Meridian Shopping Centre Security
461.32500		NFM	Heathrow	Taxi/Car Hire Company
461.32500		NFM	Ipswich	Co-Op, Boss Hall Depot Loaders (127.3)
461.32500		NFM	Ipswich	Port
461.32500		NFM	Ipswich	Shout Nightclub (167.9)
461.32500		NFM	Jersey	General Hospital
461.32500		NFM	Liverpool Airport	Emerald Operations
461.32500		NFM	London	Barbican Theatre Production Comms.
461.32500		NFM	London	Blackwell Cleaning Company
461.32500		NFM	London	Central Middlesex Hospital Security
461.32500		NFM	London	Dickins & Jones, Richmond (82.5)
461.32500		NFM	London	Earls Court Olympia Ch.11 Rigging
461.32500		NFM	London	Groen Cleaning Group, Blackwall
461.32500		NFM	London	Hillingdon Hospital Security
461.32500		NFM	London	Imperial College, South Kensington
461.32500		NFM	London	Kings College Halls of Residence Ch.1 (233.6)
461.32500		NFM	London	London Underground, Angel Road Works
461.32500		NFM	London	Ministry Of Defence, Whitehall
461.32500		NFM	London	Olympia Exhibition Centre Ch.12 Sound
461.32500		NFM	London	Plaza Shopping Centre, Victoria
461.32500		NFM	London	The Football Hall of Fame, Southbank
461.32500		NFM	London	The London Dungeon Staff, SE1 (167.9)
461.32500		NFM	London	Tiffany's Jewellery Store Security, Bond St (225.7)
461.32500		NFM	London	Walton First Scout Camp, Walton on Thames
461.32500		NFM	Newhaven	Stena Sealink Ferries

Base	Mobile	Mode	Location	User and Notes
461.32500		NFM	Nationwide	British Aerospace Security
461.32500		NFM	Oxford	Templers Square Shopping Centre, Cowley
461.32500		NFM	Retford	Halcroft Industrial Estate CCTV
461.32500		NFM	Rochdale	Wheatsheaf Centre
461.32500		NFM	Romford	Marks Gate Sports Ground
461.32500		NFM	Sheffield	Debenhams Department Store Security
461.32500		NFM	Sheffield	Hallam FM Arena Security
461.32500		NFM	Sittingbourne	Kemsley Paper Mill Staff
461.32500		NFM	Southampton	TK Maxx Security (71.9)
461.32500		NFM	Stranraer	Seacat
461.32500		NFM	Stansted	Airport Maintenance
461.32500		NFM	Sunderland	B&Q Store Security
461.32500		NFM	Weymouth	Harry's Nightclub & Bar
461.33750		NFM	Barnstaple	Green Lanes Shopping Centre Security
461.33750		NFM	Barrow In Furness	Furness General Hospital (114.8)
461.33750		NFM	Biggleswade	Jordans Cereals Ch.3
461.33750		NFM	Bricketwood	Coldharbour Plantation Security
461.33750		NFM	Burton upon Trent	Shopping Centre Security
461.33750		NFM	Cardiff	Marks & Spencer, Culverhouse Cross (71.9)
461.33750		NFM	Chatham	Wilkinson's Shop Security
461.33750		NFM	Cheadle	Top Shop Staff
461.33750		NFM	Doncaster	Warner Bros. Cinema
461.33750		NFM	Eastbourne	UGC Cinema
461.33750		NFM	East Molesey	Field Common Construction Co.
461.33750		NFM	Edinburgh	Big W, New Craighall Retail Park
461.33750		NFM	Gillingham	Marks & Spencer
461.33750		NFM	Ipswich	Maidenhall Sports Centre
461.33750		NFM	Ipswich	Marks & Spencer Staff
461.33750		NFM	Ipswich	Northgate Sports Centre
461.33750		NFM	Ipswich	Whitton Sports Centre
461.33750		NFM	Kilmarnock	Galleon Leisure Centre
461.33750		NFM	Liverpool	Docks Fire Crew
461.33750		NFM	London	Covent Garden Hotel
461.33750		NFM	London	Harrow Crown Court
461.33750		NFM	London	London Underground Maintenance Depots (141.3)
461.33750		NFM	London	Top Shop, Oxford Street (146.2)
461.33750		NFM	London	Twickenham Rugby Ground
461.33750		NFM	London	Whipps Cross Hospital, Walthamstow
461.33750		NFM	Luton Airport	Alpha Flight Catering Outlets
461.33750		NFM	Newmilns	Vesuvius Club Office Staff
461.33750		NFM	Poole	Tesco Supermarket, Fleetsbridge
461.33750		NFM	Portsmouth	Ferry Loaders (118.8)
461.33750		NFM	Portsmouth	Homebase, Ocean Park
461.33750		NFM	Sheffield	Hallam FM Arena Security
461.33750		NFM	Southend on Sea	Marks & Spencer (146.2)
461.33750		NFM	Street	Tesco Superstore (107.2)
461.33750		NFM	Torquay	Debenhams Department Store (162.2)
461.33750		NFM	Widnes	Kingsway Leisure Centre
461.35000		NFM	Ashford	Eastwell Manor Hotel
461.35000		NFM	Ayr	Kyle Centre Security
461.35000		NFM	Borehamwood	Elstree Studios
461.35000		NFM	Borehamwood	Tesco Staff/Security (123)
461.35000		NFM	Chatham	World Naval Base Security Ch.4 (173.8)
461.35000		NFM	Coventry	Airport Security (167.9)
461.35000		NFM	Coventry	Wilkinson's Store
461.35000		NFM	Dover	Euroline Coaches Control

Base	Mobile	Mode	Location	User and Notes
461.35000		NFM	Eastbourne	Boots Security (82.5)
461.35000		NFM	Hadleigh	Buyright of Hadleigh
461.35000		NFM	Heathrow	Airline Ops. (186.2)
461.35000		NFM	Ipswich	Ipswich Town Football Club Bar/Catering
461.35000		NFM	Kirkby Mallory	Mallory Park Motor Racing Circuit
461.35000		NFM	Leeds	Kirkgate Market Car Park
461.35000		NFM	Littlehampton	Bodyshop Warehouse Security (131.8)
461.35000		NFM	London	Caesars Nightclub Security, Streatham (151.4)
461.35000		NFM	London	Equinox Nightclub Security, Leicester Square (94.8)
461.35000		NFM	London	Hilton Hotel, Park Lane (162.2)
461.35000		NFM	London	Hurlingham Club
461.35000		NFM	London	Kodak Film Plant, Harrow
461.35000		NFM	London	Merk Sharpe Dohme, Ponders End
461.35000		NFM	London	Twickenham Rugby Ground Maintenance
461.35000		NFM	Romford	Crown Court Security
461.35000		NFM	Sheffield	Williams Brothers Ltd.
461.35000		NFM	Stevenage	ICL Computers Ch.1
461.35000		NFM	Tamworth	Snowdome/Leisure Island Staff
461.36250		NFM	Ashford	Gap Clothes Store Security, Designer Village
461.36250		NFM	Basildon	Jumbo Car Boot Sale
461.36250		NFM	Bletchley	Bletchley Park Trust Staff
461.36250		NFM	Cambridge	Cambridge University Press
461.36250		NFM	Chesterfield	Dema Glass
461.36250		NFM	Colney	Ventura Park Industrial Estate Security
461.36250		NFM	Coventry	B&Q Warehouse
461.36250		NFM	Ipswich	Marks & Spencer Security Ch.2
461.36250		NFM	Liverpool	Marks & Spencer Plain Clothes Store Detectives
461.36250		NFM	London	British Airways Offices, Victoria
461.36250		NFM	London	Fulham Football Club (146.2)
461.36250		NFM	London	Gap Store Security, Marble Arch (103.5/233.6)
461.36250		NFM	London	Harrods Valet Parking Ch.2, Knightsbridge
461.36250		NFM	London	Islington Leisure Centre
461.36250		NFM	London	Keyline Builders Merchants, NW10
461.36250		NFM	London	Queens Ice Rink, Bayswater
461.36250		NFM	London	Servisair/GlobeGround Check-in, City Airport
461.36250		NFM	London	St Georges's Shopping Centre Security, Harrow
461.36250		NFM	London	Top Shop/Top Man, Oxford Street
461.36250		NFM	London	Twickenham Rugby Ground
461.36250		NFM	London	Warner Bros. Cinema, Finchley
461.36250		NFM	Luton Airport	Servisair/GlobeGround
461.36250		NFM	Manchester	Marks & Spencer Plain Clothes Store Detectives
461.36250		NFM	Norwich	Airport Baggage Handlers
461.36250		NFM	Peterborough	Boots, Queensgate Shopping Centre
461.36250		NFM	Peterborough	Chicago Rock Cafe/Club Security (167.9)
461.36250		NFM	Poole	Tesco Supermarket, Branksome
461.36250		NFM	Portadown	High Street Shopping Mall Security (136.5)
461.36250		NFM	Portsmouth	Guildhall Security (118.8)
461.36250		NFM	Southampton	Lowe Security
461.36250		NFM	Stowmarket	Stowmarket Country Farms
461.36250		NFM	Strathclyde	Phase Four Shopping Area, Cumbernauld
461.36250		NFM	Swansea	Morriston Hospital Engineers
461.36250		NFM	Watford	Leisure Centre
461.36250		NFM	Welwyn	Roche Pharmaceuticals Maintenance
461.36250		NFM	Worcester	Crowngate Shopping Centre Security
461.37500		NFM	Ascot	Racecourse Staff.
461.37500		NFM	Basildon	Hospital Car Park Security

Base	Mobile	Mode	Location	User and Notes
461.37500		NFM	Belfast	Virgin Megastore Security
461.37500		NFM	Birmingham	Virgin Megastore Security
461.37500		NFM	Bristol	Virgin Megastore Security, Cribbs Causeway
461.37500		NFM	Carlisle	Virgin Megastore Security
461.37500		NFM	Cheltenham	Racecourse Tic-Tac Men
461.37500		NFM	Chesterfield	Motorcycle Training
461.37500		NFM	Coventry	Virgin Megastore Security
461.37500		NFM	Croydon	Virgin Megastore Security
461.37500		NFM	Dartford	Virgin Megastore Security, Bluewater Centre
461.37500		NFM	Fishguard	Stena Line
461.37500		NFM	Leicester	Virgin Megastore Security
461.37500		NFM	Liverpool	Virgin Megastore Security
461.37500		NFM	London	Construction, O2 Leisure Complex, Finchley (186.2)
461.37500		NFM	London	Limelight Club, Shaftesbury Avenue
461.37500		NFM	London	London Underground (Confined Spaces) (233.6)
461.37500		NFM	London	Scorpion Security (210.7)
461.37500		NFM	London	Showsec Security
461.37500		NFM	London	Sports Cafe, Haymarket (162.2)
461.37500		NFM	London	Twickenham Rugby Ground
461.37500		NFM	London	Virgin Megastore Security, Piccadilly (186.2)
461.37500		NFM	London	Virgin Megastore Security, Harrow
461.37500		NFM	Manchester	Virgin Megastore Security
461.37500		NFM	Nationwide	Abbey Investigations Private Detectives
461.37500		NFM	Nationwide	BT Engineers (186.2)
461.37500		NFM	Nationwide	Gold Link Security (179.9)
461.37500		NFM	Nationwide	Often Used By Government Agencies For Surveillance
461.37500		NFM	Nationwide	Sky TV Engineers
461.37500		NFM	Newcastle	Virgin Megastore Security
461.37500		NFM	Newmarket	Racecourse Bookmaker
461.37500		NFM	Sheffield	Hallam FM Arena Security
461.37500		NFM	Southend on Sea	Virgin Megastore Security
461.37500		NFM	Suffolk	Bickers Films Ch.2
461.37500		NFM	Westcliff	Private Detective Company
461.38750		NFM	Ascot	Racecourse Staff Network Ch.8
461.38750		NFM	Ashford	Middlesex Manor Golf Club
461.38750		NFM	Bury St Edmunds	Council CCTV Link
461.38750		NFM	Cheltenham	General Hospital Catering/Car Parks
461.38750		NFM	Coventry	Midland Lewis Wood Yard
461.38750		NFM	Derby	Alpha Flight Catering, East Midlands Airport
461.38750		NFM	Dover	Seafrance Ferries
461.38750		NFM	Eastbourne	Sovereign Leisure Centre & Swimming Pool
461.38750		NFM	Elstree	Sainsbury Distribution Depot Engineers Ch.3 (241.8)
461.38750		NFM	Hatfield	Brookmans Park Golf Club
461.38750		NFM	Havant	B&Q Store
461.38750		NFM	Heathrow	Holiday Inn Hotel, Heathrow Airport
461.38750		NFM	Ipswich	Hollywood Nightclub
461.38750		NFM	Kent	Wrotham Cement Works
461.38750		NFM	Leeds Airport	Aviance Ground Handling
461.38750		NFM	London	Arnos Grove School
461.38750		NFM	London	Broadway Shopping Centre, Ealing
461.38750		NFM	London	Business Design Centre, Islington (110.9)
461.38750		NFM	London	Eltham School
461.38750		NFM	London	Jones Laing La Salle Ltd HQ, Hannover Square
461.38750		NFM	London	Kingston Upon Thames University
461.38750		NFM	London	Russell Square Hotel
461.38750		NFM	London	St Edward The Confessor Church, Golders Green

Base	Mobile	Mode	Location	User and Notes
461.38750		NFM	London	South Herts. Golf Course, Whetstone
461.38750		NFM	London	Southside Shopping Centre, Wandsworth
461.38750		NFM	London	Tate & Lyle Sugar Refinery, Silvertown
461.38750		NFM	London	The Mail Newspaper Group, Rotherhithe
461.38750		NFM	London	University Of Westminster, Marylebone
461.38750		NFM	London	Versace Couture Security, Bond Street (77)
461.38750		NFM	London	Vyners Secondary School, Hillingdon
461.38750		NFM	Melton	CEL Containers
461.38750		NFM	Newmilns	Vesuvius Club Maintenance Engineers
461.38750		NFM	Oldham	Swimming Stadium
461.38750		NFM	Purfleet	Vopak Oil Terminal (88.5)
461.38750		NFM	Southend on Sea	Debenhams Department Store Security (173.8)
461.38750		NFM	Surrey	Woldingham Garden Village
461.38750		NFM	Thurrock	West Thurrock Oil Depot
461.40000		NFM	Barnet	Chase Farm Hospital
461.40000		NFM	Blackpool	Sandcastle Centre
461.40000		NFM	Bushey	Moor Park Golf Course
461.40000		NFM	Dagenham	Dagenham Town Football Club Stewards
461.40000		NFM	Dover	Norfolk Line
461.40000		NFM	Edinburgh	Kinnaird Park Security
461.40000		NFM	Harwell	UKAEA
461.40000		NFM	Harwich	Scandinavian Seaways Staff
461.40000		NFM	Hitchin	Wilkinson Home & Garden Store Security
461.40000		NFM	Holyhead	Train Maintenance Depot (67)
461.40000		NFM	Ipswich	Co-Op, Boss Hall Depot Management (156.7)
461.40000		NFM	Isle of Man	Emerald Airlines, Ronaldsway Airport
461.40000		NFM	Liverpool	Mecca Bingo Security Ch.3
461.40000		NFM	London	Chelsea Hotel, Sloane Street
461.40000		NFM	London	Dolphin Square Flats, Pimlico
461.40000		NFM	London	Her Majesty's Theatre, Haymarket
461.40000		NFM	London	Holiday Inn Hotel, Brent Cross
461.40000		NFM	London	JD Sports, W1 (131.8)
461.40000		NFM	London	London Palladium Front Of House Staff
461.40000		NFM	London	Miss Selfridge Security, Oxford Street (151.4)
461.40000		NFM	London	Prince of Wales Theatre Staff, Coventry Street
461.40000		NFM	London	Regents Park Hotel
461.40000		NFM	London	Snaresbrook Magistrates Court
461.40000		NFM	London	Theatre Royal Staff, Drury Lane
461.40000		NFM	London	The Edge Cafe, Harrow
461.40000		NFM	London	Top Shop Security, Oxford Street (151.4)
461.40000		NFM	Manchester	Namco Station, Trafford Centre
461.40000		NFM	Oldham	Grange School
461.40000		NFM	Sheffield	Sheffield University
461.40000		NFM	Southend on Sea	Victoria Plaza Security (173.8)
461.40000		NFM	Stevenage	Smiling Sams Casino Staff
461.40000		NFM	Warwick	Warwick Castle Staff Ch.3
461.40000		NFM	Watford	Bushey Hill Hospital
461.40000		NFM	Weybridge	Performance Papers Ltd
461.42500		NFM	Farnborough	Maintenance Contractors For Qinetiq
461.45000		NFM	Ascot	Racecourse
461.45000		NFM	Ashford	Shopwatch
461.45000		NFM	Basildon	Basildon Hospital Car Park Security
461.45000		NFM	Birmingham	Children's Hospital Car Park Security
461.45000		NFM	Chesterfield	Motorcycle Training
461.45000		NFM	Dover	Port of Dover Maintenance

Base	Mobile	Mode	Location	User and Notes
461.45000		NFM	Heathrow	Terminal 4 (203.4)
461.45000		NFM	Ipswich	Anglia TV News
461.45000		NFM	Jersey	CA Mauger Builders
461.45000		NFM	Leicester	D & J Event Caterers (167.9)
461.45000		NFM	Liverpool	Mecca Bingo Security Ch.4
461.45000		NFM	London	Central Parking Systems, Southbank
461.45000		NFM	London	Debenhams Store Security, Oxford Street
461.45000		NFM	London	European Passenger Services, Waterloo
461.45000		NFM	London	George Wimpey Plc, Hammersmith
461.45000		NFM	London	Laing Construction, Cannon Street
461.45000		NFM	London	London Underground Lift/Escalator Maintenance
461.45000		NFM	London	Royal Court Theatre Staff, Sloane Square
461.45000		NFM	London	Sainsbury Security, O2 Centre Finchley (186.2)
461.45000		NFM	London	Twickenham Rugby Ground
461.45000		NFM	London	UCI Cinema Staff, Piccadilly
461.45000		NFM	London	UCI Cinema Staff, Whitley Shopping Centre
461.45000		NFM	Nationwide	Ordnance Survey Teams
461.45000		NFM	Nationwide	Scouts Association Ch.3
461.45000		NFM	Newmarket	Racecourse Bookmaker
461.45000		NFM	Poole	UCI Cinema Staff, Tower Park Leisure Centre
461.45000		NFM	SE UK	ADT Alarm Engineers
461.45000		NFM	Southsea	Beach Rescue (88.5)
461.45000		NFM	Tamworth	UCI Cinema Staff
461.46250		NFM	Ascot	Racecourse Network Ch.5
461.46250		NFM	Barrow in Furness	Furness General Hospital (103.5)
461.46250		NFM	Barton	Barton Airfield Fire/Crash Ch.2
461.46250		NFM	Blandford Forum	Countrywise
461.46250		NFM	Brands Hatch	Car Parking (218.1)
461.46250		NFM	Cardiff	Millennium Stadium Security/Maintenance (131.8)
461.46250		NFM	Carlisle	Gap Fashion Store
461.46250		NFM	Chelmsford	Meadows Shopping Centre Security
461.46250		NFM	Cheltenham	Racecourse Car Parks (218.1)
461.46250		NFM	Chesterfield	Acorn Vehicle Hire
461.46250		NFM	Coventry	Pool Meadow Bus Depot
461.46250		NFM	Coventry	Hilton Hotel, Walsgrave Triangle
461.46250		NFM	Dagenham	Rhone Poulenc Chemicals Security
461.46250		NFM	Dartford	Bluewater Shopping Centre
461.46250		NFM	Duxford	Imperial War Museum Events (192.8)
461.46250		NFM	Duxford	Imperial War Museum Security/Emergency (103.4)
461.46250		NFM	Hatfield	Hatfield Business Park
461.46250		NFM	Heathrow	Sterling Hotel, Heathrow Airport
461.46250		NFM	Hull	Princes Quay Shopping Centre Security
461.46250		NFM	Ipswich	Marks & Spencer Security
461.46250		NFM	Ipswich	Regent Theatre Seating/Staff (94.8)
461.46250		NFM	Liverpool	Top Shop/Top Man
461.46250		NFM	London	Barnet Football Club
461.46250		NFM	London	Fortnum & Masons Security, Piccadilly (151.4)
461.46250		NFM	London	Ham House, Ham
461.46250		NFM	London	Hawker Siddeley Power Transformers, Walthamstow
461.46250		NFM	London	Inner Temple Security
461.46250		NFM	London	Law Courts, Aldwych
461.46250		NFM	London	Lewisham College
461.46250		NFM	London	London Borough of Newham Council
461.46250		NFM	London	National Advisory Council for Education & Training
461.46250		NFM	London	National Audit Commission, Buckingham Palace Road
461.46250		NFM	London	Red Bull Company Ltd., Hanover Square

Base	Mobile	Mode	Location	User and Notes
461.46250		NFM	London	Sutton Hospital, Belmont
461.46250		NFM	London	Top Shop Staff/Security, Oxford Circus (67)
461.46250		NFM	Londonderry	Marks & Spencer Security
461.46250		NFM	Nationwide	DSS Fraud Teams
461.46250		NFM	Sheffield	Crucible Theatre Staff
461.46250		NFM	Silverstone	Silverstone Race Track
461.46250		NFM	Southampton	Docks Security (151.4)
461.46250		NFM	St Helens	Marks & Spencer Security
461.46250		NFM	Stockport	Top Shop Security
461.46250		NFM	Weymouth	Lodmoor Country Park
461.46250		NFM	Windsor	Royal Station Shopping Mall Staff/Cleaners (88.5)
461.46250		NFM	Woodbridge	Farlingaye High School Caretakers (173.8)
461.46250		NFM	Worcester	Lychgate Shopping Centre
461.46250		NFM	Yorkshire	North Yorkshire Moors Railway

461.500 - 462.500 MHz — PMR (Should be Duplex but often Simplex)

Base	Mobile	Mode	Location	User and Notes
461.50000		NFM	Lancaster	St Nicholas Arcade Security Ch.2
461.50000		NFM	Nationwide	Securicor Radio Alarms
461.50000		NFM	Rochdale	Indoor Market
461.50000		NFM	Southend on Sea	Wilkinson's Store Security
461.51250		NFM	Borehamwood	Big Brother (2002) Production
461.51250		NFM	Borehamwood	Big Brother (2003) Production (DCS 412)
461.83750		NFM	Borehamwood	Big Brother (2002) Production (DCS 413)
461.83750		NFM	Borehamwood	Big Brother (2003) Production (DCS 413)
461.85000		NFM	London	Olympia Ch.6 general
461.85000		NFM	Sizewell	Power Station
461.87500		NFM	Essex	DSS Fraud Teams (71.9)
461.87500		NFM	Felixstowe	HM Revenue & Customs
461.87500		NFM	London	DSS Fraud Teams
461.87500		NFM	Lowestoft	HM Revenue & Customs
461.87500		NFM	Nottingham	DSS Fraud Teams
461.87500		NFM	Sheffield	DSS Fraud Teams
461.87500		NFM	S Wales	HM Revenue & Customs Surveillance (94.8)
461.87500		NFM	York	DSS Fraud Teams
461.88750		NFM	Bristol	Premier Travel Inn Staff
461.88750		NFM	Cardiff	Millennium Stadium Hospitality (171)
461.88750		NFM	Cardiff Bay	Mermaid Quay Shops/Restaurants (94.8)
461.88750		NFM	Chichester	Chichester Gate Leisure Park (79.7)
461.88750		NFM	Coventry	Britannia Hotel
461.88750		NFM	Duxford	Imperial War Museum Duxford Events (131.8)
461.88750		NFM	Hitchin	The Loft Night Club Security
461.88750		NFM	Hull	North Sea Ferries Cabin Crews
461.88750		NFM	Ipswich	Chicago Rock Cafe/Club Staff
461.88750		NFM	London	Apollo Theatre Stage Production, Victoria (192.8)
461.88750		NFM	London	Aura Nightclub 48-49 St James Street SW1
461.88750		NFM	London	Cafe de Paris, Coventry Street
461.88750		NFM	London	Fulham Football Club Staff/Admin.
461.88750		NFM	London	Funland, Trocadero Centre, Piccadilly (127.3)
461.88750		NFM	London	Greater London Authority Heritage Wardens (162.2)
461.88750		NFM	London	Greater London Authority Offices Security (67)
461.88750		NFM	London	Gucci Fashion Store Security, Old Bond Street
461.88750		NFM	London	Marks & Spencer, Oxford Street
461.88750		NFM	London	The Queens Theatre Staff, Shaftesbury Ave
461.88750		NFM	Nationwide	British Motorcycle Federation Events (173.8)
461.88750		NFM	Northampton	Santa Pod Raceway Ch.4 (103.5)
461.88750		NFM	Portsmouth	Argos Superstore Staff/Security

Base	Mobile	Mode	Location	User and Notes
461.88750		NFM	Portsmouth	Woolworths Staff
461.88750		NFM	Rugby	Christian Salvesen Ch.6
461.88750		NFM	Sheffield	HMV Store
461.88750		NFM	Silverstone	Silverstone Driving School
461.90000		NFM	Essex	DSS Fraud Teams (MASC in clear)
461.90000		NFM	Felixstowe	HM Revenue & Customs
461.90000		NFM	London	HM Revenue & Customs/DSS (MASC in clear)
461.90000		NFM	Lowestoft	HM Revenue & Customs
461.90000		NFM	M1	HM Revenue & Customs Surveillance
461.90000		NFM	Nationwide	HM Revenue & Customs Covert Repeater
461.90000		NFM	Nationwide	HM Revenue & Customs Surveillance
461.91250		NFM	Chesterfield	DSS Fraud Teams (MASC in clear)
461.91250		NFM	Felixstowe	HM Revenue & Customs
461.91250		NFM	London	DSS Ch.2
461.91250		NFM	Lowestoft	HM Revenue & Customs
461.91250		NFM	Manchester	DSS Ch.2
461.96250		NFM	Borehamwood	Big Brother (2002) Production (DCS 423)
461.96250		NFM	Borehamwood	Big Brother (2003) Production (DCS 423)
461.97500		NFM	Heathrow	Hertz Courtesy Bus
462.00000		NFM	Doncaster	Tesco Supermarket
462.00000		NFM	Dungeness	Power Station
462.00000		NFM	Elstree	Sainsbury Distribution Depot Security (82.5)
462.00000		NFM	Nationwide	Sainsbury Supermarkets National Allocation
462.02500		NFM	Bradford	Arndale Shopping Centre Security
462.02500		NFM	Dover	P & O Ferries CH.10
462.02500		NFM	Dublin	Airport, Rianta Ramp Ops.
462.02500		NFM	Salisbury	Arrow Crane Hire
462.05000		NFM	Aldershot	Tesco Store
462.05000		NFM	Ascot	Racecourse Bookmaker
462.05000		NFM	Aylesbury	Tesco Store, Broadfields Retail Park
462.05000		NFM	Baldock	Tesco Superstore
462.05000		NFM	Bridlington	Tesco Superstore
462.05000		NFM	Cambridge	Tesco Superstore
462.05000		NFM	Cardiff	Tesco, Western Avenue
462.05000		NFM	Coventry	WH Smith Ch.2
462.05000		NFM	Dorchester	Tesco Store
462.05000		NFM	Gillingham	Tesco Store
462.05000		NFM	Llanelli	Tesco Superstore
462.05000		NFM	London	Mercury Asset Management Ch.2, City of London
462.05000		NFM	London	Next Shop, Oxford Street
462.05000		NFM	London	Tesco Store, Oxford Street
462.05000		NFM	London	Tesco Superstore, Surrey Quays
462.05000		NFM	London	Tower Thistle Hotel, St Katherine's Dock
462.05000		NFM	London	WH Smith, Brent Cross Shopping Centre
462.05000		NFM	London	WH Smith, Kings Cross Station (107.2)
462.05000		NFM	London	WH Smith, Victoria Station
462.05000		NFM	London	WH Smith, Waterloo Station
462.05000		NFM	Lowestoft	Tesco Store
462.05000		NFM	Middleton	Mall Security
462.05000		NFM	Milton Keynes	WH Smith
462.05000		NFM	Nationwide	Tesco (Used By Nearly All Stores)
462.05000		NFM	Nationwide	WH Smith (Used By Nearly All Stores)
462.05000		NFM	Newmarket	Racecourse Bookmaker
462.05000		NFM	Norwich	Tesco Store
462.05000		NFM	Penarth	Tesco Store
462.05000		NFM	Pitsea	Tesco Superstore

Base	Mobile	Mode	Location	User and Notes
462.05000		NFM	Reading	Tesco Store
462.05000		NFM	Redbridge	WH Smith
462.05000		NFM	Rochester	Furniture Shop
462.05000		NFM	Sheerness	Tesco Superstore
462.05000		NFM	St Andrews	Tesco Store
462.05000		NFM	Stevenage	Tesco Store
462.05000		NFM	Stirling	Stirling Castle Security
462.05000		NFM	Suffolk	Tesco Superstore
462.05000		NFM	Swansea	Tesco Store, Parc Fforestfach (179.9)
462.05000		NFM	Weymouth	Tesco Superstore
462.05000		NFM	Winchester	Tesco Store
462.07500		NFM	Coventry	Cathedral Lanes Shopping Centre Security (123)
462.07500		NFM	Felixstowe	Docks
462.07500		NFM	London	St James Park (156.7)
462.07500		NFM	London	Woolwich Arsenal Explosives Museum
462.07500		NFM	Luton Airport	Reed Aviation
462.07500		NFM	Sizewell	Power Station Management Ch.18
462.07500		NFM	Stevenage	Stevenage Football Club Stewards
462.10000		NFM	Basildon	Sainsbury Savacentre Security
462.10000		NFM	Brentwood	Sainsbury Savacentre Security
462.10000		NFM	Gillingham	Sainsbury Savacentre Security
462.10000		NFM	Havant	Havant Rail Station Staff
462.10000		NFM	Leicester	Shopwatch
462.10000		NFM	Liverpool	Haydock Racecourse
462.10000		NFM	London	British Library Secondary Channel, NW1
462.10000		NFM	London	Littlewoods Security, Oxford Street
462.10000		NFM	London	New Covent Garden Market, Nine Elms
462.10000		NFM	London	Sainsbury Savacentre Security, Merton
462.10000		NFM	London	Tower of London
462.10000		NFM	London	Treaty Centre Security, Hounslow (210.7)
462.10000		NFM	Maidstone	Littlewoods Security
462.10000		NFM	Manchester	Littlewoods Security
462.10000		NFM	Nationwide	Sabrewatch Security
462.12500		NFM	Dover	P & O Ferries Ch.7
462.12500		NFM	London	Engineering Works, North Greenwich
462.12500		NFM	London	Liberty Store Staff/Security, Regent Street
462.12500		NFM	London	Network Rail Retail Distribution Depot, Stratford
462.12500		NFM	London	News International Security, Wapping
462.12500		NFM	London	White Arrow Express Couriers, Wembley
462.12500		NFM	Portsmouth	P & O Ferries (151.4)
462.12500		NFM	Sittingbourne	Kemsley Paper Mill
462.12500		NFM	Stevenage	Gordon Craig Leisure Centre (141.3)
462.12500		NFM	Tilbury	Docks
462.12500		NFM	Warrington	Ineos Glass Plant (82.5)
462.15000		NFM	Oxford	John Radcliffe Hospital Security
462.15000		NFM	Sheffield	Meadowhall Shopping Centre Security
462.17500		NFM	Felixstowe	Docks
462.17500		NFM	Immingham	Docks
462.17500		NFM	Kings Lynn	Campbells Produce
462.17500		NFM	Kirkby Mallory	Mallory Park Motor Racing Circuit
462.17500		NFM	London	British Library, St Pancras
462.17500		NFM	London	City Airport Ramp Ops. (225.7)
462.17500		NFM	London	Earls Court Ch.5 Beeton Rumford
462.17500		NFM	Silverstone	Race Track Security
462.17500		NFM	Woburn	Wildlife Park
462.20000		NFM	Basildon	Eastgate Shopping Centre

Base	Mobile	Mode	Location	User and Notes
462.20000		NFM	Dover	P & O Ferries
462.20000		NFM	East Anglia	Hostess Outside Caterers
462.20000		NFM	Felixstowe	Docks
462.20000		NFM	Nationwide	John Sisk & Son Construction Ch.2
462.20000		NFM	Spelthorne	Council Car Parks Ch.1
462.20000		NFM	Thurrock	Lakeside Shopping Centre Car Parks
462.22500		NFM	Belfast	Zoo
462.22500		NFM	Bury	Marks & Spencer Sabrewatch Security
462.22500		NFM	Dover	P & O Ferries Ch.8
462.22500		NFM	Felixstowe	Docks
462.22500		NFM	Hull	Docks
462.22500		NFM	Leeds	Shopwatch
462.22500		NFM	London	National Army Museum Security, Chelsea (77)
462.22500		NFM	London	National Physical Laboratory, Teddington
462.22500		NFM	London	Newham General Hospital
462.22500		NFM	London	St George's Hospital, Tooting
462.22500		NFM	Manchester	Marks & Spencer Sabrewatch Security
462.22500		NFM	Strathclyde	Phase One Shopping Centre, Cumbernauld
462.22500		NFM	Ramsgate	Dock Loading
462.22500		NFM	Swindon	The Gap Store Factory Retail Outlet
462.22500		NFM	Tyne & Wear	Tyne Yard Ch.3
462.25000		NFM	Altrincham	Littlewoods Sabrewatch Security
462.25000		NFM	Barrow in Furness	VSEL Nuclear Incident Channel
462.25000		NFM	Basildon	Bhs Security
462.25000		NFM	Bexleyheath	Shopping Centre security
462.25000		NFM	Bournemouth	Marks & Spencer Sabrewatch Security
462.25000		NFM	Bristol	Marks & Spencer Sabrewatch Security
462.25000		NFM	Coventry	Marks & Spencer Sabrewatch Security
462.25000		NFM	Doncaster	Marks & Spencer Sabrewatch Security
462.25000		NFM	Eastbourne	Marks & Spencer Sabrewatch Security (107.2)
462.25000		NFM	Hove	Marks & Spencer Sabrewatch Security, Holmbush Centre
462.25000		NFM	Hull	House of Fraser, Hammonds (71.9)
462.25000		NFM	Ipswich	Littlewoods Security, Tower Ramparts
462.25000		NFM	Kirkby	Gala Bingo Security Ch.1
462.25000		NFM	Kirkcaldy	Marks & Spencer Sabrewatch Security
462.25000		NFM	Leeds	Marks & Spencer Sabrewatch Security
462.25000		NFM	Liverpool	Marks & Spencer Sabrewatch Security
462.25000		NFM	London	DH Evans Staff/Security, Oxford Street
462.25000		NFM	London	Marks & Spencer Sabrewatch Security, Brent Cross
462.25000		NFM	London	Marks & Spencer Sabrewatch Security, Islington (71.9)
462.25000		NFM	London	Marks & Spencer Sabrewatch Security, Kensington (71.9)
462.25000		NFM	London	Marks & Spencer Sabrewatch Security, Kings Road (71.9)
462.25000		NFM	London	Marks & Spencer Sabrewatch Security, Marble Arch
462.25000		NFM	Londonderry	Marks & Spencer Sabrewatch Security
462.25000		NFM	Nationwide	Marks & Spencer Sabrewatch Security (Almost All Stores)
462.25000		NFM	Peterborough	Marks & Spencer Sabrewatch Security
462.25000		NFM	Poole	Marks & Spencer Sabrewatch Security
462.25000		NFM	Rochdale	Marks & Spencer Sabrewatch Security
462.25000		NFM	Southampton	Marks & Spencer Sabrewatch Security
462.25000		NFM	Southend on Sea	Marks & Spencer Sabrewatch Security (71.9)
462.25000		NFM	St Albans	Marks & Spencer Sabrewatch Security (71.9)
462.25000		NFM	St Helens	Marks & Spencer Sabrewatch Security
462.25000		NFM	Staines	Marks & Spencer Sabrewatch Security
462.25000		NFM	Stevenage	Marks & Spencer Sabrewatch Security
462.25000		NFM	Thurrock	Marks & Spencer Sabrewatch Security, Lakeside Centre
462.25000		NFM	Weymouth	Marks & Spencer Sabrewatch Security

Base	Mobile	Mode	Location	User and Notes
462.26250		NFM	Morecambe	Morecambe Football Club, Christie Park
462.27500		NFM	Aberdeen	BP, Dyce Airport
462.27500		NFM	Belfast	Royal Victoria Hospital Porters
462.27500		NFM	Bexleyheath	Shopping Centre Security
462.27500		NFM	Blackpool	Pleasure Beach Patrols
462.27500		NFM	Dartford	Europort Loaders (123)
462.27500		NFM	Hull	Docks
462.27500		NFM	Ipswich	Docks, Roll On Roll Off (67)
462.27500		NFM	Leeds	St Aidans Opencast Coal Mine
462.27500		NFM	Manchester	Manchester Royal Hospital
462.27500		NFM	Nationwide	John Sisk & Son Construction
462.27500		NFM	Portsmouth	P & O Ferries On-Board Ch.3 (151.4)
462.27500		NFM	Southend on Sea	Gap Clothes Store (141.3)
462.30000		NFM	Blackpool	Shopwatch, Town Centre Stores
462.30000		NFM	Carlisle	House of Fraser, Binns (71.9)
462.30000		NFM	Denham	Denham Media Park Security
462.30000		NFM	Edinburgh	Gap Clothes Store, Kinnaird Park
462.30000		NFM	Guildford	House of Fraser, Army & Navy Store
462.30000		NFM	Leeds	House of Fraser, Rackhams (71.9)
462.30000		NFM	London	Gap Clothes Store, Whitely Centre, Bayswater
462.30000		NFM	Manchester	Dorothy Perkins Staff
462.30000		NFM	Windsor	Windsor & Eton Riverhead Station Staff.
462.32500		NFM	Brighton	Sussex University
462.32500		NFM	Coventry	Warwick University
462.32500		NFM	Edinburgh	Edinburgh University
462.32500		NFM	Glasgow	House of Fraser, Arnotts (173,8)
462.32500		NFM	Guildford	Surrey University Security
462.32500		NFM	Ipswich	Port Authority Ch.4
462.32500		NFM	Liverpool	Gala Bingo Security Ch.2, Kirkby
462.32500		NFM	London	St Georges's Shopping Centre Security, Harrow
462.32500		NFM	Sheerness	Docks
462.35000		NFM	Hull	Docks
462.35000		NFM	Tilbury	Docks
462.36250		NFM	Ascot	Racecourse Network
462.36250		NFM	Ayr	Racecourse Officials
462.36250		NFM	Borehamwood	Big Brother (2002), Olympus Security (!03.5)
462.36250		NFM	Borehamwood	Big Brother (2003), Olympus Security (!03.5)
462.36250		NFM	Bournemouth	Marks & Spencer Staff
462.36250		NFM	Brighton	Police Fingerprint Bureau, Sussex House
462.36250		NFM	Bristol	Pinkerton Security
462.36250		NFM	Bristol	Clarks Shoes
462.36250		NFM	Cardiff	Council Crowd Control/Safestyle Security (123)
462.36250		NFM	Cardiff	Millennium Plaza Security
462.36250		NFM	Dartford	Bluewater Shopping Centre
462.36250		NFM	Dorset	Council Highways Department
462.36250		NFM	Duxford	Imperial War Museum Events Net (131.8)
462.36250		NFM	Edinburgh	Debenhams Store Staff
462.36250		NFM	Gateshead	Next Store, Metro Centre
462.36250		NFM	Gt Yarmouth	Go Karting Circuit
462.36250		NFM	Iver	Pinewood Studios
462.36250		NFM	Kirkby	Gala Bingo Security Ch.3
462.36250		NFM	Letchworth	Superkarts Go Kart Track (94.8)
462.36250		NFM	Liverpool	JD Sports
462.36200		NFM	London	Benetton, Oxford Street
462.36250		NFM	London	BP Headquarters, City of London
462.36250		NFM	London	Cafe de Paris, Coventry Street

Base	Mobile	Mode	Location	User and Notes
462.36250		NFM	London	Cinema, Coventry Street
462.36250		NFM	London	Dolcis Shoes, Oxford Street
462.36250		NFM	London	Fulham Football Club Staff/Admin (218.1)
462.36250		NFM	London	Funland Amusements, Trocadero Centre (127.3)
462.36250		NFM	London	Gap Clothes Store, Oxford Street
462.36250		NFM	London	Greys Advertising
462.36250		NFM	London	Grosvenor Hotel Security, Park Lane
462.36250		NFM	London	Kings College Halls of Residence Ch.2 (186.2)
462.36250		NFM	London	London Eye
462.36250		NFM	London	Mallinson TV Productions
462.36250		NFM	London	Marks & Spencer Food Hall Staff, Queensway (103.5)
462.36250		NFM	London	Mitzushoki Japanese Store Security Ch.8 (71.9)
462.36250		NFM	London	Oval Cricket Ground Catering, Kennington
462.36250		NFM	London	Planet Hollywood Staff, Coventry Street
462.36250		NFM	London	Plaza Centre Security, Oxford Street (173.8)
462.36250		NFM	London	Rock Garden Club/Restaurant, WC2
462.36250		NFM	London	Shaw Park Plaza Hotel, NW1 (141.3)
462.36250		NFM	London	Twickenham Rugby Ground Security (103.5)
462.36250		NFM	London	Warner Bros Store, Regent Street
462.36250		NFM	London	Woolworths Staff/Security, Brixton
462.36250		NFM	Milton Keynes	Dolcis Shoes
462.36250		NFM	Newcastle	USC Clothes Store, Eldon Gardens (141.3)
462.36250		NFM	Nationwide	British Motorcycle Federation Events (173.8)
462.36250		NFM	Nationwide	Olympus Events Security (103.5)
462.36250		NFM	Nationwide	Pearson TV Production, The Bill
462.36250		NFM	Nationwide	Rock Steady Event Safety Ch.1
462.36250		NFM	Northampton	Santa Pod Race Way Ch.1 (103.5)
462.36250		NFM	Peterborough	Dolcis Shoes, Queensgate Centre
462.36250		NFM	Prestwick	Centrum Arena Stewards (Centrum)
462.36250		NFM	Rugby	Christian Salvesen Ch.2
462.36250		NFM	Silverstone	Racing Circuit Maintenance
462.36250		NFM	St Helens	Rugby League Coaches
462.36250		NFM	Staines	Railway Station Staff
462.37500		NFM	Basildon	Boots Security
462.37500		NFM	Belfast	Boots Security, Donegal Place
462.37500		NFM	Bournemouth	Castlepoint Shopping Centre Security (114.8)
462.37500		NFM	Brighton	Racetech Winning Post Camera Set Up (131.8)
462.37500		NFM	Doncaster	Car Park Security
462.37500		NFM	Glasgow	St. Enoch Shopping Centre
462.37500		NFM	London	Barbican Centre Staff
462.37500		NFM	London	Dolce & Gabbana Security, Bond Street (167.9)
462.37500		NFM	London	Gloucester Hotel, Earls Court
462.37500		NFM	London	Gucci Security, Old Bond Street (167.9)
462.37500		NFM	London	Gucci Security, Sloane Street
462.37500		NFM	London	Tommy Hilfiger Security, Knightsbridge
462.37500		NFM	London	Versace Couture Security, Bond Street
462.37500		NFM	Nationwide	Racetech Winning Post Camera Set Up (131.8)
462.37500		NFM	Newmarket	Racecourse Bookmaker
462.37500		NFM	Peterborough	Boots Security
462.37500		NFM	Southend on Sea	Boots Security Ch.1
462.40000		NFM	Ascot	Racecourse Bookmaker
462.40000		NFM	Borehamwood	Council Services
462.40000		NFM	Cardiff Airport	Servisair/GlobeGround
462.40000		NFM	Chelmsford	High Chelmer Shopping Centre Security
462.40000		NFM	Ipswich	St Clements Mental Hospital Security (67)
462.40000		NFM	London	Container Terminal, Stratford

Base	Mobile	Mode	Location	User and Notes
462.40000		NFM	London	Corporation of London, City of London (82.5)
462.40000		NFM	London	Tower Hill Security, City of London
462.40000		NFM	London	Brook General Hospital, Greenwich
462.40000		NFM	London	World Trade Centre Security, Wapping
462.40000		NFM	Newport, Gwent	Celtic Manor Resort Concierge Department
462.40000		NFM	Poole	Megabowl, Tower Park
462.40000		NFM	Portsmouth	P & O Ferries On-Board (151.4)
462.40000		NFM	Stevenage	North Herts College Staff/Security (177.3)
462.40000		NFM	Wigan	Mall Shopping Centre Security
462.41250		NFM	Ascot	Racecourse Bookmaker
462.41250		NFM	Cheltenham	Racecourse Bookmaker
462.41250		NFM	Newmarket	Racecourse Bookmaker
462.42500		NFM	Ascot	Racecourse Network
462.42500		NFM	Birmingham	Barratts Shoes Staff
462.42500		NFM	Birmingham	Virgin Intercity Staff/Porters
462.42500		NFM	Borehamwood	Big Brother (2002) Production (DCS 445)
462.42500		NFM	Borehamwood	Big Brother (2003) Production (DCS 445)
462.42500		NFM	Brands Hatch	Race Stewards
462.42500		NFM	Bristol	Zoo
462.42500		NFM	Cardiff	Brewery Quarter Staff/Security (141.3)
462.42500		NFM	Coventry	Cathedral Staff
462.42500		NFM	Dartford	John Lewis Maintenance, Bluewater Centre (233.6)
462.42500		NFM	Epsom	Ashley Shopping Centre
462.42500		NFM	Gillingham	Motorcycle Training
462.42500		NFM	Hull	Docks
462.42500		NFM	Iver	Pinewood Studios
462.42500		NFM	Ipswich	Nighthawk Security
462.42500		NFM	Kent	County Showground Ch.4
462.42500		NFM	Leeds	Lilywhites Security, Headrow Centre
462.42500		NFM	Liverpool	Bhs Security
462.42500		NFM	London	Ashley Shopping Centre, Epsom
462.42500		NFM	London	BP Headquarters, City of London
462.42500		NFM	London	Browns Club, Covent Garden
462.42500		NFM	London	Funland Amusements, Trocadero Centre (127.3)
462.42500		NFM	London	Gap Clothes Store, Marble Arch (77)
462.42500		NFM	London	Her Majesty's Theatre Backstage
462.42500		NFM	London	JJB Sports, Oxford Street
462.42500		NFM	London	Lea Valley Leisure Centre, Edmonton
462.42500		NFM	London	Lyceum Theatre Staff, Wellington Street
462.42500		NFM	London	Marks & Spencer, Oxford Street
462.42500		NFM	London	Mitzushoki Japanese Store Security Ch.1 (82.5)
462.42500		NFM	London	N1 Shopping Centre Security, Islington
462.42500		NFM	London	National Theatre Museum, Covent Garden (192.8)
462.42500		NFM	London	Oval Cricket Ground, Kennington
462.42500		NFM	London	O'Henry's Bar Security, Finchley Road (123)
462.42500		NFM	London	Plaza Shopping Centre Cleaners, Oxford Street
462.42500		NFM	London	RADA Security, Piccadilly
462.42500		NFM	London	Royal Festival Hall Catering, Southbank
462.42500		NFM	London	Sandersons Hotel Security, Berners Street
462.42500		NFM	London	Virgin Megastore, Tottenham Court Road (94.8)
462.42500		NFM	Newcastle	HMV Records
462.42500		NFM	Newmarket	Racecourse Bookmaker
462.42500		NFM	Poole	Marks & Spencer
462.42500		NFM	Reading	House of Fraser Security, Oracle Centre
462.42500		NFM	Sheffield	Hallam FM Arena Security
462.42500		NFM	Staines	Warner Village Cinemas, Two Rivers (110.9)

Base	Mobile	Mode	Location	User and Notes
462.42500		NFM	Stansted	Airport Ops
462.42500		NFM	Southend on Sea	Victoria Circus Shopping Precinct Security
462.47500		NFM	Ascot	Racecourse Network Ch.7
462.47500		NFM	Ashford	Shopwatch
462.47500		NFM	Belfast	Nutts Corner Market Management
462.47500		NFM	Belfast	Woolworths Security
462.47500		NFM	Belfast	Yorkgate Shopping Centre Security
462.47500		NFM	Birmingham	Fort Retail Park Car Park Security (103.5)
462.47500		NFM	Borehamwood	Big Brother (2003) Production (DCS 723)
462.47500		NFM	Brands Hatch	Stewards
462.47500		NFM	Canvey Island	Waterside Farm Sports Centre
462.47500		NFM	Cardiff	Millennium Plaza (71.9)
462.47500		NFM	Cardiff	Millennium Stadium Events
462.47500		NFM	Chichester	Bhs Store Security Ch.1 (88.5)
462.47500		NFM	Dagenham	Shopwatch
462.47500		NFM	Dartford	Bhs Store Security/Staff, Lakeside Centre (141.3)
462.47500		NFM	Duxford	Imperial War Museum Events Net (131.8)
462.47500		NFM	Eastbourne	Marks & Spencer (225.7)
462.47500		NFM	Edinburgh	Bhs Store Security, Princes Street
462.47500		NFM	Gillingham	Carlton Motorcycle Training
462.47500		NFM	Gt. Yarmouth	Birds Eye Cold Storage
462.47500		NFM	Ipswich	Distinction Nightclub
462.47500		NFM	Iver	Pinewood Studios
462.47500		NFM	Kent	County Show Ground Ch.5
462.47500		NFM	Liverpool	Bhs Store Security
462.47500		NFM	London	Arsenal Football Club Box Office
462.47500		NFM	London	Bhs Security, Oxford Street
462.47500		NFM	London	BP Gas HQ Office Security, EC Ch.2
462.47500		NFM	London	Camden Lock Market Security
462.47500		NFM	London	Channel One TV Production Company Staff
462.47500		NFM	London	Debenhams Restaurant Staff, Oxford Street
462.47500		NFM	London	Funland Amusements, Trocadero Centre (127.3)
462.47500		NFM	London	Gap Clothes Store, Oxford Street
462.47500		NFM	London	Greater London Authority Heritage Wardens (203.5)
462.47500		NFM	London	Kings College Halls of Residence Security (233.1)
462.47500		NFM	London	Lea Valley Leisure Centre Security (218.1)
462.47500		NFM	London	Marks & Spencer Security, Oxford Street
462.47500		NFM	London	Moon Under Water Pub, Leicester Square
462.47500		NFM	London	Sogo Japanese Department Store, Piccadilly
462.47500		NFM	London	Sound Republic Staff, Leicester Square (74)
462.47500		NFM	London	Sports Division Shoes, Oxford Street (103.5)
462.47500		NFM	London	Tower Records, Piccadilly (131.8)
462.47500		NFM	London	Venture Security
462.47500		NFM	Nationwide	Bhs Stores Security Ch.1
462.47500		NFM	Nationwide	Chubb Fire
462.47500		NFM	Newcastle	HMV Records Security (103.5)
462.47500		NFM	Newmarket	Racecourse Bookmaker
462.47500		NFM	Northampton	Santa Pod Race Way Ch.2 (103.5)
462.47500		NFM	Norwich	Anglia TV Studio Security (Securicor) (162.2)
462.47500		NFM	Peterborough	The Solstice Broadways Club
462.47500		NFM	Poole	Flight Refuelling
462.47500		NFM	Poole	Marks & Spencer Food Hall Staff
462.47500		NFM	Portland	Queens Harbourmaster
462.47500		NFM	Rugby	Christian Salvesen Ch.8
462.47500		NFM	Sudbury	Dragon Boat Racing Rescue/Marshals

Base	Mobile	Mode	Location	User and Notes
462.48750		NFM	Ascot	Racecourse Bookmaker
462.48750		NFM	Barking	Shopwatch
462.48750		NFM	Belfast	Royal Victoria Hospital Security
462.48750		NFM	Birmingham	Sports Division Shoe Store
462.48750		NFM	Brighton	Asda Supermarket, Brighton Marina
462.48750		NFM	Cardiff	Barry Island Staff/Security
462.48750		NFM	Cardiff	Cardiff City Football Club Security (123)
462.48750		NFM	Cardiff	Millennium Stadium Security (123)
462.48750		NFM	Doncaster	Clarks Shoes
462.48750		NFM	Duxford	Imperial War Museum Events Net (131.8)
462.48750		NFM	London	Callaghan's Irish Bar, Regent Palace Hotel, Piccadilly
462.48750		NFM	London	Benetton Store, Oxford Street
462.48750		NFM	Nationwide	British Motorcycle Federation Events (173.8)
462.48750		NFM	Rugby	Christian Salvesen Ch.5

462.500 - 462.750 MHz — Emergency Services & American Radios

Base	Mobile	Mode	Location	User and Notes
462.53750		NFM	Fife	Fire Brigade Ch.8
462.53750		NFM	W Sussex	Fire Brigade Ch.8
462.55000	(467.55000)	NFM	USA	GMRS - Often Used Illegally In UK Ch.1
462.56250		NFM	Nationwide	Fire Brigade
462.56250		NFM	USA	GMRS - Often Used Illegally In UK Ch.2
462.56250		NFM	USA	FRS - Often Used Illegally In UK Ch.1
462.57500	(467.57500)	NFM	USA	GMRS - Often Used Illegally In UK Ch.3
462.57500		NFM	USA	BRS (White Dot Channel) - Often Used Illegally In UK
462.58750		NFM	USA	FRS - Often Used Illegally In UK Ch.2
462.58750		NFM	USA	GMRS - Often Used Illegally In UK Ch.4
462.60000	(467.60000)	NFM	USA	GMRS - Often Used Illegally In UK Ch.5
462.61250		NFM	USA	FRS - Often Used Illegally In UK Ch.3
462.61250		NFM	USA	GMRS - Often Used Illegally In UK Ch.6
462.62500	(467.62500)	NFM	USA	GMRS - Often Used Illegally In UK Ch.7
462.62500		NFM	USA	BRS (Black Dot Channel) - Often Used Illegally In UK
462.63750		NFM	USA	FRS - Often Used Illegally In UK Ch.4
462.63750		NFM	USA	GMRS - Often Used Illegally In UK Ch.8
462.65000	(467.65000)	NFM	USA	GMRS - Often Used Illegally In UK Ch.9
462.66250		NFM	USA	FRS - Often Used Illegally In UK Ch.5
462.66250		NFM	USA	GMRS - Often Used Illegally In UK Ch.10
462.67500	(467.67500)	NFM	USA	GMRS - Often Used Illegally In UK Ch.11
462.67500		NFM	USA	BRS (Orange Dot Channel) - Often Used Illegally In UK
462.66875		NFM	USA	FRS - Often Used Illegally In UK Ch.6
462.66875		NFM	USA	GMRS - Often Used Illegally In UK Ch.12
462.70000	(467.70000)	NFM	USA	GMRS - Often Used Illegally In UK Ch.13
462.71250		NFM	USA	FRS - Often Used Illegally In UK Ch.7
462.71250		NFM	USA	GMRS - Often Used Illegally In UK Ch.14
462.72500	(462.72500)	NFM	USA	GMRS - Often Used Illegally In UK Ch.15
462.72500		NFM	Belfast	Nutts Corner Market

462.75625 - 464.000 MHz — Fixed Links, Telemetry, PMR & Talkback

Base	Mobile	Mode	Location	User and Notes
462.75625		NFM	Corby	ASCAR (2004) Olly Playle West-Tec Car 88
462.75625	469.61875	NFM	London	Dominion Theatre Talkback
462.75625		NFM	London	Lyceum Theatre Front of House
462.75625	469.61875	NFM	London	Palladium Theatre Talkback
462.75625		NFM	Nationwide	JFMG Long Term Fixed Talkback TX
462.76125		NFM	Corby	ASCAR (2004) Peter Falding Intersport Car 33
462.76875		NFM	Nationwide	JFMG Long Term Fixed Talkback TX
462.76875		NFM	Peterborough	The Ideal Home Shopping Channel Studio

Base	Mobile	Mode	Location	User and Notes
462.78125		NFM	Nationwide	JFMG Long Term Fixed Talkback TX
462.79375		NFM	Nationwide	JFMG Long Term Fixed Talkback TX
462.80625		NFM	Corby	ASCAR (2004) Michael Vergers West-Tec Car 28
462.80625		NFM	Nationwide	JFMG Long Term Fixed Talkback TX
462.81875		NFM	Nationwide	JFMG Long Term Fixed Talkback TX
462.83125		NFM	London	Prince of Wales Theatre Talkback
462.83125		NFM	Nationwide	JFMG Long Term Fixed Talkback TX
462.83125	469.56875	NFM	London	Prince Edward Theatre Talkback
462.84375		NFM	Nationwide	JFMG Long Term Fixed Talkback TX
462.84375		NFM	London	Lyceum Theatre Back of House
462.84375	469.58125	NFM	London	Channel 5 TV Productions, Whitehall Theatre
462.85625		NFM	Nationwide	JFMG Long Term Fixed Talkback TX
462.86875		NFM	Nationwide	JFMG Long Term Fixed Talkback TX
462.86875	469.60625	NFM	London	Channel 5 TV Productions, Whitehall Theatre
462.88125		NFM	Corby	ASCAR (2004) Jon Higgins Renegade Car 19
462.88125		NFM	London	Lyceum Theatre Back of House
462.88125		NFM	London	Sadlers Wells Theatre Talkback
462.88125		NFM	Nationwide	JFMG Long Term Fixed Talkback TX
462.89375		NFM	Nationwide	JFMG Long Term Fixed Talkback TX
462.90625	469.69375	NFM	Borehamwood	BBC Eastenders Studio Talkback
462.90625		NFM	Llanelli	Agenda Studio Talkback
462.90625		NFM	Nationwide	JFMG Long Term Fixed Talkback TX
462.91875		NFM	London	The Palace Theatre Director
462.91875		NFM	Nationwide	JFMG Long Term Fixed Talkback TX
462.93125	469.83125	NFM	Borehamwood	BBC Eastenders Studio Talkback
462.93125		NFM	Corby	ASCAR (2004) Mark Proctor Fast-Tec Car 12
462.93125		NFM	Nationwide	JFMG Long Term Fixed Talkback TX
462.94375		NFM	Nationwide	JFMG Long Term Fixed Talkback TX
462.95625		NFM	Corby	ASCAR (2004) Duncan Grey Catchpole Car 77
462.95625		NFM	Nationwide	JFMG Long Term Fixed Talkback TX
462.96875		NFM	Nationwide	JFMG Long Term Fixed Talkback TX
462.98125		NFM	Corby	ASCAR (2004) Chris Cooke West-Tec Car 8
462.98125		NFM	Nationwide	JFMG Long Term Fixed Talkback TX
462.99375	469.86875	NFM	Borehamwood	BBC Eastenders Studio Talkback
462.99375		NFM	London	Dominion Theatre Talkback
462.99375		NFM	London	Lyceum Theatre Back of House
462.99375		NFM	Nationwide	JFMG Long Term Fixed Talkback TX
463.27500	457.77500	NFM	Fulmar	FSU Shell Telemetry Link
463.50000		NFM	Lincoln	EMEB Sub-Station Telemetry Link

.464.0000 - 467.0000 MHz Police/Fire/PMR Base & Repeater System
Scotland - Limited Use in England

Base	Mobile	Mode	Location	User and Notes
464.0125	450.0750	NFM	Falkirk	Police Falkirk Football Club Control
464.0125	450.0125	NFM	Strathclyde	Police Special Events
464.0250	450.0250	NFM	Strathclyde	Police Special Events Ibrox Stadium
464.0500	450.0500	NFM	Strathclyde	Police Special Events
464.0750	450.0750	NFM	Strathclyde	Police Special Events
464.0875	450.0875	NFM	Strathclyde	Police Special Events Glasgow E Division
464.1000	464.1000	NFM	Strathclyde	Police Special Events
464.1500	464.1500	NFM	Strathclyde	Police East Dunbartonshire
464.1750	451.1750	NFM	Strathclyde	Police North Ayrshire Irvine
464.2000	450.2000	NFM	Strathclyde	Police North Lanarkshire Cumbernauld
464.2250	450.2250	NFM	Strathclyde	Police South Ayrshire Ayr
464.3500		NFM	Heathrow	El Al Security
464.4500		NFM	USA	BRS (Brown Dot Channel) - Often Used Illegally In UK
464.5500		NFM	USA	BRS (Yellow Dot Channel) - Often Used Illegally In UK

Base	Mobile	Mode	Location	User and Notes
464.6000	450.6000	NFM	Strathclyde	Police West Dunbartonshire Clydebank
464.7750	450.7750	NFM	Strathclyde	Police Use During Fire Strike
464.8750	450.8750	NFM	Nationwide	Police Reverse Working Channel Ch.91
464.8750	450.8750	NFM	Nottinghamshire	Police, Sutton & Kirkby Ch.91
464.9000	450.9000	NFM	Strathclyde	Police 'Q' Division, Cambuslang South Area
464.9250	450.9250	NFM	Strathclyde	Police N Lanarkshire Broadwood Stadium Clyde FC
464.9500	450.9500	NFM	Edinburgh	Holyrood Palace Admin/Maintenance (88.5)
465.0000	451.0000	NFM	Lothian	Police 'E' Division, Tranent/Mussleburgh
465.0000	451.0000	NFM	Tayside	Police Crieff, Montrose, Blairgowrie
465.0250	451.0250	NFM	Lothian	Police 'E' Division, N. Berwick/Haddington
465.0500	451.0500	NFM	Lothian	Police 'F' Division, Bathgate/Armamdale
465.0750	451.0750	NFM	Lothian	Police 'F' Division, Bathgat /Armamdale
465.1000	451.1000	NFM	Lothian	Police 'F' Division, South Queensferry
465.1250	451.1250	NFM	Lothian	Police 'E' Division
465.1500	451.1500	NFM	Lothian	Police 'F' Division, Broxburn / Livingston
465.1500	451.1500	NFM	Nationwide	Divisional Reverse Working Channel Ch.92
465.1750	451.1750	NFM	Lothian	Police 'E' Division, Dunbar
465.1750	451.1750	NFM	Strathclyde	Police North Ayrshire Saltcoats
465.2000	451.2000	NFM	Edinburgh	Castle/Holyrood/Parliament Police & Security
465.2500	451.2500	NFM	Lothian	Police 'C' Division, Oxgangs
465.2750	451.2750	NFM	Lothian	Police 'C' Division, Wester Hailes
465.3000	451.3000	NFM	Central Scotland	Police Denny, Camelon, Larbert
465.3000	451.3000	NFM	Strathclyde	Police North Ayrshire Kilmarnock
465.3250	451.3250	NFM	Lothian	Police 'F' Division, Linlithgow
465.3500	451.3500	NFM	Central Scotland	Police Bridge of Allan, Bannockburn
465.3750	451.3750	NFM	Strathclyde	Police East Ayrshire Cumnock
465.4000	451.4000	NFM	Lothian	Police 'E' Division, Port Seton
465.4750	451.4750	NFM	Tayside	Police Comrie, Alyth, Carnoustie
465.4750	451.4750	NFM	Tayside	Police 'E' Division, Brechin & Montrose
465.5000	451.5000	NFM	Strathclyde	Police VHF-UHF Repeater
465.5250	451.6250	NFM	London	City Police/GT Metropolitan Police Link
465.5750	451.5750	NFM	Strathclyde	Police Bute Isle Of Rothesay
465.5750	451.5750	NFM	Tayside	Police 'W' Division, Kinross
465.6000	451.6000	NFM	Strathclyde	Police South Lanarkshire Lanark
465.6250	451.7250	NFM	London	City Police/GT Metropolitan Police Link
465.6250	451.6250	NFM	Nationwide	Police Special Events
465.6250	451.6250	NFM	Strathclyde	Police Special Events
465.6250	451.6250	NFM	Tayside	Police Errol, Methven
465.6500	451.6500	NFM	Lothian	Police Edinburgh
465.6500	451.6500	NFM	Strathclyde	Police South Lanarkshire Hamilton
465.6750	451.6750	NFM	London	City Police/GT Metropolitan Police Link
465.6750	451.6750	NFM	Nationwide	Police Special Events
465.6750	451.6750	NFM	Strathclyde	Party Conference (L Control)
465.6750		NFM	Tayside	Police Back to Back
465.7000	451.7000	NFM	Strathclyde	Police North Lanarkshire Motherwell
465.7250	451.7250	NFM	Nationwide	Police Special Events
465.7250	451.7250	NFM	Strathclyde	Police Special Events
465.7250	451.7250	NFM	Tayside	Police Dundee (Spare), Dunkeld
465.7500	451.7500	NFM	Strathclyde	Police Wishaw
465.7750	451.7750	NFM	Aberdeen	Police Grampian Football Control
465.7750	451.7750	NFM	London	City Police/GT Metropolitan Police Link
465.7750	451.7750	NFM	Tayside	Police Incident Channel
465.7750	451.7750	NFM	Strathclyde	Police Special Events
465.8000	451.8000	NFM	Lothian	Police 'E' Division, Haddington
465.8250	465.8250	NFM	Central Scotland	Police Special Use
465.8250	465.8250	NFM	Strathclyde	Police VHF-UHF Repeater

Base	Mobile	Mode	Location	User and Notes
465.8750	465.8750	NFM	Tayside	Police Monifieth, Kinross, Auchterarder, Kirriemuir
465.9000	465.9000	NFM	Strathclyde	Police South Lanarkshire Ruthgerglen
465.9250	451.9250	NFM	Glasgow	Police Glasgow Airport
465.9750	451.9750	NFM	Strathclyde	Police Support Units General Use Low Power
466.0250	452.2500	NFM	Central Scotland	Police Inter-Force Link (Constant Carrier)
466.1000	452.6000	NFM	Newtownabbey	Abbeycentre Security
466.1500	452.1500	NFM	Edinburgh	Holyrood Park Rangers (107.2)
466.2250		NFM	Nationwide	BBC O/B On-Site Handhelds
466.2250	452.2500	NFM	Fife	Scottish Police Training College, Tulliallian
466.2500	452.2500	NFM	Edinburgh	Police 'B' Division, Edinburgh City
466.2500	452.2500	NFM	Grampian	Police Dalkeith
466.2500	452.2500	NFM	Grampian	Police/Special Branch/Royalty Protection Balmoral
466.2500	452.2500	NFM	Strathclyde	Police VHF-UHF Repeater
466.2500	452.2500	NFM	Tayside	Police Emergency, Mutual Aid & Sports Use
466.2500	452.2500	NFM	Edinburgh	St Leonards Division HQ (B) Ch.2
466.2500	452.2500	NFM	Glasgow	Police Firearms Support Group
466.2500	452.2500	NFM	Lanark	Police
466.2750	452.2750	NFM	Grampian	Traffic Wardens
466.2750	452.2750	NFM	Inverness	Traffic Wardens
466.2750	452.2750	NFM	Lothian	Police 'C' Division
466.2750	452.2750	NFM	Nationwide	Scottish Traffic Wardens
466.2750	452.2750	NFM	Strathclyde	Police Glasgow City Special Events A Division
466.2750		NFM	Tayside	Traffic Wardens
466.3000	452.3000	NFM	Dunfermline	Traffic Wardens
466.3000	452.3000	NFM	Fife	Traffic Wardens
466.3000		NFM	Tayside	Fireground Repeater
466.3250	452.3250	NFM	Edinburgh	Police 'C' Division, Edinburgh, West End
466.3250	452.3250	NFM	Strathclyde	Police West Dumbartonshire/Helensburgh
466.3500	451.3500	NFM	Strathclyde	Police Glasgow East
466.3750	452.3750	NFM	Strathclyde	Police Renfrewshire
466.4000	451.4000	NFM	Aberdeen	HM Prison Aberdeen
466.4000	451.4000	NFM	Dumfries	Young Offenders Institution
466.4000	451.4000	NFM	Edinburgh	HM Prison Saughton
466.4000	451.4000	NFM	Forfar	HM Prison Noranside
466.4000	451.4000	NFM	Glasgow	HM Prison Barlinnie
466.4000	451.4000	NFM	Nationwide	Scottish Office Prison Service Common
466.4000	451.4000	NFM	Perth	HM Prison Friarton
466.4000	451.4000	NFM	Stirling	HM Prison Cornton Vale
466.4250	452.4250	NFM	Edinburgh	Police Edinburgh Airport
466.4500	452.4500	NFM	Strathclyde	Police Glasgow North West
466.4500	452.4500	NFM	Tayside	Police Dundee 1,3
466.4750	452.4750	NFM	Grampian	Police Peterhead
466.5000	452.5000	NFM	Strathclyde	Police Glasgow City
466.5000	452.5000	NFM	Strathclyde	Police Argyll Main Towns Only
466.5000	452.5000	NFM	Tayside	Police Perth, Forfar, Edzell
466.5250	452.5250	NFM	Edinburgh	Police 'B' Division Edinburgh St Leonards
466.5250	452.5250	NFM	Central Scotland	Police Callender & Balfron
466.5500	452.5500	NFM	Central Scotland	Police Stirling
466.5500	452.5500	NFM	Inverness	Northern Constabulary Main PR
466.5500	452.5500	NFM	Strathclyde	Police Glasgow West
466.5500	452.5500	NFM	Tayside	Police, Aberfeldy, Brechin, Dundee 2, 4
466.5500	452.5500	NFM	Tayside	Police, Pitlochry, Perth (Football), Rannoch
466.5750	452.5750	NFM	Edinburgh	Police 'C' Division, Edinburgh West
466.6000	452.6000	NFM	Aberdeen	Police
466.6000	452.6000	NFM	Inverness	Northern Constabulary Events
466.6000	452.6000	NFM	Strathclyde	Police Glasgow North

Base	Mobile	Mode	Location	User and Notes
466.6000	452.6000	NFM	Strathclyde	Police 'D' Division, Bishopbriggs, Kirkintilloch
466.6000	452.6000	NFM	Tayside	Police Dundee 5, 6
466.6250	452.6250	NFM	Edinburgh	Police 'B' Division, Edinburgh City Gayfield Sq
466.6500	452.6500	NFM	Grampian	Police Elgin, Bucksburn Aberdeen North Half
466.6500	452.6500	NFM	Strathclyde	Police Glasgow South
466.6750		NFM	Lothian	Police 'D' Division, Portobello
466.7000		NFM	Lothian	Police 'E' Division
466.7000	452.7000	NFM	Strathclyde	Police Inverclyde
466.7250	452.7250	NFM	Lothian	Police 'F' Division, Balerno
466.7250	452.7250	NFM	Tayside	Police Mobile Repeater
466.7500	452.7500	NFM	Strathclyde	Police Glasgow South East E Renfrewshire
466.7750	452.7750	NFM	Central Scotland	Police Grangemouth, Bo'ness & Braes Area
466.7750	452.7750	NFM	Strathclyde	Police South Lanarkshire East Kilbride
466.7750		NFM	Tayside	Police Firearms Back-Back
466.8000		NFM	Derbyshire	Fire Brigade Link
466.8000	452.8000	NFM	Strathclyde	Police Support Unit/Dog Branch/SOC Search
466.8000		NFM	Tayside	Police Air Support-Ground
466.8250	452.8250	NFM	Lothian	Police 'D' Division, Leith Area
466.8250	452.8250	NFM	Strathclyde	Police North Lanarkshire Coatbridge
466.8250		NFM	Tayside	Police Firearms Back-Back
466.8250	452.8250	NFM	Nationwide	Army Air Corps Parachute Team Loader
466.8500		NFM	Bedfordshire	Fire Brigade Link
466.8500	452.8500	NFM	Holyhead	Police Hilltop Link
466.8750	452.8750	NFM	Stirling	HM Prison Cornton Vale
466.8750		NFM	Tayside	Police Firearms Back-Back
466.8750		NFM	W Sussex	Fire Brigade Hilltop Link
466.8875	452.8875	NFM	Tayside	Police Coupar Angus, Arbroath
466.9000	452.9000	NFM	Strathclyde	Police Event Control (Ibrox & Parkhead)
466.9250	452.9250	NFM	Strathclyde	Police VHF-UHF Repeater
466.9500		NFM	Grampian	Police 'A' Division, Fochabers & Forres
466.9500		NFM	Suffolk	Fire Brigade Link
466.9750	452.9750	NFM	Tayside	Police Firearms Repeater
467.2000		NFM	Grampian	Police Queen Street Aberdeen

467.25625 - 470.0000 MHz   Broadcasting Links and Maritime

Base	Mobile	Mode	Location	User and Notes
467.25625		NFM	Borehamwood	BBC Radio O/B (179.9)
467.26875		NFM	Borehamwood	BBC Radio O/B (179.9)
467.29375		NFM	London	BBC Radio News Talk Back London
467.30000		NFM	Nationwide	BBC Radio O/B
467.35000		NFM	Nationwide	USS Winston Churchill On Board Trunked
467.36250		NFM	Nationwide	USS Winston Churchill On Board Trunked
467.37500		NFM	Nationwide	USS Winston Churchill On Board Trunked
467.38750		NFM	Nationwide	USS Winston Churchill On Board Trunked
467.40000		NFM	Nationwide	USS Winston Churchill On Board Trunked
467.40625		NFM	Corby	ASCAR (2004) Rob Speak Team Turn Four Car 5
467.42500		NFM	Nationwide	BBC Radio 5 O/B
467.42500		NFM	Nationwide	BBC Radio Engineers
467.47500		NFM	Burnley	Granada TV O/B
467.49375		NFM	London	Carlton TV Talkback
467.49370		NFM	London	ITV Weather
467.52500		NFM	Dover	P & O Ferries Ch.4
467.52500		NFM	Newhaven	Transmanche Ferries MV Dieppe/MV Sardinia
467.52500		NFM	Worldwide	On-Board Ship Handhelds
467.53125		NFM	Japan	Japanese FRS - Often Used Illegally in UK
467.53750		NFM	Worldwide	On-Board Ship Handhelds
467.55000		NFM	Dover	P & O Ferries Ch.5

Base	Mobile	Mode	Location	User and Notes
467.55000		NFM	Holyhead	Ulysses On-Board Ops.
467.55000		NFM	Worldwide	On-Board Ship Handhelds
467.56250		NFM	USA	FRS - Often Used Illegally In UK Ch.8
467.56250		NFM	Worldwide	On-Board Ship Handhelds
467.57500		NFM	Belfast	Downtown Radio O/B
467.57500		NFM	Dover	P & O Ferries Ch.6
467.57500		NFM	Worldwide	On-Board Ship Handhelds
467.58750		NFM	USA	FRS - Often Used Illegally In UK Ch.9
467.60000		NFM	Holyhead	Ulysses On-Board Ops.
467.61250		NFM	Belfast	Downtown Radio Belfast
467.61250		NFM	Glasgow	Radio Clyde
467.61250		NFM	Hereford	Radio Wyvern
467.61250		WFM	Lincolnshire	Lincs FM O/B Radio Mics.
467.61250		NFM	London	Capital Radio 95.8
467.61250		NFM	Nationwide	Independent Local Radio Ch.C1
467.61250		WFM	Salisbury	Spire FM O/B
467.61250		WFM	USA	FRS - Often Used Illegally In UK Ch.10
467.63750		NFM	USA	FRS - Often Used Illegally In UK Ch.11
467.66250		NFM	Ayr	West Sound Radio
467.66250		NFM	Cardiff	CBC Radio
467.66250		NFM	Coventry	Mercia Sound O/B
467.66250		NFM	Ipswich	SGR FM Radio
467.66250		NFM	London	Capital Radio (95.8 & Gold) Flying Eye
467.66250		NFM	Manchester	Piccadilly Radio
467.66250		NFM	Nationwide	Independent Local Radio ChC2
467.66250		NFM	Teesside	Radio Tees
467.66250		NFM	USA	FRS - Often Used Illegally In UK Ch.12
467.66250		NFM	Wiltshire	Wiltshire Radio
467.68750		NFM	USA	FRS - Often Used Illegally In UK Ch.13
467.71250		NFM	Aberdeen	Northsound Radio
467.71250		NFM	Glasgow	Radio Clyde
467.71250		NFM	Gloucester	Severn Radio
467.71250		NFM	London	Virgin Radio O/B Link
467.72500		NFM	Nationwide	Independent Local Radio Ch.C3
467.71250		NFM	Plymouth	Plymouth Sound
467.71250		WFM	Reading	Radio 210 O/B
467.71250		NFM	Southend	Essex Radio
467.71250		NFM	Swansea	Swansea Sound O/B
467.71250		WFM	Strathclyde	Tay AM
467.72500		NFM	USA	FRS - Often Used Illegally In UK Ch.14
467.72500		NFM	Holyhead	On-Board Radio Ops. Stena Adventurer (114.8)
467.72500		NFM	Worldwide	On-Board Handhelds 2 Watts
467.72500	457.5250	NFM	Worldwide	On-Board Handhelds 2 Watts Repeaters
467.75625		NFM	Corby	ASCAR (2004) Malcolm Clein CWS Car 85
467.75625		NFM	Nationwide	JFMG Programme Making/Special Events
467.76250		NFM	USA	BRS (J Dot Channel) - Often Used Illegally In UK
467.76875		NFM	Nationwide	JFMG Programme Making/Special Events
467.77500		NFM	Worldwide	On-Board Handhelds 2 Watts
467.77500	457.55000	NFM	Worldwide	On-Board Handhelds 2 Watts Repeaters
467.78125		NFM	Nationwide	JFMG Programme Making/Special Events
467.79375		NFM	Nationwide	JFMG Programme Making/Special Events
467.80000		NFM	Worldwide	On-Board Handhelds 2 Watts
467.80000	457.57500	NFM	Worldwide	On-Board Handhelds 2 Watts Repeaters
467.80625		NFM	Nationwide	JFMG Programme Making/Special Events
467.81825		NFM	Nationwide	JFMG Programme Making/Special Events

Base	Mobile	Mode	Location	User and Notes
467.81250		NFM	USA	BRS (K Dot Channel) - Often Used Illegally In UK
467.81875		NFM	Nationwide	JFMG Programme Making/Special Events
467.82500		NFM	Worldwide	On-Board Handhelds 2 Watts
467.82500	457.60000	NFM	Worldwide	On-Board Handhelds 2 Watts Repeaters
467.83125		NFM	Nationwide	JFMG Programme Making/Special Events
467.84375		NFM	Nationwide	JFMG Programme Making/Special Events
467.85000		NFM	USA	BRS (Silver Star Channel) - Often Used Illegally In UK
467.85625		NFM	Corby	ASCAR (2004) Skid Carrera KR Racing Car 11
467.85625		NFM	Nationwide	JFMG Programme Making/Special Events
467.86875		NFM	Nationwide	JFMG Programme Making/Special Events
467.87500		NFM	USA	BRS (Gold Star Channel) - Often Used Illegally In UK
467.89375		NFM	Nationwide	JFMG Programme Making/Special Events
467.90000		NFM	USA	BRS (Red Star Channel) - Often Used Illegally In UK
467.90625		NFM	Nationwide	JFMG Programme Making/Special Events
467.91875		NFM	Nationwide	JFMG Programme Making/Special Events
467.92500		NFM	USA	BRS (Blue Star Channel) - Often Used Illegally In UK
467.93125		NFM	Nationwide	JFMG Programme Making/Special Events
467.94375		NFM	Nationwide	JFMG Programme Making/Special Events
467.94375		NFM	Nationwide	Premiership Football Referees, Scrambled (103.5)
467.95625		NFM	Nationwide	JFMG Programme Making/Special Events
467.96875		NFM	Corby	ASCAR (2004) Duncan Gray Team Catchpole Car 77
467.96875		NFM	Nationwide	JFMG Programme Making/Special Events
467.98125		NFM	Nationwide	JFMG Programme Making/Special Events
467.99375		NFM	Nationwide	ASCAR (2004) Tony King HTML Car 17
467.99375		NFM	Nationwide	JFMG Programme Making/Special Events
467.99375		NFM	Nationwide	Sky TV O/B Sound Gallery
468.00000		NFM	London	LWT
468.01875		NFM	Nationwide	Anglia TV O/B Camera Link
468.05000		NFM	Jersey	Channel TV Talkback
468.05625		NFM	Nationwide	BBC TV O/B Link
468.08125		NFM	Kent	Invicta FM Radio
468.08750		NFM	Dundee	Radio Tay Talkback
468.08750		NFM	Exeter	Gemini FM
468.08750		NFM	Guildford	County Sound Radio
468.08750		NFM	Inverness	Moray Firth Radio
468.08750		NFM	Leeds	Radio Aire
468.08750		NFM	Leicester	Sunrise Radio O/B
468.08750		NFM	Nationwide	Independent Local Radio Ch.B1
468.13670		NFM	London	Spectrum 558 Radio O/B
468.13750		NFM	London	Sunrise Radio OB Link
468.13750		NFM	Nationwide	BBC Radio O/B
468.15000		NFM	Nationwide	BBC Radio O/B
468.20625		NFM	Nationwide	BBC News 24 Handhelds Production Channel
468.25000		NFM	Nationwide	BBC Radio O/B
468.25000		NFM	Nationwide	BBC Radio 1 Roadshow Talkback
468.27500		NFM	Nationwide	BBC Radio O/B
468.27500		NFM	Nationwide	BBC Radio 5 Live Talkback
468.31250		NFM	Nationwide	Anglia TV O/B Camera Link
468.37500		NFM	Nationwide	ITV Cameras
468.38750		NFM	London	Metropolitan Police Federation (131.8)
468.38750		NFM	Nationwide	JFMG Common Special Use Allocation
468.39000		NFM	Jersey	Channel TV Talkback
468.45625		NFM	London	Capital Gold O/B
468.46250		NFM	Bristol	Radio West
468.46250		NFM	Crawley	Oak Ridge Radio

Base	Mobile	Mode	Location	User and Notes
468.46250		NFM	Edinburgh	Radio Forth
468.46250		NFM	Inverness	Moray Firth Radio O/B
468.46250		NFM	London	Capital Radio Gold O/B
468.46250		NFM	Nationwide	Independent Local Radio Ch.B2
468.46250		NFM	Nottingham	Radio Trent
468.46250		NFM	Tyne & Wear	Metro Radio
468.46250		NFM	Wolverhampton	Beacon Radio
468.47500		NFM	Nationwide	IBA Riggers
468.50000		NFM	Nationwide	ITV O/B
468.58750		WFM	S Wales	Flying Eye Traffic Reports
468.58750		WFM	Yorkshire	Flying Eye Traffic Reports
468.59375		NFM	Bedfordshire	Chiltern Radio Eye In The Sky
468.59375		NFM	London	Virgin Radio Chopper O/B
468.64375		NFM	Leeds	Flying Eye for Magic 828, Hallam & Viking
468.68750		NFM	Herts/Beds	Chiltern Radio O/B
468.69375		NFM	Manchester	Piccadilly Radio Eye In The Sky
468.74375		NFM	Manchester	Red Rose Radio Eye In The Sky
468.79375		NFM	Herts/Beds	Q103 FM Eye In The Sky
468.79375		NFM	Manchester	Radio City Eye In The Sky
468.79375		NFM	West Country	Severn Sound Radio Air-Ground Talkback
468.84750		NFM	Doncaster	Doncaster Radio Eye In Sky
468.94375		NFM	Cambridge	Horizon FM Eye In The Sky
468.94375		NFM	West Country	GWR Radio Air-Ground Talkback
468.95625		NFM	London	BBC Air-Ground
469.00000		NFM	Preston	Radio Lancashire O/B
469.01250		NFM	Berkshire	BBC Radio Berkshire Radio Car
469.01250		NFM	Humberside	BBC Radio Humberside O/B
469.01250		NFM	Shropshire	BBC Radio Shropshire O/B
469.06250		NFM	Nationwide	BBC Radio 5 Live O/B
469.11250		NFM	Lincoln	BBC Radio Lincolnshire O/B
469.11250		NFM	London	Smooth FM Flying Eye
469.11250		NFM	Wiltshire	BBC Wiltshire Sound
469.11250		NFM	York	BBC Radio York
469.16250		NFM	Nationwide	BBC Radio 5 Live Talkback
469.21250		NFM	Blackpool	Rock FM Flying Eye
469.21250		NFM	London	Evening Standard Sky Patrol
469.21250		NFM	London	Smooth FM O/B
469.21250		NFM	Midlands	Gem AM Radio OB
469.21250		NFM	Midlands	Ram FM Radio OB
469.21250		NFM	Midlands	Trent AM Radio O/B
469.26250		NFM	Aberdeen	North Sound Radio
469.26250		NFM	Ayr	West Sound Radio
469.26250		WFM	Liverpool	Magic 1548/Radio City O/B
469.26250		NFM	London	AA Skywatch O/B
469.26250		NFM	Nationwide	Independent Radio Ch A1
469.26250	455.16250	NFM	Norfolk	Radio Broadland O/B
469.31250		NFM	Cardiff	CBC Radio
469.31250		NFM	Ipswich	SGR FM Radio O/B
469.31250		NFM	Nationwide	Independent Radio Ch.A2
469.31250		NFM	Swindon	Wiltshire Radio
469.31250		NFM	Teesside	Radio Tees
469.35000		NFM	Essex	Essex Radio O/B
469.35000		NFM	Kent	Invicta FM Radio O/B
469.36250		NFM	Essex	Breeze AM Radio O/B

Base	Mobile	Mode	Location	User and Notes
469.36250		NFM	Essex	Essex Radio O/B
469.36250		NFM	Gloucester	Severn Radio
469.36250		NFM	Nationwide	Independent Radio Ch.A3
469.36250		NFM	Plymouth	Plymouth Sound
469.36250		NFM	Reading	Radio 210 O/B
469.36250		NFM	Swansea	Swansea Sound O/B
469.36250		NFM	Wrexham	Marcher Gold Talkback
469.36875		NFM	Essex	BBC Radio Essex Flying Eye
469.41250	468.08750	NFM	Bury St. Edmunds	SGR FM Radio O/B
469.41250		NFM	Londonderry	Northside Sound Radio
469.41250		NFM	Medway	Northdown Radio
469.41250		NFM	Nationwide	Independent Radio Ch.A4
469.46250		NFM	Exeter	Gemini FM
469.46250		NFM	Guildford	County Sound
469.46250		NFM	London	Kiss FM Flying Eye
469.46250		NFM	London	Spectrum 558 O/B
469.46250		NFM	London	Sunrise Radio O/B
469.46250		NFM	Nationwide	Independent Radio Ch.A5
469.49375		NFM	Nationwide	JFMG Long Term Fixed Talkback Rx
469.49375		NFM	Nationwide	JFMG Long Term Paired With 462.75625
469.50625		NFM	Nationwide	JFMG Long Term Fixed Talkback Rx
469.51875		NFM	Nationwide	JFMG Long Term Fixed Talkback Rx
469.53125		NFM	London	Big Brother Site Security Three Mill Studio (114.8)
469.53125		NFM	Nationwide	JFMG Long Term Fixed Talkback Rx
469.54375		NFM	Nationwide	JFMG Long Term Fixed Talkback Rx
469.55625		NFM	Nationwide	JFMG Long Term Fixed Talkback Rx
469.56875		NFM	Nationwide	JFMG Long Term Fixed Talkback Rx
469.57500		NFM	Doncaster	Continental Landscapes Ltd
469.58125		NFM	Corby	ASCAR (2004) Anthony Swan Torquespeed Car 23
469.58125		NFM	Nationwide	JFMG Long Term Fixed Talkback Rx
469.59375		NFM	Nationwide	JFMG Long Term Fixed Talkback Rx
469.60625		NFM	Nationwide	JFMG Long Term Fixed Talkback Rx
469.61875		NFM	Nationwide	JFMG Long Term Fixed Talkback Rx
469.63125		NFM	Nationwide	JFMG Long Term Fixed Talkback Rx
469.64375		NFM	Nationwide	JFMG Long Term Fixed Talkback Rx
469.65625		NFM	Nationwide	JFMG Long Term Fixed Talkback Rx
469.66250		NFM	Manchester	Piccadilly Radio Programme link
469.66875		NFM	Nationwide	JFMG Long Term Fixed Talkback Rx
469.68125		NFM	Nationwide	JFMG Long Term Fixed Talkback Rx
469.69375		NFM	Nationwide	JFMG Long Term Fixed Talkback Rx
469.70625		NFM	Nationwide	JFMG Long Term Fixed Talkback Rx
469.71875		NFM	Nationwide	JFMG Long Term Fixed Talkback Rx
469.73125		NFM	Nationwide	JFMG Long Term Fixed Talkback Rx
469.74375		NFM	Nationwide	JFMG Long Term Fixed Talkback Rx
469.75625		NFM	Nationwide	JFMG Long Term Fixed Talkback Rx
469.76875		NFM	Nationwide	JFMG Long Term Fixed Talkback Rx
469.78125		NFM	Nationwide	JFMG Long Term Fixed Talkback Rx
469.79375		NFM	Nationwide	JFMG Long Term Fixed Talkback Rx
469.80625		NFM	Nationwide	JFMG Long Term Fixed Talkback Rx
469.81875		NFM	Nationwide	JFMG Long Term Fixed Talkback Rx
469.83125		NFM	Nationwide	JFMG Long Term Fixed Talkback Rx
469.84375		NFM	Nationwide	JFMG Long Term Fixed Talkback Rx
469.85625		NFM	Nationwide	JFMG Long Term Fixed Talkback Rx
469.86875		NFM	Nationwide	JFMG Long Term Fixed Talkback Rx

UK TV Channels, Local Radio Talkback & Theatre Radio Microphones

UK Television Channels

Ch.	Vision	Sound		Ch.	Vision	Sound
21	471.25	477.25		45	663.25	669.25
22	479.25	485.25		46	671.25	677.25
23	487.25	493.25		47	679.25	685.25
24	495.25	501.25		48	687.25	693.26
25	503.25	509.25		49	695.25	701.25
26	511.25	517.25		50	703.25	709.25
27	519.25	525.25		51	711.25	717.25
28	527.25	533.25		52	719.25	725.25
29	535.25	541.25		53	727.26	733.25
30	543.25	549.25		54	735.25	741.25
31	551.25	557.25		55	743.25	749.25
32	559.25	565.25		56	751.25	757.25
33	567.25	573.25		57	759.25	765.25
34	575.25	581.25		58	767.25	773.25
35	583.25	589.25		59	775.25	781.25
36	591.25	597.25		60	783.25	789.25
37	599.25	605.25		61	791.25	797.25
38	607.25	613.25		62	807.25	813.25
39	615.25	621.25		64	815.25	821.25
40	623.36	629.25		65	823.25	829.25
41	631.25	627.25		66	831.25	837.25
42	629.25	645.25		67	839.25	845.25
43	647.25	653.25		68	847.25	853.25
44.	655.25	661.25				

SCOTLAND	BBC1	BBC2	ITV	CH4		BBC1	BBC2	ITV	CH4
Aberfoyle	58	64	61	54	Abington	57	63	60	53
Acharacle	40	46	43	50	Angus	57	63	60	53
Ardentinny	39	45	49	52	Ardintoul	39	45	49	42
Ardnadam	51	44	41	47	Arisaig	33	26	23	29
Arrochar	21	27	24	31	Attadale	22	28	25	32
Auchmore Wood	22	28	25	32	Auchtermuchty	39	45	49	42
Aviemore	22	28	25	32	Avoch	63	57	53	60
Ayr South	51	44	41	47	Badachro	40	46	43	50
Balblair Wood	55	62	59	65	Balgownie	40	46	43	50
Ballachulish	33	26	23	29	Balmullo	39	45	49	42
Balnaguard	42	49	39	45	Baltasound	39	45	42	49
Banff	39	45	42	49	Bellanoch	39	45	42	49
Ben Tongue	39	45	49	42	Biggar	22	28	25	32
Black Hill	40	46	43	50	Blackwaterfoot	40	46	43	50
Blair Atholl	40	46	43	50	Boddam	39	45	42	49
Borve	22	28	32	25	Bowmore	39	45	49	42
Braemar	39	45	42	49	Brechin	40	46	43	50
Bressay	22	28	25	32	Bridge of Allan	33	26	23	29
Broughton	21	27	24	31	Bruernish	40	46	43	50
Burgar Hill	21	27	24	31	Callander	22	28	25	32
Campbeltown	57	63	60	53	Camperdown	33	26	23	29
Canongate	58	64	61	54	Carie	21	27	24	31
Carradale	51	44	41	47	Castlebay	21	27	24	31
Cathcart	57	63	60	53	Catrine	55	62	59	65
Clachan	40	46	43	50	Claonaig	55	62	59	65
Clettraval	51	44	41	47	Collafirth Hill	51	44	41	47
Cow Hill	40	46	43	50	Craigellachie	57	63	60	53

Craigkelly	31	27	24	21	Crieff	33	26	23	29
Cromarty	22	28	25	32	Cumbernauld Village	58	64	61	54
Cupar	51	44	41	47	Daliburgh	57	63	60	53
Dalmally	51	44	41	47	Darvel	33	26	23	29
Deanston	53	60	63	57	Dollar	58	64	61	54
Duncraig	51	44	41	47	Dunkeld	51	44	41	47
Dukeld Town	33	26	23	29	Dunoon	21	24	27	31
Dunure	40	46	43	50	Durness	57	63	53	60
Durris	22	28	25	32	Dychliemore	22	28	25	32
Easdale	39	45	49	42	Eitshal (Lewis)	33	26	23	29
Ellon	39	45	49	42	Fetlar	40	46	43	50
Fintry	34	27	24	31	Fitful Head	39	45	42	49
Fiunary	40	46	43	50	Fodderty	57	63	60	53
Fort Augustus	33	26	23	29	Garelochhead	51	44	41	47
Gartly Moor	58	64	61	54	Gigha Island	51	44	41	47
Girvan	55	62	59	65	Glasgow (W Central)	68	62	56	66
Glen Convinth	21	27	24	31	Glen Urquhart	51	44	41	47
Glengorm	56	52	48	54	Glespin	58	64	61	54
Gourdon	55	62	65	59	Grandtully	58	64	61	54
Grangemouth	57	63	60	53	Grantown	51	44	41	47
Haddington	58	64	61	54	High Keil	51	44	47	41
Holmhead	51	44	41	47	Inverarish	40	46	43	50
Inverness	55	62	65	59	Keelylang Hill	40	46	43	50
Kelvindale	34	52	30	48	Kenmore	33	26	23	29
Kilbride (South Uist)	39	45	49	42	Killearn	65	62	59	55
Killin	39	45	49	42	Kilmacolm	21	27	42	31
Kilmelford	55	62	59	65	Kingussie	40	46	43	50
Kinlochbervie	40	46	43	50	Kinlochleven	55	62	59	65
Kinross	61	67	64	54	Kintraw	40	46	43	50
Kirkconnel	58	64	61	54	Kirkfieldbank	57	63	60	53
Kirkmichael	39	45	49	52	Kirkoswald	22	28	25	32
Knock More	33	26	23	29	Kylerhea	51	44	41	47
Lairg	51	44	41	47	Largs	39	45	42	49
Leadhills	58	64	61	54	Lethanhill	57	63	60	53
Lindores	40	46	43	50	Loch Feochan	58	64	61	68
Lochearnhead	58	64	61	54	Lochgoilhead	57	63	53	60
Lochinver	40	46	43	50	Lochmaddy	22	28	25	32
Lochwinnoch	57	63	60	53	Lumphanan	49	42	39	45
Mallaig	43	46	40	50	Melvich	51	44	41	47
Methven	22	28	25	32	Millburn Muir	39	52	42	49
Millport	58	64	61	54	Muirkirk	51	44	41	47
Ness of Lewis	51	44	41	47	Netherton Braes	22	28	25	32
New Cumnock	40	46	43	50	Newbattle	55	62	59	65
Oban	51	44	41	47	Onich	58	64	61	54
Penicuik	58	64	61	54	Penifiler	39	45	49	42
Perth	39	45	49	42	Peterhead	55	62	59	65
Pierowall	33	26	23	29	Pitlochry	22	28	25	32
Poolewe	51	44	47	41	Port Ellen	22	28	25	32
Portnahaven	33	26	23	29	Ravenscraig	21	27	24	31
Rosehearty	51	44	41	47	Rosemarkie	39	45	49	42
Rosneath	58	64	61	54	Rothesay	22	28	25	32
Rothesay Town	55	62	59	65	Rumster Forest	31	27	24	21
Scalloway	55	62	59	65	Scoval	55	62	59	65
Skriaig (Skye)	21	27	24	31	Sorn	40	46	43	50
South Knapdale	57	63	60	53	Spean Bridge	21	27	24	31
St. Fillans	51	44	47	41	Staffin	39	45	49	42
Strachur	33	26	23	29	Strathallan	39	45	49	42
Strathblane	21	27	24	31	Strathyre	21	27	24	31

Strathyre Link	40	46	43	50	Strontian	42	49	39	45
Swinister	55	62	59	65	Tarbert (Harris)	39	45	49	52
Tarbert (Loch Fyne)	21	27	24	31	Tay Bridge	51	44	41	47
Taynuilt	40	46	43	50	Tayvallich	40	46	43	50
Thurso	57	63	60	53	Tighnabruaich	39	45	49	42
Tillicoultry	57	63	60	53	Tomatin	22	28	25	32
Tomich	21	27	24	31	Tomich Link	39	45	49	42
Tomintoul	40	46	43	50	Torosay	22	28	25	32
Troon	58	64	61	54	Tullich	55	62	59	65
Tummel Bridge	39	45	49	42	Twechar	22	28	25	32
Uig	53	46	43	50	Ullapool	39	45	49	52
Uplawmoor	58	64	61	54	Voe	57	63	60	53
Wanlockhead	51	44	47	41	Weisdale	58	64	61	54
West Kilbride	51	44	41	47	West Linton	33	26	23	29
Wester Erchite	21	27	24	31					

BORDERS & NORTHERN ENGLAND

Addingham	40	46	43	50	Ainstable	43	51	47	49
Aislaby	39	45	52	49	Allenheads	21	27	31	24
Alston	52	45	49	42	Armitage Bridge	58	64	61	54
Austwick	39	45	49	42	Backbarrow	57	63	60	50
Bacup	40	46	43	53	Bainbridge	57	63	60	53
Ballantrae	58	64	61	54	Barrow Town Hall	51	44	41	47
Barskeoch Hill	55	62	59	65	Bassenthwaite	52	45	49	42
Batley	57	63	60	67	Beary Peark (IoM)	40	46	43	50
Beecroft Hill (Leeds)	55	62	59	65	Bellingham	21	27	24	31
Belmont	22	28	25	32	Berwick on Tweed	21	27	24	31
Bidston	51	44	41	47	Bilsdale (W Moor)	33	26	29	23
Birch Vale	40	46	43	53	Blackburn	51	44	41	31
Blackburn in Rother'm	57	63	60	53	Blaydon Burn	51	44	41	48
Bleachgreen	57	63	60	53	Bollington	21	27	24	31
Bonchester Bridge	39	45	49	42	Bradford West	57	62	49	67
Brinscall	27	21	24	31	Broadbottom	39	45	42	49
Brockwell	66	39	68	49	Brook Bottom	58	64	61	68
Burbage	44	51	41	47	Buxton	21	27	24	31
Byrness	21	27	31	24	Caldbeck	30	34	28	32
Calver Peak	39	45	49	42	Cambret Hill	44	51	41	47
Cartmel	22	28	25	32	Castleton	55	62	59	65
Catton Beacon	40	46	43	50	Chatburn	33	26	23	29
Chatton	39	45	49	42	Chesterfield	33	26	23	29
Chinley	57	64	61	67	Cleckheaton	55	62	59	65
Clovenfords	21	27	24	31	Congleton	51	44	41	47
Conisbrough	57	63	60	53	Coniston High Man	21	27	24	31
Cop Hill	22	28	25	32	Copley	62	55	59	65
Cornholme	58	64	61	54	Cowling	40	46	43	50
Cragg Vale	58	64	61	54	Creeetown	58	64	61	54
Crosby Ravensworth	57	63	60	53	Crosthwaite	57	63	60	53
Cullingworth	66	39	49	68	Dalton	40	46	43	53
Darwen	39	45	49	42	Delph	33	26	23	29
Dentdale	57	63	60	53	Dog Hill	40	46	43	53
Douglas (IoM)	68	66	48	56	Dronfield	55	62	59	65
Dumfries South	40	48	46	50	Durham	40	46	43	50
Edale	57	63	60	53	Elland	58	64	61	54
Elton	21	27	24	31	Emley Moor	44	52	47	41
Esh	39	45	49	42	Eskdale Green	22	28	25	32
Eston Nab	40	46	43	50	Eyemouth	33	26	23	29
Falstone	51	44	41	47	Far Highfield	48	66	56	68

Location				
Felling	52	50	46	66
Foxdale	33	26	23	29
Glencoyne	21	27	24	31
Glenmaye (IoM)	58	64	61	54
Glossop	22	28	25	32
Grasmere	57	63	60	53
Greystoke	57	63	60	53
Grinton Lodge	40	46	43	50
Hagg Wood	55	62	59	65
Haltwhistle	55	62	59	65
Haslingden	33	26	23	29
Hawick	33	26	23	29
Haydon Bridge	51	44	41	47
Hebden Bridge	22	28	25	32
Heyshaw	57	63	60	53
Holmfirth	39	66	56	68
Hulme	51	44	41	47
Hunmanby	40	46	43	50
Innerleithen	58	64	61	54
Jedburgh	68	44	41	47
Keighley Town	33	26	23	29
Kendal Fell	40	46	43	50
Kettlewell	49	42	39	45
Kimmeragh (IoM)	57	63	60	53
Kirkcudbright	21	27	24	31
Lancaster	31	27	24	21
Langley	21	27	24	31
Laxey	58	64	61	54
Limber Hill	40	46	43	50
Littleborough	21	27	24	31
Lorton	57	63	60	53
Luddenden	57	63	60	67
Macclesfield	22	28	25	32
Middleton	57	34	30	37
Millom Park	22	28	25	32
Minnigaff	33	26	29	23
Morpeth	22	28	25	32
Mottram	40	46	43	53
Newchurch	27	21	24	31
Norden	34	37	30	57
Oakenhead	51	44	41	47
Orton	40	46	43	50
Over Biddulph	34	57	30	48
Parbold	51	44	41	47
Pendle Forest	22	28	25	32
Peterlee	45	52	49	39
Pontop Pike	58	64	61	54
Port St Mary (IoM)	58	64	61	54
Portwood	22	28	32	25
Primrose Hill	57	62	60	67
Ravenscar	58	64	61	54
Ribblesdale	51	44	41	47
Romaldkirk	51	44	41	47
Rookhope	40	46	43	50
Rosedale Abbey	40	46	43	50
Saddleworth	52	45	49	42
Seaham	51	44	41	47
Selkirk	55	62	59	65
Fenham	21	27	24	31
Galashield	68	44	41	47
Glenluce	58	64	61	54
Glenridding	60	53	57	63
Gosforth	58	64	61	54
Grassington	33	26	23	29
Grimsby	39	45	42	49
Guisborough	57	63	60	53
Halifax	21	27	24	31
Hasland	57	63	60	53
Haughton Green	40	46	43	53
Hawkshead	33	26	23	29
Headingley	58	64	61	54
Hedleyhyope	40	46	43	50
Holmfield	55	62	59	65
Hope	22	28	25	32
Humshaugh	39	45	49	42
Idle	21	27	24	31
Ireshopeburn	55	62	59	65
Keighley	58	64	61	54
Kendal	58	64	61	54
Keswick	21	27	24	31
Kielder	33	26	23	29
Kirkby Stephen	57	63	60	53
Ladder Hill	33	26	23	29
Langholm	57	63	60	53
Lauder	22	28	25	32
Lees	22	28	32	25
Lincoln Central	39	45	42	52
Longwood Edge	55	62	59	65
Lowther Valley	48	40	46	50
Lydgate	33	26	23	29
Melling	57	63	60	53
Millhouse Green	58	64	61	54
Millthrop	48	66	56	68
Moffar	52	45	42	49
Moss Bank	21	27	24	31
New Galloway	33	26	23	29
Newton	33	26	23	29
North Oldham	21	27	24	31
Olivers Mount	57	63	60	53
Oughtibridge	55	62	59	65
Oxenhope	22	28	25	32
Peebles	22	28	25	32
Penny Bridge	33	26	23	29
Pinwherry	22	28	25	32
Pooley Bridge	48	40	46	50
Portpatrick	58	64	61	54
Prestbury	40	46	43	50
Ramsbotton	58	64	61	54
Ravenstonedale	57	63	60	53
Ripponden	58	64	61	54
Romiley	51	44	41	47
Roose	26	33	29	39
Rothbury	55	62	65	59
Sandale	22	67	-	-
Sedbergh	40	46	43	50
Shatton Edge	52	58	48	54

Sheffield	31	27	24	21	Shotleyfield	22	28	25	32
Skinningrove	40	46	43	50	Skipton	39	45	49	42
Skipton Town	21	27	24	31	St. Bees	58	64	61	54
Staithes	51	44	41	47	Staveley in Cartmel	40	46	43	53
Stockport	27	24	21	31	Stocksbridge	58	64	61	54
Storeton	22	28	25	32	Stow	33	26	23	29
Stranraer	57	63	60	53	Sunderland	40	46	43	50
Sutton in Craven	33	26	23	29	Thornhill	57	63	60	53
Threlkeld	57	63	60	53	Tideswell Moor	56	63	60	66
Todmorden	39	45	49	42	Totley Rise	39	45	49	42
Trawden	57	63	60	67	Union Mills (IoM)	39	45	52	42
Urswick	51	44	41	47	Wall	40	46	43	50
Walsden	57	63	60	67	Walsden South	40	46	43	53
Walton le Dale	21	27	24	31	Wardle	22	28	25	32
Weardale	44	51	41	47	Weaverthorpe	55	62	59	65
West Burton	40	46	43	50	West Kirby	21	27	24	31
Whaley Bridge	39	45	49	52	Whalley	40	46	43	53
Wharfedale	22	28	25	32	Wheatley	58	64	61	54
Whitaside	51	44	41	47	Whitby	55	62	59	65
Whitehaven	46	40	43	50	Whitewell	57	63	60	67
Whitworth	22	28	25	32	Wincobank	55	62	59	65
Windermere	51	44	41	47	Winter Hill	55	62	59	65
Woodnook	39	45	49	52	Wooler	22	28	25	32
Workington	58	64	61	54	Yetholm	51	44	41	47

MIDLANDS AND EASTERN ENGLAND

Aldeburgh	33	26	23	30	Allesley Park	22	28	25	32
Ambergate	22	28	25	32	Andoversford	55	62	59	65
Ascott u. Wychwood	21	27	24	31	Ashbourne	22	28	25	32
Ashford in Water	33	26	23	29	Belper	66	56	68	62
Birchover	39	45	49	42	Bolehill	63	57	53	60
Brailes	30	52	34	59	Bramford	21	27	24	31
Bretch Hill	65	48	55	67	Bridgnorth	62	68	56	66
Brierley Hill	57	63	60	53	Bromsgrove	31	27	24	21
Bucknell	39	45	49	42	Burnham	40	-	46	-
Bury St Edmunds	22	28	25	32	Charlbury	51	44	41	47
Cheadle	48	66	56	68	Clun	55	62	59	65
Coalbrookdale	51	44	47	41	Creake	39	45	49	42
Dallington Park	66	62	56	68	Darley Dale	30	48	34	52
Derby	48	-	30	-	Eardiston	58	64	61	54
Earl Sterndale	58	64	61	54	Eastwood	33	26	23	29
Edgbaston	21	27	24	31	Ewyas Harold	51	44	67	47
Felixstowe	31	63	60	67	Fenton	31	27	24	21
Garth Hill	57	63	60	53	Gib Heath	56	66	62	68
Gorleston on Sea	33	26	23	39	Gravelly Hill	66	56	62	68
Guiting Power	51	44	41	47	Haden Hill	39	52	49	42
Halesowen	58	64	61	54	Hamstead	21	27	24	31
Harborne	30	48	34	67	Hartington	66	48	56	68
Hazler Hill	51	44	41	47	Hereford	51	44	41	47
Hope Under Dinmore	63	57	60	53	Icomb Hill	22	28	25	32
Ipstones Edge	57	63	60	53	Ipswich	22	28	25	32
Ironbridge	58	64	61	54	Kenilworth	57	63	60	53
Kidderminster	58	64	61	54	Kimpton	45	56	52	48
King's Lynn	39	-	52	-	Kington	39	45	49	42
Kinver	66	48	56	68	Knucklas	39	45	42	49
Lark Stoke	33	26	23	29	Leamington Spa	56	62	66	68
Leek	22	28	25	32	Leicester City	22	28	25	32
Linnet Valley	33	26	23	29	Little Eaton	33	26	23	29

Little Walsingham	51	44	41	47	Long Compton	22	28	25	32
Ludlow	39	45	42	49	Luton	55	62	59	65
Malvern	56	62	66	68	Matlock	21	27	24	31
New Radnor	51	44	41	47	Norwich (Central)	39	45	49	42
Nottingham	21	27	24	31	Oakamoor	21	27	24	31
Oakeley Mynd	39	45	49	42	Over Norton	65	48	55	67
Overstrand	51	44	41	47	Oxford	57	63	60	53
Parwich	21	27	24	31	Perry Beaches	22	28	25	32
Peterchurch	57	63	60	53	Presteigne	48	56	52	66
Questlett	58	64	61	54	Redditch	22	28	25	32
Repton	48	68	56	66	Ridge Hill	22	28	25	32
Ross-on-Wye	55	62	65	59	Rugeley	66	48	56	68
Sandy Heath	31	27	24	21	Somersham	22	28	25	32
St. Briavels	40	46	43	50	Stamford	39	45	49	42
Stanton Moor	55	62	59	65	Sudbury	51	44	41	47
Sutton Coldfield	46	40	43	50	Tacolneston	62	55	59	65
Tenbury Wells	57	63	60	53	The Wrekin	26	33	23	29
Thetford	33	26	23	29	Turves Green	56	66	62	68
Upper Soudley	40	46	43	50	Waltham	58	64	61	54
Wells-next-the-Sea	43	-	50	-	West Runton	33	26	23	29
Whittingslow	57	63	60	53	Winchcombe	58	64	61	54
Winshill	66	48	56	68	Wivenhoe Park	58	64	61	54
Woodbridge	58	64	61	54	Woodford Halse	22	28	25	32

SOUTHERN ENGLAND

Aldbourne	21	27	24	31	Alderney	58	64	61	68
Alexandra Palace	58	64	61	54	Alton	49	62	59	52
Alverton	21	27	24	31	Ashburton	21	27	24	31
Assendon	55	68	58	65	Avening	51	44	41	47
Aveton Gifford	51	44	66	47	Backwell	22	28	25	32
Bampton	39	49	45	52	Barnstaple	40	46	43	30
Bath	22	28	25	32	Beacon Hill	57	63	60	53
Beaminster	55	62	59	65	Beer	55	62	59	65
Berrynarbor	22	28	25	32	Bevendean	40	46	43	29
Biggin Hill	45	52	49	67	Bincombe Hill	55	62	65	59
Bishop's Stortford	55	62	59	49	Blakeney	21	27	24	31
Bluebell Hill	40	46	43	65	Boscastle	33	26	23	29
Bossiney	58	64	61	54	Bovey Tracey	39	45	49	42
Bovington	51	44	41	47	Box	40	46	43	50
Brading	51	44	41	47	Branscombe	51	44	47	41
Braunton	39	45	49	42	Bridport	51	44	41	47
Brighstone	51	44	41	47	Brighton (Central)	39	45	41	47
Brighton (W'hawk Hill)	57	63	60	53	Bristol Barton House	21	27	24	31
Bristol Warmley	66	49	39	68	Brixham	40	46	43	50
Brushford	21	27	24	31	Bruton	40	46	43	50
Buckfastleigh	51	44	41	47	Burrington	57	63	60	53
Calne	21	27	24	31	Cane Hill	61	54	58	68
Canford Heath	39	45	68	42	Caradon Hill	22	28	25	32
Carhampton	21	27	24	31	Caterham	55	62	59	65
Cerne Abbas	22	28	25	32	Chagford	21	27	24	31
Chalford	21	27	24	31	Chalford Vale	68	46	43	50
Chambercombe	21	27	24	31	Charmouth	51	44	41	47
Chartham	21	27	24	31	Chatham Town	58	68	61	54
Chepping Wycombe	51	44	41	47	Chepstow	21	27	24	31
Cheselbourne	57	63	53	60	Chesham	40	46	43	50
Chideock	49	45	39	42	Chilfrome	39	49	45	52
Chingford	56	50	52	48	Chisbury	55	62	59	52
Chiseldon	30	49	34	67	Chitterne	40	46	43	50

Chudleigh	51	44	41	47	Cirencester	33	26	23	29
Clearwell	66	48	68	56	Clennon Valley	39	45	49	42
Coldean	65	42	44	68	Coleford	42	52	45	39
Combe Martin	39	45	49	42	Compton	51	44	68	47
Coombe	21	27	24	31	Corfe Castle	51	44	41	47
Corsham	51	44	41	47	Countisbury	39	66	49	68
Crediton	40	46	43	50	Crewkerne	40	46	43	50
Crockerton	51	44	41	47	Croyde	51	44	41	47
Croydon (Old Town)	49	56	52	67	Crystal Palace	26	33	23	30
Culm Valley	39	45	49	42	Dartmouth	51	44	41	47
Dawlish	55	62	59	65	Donhead	51	44	41	47
Dorking	51	44	41	47	Dover	50	56	66	53
Dover Town	33	26	23	30	Downderry	55	62	59	65
Dunsford	45	67	39	49	Dursley	40	46	43	50
East Dean	62	44	54	42	East Grinstead	40	56	46	59
Eastbourne	33	26	23	30	Eastbourne (Old Town)	40	46	43	58
Easter Compton	63	57	53	60	Edginswell	39	49	45	67
Edmonton	57	42	60	53	Elham	33	26	23	30
Exford	51	44	41	47	Farleigh	28	57	21	54
Farningham	48	56	50	58	Faversham	22	28	25	32
Finchley	52	56	49	67	Findon	51	44	41	47
Folkstone	33	26	23	30	Forest Row	48	54	62	66
Fowey	58	64	61	54	Fremont Point	51	44	41	47
Frome	21	27	24	31	Gorey	54	26	23	29
Gravesend	55	62	59	49	Great Missenden	58	64	61	54
Great Torrington	39	45	49	42	Greenwich	56	50	52	48
Guildford	40	46	43	50	Gulval	33	26	23	29
Gunnislake	40	46	43	50	Halwell	44	51	47	41
Hammersmith	48	62	59	65	Hampstead Heath	51	44	47	41
Hamstreet	33	26	23	30	Hangleton	39	45	49	42
Hannington	39	45	42	66	Harbertonford	39	45	49	42
Hartland	48	56	52	66	Haslemere	22	28	25	32
Hastings	22	25	28	32	Hastings Old Town	45	39	42	55
Hatch Bottom	-	49	-	-	Haywards Heath	39	45	43	41
Heathfield	49	52	64	67	Hele	40	46	43	50
Helston	58	64	61	54	Hemdean	49	52	56	59
Hemel Hempstead	51	44	41	47	Hemel Hempstead	58	63	61	54
Henley-on-Thames	48	64	67	54	Hertford	58	64	61	54
High Wycombe	55	62	59	65	Hollington Park	45	39	42	55
Honiton	49	39	52	45	Horn Street	58	44	41	47
Horndean	56	64	50	62	Hughenden	40	46	43	50
Huntshaw Cross	55	62	59	65	Hurstbourne Tarrant	22	28	32	25
Hutton	49	66	39	68	Hythe	21	27	24	31
Hythe (Hants)	-	59	-	-	Ilchester Crescent	40	46	43	50
Ilfracombe	58	64	61	54	Isles of Scilly	21	27	24	31
Ivybridge	39	45	42	49	Kenley	40	46	43	50
Kensal Town	56	49	52	67	Kewstoke	40	46	43	50
Kilve	49	66	39	68	Kings Weston Hill	45	48	42	52
Kingsbridge	40	46	43	50	Kingskerswell	55	68	48	65
Lamberhurst	54	60	58	62	Lambourn	55	62	59	52
Lea Bridge	55	62	39	59	Les Touillets	56	48	54	52
Lewes	22	28	25	32	Liverton	55	68	48	65
Looe	40	46	43	50	Lostwithiel	40	46	43	50
Luccombe	56	62	59	34	Lulworth	55	62	59	65
Luscombe Valley	39	45	49	42	Lydbrook	40	46	43	50
Lydden	43	46	40	64	Lyminge	22	28	25	32
Margate	22	28	25	32	Marlborough	22	28	25	32
Marlow Bottom	58	64	61	54	Marystow	39	45	49	42

Mendip	58	64	61	54	Mevagissey	40	46	43	50
Micklefield	54	64	57	67	Mickleham	61	55	58	68
Midhurst	61	55	58	68	Millbrook	51	44	41	47
Modbury	55	62	59	54	Monksilver	45	48	52	42
Montpelier	33	26	23	29	Mountfield	21	27	24	31
Muddiford	51	44	41	47	Nailsworth	33	26	23	29
New Addington	64	48	54	68	New Barnet	55	62	59	48
Newhaven	39	45	43	41	Newnham (Kent)	21	27	24	31
Newton Abbot	40	46	43	50	Newton Ferrers	55	62	59	54
North Bovey	40	46	43	50	North Hessary Tor	55	62	59	65
North Winchester	-	56	-	-	Occombe Valley	21	27	24	31
Ogbourne St George	40	46	43	50	Okehampton	39	45	49	42
Old Coulsdon	48	64	45	66	Orpington	55	62	59	66
Otford	57	63	60	53	Ovingdean	65	42	44	68
Parkend	51	44	41	47	Patcham	46	40	43	50
Penaligon Down	39	45	49	42	Pennsylvania	58	64	61	54
Penryn	55	62	59	65	Perranporth	55	62	59	65
Piddletrenthide	39	45	49	42	Pillowell	40	46	43	50
Plymouth North Rd	40	46	43	50	Plympton	58	64	61	54
Polperro	57	63	60	53	Poole	57	63	60	53
Poplar	45	66	49	68	Porlock	48	45	42	52
Port Isaac	55	62	65	59	Portbury	21	27	24	31
Porthleven	33	26	23	29	Porthtowan	21	27	24	31
Portishead	66	39	49	68	Portreath	33	26	23	29
Portslade	51	44	41	47	Poulner	39	45	68	42
Praa Sands	55	62	59	65	Preston	58	64	61	54
Rampisham	40	46	43	50	Ramsgate	33	26	23	30
Redbrook	39	45	42	52	Redcliff Bay	57	63	53	60
Redruth	51	44	41	47	Reigate	57	63	60	53
Roadwater	21	27	24	31	Rowridge	31	24	27	21
Rye	58	44	41	47	Salcombe	51	41	44	30
Salisbury	57	63	60	53	Saltdean	51	66	55	47
Seagry Crt, Swindon	44	51	41	47	Sedlescombe	33	26	23	30
Shrewton	51	44	41	47	Sidmouth	39	49	45	67
Singleton	51	44	41	47	Siston	31	24	34	21
Skirmett	51	44	41	47	Slad	33	26	23	29
Slapton	48	66	55	68	South Brent	40	46	43	50
Southway	55	62	59	65	St. Albans	49	63	57	67
St. Anthony Roseland	33	26	23	29	St. Austell	55	62	59	65
St. Brelades	57	67	63	54	St. Helier	55	62	59	65
St. Just	58	64	61	54	St. Marks	57	63	60	53
St. Neot	39	45	49	42	St. Peter Port	21	27	24	31
St. Thomas (Exeter)	51	44	41	47	Steyning	45	59	62	56
Stockland Hill	33	26	23	29	Stokeinteignhead	51	44	41	47
Stroud	48	45	42	52	Sutton	55	62	59	65
Sutton Row	22	28	25	32	Swimbridge	33	26	23	29
Tavistock	57	63	60	53	Tedburn St. Mary	42	48	52	31
Teignmouth	39	49	45	67	The Bournes	47	51	59	49
Tidworth	22	28	32	25	Till Valley	46	40	43	50
Tintern	21	27	24	31	Tiverton	40	46	43	50
Torquay Town	51	44	41	47	Torteval	50	40	46	66
Totnes	21	27	24	31	Truro	58	64	61	54
Tunbridge Wells	51	44	41	47	Turnpike Hill	58	44	41	47
Ubley	21	27	24	31	Upavon	33	26	23	29
Ventnor	39	45	49	42	Walthamstow North	45	66	49	68
Washford	49	66	39	68	Welwyn	40	46	43	50
West Lavington	21	27	24	31	West Wycombe	40	46	43	67
Westbourne	51	44	41	47	Weston Mill	49	42	39	45

	BBC1	BBC2	ITV	CH4		BBC1	BBC2	ITV	CH4
Westward Ho!	21	27	24	31	Westwood	40	46	43	50
Weymouth	40	46	43	50	Wid'combe in Moor	40	46	43	50
W'bourne Steepleton	39	49	45	66	W'bourne Stickland	40	46	43	50
Wonersh	48	65	52	67	Wooburn	49	52	56	68
Woodcombe	63	57	53	60	Woolacombe	39	45	42	49
Woolwich	57	63	60	67	Wootton Courtenay	22	28	25	32
Worlds End	43	50	46	68	Wye (Ashford)	22	28	25	32

N. IRELAND

	BBC1	BBC2	ITV	CH4		BBC1	BBC2	ITV	CH4
Armagh	39	45	49	42	Ballintoy	39	45	49	42
Ballycastle	39	45	49	42	Banbridge	44	48	46	50
Bangor	62	55	69	65	Belcoo	51	44	41	47
Bellair	48	56	52	67	Benagh	22	28	25	32
Black Mountain	39	45	49	41	Brougher Mountain	22	28	25	32
Buckna	51	44	41	47	Bushmills	51	44	41	47
Camlough	58	64	61	54	Carnmoney Hill	40	46	43	50
Castlederg	55	62	65	59	Claudy	57	63	60	53
Conlig	39	45	49	42	Cushendall	40	46	43	50
Cushendun	22	28	32	25	Derrygonnelly	51	44	47	66
Divis	31	27	24	21	Draperstown	39	45	49	42
Dromore	58	64	61	54	Ederny	65	59	62	55
Glenariff	58	64	61	54	Glenelly Valley	33	26	23	29
Glynn	58	64	61	54	Gornalee	21	27	24	31
Gortnageeragh	39	45	42	49	Kilkeel	39	45	49	42
Killowen Mountain	31	27	24	21	Larne	39	45	49	42
Leitrim	57	63	60	53	Limavady	55	62	59	65
Lisbellaw	55	62	59	65	Londonderry	51	44	41	47
Moneymore	39	45	49	42	Muldonagh	22	28	32	25
Newcastle (NI)	55	62	59	65	Newry North	51	44	41	47
Newry South	39	45	49	42	Newtownards	58	64	61	54
Plumbridge	52	66	56	68	Rostrevor Forest	48	40	46	50
Strabane	39	45	49	42	Whitehead	48	56	52	67

WALES

	BBC1	BBC2	ITV	C4/S4		BBC1	BBC2	ITV	C4/S4
Aberbeeg	40	46	43	50	Abercraf	22	28	25	32
Abercynon	64	66	58	54	Aberdare	21	27	24	31
Abergavenny	39	45	49	42	Abergwynfi	21	27	24	31
Abertillery	22	28	25	32	Abertridwr	57	63	60	53
Aberystwyth	58	64	61	54	Afon Dyfi	22	28	25	32
Alltwen	40	46	43	50	Amlwch	22	28	25	32
Arfon	51	44	41	47	Bagillt	57	-	-	53
Bala	33	26	23	29	Bargoed	21	27	24	31
Beddgelert	55	62	59	65	Bedlinog	21	27	24	31
Bethesda	57	63	60	53	Bethesda North	28	22	25	32
Betws-y-Coed	21	27	24	31	Betws-yn-Rhos	21	27	24	31
Blackmill	22	28	25	32	Blaenau Gwent	57	63	60	53
Blaenavon	57	63	60	53	Blaenllechau	21	27	24	31
Blaenplwyf	31	27	24	21	Blaina	40	46	43	50
Bow Street	51	44	41	47	Brechfa	21	27	31	24
Brecon	58	64	61	54	Briton Ferry	46	40	43	50
Broad Haven	58	64	61	54	Broeirion	33	26	29	23
Bronnant	34	26	23	30	Bronwydd Arms	21	27	31	24
Builth Wells	22	28	25	32	Burry Port	58	64	61	54
Caergybi	21	27	24	31	Caerhendy	21	27	24	31
Caernarfron	21	27	24	31	Carmel	57	63	60	53
Carno	21	27	24	31	Castle Caereinion	40	46	43	50
Cefn-Mawr	51	44	41	47	Cefn-Mawr B	58	64	61	54
Cemaes	40	46	43	50	Cerrigydrudion	33	26	23	29

Location					Location			
Chepstow	21	27	24	31	Cilfrew	39	45	49	52
Cilycym	21	27	31	24	Clydach	33	26	23	29
Clyro	51	44	41	47	Coed Derw	51	44	41	47
Conway	40	46	43	50	Corris	39	45	49	42
Corwen	22	28	25	32	Craig-Cefn-Parc	46	40	43	50
Crickhowell	21	27	24	31	Croeserw	58	64	61	54
Crucorney	21	27	24	31	Crumlin	56	66	60	68
Cwm Ffrwd-oer	39	46	43	50	Cwm Twrch	21	27	24	31
Cwmafon	21	27	24	31	Cwmaman	39	45	49	42
Cwmferlinfach	52	45	48	42	Cwmgors	21	27	24	31
Cwrtnewydd	51	44	41	47	Cyffylliog	22	28	25	32
Cynwyl Elfed	22	28	25	32	Deiniolen	22	28	25	32
Deri	22	28	25	32	Dolgellau	55	62	59	65
Dolwyddelan	51	44	41	47	Dolybont	58	64	61	54
Dowlais	58	64	61	54	Duffryn	22	28	25	32
Ebbw Vale	55	62	59	65	Efail Fach	39	45	49	52
Erwood	57	63	60	53	Evvw Vale South	27	21	24	31
Ferndale	57	63	60	53	Fernhill	55	62	59	65
Ferryside	21	27	24	31	Ffestiniog	22	28	25	32
Fishguard	58	64	61	54	Flint	46	-	-	44
Gelli-fendigaid	55	62	59	65	Gilfach	21	27	24	31
Glyn Ceiriog	58	64	61	54	Glyncorrwg	39	45	49	42
Glyndyfrdwy	55	62	59	65	Greenhill	21	27	24	31
Gronant	26	33	29	23	Haverfordwest	52	66	56	68
Holywell	47	-	-	51	Kerry	21	27	24	31
Kilvey Hill	33	26	23	29	Llanarmon-yn-lal	21	27	24	31
Llanbrynmair	22	28	25	32	Llandderfel	55	62	65	59
Llanddona	57	63	60	53	Llanddulas	33	26	23	29
Llandecwyn	58	64	61	54	Llandinam	44	51	41	47
Llandrindod Wells	39	45	49	42	Llandyfriog	22	28	25	32
Llandysul	57	63	60	53	Llanengan	58	64	61	54
Llanfach	57	63	60	53	Llanfoist	57	63	60	53
Llanfyllin	22	28	25	32	Llangadfan	22	28	25	32
Llangybi	22	28	25	32	Llangeinor	55	62	59	65
Llangernyw	22	28	32	25	Llangollen	57	63	60	53
Llangranog	22	28	25	32	Llangurig	33	26	23	29
Llangynog	55	62	65	59	Llanharan	21	27	24	31
Llanhilleth	39	45	49	42	Llanidloes	22	28	25	32
Llanrhaeadr-ym-Mct.	39	45	49	42	Llansawel	22	28	32	25
Llanuwchllyn	40	46	43	50	Llanwrtyd Wells	21	27	24	31
Llanelli	39	45	49	67	Llsywen	21	27	24	31
Llwyn Onn	22	28	25	32	Long Mountain	58	64	61	54
Machen Upper	55	65	62	68	Machynlleth	57	63	60	53
Maentwrog	40	46	43	50	Maesteg	22	28	25	32
Merthyr Tydfil	22	28	25	32	Mochdre	33	26	23	29
Moel-y-Parc	52	45	49	42	Moel-y-Sant	34	27	24	31
Monmouth	55	62	59	65	Morfa Nefyn	22	28	25	32
Mynydd Bach	58	64	61	54	Mynydd Emroch	40	46	43	50
Mynydd Machen	33	26	23	29	Mynydd Pencarreg	58	64	61	54
Nant-y-Moel	21	27	31	24	Nantyglo	57	63	60	53
Neath Abbey	66	48	42	56	Newport Bay	57	63	60	67
Ogmore Vale	57	63	60	53	Pembroke Dock	58	64	61	54
Pen-y-Banc	21	27	24	31	Pencader	33	26	23	29
Penderyn	39	45	49	42	Penmaen Rhos	22	28	25	32
Pennar	40	46	43	50	Pennorth	33	26	23	29
Penrhiwceiber	57	63	53	60	Penryhn-Coch	55	62	59	65
Pontardawe	58	64	61	68	Pontfadog	22	28	25	32
Pontypool	21	27	24	31	Pontypridd	22	28	25	32

Porth	40	46	43	50	Presely	46	40	43	50
Prestatyn	22	28	25	32	Pwll-glas	33	26	23	29
Rhayader	33	26	23	29	Rheola	55	62	59	65
Rhondda A	33	26	23	29	Rhondda B	66	39	49	68
Rhondda Fach	22	28	25	32	Rhymney	57	63	60	53
Risca	40	46	43	50	Sennybridge	40	46	43	50
South Maesteg	55	62	59	65	South Tredegar	52	45	49	39
St. Davids	33	26	23	29	St. Dogmaels	33	26	23	29
Taffs Well	55	62	59	65	Talley	39	45	49	42
Tenby	39	45	49	42	Ton Pentre	58	64	61	54
Tonypandy	55	62	59	65	Tonyrefail	55	62	59	65
Trebanog	21	27	24	34	Trecastle	22	28	25	32
Trefechan	39	45	42	49	Trefilan	57	63	60	53
Trefin	22	28	25	32	Trefor	39	45	49	42
Tregaron	62	68	56	66	Tregynon	22	28	25	32
Treharris	56	48	52	68	Tynewydd	55	62	59	65
Upper Killay	21	27	24	31	Usk	21	27	24	31
Van Terrace	39	45	49	42	Wattsville	63	57	60	53
Waunfawr	22	28	25	32	Wenvoe	44	51	41	47
Wrexham-Rhos	22	28	32	25	Ynys Owen	55	62	59	65
Ynys-Pennal	51	44	41	47	Ystalyfera	39	45	49	42
Ystumtuen	39	45	49	42					

CHANNEL 5

Belmont	56	Bilsdale	35	Black Hill	37
Black Mountain	37	Blaen Plwyf	56	Brighton	35
Burnhope	68	Caldbeck	56	Cambret Hill	37
Chelmsford	63	Churchdown Hill	48	Craigkelly	48
Croydon	37	Darvel	35	Durris	67
Emley Moor	37	Fawley	34	Fenham	56
Fenton	35	Hannington	35	Hastings	35
Huntshaw Cross	67	Kilvey Hill	35	Lichfield	37
Londonderry	31	Madingley	34	Mendip	37
Middleton	22	Milburn Muir	45	Mounteagle	67
Norwich Central	33	Nottingham	34	Olivers Mount	66
Oxford	49	Perth	55	Peterhead	68
Plympton	30	Presely	37	Redruth	37
Reigate	42	Ridge Hill	35	Salisbury	39
Sandy Heath	39	Selkirk	52	Sheffield	67
Storeton	39	Sudbury	35	Tacolneston	52
Tay Bridge	34	The Wrekin	35	Tunbridge Wells	37
Waltham	35	Winter Hill	48		

IRELAND

	RTE1	RTE2	TV3	TG4		RTE1	RTE2	TV3	TG4
Abbeyfeale	39	42	45	49	Ashleam	21	24	27	31
Achill	40	43	46	50	Avoca A	60	63	-	-
Aghavannagh	54	58	61	64	Avoca B	30	34	-	-
Annagary	23	26	30	34	Ballinastoe	30	34	-	-
Annascaul	30	34	-	-	Ballineen	40	43	46	50
Araglin	54	58	61	64	Ballingeary	54	58	61	64
Arainn Mhor	39	42	45	49	Ballinglen	21	24	27	31
Ardmore	54	58	61	64	Ballintrillick	30	34	67	37
Arklow	28	22	25	32	Ballyandreen	29	33	37	35
Arthurstown	55	59	62	65	Ballybofey/Stranorlar	54	58	61	64
Ashford	22	25	28	32	Ballydavid	22	25	28	32

	RTE1	RTE2	TV3	TG4
Ballymacarbry	54	58	61	64
Ballynakilly	22	25	28	32
Ballyporeen	48	52	-	-
Bandon	41	44	47	51
Bandon 1	22	25	30	34
Bandon 2	54	56	58	60
Bantry	-	-	45	-
Bantry	40	43	46	50
Barrroe	61	64	66	68
Bawnfine	22	25	28	32
Bealanabrack	39	42	45	49
Belgooly	54	58	61	64
Belgooly	21	23	25	29
Belgooly	29	33	35	37
Bellevue Greystones	53	57	60	63
Ben Gorm	54	58	61	64
Blarney	29	33	26	23
Bonane	39	42	45	49
Briska	54	58	61	64
Brittas Bay	29	33	35	-
Broadford	40	43	46	50
Cahir	40	43	46	50
Cahirciveen	39	42	45	49
Cairn Hill	40	43	46	50
Cappoquin/Dungvarvin	53	57	60	63
Carhan	48	52	-	-
Carlingford/Greenore	47	41	51	44
Carrick	21	24	27	31
Carrickmourne	54	58	61	64
Carrigadrohid	54	58	61	64
Carrigaline HP	40	42	45	48
Carriganes	41	44	47	51
Carriganes	41	44	47	51
Carriganimmy	23	25	29	33
Cashel	28	22	25	32
Casla	39	42	45	49
Castlebar	29	33	26	23
Castletownbere	53	57	60	63
Clemont Carn	52	56	66	68
Clermont Carn B	29	33	23	26
Clifden	22	25	28	32
Clifden Glen	39	42	45	49
Cloghan	40	43	46	50
Cloghane	30	34	-	-
Cloghroe	61	64	66	69
Clonakilty	39	42	45	49
Clnakilty	61	64	66	69
Clonmany	39	42	45	49
Clonmel	46	40	43	50
Collins Barracks	39	49	46	43
Cornamona	21	24	27	31
Craffield	48	52	-	-
Crossbarry/Halfway	54	58	61	64
Crosshaven	55	59	62	65

	RTE1	RTE2	TV3	TG4
Crosshaven	22	25	30	34
Curraun	30	34	-	-
Dingle	23	26	29	33
Donard	39	42	45	49
Dooncrton	21	24	27	31
Dowra	39	42	49	45
Drimoleague	39	42	49	45
Dromanassig	54	58	61	64
Dromor	54	58	61	64
Dromore Cork	41	44	47	51
Droumgarrif	22	25	28	32
Drummin	53	57	59	-
Drumshambo	30	34	37	48
Dunlewy	39	42	45	49
Dunmanway	41	44	47	51
Dunmore East	55	59	62	65
Dunquin	30	34	26	23
East Ferry	21	24	28	32
Enniskeane	55	59	62	65
Ennistymon	54	58	61	64
Failmore	54	58	61	64
Falcarragh	21	24	31	27
Fallmoe	22	25	28	32
Fanad	67	58	61	64
Fanore	30	34	-	-
Fennell's Bay	41	44	47	51
Feohanagh	21	24	27	31
Feroy	39	42	45	49
Fermoy	23	25	29	33
Finvarra	21	24	27	31
Fountainstown	30	34	-	-
Fountainstown	40	42	45	48
Glanlea	29	33	35	37
Glanmire	41	44	47	51
Gleann Na Ngealt	40	43	46	50
Gleann Na Ngealt	30	34	-	-
Glenbeigh	39	42	45	49
Glencar (Co. Kerry)	22	25	28	32
Glencar (Co. Leitrim)	39	42	45	49
Glencolumbkille	39	42	45	49
Glencullen	54	58	61	64
Glenisland	30	34	37	-
Glenmalure	30	34	-	-
Glennagevlagh	39	42	45	49
Glenties	40	43	46	50
Glounaclohy	23	25	29	33
Gorey	54	58	61	64
Headford	39	42	45	49
Hilltown	23	26	29	33
Hollyford	30	34	-	-
Holywell Hill	23	26	29	33
Inchigeelagh	40	43	46	50
Iniscleire	54	58	61	64
Inishannon	40	43	46	50

	RTE1	RTE2	TV3	TG4		RTE1	RTE2	TV3	TG4
Inishannon	21	23	29	33	Monaghan NW	62	55	59	65
Inistioge	53	57	60	63	Monasootagh	54	58	61	64
Iorras	27	21	24	31	Monavullagh	61	64	66	69
Keimineigh	30	34	-	-	Morley's Bridge	29	33	35	37
Kells Bay	22	25	28	32	Mossy Glen	53	57	60	63
Kilbane	30	34	-	-	Mount Eagle	40	43	46	50
Kilduff	41	44	47	51	Mount Gabriel	29	33	23	26
Kilgarvan	49	39	42	45	Mount Leinster	30	34	26	23
Kilkee	54	58	61	64	Mountainstage	22	25	28	32
Killaloe	54	58	61	64	Moville	40	43	46	50
Killeagh	54	58	61	64	Mullaghanish	21	24	27	31
Kilmacomma	22	25	28	32	Mulrany	55	59	62	65
Kilmacthomas	54	58	61	64	Myrtleville Bay	46	39	43	-
Kilpedder	30	34	-	-	Nebaun	55	59	62	65
Kinsale	30	34	-	-	Nire Valley	21	24	27	31
Kinsale	41	44	47	51	Passge West A	29	33	26	23
Kinsale	54	56	58	62	Rathmullen	54	58	61	64
Kippure	37	65	62	59	Rinvyle	53	57	60	63
Knockalafalla	55	59	62	65	Rockchapel	40	43	46	50
Knockanedin	30	34	-	-	Rosscarbery	53	57	60	63
Knockfola	30	34	-	-	Rossinver	30	34	37	48
Knockgraffon	21	24	27	31	Rushbrooke	32	36	38	68
Knockmoyle	53	57	60	63	Schull	30	34	-	-
Knocknascrow	52	54	56	58	Slveen	34	39	49	52
Lahinch	40	43	46	50	Sligo Twn	41	44	51	47
Laragh/Glendalough	41	44	47	51	Spur Hill	53	57	60	63
Lauragh	55	59	62	65	Srahmore	30	34	-	-
Leap	41	44	47	51	Suir Valley	53	57	60	63
Leenaun	21	24	27	31	Tawnycullawee	-	-	39	-
Letterkenny	52	56	66	68	Termo	54	58	61	64
Listowel	53	57	60	63	The Gle	29	33	35	37
Lomanaugh	29	33	35	37	Three Rock	29	33	35	55
Loughtalt	63	67	-	-	Timoleague	30	34	-	-
Maam	21	24	27	31	Tinahely	48	52	-	-
Macroom	62	65	59	55	Tomriland	21	24	27	31
Maghera	52	56	66	68	Toomes Bridge	41	44	47	51
Magheroarty	21	24	-	31	Tracton/Minane	48	52	-	-
Malin	22	25	28	32	Truskmore	53	57	60	63
Mamclasach	40	43	46	50	Upper Pembrook	61	64	66	69
Meenacreeva	23	26	30	34	West Port	54	58	61	64
Meenacuing	30	24	-	-	Wexford	66	52	56	68
Midleton	46	40	43	50	Wicklow	66	49	56	68
Miltown Malbay	53	57	60	63	Woodcoc Hill	39	42	45	49
Minane Brdge	54	56	58	60	Woodenbridge	30	34	-	-
Mitchestown	41	44	47	51	Youghal East	41	44	47	51
Monaghan Lugad	54	58	61	64	Youghal South	29	33	35	37

Local Radio and TV Talkback, Links and Theatre Radio Microphones

Base	Mobile	Mode	Location	User and Notes
470.00000		NFM	Nationwide	JFMG Radio Microphone Ch.21
470.05000		NFM	Borehamwood	Big Brother (2002) Production
473.68750		NFM	London	Radio Mic Canadian Broadcasting Corporation
473.95000		NFM	Newcastle	Metro Radio Talkback
474.01250		NFM	Borehamwood	Big Brother (2002) Production Talkback
474.05000		NFM	Borehamwood	Big Brother (2002) Production Talkback
474.05000		NFM	Norwich	Anglia TV Studio Ch.1
474.10000		NFM	London	Southbank Studio
474.10000		NFM	Norwich	Anglia TV Studio Ch.2
474.20000		NFM	Norwich	Anglia TV Studio Ch.3
474.40000		NFM	Norwich	Anglia TV Studio Ch.4
474.75000	470.25000	NFM	London	BBC O/B Producers Link
475.00000	470.40000	NFM	London	BBC O/B Producers Link
475.17500	470.57500	NFM	London	BBC O/B Producers Link
475.25000		NFM	London	BBC O/B Producers Link
476.97500		NFM	England SE	BBC Southeast TV O/B
478.00000		NFM	Nationwide	JFMG Radio Microphone Ch.21
478.70000		NFM	London	Palladium Radio Microphone
479.65000		NFM	London	Her Majesty's Theatre Radio Microphone
479.65000		NFM	London	Palladium Radio Microphone
479.95000		NFM	London	Her Majesty's Theatre Radio Microphone
480.20000		NFM	London	Her Majesty's Theatre Radio Microphone
480.20000		NFM	London	Palladium Radio Microphone
483.75000		NFM	London	Prince Edward Theatre Radio Microphone
486.00000		NFM	Nationwide	JFMG Radio Microphone Ch.22
494.00000		NFM	Nationwide	JFMG Radio Microphone Ch.23
495.56750		NFM	Glasgow	Victoria's Nightclub Radio Microphone
498.72500		NFM	London	Prince Edward Theatre Radio Microphone
500.00000		AM	Nationwide	NATO Mayday Discrete
502.00000		NFM	Nationwide	JFMG Radio Microphone Ch.24
510.00000		NFM	Nationwide	JFMG Radio Microphone Ch.25
518.00000		NFM	Nationwide	JFMG Radio Microphone Ch.26
526.00000		NFM	Nationwide	JFMG Radio Microphone Ch.27
534.00000		NFM	Nationwide	JFMG Radio Microphone Ch.28
542.00000		NFM	Nationwide	JFMG Radio Microphone Ch.29
550.00000		NFM	Nationwide	JFMG Radio Microphone Ch.30
558.00000		NFM	Nationwide	JFMG Radio Microphone Ch.31
566.00000		NFM	Nationwide	JFMG Radio Microphone Ch.32
574.00000		NFM	Nationwide	JFMG Radio Microphone Ch.33
582.00000		NFM	Nationwide	JFMG Radio Microphone Ch.34
590.00000		NFM	Nationwide	JFMG Radio Microphone Ch.35

590.0000 - 598.0000 MHz   Civil & Defence Radar

Local Radio and TV Talkback, Links and Theatre Radio Microphones

Base	Mobile	Mode	Location	User and Notes
598.00000		NFM	Nationwide	JFMG Radio Microphone Ch.36
602.20250	608.20250	NFM	Nationwide	UK Mod Satcom H45/H46 Tx10/Nx10
602.21250	608.21250	NFM	Nationwide	UK Mod Satcom H45 Tx1(602) H46 Nx1(608)
602.22250	608.22250	NFM	Nationwide	UK Mod Satcom TX2/NX2
602.23250	608.23250	NFM	Nationwide	UK Mod Satcom TX3/NX3
602.24250	608.24250	NFM	Nationwide	UK Mod Satcom TX4/NX4
602.25250	608.25250	NFM	Nationwide	UK Mod Satcom TX5/NX5
602.26250	608.26250	NFM	Nationwide	UK Mod Satcom TX6/NX6
602.27250	608.27250	NFM	Nationwide	UK Mod Satcom TX7/NX7

Base	Mobile	Mode	Location	User and Notes
602.28250	608.28250	NFM	Nationwide	UK Mod Satcom TX8/NX8
602.29250	608.29250	NFM	Nationwide	UK Mod Satcom TX9/NX9
606.00000		NFM	Nationwide	JFMG Radio Microphone Ch.37
614.00000		NFM	Nationwide	JFMG Radio Microphone Ch.38
622.00000		NFM	Nationwide	JFMG Radio Microphone Ch.39
630.00000		NFM	Nationwide	JFMG Radio Microphone Ch.40
638.00000		NFM	Nationwide	JFMG Radio Microphone Ch.41
646.00000		NFM	Nationwide	JFMG Radio Microphone Ch.42
654.00000		NFM	Nationwide	JFMG Radio Microphone Ch.43
662.00000		NFM	Nationwide	JFMG Radio Microphone Ch.44
670.00000		NFM	Nationwide	JFMG Radio Microphone Ch.45
678.00000		NFM	Nationwide	JFMG Radio Microphone Ch.46
686.00000		NFM	Nationwide	JFMG Radio Microphone Ch.47
694.00000		NFM	Nationwide	JFMG Radio Microphone Ch.48
702.00000		NFM	Nationwide	JFMG Radio Microphone Ch.49
710.00000		NFM	Nationwide	JFMG Radio Microphone Ch.50
718.00000		NFM	Nationwide	JFMG Radio Microphone Ch.51
726.00000		NFM	Nationwide	JFMG Radio Microphone Ch.52
734.00000		NFM	Nationwide	JFMG Radio Microphone Ch.53
742.00000		NFM	Nationwide	JFMG Radio Microphone Ch.54
750.00000	758.00000	NFM	London	BBC Eastenders Radio Microphones
750.00000		NFM	Nationwide	JFMG Radio Microphone Ch.55
758.00000		NFM	Nationwide	JFMG Radio Microphone Ch.56
766.00000		NFM	Nationwide	JFMG Radio Microphone Ch.57
768.30000		NFM	London	Cirque De Soleil Talkback
774.00000		NFM	Nationwide	JFMG Radio Microphone Ch.58
782.00000		NFM	Nationwide	JFMG Radio Microphone Ch.59
790.00000		NFM	Nationwide	JFMG Radio Microphone Ch.60
798.00000		NFM	Nationwide	JFMG Radio Microphone Ch.61
802.60000		WFM	London	Cirque De Soleil Radio Microphones
806.00000		NFM	Nationwide	JFMG Radio Microphone Ch.62
806.30000		WFM	Borehamwood	Big Brother (2002) Radio Microphone
806.30000		WFM	Borehamwood	Big Brother (2003) Radio Microphone
806.95000		WFM	Borehamwood	Big Brother (2003) Radio Microphone
807.50000		WFM	Borehamwood	Big Brother (2002) Radio Microphone
807.50000		WFM	Borehamwood	Big Brother (2003) Radio Microphone
807.90000		WFM	Borehamwood	Big Brother (2002) Radio Microphone
807.90000		WFM	Borehamwood	Big Brother (2003) Radio Microphone
808.40000		WFM	Borehamwood	Big Brother (2002) Radio Microphone
808.40000		WFM	Borehamwood	Big Brother (2003) Radio Microphone
808.90000		WFM	Borehamwood	Big Brother (2002) Radio Microphone
809.30000		WFM	Borehamwood	Big Brother (2002) Radio Microphone
809.30000		WFM	Borehamwood	Big Brother (2003) Radio Microphone
809.95000		WFM	Borehamwood	Big Brother (2003) Radio Microphone
810.40000		WFM	Borehamwood	Big Brother (2002) Radio Microphone
811.10000		WFM	Borehamwood	Big Brother (2002) Radio Microphone
811.10000		WFM	Borehamwood	Big Brother (2003) Radio Microphone
811.60000		WFM	Borehamwood	Big Brother (2002) Radio Microphone
812.20000		WFM	Borehamwood	Big Brother (2002) Radio Microphone
813.30000		WFM	London	Cirque de Soleil Radio Microphone
814.00000		NFM	Nationwide	JFMG Radio Microphone Ch.63
820.25000		WFM	Widnes	RefCall Rugby League
820.25000		WFM	Leigh	RefCall Rugby League
822.00000		NFM	Nationwide	JFMG Radio Microphone Ch.64
830.00000		NFM	Nationwide	JFMG Radio Microphone Ch.65
838.00000		WFM	Nationwide	JFMG Radio Microphone Ch.66

Base	Mobile	Mode	Location	User and Notes
838.10000		WFM	Torquay	Babbacombe Theatre Radio Microphone
839.40000		WFM	Torquay	Babbacombe Theatre Radio Microphone
841.10000		WFM	Torquay	Babbacombe Theatre Radio Microphone
846.00000		WFM	Nationwide	JFMG Radio Microphone Ch.67
849.70000		WFM	Torquay	Babbacombe Theatre Radio Microphone
850.00000		WFM	Anglia	Anglia TV Radio Microphones
852.20000		WFM	Nationwide	Sky TV Radio Microphones
852.75000		WFM	Cardiff	BBC O/B
854.00000		NFM	Nationwide	JFMG Radio Microphone Ch.68
854.62500		NFM	Nationwide	Radio Microphones
854.77500		NFM	Nationwide	JFMG Mono High Power Sound Link
854.90000		WFM	London	This Morning Link Southbank Studio
854.90000		NFM	London	Prince Edward Theatre Radio Microphone
854.90000		NFM	London	Carling Apollo Theatre Radio Microphone
854.90000		WFM	Wales	Rugby Union Referees Radio Microphones
854.90000		NFM	London	JFMG Radio Microphone Mobile Ch.MI 14
855.07500		NFM	Nationwide	JFMG Mono High Power Sound Link
855.27500		NFM	London	Palladium Radio Microphone
855.27500		NFM	London	Prince Edward Theatre Radio Microphone
855.27500		NFM	Nationwide	JFMG Radio Microphone Mobile Ch.MI 15
855.40000		NFM	Nationwide	JFMG Mono Low Power Sound Link
855.45000		NFM	Nationwide	JFMG Mono Low Power Sound Link
855.47500		NFM	Nationwide	JFMG Stereo Low Power Sound Link
855.50000		NFM	Nationwide	JFMG Mono Low Power Sound Link
855.55000		NFM	Nationwide	JFMG Mono Low Power Sound Link
855.60000		NFM	Nationwide	JFMG Mono Low Power Sound Link
855.65000		NFM	Nationwide	JFMG Mono Low Power Sound Link
855.67500		NFM	Nationwide	JFMG Stereo Low Power Sound Link
855.70000		NFM	Nationwide	JFMG Mono Low Power Sound Link
855.75000		NFM	Nationwide	JFMG Mono Low Power Sound Link
855.87500		NFM	London	Palladium Radio Microphone
855.90000		NFM	London	Prince Edward Theatre Radio Microphone
855.90000		NFM	London	Carling Apollo Theatre Radio Microphone
855.90000		WFM	Anglia	Anglia TV Radio Microphone
855.90000		WFM	Nationwide	JFMG Radio Microphone Mobile Ch.MI 16
856.10000		WFM	Woodbridge	Riverside Theatre Radio Microphone
856.17500		NFM	London	Prince Edward Theatre Radio Microphone
855.17500		WFM	Nationwide	JFMG Radio Microphone Mobile Ch.MI 20
856.22500		NFM	London	Carling Apollo Theatre Radio Microphone
856.22500		NFM	London	Palace Theatre Radio Microphone
856.22500		NFM	London	Palladium Radio Microphone
856.30000		NFM	Nationwide	JFMG Mono Low Power Sound Link
856.35000		NFM	Nationwide	JFMG Mono Low Power Sound Link
856.37500		NFM	Nationwide	JFMG Mono Low Power Sound Link
856.40000		NFM	Nationwide	JFMG Mono Low Power Sound Link
856.40000		WFM	Woodbridge	Riverside Theatre Radio Microphone
856.45000		NFM	Nationwide	JFMG Mono Low Power Sound Link
856.47500		NFM	Suffolk	BBC Radio Suffolk Radio Microphone
856.50000		NFM	London	London Underground Wireless PA, Kings Cross
856.57500		NFM	London	Palace Theatre Radio Microphone
856.57500		NFM	London	Palladium Radio Microphone
856.57500		NFM	London	Prince of Wales Theatre Radio Microphone
856.57500		NFM	London	JFMG Radio Microphone Mobile Ch.MI 21
856.72500		NFM	Nationwide	JFMG Mono Low Power Sound Link
856.77500		NFM	Nationwide	JFMG Mono Low Power Sound Link
856.80000		NFM	Nationwide	JFMG Stereo Low Power Sound Link

Base	Mobile	Mode	Location	User and Notes
856.82500		NFM	Nationwide	JFMG Mono Low Power Sound Link
856.87500		NFM	Nationwide	JFMG Mono Low Power Sound Link
856.97500		NFM	London	Carling Apollo Theatre Radio Microphone
856.97500		NFM	London	Palace Theatre Radio Microphone
856.97500		NFM	London	Palladium Radio Microphone
856.97500		NFM	London	Prince of Wales Theatre Radio Microphone
857.15000		WFM	Woodbridge	Riverside Theatre Radio Microphone
857.20000		NFM	London	Palace Theatre Radio Microphone
857.30000		WFM	Torquay	Babbacombe Theatre Radio Microphone
857.35000		NFM	Nationwide	JFMG Mono Low Power Sound Link
857.40000		NFM	Nationwide	JFMG Mono Low Power Sound Link
857.40000		NFM	Woodbridge	Riverside Theatre Radio Microphone
857.42500		NFM	Nationwide	JFMG stereo High/Low Power Alternate
857.45000		NFM	Nationwide	JFMG Mono Low Power Sound Link
857.50000		NFM	Nationwide	JFMG Mono Low Power Sound Link
857.62500		NFM	Nationwide	JFMG Radio Microphone Mobile Ch.M1 22
857.70000		NFM	London	Carling Apollo Radio Microphone
857.70000		NFM	London	Palace Theatre Radio Microphone
857.70000		NFM	London	Palladium Radio Microphone
857.70000		NFM	London	Prince of Wales Theatre Radio Microphone
857.77500		NFM	Nationwide	JFMG set 3 Radio Mic co-ord Ch.68
857.95000		NFM	London	Prince Edward Theatre Radio Microphone
857.95000		NFM	Nationwide	JFMG Radio Microphone Mobile Ch.M1 23
858.12500		NFM	London	Carling Apollo Radio Microphone
858.12500		NFM	London	Palace Theatre Radio Microphone
858.12500		NFM	London	Prince of Wales Theatre Radio Microphone
858.20000		NFM	London	Prince Edward Theatre Radio Microphone
858.20000		NFM	Nationwide	JFMG Radio Microphone Mobile Ch.M1 24
858.25000		NFM	London	Hare Chrisna Band Radio Microphone
858.57500		NFM	England SE	BBC News Southeast Radio Microphone
858.57500		NFM	London	Carling Apollo Radio Microphone
858.57500		NFM	London	Palace Theatre Radio Microphone
858.57500		NFM	London	Palladium Radio Microphone
858.57500		NFM	London	Prince of Wales Theatre Radio Microphone
858.65000		NFM	Nationwide	JFMG Radio Microphone Mobile Ch.M1 24
858.70000		WFM	London	London Underground Wireless PA Leicester Square
858.90000		WFM	Woodbridge	Riverside Theatre Radio Microphone
858.97500		NFM	London	Prince Edward Theatre Radio Microphone
859.15000		NFM	London	Carling Apollo Radio Microphone
859.15000		NFM	London	Palace Theatre Radio Microphone
859.15000		NFM	London	Prince of Wales Theatre Radio Microphone
859.47500		WFM	Suffolk	BBC Radio Suffolk Radio Microphone
859.50000		NFM	London	Prince Edward Theatre Radio Microphone
859.52500		WFM	Woodbridge	Riverside Theatre Radio Microphone
859.70000		WFM	Torquay	Babbacombe Theatre Radio Microphone
859.80000		WFM	Norwich	BBC Look East Talkback
860.27500		NFM	Nationwide	JFMG Mono High Power O/B sound link
860.40000		NFM	London	Carling Apollo Radio Microphone
860.40000		NFM	London	Prince Edward Theatre Radio Microphone
860.40000		NFM	Nationwide	JFMG Radio Microphone Mobile Ch.MI
860.52500		NFM	Nationwide	JFMG Mono High Power O/B sound link
860.52500		NFM	Nationwide	JFMG Mono Low Power O/B sound link
860.57500		NFM	Nationwide	JFMG Mono High Power O/B sound link
860.57500		NFM	Nationwide	JFMG Mono Low Power O/B sound link
860.60000		NFM	Nationwide	JFMG Stereo High Power Sound Link
860.60000		NFM	Nationwide	JFMG Stereo Low Power Sound Link

Base	Mobile	Mode	Location	User and Notes
860.62500		NFM	Nationwide	JFMG Mono High Power Sound Link
860.62500		NFM	Nationwide	JFMG Mono Low Power Sound Link
860.67500		NFM	Nationwide	JFMG Mono High Power Sound Link
860.67500		NFM	Nationwide	JFMG Mono Low Power Sound Link
860.72500		NFM	Nationwide	JFMG Mono High Power Sound Link
860.90000		NFM	London	Carling Apollo Radio Microphone
859.90000		NFM	London	Palace Theatre Radio Microphone
860.90000		NFM	London	Prince Edward Theatre Radio Microphone
860.90000		NFM	Wales	Rugby Union Referees Radio Microphones
860.90000		NFM	Nationwide	JFMG Radio Microphone Mobile Ch.MI 18
861.15000		WFM	Torquay	Babbacombe Theatre Radio Microphone
861.20000		NFM	London	Carling Apollo Radio Microphone
861.20000		NFM	London	Palace Theatre Radio Microphone
861.20000		NFM	London	Prince Edward Theatre Radio Microphone
861.20000		NFM	London	Prince of Wales Theatre Radio Microphone
861.20000		NFM	Nationwide	JFMG Radio Microphone Mobile Ch.MI 26
861.55000		NFM	London	Prince Edward Theatre Radio Microphone
861.55000		NFM	Nationwide	JFMG Radio Microphone Mobile Ch.MI 27
861.55000		WFM	Woodbridge	Riverside Theatre Radio Microphone
861.60000		WFM	Torquay	Babbacombe Theatre Radio Microphone
861.75000		NFM	London	Carling Apollo Radio Microphone
861.75000		NFM	London	Palace Theatre Radio Microphone
861.75000		NFM	London	Palladium Radio Microphone
861.75000		NFM	London	Prince Edward Theatre Radio Microphone
861.75000		NFM	Nationwide	JFMG Radio Microphone Mobile Ch.MI 19
861.92500		NFM	Nationwide	JFMG Set 3 Radio Mic Co-Ord Ch.68

863.000 - 865.000 MHz — Licence Free Band for Low Power Devices such as Cordless Headphones & Speakers

Base	Mobile	Mode	Location	User and Notes
863.70000		WFM	Nationwide	Sennheiser Headphones/Ross Wireless Speakers
863.72500		WFM	Nationwide	Sennheiser Headphones/Ross Wireless Speakers
863.77500		WFM	Nationwide	Sennheiser Headphones/Ross Wireless Speakers
863.80000		WFM	Nationwide	Sennheiser Headphones/Ross Wireless Speakers
863.82500		WFM	Nationwide	Sennheiser Headphones/Ross Wireless Speakers
863.85000		WFM	Nationwide	Sennheiser Headphones/Ross Wireless Speakers
863.87500		WFM	Nationwide	Sennheiser Headphones/Ross Wireless Speakers
863.97500		WFM	Nationwide	Sennheiser Headphones/Ross Wireless Speakers
864.00000		WFM	Nationwide	Sennheiser Headphones/Ross Wireless Speakers

866.000 - 868.000 MHz — Cordless Audio Devices & Asset Tracking Systems

868.000 - 870.000 MHz — Short Range Devices

870.000 - 888.000 MHz — Government, Fixed & Mobile
871.000 - 876.000   Tetra (Mobile)

888.000 - 889.000 MHz — Low Power Systems & Anti-Theft Devices

880-000 - 915.000 MHz — Digital Cellular Radio (GSM) Telephones

915.000 - 933.000 MHz — Fixed, Mobile & Radiolocation
916.000 - 921.000   Harmonised Band for TETRA (Base)
917.000 - 933.000   Was Used for ETACS
926.000 - 934.000   Radio Astronomy - Used for Pulsars

Base	Mobile	Mode	Location	User and Notes

925.000 - 960.000 MHz   **Digital Cellular Radio Telephones (GSM)**

935.000 - 942.000 MHz   **Radio Location Devices**

959.0125 - 959.9875 MHz   **Cybernet/Uniden Cordless Telephones**

Base	Mobile	Mode	Location	User and Notes
959.01250	914.01250	NFM	Nationwide	Channel 1
959.02500	914.02500	NFM	Nationwide	Channel 2
959.03750	914.03750	NFM	Nationwide	Channel 3
959.05000	914.05000	NFM	Nationwide	Channel 4
959.06250	914.06250	NFM	Nationwide	Channel 5
959.07500	914.07500	NFM	Nationwide	Channel 6
959.08750	914.08750	NFM	Nationwide	Channel 7
959.10000	914.10000	NFM	Nationwide	Channel 8
959.11250	914.11250	NFM	Nationwide	Channel 9
959.12500	914.12500	NFM	Nationwide	Channel 10
959.13750	914.13750	NFM	Nationwide	Channel 11
959.15000	914.15000	NFM	Nationwide	Channel 12
959.16250	914.16250	NFM	Nationwide	Channel 13
959.17500	914.17500	NFM	Nationwide	Channel 14
959.18750	914.18750	NFM	Nationwide	Channel 15
959.20000	914.20000	NFM	Nationwide	Channel 16
959.21250	914.21250	NFM	Nationwide	Channel 17
959.22500	914.22500	NFM	Nationwide	Channel 18
959.23750	914.23750	NFM	Nationwide	Channel 19
959.25000	914.25000	NFM	Nationwide	Channel 20
959.26250	914.26250	NFM	Nationwide	Channel 21
959.27500	914.27500	NFM	Nationwide	Channel 22
959.28750	914.28750	NFM	Nationwide	Channel 23
959.30000	914.30000	NFM	Nationwide	Channel 24
959.31250	914.31250	NFM	Nationwide	Channel 25
959.32500	914.32500	NFM	Nationwide	Channel 26
959.33750	914.33750	NFM	Nationwide	Channel 27
959.35000	914.35000	NFM	Nationwide	Channel 28
959.36250	914.36250	NFM	Nationwide	Channel 29
959.37500	914.37500	NFM	Nationwide	Channel 30
959.38750	914.38750	NFM	Nationwide	Channel 31
959.40000	914.40000	NFM	Nationwide	Channel 32
959.41250	914.41250	NFM	Nationwide	Channel 33
959.42500	914.42500	NFM	Nationwide	Channel 34
959.43750	914.43750	NFM	Nationwide	Channel 35
959.45000	914.45000	NFM	Nationwide	Channel 36
959.46250	914.46250	NFM	Nationwide	Channel 37
959.47500	914.47500	NFM	Nationwide	Channel 38
959.48750	914.48750	NFM	Nationwide	Channel 39
959.50000	914.50000	NFM	Nationwide	Channel 40
959.51250	914.51250	NFM	Nationwide	Channel 41
959.52500	914.52500	NFM	Nationwide	Channel 42
959.53750	914.53750	NFM	Nationwide	Channel 43
959.55000	914.55000	NFM	Nationwide	Channel 44
959.56250	914.56250	NFM	Nationwide	Channel 45
959.57500	914.57500	NFM	Nationwide	Channel 46
959.58750	914.58750	NFM	Nationwide	Channel 47
959.60000	914.60000	NFM	Nationwide	Channel 48
959.61250	914.61250	NFM	Nationwide	Channel 49
959.62500	914.62500	NFM	Nationwide	Channel 50

Base	Mobile	Mode	Location	User and Notes
959.63750	914.63750	NFM	Nationwide	Channel 51
959.65000	914.65000	NFM	Nationwide	Channel 52
959.66250	914.66250	NFM	Nationwide	Channel 53
959.67500	914.67500	NFM	Nationwide	Channel 54
959.68750	914.68750	NFM	Nationwide	Channel 55
959.70000	914.70000	NFM	Nationwide	Channel 56
959.71250	914.71250	NFM	Nationwide	Channel 57
959.72500	914.72500	NFM	Nationwide	Channel 58
959.73750	914.73750	NFM	Nationwide	Channel 59
959.75000	914.75000	NFM	Nationwide	Channel 60
959.76250	914.76250	NFM	Nationwide	Channel 61
959.77500	914.77500	NFM	Nationwide	Channel 62
959.78750	914.78750	NFM	Nationwide	Channel 63
959.80000	914.80000	NFM	Nationwide	Channel 64
959.81250	914.81250	NFM	Nationwide	Channel 65
959.82500	914.82500	NFM	Nationwide	Channel 66
959.83750	914.83750	NFM	Nationwide	Channel 67
959.85000	914.85000	NFM	Nationwide	Channel 68
959.86250	914.86250	NFM	Nationwide	Channel 69
959.87500	914.87500	NFM	Nationwide	Channel 70
959.88750	914.88750	NFM	Nationwide	Channel 71
959.90000	914.90000	NFM	Nationwide	Channel 72
959.91250	914.91250	NFM	Nationwide	Channel 73
959.92500	914.92500	NFM	Nationwide	Channel 74
959.93750	914.93750	NFM	Nationwide	Channel 75
959.95000	914.95000	NFM	Nationwide	Channel 76
959.96250	914.96250	NFM	Nationwide	Channel 77
959.97500	914.97500	NFM	Nationwide	Channel 78
959.98750	914.98750	NFM	Nationwide	Channel 79

962.000 - 970.000 MHz — Radio Astronomy (Used for Pulsars)

960.000 - 1215.000 MHz — DME Aeronautical Radio Navigation & Transponder Equipment

Base	Mobile	Mode	Location	User and Notes
962.00000	1025.00000	AM	Nationwide	DME Channel 1X Not Used
963.00000	1026.00000	AM	Nationwide	DME Channel 2X Not Used
964.00000	1027.00000	AM	Nationwide	DME Channel 3X Not Used
965.00000	1028.00000	AM	Nationwide	DME Channel 4X Not Used
966.00000	1029.00000	AM	Nationwide	DME Channel 5X Not Used
967.00000	1030.00000	AM	Nationwide	DME Channel 6X Not Used
968.00000	1031.00000	AM	Nationwide	DME Channel 7X Not Used
969.00000	1032.00000	AM	Nationwide	DME Channel 8X Not Used
970.00000	1033.00000	AM	Nationwide	DME Channel 9X Not Used
971.00000	1034.00000	AM	Nationwide	DME Channel 10X Not Used
972.00000	1035.00000	AM	Nationwide	DME Channel 11X Not Used
973.00000	1036.00000	AM	Nationwide	DME Channel 12X Not Used
974.00000	1037.00000	AM	Nationwide	DME Channel 13X Not Used
975.00000	1038.00000	AM	Nationwide	DME Channel 14X Not Used
976.00000	1039.00000	AM	Nationwide	DME Channel 15X Not Used
977.00000	1040.00000	AM	Nationwide	DME Channel 16X Not Used
978.00000	1041.00000	AM	Nationwide	DME Ch 17X (108.00 MHz)
979.00000	1042.00000	AM	Dundee Airport	DME
979.00000	1042.00000	AM	Nationwide	DME Ch 18X (108.10 MHz)
979.00000	1042.00000	AM	RAF Cottesmore	TACAN
980.00000	1043.00000	AM	Boscombe Down (MoD)	TACAN

Base	Mobile	Mode	Location	User and Notes
980.00000	1043.00000	AM	Nationwide	DME Ch 19X (108.20 MHz)
981.00000	1044.00000	AM	Nationwide	DME Ch 20X (108.30 MHz)
982.00000	1045.00000	AM	Nationwide	DME Ch 21X (108.40 MHz)
982.00000	1045.00000	AM	RAF Valley	TACAN
983.00000	1046.00000	AM	Nationwide	DME Ch 22X (108.50 MHz)
983.00000	1046.00000	AM	Sumburgh Airport	DME
983.00000	1046.00000	AM	Teesside Airport	DME
984.00000	1047.00000	AM	Kirkwall Airport	DME
984.00000	1047.00000	AM	Nationwide	DME Ch 23X (108.60 MHz)
985.00000	1048.00000	AM	Nationwide	DME Ch 24X (108.70 MHz)
985.00000	1048.00000	AM	Newton Point	TACAN
986.00000	1049.00000	AM	Nationwide	DME Ch 25X (108.80 MHz)
986.00000	1049.00000	AM	Weathersfield	TACAN
987.00000	1050.00000	AM	Edinburgh Airport	DME
987.00000	1050.00000	AM	Nationwide	DME Ch 26X (108.90 MHz)
987.00000	1050.00000	AM	Ventnor	TACAN
988.00000	1051.00000	AM	Nationwide	DME Ch 27X (109.00 MHz)
989.00000	1052.00000	AM	Nationwide	DME Ch 28X (109.10 MHz)
990.00000	1053.00000	AM	Inverness Airport	DME
990.00000	1053.00000	AM	Nationwide	DME Ch 29X (109.20 MHz)
990.00000	1053.00000	AM	Swansea Aerodrome	DME
991.00000	1054.00000	AM	Nationwide	DME Ch 30X (109.30 MHz)
992.00000	1055.00000	AM	Barrow Airport	DME
992.00000	1055.00000	AM	Nationwide	DME Ch 31X (109.40 MHz)
993.00000	1056.00000	AM	London, Heathrow	DME
993.00000	1056.00000	AM	Manchester Airport	DME
993.00000	1056.00000	AM	Nationwide	DME Ch 32X (109.50 MHz)
993.00000	1056.00000	AM	Plymouth Airport	DME
994.00000	1057.00000	AM	Nationwide	DME Ch 33X (109.60 MHz)
994.00000	1057.00000	AM	RAF Linton-on-Ouse	TACAN
994.00000	1057.00000	AM	RAF Odiham	TACAN
995.00000	1058.00000	AM	Nationwide	DME Ch 34X (109.70 MHz)
996.00000	1059.00000	AM	Nationwide	DME Ch 35X (109.80 MHz)
996.00000	1059.00000	AM	RAF Kinloss	TACAN
997.00000	1060.00000	AM	Nationwide	DME Ch 36X (109.90 MHz)
997.00000	1060.00000	AM	Warton (MoD)	DME
998.00000	1061.00000	AM	Nationwide	DME Ch 37X (110.00 MHz)
999.00000	1062.00000	AM	Birmingham International	DME
999.00000	1062.00000	AM	Nationwide	DME Ch 38X (110.10 MHz)
1000.00000	1063.00000	AM	Nationwide	DME Ch 39X (110.20 MHz)
1000.00000	1063.00000	AM	USAF Lakenheath	TACAN
1001.00000	1064.00000	AM	Nationwide	DME Ch 40X (110.30 MHz)
1002.00000	1065.00000	AM	Bournemouth (Hurn)	DME
1002.00000	1065.00000	AM	Nationwide	DME Ch 41X (110.40 MHz)
1003.00000	1066.00000	AM	Nationwide	DME Ch 42X (110.50 MHz)
1003.00000	1066.00000	AM	RAF Leuchars	TACAN
1003.00000	1066.00000	AM	Stansted	DME
1004.00000	1067.00000	AM	Cardiff Airport	DME
1004.00000	1067.00000	AM	Carlisle Airport	DME
1004.00000	1067.00000	AM	London, Heathrow	DME
1004.00000	1067.00000	AM	Nationwide	DME Ch 43X (110.60 MHz)
1005.00000	1068.00000	AM	Nationwide	DME Ch 44X (110.70 MHz)
1006.00000	1069.00000	AM	Nationwide	DME Ch 45X (110.80 MHz)
1007.00000	1070.00000	AM	Jersey Airport	DME
1007.00000	1070.00000	AM	London, Gatwick	DME
1007.00000	1070.00000	AM	Nationwide	DME Ch 46X (110.90 MHz)

Base	Mobile	Mode	Location	User and Notes
1007.00000	1070.00000	AM	Ronaldsway, Isle of Man	DME
1008.00000	1071.00000	AM	Nationwide	DME Ch 47X (111.00 MHz)
1008.00000	1071.00000	AM	RNAS Yeovilton	TACAN
1009.00000	1072.00000	AM	Nationwide	DME Ch 48X (111.10 MHz)
1010.00000	1073.00000	AM	Nationwide	DME Ch 49X (111.20 MHz)
1011.00000	1074.00000	AM	London, Heathrow	DME
1011.00000	1074.00000	AM	Nationwide	DME Ch 50X (111.30 MHz)
1012.00000	1075.00000	AM	Nationwide	DME Ch 51X (111.40 MHz)
1012.00000	1075.00000	AM	RAF Coningsby	TACAN
1013.00000	1076.00000	AM	London, City Airport	DME
1013.00000	1076.00000	AM	Nationwide	DME Ch 52X (111.50 MHz)
1013.00000	1076.00000	AM	Newcastle Airport	DME
1013.00000	1076.00000	AM	USAF Fairford	TACAN
1014.00000	1077.00000	AM	Nationwide	DME Ch 53X (111.60 MHz)
1014.00000	1077.00000	AM	RAF Chivenor	TACAN
1015.00000	1078.00000	AM	Nationwide	DME Ch 54X (111.70 MHz)
1016.00000	1079.00000	AM	Nationwide	DME Ch 55X (111.80 MHz)
1017.00000	1080.00000	AM	Nationwide	DME Ch 56X (111.90 MHz)
1017.00000	1080.00000	AM	RAF Brize Norton	TACAN
1018.00000	1081.00000	AM	Nationwide	DME Ch 57X (112.00 MHz)
1019.00000	1082.00000	AM	Nationwide	DME Ch 58X (112.10 MHz)
1019.00000	1082.00000	AM	Pole Hill	DME
1020.00000	1083.00000	AM	Nationwide	DME Ch 59X (112.20 MHz)
1020.00000	1083.00000	AM	Ronaldsway, Isle of Man	DME
1021.00000	1084.00000	AM	Nationwide	DME Ch 60X (112.30 MHz)
1022.00000	1085.00000	AM	Nationwide	DME Ch 61X Not Used
1023.00000	1086.00000	AM	Nationwide	DME Ch 62X Not Used
1024.00000	1087.00000	AM	Nationwide	DME Ch 63X Not Used
1025.00000	1088.00000	AM	Nationwide	DME Ch 64X Not Used
1026.00000	1089.00000	AM	Nationwide	DME Ch 65X Not Used
1027.00000	1090.00000	AM	Nationwide	DME Ch 66X Not Used
1028.00000	1091.00000	AM	Nationwide	DME Ch 67X Not Used
1029.00000	1092.00000	AM	Nationwide	DME Ch 68X Not Used
1030.00000	1090.00000	AM	Nationwide	Transponder Interrog./Reply
1030.00000	1093.00000	AM	Nationwide	DME Ch 69X Not Used
1031.00000	1094.00000	AM	Nationwide	DME Ch 70X (112.30 MHz)
1032.00000	1095.00000	AM	Nationwide	DME Ch 71X (112.40 MHz)
1033.00000	1096.00000	AM	Nationwide	DME Ch 72X (112.50 MHz)
1033.00000	1096.00000	AM	St Abbs	DME
1034.00000	1097.00000	AM	Nationwide	DME Ch 73X (112.60 MHz)
1034.00000	1097.00000	AM	RAF St Mawgan	TACAN
1035.00000	1098.00000	AM	Berry Head	DME
1035.00000	1098.00000	AM	Donegal Aerodrome	DME
1035.00000	1098.00000	AM	Nationwide	DME Ch 74X (112.70 MHz)
1036.00000	1099.00000	AM	Gamston Aerodrome	DME
1036.00000	1099.00000	AM	Nationwide	DME Ch 75X (112.80 MHz)
1037.00000	1100.00000	AM	Nationwide	DME Ch 76X (112.90 MHz)
1038.00000	1101.00000	AM	Nationwide	DME Ch 77X (113.00 MHz)
1039.00000	1102.00000	AM	Nationwide	DME Ch 78X (113.10 MHz)
1039.00000	1102.00000	AM	Strumble	DME
1040.00000	1103.00000	AM	Nationwide	DME Ch 79X (113.20 MHz)
1040.00000	1103.00000	AM	Warton (MoD)	TACAN
1041.00000	1104.00000	AM	Nationwide	DME Ch 80X (113.30 MHz)
1042.00000	1105.00000	AM	Nationwide	DME Ch 81X (113.40 MHz)
1043.00000	1106.00000	AM	Nationwide	DME Ch 82X (113.50 MHz)
1044.00000	1107.00000	AM	London, Heathrow	DME

Base	Mobile	Mode	Location	User and Notes
1044.00000	1107.00000	AM	Nationwide	DME Ch 83X (113.60 MHz)
1044.00000	1107.00000	AM	Wick Aerodrome	TACAN
1045.00000	1108.00000	AM	Nationwide	DME Ch 84X (113.70 MHz)
1046.00000	1109.00000	AM	Nationwide	DME Ch 85X (113.80 MHz)
1046.00000	1109.00000	AM	Talla	DME
1047.00000	1110.00000	AM	Nationwide	DME Ch 86X (113.90 MHz)
1047.00000	1110.00000	AM	Ottringham	DME
1048.00000	1111.00000	AM	Midhurst	DME
1048.00000	1111.00000	AM	Nationwide	DME Ch 87X (114.00 MHz)
1049.00000	1112.00000	AM	Nationwide	DME Ch 88X (114.10 MHz)
1049.00000	1112.00000	AM	Wallasey	DME
1050.00000	1113.00000	AM	Land's End Airport	DME
1050.00000	1113.00000	AM	Nationwide	DME Ch 89X (114.20 MHz)
1051.00000	1114.00000	AM	Aberdeen (DyceAirport)	DME
1051.00000	1114.00000	AM	Nationwide	DME Ch 90X (114.30 MHz)
1052.00000	1115.00000	AM	Benbecula Airport	TACAN
1052.00000	1115.00000	AM	Nationwide	DME Ch 91X (114.40 MHz)
1053.00000	1116.00000	AM	Koksijde	DME
1053.00000	1116.00000	AM	Nationwide	DME Ch 92X (114.50 MHz)
1054.00000	1117.00000	AM	Nationwide	DME Ch 93X (114.60 MHz)
1055.00000	1118.00000	AM	Nationwide	DME Ch 94X (114.70 MHz)
1056.00000	1119.00000	AM	Nationwide	DME Ch 95X (114.80 MHz)
1057.00000	1120.00000	AM	Nationwide	DME Ch 96X (114.90 MHz)
1057.00000	1120.00000	AM	Vallafield	TACAN
1058.00000	1121.00000	AM	Nationwide	DME Ch 97X (115.00 MHz)
1058.00000	1121.00000	AM	Stornoway Airport	TACAN
1059.00000	1122.00000	AM	Biggin Hill	DME
1059.00000	1122.00000	AM	Nationwide	DME Ch 98X (115.10 MHz)
1060.00000	1123.00000	AM	Dean Cross	DME
1060.00000	1123.00000	AM	Nationwide	DME Ch 99X (115.20 MHz)
1061.00000	1124.00000	AM	Nationwide	DME Ch 100X (115.30 MHz)
1061.00000	1124.00000	AM	Ockham	DME
1062.00000	1125.00000	AM	Glasgow	DME
1062.00000	1125.00000	AM	Nationwide	DME Ch 101X (115.40 MHz)
1063.00000	1126.00000	AM	Nationwide	DME Ch 102X (115.50 MHz)
1064.00000	1127.00000	AM	Lambourne	DME
1064.00000	1127.00000	AM	Nationwide	DME Ch 103X (115.60 MHz)
1065.00000	1128.00000	AM	Nationwide	DME Ch 104X (115.70 MHz)
1065.00000	1128.00000	AM	Stoke on Trent	DME
1066.00000	1129.00000	AM	Nationwide	DME Ch 105X (115.80 MHz)
1067.00000	1130.00000	AM	Nationwide	DME Ch 106X (115.90 MHz)
1067.00000	1130.00000	AM	USAF Mildenhall	TACAN
1068.00000	1131.00000	AM	Nationwide	DME Ch 107X (116.00 MHz)
1069.00000	1132.00000	AM	Nationwide	DME Ch 108X (116.10 MHz)
1070.00000	1133.00000	AM	Blackbushe	DME
1070.00000	1133.00000	AM	Nationwide	DME Ch 109X (116.20 MHz)
1071.00000	1134.00000	AM	Nationwide	DME Ch 110X (116.30 MHz)
1072.00000	1135.00000	AM	Daventry	DME
1072.00000	1135.00000	AM	Nationwide	DME Ch 111X (116.40 MHz)
1073.00000	1136.00000	AM	Nationwide	DME Ch 112X (116.50 MHz)
1073.00000	1136.00000	AM	RAF Coltishall	TACAN
1074.00000	1137.00000	AM	Nationwide	DME Ch 113X (116.60 MHz)
1075.00000	1138.00000	AM	Nationwide	DME Ch 114X (116.70 MHz)
1076.00000	1139.00000	AM	Nationwide	DME Ch 115X (116.80 MHz)
1077.00000	1140.00000	AM	Nationwide	DME Ch 116X (116.90 MHz)
1078.00000	1141.00000	AM	Nationwide	DME Ch 117X (117.00 MHz)

Base	Mobile	Mode	Location	User and Notes
1078.00000	1141.00000	AM	Seaford	DME
1079.00000	1142.00000	AM	Nationwide	DME Ch 118X (117.10 MHz)
1080.00000	1143.00000	AM	Nationwide	DME Ch 119X (117.20 MHz)
1081.00000	1144.00000	AM	Detling	DME
1081.00000	1144.00000	AM	Nationwide	DME Ch 120X (117.30 MHz)
1082.00000	1145.00000	AM	Connaught Airport	DME
1082.00000	1145.00000	AM	Nationwide	DME Ch 121X (117.40 MHz)
1082.00000	1145.00000	AM	RAF Cranwell	TACAN
1083.00000	1146.00000	AM	Brookmans Park	DME
1083.00000	1146.00000	AM	Nationwide	DME Ch 122X (117.50 MHz)
1083.00000	1146.00000	AM	Turnberry	DME
1084.00000	1147.00000	AM	Nationwide	DME Ch 123X (117.60 MHz)
1084.00000	1147.00000	AM	RAF Wittering	TACAN
1085.00000	1148.00000	AM	Nationwide	DME Ch 124X (117.70 MHz)
1085.00000	1148.00000	AM	Oxford/Kidlington	DME
1085.00000	1148.00000	AM	Tiree	DME
1086.00000	1149.00000	AM	Nationwide	DME Ch 125X (117.80 MHz)
1087.00000	1150.00000	AM	Mayfield	DME
1087.00000	1150.00000	AM	Nationwide	DME Ch 126X (117.90 MHz)
1088.00000	1025.00000	AM	Nationwide	DME Channel 1Y Not Used
1089.00000	1026.00000	AM	Nationwide	DME Channel 2Y Not Used
1090.00000	1027.00000	AM	Nationwide	DME Channel 3Y Not Used
1091.00000	1028.00000	AM	Nationwide	DME Channel 4Y Not Used
1092.00000	1029.00000	AM	Nationwide	DME Channel 5Y Not Used
1093.00000	1030.00000	AM	Nationwide	DME Channel 6Y Not Used
1094.00000	1031.00000	AM	Nationwide	DME Channel 7Y Not Used
1095.00000	1032.00000	AM	Nationwide	DME Channel 8Y Not Used
1096.00000	1033.00000	AM	Nationwide	DME Channel 9Y Not Used
1097.00000	1034.00000	AM	Nationwide	DME Channel 10Y Not Used
1098.00000	1035.00000	AM	Nationwide	DME Channel 11Y Not Used
1099.00000	1036.00000	AM	Nationwide	DME Channel 12Y Not Used
1100.00000	1037.00000	AM	Nationwide	DME Channel 13Y Not Used
1101.00000	1038.00000	AM	Nationwide	DME Channel 14Y Not Used
1102.00000	1039.00000	AM	Nationwide	DME Channel 15Y Not Used
1103.00000	1040.00000	AM	Nationwide	DME Channel 16Y Not Used
1104.00000	1041.00000	AM	Lydd Airport	DME
1104.00000	1041.00000	AM	Nationwide	DME Ch 17Y (108.05 MHz)
1105.00000	1042.00000	AM	Blackpool	DME
1105.00000	1042.00000	AM	Nationwide	DME Ch 18Y (108.15 MHz)
1106.00000	1043.00000	AM	Nationwide	DME Ch 19Y (108.25 MHz)
1107.00000	1044.00000	AM	Nationwide	DME Ch 20Y (108.35 MHz)
1108.00000	1045.00000	AM	Nationwide	DME Ch 21Y (108.45 MHz)
1109.00000	1046.00000	AM	Nationwide	DME Ch 22Y (108.55 MHz)
1110.00000	1047.00000	AM	Nationwide	DME Ch 23Y (108.65 MHz)
1111.00000	1048.00000	AM	Humberside Airport	DME
1111.00000	1048.00000	AM	Nationwide	DME Ch 24Y (108.75 MHz)
1112.00000	1049.00000	AM	Nationwide	DME Ch 25Y (108.85 MHz)
1113.00000	1050.00000	AM	Nationwide	DME Ch 26Y (108.95 MHz)
1113.00000	1050.00000	AM	Woodford	DME
1114.00000	1051.00000	AM	Nationwide	DME Ch 27Y (109.05 MHz)
1114.00000	1051.00000	AM	Yeovil Aerodrome	DME
1115.00000	1052.00000	AM	Luton Airport	DME
1115.00000	1052.00000	AM	Nationwide	DME Ch 28Y (109.15 MHz)
1116.00000	1053.00000	AM	Nationwide	DME Ch 29Y (109.25 MHz)
1117.00000	1054.00000	AM	Nationwide	DME Ch 30Y (109.35 MHz)
1118.00000	1055.00000	AM	Nationwide	DME Ch 31Y (109.45 MHz)

Base	Mobile	Mode	Location	User and Notes
1119.00000	1056.00000	AM	Nationwide	DME Ch 32Y (109.55 MHz)
1120.00000	1057.00000	AM	Nationwide	DME Ch 33Y (109.65 MHz)
1121.00000	1058.00000	AM	Nationwide	DME Ch 34Y (109.75 MHz)
1122.00000	1059.00000	AM	Fairoaks Aerodrome	DME
1122.00000	1059.00000	AM	Nationwide	DME Ch 35Y (109.85 MHz)
1123.00000	1060.00000	AM	Nationwide	DME Ch 36Y (109.95 MHz)
1124.00000	1061.00000	AM	Nationwide	DME Ch 37Y (110.05 MHz)
1125.00000	1062.00000	AM	Nationwide	DME Ch 38Y (110.15 MHz)
1126.00000	1063.00000	AM	Nationwide	DME Ch 39Y (110.25 MHz)
1127.00000	1064.00000	AM	Nationwide	DME Ch 40Y (110.35 MHz)
1128.00000	1065.00000	AM	Nationwide	DME Ch 41Y (110.45 MHz)
1129.00000	1066.00000	AM	Nationwide	DME Ch 42Y (110.55 MHz)
1130.00000	1067.00000	AM	Nationwide	DME Ch 43Y (110.65 MHz)
1131.00000	1068.00000	AM	Nationwide	DME Ch 44Y (110.75 MHz)
1132.00000	1069.00000	AM	Nationwide	DME Ch 45Y (110.85 MHz)
1133.00000	1070.00000	AM	Nationwide	DME Ch 46Y (110.95 MHz)
1134.00000	1071.00000	AM	Nationwide	DME Ch 47Y (111.05 MHz)
1135.00000	1072.00000	AM	Nationwide	DME Ch 48Y (111.15 MHz)
1136.00000	1073.00000	AM	Nationwide	DME Ch 49Y (111.25 MHz)
1137.00000	1074.00000	AM	Nationwide	DME Ch 50Y (111.35 MHz)
1137.00000	1074.00000	AM	Southend Airport	DME
1138.00000	1075.00000	AM	Nationwide	DME Ch 51Y (111.45 MHz)
1139.00000	1076.00000	AM	Nationwide	DME Ch 52Y (111.55 MHz)
1140.00000	1077.00000	AM	Nationwide	DME Ch 53Y (111.65 MHz)
1141.00000	1078.00000	AM	Liverpool Airport	DME
1141.00000	1078.00000	AM	Nationwide	DME Ch 54Y (111.75 MHz)
1142.00000	1079.00000	AM	Nationwide	DME Ch 55Y (111.85 MHz)
1143.00000	1080.00000	AM	Nationwide	DME Ch 56Y (111.95 MHz)
1144.00000	1081.00000	AM	Nationwide	DME Ch 57Y (112.05 MHz)
1145.00000	1082.00000	AM	Nationwide	DME Ch 58Y (112.15 MHz)
1146.00000	1083.00000	AM	Nationwide	DME Ch 59Y (112.25 MHz)
1147.00000	1084.00000	AM	Nationwide	DME Channel 60Y Not Used
1148.00000	1085.00000	AM	Nationwide	DME Channel 61Y Not Used
1149.00000	1086.00000	AM	Nationwide	DME Channel 62Y Not Used
1150.00000	1087.00000	AM	Nationwide	DME Channel 63Y Not Used
1151.00000	1088.00000	AM	Nationwide	DME Channel 64Y Not Used
1152.00000	1089.00000	AM	Nationwide	DME Channel 65Y Not Used
1153.00000	1090.00000	AM	Nationwide	DME Channel 66Y Not Used
1154.00000	1091.00000	AM	Nationwide	DME Channel 67Y Not Used
1155.00000	1092.00000	AM	Nationwide	DME Channel 68Y Not Used
1156.00000	1093.00000	AM	Nationwide	DME Channel 69Y Not Used
1157.00000	1094.00000	AM	Nationwide	DME Ch 70Y (112.35 MHz)
1158.00000	1095.00000	AM	Nationwide	DME Ch 71Y (112.45 MHz)
1159.00000	1096.00000	AM	Nationwide	DME Ch 72Y (112.55 MHz)
1160.00000	1097.00000	AM	Nationwide	DME Ch 73Y (112.65 MHz)
1161.00000	1098.00000	AM	Nationwide	DME Ch 74Y (112.75 MHz)
1162.00000	1099.00000	AM	Nationwide	DME Ch 75Y (112.85 MHz)
1163.00000	1100.00000	AM	Nationwide	DME Ch 76Y (112.95 MHz)
1164.00000	1101.00000	AM	Nationwide	DME Ch 77Y (113.05 MHz)
1165.00000	1102.00000	AM	Nationwide	DME Ch 78Y (113.15 MHz)
1166.00000	1103.00000	AM	Nationwide	DME Ch 79Y (113.25 MHz)
1167.00000	1104.00000	AM	Nationwide	DME Ch 80Y (113.35 MHz)
1168.00000	1105.00000	AM	Nationwide	DME Ch 81Y (113.45 MHz)
1169.00000	1106.00000	AM	Manchester Airport	DME
1169.00000	1106.00000	AM	Nationwide	DME Ch 82Y (113.55 MHz)

Base	Mobile	Mode	Location	User and Notes
1170.00000	1107.00000	AM	Honiley	DME
1170.00000	1107.00000	AM	Nationwide	DME Ch 83Y (113.65 MHz)
1171.00000	1108.00000	AM	Bovingdon	DME
1171.00000	1108.00000	AM	Nationwide	DME Ch 84Y (113.75 MHz)
1172.00000	1109.00000	AM	Nationwide	DME Ch 85Y (113.85 MHz)
1173.00000	1110.00000	AM	Nationwide	DME Ch 86Y (113.95 MHz)
1174.00000	1111.00000	AM	Nationwide	DME Ch 87Y (114.05 MHz)
1175.00000	1112.00000	AM	Nationwide	DME Ch 88Y (114.15 MHz)
1176.00000	1113.00000	AM	Nationwide	DME Ch 89Y (114.25 MHz)
1177.00000	1114.00000	AM	Compton	DME
1177.00000	1114.00000	AM	Nationwide	DME Ch 90Y (114.35 MHz)
1178.00000	1115.00000	AM	Nationwide	DME Ch 91Y (114.45 MHz)
1179.00000	1116.00000	AM	Clacton Aerodrome	DME
1179.00000	1116.00000	AM	Nationwide	DME Ch 92Y (114.55 MHz)
1180.00000	1117.00000	AM	Nationwide	DME Ch 93Y (114.65 MHz)
1181.00000	1118.00000	AM	Nationwide	DME Ch 94Y (114.75 MHz)
1182.00000	1119.00000	AM	Nationwide	DME Ch 95Y (114.85 MHz)
1183.00000	1120.00000	AM	Dover	DME
1183.00000	1120.00000	AM	Nationwide	DME Ch 96Y (114.95 MHz)
1184.00000	1121.00000	AM	Nationwide	DME Ch 97Y (115.05 MHz)
1185.00000	1122.00000	AM	Nationwide	DME Ch 98Y (115.15 MHz)
1186.00000	1123.00000	AM	Nationwide	DME Ch 99Y (115.25 MHz)
1187.00000	1124.00000	AM	Nationwide	DME Ch 100Y (115.35 MHz)
1188.00000	1125.00000	AM	Nationwide	DME Ch 101Y (115.45 MHz)
1189.00000	1126.00000	AM	Gloucestershire Airport	DME
1189.00000	1126.00000	AM	Nationwide	DME Ch 102Y (115.55 MHz)
1190.00000	1127.00000	AM	Nationwide	DME Ch 103Y (115.65 MHz)
1191.00000	1128.00000	AM	Nationwide	DME Ch 104Y (115.75 MHz)
1192.00000	1129.00000	AM	Nationwide	DME Ch 105Y (115.85 MHz)
1193.00000	1130.00000	AM	Nationwide	DME Ch 106Y (115.95 MHz)
1194.00000	1131.00000	AM	Nationwide	DME Ch 107Y (116.05 MHz)
1195.00000	1132.00000	AM	Nationwide	DME Ch 108Y (116.15 MHz)
1196.00000	1133.00000	AM	Barkway	DME
1196.00000	1133.00000	AM	Nationwide	DME Ch 109Y (116.25 MHz)
1197.00000	1134.00000	AM	Nationwide	DME Ch 110Y (116.35 MHz)
1198.00000	1135.00000	AM	Nationwide	DME Ch 111Y (116.45 MHz)
1199.00000	1136.00000	AM	Nationwide	DME Ch 112Y (116.55 MHz)
1200.00000	1137.00000	AM	Nationwide	DME Ch 113Y (116.65 MHz)
1201.00000	1138.00000	AM	Cambridge Airport	DME
1201.00000	1138.00000	AM	Nationwide	DME Ch 114Y (116.75 MHz)
1202.00000	1139.00000	AM	Nationwide	DME Ch 115Y (116.85 MHz)
1203.00000	1140.00000	AM	Nationwide	DME Ch 116Y (116.95 MHz)
1204.00000	1141.00000	AM	Nationwide	DME Ch 117Y (117.05 MHz)
1205.00000	1142.00000	AM	Nationwide	DME Ch 118Y (117.15 MHz)
1206.00000	1143.00000	AM	Nationwide	DME Ch 119Y (117.25 MHz)
1207.00000	1144.00000	AM	Nationwide	DME Ch 120Y (117.35 MHz)
1207.00000	1144.00000	AM	Sumburgh Airport	DME
1208.00000	1145.00000	AM	Brecon	DME
1208.00000	1145.00000	AM	Nationwide	DME Ch 121Y (117.45 MHz)
1209.00000	1146.00000	AM	Nationwide	DME Ch 122Y (117.55 MHz)
1210.00000	1147.00000	AM	Nationwide	DME Ch 123Y (117.65 MHz)
1211.00000	1148.00000	AM	Nationwide	DME Ch 124Y (117.75 MHz)
1212.00000	1149.00000	AM	Nationwide	DME Ch 125Y (117.85 MHz)
1213.00000	1150.00000	AM	Nationwide	DME Ch 126Y (117.95 MHz)

Base	Mobile	Mode	Location	User and Notes

1215.000 - 1260.000 MHz — Radio Location, Satellite Positioning Systems, Civil Radar & Amateur Radio

Base	Mobile	Mode	Location	User and Notes
1227.60000		NFM	Nationwide	Military GPS Navstar
1246.00000		NFM	Nationwide	Military Glonass Ch 0
1246.43750		NFM	Nationwide	Military Glonass Ch 1
1246.87500		NFM	Nationwide	Military Glonass Ch 2
1247.31250		NFM	Nationwide	Military Glonass Ch 3
1247.75000		NFM	Nationwide	Military Glonass Ch 4
1248.18750		NFM	Nationwide	Military Glonass Ch 5
1248.62500		NFM	Nationwide	Military Glonass Ch 6
1249.06250		NFM	Nationwide	Military Glonass Ch 7
1249.50000		NFM	Nationwide	Military Glonass Ch 8
1249.93750		NFM	Nationwide	Military Glonass Ch 9
1250.37500		NFM	Nationwide	Military Glonass Ch 10
1250.81250		NFM	Nationwide	Military Glonass Ch 11
1251.25000		NFM	Nationwide	Military Glonass Ch 12
1251.68750		NFM	Nationwide	Military Glonass Ch 13
1252.12500		NFM	Nationwide	Military Glonass Ch 14
1252.56250		NFM	Nationwide	Military Glonass Ch 15
1253.00000		NFM	Nationwide	Military Glonass Ch 16
1253.43750		NFM	Nationwide	Military Glonass Ch 17
1253.87500		NFM	Nationwide	Military Glonass Ch 18
1254.31250		NFM	Nationwide	Military Glonass Ch 19
1254.75000		NFM	Nationwide	Military Glonass Ch 20
1255.18750		NFM	Nationwide	Military Glonass Ch 21
1255.62500		NFM	Nationwide	Military Glonass Ch 22
1256.06250		NFM	Nationwide	Military Glonass Ch 23
1256.50000		NFM	Nationwide	Military Glonass Ch 24

1240.000 - 1325.000 MHz — 23 cm Amateur Radio Band (Secondary)

Base	Mobile	Mode	Location	User and Notes
1240.1500		SSB	Nationwide	Packet Radio
1248.0000		SSB	Nationwide	Amateur TV
1255.0000		WFM	Nationwide	Amateur TV
1276.0000		AM	Nationwide	Amateur TV
1296.0000		CW	Space	Moonbounce
1296.2000		SSB	Nationwide	Centre of Activity
1296.6000		SSB	Nationwide	RTTY
1296.7000		SSB	Nationwide	Fax
1296.8100		CW	Orpington	Beacon (GB3NWK)
1296.8300		CW	Martlesham	Beacon (GB3MHL)
1296.8500		CW	Farnborough	Beacon (GB3FRS)
1296.8600		CW	St. Austell	Beacon (GB3MCB)
1296.8750		CW	Bristol	Beacon (GB3USK)
1296.8900		CW	Dunstable	Beacon (GB3DUN)
1296.9000		CW	Newport, IOW	Beacon (GB3IOW)
1296.9100		CW	Clee Hill, Salop	Beacon (GB3CLE)
1296.9300		CW	Emley Moor	Beacon (GB3MLE)
1296.9650		CW	Dundee	Beacon (GB3ANG)
1296.9900		CW	Edinburgh	Beacon (GB3EDN)
1297.0000	1291.0000	NFM	Alveston	Repeater (GB3AA) (118.8)
1297.0000	1291.0000	NFM	Horwich.	Repeater (GB3MC) (82.5)
1297.0000	1291.0000	NFM	Norwich	Repeater (GB3NO) (94.8)
1297.0500	1291.0500	NFM	Farnham	Repeater (GB3FM) (100)
1297.0750	1291.0750	NFM	Royston	Repeater (GB3PS) (77)
1297.0750	1291.0750	NFM	Stoke on Trent	Repeater (GB3SE) (103.5)
1297.1250	1291.1250	NFM	Northampton	Repeater (GB3CN) (77)

Base	Mobile	Mode	Location	User and Notes
1297.1250	1291.1250	NFM	Weston-Super-Mare	Repeater (GB3BW) (77)
1297.1500	1291.1500	NFM	Wolverhampton	Repeater (GB3MM) (67)
1297.2000	1291.2000	NFM	Corby	Repeater (GB3CO) (77)
1297.2250	1291.2250	NFM	Chelmsford	Repeater (GB3ZP) (110.9)
1297.3750	1291.3750	NFM	Wakefield	Repeater (GB3WC) (82.5)
1297.5000		NFM	Nationwide	Channel 20
1297.5250		NFM	Nationwide	Channel 21
1297.5500		NFM	Nationwide	Channel 22
1297.5750		NFM	Nationwide	Channel 23
1297.6000		NFM	Nationwide	Channel 24
1297.6250		NFM	Nationwide	Channel 25
1297.6500		NFM	Nationwide	Channel 26
1297.6750		NFM	Nationwide	Channel 27
1297.7000		NFM	Nationwide	Channel 28
1297.7250		NFM	Nationwide	Channel 29
1297.7500		NFM	Nationwide	Channel 30
1299.0000		SSB	Nationwide	Remote Control
1299.4250		NFM	Nationwide	Packet Radio
1308.0000	1248.0000	NFM	East Yorkshire	Repeater (TV) (GB3EY)
1308.0000	1248.0000	NFM	High Wycombe	Repeater (TV) (GB3HV)
1310.0000	1248.0000	NFM	Lincoln	Repeater (TV) (GB3VL)
1310.0000	1248.0000	NFM	Bournemouth	Repeater (TV) (GB3SQ)
1310.0000	1249.0000	NFM	Eastbourne	Repeater (TV) (GB3VX)
1310.0000	1249.0000	NFM	Liskeard	Repeater (TV) (GB3WV)
1310.0000	1249.0000	NFM	Sheerness	Repeater (TV) (GB3KT)
1310.0000	1280.0000	NFM	Criccieth	Repeater (TV) (GB3GW)
1310.0000	2388.0000	NFM	Bournemouth	Repeater (TV) (GB3SQ)
1311.5000	1249.0000	NFM	Bath,	Repeater (TV) (GB3UT)
1312.0000	1249.0000	NFM	North London	Repeater (TV) (GB3EN)
1312.0000	2390.0000	NFM	Wisbech	Repeater (TV) (GB3FV)
1316.0000	10340.000	NFM	Anglesey	Repeater (TV) (GB3TM)
1316.0000	10340.000	NFM	Anglesey	Repeater (TV) (GB3TM)
1316.0000	1249.0000	NFM	Bradford	Repeater (TV) (GB3YT)
1316.0000	1249.0000	NFM	Brighton	Repeater (TV) (GB3VR)
1316.0000	1249.0000	NFM	Bristol	Repeater (TV) (GB3ZZ)
1316.0000	1249.0000	NFM	Cambridge	Repeater (TV) (GB3PV)
1316.0000	1249.0000	NFM	Carrickfergus	Repeater (TV) (GB3TX)
1316.0000	1249.0000	NFM	Coventry	Repeater (TV) (GB3RT)
1316.0000	1249.0000	NFM	Fakenham	Repeater (TV) (GB3TN)
1316.0000	1249.0000	NFM	Isle of Wight	Repeater (TV) (GB3IV)
1316.0000	1249.0000	NFM	Lowestoft	Repeater (TV) (GB3LO) (77)
1316.0000	1249.0000	NFM	Markfield.	Repeater (TV) (GB3GV)
1316.0000	1249.0000	NFM	Northampton	Repeater (TV) (GB3MV)
1316.0000	1249.0000	NFM	St Austell	Repeater (TV) (GB3NQ)
1316.0000	1249.0000	NFM	Torquay	Repeater (TV) (GB3TB)
1316.0000	1249.0000	NFM	Winchester	Repeater (TV) (GB3AT)
1318.5000	1249.0000	NFM	Dunstable	Repeater (TV) (GB3TV)
1318.5000	1249.0000	NFM	Stoke on Trent	Repeater (TV) (GB3UD)

1325.000 - 1400.000 MHz Civil Fixed Links

Base		Mode	Location	User and Notes
1328.02000		MUX	Poole	Bulbarrow Main Site
1331.20000		MUX	Poole	Bulbarrow Main Site
1334.00000		MUX	Poole	Bulbarrow Main Site

1350.000 - 1375.000 MHz Civil Fixed Links & Airport Radar

1362.500 MHz   Maritime Seismic Streamer Tailbouys

1370.000 - 1400.000 MHz   Radio Astronomy

Used for the Study of Redshifted Hydrogen Lines

1375.000 - 1400.000 MHz   Government & Civil Fixed Links

1389.500 MHz	Maritime Seismic Streamer Tailbouys
1394.000 MHz	Civil Video Links

1400.000 - 1427.000 MHz   Radio Astronomy

Used for the study of Hydrogen lines, MERLIN, Pulsars and for Mapping Radio Sources

1427.000 - 1452.000 MHz   Mainly Government Fixed Links

1452.000 - 1530.000 MHz   Civil Fixed Links (Primary), Broadcasting Satellite (Secondary until 2007)

Base	Mobile	Mode	Location	User and Notes
1455.35000		NFM	Merseyside	Police DCR Link
1457.64000		MUX	Poole	Fire Brigade Link
1458.24750		NFM	Badminton	Palace Link
1459.15000		MUX	Poole	Microwave Link
1460.43000		MUX	Poole	Microwave Link
1461.62500		NFM	Wiltshire	Fire Brigade Link
1461.64000		MUX	Poole	Microwave Link
1466.87500	1529.37500	NFM	Nationwide	UK Test & Development
1467.12500	1529.62500	NFM	Nationwide	UK Test & Development
1468.77000		MUX	Poole	Microwave Link
1469.68000		MUX	Poole	171.2875 MHz Feeder
1470.33000		MUX	Poole	Bulbarrow Main Site
1472.00000		MUX	Poole	Corfe Castle
1472.65000		MUX	Poole	Microwave Link
1472.98750	1492.85000	NFM	Channel Islands	Aurigny Airlines Link
1473.15000		MUX	Poole	Bulbarrow Main Site
1492.30000		MUX	Poole	Paging Feeder
1492.30000		MUX	Poole	Microwave Link

1530.000 - 1535.000 MHz   Satellites (Earth to Space & Space to Earth) and Some Fixed Links

1535.000 - 1544.000 MHz   Satellites (Space to Earth)

1544.000 - 1545.000 MHz   Satellites (Space to Earth Distress & Safety Communications)

1545.000 - 1555.000 MHz   Satellites (Aircraft Public Telephones) (Mobile +101.500 MHz)

1555.000 - 1559.000 MHz   Satellites (Space to Earth)

1559.420 - 1616.500 MHz   Radio Navigation Receive Band

Base	Mode	Location	User and Notes
1575.42000	NFM	Nationwide	Civilian GPS Navstar
1602.00000	NFM	Nationwide	Civil Glonass Ch 0
1602.56250	NFM	Nationwide	Civil Glonass Ch 1
1603.12500	NFM	Nationwide	Civil Glonass Ch 2
1603.67850	NFM	Nationwide	Civil Glonass Ch 3
1604.25000	NFM	Nationwide	Civil Glonass Ch 4
1604.81250	NFM	Nationwide	Civil Glonass Ch 5
1605.37500	NFM	Nationwide	Civil Glonass Ch 6
1605.93750	NFM	Nationwide	Civil Glonass Ch 7
1606.50000	NFM	Nationwide	Civil Glonass Ch 8
1607.06250	NFM	Nationwide	Civil Glonass Ch 9
1607.62500	NFM	Nationwide	Civil Glonass Ch 10

Base	Mobile	Mode	Location	User and Notes
1608.18750		NFM	Nationwide	Civil Glonass Ch 11
1608.75000		NFM	Nationwide	Civil Glonass Ch 12
1609.31250		NFM	Nationwide	Civil Glonass Ch 13
1609.87500		NFM	Nationwide	Civil Glonass Ch 14
1610.43750		NFM	Nationwide	Civil Glonass Ch 15
1611.00000		NFM	Nationwide	Civil Glonass Ch 16
1611.56250		NFM	Nationwide	Civil Glonass Ch 17
1612.12500		NFM	Nationwide	Civil Glonass Ch 18
1612.67850		NFM	Nationwide	Civil Glonass Ch 19
1613.25000		NFM	Nationwide	Civil Glonass Ch 20
1613.81250		NFM	Nationwide	Civil Glonass Ch 21
1614.37500		NFM	Nationwide	Civil Glonass Ch 22
1614.93750		NFM	Nationwide	Civil Glonass Ch 23
1616.50000		NFM	Nationwide	Civil Glonass Ch 24

1626.500 - 1645.500 MHz — Up-Band for Maritime Mobile Terminals

1645.500 - 1646.500 MHz — Up-Band for Mobile Terminals (Distress & Safety Operations)

1646.500 - 1656.500 MHz — Satellites (Aircraft Public Telephones) (Base -101.500 MHz)

1656.500 - 1660.000 MHz — Up-Band for Mobile Terminals

1660.000 - 1668.000 MHz — Radio Astronomy
Used for the Study of MERLIN and Hydroxyl Lines

1668.000 - 1670.000 MHz — Radio Astronomy (Co-Primary)
Used for the Study of MERLIN and Hydroxyl Lines

1668.000 - 1670.000 MHz — Fixed Government (Co-Primary)
Home Office & Scottish Executive Emergency Services Fixed Links

1670.0000 - 1675.0000 MHz — Meteorological Satellites

1675.000 - 1690.000 MHz — Meteorological Satellites
1677.000 - 1685.000   Home Office & Scottish Executive Emergency Services Fixed Links

1690.000 - 1698.000 MHz — Meteorological Satellites

Base	Mobile	Mode	Location	User and Notes
1691.00000		NFM	Nationwide	Meteosat Ch A1/GOES
1694.50000		NFM	Nationwide	Meteosat Ch A2/FAX
1698.00000		NFM	Nationwide	NOAA-10

1698.000 - 1700.000 MHz — Meteorological Satellites

1698.000 - 1700.000 MHz — Fixed Links
Home Office & Scottish Executive Emergency Services Fixed Links

1700.000 - 1710.000 MHz — Meteorological Satellites & Land Mobile

1710.000 - 1880.000 MHz — Fixed, Mobile & Radio Astronomy
1710.000 - 1785.000	PCN Base Receive MPT1378
1710.000 - 1750.000	Some Residual Fixed Services Being Phased Out.
1765.500 - 1789.500	Fixed Use for Offshore Links
1800.000 - 1805.000	TFTS (Aircraft Stations)
1807.500 - 1815.500	Home Office & Scottish Executive Emergency Services Fixed Links
1820.000 - 1860.000	Some Residual Fixed Services Being Phased Out.

1880.000 - 1900.000 MHz — DECT Telephones

1873.500 - 1897.500   Fixed Use for Offshore Links

1885.000 - 2025.000 MHz — Future UMTS/IMT- 2000 Band

2025.000 - 2120.000 MHz — Fixed, Mobile & Space Operations

2120.000 - 2170.000 MHz — Fixed & Mobile

2170.000 - 2200.000 MHz — Fixed & Mobile & Satellite (Space-Earth)

2200.000 - 2290.000 MHz — Fixed, Land Mobile & Space Operations

2290.000 - 2300.000 MHz — Fixed, Mobile (MoD) & Space Operations

2300.000 - 2302.000 MHz — Fixed (Government) & Mobile (MoD)

2302.000 - 2310.000 MHz — Fixed

Home Office & Scottish Executive Emergency Services Fixed Links

2310.000 - 2450.000 MHz — Fixed, Mobile, Radiolocation & Amateur

Military Band - Mainly Fixed and Transportable Links

2310.000 - 2450.000 — Fixed, Mobile, Radiolocation & Amateur

2320.500 - 2380.500   Home Office & Scottish Executive Emergency Services Fixed Links
2390.000 - 2690.000   Programme Making & Special Events
2400.000 - 2500.000   Industrial, Scientific & Medical

2390.000 - 2400.000   Amateur (Primary)

Base	Mobile	Location	User and Notes
2326.0000	2388.0000	Luton	TV Repeater (GB3TZ)
2420.0000	2355.0000	Barnsley	TV Repeater (GB3ZE)
2420.0000	1248.0000	Grimsby	TV Repeater (GB3GG)
2420.0000	2388.0000	Grimsby	TV Repeater (GB3GG)
2435.0000	2335.0000	Brighton	TV Repeater (GB3VV)
2435.0000	2330.0000	E Yorkshire	TV Repeater (GB3VW)
2435.0000	2388.0000	Birmingham	TV Repeater (GB3LB)
2440.0000	2388.0000	Bradford	TV Repeater (GB3YV)
2440.0000	2388.0000	Coventry	TV Repeater (GB3RX)
2440.0000	2388.0000	Derby	TV Repeater (GB3DH)
2440.0000	2388.0000	Luton	TV Repeater (GB3TZ)
2440.0000	2388.0000	Newbury	TV Repeater (GB3FT)
2440.0000	2388.0000	Spennymoor	TV Repeater (GB3KM)
2440.0000	2328.0000	Spennymoor	TV Repeater (GB3KM)
2440.0000	2340.0000	Watford	TV Repeater (GB3BH)

2400.000 - 2402.000   Amateur Satellite (Shared)
2400.000 - 2483.500   Spread Spectrum Devices such as Wireless LANs
2445.000 - 2455.000   Civil Low Power Devices such as Tags

2450.000 - 2483.5000 MHz — Fixed, Mobile & Radiolocation

Civil Band

2483.5000 - 2500.0000 MHz — Fixed, Mobile, Radiolocation & Satellite

UK & Irish Airports in
Alphabetical Order

Abbeyshrule, Eire	
Air-Ground	122.600
Aberdeen (Dyce Airport)	
Approach	119.050
ATIS	121.850
Bristow Helicopters	123.450
Caledonian Ops	130.625
Fire Service	121.600
Ground	121.700
Lion Ops	126.900
Radar	119.050
Radar	128.300
Scotia Ops	130.575
Servisair/GlobeGround	130.600
Tower	118.100
Aberporth (MoD)	
AFIS	119.650
AFIS	259.000
Alderney	
Approach (Guernsey)	128.650
Aurigny Airlines	122.300
Ground	130.500
Tower	125.350
Trinity Lightship Heliport	129.700
Andrewsfield	
Air-Ground	130.550
Ashcroft Farm	
Air-Ground	122.525
Audley End	
Air-Ground	120.625
Badminton	
Air-Ground	123.175
Bagby (Thirsk)	
Air-Ground	123.250
Baldonnel	
Approach	122.000
Area Control	122.800
Dublin Military Radar	122.000
Dublin Military Radar	122.300
Ground	123.100
Talkdown	129.700
Tower	123.500
Ballykelly (Army)	
Approach (Aldergrove)	120.900
Approach (Eglington Tower)	134.150
Approach (Eglington)	123.625
Dropping Zone	129.950
Ops (Bellarena Ops)	130.100

Bantry, Eire	
Air-Ground	122.400
Barkston Heath (RAF)	
Approach (Cranwell)	340.475
DATIS	269.900
Departure	119.375
Departure	291.700
Ground	340.525
Radar	379.525
Talkdown	123.300
Talkdown	360.725
Tower	120.425
Tower	342.075
Barra, Scotland	
AFIS	118.075
Barrow (Walney Island)	
Air-Ground	123.200
Barton Aerodrome, Manchester	
Air-Ground	122.700
Beccles Heliport	
Air-Ground	120.375
Belfast (Aldergrove)	
Approach	128.500
Approach	310.000
ATIS	128.200
Aviance	131.675
British Airways Ops	131.850
British Midland	131.575
Ground	121.750
Ops (RAF)	241.825
Radar	120.900
Radar	243.000
Radar	310.000
Tower	118.300
Belfast (City)	
AFIS	136.625
Approach (Belfast)	128.500
Handling	129.750
Radar (Belfast)	120.900
Tower	130.850
Bellarena	
Air-Ground Gliders	130.100
Belmullet, Eire	
AFIS & Air-Ground	123.600
Bembridge, Isle of Wight	
AFIS & Air-Ground	123.250
Benbecula	
Approach/Tower & AFIS	119.200
ATIS	113.950

Benson (RAF)	
Approach	120.900
Approach	268.825
Approach (London Military)	275.475
DATIS	241.625
Director	136.450
Director	315.750
Ground	340.325
MATZ	120.900
Radar	122.100
Radar	130.250
Radar	315.750
Radar	362.300
Talkdown	361.875
Tower	127.150
Tower	279.350

Berwick on Tweed (Winfield)	
Winfield Radio	123.500

Beverley (Linley Hill)	
Tower	123.050

Biggin Hill	
Approach	129.400
ATIS	121.875
Srikair	130.025
Tower	134.800

Birmingham International	
Approach	118.050
ATIS	126.275
Birmingham Executive	130.650
British Airways Ops	131.850
Fire Service	121.600
Goldstar Ops	122.050
Ground	121.800
Loganair	131.575
Ogden Aviation	131.425
Radar	118.050
Radar	131.325
Servisair/GlobeGround	131.425
TEA Operations	131.575
Tower	118.300

Birr Aerodrome, Eire	
Air-Ground	122.950

Bitteswell Aerodrome	
Air-Ground	122.500

Blackbushe	
AFIS & Air-Ground	122.300
Air Lynton Ops	130.175
ATS	129.700
Premiair Ops	130.170

Blackpool	
Approach/Radar	119.950
ATIS	121.750
Keenair Ops	122.050
Radar	135.950
Scotia Helibus Ops	122.375
Servisair/GlobeGround	130.600
Tower	118.400

Bodmin	
Tower	122.700

Boscombe Down (MoD)	
Approach	130.000
Approach	291.650
DATIS	263.500
Director	291.650
Director	359.775
Ground	130.750
Ground	299.400
MATZ	126.700
MATZ	362.650
Radar	276.850
Talkdown	130.750
Talkdown	336.150
Tower	130.750
Tower	386.700

Boulmer (RAF)	
Air-Ground	282.800
Air-Ground	299.100
Air-Ground SAR	123.100

Bourn Aerodrome	
Air-Ground	124.350

Bournemouth (Hurn)	
Approach	119.475
ATIS	121.950
Channel Express	130.600
Europe Air Charter	119.475
Fire Service	121.600
FR Aviation (Broadway Ops)	123.650
Ground	121.700
Radar	118.650
Servisair/GlobeGround	129.750
Tower	125.600

Braintree Airfield	
Air-Ground	125.050

Breighton	
Air-Ground	129.800

Brimpton	
Air-Ground	135.125

Bristol Airport			Campbeltown		
	Approach	126.650		AFIS	125.900
	ATIS	126.025	Canterbury		
	City Express Ops	122.050		Traffic Information (Manston)	126.350
	Clifton Ops	130.625	Cardiff Airport		
	Radar	136.075		Approach	125.850
	Servisair/GlobeGround	130.600		Approach	277.225
	Tower	133.850		ATIS	132.475
Brittas Bay				Aviance	129.750
	Air-Ground	118.250		Execair	122.350
Brize Norton				Execair	122.750
	Approach	127.250		Radar	125.850
	Approach	342.450		Radar	126.625
	Approach	362.300		Radar	277.225
	ATIS	254.475		Red Dragon Ops	130.650
	Crew Commander	121.600		Servisair/GlobeGround	130.600
	Director	133.750		Tower	125.000
	Ground	121.725		Tremorfa Heliport	120.650
	Ground	370.300	Cark		
	MATZ	124.275		Cark Radio	129.900
	Ops	130.075	Carlisle Airport		
	Ops	357.475		Approach/Tower/Ground	123.600
	Radar	119.000		ATIS	132.475
	Radar	268.500	Castlebar, Eire		
	Radar	344.000		Air-Ground	122.600
	Radar	356.875	Castleforbes, Eire		
	Talkdown	126.500		Air-Ground	130.500
	Talkdown	338.650		Tower	125.400
	Talkdown	385.400	Chetwynd (RAF)		
	Tower	123.725		Approach	356.325
	Tower	257.800		Tower	309.550
	Tower	396.700	Chichester (Goodwood)		
Brooklands				AFIS	122.450
	Air-Ground	122.350	Chivenor (RAF)		
Brough Aerodrome				Air-Ground	130.200
	Tower & Air-Ground	130.550		Air-Ground	252.800
Bruntingthorpe			Church Fenton		
	Air-Ground	122.825		Approach	126.500
Caernarfon Aerodrome				Approach	254.525
	Air-Ground	122.250		Approach	362.300
Cambridge Airport				Ground	121.950
	Approach	123.600		Ground	340.200
	ATIS	133.700		Radar	344.000
	Fire Service	121.600		Radar	375.325
	Magnet Air	130.175		Talkdown	123.300
	Marshalls Ops	129.700		Talkdown	385.400
	Radar	124.975		Talkdown	386.725
	Radar	372.425		Tower	122.100
	Scot Airways Ops	130.175		Tower	275.500
	Suckling Ops	130.175	Clacton Aerodrome		
	Tower	122.200		Air-Ground	118.150
	Tower	372.425			

Clonbullogue, Eire		**Connemara, Eire**	
Air-Ground	128.550	Air-Ground	123.000
Colerne (RAF)		**Coonagh, Eire**	
Approach	120.075	Air-Ground	129.900
Approach	277.275	**Cork Airport**	
Approach	362.300	Aer Lingus Ops	131.500
Ground	360.750	Aer Lingus Ops	131.850
Tower	120.075	Approach	119.900
Tower	258.975	ATIS	120.925
Coltishall (RAF)		Ground	121.800
Approach	122.100	Radar	118.800
Approach	315.325	Tower	119.300
Approach	342.250	Tower	121.700
CAC (London Military)	299.975	**Cosford (RAF)**	
Director	123.300	Approach	135.875
FIS	293.425	Approach	276.125
Ground	254.250	Ground	128.850
MATZ	119.350	Ground	269.700
MATZ	125.900	Tower	128.650
Ops.	364.800	Tower	357.125
Radar	125.900	**Cottesmore (RAF)**	
Radar	293.425	Approach	130.200
Radar	342.250	Approach	358.725
Talkdown	123.300	CAC (London Military)	299.975
Talkdown	275.975	DATIS	242.325
Talkdown	387.775	Director	123.300
Tower	122.100	Director	312.075
Tower	339.950	Ground	122.100
Compton Abbas Aerodrome		Ground	336.375
Air-Ground	122.700	MATZ	130.200
Coningsby (RAF)		Radar	340.575
Approach	120.800	Radar	376.575
Approach	122.100	Talkdown	123.300
Approach	312.225	Talkdown	262.900
Approach	344.625	Talkdown	337.875
Approach	362.300	Tower	122.100
CAC (London Military)	299.975	Tower	257.800
DATIS	281.500	Tower	370.050
Ground	122.100	**Coventry Airport**	
Ground	358.550	Air Atlantique Ops	130.625
Ops.	268.700	Approach	119.250
Radar	262.950	ATIS	126.050
Radar	344.000	Fire Service	121.600
Talkdown	123.300	Ground	121.700
Talkdown	300.925	Handling	130.075
Talkdown	337.975	Radar	122.000
Tower	119.975	Tower	119.250
Tower	122.100	Tower	124.800
Tower	275.875	**Cowden Range**	
Connaught (Knock) Airport		Range Control	122.750
Ground	121.900		
Tower	130.700		

Cranfield			Dishforth (Army)		
Approach	122.850		Air-Ground	130.100
ATIS	121.875		Approach	122.100
Tower	134.925		Approach	125.000
Cranwell (RAF)			Approach	357.375
Approach	119.375		Approach	362.300
Approach	340.475		Ground	122.100
Approach	362.300		Ground	379.675
DATIS	135.675		Ops	252.900
DATIS	247.175		Tower	122.100
Ground	297.900		Tower	259.825
MATZ	119.375		Doncaster (Robin Hood)	
Radar	250.050		Approach	126.225
Radar	282.000		ATIS	134.950
Radar	344.000		Radar	129.050
Talkdown	123.300		Tower	128.775
Talkdown	285.150		Donegal, Eire	
Talkdown	356.925		ATIS	129.925
Tower	125.050		Tower	129.800
Tower	257.800		Donna Nook Range	
Cromer (Northrepps)			Control	122.750
Air-Ground (Microlight)	129.825		Control	342.175
Croughton (USAF)			Control	387.675
Air-Ground	343.600		Dounreay Aerodrome	
Crowfield Aerodrome			Tower	122.400
Air-Ground	122.775		Dublin Airport	
Culdrose (RN)			City Jet Ops	136.825
Approach	134.050		Aer Lingus Shamrock Ops	131.500
Approach	241.950		Air Contractor Ops	122.350
ATIS	282.100		Approach	119.550
Ground	299.400		Approach	119.925
MATZ	134.050		Approach	121.100
Radar	241.950		ATIS	124.525
Radar	339.950		British Midland/Aviance	131.425
Talkdown	122.100		Clearance/Delay	121.875
Talkdown	123.300		Director	118.500
Talkdown	259.750		Dublin Military ATC	123.300
Talkdown	262.775		Dublin VOLMET	127.000
Tower	122.100		Ground	121.800
Tower	123.300		Park Aviation	131.825
Tower	386.525		Ryanair Ops	131.550
Cumbernauld Airport			Servisair/GlobeGround	131.450
Air-Ground	120.600		Tower	118.600
Denham			Translift Ops	131.475
Air-Ground & AFIS	130.725		Dublin Area Control Centre	
Derby (Burnaston)			Control North	129.175
Air-Ground	118.350		Control North	136.050
Approach (East Midlands)	134.175		Control North	136.150
Derry			Control South	124.650
Approach	123.625		Control South	136.050
Fire Service	121.600		Control South	136.150
Tower	134.150			

Dundalk		
Air-Ground	122.900	
Dunkeswell Aerodrome		
Air-Ground	123.475	
Dunstable Downs		
Gliders Air-Ground	119.900	
Duxford		
AFIS	122.075	
AFIS	122.675	
Air-Ground	121.175	
Eaglescott		
Air-Ground	123.000	
Earls Colne		
Air-Ground	122.425	
East Midlands Airport/ Nottingham		
Air Bridge Carriers Ops	122.350	
Approach	134.175	
ATIS	128.225	
British Midland	131.575	
Donington Aviation	130.250	
Donington Aviation	130.625	
Excalibur Ops	131.575	
Fire Service	121.600	
Ground	121.900	
Radar	120.125	
Radar	124.000	
Radar	134.175	
Tower	124.000	
UPS Ops	131.600	
Edinburgh Airport		
Approach	121.200	
ATIS	131.350	
British Airways	131.800	
British Midland	131.575	
Execair Ops	122.350	
Fire Service	121.600	
Fishery Protection	130.625	
Ground	121.750	
Servisair/GlobeGround	130.600	
Tower	118.700	
Elmsett		
Air-Ground	130.900	
Elstree Aerodrome		
Air-Ground & AFIS	122.400	
English Channel		
Fisheries Protection	130.800	
Trinity House Lightships	129.700	
Enniskillen (St. Angelo)		
Air-Ground	123.200	
Enstone Aerodrome		
Air-Ground	129.875	

Errol Aerodrome		
Drop Zone Control	123.450	
Eshott		
Air-Ground	122.850	
Eskmeals Range (MoD)		
London Information	125.475	
Range	122.750	
Range	288.950	
Exeter Airport		
Approach	128.975	
ATIS	119.325	
Handling	130.175	
Markair Ops	130.175	
Radar	119.050	
Radar	128.975	
Tower	119.800	
Fadmoor Aerodrome		
Air-Ground	123.225	
Fair Isle		
Air-Ground	123.150	
Fairford (USAF)		
Approach	127.250	
Approach	362.300	
Approach (Brize)	342.450	
CAC (Brize)	124.275	
CAC (Brize)	311.825	
Ground	259.975	
MATZ	124.275	
Ops	379.475	
Radar	119.000	
Tower	119.150	
Tower	337.575	
Fairoaks		
Tower & AFIS	123.425	
Farnborough		
Approach	134.350	
ATIS	128.400	
Fire Service	121.600	
Precision Approach Radar	130.050	
Radar	125.250	
TAG Executive Ops	130.375	
Tower	122.500	
Farway Common		
Air-Ground	119.425	
Felthorpe Aerodrome		
Tower	123.500	
Fenland		
Air-Ground & AFIS	122.925	
Fife		
Air-Ground	130.450	

Filton (BAe) Bristol		Grimsby (Cuxwold)	
Approach	122.725	Air-Ground	122.350
Filton Ops	134.500	Guernsey	
Radar	124.950	Approach	128.650
Radar	129.975	ATIS	109.400
Rolls Royce Ops	129.750	Aurigny Air Services	122.350
Tower	132.350	British Midland Ops	131.575
Fishburn		FlyBe Ops	122.050
Air-Ground	118.275	Ground	121.800
Flotta Airfield		Radar	118.900
Tower	122.125	Radar	124.500
Foulsham Aerodrome		Servisair/GlobeGround	130.600
Tower	130.650	Tower	119.950
Fowlemere		Halfpenny Green (See Wolverhampton)	
Air-Ground	135.700	FIS	123.000
Full Sutton		Halton (RAF)	
Air-Ground	132.325	Air-Ground	130.425
Galway, Eire		Haverfordwest	
CAC	124.700	Air-Ground	122.200
Tower & AFIS	122.500	Hawarden/Chester	
Glasgow		Approach	123.350
Air Canada	131.375	Radar	130.250
Approach	119.100	Tower	124.950
ATIS	129.575	Haydock Park Racecourse	
British Airways Ops	131.800	Air-Ground	119.400
British Airways Ops	131.850	Hayes Heliport	
Execair Ops	122.350	Air-Ground (Macline Hayes)	123.650
Fire Service	121.600	Henlow (RAF)	
Ground	121.700	Air-Ground	121.100
Jetset Ops Air 2000	131.700	Henstridge	
Loganair Ops	130.650	Air-Ground	130.250
Oceanic Clearance	120.350	Hethel	
Radar	119.100	Air-Ground	122.350
Radar	119.300	Hethersett Aerodrome	
Radar	121.300	Air-Ground	129.875
Servisair/GlobeGround	130.600	Highland Ranges/Tain(RAF)	
Tower	118.800	Range	122.750
Glasgow Heliport		Hinton in the Hedges	
Air-Ground	122.950	Air-Ground	119.450
Glenrothes		Hitchin (Rush Green)	
Air-Ground	130.450	Air-Ground	122.350
Gloucestershire Staverton		Holbeach Range	
Approach	128.550	Control	124.600
ATIS	127.475	Control	343.375
Fire Service	121.600	Honington (RAF)	
Radar	120.975	Radar	128.900
Tower	122.900	Radar	264.675
Gormanston, Eire (Military)		Tower	122.100
Approach/Tower	122.200	Tower	282.275
Great Yarmouth (North Denes)		Hucknall Aerodrome	
Air-Ground	122.950	Air-Ground	130.800

Huddersfield (Crosland Moor)		Kinloss (RAF)	
Air-Ground	128.375	Approach	119.350
Humberside Airport		Approach	362.300
Approach	119.125	Approach	376.650
ATIS	124.125	Departures	118.900
Radar	119.125	Departures	258.850
Radar	129.250	Director	123.300
Scotia Helibus Ops	122.375	Ground	296.725
Tower	124.900	Ops	358.475
Inisheer, Eire		Radar	259.975
Air-Ground	123.000	Talkdown	118.350
Inishman, Eire		Talkdown	370.050
Air-Ground	123.000	Talkdown	376.525
Inishmore, Eire		Tower	122.100
Air-Ground	123.000	Tower	257.800
Insch Airfield		Tower	336.350
Air-Ground	129.825	Kirkcudbridght Ranges	
Inverness Airport		Kirkcoobree Range	122.100
Approach/Tower	122.600	West Freugh Range	130.050
ATIS	109.200	Kirkwall Airport	
British Airways Ops	131.850	ATIS	108.600
Radar	119.350	Tower/Approach/Weather	118.300
Ipswich Airport		Kyle of Lochalsh	
AFIS	118.325	RN Heliport	130.650
Islay Airport		Lakenheath (USAF)	
AFIS	123.150	Approach	136.500
Jersey Airport		Approach	337.600
Approach	120.300	ATIS	249.700
ATIS	129.725	CAC (London Military)	299.975
ATZ Zone/Radar	120.450	Civil Transit	128.900
ATZ Zone/Radar	125.200	Departure	242.075
Aviation Beauport Ops	129.700	Ground	231.425
British Airways Jersey Ops	131.850	Information	249.700
British Midland Jersey Ops	131.575	MATZ Crossing	365.975
Fire Service	121.600	Metro	257.750
Ground	121.900	Ops (Command Post)	269.075
Radar	118.550	Ops (Dispatcher)	300.825
Radar	120.300	Radar	259.050
Radar	120.450	Radar	315.575
Radar	125.200	Radar	369.075
Servisair/GlobeGround	130.600	RAPCon	136.500
Tower	119.450	RAPCon	337.600
Kemble		Tower	122.100
AFIS	118.900	Tower	358.675
Kent		Weather	257.750
Air Ambulance	132.650	Land's End (St Just)	
Kerry		Air-Ground	130.700
Ground	121.600	Langar Airfield	
Tower	123.325	Approach	130.200
Kilkenny		Drop Zone	129.900
Air-Ground	122.900		

Lasham Aerodrome		MATZ	126.500
Approach (Farnborough)	125.250	Ops	285.025
Glider Ops	131.025	Radar	255.400
Lashenden (Headcorn)		Talkdown	259.925
Air-Ground	122.000	Talkdown	370.075
Leconfield (RAF)		Talkdown	385.400
Air-Ground	123.050	Tower	122.100
Air-Ground	244.875	Tower	257.800
Air-Ground	282.800	Tower	259.125
Lee on Solent (Fleetlands)		Lewes (Deanland)	
Tower	135.700	Air-Ground	129.725
Leeds/Bradford Airport		Limerick (Coonagh)	
Approach	123.750	Air-Ground	129.900
ATIS	118.025	Linton on Ouse (RAF)	
Aviance Ops	131.575	Approach	129.150
Coney Park Heliport	129.750	Approach	292.800
Multiflight	130.650	Approach	362.300
Radar	121.050	Approach	362.675
Servisair/GlobeGround	130.600	ATIS	241.650
Tower	120.300	Departures	277.625
Leeming (RAF)		Departures	292.800
AFIS	249.525	Ground	122.100
Approach	127.750	Ground	340.025
Approach	358.650	Radar	123.300
Approach	362.300	Radar	129.150
Director	292.700	Radar	292.800
Director	344.000	Radar	344.000
Ground	386.525	Radar	344.475
MATZ	127.750	Talkdown	123.300
Ops	356.725	Talkdown	129.150
Radar	337.825	Talkdown	259.875
Talkdown	123.300	Talkdown	358.525
Talkdown	309.875	Tower	122.100
Talkdown	336.350	Tower	257.800
Talkdown	385.400	Tower	300.425
Tower	120.500	Liskeard	
Tower	122.100	Civil Heliport	129.900
Leicester Aerodrome		Little Gransden Aerodrome	
Air-Ground	122.125	Air-Ground	130.850
Lerwick (Tingwall)		Little Snoring Aerodrome	
Air-Ground & Air Ambulance	122.600	Air-Ground	124.150
Leuchars (RAF)		Little Staughton	
Approach	126.500	Air-Ground	123.925
Approach	292.475	Liverpool John Lennon	
Approach	362.300	Approach	119.850
DATIS	249.575	ATIS	124.325
Director	123.300	Aviance	131.875
Ground	122.100	Gemstone Ops Emerald Airways	130.075
Ground	297.900	Gemstone Ops Emerald Airways	130.175
Have Quick	338.025	Ground	121.950

Liverpool John Lennon (Cont.)	
Liverpool Aviation (Keenair) Ops	131.175
Mail Flights (Air-Air)	135.975
Radar	118.450
Radar	119.850
Raven Air Ops	130.175
Reed Aviation Ops	122.350
Royal Mail Ops	130.175
Servisair/GlobeGround	130.600
Tower	126.350

Llanbedr	
Air-Ground	122.500

Lochaber	
Air Ambulance	121.300
PLM Helicopters	122.350

London	
Air Ambulance G-HEMS	122.950
Capital Radio Flying Eye Ops	130.025
Special Flypasts Air-Ground	123.100

London City Airport	
Approach/Thames Radar	132.700
ATIS	136.350
City Handling Ops	131.475
City Jet Ops	136.825
Ground	121.775
KGS Handling Ops	130.625
Radar (Thames Radar)	132.700
Radar (City Radar)	128.025
Tower	118.075
Tower	118.400

London Gatwick	
Air New Zealand Ops	131.425
Approach	118.950
Approach	126.825
Approach	129.025
Approach	135.575
ATIS	136.525
ATIS	136.525
Aviance	122.350
Aviance	130.650
British Airways Maintenance	131.475
British Airways Ops	131.875
British Airways/GB Air	131.625
City Flyer Ops	131.600
Clearance	121.950
Continental Airlines Ops	131.750
Delivery	121.950
Excelair Ops	130.075
Fire Service	121.600
First Choice	131.700

Flystar Ops	131.425
Ground	121.800
Groundstar Ops	122.050
Interflight Ops	130.175
Korean Airlines	130.650
London VOLMET (Main)	135.375
Monarch Airlines Ops	136.875
Ogden Aviation Ops	131.425
Police Helicopter Ops	119.800
Radar	118.950
Radar Standby	129.025
Thos. Cook Airlines	122.350
Tower	124.225
Tower	134.225
Virgin Ops	131.425

London Heathrow	
Aer Lingus Ops	131.750
Aeroflot	131.775
Air Canada Ops	131.450
Air France Ops	131.500
Air India Ops	131.925
Air Malta Ops	131.650
Air Singapore Ops	131.500
Alitalia Ops	131.450
All Nippon Airlines Ops	131.475
American Airlines Maintenance	131.925
American Airlines Ops	131.925
Approach	120.400
Approach	127.525
Approach	134.975
Approach (Director)	119.725
ATIS (Arrivals)	128.075
ATIS (Departures)	121.850
ATIS (VOR)	113.750
ATIS (VOR)	115.100
Aviance	131.425
British Airways Ops	131.950
British Airways Ops	131.775
British Airways Ops	131.800
British Airways Terminal 1	131.550
British Airways Terminal 4	131.900
British Mediterranean	131.775
British Midland Ops	131.575
British Midland Ops	131.700
Cathay Pacific Ops	131.925
Clearance/Delivery	121.975
Corporate Jet Ops	130.175
CSA	131.400
Delta Ops	131.700
El Al	131.575

London Heathrow (Cont.)

Excelair	123.650
Federal Express Ops	131.825
Globe Air Ops	131.825
Ground	121.700
Ground	121.900
Gulf Air Terminal 3	122.350
Iberia Airlines Ops	131.950
KLM Ops	131.650
Korean Air Ops	131.775
Kuwait Airways Ops	131.500
London VOLMET (Main)	135.375
London Zone	134.450
LOT	131.775
Lufthansa Ops	131.925
Medivac	132.650
Olympic Airways Ops	131.950
Pakistan International Ops	131.450
Quantas Ops	131.875
Radar	125.625
Royal Jordanian Ops	131.425
SAS Ops	131.700
Saudia Ops	131.425
Singapore Airlines Ops	130.675
South African Airlines	131.900
Standby Tower	124.475
Swissair Ops	131.750
TAP Air Portugal	131.750
Thai Airways Ops	131.450
Thames Radar	132.700
Tower	118.500
Tower	118.700
Tower	124.475
Tower (Special Flights)	125.625
United Airlines Ops	131.850
United Airlines Ops	131.975
Virgin Ops	131.425

London TCC (Terminal Control)

Biggin	120.525
Bovingdon	119.775
Bovingdon	121.275
Brookmans Park	118.825
Compton	135.800
Cowley	121.025
Cowley	133.075
Dogga	124.925
Gatwick	118.950
Gatwick	126.825
Gatwick	129.025
Gatwick	135.575
Heathrow	119.725
Heathrow	120.400
Heathrow	127.525
Heathrow	134.975
Lambourne	123.900
Logan	120.025
London	120.475
London	133.975
Lorel	129.275
Low	129.075
Luton	128.750
Luton	129.550
Ockham	134.125
Redfa	121.225
Sabre	129.600
Stansted	120.625
Stansted	126.950
Thames	125.625
Thames	132.700
Timba	120.175
Vaton	127.950
Welin	128.475
Welin	130.925
Willo	133.175

London, Lippits Hill

Met Police Helicopter	130.475

London, Westland Heliport

Tower (Battersea)	122.900

Londonderry

Approach	123.625
Tower	134.150

Long Marston Aerodrome

Tower	130.125

Lossiemouth (RAF)

Approach	123.300
Approach	311.325
Approach	362.300
Approach	376.650
DATIS	269.025
Departures	118.900
Departures	258.850
Director	123.300
Ground	118.200
Ground	299.400
Radar	119.350
Radar	259.975
Talkdown	123.300
Talkdown	231.425
Talkdown	312.400
Tower	118.200
Tower	337.750

Luton Airport		Control	125.950
Approach	128.750	Control	128.050
Approach	129.550	Control	133.050
ATIS	120.575	Control	133.400
Aviance	122.050	Control	133.425
Aviance	122.350	Control	133.800
British Airways Maintenance	131.775	Pennine Radar	128.675
Britannia Airways	131.675	Manchester Airport	
Director	128.750	Aer Lingus Ops	131.750
easyJet Ops	131.400	Air Kilroe Ops	122.350
Gemstone Ops Emerald Airways	131.650	American Airlines Ops	136.825
Ground	121.750	Approach	118.575
Magec Ops	130.175	Approach	119.525
Monarch Airlines Ops	131.525	Approach (Director)	121.350
Monarch Airlines Ops	136.875	ATIS (Arrivals)	128.175
Radar	126.725	ATIS (Departures)	121.975
Reed Aviation	122.350	Aviance	131.575
Ryanair Ops	131.525	British Airways Ops	131.850
Servisair/GlobeGround	130.600	Clearance	121.700
Signature Executive Ops	130.175	Delivery	121.700
Thames Valley Police Ops	130.650	Departure Information	121.975
Tower	132.550	Director	121.350
Lydd Airport		Euro Manx Ops	131.875
AFIS	120.700	Federal Express	131.950
Lyneham (RAF)		Fire Service	121.600
Approach	118.425	FLS Engineering Ops	130.375
Approach	123.400	Ground	121.375
Approach	359.500	Ground	121.850
Approach	362.300	Kestrel Ops My Travel	136.800
ATIS	277.925	Lufthansa	131.925
CAC	275.475	Monarch Airlines Ops	136.875
Crew Commander	121.600	Northern Executive Handling	130.650
Director	118.425	Radar Standby	118.575
Ground	129.475	Ringway Handling	136.650
Ground	340.175	Ryanair Ops	130.175
MATZ	345.025	Servisair/GlobeGround	130.600
Ops	254.650	Swissair Ops	131.700
Radar	123.400	Swissport Handling Ops	122.050
Radar	300.475	Thos. Cook Airlines	122.350
Radar	344.000	Tower	118.625
Talkdown	123.300	Tower	121.850
Talkdown	375.200	Manston	
Talkdown	385.400	Approach	119.925
Tower	119.225	Approach	126.350
Tower	122.100	Approach	129.450
Tower	386.825	ATIS	133.875
Manchester Control Centre		Director	129.450
Control	118.775	Fire Service	121.600
Control	119.400	Radar	126.350
Control	125.100	Tower	119.925

Marham (RAF)		Morecambe Bay	
Approach	268.875	British Gas Helicopters	123.375
Approach	362.300	Mull	
Approach	362.750	Mull Traffic	123.450
ATIS	261.200	Nationwide	
Director	344.000	AAC Blue Eagles Display Team	135.950
Ground	336.350	AAC Blue Eagles Display Team	135.975
MATZ	124.150	AAC Blue Eagles Display Team	136.975
Ops	312.550	AAC Blue Eagles Display Team	259.600
Radar	124.150	AAC Blue Eagles Display Team	382.000
Radar	293.775	ACARS Frequency	131.525
Talkdown	123.300	ACARS Frequency	131.725
Talkdown	344.900	ACARS Frequency	131.825
Talkdown	379.650	ACARS Frequency	136.750
Tower	122.100	ACARS Frequency	136.900
Tower	257.800	ACARS Frequency	136.925
Tower	337.900	Air Ambulance Common	122.950
Merryfield (RN)		Air Ambulance Common	132.650
Tower	122.100	Air-Air Common	118.000
Tower	312.700	Air-Air Common	123.450
Middle Wallop (Army)		Airfield Fire & Rescue	121.600
Approach	118.275	Aquilla Spanish Display Team	130.500
Approach	312.000	Aquilla Spanish Display Team	337.975
Radar	275.400	Army Air-Air	135.975
Talkdown	364.825	Army Helicopter Common	252.900
Tower	118.275	Battle of Britain Flight	120.800
Tower	123.300	Battle of Britain Flight	122.700
Tower	312.625	CAA Calibrator Aircraft	122.275
Mildenhall (USAF)		CAA Events (Rarely Used)	121.700
AMC Ops	396.450	CAA Events Air-Ground	136.775
Approach	142.800	CAA Events/Airshows	121.175
Approach	337.600	CAA Events/Airshows	130.500
ATIS	277.075	CAA Events/Airshows	130.625
CAC	299.975	CAA Events/Airshows	130.675
Departure	242.075	CAA Events/Airshows	132.900
Ground	142.275	CAA Events/Airshows	134.550
Ground	278.150	CAA Special Reserve	122.375
Navy Ops	315.375	CAA Test Flights	127.050
Ops (Command Post)	312.450	CAA Test Flights	134.975
Ops (Dispatcher)	365.100	CAA Test Flights	135.000
Tower	122.550	CAA Test Flights	135.750
Tower	370.250	Civil Aviation Distress Channel	121.500
Weather	257.750	Coastguard Standby	132.650
Mona (RAF)		Dutch F-16 Display Team	130.900
AFIS	118.950	Falcons Parachute Team	256.900
Approach	379.700	Falcons Parachute Team (Primary)	255.100
Flying Club	119.175	Fisheries Protection	122.100
Radar	258.825	Fisheries Protection	123.650
Radar	372.325	Fisheries Protection	131.800
Tower	358.750	Fisheries Protection	373.700
		Flight Checker Navaid Calibrator	134.650

Nationwide (Cont.)	
Frecce Tricolori Display Team	140.600
Frecce Tricolori Display Team	307.800
Glider Training	130.125
Gliders	130.100
Gliders	130.400
Gliders	129.975
Hang Gliding	129.900
Honda Display Team Air-Air	118.000
Hot Air Ballooning	129.900
Hot Air Ballooning Air-Ground	122.475
Los Halcones Chilean Display Team	135.175
Low Level Military	300.800
Marine Emergency/Helicopters (NFM)	156.000
Marine Emergency/Helicopters (NFM)	156.300
Marine Emergency/Helicopters (NFM)	156.800
Microlight Common	129.825
Military Airfield Radar	123.300
Military Tower Common	122.100
Moroccan Green March Display Team	135.925
Parachute DZ	129.900
Parachute DZ	130.525
Paragliding Below 5000 Feet	118.675
Patrouille De France Display Team	141.825
Patrouille De France Display Team	143.100
Patrouille De France Display Team	242.650
Patrouille De France Display Team	243.850
Patrouille Suisse Display Team	266.775
Patrouille Suisse Display Team	388.075
Royal Flights Helicopters Air-Ground	132.650
Royal Navy Lynx Duo	132.650
SAFETYCOMM	135.475
Search and Rescue Incident	130.425
Search and Rescue (Primary)	123.100
Shape Sky Divers	118.000
Trinity House Helicopters	129.700
Utterly Butterly Wing Walking Team	118.000
YAK Display Team	124.450
Nesscliffe Camp (Army)	
Air-Ground	356.325
Netheravon (Army)	
AFIS	128.300
AFIS	290.950
Air-Ground (Salisbury Plain)	128.300
Air-Ground (Salisbury Plain)	282.250
Drop Zone Radio	128.300
Information	128.300
Netherthorpe	
Air-Ground	123.275

Newcastle Airport	
Approach	124.375
Approach	284.600
Apron (Samson Ops)	130.650
ATIS	118.375
British Airways Ops	131.850
Radar	118.500
Radar	124.375
Radar	284.600
Servisair/GlobeGround	130.600
Tower	119.700
Newcastle Helipad	
Air-Ground	118.075
Newtownards	
Air-Ground	128.300
North Coates	
Air-Ground	120.150
Air-Ground Donna Nook Range	122.750
North Sea	
Alwyn North Oil Field log	130.200
Amethyst Field deck	129.875
Amoco Arbroath Field	129.700
Amoco Indefatigable Field	123.625
Amoco Leman Field	123.625
Amoco Montrose Field	122.325
Amoco NW Hutton Deck	130.800
Amoco Valhall Field	130.550
Andrew Oil Field deck	123.550
Arco Thames Field	123.225
Barque Oil Field deck	133.525
Beatrice Field deck	122.800
Bessemer Oil Field deck	123.625
BP Buchan Field	122.000
BP Cleeton Field deck	122.025
BP Cyprus Field	122.000
BP Forties Field	122.000
BP Gyda Field	122.000
BP Magnus Field Deck	122.375
BP Ravenspurn North Field deck	129.875
BP West Sole Field deck	129.875
Brae Oil Field deck	123.650
Brent Oil Field Deck	122.050
Brent Oil Field log	123.050
British Gas Rough Field deck	129.875
Bruce Oil Field deck	123.225
Caister Oil Field deck	122.025
Camelot Oil Field deck	123.625
Captian Oil Field deck	123.550
Chevron Ninian Field log	122.050
Claymore & Tartan	122.450

North Sea (Cont.)

Clipper Oil Field deck	133.575	Nelson Oil Field deck	122.650
Clyde Oil Field deck	122.525	Ninian Field Deck	130.200
Conoco Hutton Deck	130.800	Ninian Field Log	122.050
Conoco Murchison Field Deck	122.050	Noordwinning Oil Field deck	129.775
Conoco oil rig	129.950	Noordwinning/Zanddijk Field	123.450
Conoco Viking Field	122.625	North Cormorant deck	129.950
Dab Duc Dan Field	123.450	North Cormorant log	123.050
Dab Duc Gorm Field	123.450	North Hamilton Oil Field deck	129.775
Dab Duc Skjold Field	123.400	Occidental Claymore Field	122.450
Davey Oil Field deck	123.625	Oil Rig Heliport Common	120.450
Dunbar Oil Field deck	130.200	Penzoil Noordwinning	122.950
East Brae Oil Field deck	123.650	Petroland Oil Field deck	125.175
Eider Oil Field deck	129.900	Petroland Petroland Field	122.950
Eko/Tees Pip Oil Field deck	122.950	Phillip Ekofisk Field	122.925
Elf Aquataine Norge Frigg	129.750	Phillips Albuskjell Field	130.550
Everest Oil Field deck	129.700	Phillips Cod Field	130.550
Excalibur Oil Field deck	122.875	Phillips Edda Field	130.550
FRG/STFS Pipe	130.725	Phillips Eko/EMB Pipe deck	129.900
Frigg Oil Field deck	118.050	Phillips Ekofisk Field	130.550
Galahad Oil Field deck	122.875	Phillips Eldfisk Field	130.550
Galleon Oil Field deck	133.575	Phillips Hewett Field	122.875
Gannet Oil Field deck	122.325	Phillips Tor Field	130.550
Gryphon Oil Field deck	123.025	Pickerill Oil Field deck	122.875
Guinevere Oil Field deck	122.875	Piper Oil Field deck	122.450
Hamilton Argyll Field	122.125	Placid Oil Field deck	125.175
Hamilton Esmond Field	122.325	Placid Placid Field	122.950
Hamilton Forbes Field	122.325	Ravenspun Deck	129.875
Hamilton Gordon Field	122.325	Rolf Oil Field deck	123.450
Hamilton Pipe Field	122.525	Saltire Oil Field deck	122.450
Hamilton Ravenspurnn North	123.025	Scott Oil Field deck	122.775
Helicopter Common	129.975	Shell/Esso Auk Field	122.050
Ivanhoe Oil Field deck	123.000	Shell/Esso Brent Field	122.250
Judy Oil Field deck	122.525	Shell/Esso Dunlin field deck	129.950
Kewanee Nordsee Field	129.750	Shell/Esso Eider Field log	123.050
Kittiwake Oil Field deck	130.870	Shell/Esso Fulmar Field	122.750
Kotter Oil Field deck	122.950	Shell/Esso Indefatigable	123.625
Lancelot Oil Field deck	122.875	Shell/Esso Kittiwake Field	122.050
Lennox Oil Field deck	122.375	Shell/Esso Leman Field	123.625
Logger Oil Field deck	122.950	Shell/Esso Sean Field	123.625
Lomond Oil Field deck	122.325	Shell/Esso Tern field deck	129.950
Magnus BP	122.395	Shell/Esso Tern Field log	123.050
Marathon East Kinsale	123.450	South Cormorant log	123.050
Marathon West Kinsale	123.450	South Cormorant oil field deck	129.950
Markham Oil Field deck	125.175	Statfjord Oil Field deck	129.650
Maureen Oil Field deck	123.875	Sun Balmoral Field	123.550
Mobil Beryl Field	122.175	Texaco Tartan Field	122.450
Murdoch Oil Field deck	122.025	Thames Oil Field deck	123.625
Nam Nam Field	122.950	Thistle Field Deck	122.050
Nam Noordwinning	121.175	Tiffany Oil Field deck	123.575
		Total Alwyn Field	122.350

North Sea (Cont.)			Odiham (RAF)	
Total/Elf Frigg Field	129.750		Approach/Radar	131.300
Trent Oil Field deck	120.075		Approach/Radar	386.775
Tyne Oil Field deck	120.075		ATIS	276.175
Tyra Oil Field deck	123.450		Director	370.075
Unionoil Heather Field	122.800		Flight Information	122.100
Unity Oil Field deck	122.000		Flight Information	315.975
Valhall Oil Field deck	130.550		Ground	372.500
Viking Oil Field log	120.075		MATZ	125.250
Welland Oil Field Deck	123.625		Talkdown	123.300
Welland Oil Field Log	123.225		Talkdown	300.450
West Sole Oil Field deck	129.875		Talkdown	385.400
Zanddijk	122.950		Tower	122.100
North Weald			Tower	257.800
Aceair Company Channel	130.175		Tower	309.625
Air-Ground	123.525		Old Sarum	
Gliders	129.975		Air-Ground	123.200
Northampton (Sywell)			Old Warden (Biggleswade)	
AFIS	134.875		Tower (Display Days Only)	130.700
Northolt (RAF)			Oxford	
Approach	126.450		Churchill Hospital Helicopter	132.650
Approach	344.975		Oxford (Kidlington Airport)	
Approach	362.300		Approach	125.325
ATIS	125.125		ATIS	136.225
ATIS	300.350		Ground	121.950
Departures	120.320		Tower	133.425
Director	130.350		Panshanger	
Director	379.425		Air-Ground	120.250
Ground	124.975		Pembrey Range (RAF)	
Ops	244.425		Air-Ground	124.200
Radar	375.500		Range	122.750
Talkdown	125.875		Range	379.875
Talkdown	375.500		Penzance Heliport	
Talkdown	385.400		Tower	118.100
Tower	120.675		Perranporth	
Tower	257.800		Air-Ground	119.750
Tower	312.350		Glider Ops	130.100
Norwich Airport			Perth (Scone)	
Approach	119.350		Air-Ground & AFIS	119.800
ATIS	128.625		Peterborough (Conington)	
Radar	119.350		Air-Ground	129.725
Radar	128.325		Peterborough (Sibson)	
Tower	124.250		Approach/Radar	122.300
Nottingham/Tollerton			Peterhead/Longside	
Air-Ground	134.875		Air-Ground Bond Helicopters	122.375
Hutchins Crop Sprayers	122.050		Plockton Airfield	
Nuthampstead, Royston			Air-Ground	130.650
Air-Ground	123.050		Plymouth City Airport	
Oaksey Park			Approach	133.550
Air-Ground	122.775		Tower	118.150
Oban				
Air-Ground	118.050			

Plymouth Military Radar (RN)		Ronaldsway, Isle of Man	
Radar	121.250	Approach	120.850
Radar	124.150	ATIS	123.875
Radar	300.175	Citiexpress Ops	129.750
Radar	370.325	Fire Service	121.600
Pocklington		FlyBe Ops	122.050
Air-Ground Gliders	130.100	Gemstone Ops Emerald Airways	131.875
Gliders	129.975	Islavia Ops	130.625
Popham Aerodrome		Manx Handling	129.750
Air Ground	129.800	Manxair Ops	130.175
Portishead		Radar	118.200
Aero Radio Telephones	131.625	Radar	120.850
Portland (RN)		Radar	125.300
Approach	122.100	Tower	118.900
Approach	124.150	Woodgate Aviation	130.175
MATZ	124.150	Rufforth, York	
Radar	124.150	Air-Ground	129.975
Tower	122.100	Salisbury Plain (Army)	
Tower	123.300	Air-Ground	122.750
Predannack (RN)		Air-Ground	282.250
Approach	241.950	Sandown, Isle of Wight	
Approach (Culdrose)	134.050	Air-Ground	119.275
Tower	338.975	Sandtoft	
Tower	370.000	Tower	130.425
Tower (Culdrose)	122.100	Scampton (RAF)	
Prestwick Airport		Ground	258.500
Air Canada Ops	131.450	Talkdown	309.825
Approach	120.550	Talkdown	379.250
ATIS	121.125	Tower	282.400
Greer Aviation Ops	122.050	Scarborough	
Highland Radar	126.100	Air-Ground	130.125
Highland Radar	134.100	Scatsa	
PIK Handling	129.700	Approach/Tower	123.600
Radar	119.450	Radar	122.400
Radar	120.550	Scilly Isles (St. Marys)	
Tower	118.150	Approach/Tower	123.825
Tower	121.800	Scottish Air Traffic Control Centre - Prestwick	
Prestwick Navy (RN)		Scottish ACC (Entire Route)	133.675
Ops	337.750	Scottish ACC (Information)	119.875
Punchestown		Scottish ACC (Information)	127.275
Air-Ground (Parachute/Glider Ops)		Scottish Air Traffic Control	121.325
130.400		Scottish Air Traffic Control	135.850
Rathkenny		Scottish Control	123.775
Air-Ground	123.600	Scottish Control	124.050
Redhill Aerodrome		Scottish Control	124.500
Tower/AFIS	119.600	Scottish Control	125.675
Retford		Scottish Control	126.850
Air-Ground	130.475	Scottish Control	126.925
Rochester Aerodrome		Scottish Control	133.675
AFIS	122.250	Scottish Control	133.875

Scottish Control (0630-2130)	124.825	Sherburn in Elmet Aerodrome	
Scottish Control (2131-0629)	126.300	Air-Ground	122.600
Scottish Control (Information)	126.250	Shetlands	
Scottish Control (Stornoway)	123.500	East Shetland Information	119.000
Scottish Control UIR	135.875	Radar	134.150
Scottish Low Level Climbout	249.475	Viking Approach	129.950
Scottish Military	134.300	Shipdam	
Scottish Military	249.475	Air-Ground & AFIS	119.550
Scottish VOLMET	125.725	Shobdon Aerodrome	
Shanwick Oceanic (Clearances)	135.525	Air-Ground	123.500
Seething Aerodrome		Shoreham by Sea	
Air-Ground	122.600	Approach/Tower	123.150
Shannon Airport		ATIS	125.300
Approach	120.200	Silverstone	
Approach	121.400	Air-Ground	121.075
ATIS	130.950	Skegness Aerodrome	
Clearance	121.700	Air-Ground	130.450
Ground	121.800	Skye	
Radar	121.400	Air-Ground	130.650
Servisair/GlobeGround	131.450	Sleap Aerodrome	
Tower	118.700	Air-Ground	122.450
Shannon Area Control Centre		Sligo	
Centre	121.700	Tower/AFIS	122.100
Control	124.700	Solent	
Control	127.500	Initial Contact Frequency	120.255
Control	132.150	Southampton Airport	
Control	134.275	Approach	128.850
Control	135.600	ATIS	113.350
Control Cork Sector	131.150	Ground	121.775
Control Southern Sector	135.225	Ops	130.650
Shanwick Oceanic Area Control Centre		Radar	128.850
Air-Ground Shanwick Radio	127.900	Tower	118.200
ATC Shanwick Oceanic	120.350	Zone	120.225
ATC Shanwick Oceanic	123.950	Southend Airport	
ATC Shanwick Oceanic	127.650	Approach	130.775
Shawbury (RAF)		ATIS	121.800
Approach	311.100	Express Flight Handling	129.700
DATIS	292.575	Heavilift Ops	122.050
Director	254.200	Radar	128.950
Ground	337.900	Radar	130.775
MATZ	120.775	Tower	127.725
Radar	124.150	Spadeadam (RAF)	
Radar – Low Level	356.325	LARS	124.375
Talkdown	123.300	Radar	122.100
Talkdown	356.975	Radar	369.150
Talkdown	376.675	Secondary	340.300
Tower	122.100	Spalding (Crowland)	
Tower	340.350	Tower (Gliders)	130.400
Sheffield City		Spanish Point, Eire	
Air/ Ground	128.525	Air-Ground	123.300

St. Angelo		Servisair/GlobeGround	130.600	
Tower	123.200	Servisair/GlobeGround	129.750	
St. Athan (RAF)		Swissport Handling Ops	122.050	
Approach	125.850	Tower	123.800	
Approach	277.225	Tower	125.550	
Approach	362.300	Universal Air Handling	130.575	
ATIS	284.925	Zap Ops Titan Airways	130.625	
Ground	386.500	Stapleford Tawney		
Talkdown	123.300	Aeromega Ops (Helicopter Ops)	122.050	
Talkdown	340.100	Air-Ground	122.800	
Talkdown	372.375	Stapleford Ops	130.625	
Tower	118.125	Staxton Wold (RAF)		
Tower	257.800	Danger Area Information	124.750	
Tower	336.525	Stornoway Airport		
St. Kilda (RAF)		Approach/Tower & AFIS	123.500	
Tower	128.100	Strathallan Aerodrome		
St. Mawgan (RAF)		Air-Ground	129.900	
Approach	122.100	Strubby Aerodrome		
Approach	128.725	Air-Ground Gliders	130.100	
Approach	357.200	Air-Ground	122.375	
DATIS	252.525	Stubton Park		
Ground	376.625	Air-Ground	119.425	
MATZ	126.500	Sturgate Aerodrome		
Ops	260.000	Air-Ground	130.300	
Radar	123.300	Sumburgh Airport		
Radar	125.550	Approach	123.150	
Radar	344.000	ATIS	125.850	
Radar	360.550	Fire Service	121.600	
Talkdown	123.300	Helicopter Information	129.950	
Talkdown	385.400	North Sea Offshore	123.150	
Talkdown	387.450	Radar (N Sea Offshore)	131.300	
Tower	122.100	Tower	118.250	
Tower	123.400	Swansea Airport		
Tower	241.825	Air Sea Rescue	132.650	
Stanford (Army)		Air-Ground	119.700	
Air-Ground	307.800	ATC Glider Training	129.975	
Danger Area Information	128.900	Swanton Morley Aerodrome		
Stansted Airport		Air-Ground	123.500	
Air Foyle	131.775	Swanwick Civil ATC		
Approach	120.625	London Control	118.475	
ATIS	127.175	London Control	119.775	
Aviance	131.575	London Control	120.025	
FedEx Ops	131.475	London Control	121.225	
Fire	122.600	London Control	121.275	
Ground	121.725	London Control	124.275	
Hijack Negotiations	122.275	London Control	126.075	
Radar	126.950	London Control	127.100	
Ryanair Engineering Ops	131.975	London Control	127.700	
Ryanair Ops	130.175	London Control	127.875	
Ryanair Ops	131.600	London Control	128.425	

Swanwick Civil ATC (Cont.)

London Control	129.075	Lower Airspace (Northwest)	254.270
London Control	129.100	Lower Airspace (Southeast)	251.225
London Control	129.200	Middle Airspace (East)	135.275
London Control	129.375	Middle Airspace (East)	299.975
London Control	129.425	Middle Airspace (Northwest)	127.450
London Control	129.600	Middle Airspace (Northwest)	254.270
London Control	131.125	Middle Airspace (Scottish)	134.300
London Control	132.450	Middle Airspace (Scottish)	249.475
London Control	132.8416	Middle Airspace (West)	135.150
London Control	132.950	Middle Airspace (West)	275.450
London Control	133.175	Upper Airspace (East)	299.975
London Control	133.450	Upper Airspace (Scottish)	249.475
London Control	133.600	Upper Airspace (West)	275.350
London Control	133.700	Swindon (Draycott)	
London Control	134.125	Air-Ground	129.825
London Control	134.900	Syerston (RAF)	
London Control	135.050	Air-Ground	125.425
London Control	135.425	Tain Range (RAF)	
London Control (Bristol)	132.800	Range	122.750
London Control (Cardiff)	135.250	Range	337.600
London Control (Cardiff)	135.325	Range	358.675
London Control (Hurn)	134.450	Tatenhill Aerodrome	
London Control (Standby)	136.600	Air-Ground	124.075
London Control ACC	118.825	Tees Valley/Durham Airport	
London Control ACC	120.525	Air Cam	122.350
London Control FIR Information	124.600	Approach	118.850
London Control Inbound	120.175	ATIS	136.200
London Control Inbound	126.300	Radar	118.850
London Control Inbound	126.875	Radar	128.850
London Control Information	124.750	Tower	119.800
London Control Information	125.475	Ternhill (RAF)	
London Control Irish Sea	134.425	Approach	356.325
London Control North East UIR	131.050	Tower	122.100
London Control North Sea	128.125	Tower	338.825
London Control North Sea	133.525	Thirsk (Sutton Bank)	
London Control North Sea	134.250	Air-Ground Gliders	130.400
London Control Radar Dep.	125.800	Thruxton Aerodrome	
London Control SIDs	120.475	Air-Ground	130.450
London Control SW Approach	132.600	Tibenham	
London Control TMA	121.325	Air-Ground	129.975
London Control TMA	130.925	Air-Ground Gliders	130.100
London Control Upper East	127.425	Tiree	
London Control Upper West	134.750	AFIS	122.700
London VOLMET (Main)	135.375	Topcliffe (RAF)	
London VOLMET (South)	128.600	Approach	122.100
Oceanic Clearance (E of 30W)	127.650	Approach	125.000
Swanwick Military/London Joint Area Org.		Approach	357.375
Lower Airspace (Central)	275.350	Approach	362.300
Lower Airspace (Northwest)	127.450	Ground	387.450
		Talkdown	123.300

Base	Mobile	Mode	Location	User and Notes

Base	Mobile	Mode	Location	User and Notes
Topcliffe (RAF) (Cont.)				
	Talkdown		344.350	
	Talkdown		385.400	
	Tower		122.100	
	Tower		257.800	
	Tower		309.725	
Tresco				
	Civil Heliport Air-Ground		130.250	
Trevose Head (RAF)				
	Danger Area Information		124.750	
	Danger Area Information		126.500	
Trim, Eire				
	Air-Ground		123.300	
Truro Aerodrome				
	Air-Ground		129.800	
Turweston Aerodrome				
	Air-Ground		122.175	
Unst (Saxa Vord)				
	Air-Ground		130.350	
	Flight Information		130.350	
	Ops		123.450	
Upavon (Army)				
	Tower		275.800	
Valley (RAF)				
	Approach		122.250	
	Approach		134.350	
	Approach		362.300	
	Approach		372.325	
	ATIS		120.725	
	Director		125.225	
	Director		337.725	
	Director		344.000	
	Ground		122.100	
	Ground		356.750	
	MATZ		119.750	
	Radar		123.300	
	Radar		134.350	
	Radar		258.825	
	Talkdown		123.300	
	Talkdown		358.675	
	Talkdown		385.400	
	Tower		122.100	
	Tower		257.800	
	Tower		340.175	
Waddington (RAF)				
	Approach		121.725	
	Approach		312.500	
	Approach		362.300	
	CAC		299.975	
	DATIS		291.675	
	Director		300.575	
	Director		344.000	
	Ground		342.125	
	MATZ		127.350	
	Ops		374.500	
	Radar		123.300	
	Radar		125.350	
	Radar		249.850	
	Talkdown		309.675	
	Talkdown		385.400	
	Tower		122.100	
	Tower		257.800	
	Tower		370.125	
Wainfleet Range (RAF)				
	Range		122.750	
	Range		356.800	
Walton Wood				
	Air-Ground		123.625	
Warton (BAe)				
	Approach		129.525	
	Approach		130.800	
	Approach		311.300	
	Approach		336.475	
	ATIS		121.725	
	Director		343.700	
	Ops		127.975	
	Radar		129.525	
	Radar		311.300	
	Radar		336.475	
	Tower		130.800	
	Tower		311.300	
Waterford				
	ATIS		121.725	
	CAC		124.700	
	Fire Service		121.600	
	Tower & AFIS		129.850	
Wattisham (Army Airfield)				
	Air-Air		118.000	
	Approach		123.300	
	Approach		125.800	
	Approach		291.125	
	Director		123.300	
	Director		283.575	
	MATZ		125.800	
	Talkdown		123.300	
	Talkdown		356.175	
	Tower		122.100	
	Tower		358.600	
Wellesbourne Mountford				
	Air-Ground		124.025	

Welshpool			Wolverhampton (Halfpenny Green)	
Air-Ground	128.000		Air-Ground	123.000
West Freugh (MoD)			ATIS	124.875
Approach	130.050		Woodford (BAe)	
Approach	260.025		Approach	130.750
West Midlands			Tower	120.700
Air Ambulance	127.900		Approach	121.000
Weston (Dublin), Eire			Approach	312.800
Air-Ground	122.400		Tower	119.750
Weston on the Green			Tower	259.950
Weston Radio	133.650		Wycombe Air Park (Booker)	
Weston-super-Mare			Ground	121.775
Danger Area Information	134.300		Tower & AFIS	126.550
Tower	122.500		Wyton (RAF)	
Wethersfield (RAF)			Air-Ground	134.050
MATZ	122.100		Approach	134.050
Radar	123.300		Approach	375.125
Whitchurch (Tilstock)			ATIS	315.700
Air-Ground	122.075		Ground	122.100
White Waltham Aerodrome			Ground	249.400
Air-Ground	122.600		Tower	119.975
Wick			Tower	245.375
Air-Ground	119.700		Yeovil (Westland)	
Fuellers (FarNor)	130.375		Air-Ground	125.400
Wickenby Aerodrome			Approach	130.800
Air-Ground	122.450		Approach	369.975
Wigtown			Radar	130.800
Tower	123.050		Radar	300.675
Wittering (RAF)			Tower	125.400
Approach	130.200		Tower	372.425
Approach	362.300		Westland Helicopter Tests	118.000
Approach	374.925		Yeovilton (RN)	
CAC (Easterly Departures)	299.975		Approach	362.300
CAC (Westerly Departures)	275.475		Approach	369.875
Departure	344.000		ATIS	379.750
Departure	376.575		Director	123.300
Director	362.300		Director	338.875
Director	374.925		Director	362.300
Ground	311.950		Ground	311.325
MATZ	130.200		MATZ	127.350
Talkdown	123.300		Radar	127.350
Talkdown	337.950		Radar	369.875
Talkdown	396.850		Talkdown	123.300
Tower	125.525		Talkdown	339.975
Tower	257.800		Talkdown	344.350
Tower	357.150		Tower	122.100

AFIS = Aerodrome Flight Information Service   ATIS = Automatic Terminal Information Service
CAC = Centralised Approach Control   DATIS = Digital Automatic Terminal Information Service
FIS = Flight Information Service   Ops = Operations

Late News

These frequencies arrived too late to be included in the main body of the book

Base	Mobile	Mode	Location	User and Notes
85.66250	72.16250	NFM	Greenock	McGills Buses
118.02500		AM	Fair Isle Airfield	Air-Ground
118.12500		AM	Little Snoring Airfield	Air-Ground
118.55000		AM	RAF Linton on Ouse	Approach
118.75000		AM	Strubby Airfield	Air-Ground
118.90000		AM	Rougham Airfield	Air-Ground
119.10000		AM	Defford Airfield	Air-Ground
119.10000		AM	Dunsfold	Aces High Operations
121.72500		AM	Newcastle Airport	Ground
122.82500		AM	Belfast City Airport	Tower
123.17500		AM	Elwood Heliport Hexham	Air-Ground
123.82500		AM	Little Staughton Airfield	Air-Ground
129.02500		AM	Nationwide	Breitling L39 Display Team
129.90000		AM	Tremorfa Helipad Cardiff	Veritair Operations
130.27500		AM	Belfast Aldergrove Airport	Safety Officer Ops
130.90000		AM	Little Gransden Airfield	Air-Air
130.90000		AM	RAF Leuchars	UAS Ops Claymore
131.40000		AM	Edinburgh Airport	Menzies Aviation Handling Operations
131.57500		AM	Heathrow Airport	East African Airways Ops
131.62500		AM	Heathrow Airport	DHL Aviation Flightwatch Ops
131.65000		AM	Heathrow Airport	Northwest Airlines Ops
131.70000		AM	Heathrow Airport	Hellas Jet Operations
131.70000		AM	Heathrow Airport	Swissair Operations
131.80000		AM	Bristol Airport	Speedbird Ops British Airways
131.87500		AM	Liverpool	Emerald Operations, John Lennon Airport
132.42500		AM	Skegness	Air-Ground
134.60000		AM	Cambridge Airport	ATIS
147.87500		AM	Suffolk	Police Vehicle-Vehicle Ch.21
147.87500		AM	West Midlands	Police Traffic Department Ch.21
156.45000		NFM	Scrabster/Stromness	John O'Groats Ferries
157.85000		NFM	Loch Lomond	Loch Lomond Rangers
158.50000		NFM	Southsea	Lifeguards Ch.50
159.51250		NFM	Cairnryan	P & O Express (110.9)
159.51250		NFM	Troon	P & O Express (110.9)
161.22500		NFM	Nationwide	RNLI Beach Lifeguards
161.22500		NFM	Newquay	RNLI Beach Lifeguards, Crantock Beach
161.22500		NFM	Newquay	RNLI Beach Lifeguards, Fistral Beach
161.22500		NFM	Newquay	RNLI Beach Lifeguards, Great Western Beach
161.22500		NFM	Newquay	RNLI Beach Lifeguards, Mawgan Porth Beach
161.22500		NFM	Newquay	RNLI Beach Lifeguards, Porth Beach
161.22500		NFM	Newquay	RNLI Beach Lifeguards, Tolcarne Beach
161.22500		NFM	Newquay	RNLI Beach Lifeguards, Towan Beach
161.22500		NFM	Newquay	RNLI Beach Lifeguards, Watergate Beach
161.22500		NFM	Poole	RNLI Beach Lifeguards, Branksome Chine Beach
161.22500		NFM	Poole	RNLI Beach Lifeguards, Canford Cliffs Beach
161.22500		NFM	Poole	RNLI Beach Lifeguards, Sandbanks Beach
161.22500		NFM	Poole	RNLI Beach Lifeguards, Shore Road Beach
161.22500		NFM	Weymouth	RNLI Beach Lifeguards, Greenhill Beach
161.22500		NFM	Weymouth	RNLI Beach Lifeguards, Weymouth Beach
161.47500		NFM	Felixstowe	Seawheel Ferries
163.07500	158.47500	NFM	Lewes	Community Repeater Council Services (156.7)
163.07500	158.47500	NFM	Newhaven	Community Repeater Taxi Company (94.8)
163.11250	158.61250	NFM	Billingshurst	Community Repeater Abbey Cars (210.7)
163.86250	159.36250	NFM	Detling	Kent County Showground (82.5)

Base	Mobile	Mode	Location	User and Notes
163.90000		NFM	Gt Yarmouth	Race Course (71.9)
163.92500		NFM	Gt Yarmouth	Race Course (71.9)
164.45000	159.95000	NFM	Sussex	Community Repeater Patient Transport (123)
164.95000	160.45000	NFM	Hollingdean	Council Cleaning/Environmental Services (123)
165.08750	169.98750	NFM	Gt Yarmouth	Anglia Taxis (123)
165.16250	169.96250	NFM	Lowestoft	Caister Holiday Centre (77)
165.30000	170.10000	NFM	Breckland	District Council Refuse Service (250.3)
165.36250	170.16250	NFM	London	Community Repeater St John Ambulance (210.7)
165.40000	170.20000	NFM	Billingshurst	Community Repeater Abbey Cars (74.4)
165.41250	170.21250	NFM	Billingshurst	Community Repeater Abbey Cars (250.3)
165.41250	170.21250	NFM	Lewes	Community Repeater Council Refuse Service (131.8)
165.41250	170.21250	NFM	Sussex	Community Repeater Delivery Company (88.5)
165.41250	170.21250	NFM	Worthing	Community Repeater Council Services (141.3)
165.42500	170.22500	NFM	Gt Yarmouth	Diamond Cars (107.2)
166.07500	170.97500	NFM	Edwinstowe	Sherwood Forrest Park
166.18750	170.98750	NFM	Lowestoft	Council Works Department (186.2)
167.66250		NFM	Chesterfield	Royal Mail Security
167.66250		NFM	Nationwide	Royal Mail Security
168.13750	172.93750	NFM	Doncaster	Doncaster College Security
168.85000		NFM	East Fortune Airfield	Museum Of Flight (71.9)
169.08750		NFM	Scrabster/Stromness	Pentland Ferries
169.11250		NFM	Felixstowe	Docks North Freightliner Terminal
169.16250		NFM	Thruxton Airfield	Crash/Fire Team (Callsign Alert 1/2/3) (103.5)
169.32500		NFM	Eastbourne	Benjys Coffee Shop/Food Outlets, Esplanade (151.4)
169.33750		NFM	Pagham Chichester	Church Farm Holiday Village Maint/Admin/Security
169.41250		NFM	Gt Yarmouth	Speedeworth Stock Car Racing
169.83750		NFM	Felixstowe	Docks North Freightliner Terminal
169.96250		NFM	Felixstowe	Docks South Freightliner Terminal
205.20000	197.20000	NFM	Felixstowe	Docks North Freightliner Terminal
205.25000	197.25000	NFM	Felixstowe	Docks South Freightliner Terminal
252.47500		AM	Scottish Military Radar	ACC
259.17500		AM	Scottish Military Radar	ACC
268.57500		AM	Scottish Military Radar	ACC
268.92500		AM	Scottish Military Radar	ACC
279.25000		AM	RAF Lakenheath	USAFE Air-Air
292.30000		AM	Nationwide	USAFE Common Air-Air
292.67500		AM	Scottish Military Radar	ACC
358.87500		AM	Scottish Military Radar	ACC
359.47500		AM	RAF Coningsby	29 Squadron Air-Air
369.90000		AM	RAF Coningsby	29 Squadron Operations
389.65000		AM	RAF Valley	208 Squadron Air-Air
409.50000		NFM	RAF Shawbury	Rafpol
409.75000		NFM	RAF Shawbury	Tower
426.32500		NFM	Nationwide	HM Revenue & Customs Surveillance Astro DVP
426.35000		NFM	Nationwide	HM Revenue & Customs Surveillance Astro DVP
426.37500		NFM	Nationwide	HM Revenue & Customs Surveillance Astro DVP
426.77500		NFM	Nationwide	HM Revenue & Customs Surveillance Astro DVP
440.76250	426.76250	NFM	London	Hammersmith & Fulham Parks Police
440.77500	426.77500	NFM	Nationwide	HM Revenue & Customs Surveillance Astro DVP
440.78750	426.28750	NFM	Manchester Airport	Parking Enforcement (127.3)
446.15000		NFM	Edinburgh	Vue Cinema, Ocean Terminal Shopping Centre (94.8)
446.20000		NFM	Edinburgh	Ocean Terminal Shopping Centre (131.8)
446.26250		NFM	Edinburgh	Gyle Shopping Centre Security (118.8)
446.27500		NFM	Edinburgh	Gyle Shopping Centre Admin/Cleaners (118.8)
446.40000		NFM	London	UCG Cinema Staff, Trocadero Centre (127.3)
447.71250		NFM	Scrabster/Stromness	Northlink Ferries
449.31250		NFM	Coventry	St John Ambulance, Ricoh Arena Ch.1 (186.2)

Base	Mobile	Mode	Location	User and Notes
449.31250		NFM	Stirling	Blair Drummond Safari Park Admin Ch.1 (77)
449.40000		NFM	Coventry	St John Ambulance, Ricoh Arena Ch.2
449.40000		NFM	Stirling	Blair Drummond Safari Park Shops Ch.2 (179.9)
449.47500		NFM	Coventry	St John Ambulance, Ricoh Arena Ch.3
449.47500		NFM	Stirling	Blair Drummond Safari Park Ch.3
449.47500		NFM	Stoke on Trent	Tesco Security, Longton
450.07500		NFM	Edgbaston	Tally Ho Police Training Centre Ch.78
450.25000		NFM	London	Metropolitan Police ANPR Channel
450.25000	464.25000	NFM	Sussex	Police Cadets Ch.68, (131.8)
451.32500		NFM	Sussex	Police Cadets Ch.07
452.12500		NFM	Nationwide	Ofcom Investigations
453.10000	459.60000	NFM	Dudley	Russels Hall Hospital Porters/Maint. Trunked Voice
453.20000	459.70000	NFM	Edinburgh	PDQ Couriers (118.8)
453.30000		NFM	London	Apple Computers Superstore, Regent Street (71.9)
453.50000	460.00000	NFM	Dudley	Russels Hall Hospital Porters/Maint. Trunked Control
453.50000	460.00000	NFM	Edinburgh	Ikea Furniture Superstore, Straiton (103.5)
453.52500		NFM	Edinburgh Airport	Airline Ramp Ops (123)
453.77500	460.27500	NFM	Brighton	Sassco Doormen/Security/Staff/CCTV Ch.2 (82.5)
453.77500	460.27500	NFM	Brighton	Sassco Management Ch.3 (131.8)
453.77500	460.27500	NFM	Romford	The Mall Shopping Centre Trunked Control Channel
453.80000	460.30000	NFM	Dudley	Russels Hall Hospital Porters/Maint. Trunked Voice
453.82500	460.32500	NFM	Worthing	Parking Enforcement (107.2)
453.90000		NFM	Edinburgh Airport	Menzies Aviation Handling (77)
453.98750	460.48750	NFM	Southampton	Shopwatch
456.01250	461.51250	NFM	Coventry	Ricoh Arena Trunked Data Control
456.02500	461.52500	NFM	Birmingham	Birmingham Womens Hospital (67)
456.33750	461.73750	NFM	Coventry	Ricoh Arena Trunked Net Voice
456.35000	461.85000	NFM	London	Gap Store Staff, Marble Arch (118.8)
456.35000	461.85000	NFM	Plymouth	City Centre Tourist Hosts
456.38750		NFM	London	Palace Of Westminster Tour Guides (69.3)
456.46250	461.96250	NFM	Coventry	Ricoh Arena Trunked Voice
456.47500	461.97500	NFM	Gt Yarmouth	Vauxhall Holiday Camp (67)
456.56250	462.06250	NFM	Coventry	Ricoh Arena Trunked Voice
456.60000	462.10000	NFM	Romford	The Mall Shopping Centre Trunked Voice
456.68750	462.18750	NFM	Coventry	Ricoh Arena Trunked Voice
456.70000	462.20000	NFM	Southampton Airport	AirRadio Trunked Multi User/Aviance/Security Voice
456.75000	462.25000	NFM	Shoreham by Sea	Marks & Spencer, Holmebush (71.9)
456.82500	462.32500	NFM	Telford	Telford Centre Security/Management (118.8)
456.86250		NFM	Llandudno	Llandudno Pier Security/Staff
456.87500	462.27500	NFM	Portsmouth	Shopwatch (DCS 073)
456.95000	462.45000	NFM	Edinburgh	Royal Yacht Britannia (136.5)
456.98750		NFM	Northampton	Royal Mail National Distribution Centre (69.3)
457.52500		NFM	Felixstowe	Seawheel Ferries
459.57500		NFM	Colchester	Colchester Zoo, Keepers
459.62500		NFM	Enfield	Chase Farm Hospital
460.12500		NFM	Sussex	Global Ballooning Air-Ground/Recovery Crew (127.3)
461.32500		NFM	Colchester	Colchester Zoo, Catering
461.33750		NFM	London	Gap Store, Marble Arch (110.9)
461.46250		NFM	Coventry	Ikon/Diva Door Staff (218.1)
461.88750		NFM	Northampton	Royal Mail National Distribution Centre (69.3)
462.12500		NFM	London	WAGN, Finsbury Park Station (DCS 243)
462.25000		NFM	Brighton	Marks & Spencer Security, Churchill Square (94.8)
462.25000		NFM	Welwyn Garden City	Marks & Spencer Security (71.9)
462.37500		NFM	Felixstowe	Docks Rail Shunting All Areas
466.20000	452.20000	NFM	Edinburgh	Edinburgh Castle Police (88.5)
467.52500		NFM	Felixstowe	Docks Norfolk Line
467.71250		NFM	Deal	Air Training Corps Band